A TEXTBOOK

OF

PRODUCTION TECHNOLOGY

(MANUFACTURING PROCESSES)

Dr. P.C. Sharma

B.Sc. Engg. (Mech.) (Hons.)
M.Sc. Engg. (Mech.) (Distinction)
Ph.D. (I.I.T. Delhi)

LMISME, MISTE
Ex. Principal SUSCET
Tangori (Mohali), PUNJAB
Formerly of
Punjab Engineering College
CHANDIGARH

S. CHAND & COMPANY LTD.

(AN ISO 9001 : 2008 COMPANY)
RAM NAGAR, NEW DELHI - 110 055

S. CHAND & COMPANY LTD.
(An ISO 9001 : 2008 Company)

Head Office: 7361, RAM NAGAR, NEW DELHI - 110 055
Phone: 23672080-81-82, 9899107446, 9911310888
Fax: 91-11-23677446

Shop at: **schandgroup.com**; e-mail: **info@schandgroup.com**

Branches:

AHMEDABAD : 1st Floor, Heritage, Near Gujarat Vidhyapeeth, Ashram Road, **Ahmedabad** - 380 014,
Ph: 27541965, 27542369, ahmedabad@schandgroup.com

BENGALURU : No. 6, Ahuja Chambers, 1st Cross, Kumara Krupa Road, **Bengaluru** - 560 001,
Ph: 22268048, 22354008, bangalore@schandgroup.com

BHOPAL : Bajaj Tower, Plot No. 243, Lala Lajpat Rai Colony, Raisen Road, **Bhopal** - 462 011,
Ph: 4274723. bhopal@schandgroup.com

CHANDIGARH : S.C.O. 2419-20, First Floor, Sector - 22-C (Near Aroma Hotel), **Chandigarh** -160 022,
Ph: 2725443, 2725446, chandigarh@schandgroup.com

CHENNAI : 152, Anna Salai, **Chennai** - 600 002, Ph: 28460026, 28460027, chennai@schandgroup.com

COIMBATORE : No. 5, 30 Feet Road, Krishnasamy Nagar, Ramanathapuram, **Coimbatore** -641045,
Ph: 0422-2323620 coimbatore@schandgroup.com **(Marketing Office)**

CUTTACK : 1st Floor, Bhartia Tower, Badambadi, **Cuttack** - 753 009, Ph: 2332580; 2332581,
cuttack@schandgroup.com

DEHRADUN : 1st Floor, 20, New Road, Near Dwarka Store, **Dehradun** - 248 001,
Ph: 2711101, 2710861, dehradun@schandgroup.com

GUWAHATI : Pan Bazar, **Guwahati** - 781 001, Ph: 2738811, 2735640 guwahati@schandgroup.com

HYDERABAD : Padma Plaza, H.No. 3-4-630, Opp. Ratna College, Narayanaguda, **Hyderabad** - 500 029,
Ph: 24651135, 24744815, hyderabad@schandgroup.com

JAIPUR : 1st Floor, Nand Plaza, Hawa Sadak, Ajmer Road, **Jaipur** - 302 006,
Ph: 2219175, 2219176, jaipur@schandgroup.com

JALANDHAR : Mai Hiran Gate, **Jalandhar** - 144 008, Ph: 2401630, 5000630, jalandhar@schandgroup.com

JAMMU : 67/B, B-Block, Gandhi Nagar, **Jammu** - 180 004, (M) 09878651464 **(Marketing Office)**

KOCHI : Kachapilly Square, Mullassery Canal Road, Ernakulam, **Kochi** - 682 011, Ph: 2378207,
cochin@schandgroup.com

KOLKATA : 285/J, Bipin Bihari Ganguli Street, **Kolkata** - 700 012, Ph: 22367459, 22373914,
kolkata@schandgroup.com

LUCKNOW : Mahabeer Market, 25 Gwynne Road, Aminabad, **Lucknow** - 226 018, Ph: 2626801,
2284815, lucknow@schandgroup.com

MUMBAI : Blackie House, 103/5, Walchand Hirachand Marg, Opp. G.P.O., **Mumbai** - 400 001,
Ph: 22690881, 22610885, mumbai@schandgroup.com

NAGPUR : Karnal Bag, Model Mill Chowk, Umrer Road, **Nagpur** - 440 032, Ph: 2723901, 2777666
nagpur@schandgroup.com

PATNA : 104, Citicentre Ashok, Govind Mitra Road, **Patna** - 800 004, Ph: 2300489, 2302100,
patna@schandgroup.com

PUNE : 291/1, Ganesh Gayatri Complex, 1st Floor, Somwarpeth, Near Jain Mandir,
Pune - 411 011, Ph: 64017298, pune@schandgroup.com **(Marketing Office)**

RAIPUR : Kailash Residency, Plot No. 4B, Bottle House Road, Shankar Nagar, **Raipur** - 492 007,
Ph: 09981200834, raipur@schandgroup.com **(Marketing Office)**

RANCHI : Flat No. 104, Sri Draupadi Smriti Apartments, East of Jaipal Singh Stadium, Neel Ratan
Street, Upper Bazar, **Ranchi** - 834 001, Ph: 2208761,
ranchi@schandgroup.com **(Marketing Office)**

SILIGURI : 122, Raja Ram Mohan Roy Road, East Vivekanandapally, P.O., **Siliguri**-734001,
Dist., Jalpaiguri, (W.B.) Ph. 0353-2520750 **(Marketing Office)**

VISAKHAPATNAM: Plot No. 7, 1st Floor, Allipuram Extension, Opp. Radhakrishna Towers, Seethammadhara
North Extn., **Visakhapatnam** - 530 013, (M) 09347580841,
visakhapatnam@schandgroup.com **(Marketing Office)**

First Edition 1996, Second Edition 1999
Thoroughly Revised and Enlarged Third Edition 2001
Reprints 2004, 2005, Revised Edition 2007, 2008, 2009, 2010, 2011
Reprint with corrections 2012
ISBN : 81-219-1114-1   **Code : 10A 160**

PRINTED IN INDIA
By Nirja Publishers & Printers Pvt. Ltd., 54/3/2, Jindal Paddy Compound, Kashipur Road, Rudrapur-263153, Uttarakhand and published by S. Chand & Company Ltd., 7361, Ram Nagar, New Delhi -110 055.

PREFACE TO THE SEVENTH EDITION

The printing of the seventh edition of the book has provided the author with an opportunity to completely go through the text. Minor Additions and Improvements have been carried out, whereever needed. All the figure work has been redone on computer, with the result that all the figures are clear and sharp.

The author is really thankful to S.Chand & Company Ltd. for doing an excellent job in publishing the latest edition of the book.

Pointing out of errors and misprints in the text will be highly obliged and thankfully acknowledged. Any suggestion for further improvement in the text will be highly appreciated.

P.C. SHARMA

PREFACE TO THE FIRST EDITION

The book "A Textbook of Production Engineering" by the author, has been very popular with the readers, for the last fourteen years. The readers have been writing to the author to bring out a book exclusively dealing with manufacturing processes. The author feels very happy to bring out this book **A Textbook of Production Technology** to meet the long standing demand of the readers. It has been author's intention to provide a broad-based introduction to a wide variety of manufacturng processes. The text is designed to be used by engineering (Mechanical, production, Industrial and Aeronautical) students. The book will also be useful to students appearing in various professional and competitive examinations (A.M.I.E., Engineering Services, Administrative Services, GATE, and so on). The author hopes that practicing engineers too will find the book useful.

Author's sincere thanks are due to M/s S. Chand & Company Ltd., for the excellent work done in publishing this book at a reasonable price. I am thankful to our Publishers S. Chand & Company Ltd., for bringing out the book in a record time and such a nice format. I am also grateful to Managing Director, Shri Rajendra Kumar Gupta and Director, Shri Ravindra Kumar Gupta for showing personal interest.

Finally, the author sincerely hopes that the book will meet the needs of the readers. All the suggestions to improve the text of the book will always be welcome.

P.C. SHARMA

CONTENTS

Chapter

1

Introduction

1.1. INTRODUCTION

The main aim behind advances in engineering and technology has been to raise the standard of living of man and to make his life more comfortable. The major role in this direction has been played by manufacturing science. Manufacturing is an essential component of any industrialised economy. The word 'Manufacturing' is derived from the Latin, *manus* = hand and *factus* = made, that is, the literal meaning is "made by hand". However, in the broader sense, the word 'Manufacturing' means the making of goods and articles by hand and/or by machinery. Thus 'Manufacturing engineering' or "Production Engineering" can be defined as the study of the various processes required to produce parts and to assemble them into machines and mechanisms. Production or Manufacturing is a critical link in the design cycle, which starts with a creative idea and ends with a successful product, Fig. 1.1.

1.2. CLASSIFICATION OF MANUFACTURING PROCESSES

When one thinks as to how the various components of machines are produced, many techniques come to the mind, for example, casting, forging, rolling, machining, welding etc. The manufacturing processes are so varied that there is no simple and universally accepted criteria of classifying these. However, all the manufacturing processes may be grouped into the following main categories:

1. Casting Processes. Here, the metal in the molten state is poured into a mould and allowed to solidify into a shape. The mould may be expendable or permanent.

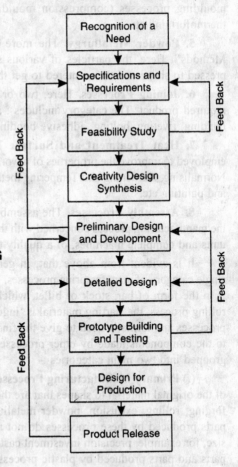

Recognition of a Need

Specifications and Requirements

Feasibility Study

Creativity Design Synthesis

Preliminary Design and Development

Detailed Design

Prototype Building and Testing

Design for Production

Product Release

Feed Back

Fig. 1.1. Design Cycle.

The examples are : Sand casting, Permanent mould casting, Die casting, Precision investment casting and centrifugal casting etc.

2. Deformation Processes. In these processes, the material is plastically deformed (hot or cold) under the action of an external force, to produce the required shape. No material is removed, but is only displaced and deformed to get the final shape. This category includes metal working/ forming processes such as : forging, rolling, extrusion and drawing etc. and also sheet metal working processes such as deep drawing and bending etc. The unconventional forming processes such as High Energy Rate Forming (HERF) and High Velocity Forming (HVF) methods also fall under this category.

3. Machining Processes. In machining processes, also known as Metal cutting or chip forming processes, material is removed from a work piece to get the final shape of the product. The processes include : Turning, milling, drilling, broaching, shaving, grinding, polishing, lapping, honing, buffing and sawing etc. The modern unconventional machining processes such as ECM, EDM, USM, AJM and LBM etc. are also included in this category.

4. Plastic Materials/Polymers processing methods. Under this category are included the various methods for processing plastic materials/ polymers, for example, shape casting, the various moulding processes (compression moulding, injection moulding, transfer moulding etc.) and thermoforming etc.

5. Powder Metallurgy. The more appropriate name should be "Particulate Processing Methods". Here, the particles of various sizes of metals, ceramics, polymers and glass etc. are pressed to shape and then sintered to get the final product.

6. Joining Processes. Here, two or more components are joined together to produce the required product. The category includes : all the welding processes, brazing, soldering, diffusion bonding, riveting, bolting, adhesive bonding etc.

7. Heat Treatment and Surface Treatment Processes. Heat treatment processes are employed to improve the properties of a work piece. The category includes the processes : Annealing, Normalising, Hardening and Tempering methods. Surface treatment processes include electro-plating and painting etc.

8. Assembly Processes. The assembly process for machines and mechanisms is the part of the manufacturing process concerned with the consecutive joining of the finished parts into assembly units and complete machines, of a quality that meets the manufacturing specifications.

It is evident from above that, in general, no component can be produced entirely by one single category of manufacturing processes. For example, the starting material for the forging process is in the form of bar, stock or billet, which are the end-products of rolling process. And, for the rolling process, the starting material is 'ingot', which is produced by casting process. Metal cutting processes are normally used to give the final shape and size (surface finish, dimensional accuracy) to the components made by other processes. Accordingly, all the manufacturing processes can be grouped into two main categories :-

(*i*) **Primary Manufacturing Processes.** These processes are involved in the initial breakdown of the original material to shapes that are then processed for the final product; for example, casting, forging, rolling, extrusion, powder metallurgy and plastic technology. However, in many cases, parts produced by these processes do not need other processes for producing the final shape and size, for example, precision investment casting, die-castings, precision forgings, powder metallurgy parts and parts produced by plastic processing methods.

(*ii*) **Secondary Manufacturing Processes.** These processes take the products of some primary process and change their geometry and properties to the semifinished or finished stage, *e.g.*, all metal removal processes and the rest of the metal forming processes, that is, drawing, spinning, swaging, coining, stretching, bending, deep drawing, wire/rod/ tube drawing, sheet metal forming and rubber forming etc.

1.3. VARIOUS KINDS OF PRODUCTION

Depending upon the scale of production and the type of components being produced, the production or manufacturing can be classified as : piece or job-lot production; medium lot, moderate lot, or batch production; and mass production.

1. Piece or Job-lot Production. Here, the parts are produced in small quantities to order, which are not periodically repeated. Companies engaged in piece production employ mainly general purpose equipment. Standard cutting tools and universal measuring facilities are used. The principle of complete inter changeability is not complied with. Hence, fitting is resorted to in assembly operations. The labour employed is more skilled. Lot sizes usually vary from 10 to 500 parts per lot, for example, manufacture of aeroplanes and oil field equipment, machine tools, giant hydroturbines, rolling mills and other heavy equipment etc.

2. Medium Production. It is characterized by the manufacture of parts in repeating lots or batches and to order. Mostly, the equipment used is general purpose type, equipped with universal, adjustable and sectional built up jigs, fixtures and tools. This enables the labour input and cost of production to be substantially reduced. Principles of interchangeability are to be strictly complied with. Lot size may range from a few parts to over 300 parts per lot and the yearly production may range from 2500 to 100,000 parts. An example of medium production is printing of books. Other examples are : machine tools, pumps, compressors, stationary I.C. engines etc.

3. Mass Production. It is characterized primarily by an established and stable object of production. The parts are produced in large quantities either intermittently or continuously, but are not dependent upon individual orders. The quantity is usually over 100,000 parts per year. A mass-production enterprise deals with standardized products of limited variety, such as consumer durable and products for industrial use. Other features typical of mass production are : an extensive use of specialized (usually permanently set up) and single purpose machine tools, and mechanization and automation of production processes, with strict compliance of the principle of interchangeability. The latter greatly reduces the time required for assembly operations. Examples of mass production are :- nuts, bolts, screws, washers, pencils, matches, engine blocks, automobiles, bicycles, electric motors, sewing machines and tractors etc.

The most advanced form of mass production is 'Continuous-flow production', whose main feature is that the time required for each operation of the production line is equal to or a multiple of the set standard time all along the line. This enables work to be done without providing stock piles and in strictly definite intervals of time. Examples include : oil refineries and continuous chemical plants.

In mass production type of production, semi-skilled or even unskilled workers are needed to operate the machines. This type of production is capital-intensive and the unit cost is low.

1.4. COMPUTERS IN MANUFACTURING

Computers are being increasingly used in the design/production cycle of a part. Computer-aided design (CAD) and computer aided manufacturing (CAM) are performing greater role in manufacturing industry. Computers are being used in every aspect of manufacturing, for example,

   (*i*) For the control of production processes and machines with the aid of NC (numerical control), CNC (Computer Numerical Control) and DNC (Direct Numerical Control)
   (*ii*) Computer-Aided Process Planning, (CAPP)
   (*iii*) Production planning and control
   (*iv*) Inventory management and for material management planning (MRP)

(v) Computer-Aided Quality Control, (CAQC)

(vi) Flexible Manufacturing Systems, (FMS)

(vii) Industrial Robots

(viii) Group Technology, (GT)

(ix) Computer Integrated Manufacturing System, (CIMS), and so on.

The use of computers in manufacturing has resulted in : improved productivity, quality, equipment utilization, reduced inventory and faster delivery.

1.5. SELECTION OF A MANUFACTURING PROCESS

From the above, it is thus clear that a manufacturer has the choice of selecting one of the many manufacturing processes for producing a given component. There are many factors involved in this exercise, but the selection of a suitable process can be made on the basis of the following considerations :-

(i) Type and nature of the starting material

(ii) Volume of production

(iii) Expected Quality and properties of the components.

(iv) Technical viability of the process

(v) Economy

Other factors influencing the choice of a manufacturing process are : Geometrical shape, Toolings, jigs, fixtures and gauges needed, available equipment and delivery date.

The selection of material for a component should be based on the processing factors as well as the functional requirements of the component (Refer to Tables 1.1 to 1.3). The cheapest material meeting these requirements should be selected, because higher the alloy content, the higher the cost. Also, standard alloys should be selected. Selection of many different alloys should be avoided to reduce inventory costs.

The type of material is also an important factor. Hard and brittle materials cannot be mechanically worked conveniently, whereas these can be cast or machined by many methods.

A manufacturing method usually alters the properties of the material. For example, cold working renders a material stronger, harder and brittle (less ductile). A very good surface finish and close tolerances can be obtained by cold working operations as compared to hot working operations. However, they will be needing higher capacity equipment.

Size, shape and shape complexity are also important factors. Flat components with thin cross-sections cannot be cast conveniently, whereas complex parts can't be mechanically worked. However, these can be conveniently cast or fabricated from individual parts. Complex shapes can be produced by forging and subsequent machining and finishing operations, and they have a toughness that is far superior to that of casting and P/M parts. Landing gear of a jet liner is manufactured by forging and machining processes. Very thin sections can be producted by cold rolling.

The geometrical shape of the component dictates the shape of the starting material and the processing method. For simple shaped components, for example, straight shafts, bolts, rivets etc., the selection of the shape and the starting material and the manufacturing method is easily made. As the complexity of the shape increases, there is a wide choice of the shape of the starting material and the manufacturing process. For example, a small pinion can either be machined from a bar stock or from a precision forged gear blank. The final choice will be dictated by economics. For this, volume of production is an important factor. Larger the volume of production, more economical it will be to invest in special equipment so as to reduce the cost per unit. Similarly, higher the production rate, economical it will be to select special purpose/automatic equipment. They will also be capable of meeting the delivery dates.

Production volume depends upon the product. For example, paper pins, paper clips, nuts, bolts, washers, sparks plugs, ball bearings and ball point pens are produced in very large quantities. Whereas, jet engines for large commercial air craft, diesel engines for locomotives etc. are manufactured in limited quantities. Production volume also plays a very significant role in determining, Economic Order Quantity (EOQ) and Economic Lot or Batch quantity.

As for the production rate, processes such as Die Casting, P/M, sheet metal working processes and roll forming etc. are high production-rate processes. Whereas, processes such as sand Casting, conventional machining process, Unconventional machining and forming processes and the various adhesive and diffusion bonding processes are relatively slow processes. The production rates can, however, be increased by automation or by the use of multiple machines.

Lead time also greatly influences the choice of a process. It is defined as the time to start production. Process such as rolling, forging, extrusion, die casting, roll forming and various sheet metal working process, require extensive and expensive dies, tools and equipment, resulting in long lead-time. On the other hand, the various conventional machining processes are very flexible and can be adapted to most requirements in a relatively short time. Lead time is also very small in the case of machining centres, Flexible Manufacturing Cells (FMC) and Flexible Manufacturing Systems (FMS). They can respond quickly and effectively to product changes (both in design and quantity).

It is clear from Table 1.3 that each manufacturing process has the capability of manufacturing a component within a certain tolerance range and surface quality. As the tolerance decreases and surface quality increases, the cost/unit increases. Therefore the widest tolerances and minimum surface quality that will meet the functional requirements of the component, should be specified.

Each manufacturing process has its own limitation of producing complex shapes and maximum and minimum size of the component (Table 1.3).

It is not always an easy task to select the best manufacturing process. Sometimes a product can be made by more than one competitive processes. So, in the final selection, cost is a very important factor. The cost of manufacturing a component by these methods should be compared and the optimum process selected. While doing these evaluations, along with the cost of processing the material to the finished product, the other important considerations are : material utilization factor, the effect of processing method on the material properties and the subsequent performance of the component in service.

The various manufacturing processes have been compared in Tables 1.1 to 1.4 on the basis of joinability, metal forming, design and cost considerations.

Production technology has become much more sophisticated since World War – II, due to technological innovations and advances in computerisation and quality management. The economic implications of new technology for manufacturing companies are complex. Changes in Production Technology, such as the development of CAD/CAM, have allowed the manufacturing of high quality, tailor made goods at low cost. Changes in Production Technology create whole classes of highly skilled positions to operate the machines and co-ordinate more complex organizational structures that originate from the technologies.

Table 1.1. Manufacturing Processes : Joinability Considerations

Material	Welding			Brazing	Soldering	Adhesive bond [TS, TP, EM]¹	Adhesive bond²	Thread Fastening	Riveting
	Arc	Oxy. Acet	Resistance						
Cast Iron	C	R	O	D	O	(TS) C, (TP) O	C	C	R
Carbon steel	R	R	R	R	D	(TS) C, (TP) O	C	C	R
Stainless steel	R	C	R	R	C	(TS) C, (TP) O	C	R	C
Aluminium-Magnesium	C	C	C	C	O	(TS) R, (TP) O	R	R	C
Copper	C	C	C	R	R	(TS) C, (TP) O	C	C	C
Nickel	R	C	R	R	C	(TS) C, (TP) O	C	C	C
Titanium	C	X	C	D	O	(TS) O, (TP) X	O	R	X
Lead	C	C	X	X	R	R		C	R
Zinc	C	C	O	X	R	R		R	R
Thermoplastics	R	R	C	X	X	C		R	R
Ceramics	X	O	X	X	X	R	R	O	O
Leather	X	X	X	X	X	(EM) R, (TS) C		C	R
Fabric	X	X	X	X	X	(EM) R		O	R

R : Recommended ; C : Common ; D : Difficult ; O : Seldom used ; X : Not used [TS : Thermoset ; TP : Thermoplastic ; EM : Elastomeric] ; ²(Modified Compression Epoxy)

Table 1.2. Manufacturing Processes : Metal forming Considerations

Manufacturing Process	Irons	Low-C-steel alloys	Heat and corrosion resistant alloy	Aluminium alloy	Copper alloy	Lead alloy	Magnesium alloy	Nickel alloy	Precious Metals	Tin alloy	Titanium alloy	Zinc alloy
Sand casting	A	A	A	A	A	B	A	A	-	B	-	B
Shell mould casting	A	B	B	A	A	-	-	B	-	-	-	-
Permanent mould casting	A	B	-	A	B	B	A	B	-	B	-	B
Die casting	-	-	-	A	B	A	A	-	-	B	-	A
Plaster mould casting	-	-	-	A	A	-	-	-	-	-	-	-
Investment casting	-	A	B	A	A	-	A	B	B	-	-	-
Centrifugal casting	A	A	A	B	B	-	-	B	-	-	-	-
Drop forging	B	A	A	B	B	-	B	B	-	-	B	-
Press forging	-	A	A	B	B	-	B	B	-	-	B	-
Upset forging	-	A	A	B	B	-	B	B	-	-	B	-
Cold headed parts	-	A	B	A	A	B	-	B	B	-	-	-
Stampings, Drawing	-	A	B	B	A	-	B	B	B	-	B	B
Spinning	-	A	B	A	A	B	B	A	B	-	B	B
Screw machining	B	A	B	A	A	-	B	A	B	-	B	B
Roll forming	-	A	-	B	B	-	B	-	-	-	B	B
Extrusion	-	B	B	A	A	B	A	B	-	B	B	-
Powder Metallurgy	A	A	B	B	A	-	-	B	B	-	B	-
Electro forming	A	-	-	B	A	B	-	A	A	B	-	B

A : Materials most frequently used ; B : Also materials currently used

Table 1.3. Manufacturing Processes : Design Considerations

S. No.	Manufacturing Process ↓	Material choice	Complexity of part	Maximum Size	Minimum Size	Mechanical properties	Precision and Tolerance	Special Structural Properties	Surface Smoothing	Surface Detail	Remarks
1.	Sand casting	Wide ; Ferrous, Non-ferrous Light Metals	Considerable	Largest	3 mm	Fair to High	± 0.6 to 0.3 mm per mm	Good Bearing structure	Poor	Poor	Usually require some machining
2.	Shell Mould casting	Wide	Moderate	Best for smaller parts	1.5 mm	Good	± 0.003 to 0.005 mm per mm	High Quality for cast metals	Good	Good	Best of low casting methods
3.	Permanent Mould casting	Restricted : brass bronze aluminium	Limited	Moderate	2.5 mm	Fair good	±0.6 mm per mm	None	Good	Good	Economical for mass production only
4.	Plaster Mould casting	Narrow : Brass, bronze, aluminium	Considerable	Moderate	0.75 mm	Fair	±0.25 to 0.125	None	Good	Good	Little finishing required
5.	Investment casting	Wide	Considerable	Moderate	0.75 mm	Good	±0.125 mm per mm	None	Excellent	Excellent	Best for too complicated parts.
6.	Die casting	Narrow : Zinc, aluminium, brass, magnesium	Considerable	Large	0.06 mm	Fair to Good	±0.025 mm per mm	None	Good	Good	Most economical where applicable
7.	Drop Forging	Medium	Moderate	Large	Small	High	±0.25 to 0.75 mm	Toughness	Fair	Fair	Used for high strength
8.	Press Forging	Medium : best for non ferrous alloys	Limited	Moderate	Small	High	Medium better than drop forging	Toughness	Fair	Fair	Greater complexity than drop forging.
9.	Upset Forging	Medium : many ferrous and non-ferrous alloy	Limited	Medium	Moderate	High	Medium	Toughness	Medium	Medium	Best suited to small parts.
10.	Welding	Wide	Considerable	Unlimited	Moderate	Variable	Medium, not highly precise	Toughness	Depends upon components	None	Versatile process.

Table 1.4. Manufacturing Processes : Cost Considerations

S. No.	Manufacturing Process ↓	Raw Material Cost	Tool and Die Costs	Direct Labour Cost	Finishing Cost	Scrap loss
1.	Sand Casting	Low to Medium depending on metal	Low	High	High	Moderate : Scrap can be remelted.
2.	Shell Mould Casting	Low to Medium	Low to Moderate	Low	Low	Low
3.	Permanent Mould Casting	Medium	Medium	Moderate	Low to Moderate	Low
4.	Plaster Mould Casting	Medium	Medium	High	Low	Low
5.	Investment Casting	High : best for special and costly alloys	Low to Moderate	High	Low	Low : Scrap is remelted.
6.	Die Casting	Medium	High	Low to Medium	Medium	Low : Scrap can be remelted.
7.	Drop forging	Low to Moderate	High	Medium	Medium	Moderate
8.	Press forging	Low to Moderate	High	Medium	Medium	Moderate
9.	Upset forging	Low to Moderate	High	Medium	Medium	Medium : Lowest of forging processes.
10.	Welding	Low to Moderate	Low to moderate	Medium to High	Medium	Low : Practically none.

PROBLEMS

1. Discuss the importance of manufacturing science.
2. Define the term "Manufacturing".
3. Define "Manufacturing Engineering".
4. Classify the Manufacturing Processes.
5. Discuss the various types of production.
6. Discuss the importance of Computers in Manufacturing.
7. Discuss the various factors for selection of a manufacturing process for a given product.
8. Consider a product and describe how its production volume would affect selection of economical manufacturing process for it.   (PTU)
9. Give two broad classes of manufacturing processes. Explain differences in these.   (PTU)
10. Give the most important plus point of casting process of manufacturing.
11. What is the most important plus point of Deformation processes of Manufacturing.
12. Write on : Primary process and Secondary processes of manufacturing.
13. Write the attributes of "Piece Production of components.
14. Write the attributes of "Medium Production" or "Batch production".
15. Write the attributes of "Mass production" of components.
16. What is : Continuous Flow Production?
17. List the product applications of : Job lot production, Medium production, Mass production and Continuous- flow production.
18. Define the terms : CAD, CAM, NC, CNC, DNC, CAPP, MRP, GT, FMS and CAQC.
19. What are the uses of Industrial Robots in manufacturing.
20. Which manufacturing process you will recommend for the manufacture of the following components :

    (a) Pump cylinder   (b) Connecting rod of an I.C. engine (c) Porous bearings (d) Tungsten filament of electric Bulb.
21. What is lead time ? How it affects the selection of a manufacturing process ?
22. Name a few high production – rate manufacturing processes.
23. How the size, shape, and shape complexity of the component influence the selection of a manufacturing process ?
24. Manufacturing must be carriedout at the lowest cost consistent with the quality and functionality of the product. Discuss.
25. List the advantages of flow production.
26. Safety in manufacturing is everybody's responsibility. Discuss.
27. Write on the routes taken by Primary Processing Methods. The Primary Manufacturing Methods can take the following routes :-

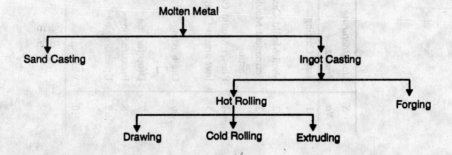

Chapter 2

Engineering Materials and Heat Treatment

2.1. ENGINEERING MATERIALS

Materials of construction can be classified into two groups :-

1. Metallic materials
2. Non-metallic materials

Metallic materials can be further split into :-

(i) Ferrous materials, and (ii) Non-ferrous materials.

Ferrous materials consist mainly of iron with comparatively small addition of other materials. Ferrous materials are iron and its alloys such as cast iron, gray cast iron, malleable cast iron, wrought iron, and steels of low carbon content and high carbon content etc.

Non-ferrous materials contain little or no iron. The materials include : Aluminium, Magnesium, Copper, Zinc, Tin, Lead, Nickel, Titanium and so on and their alloys.

Non-metallic materials included plastics, rubber, leather, carbon, wood, glass etc.

2.2. GENERAL MATERIAL PROPERTY DEFINITIONS

1. Homogeneity. A material that exhibits the same properties throughout is said to be homogeneous. Homogeneity is an ideal state that is not achievable by real materials, particularly metals. However, this variation in properties is so small that calculations for stress and deflection can easily assume that a material is homogeneous throughout.

2. Isotropy. A material that displays the same elastic properties in all loading directions is said to be isotropic. The equations of elasticity and strength of materials are based upon this assumption.

3. Anisotropy is that characteristic of a material which exhibits different property values in different directions with respect to a set of reference axes.

4. Elasticity. It is that property of a material by virtue of which deformations caused by applied load disappear upon the removal of load.

5. Plasticity of a material is its ability to undergo some degree of permanent deformation without rupture. Plastic deformation takes place only after the elastic range has been exceeded.

6. Ductility and Brittleness. Ductility is that property of a material which permits permanent deformation before fracture by stress in tension. Ductility is most commonly measured by means of elongation and reduction in area in the tensile test.

$$\% \text{ elongation} = \frac{\text{Final gauge length} - \text{Original guage length}}{\text{Original gauge length}} \times 100$$

$$\% \text{ reduction in area} = \frac{\text{Original area} - \text{Final area}}{\text{Original area}} \times 100$$

A material is generally classified as ductile if the percentage elongation is more than 5 in a gauge length of 50 mm, and as brittle if the percentage elongation is less than 5%.

7. Stiffness. Stiffness is the resistance of a material to elastic deformation or deflection. A material which suffers only a slight deformation under load has a high degree of stiffness.

8. Hardness is the property of solid bodies where by resistance is offered to plastic deformation and fracture, when two bodies in contact over a small area are pressed together.

In metal working, hardness generally implies resistance to penetration. It may, however, include resistance to scratching, abrasion or cutting.

9. Toughness of a material is its ability to withstand the plastic and elastic deformation. It is, in fact, the amount of energy a material can absorb before actual fracture or failure takes place.

10. Malleability of a material is its ability to be flattened into thin sheets without cracking, in the cold state, by pressing, rolling, hammering etc. Copper, aluminium and gold have good malleability.

11. Machinability. This property refers to the relative ease with which a material can be machined or cut. For example, brass can be easily machined as compared to steel.

12. Cold shortness. It is the brittleness that exists in some metals at temperatures below their recrystallization temperature.

13. Red shortness. It is the brittleness of steel and tendency towards cracking at high temperatures caused by the formation of iron sulphide.

14. Damping capacity is the ability of a metal to dissipate the energy of vibratory or cyclic stresses by means of internal friction. Some metals such as lead have a high damping capacity; cast iron also has good damping properties. Steel, however, has poor damping characteristics.

15. Embrittlement. Embrittlement is the loss of ductility of a metal. The loss may be due to physical or chemical changes.

16. Hydrogen embrittlement is the low ductility of a metal caused by the absorption of hydrogen.

17. Cold working. Cold working of metals means the mechanical working at temperatures below the recrystallization temperatures. Normally, it is taken to be working of metals at room temperature.

18. Hot working of metals means the working of metals when these are heated sufficiently (above the recrystallization temperature) to make them plastic and easily worked.

2.3. THE IRON-CARBON PHASE DIAGRAM

To understand the Iron Carbon Phase diagram, we need to understand the cooling process of pure metals and of alloys. Cooling curve for a pure metal is shown in Fig. 2.1. It is clear that pure metals have clearly defined freezing (as well as melting point) and solidification/melting takes place at constant temperature. However, alloys solidify/melt over a range of temperature, Fig 2.2. for Ni-Cu alloy.

Iron may exist in several allotropic forms in the solid state in accordance with the temperature. The transformation of iron from one allotropic form to another is accompanied by either the evolution of heat (on cooling curve of metal) or absorption of heat (on heating curve of metal). Fig 2.3 illustrates the cooling curve for pure molten iron (its melting point being about 1537°C) plotted in time *vs.* temperature co-ordinates. The first horizontal step appears on this curve at a temperature of 1537°C. It indicates that the heat is evolved and that iron passes from the liquid to the solid state and the mixture consists of liquid plus delta iron solid solution. Delta iron has a body centred cubic crystal lattice (b.c.c.). The second temperature effect occurs at 1392°C on the iron cooling curve and the delta iron gets transformed into a new allotropic form γ- iron which has a face centred cubic lattice (f.c.c.). Next step is at 910°C where γ-iron is transformed into β-iron with b.c.c. lattice. The last, fourth step, is observed at 768°C when β-iron is transformed into α -iron with b.c.c. lattice. α -iron acquires pronounced ferro-magnetic properties.

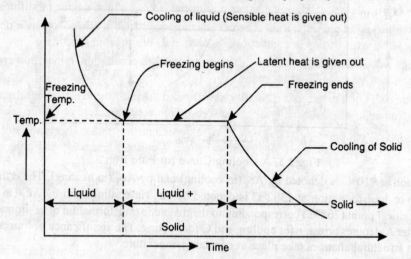

Fig. 2.1. Cooling Curve for a Pure Metal.

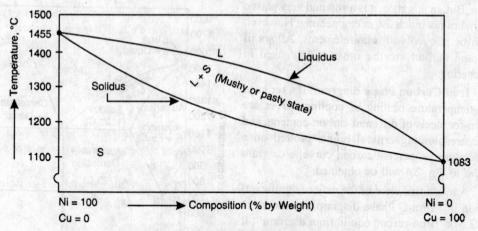

Fig. 2.2. Cooling Curve for an Alloy.

Since the space lattice does not change in the alpha-to-beta transformation, β-iron must be regarded as a paramagnetic state of α -iron. Again delta iron, which exists in the interval 1537°C to 1392°C, has a space lattice of b.c.c., the same as α -iron. Thus, there are actually two allotropic forms of iron : α -iron and γ -iron. They exist as follow : –

    Δ Iron (b.c.c) : 1392°C to 1537°C

    γ Iron (f.c.c) : 910°C to 1392°C

    β Iron (b.c.c) : 768°C to 910°C

    α Iron (b.c.c.) : < 768°C

Critical Points. On the cooling curve (or on the heating curve), the points where structural changes occur, are known as "critical points". In Fig. 2.3, the critical point of the α ⇌ γ

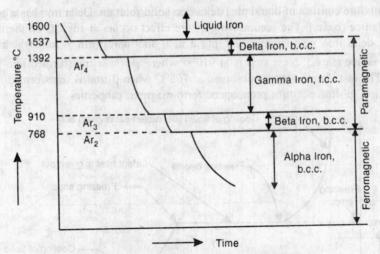

Fig. 2.3. A Cooling Curve for Pure Iron.

transformation at 910°C is denoted by Ar_3 (in cooling) and by Ac_3 (in heating). The critical point of the $\gamma \rightleftharpoons \alpha$ transformation at 1392°C is denoted by Ar_4 (in cooling) and by Ac_4 (in heating). Again, the critical point (768°C) corresponding to the magnetic transformation of α-iron is denoted by Ar_2. Letter A denotes arrest, r for cooling and C for heating. The significance of "arrest" lies in the fact that structural changes take place at constant temperature.

Absolutely pure iron is very difficult to obtain. But, in this state, it is a soft and very plastic material of not much use in engineering. However, it can be alloyed with may elements. Alloys of iron and carbon are the most widely used in engineering.

Iron-Carbon Phase diagram. If a series of time-temperature heating or cooling curves are drawn for steels of different carbon contents and the corresponding critical points plotted on a temperature vs. percent carbon curve, a diagram similar to Fig. 2.4 will be obtained.

A magnified view of the major (significant) portion of "Iron-C Phase diagram" is shown in Fig. 2.5 or "Iron-carbon equilibrium diagram". It is known as equilibrium diagram because the state of systems remains constant over an indefinite period of time. It provides a complete picture of phase relations, microstructure, and temperature for the knowledge of heat treatment of steels. In addition, it clearly indicates the division between steel and cast iron. Pure iron is on the left side of the diagram and cementite (Fe_3C), containing 6.67% carbon, on the right. Cementite is a

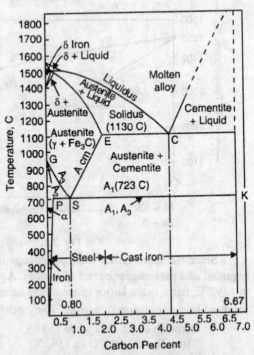

Fig. 2.4. Iron-Carbon Phase Diagram.

chemical compound of iron and carbon and may form upon rapid cooling of the iron-carbon melt from high temperatures. It is brittle, weak in tension, strong in compression, and is the hardest of any material in the equilibrium diagram. To be strictly correct, this diagram should be called as

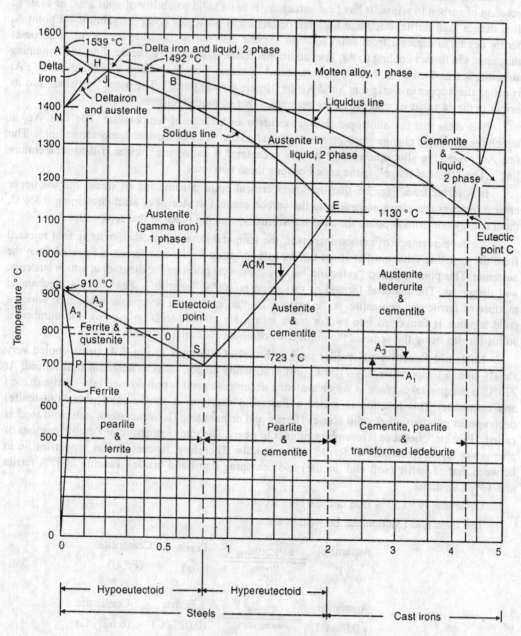

Fig. 2.5. Iron-Carbon Phase Diagram.

iron-iron carbide diagram, because the carbon in equilibrium does not appear as free carbon (graphite) but in the form of Fe_3C. Common usage, however, terms it the iron-carbon diagram.

It will be observed from Fig. 2.4 that carbon is soluble in α-iron to a maximum of 0.025% at 723°C (Point P) and only to 0.008% at room temperature. The result is an interstitial solid solution with dissolved carbon. Alpha iron is commonly called as "ferrite" or more accurately as "α-ferrite". It is the softest of all materials in the diagram.

Above critical point A_3 (Point G), the substance is known as "austenite", which is a solid solution of carbon in γ-iron. It has f.c.c. structure. It has a solid solubility of upto 2%C at 1130°C. It is denser than ferrite, ductile at high temperature and possesses good formability. At point A_3 ferrite begins to separate from solid solution. As the material is cooled to Ar_2 point, it becomes magnetic. On further cooling to Ar_1 line, additional ferrite is formed. At the Ar_1 line, the remaining austenite is transformed to a new structure called "pearlite". So, Ar_1 is also a "critical point". A_3 is called the "upper critical point" and A_1 the "lower critical point". The name "pearlite" has its origin in the fact that its microstructure resembles that of mother-of-pearl.

It is clear that the allotropic change occurs over a range of temperature. The line, Ac_1 at which the allotropic change starts on heating is called the "Lower Critical Temperature line". The line Ac_3 where the allotropic change is fully completed is called the "upper critical temperature line". The "Critical range" is the zone between these two lines.

It is sclear from Fig. 2.5 that the lower critical point is same for all steels, but the upper critical temperature varies according to the carbon content in steel. For steel containing 0.8% C, there is only one critical point, the total transformation taking place at that temperature.

As the percentage of carbon increases, the temperature at which the ferrite is first rejected from the austenite falls, until at about 0.80% carbon (point S), no free ferrite is rejected from the austenite. This point is called "eutectoid" and is the lowest point on the diagram at which austenite will disappear. The material formed at this point is 100% "pearlite". Pearlite is a mechanical mixture of ferrite and cementite. A "eutectoid" is "an isothermal reversible reaction in which a solid solution is converted into two or more intimately mixed solids on cooling, the number of solids formed being the same as the number of components in the system".

Eutectoid Reaction : Consider steel with 0.8% C (Point S in Fig. 2.4) being cooled very slowly from a temperature, say 1100°C (in the austenite range), so as to maintain equilibrium. At 723°C, a reaction takes place in which austenite decomposes and is transformed into -ferrite (b.c.c.) and cementite. This reaction is called a Eutectoid reaction. A single solid phase (austenite) decomposes into two other solid phases (ferrite and cementite). The structure of eutectoid steel is called "Pearlite", because it resembles mother of pearl. The micro-structure of Pearlite consists of alternating layers (lamellae) of ferrite and cementite. Therefore, its mechanical properties lie in between that of ferrite (soft and ductile) and cementite (hard and brittle). Pearlite is 87% ferrite and 13% Cementite.

Cementite is 93.33% Iron and 6.67% carbon.

The Eutectoid reaction can be written as:

$$\text{Austenite} \quad \xrightleftharpoons[\substack{\text{Heating}\\723°C}]{\substack{0.8\%C,\ \text{Cooling}}} \quad \text{Ferrite} \quad + \quad \text{Cementite}$$
$$(\gamma) \qquad\qquad\qquad\qquad (\alpha) \qquad\qquad (Fe_3C)$$

or

$$\text{Austenite} \quad \xrightleftharpoons[\text{Heating } 723°C]{\text{Cooling}} \quad \text{Ferrite} \quad + \quad \text{Cementite}$$
$$(\gamma\ 0.8\%\ C) \qquad\qquad\qquad (0.02\%\ C) \qquad (6.67\%\ C)$$

or

$$\text{Solid 1} \quad \xrightleftharpoons[\text{Heating}]{\text{Cooling}} \quad \text{Solid 2} + \text{Solid 3}$$

723°C is called the Eutectoid temperature, and 0.8% C steel is called the Eutectoid composition.

In steel with carbon percentage less than 0.8, the microstructure consists of Pearlite phase [Ferrite + Cementite] and a ferrite phase.

If C% is greater than 0.8, austenite transforms into Pearlite and Cementite.

If the carbon content of steel is greater than the eutectoid, a new line is observed in the iron-carbon diagram, that is line A_{cm}. The line denotes the temperature at which iron carbide is first rejected from the austenite instead of ferrite.

It is clear from the figure that the maximum solubility of carbon in γ-iron is 2% (Point E).

Point C is a "eutectic point" containing 4.3% carbon and consists of a mixture of austenite and cementite known as "lederburite". A eutectic point is a point on the phase diagram at which two constituent metals solidify simultaneously. It has the lowest liquidus temperature (above which only liquid exists), and the liquidus and the solidus (below which only solid exists) coincide, so that it melts and solidifies like a pure metal.

Eutectic Reaction. Point C in Fig. 2.5, percentage of carbon being 4.3%.

When molten alloy is cooled slowly, it will start cooling and solidifying along the liquidus line. For alloy containing 4.3% C, when it is cooled to 1130°C, a reaction takes place in which molten alloy solidifies into a mixture of two solids (austenite and cementite), known as "Lederburite". All the liquid gets solidified at 1130° C, at the same time. Crystals of austenite containing 2% C and Cementite containing 6.67% C separate from it. These crystals of austenite and cementite form the eutectic mixture known as "Lederburite", point C. Thus, eutectic alloy at point C containing 4.3% Carbon solidifies at the constant temperature of 1130°C with the formation of only Lederburite. Thus, the eutectic reaction is

$$\text{Liquid} \xrightarrow[1130°C]{4.3\%C} \underset{(\gamma)}{\text{Austenite}} + \underset{[Fe_3C]}{\text{Cementite}}$$

Thus, at eutectic point, liquid phase and two solid phases co-exist.

Lederburite is γ-Fe$_3$ C eutectic matrix.

At higher carbon content (> 4.3% C), Fe$_3$C is embedded in the eutectic matrix. As above cementite is 6.67% C and 93.33% Iron.

The carbon alloys having less than 2% carbon are called "steels" and those containing over 2% carbon are called cast irons. Steels may further be classified into two groups :- Steels having less than 0.8% carbon are called "hypo-eutectoid steels" and those having more than 0.8% carbon called "hyper-eutectoid steels".

Steels with carbon content exactly equal to 0.8% are called "Eutectoid Steels".

Similarly Cast Irons with carbon content above 2% and upto 4.3% are called "Hypo-eutectic" Cast Iron and those with carbon content above 4.3% and upto 6.67% are called "Hyper-eutectic" Cast Irons. Cast Irons with carbon content exactly equal to 4.3% are called "Eutectic" Cast Irons.

The portion of the iron-carbon phase diagram which pertains to steels and which is important for studying the heat treatment of steels is shown in Fig. 2.6

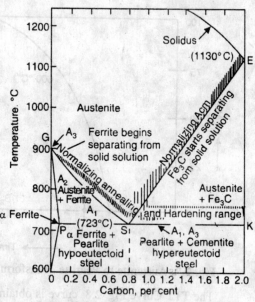

Fig. 2.6. Iron-Carbon Diagram.

Thus, as noted above, the information from Iron Carbon phase diagram is as follows .

1. Temperatures at which the alloys will start melting/solidifying and finish melting/solidifying.

2. Possible phase Change which will occur as a result of alteration in the composition or temperature.

2.3.1. TTT Curves : The Iron-carbon Phase diagram, Fig. 2.4, provides a complete picture of phase changes, corresponding microstructure and temperatures under equilibrium condition. That is, sufficient time is allowed for the reactions to complete. So, time is not a variable in this diagram and hence this also known as Equilibrium diagram. The effects of different cooling rates on the structural changes of steel are not revealed in this diagram. However, in the various heat treatment processes (particularly hardening), the austenite transformation of steel depends upon the cooling rate.

The most comprehensive conception of the kinetics involved in the structural changes of austenite may be gained by studying the isothermal transformation of decomposition of supercooled austenite, that is its transformation at constant temperature. Thus, time is also a variable. Hence, the basis for heat treatment of steels is time, temperature Transformation diagram (TTT diagram) or Isothermal transformation (IT) diagram, which because of its shape is also known as C curve or S-curve.

To construct these curves, a number of small specimens of steel are heated above the critical points where austenite is stable. These are then rapidly cooled to a number of temperatures and are held at these temperatures for different periods of time until austenite is completely decomposed. At any given time, the percentages of austenite and pearlite are also noted by examining the structure. Then, we get the curves as shown in Fig 2.7. These curves have been obtained experimentally for eutectoid steel (0.8% C), by heating steels above critical points and rapidly cooling them to 700°C, 600°C and 400°C and holding them at these temperature for various lengths of time. The higher the temperature and/or the longer the time, the greater the percentage of austenite transformed to pearlite. The transformation of austenite at constant temperatures does not begin immediately, but only after a certain time interval which is called the "incubation period".

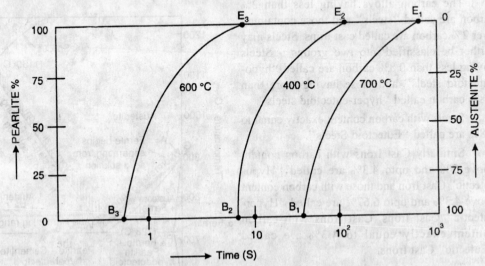

Fig. 2.7. Austenite to Pearlite Transformation as a Function of Time and Temperature.

The TTT Curve Fig. 2.8, curve is obtained from curves of Fig. 2.7. In such a curve, time is in seconds plotted along the horizontal axis in a logarithmic scale and the temperatures in °C in an ordinary scale along the vertical axis. At 700°C, the austenite decomposition begins at point B_1 and ends at point E_1. Similarly at temperatures of 600°C and 400°C, the beginning and end points are B_3, E_3 and B_2, E_2 respectively. Curves 1 and 2 are then drawn passing through these points indicating the beginning and end of austenite transformation.

At near about 700°C, austenite decomposes into pearlite. Sorbite is formed at lower temperature (600°C). Troostite is formed at 500 to 550°C. Acicular troostiteor bainite is formed when the temperature is lowered from 550 to 220°C. At 240°C (point Ms) martensite transformation begins and it ends at point MF (–50°C). These points are not affected by cooling rate, but their positions depend upon the chemical composition of steel.

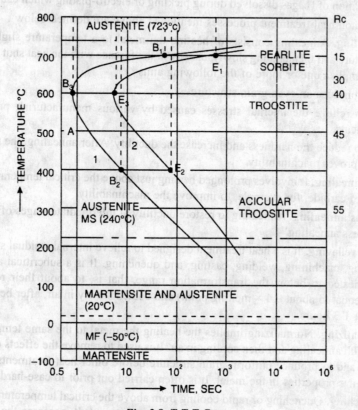

Fig. 2.8. T T T Curve.

TTT curves are drawn from non-equilibrium conditions. The information available from TTT curve is : Change of phase with the cooling rate which is used in Hardening process.

2.4. HEAT TREATMENT DEFINITIONS

The heat treatment operations can be defined as : heating a metal or alloy to various definite temperatures, holding these for various time durations and cooling at various rates. This combination of controlled heating and cooling determine not only the nature and distribution of micro-constituents (which determine the properties of a metal or alloy), but also the grain size. Thus, the main aim of the heat treatment operations is to control the properties of a metal or alloy through the alteration of the structure of the metal or alloy.

The purposes of the various heat treatment operations are as given below :

1. To remove or relieve strains os stresses induced by cold working (drawing, bending etc.) or non-uniform cooling of hot metal (for example welding) : Annealing

2. To increase strength or hardness of the material for improved wear resistance: Hardening.

3. To improve machinability : Annealing

4. To soften the material : Annealing

5. To decrease hardness and increase ductility and tougness to withstand high impact. (Tempering)

6. To improve the cutting properties of tools.

7. To change or modify the physical properties of the material such as electrical properties, magnetic properties, corrosion resistance and heat resistance etc.

8. Elimination of H_2 gas dissolved during pickling or electro-plating which causes brittleness.

The common heat treatment processes mentioned above are defined below :

1. Annealing. Annealing consists of heating the metal to a temperature slightly above the critical temperature and then cooling slowly, usually in the furnace with the heat shut off. Annealing is done to accomplish one or more of the following aims :

(*i*) To produce an even grain structure.

(*ii*) To relieve the internal stresses caused by various manufacturing processes or by previous treatments.

(*iii*) To reduce the hardness and increase the ductility. After annealing, the metal becomes soft, whisch improves machinability.

2. Full annealing. It involves prolonged heating just above the critical temperature to produce globular form of carbide, for example, to improve the machinability.

3. Process annealing. Annealing to restore ductility at intermediate stages of cold reduction is called "process annealing".

4. Stress relieving. It is a heat treatment designed to relieve internal residual stresses induced by cold working, machining, welding, casting, and quenching. It is a subcritical anneal process. The metal is heated to below the transformation range, that is, to about their recrystallization temperatures (equal to about 0.4 × melting point) and cooled slowly in air, after being held at that temperature for 1-3 hours.

5. Normalizing. Normalizing implies the heating the metal to the same temperature as that employed for full annealing and then cooling in air. It is used to remove the effects of any previous heat treatment and to produce uniform grain structure before other heat treatments are applied to develop particular properties in the metal. It is often carried out prior to case-hardening.

6. Quenching. Quenching or rapid cooling from above the critical temperature by immersion in cold water or other cooling medium, is a hardening treatment. It increases the strength of the metal and increases the wear resistance, but makes the metal brittle and of low ductility.

7. Tempering. "Tempering" or "Drawing" consists of reheating below the critical temperature the quenched metal to restore some of the ductility and reduce the brittleness. Increased toughness is obtained at the expense of high strength.

8. Case-hardening. Case-hardening or carburising is a process of hardening the outer portion of the metal by prolonged heating, free from contact with air while packed in carbon in the form of bone char or charcoal. The outer metal absorbs carbon, and, when the hot metal is quenched, this high-carbon steel hardens, whereas the low carbon steel of the core remains soft and ductile. In "gas carburising", the metal is heated in an atmosphere of gas and controlled so that the metal absorbs carbon from the gas but will not be oxidized on the surface.

9. Cyaniding. Cyaniding is case-hardening with powdered potassium cyanide, or potassium ferrocyanide mixed with potassium bichromate, substituted for carbon. For a very thin case, immersion in hot liquid cyanide is sufficient. Cyaniding produces a thin but very hard case in a very short time.

10. Nitriding. Nitriding is surface hardening, accomplished by heating certain steel alloys (Nitralloys) while immersed in ammonia fumes.

11. Flame hardening. This is a hardening process by which either selected surface areas or the entire part is thoroughly heated by means of a gas burner with subsequent quenching.

12. Induction hardening. It is hardening of parts which follows induction heating, the latter of which either has heated the case portion or the entire part.

13. Aging, Age hardening or precipitation hardening. This is the process by which the structure of a metal recovers from an unstable condition produced by quenching (quench aging) or by cold working (strain aging). The change in structure is due to the precipitation of one of the constituents from a saturated solid solution and results in a material that is stronger and harder, but usually less ductile. This type of aging takes place slowly at room temperature and is called "Natural aging". The process may be accelerated by a slight increase in temperature and is then called "Artificial aging".

The first step in age hardening is "Solution heat treatment". It is the heating of an alloy to a suitable temperature, holding it at that temperature long enough to allow one or more constituents to enter into solid solution and then cooling rapidly enough to hold the constituents in solution. The alloy is left in a supersaturated, unstable state and may subsequently exhibit quench aging.

This process of hardening is usually used for non-ferrous metals.

2.5. FERROUS METALS

Ferrous metals are composed of iron and carbon, plus a number of other elements, which are present either (1) impurity elements (such as S, P, Mn and Si) carried over from the raw materials or unavoidably introduced during the manufacturing processes, or (2) intentionally added alloying elements.

The general classes of ferrous metal products differ from one another principally in the amount of carbon content present in each. Commercially pure iron contains upto 0.01% carbon. Steels contain less than or maximum 2% carbon and cast irons over 2% carbon (some of the literature specifies 1.7% carbon as the difference between steels and cast irons).

Pig Iron. All iron and steel products are derived originally from pig iron. Pig iron is the raw material obtained from the chemical reduction of iron ore in a blast furnace. The process of reduction of iron ore to pig iron is known as "Smelting".

2.5.1. Cast Iron. Cast iron is pig iron remelted and thereby refined in a cupola or other form of remelting furnace and poured into suitable moulds. As indicated in Figure 2.2, the carbon content of cast irons is from 2 to 6.67%. Most commercial types of cast iron contains between 2.5 and 4% carbon.

It is obvious that, with such a high carbon content, cast iron is very brittle and has low ductility. Hence, cast iron can not be cold worked. However, cast iron flows readily when fluid, it is easily cast into intricate shapes that can be machined after cooling and aging. It is the cheapest of the cast materials. Cast iron without the addition of alloying elements is weak in tension and shear, strong in compression and has low resistance to impact. The damping capacity of cast iron is much greater than that of steel. The properties of cast iron can be varied extensively with the addition of alloying elements and proper heat treatment. The primary types of cast iron are :

(1) gray cast iron (2) white cast iron (3) malleable cast iron (4) ductile cast iron (5) chilled cast iron (6) alloy cast iron (7) meehanite cast iron (8) mottled cast Iron

1. Gray Cast Iron. When the molten C.I. is cooled, its final structure will depend upon the form in which the carbon solidifies, which in turn will depend upon the cooling rates as well as composition. The control will be affected by the total C and Si (also P) and their total effect is expressed by the 'carbon equivalent', (C.E.) :

$$C.E.(\%) = C\% + \frac{Si\% + P\%}{3}$$

At relatively high C.E. and slower cooling rates, the solidified cementite, being unstable, breaks up into austenite and graphite flakes. The process is called as "graphitization". The presence of certain elements, of which Si is most important, promotes graphitization. The graphite flakes give the cast iron the gray appearance when fractured, hence the name "gray" C.I.

Gray C.I. is the most widely used of all cast irons. In fact, it is common to speak of gray cast iron just as cast iron. It contains 2.50 to 3.75% C and upto 2.5% Si.

Gray cast iron is soft, easily machined and only moderately brittle. Its main advantages are : low cost, low melting point, fluidity and good damping capacity. Another good property it possesses is that the free graphite in its structure acts as a lubricant and when very large machine slides are made of it, a very free-working action is obtained.

Product Applications. Due to its low cost, gray C.I. is preferred in all fields where ductility and high strength are not required, for example, weights; frames; motor, gear and pump housings; sanitary wares; pipe fittings and gas and water pipes for underground purposes etc. Due to its high compressive strength and good damping characteristics, gray C.I. is used for machine tool bases and supports for structures. Again, due to its fluidity and excellent wear properties, gray C.I. is used extensively in the manufacture of engine blocks, brake drums, sliding surfaces of machines, gearing, gear housings, piston rings, and so on. Gray C.I. has also been used for the manufacture of engine crankshafts, because of its good damping properties, high torsional shear strength and low notch sensitivity. Other product applications of gray C.I. are : Household appliances, manhole covers, cylinder heads for engines and in rolling mill and general machinery parts.

2. White Cast Iron. At low values of C.E., < 3 (C upto 2.5% and Si < 1.5%) and rapid cooling, the cementite will not have sufficient time to break into graphite and austenite. As a result, the total carbon will be exclusively in the combined form of Iron Carbide, Fe_3C (Cementite). It is a very hard and brittle metal with the entire cross-section having a white microstructure. Due to this, the metal is virtually unmachinable except by grinding and so has very limited applications.

Product Applications. The use of white C.I. is limited for wear resistant parts such as grinding balls, liners for ore-crushing mills and cement mixers, extrusion dies and some agricultural machinery. However, it is widely used in the manufacture of wrought iron and for making malleable iron castings.

3. Malleable Cast Iron. Malleable castings are first made from white cast iron and then malleabilized by two methods : "Black heart method" and "white heart method"

(i) **Black heart Method.** In this method, the white iron castings are annealed by heating them for a prolonged period of several days (to a temperature of 850 – 1000°C) in air tight pots filled with inert material such as ferrous silicate scale (or iron oxide) or slag. The action of heat and iron oxide partially removes the carbon and reduces the remainder from combined state to a globular form of free carbon, so that after a slow cooling, a strong soft and somewhat ductile casting is obtained. This method, which is also called "decomposition" is used in U.S.A. and the material is Ferritic malleable iron.

(ii) **White heart Method.** In this method (decarburisation), the castings are placed in pots packed with an oxidising material. The oxygen combines with carbon in the castings, reducing its amount to less than 1%. This method is used in Europe, and the material is pearlitic malleable iron.

The difference between gray C.I. and malleable C.I. is the form in which the free carbon occurs. In gray C.I., the free carbon occurs in the form of flat or plate like particles, whereas in malleable C.I., the graphite is in the form of irregularly shaped spherical particles which are much more desirable from a strength point of view than flakes.

Malleable C.I. is stronger and tougher, ductile, resistant to impact and easily machinable (due to the presence of graphite). Since the carbon change reaches only to a depth of about 10 mm, this process is not suitable for heavy castings. The application of malleable C.I. is considerably more limited than that of gray C.I., because it is more expensive to produce and better mechanical properties are not required in most cases.

The use of malleable cast iron usually involves parts of complex shape that often need considerable machining to meet the specifications, such as, : in automotive and agricultural equipment industries (housings, yokes, wheel hubs), hinges, door-keys, spanners, mountings of all sorts, cranks, levers, thin walled components of sewing machines, textile machines and others, brake pedals in cars, spring hangers and so on.

4. Ductile Cast Iron. Ductile cast iron, which is also called as "Nodular Cast iron" and "Spheroidal cast iron" is of higher grade in comparison to malleable cast iron, because, the carbon is precipitated as spherical nodules of graphite which are more perfect spheres than those found in malleable cast iron. To produce ductile cast iron, the molten metal is first completely desulphurised. Then small amounts of special alloys containing magnesium or cerium are added to the molten iron in the ladle causing it, during solidification, to precipitate graphite as small spherical nodules.

Ductile cast iron possesses high fluidity, which permits the casting of intricate shapes with excellent combination of strength and ductility. Ductile cast iron can be produced in thicker pieces than those produced by malleable cast iron.

Ductile cast iron is stronger, more ductile, tougher and less porous than gray cast iron. So, it is used in parts where density and pressure tightness is a highly desirable quality. These parts include : hydraulic cylinders, valves, pipes and pipe fittings, cylinder heads for compressors and diesel engines. Ductile cast iron is also used to make rolls for rolling mills, many centrifugally cast parts, pulleys, forming dies, pump housings and, in general, for parts subjected to impact loading or requiring a high elastic modulus.

5. Chilled Cast Iron. Quick cooling is called chilling and the iron so produced is chilled iron. It is made by placing "metal chills" inside the mould but near its surface. The molten metal, when poured into the mould, cools rapidly to produce a hard wear- resistant surface (of 1 to 2 mm thick) consisting of white cast iron. Below this surface the material is gray cast iron. Chilled cast iron can only be machined by grinding and is used in making stamping dies, mill and crushing rolls, railway wheels, car wheels, cam followers and so on.

6. Alloy Cast Iron. Alloying elements are added intentionally to cast irons to overcome certain inherent deficiencies in ordinary cast irons to give the required qualities for special purposes. By controlling the rate of graphitization, these elements develop special capabilities, such as better mechanical properties, improved resistance to heat, corrosion, wear, or brittle fracture. Also, alloying can improve both the castability and machinability properties of cast iron. Common alloying elements are : nickel, copper, chromium, molybdenum, vanadium and boron.

Note. The reader should not mistake impurities such as Mn, P, S and Si for alloying elements. The process of mass producing steel, cast iron, non-ferrous metals and so on, are not designed for complete removal of all impurities.

Below, we discuss the individual effects of these impurities and alloying elements on cast iron.

(i) Effect of impurities on Iron.

Sulphur. Sulphur is generally considered harmful in C.I. In gray cast iron, it counteracts the graphitizing effect of silicon, lowers fluidity during pouring, decreases strength and makes the metal more brittle. So, it should be kept as low as possible, preferably below 0.1%.

Manganese. It encourages the formation of carbide and so, tends to whiten and harden cast iron. But it helps to control the harmful effects of sulphur. It has greater affinity for sulphur than for iron and it combines with sulphur to produce manganese sulphide, which is not objectionable. It is often kept below 0.75%.

Phosphorus. Phosphorus increases the flowability of gray cast iron. Phosphoric irons are useful for casting of intricate designs and for many light engineering castings when cheapness is essential. Phosphorus induces brittleness in cast iron and it is rarely allowed to exceed 1.0%.

Silicon. It is the important graphitizer for cast irons, which makes the cast irons soft and easily machinable. It also produces sound castings free from blow holes because of its affinity for oxygen. It is present in cast irons upto 2.5%.

(ii) Effect of alloying elements on Cast Iron

Nickel. Nickel is used in cast irons to refine grain structure, increase strength and toughness and increase resistance to corrosion. It has no effect on ductility. It also acts as a graphitizer but is only half as effective as silicon. It, thus, promotes the machinability of cast irons. In low alloy cast irons, its amount is from 0.25 to 5.0%. This alloy is used in steam and hydraulic machinery, compressors and I.C. engine parts. In heat and corrosion resistant cast irons as much as 35% nickel is used.

Chromium. Chromium also refines grain structure and increases strength, hardness and resistance to corrosion. It also increases the wear resistance and heat resistance property of cast iron. Gray cast irons which will be subjected to severe wear conditions, often contain chromium (upto 8%). This alloy is used in pumps of all types. The alloy used in higher resistance parts may contain chromium from 10 to 30%. However, chromium tends to prevent graphitization.

Copper. Copper is added to cast iron in amounts upto about 1.0%. It increases fluidity for improved mould filling ability, imparts corrosion resistance, and improves mechanical properties, notably toughness and hardness. Machinability of cast iron is also slightly improved, because copper promotes formation of graphite.

Molybdenum. The presence of molybdenum in cast iron produces fine and highly dispersed particles of graphite and good uniform structure. This increases the strength and toughness and improve high-temperature strength of cast iron. Its amount ranges from 0.25 to 1.25%. Molybdenum is frequently used in cast iron in combination with nickel or chromium or nickel and chromium.

Vanadium is added to cast iron in amounts of 0.10 to 0.50%. It promotes grain refinement, increases strength and increases resistance to fatigue stresses. However, it tends to reduce graphitization.

Boron. Until quite recently, boron received little recognition as an addition to regular gray cast iron. 0.05% boron, 3.5% carbon and 1.0% silicon in cast iron help to increase surface hardness and refine structure. This alloy is used for rolls in rolling mills.

7. Meehanite Cast Iron. Meehanite cast iron, produced under patent protection, is made with the addition of a calcium-silicon alloy. Calcium silicide acts as a graphitizer and produces a fine graphite structure giving a cast of excellent mechanical properties. The basic gray cast iron used to obtain Meehanite iron is low in silicon and moderately low in carbon (about 2.5 to 3%). Various grades of Meehanite are produced to meet special requirements.

All Meehanite irons have high strength, toughness, ductility and easy machinability. These irons also respond to heat treatment. Meehanite cast iron is ideally suited for machine tool castings.

Table 2.1 gives the chemical composition of main types of cast irons (excluding alloy cast irons)

Table 2.1

Metal	C	Si	Mn	S	P
Pig iron	3.00 – 4.00	0.50 – 3.00	0.10 – 1.00	0.02 – 0.10	0.03 – 2.00
Gray cast iron	2.50 – 3.75	1.00 – 2.50	0.40 – 1.00	0.06 – 0.12	0.10 – 1.00
Malleable cast iron	2.20 – 3.60	0.40 – 1.10	0.10 – 0.40	0.03 – 0.30	0.10 – 0.20
White cast iron	1.75 – 2.30	0.85 – 1.20	0.10 – 0.40	0.12 – 0.35	0.05 – 0.20

8. Mottled Cast Iron : It is mixture of grey and white cast irons in which the outer layers have the structure of white cast iron and the core, that of grey cast iron. It is obtained by heating cast iron to red hot with powdered red hematite in an oven. This cast iron possesses increased toughness.

2.5.2. Heat Treatment of Cast Iron. Several types of heat treatments are used to alter or to enhance some properties of cast irons and thus to increase their usefulness.

Aging. It is applied to relieve the casting stresses without materially affecting physical properties. It is carried on during 1 to 5 hours in the temperature range of 450°C to 550 °C.

Annealing. It is carried out for 1 to 5 hours at 660°C to 870°C, the temperature depending upon the size of the part. It is intended to reduce hardness and to facilitate machining. However, annealing is done at the expense of some strength.

Baking. It is applied to castings that have been pickled in acid to remove sand and scale. Pickling makes castings brittle but baking for a few hours at 150°C removes this brittleness.

Quenching. Quenching cast iron in oil or water after it has been heated above the critical range increases its hardness and also its brittleness.

Drawing or tempering. This is done by reheating the quenched metal to a temperature below the critical temperature. It reduces the brittleness but still leaves an increase of hardness. By such a treatment a Brinell hardness number from 200 to 400 can be attained, the value depending on the quenching and tempering temperature.

2.5.3. Wrought Iron. The word "Wrought" means that the metal possesses sufficient ductility to permit hot and/or cold plastic deformation.

Wrought iron is a mixture of pure iron and 1 – 3% slag. It also contains traces of carbon, silicon, manganese, sulphur and phosphorus. It is made in this manner : First of all, all the elements in the iron (C, Si, Mn, S, P) are removed, leaving almost pure iron. The molten slag from the open-hearth furnace is then intentionally added into vessels containing pure iron and thoroughly mixed into it. The final mix is then squeezed in a press to remove excess slag and reduced into billets by a rolling mill. The material will consist of fibres of pure iron separated by thin layers of slag material. These layers of glass like slag material acts as barriers to corrosion which may attempt to penetrate the iron. The billets can be reheated to form bars, tubing, plates, structural shapes, pipe, forgings, bolts and nuts, nails, rivets, chains, crane hooks, railway couplings, barbed wire, boiler tubes, fittings, and so on.

Wrought iron is ductile and soft and is most readily forged and forge welded. It can with stand sudden and excessive loads. It can neither be hardened nor tempered like steel. The strength of wrought iron can be increased by alloying, typically with nickel (1.5 – 3.5%). The ultimate strength of wrought iron can be increased by cold working and subsequent aging.

A typical chemical composition of wrought iron is as given below :-

C : 0.02 – 0.08%, Si : 0.10 – 0.20%, Mn : 0.02 – 0.10%

S : 0.02 – 0.04%, P : 0.05 – 0.20%

2.5.4. Semi-steel. Semi-steel is not steel, but the name is given to the product made by meltinmg 20 to 40% steel scrap with cast iron in the cupola. The product is a tough, close-grained cast iron.

2.5.5. Steels. Steels are alloys, the essential ingredients of which are iron and carbon (upto 2%). The carbon is distributed throughout the mass of the metal not as elemental or free carbon but as a compound with iron. Steels also contain definite amounts of inevitable impurities which include silicon, manganese, sulphur and phosphorus. Alloying elements are added to these plain carbon steels to produce special purpose steels.

Classification of Steels. Steels can be grouped into four main categories : Plain carbon steels, Alloy steels and Special alloy steels, and Cast steels

1. Plain Carbon Steels. Plain carbon steels are those containing only two elements – iron and carbon. Silicon, manganese, sulphur and phosphorus exist as impurities and not as ingredients. These constituents have negligible effect on steels when their extent does not exceed: 0.3 – 0.4% Si, 0.5 – 0.8% Mn, 0.08% P and 0.04% S.

Plain carbon steels can be classified according to their carbon content:

(*a*) Low carbon or mild steel   0.05 to 0.30% C

(*b*) Medium carbon steel   0.30 to 0.60% C

(*c*) High carbon steel   0.60 to 1.50% C

Sulphur is a harmful impurity in steel. It combines with iron chemically to produce iron sulphide which forms in the grain boundaries. Iron sulphide, because of its low melting point, produces red-shortness in steels, that is, causes brittleness at forging temperatures.

Phosphorous is also a harmful impurity in steels, because it causes brittleness.

Silicon is a very good deoxidizer. It removes the gases and oxides, prevents blowholes and thereby makes the steel tougher and harder. Manganese also serves as a good deoxidizing and purifying agent. It also combines with sulphur to form manganese sulphide and thereby reduces the harmful effects of sulphur remaining in the steel. When used in ordinary low carbon steels, it makes the metal ductile and of good bending qualities.

(*a*) **Low Carbon Steels.** Low carbon steel is used extensively to make industrial products and also in the construction industry. The product applications include : pipes, tubes, storage tanks, railroad cars, automobile frames, nuts, bolts, automobile bodies and galvanized sheet steel. These steels are soft, very ductile, easily machined, easily welded by any process. Since the carbon content is low, these steels are unresponsive to heat treatment.

Free-cutting Steel. These carbon steels have an increased sulphur content (resulphurized steels) which result in a relatively high manganese sulphide, MnS content of controlled globular shape. This steel has excellent machining properties. Free cutting or free machining steels may contain an insoluble, soft element, primarily lead (0.15 – 0.35%) (leaded steels) instead of higher percentage of sulphur. The drawback of these steels is that they become less ductile and fatigue strength and tensile strength are slightly reduced. The wear of cutting tools (due to reduced ductility) can be reduced with affecting the mechanical properties of the steel by the use of calcium as a deoxidizing agent. When cutting such steels, a complex, low-shear-strength oxide forms on the rake face of the tool. When "Tellurium" is added to a leaded steel, it will further improve the machinability of steels. Its content is 0.03 – 0.05%.

This free machining steel is extensively used in automatic screw machines.

(b) **Medium Carbon Steels.** These steels can be hardened and tempered. Thus, these steels can be used for products requiring greater strength and wear resistance. Typical product applications include : forgings, castings, axles, shafts, crank shafts, connecting rods, and any machined part that requires a greater strength than that can be provided by low carbon steels.

(c) **High Carbon Steels.** These steels respond better to heat treatment as compared to medium carbon steels. So, these are used to make products which must have high strength, hardness, and good resistance to wear. This steel is often available in annealed state and the finished product is then heat treated to its proper hardness. Typical product applications include : forgings and a wide variety of tools, such as drills, taps, reamers, dies and hand tools. This steel is also used for making products requiring edges, for example, cutlery, chisels, shear blades, planer tools and so on and also for spring wire, and for cable and wire rope. These steels are not so ductile as the medium carbon steels. In the higher carbon ranges, the extreme hardness is accompanied by excessive brittleness. The higher the carbon content, the more difficult it is to weld these steels.

2. Alloy Steels. A steel is said to be alloyed when its composition incorporates specially introduced alloying elements, absent in plain carbon steels, or when the silicon and/or manganese content exceeds the usual percentage. As already discussed, the alloying elements are added to modify and/or enhance the properties of steel, that is, to achieve one or more of the following aims :-

    to produce fine grained steel

    to improve wear resistance, corrosion resistance

    to improve hardenability and hardness

    to improve machinability

    to improve weldability

    to improve electrical properties

    to improve physical properties at high temperatures

    to improve tensile strength, ductility, elastic properties etc.

The most frequently employed elements for alloying steel are : Cr, Ni, Mn, Si, Mo, Va, W, Cu and Al, and to a lesser extent cobalt, beryllium, Titanium and boron. Often combinations of alloying elements are used.

Effects of Alloying elements in Steel

Chromium. The addition of chromium results in the formation of various carbides of chromium which are very hard, yet the resulting steel is more ductile than a steel of the same hardness produced by a simple increase in carbon content. Chromium also refines the grain structure so that these two combined effects result in both increased toughness and increased hardness. The addition of chromium increases the critical range of temperatures and raises the strength at high temperature. Alloy of chromium resists abrasion and wear. Chromium also increases resistance to corrosion and oxidation. The amount of chromium may be from a fraction of a percent to about 30%.

Nickel. It also increases the critical range of temperature. Nickel is soluble in ferrite and does not form carbides or oxides, and thus increases the strength without decreasing the ductility, Case-hardening of nickel steel results in a better core than can be obtained with plain carbon steels. Chromium is frequently used with nickel to obtain the toughness and ductility provided by the nickel and the wear resistance and hardness contributed by the chromium. The amount of nickel may be upto 50%.

Manganese. It is added to all steels as a deoxidizing and desulphurizing agent, but if the sulphur content is low and the manganese content is high (over one per cent), then it is classified as a manganese alloy. It lowers the critical range of temperatures. It increases the time required for transformation, so that oil quenching becomes practicable. The percentage of manganese varies from 0.4 to 2.0 and 11 to 14%.

Silicon. It is added to all steels as a deoxidizing agent. When added to very-low-carbon steels it produces a brittle and a high magnetic permeability. The principal use of silicon is with other alloying elements, such as manganese, chromium, and vanadium, to stabilize the carbides. The usual amount of silicon is upto 0.8%. However in heat resisting stainless steel it can be upto 3%.

Molybdenum. It acts very much like chromium but is more powerful in action. It also increases the depth of hardening after heat- treatment. Molybdenum finds its greatest use when combined with other alloying elements such as nickel, chromium or both. Nickel molybdenum and nickel-chromium-molybdenum steels retain the good features of the nickel chromium steels and in addition have better machining qualities. Molybdenum increases the critical range of temperature. Except for carbon, it has the greatest hardening effect and results in the retention of a great deal of toughness. It varies from 0.20 to 0.70%.

Vanadium. It is used to toughen and strengthen the steel to reduce the grain size and to act as a cleaner and degasifer. It has the desirable effect of increasing the life of tools, springs and other members subjected to high temperatures. As vanadium has a very strong tendency to form carbides, hence it is used only in small amounts, 0.2 to 0.5% in alloy carbon tool steels and 1 to 5% in high speed steels.

Tungsten. It is widely used in tools steel because the tool maintains its hardness even at red heat. Tungsten produces a fine dense structure and adds both toughness and hardness. Its effect is similar to molybdenum except that greater quantities must be added. The amount of tungsten in steel can vary from 0.4 to 22%.

Cobalt. Cobalt is commonly used in high speed to increase the hot hardness so that the cutting tools can be used at a higher cutting speeds and temperatures and still retain their hardness and a sharp cutting edge. Its content ranges from 5 to 12%.

Copper. Copper lowers the critical temperatures. Copper is added to steel (from 0.15 to 0.30%) only to improve its resistance to atmospheric corrosion. When more than 0.75% copper is added, steel can be precipitation hardened.

Aluminium. Aluminium deoxidizes efficiently, restricts grain growth and is the alloying element in nitriding steel. Its content ranges from 1 to 5%.

Sulphur. It is an undesirable impurity in steel because its forms iron sulphide, which can result in cracking. However, in the presence of proper amount of Mn, it forms Mn S which improves the machinability of steels. Its content may very from 0.06 – 0.30%.

Boron. Boron (not exceeding 0.003%) is very effective in increasing the hardenability of low and medium carbon steels. It has no effect on tensile strength of steel.

Classification of alloy steels. Alloy steels may be classified according to—their chemical composition, structural class and purpose.

(a) Classification according to chemical composition

(*i*) Three component steels, containing one alloying element in addition to Fe and C.

(*ii*) Four component steels, containing two alloying elements, and so on.

(b) Classification according to structural class

(*i*) **Pearlitic.** This class of steel is obtained when the amount of alloying elements is relatively small (upto 5%). It has good machinability and its mechanical properties are considerably improved by heat treatment.

(*ii*) **Martensitic.** The amount of alloying elements is greater than 5%. These steels have a very high hardness and present difficulties in machining.

(*iii*) **Austenitic.** A very large percentage (10 to 30%) of certain alloying elements (Ni, Mn or Co) enables the austenite structure to be retained in steel at room temperature. This class includes : stainless steels, nonmagnetic steels and heat-resistant steels.

(*iv*) **Ferritic.** This class contains a large amount of alloying elements (*e.g.* Cr, W or Si) but has a low carbon content. These steels do not respond to hardening. In the annealed condition, their structure comprises alloyed ferrite and a small amount of cementite.

(*v*) **Carbidic or ledeburitic.** These steels contain considerable amounts of carbon and carbide-forming elements, Cr, W, Mn, Ti, Nb and Zr.

(*c*) **Classification according to purpose**

Alloy steels can be classified as :- Structural steels, tool steels, and special alloy steels. Structural steels are used to make machine components, structural components and structures. Structural steels may be either of straight carbon or alloy types. Their carbon content does not usually exceed 0.5 or 0.6%.

(*i*) **Alloy Structural Steels.** Alloy structural steels are divided into three groups depending upon the total content of alloying elements :

low-alloy : upto 2%

medium-alloy : 2 to 5%

high-alloy : 5%

After suitable heat treatment alloy structural steels acquire higher mechanical properties than carbon structural steels. This is due to the higher hardenability and, consequently, more uniform properties along the cross-section of alloy steels. This feature is of special importance for parts with a large cross-section. Alloying elements introduced into structural steels strengthen the ferrite, refine the grain and increase the resistance to softening on heating to moderate temperatures.

Certain grades of alloy structural steels will be considered below :

Silicon Steels

1. Si 1.25 – 2.5%, C 0.5 to 0.65, Mn 0.6 to 0.9

These steels are used for all possible types of springs. Their mechanical properties after quenching and tempering are very high.

2. Si 0.5 to 1.0, Mn 0.7 – 0.95

Used for structural purposes.

3. Si 3.4% , Mn 0.3, C 0.05 (less)

This steel possesses extremely low magnetic hysterisis. It is widely used for laminations of electrical machines.

Chrome-silicon-manganese Steels

C 0.17 – 0.39, Si 0.9 – 1.2, Mn 0.8 – 1.1, Cr 0.8 – 1.0

This steel is used to make shafts, axles and weldments that are to operate under alternating loads.

Manganese Steels. Manganese steels can be of low carbon low manganese type or high carbon high manganese type.

1. Low alloy manganese structural Steels (C upto 0.5% and Mn 0.9 to 1.8%) possess good plastic properties and respond easily to elongation and rolling in both hot and cold conditions. Their weldability is also good.

2. High alloy manganese Steels (C 0.9 to 1.0%, Mn 12 to 14%) acquire purely austinitic structure after being quenched in water from 1000 to 1050°C. This steel is used for parts requiring high toughness in conjunction with high wear resistance, for example, buckets and lips of dredgers, excavators and drag lines, stone crusher jaws, railway track frogs and switches etc.

Chrome-molybdenum Steel. This steel (Cr 0.40 - 10.0%, Mo 0.2 to 1.5%) is used to make heavily loaded bolts, studs, gears and shafts. Its excellent weldability has found chrome-molybdenum steel applications in welded structures.

Plain Nickel Steels.

1. Ni 6%, Mn 0.3 to 0.8%, C 0.1 - 0.55%

This steel is used for parts subjected to alternating stresses, impacts and shocks.

2. Ni 20 - 30%, C 0.4 - 0.5%

This steel is used for steam turbine blades, I.C. engine valves etc.

Chromium Steel. Cr 0.7 to 11%, C 0.15 - 0.5% This steel is used for automobile and tractor valves, tappets, wrist pins, idler studs etc. They are also used for gears operating at high speeds and medium loads, claw clutches, bushings, worms, balls rollers and races for bearings.

Nickel-Chrome Steel

1. *Mild nickel-chrome Steels.*

Composition. 3.0 - 3.75% Ni, 0.3 to 0.6% Mn, 0.4 to 0.8% Cr, 0.25 to 0.35% C.

Product applications. Crankshafts, axles and parts requiring strength and lightness.

2. *Medium nickel-chromium Steels.*

Composition. Ni 3.0 - 3.75%, Mn 0.25 - 0.55%, Cr 0.5 - 0.8%, C 0.25 - 0.35%

Product applications. Used for highly stressed parts subjected to shock such as axles, connecting rods, tubes and plates.

3. *High tensile nickel-chrome Steels.*

Composition. Ni 4%, Mn 0.5%, Cr 1.0 - 1.25%, C 0.3%

Product applications. Used for very highly stressed parts such as crankshafts, connecting rods, piston rods etc.

4. *Air hardening Ni-Cr Steels.*

Composition. Ni 3.75 - 4.5%, Mn 0.35 - 0.65%, Cr 1.0 - 1.5%, C 0.25 - 0.32%

Product applications. Used where strong light parts are required such as gears, highly stressed shafts, tubes and turnbuckles etc.

Molybdenum Steels

Composition. Mo 0.2 - 0.7%, Mn 0.3 - 1.0%, Si 0.1 - 0.35, C 0.15 - 0.7%.

Product applications. High cost restricts its use. Can be used as rolled sections, forgings and castings. Also used for heat resistant properties.

Nickel-chrome-Molybdenum Steels. This steel is similar to nickel-chrome steel but an additional amount of molybdenum (0.3 to 0.6%) is added. Used for structural purposes.

Nickel-chrome-vanadium Steels. Vanadium (upto 0.2%) added to nickel-chrome steels hardens the steel. It is a very effective deoxidizing element and improves mechanical properties and fatigue strength.

Chrome-nickel-tungsten Steel. It is used after hardening and low-temperature tempering or after carburising followed by quenching and tempering.

(*ii*) **Alloy tool Steels.** There are two types of alloy tool steels available. Low alloy tool steels and High-alloy tool steels. Low alloy tool steels contain lower contents of alloying elements. They possess higher hardness and wear resistance in comparison with carbon steels. High-alloy tool steels contain considerable amounts of alloying elements (W, Va and Cr etc.) which are carbide forming elements that increase the ability of the steel to retain the hardness and cutting properties of the tool at elevated temperatures (red-hardness). These steels are called as "High Speed Steels" (H.S.S.) because tools made from these steels can operate at higher cutting speeds. They acquire high cutting properties only after heat treatment.

Alloy tool steels have been discussed in detail in chapter 7.

(iii) **Special alloy Steels.** These alloy steels possess special physical and chemical properties to meet the special requirements. These alloy steels can be grouped into the following groups (1) Stainless steels (2) Scale and heat resistant steels (3) Wear resistant steels (4) Magnetic steels, and (5) Alloys with special thermal properties.

1. Stainless Steels. Stainless steels are distinguished by their high resistance to corrosion in various aggressive media, that is, atmospheres of air and water vapour, sea water, solutions of acids or salts etc. There are three types of stainless steels available :

(a) **Austenitic stainless Steels.** These are chrome-nickel steels containing not over 0.12 - 0.14% C, 17 to 20% Cr, and 8 to 11% Ni. The most common steel in this group is the 18–8 stainless steel, containing 18% Cr and 8% Ni. These steels are not hardenable by quenching but respond readily to cold working, followed by quick annealing for severe cold working. These steels are difficult to machine but are readily forgeable and weldable. These steels are nonmagnetic.

Product applications. This steel is used extensively in food processing and handling machinery, kitchen equipment, dairy plants, some textile machinery, surgical and dental instruments and so on. Another most important field of application is in nuclear engineering. Stainless steels are used as cladding for fuel elements, reactor vessels, piping systems, valves, fittings and so on.

(b) **Ferritic stainless Steel.** This steel contains mainly chromium (14 to 18% or 23 to 30%). Chromium forms a dense, this film of chromium oxide on the surface of the steel which reliably protects the part against corrosion. These steels can not be hardened by heat treatment.

(c) **Martensitic stainless Steel.** This steel is also chromium iron steel (12 to 14% Cr). These steels have good impact properties and are hardenable by quenching in oil from about followed by tempering.

Product applications. These steels have wide and varied applications. These steels are used for : valves, screens, pump shafts, cutlery, bolts, nuts and various parts in the chemical and petroleum industries, steam turbine blades, jet engine compressor blades, carburetor parts, instrument parts, surgical instruments, ball bearings, bushings, valve seats and so on.

Out of three types of stainless steels, austenitic steels are superior in resisting corrosion. They possess the highest resistance to scaling and have superior high temperature strength characteristics.

2. Scale and Heat Resistant Steels. Power plant equipment, gas turbines, jet engines, petroleum refineries, chemical plants and so on, all require components made of steels that would resist oxidation and have good creep properties, for high temperature service. Steels with alloying elements Cr, Ni and Si are used for this purpose. Stainless steels have good resistance to scaling and some categories of stainless steels have been used as scale and heat resistant steels.

Chromium steels (12 to 14% Cr) are sufficiently scale resistant upto 750° – 850°C. An increase in the chromium content to 15 – 17% extends the resistance to scaling to 850° – 1000°C and at a content of 30% Cr, resistance is maintained upto 1100°C. This steel (with C% 0.35) is used principally to make furnace parts, annealing boxes etc. Silchrome (Si + Cr) steels can be used upto 800 – 1000°C. Parts subjected to high temperatures and pressures are frequently made of chrome-nickel-silicon steel (23 - 27% Cr, 18 - 21% Ni and 2 - 3% Si). Parts of steam and gas turbines and valves are made of a complex steel alloy (13 - 15% Cr, 13 - 15% Ni, 2 - 2.7% W, 0.25 - 0.40% Mo and 0.4 to 0.5% C).

3. Magnetic Steels. Magnetic steels and alloys may be classified as soft-magnet and permanent magnet types.

Soft-magnet steels and alloys are used in the production of pole cores, transformers, generators, motors and electromagnets. The most commonly used soft-magnet material is sheet steel (0.35 to 1 mm thick) with a low carbon content (not over 0.1%) and an increased silicon content (3.8 to 4.2% in transformer steel and 0.8 to 2.3% in dynamo steel).

Permanent magnets are installed in many measuring instruments, radio apparatus, loud speakers and magnetos etc. These magnets are made of complex steels alloyed with Co (15 - 40%), 1.5 to 9% Cr, upto 10% W, 0.4 - 1% C, Ni, Cu, and Al. These steels are hardened at high temperatures (1300°C) and are slowly cooled in a magnetic field. This is followed by tempering operation at 600°C.

4. Shock Resisting Steels. for resisting severe shock and fatigue stresses.

   (*i*) 0.50% C, 2.25% W, 1.50% Cr, 0.25 Va.

   (*ii*) Silicon-manganese steel : 0.55% C, 2.00% Si, 0.80% Mn and 0.30% Mo. This steel
         is mainly used for leaf and coil springs.

5. Alloys with special thermal properties. Alloys with a high nickel content (35 to 44%) and a low carbon content (upto 0.35%) have an austenitic structure which ensures a very low linear co-efficient of thermal expansion. 'Invar' (Ni 36%) is used in measuring instruments, for example, for geodetic and optical instruments. These steels are also used to make watch springs, tuning forks etc.

Cast Steels

A plain carbon steel is an alloy of iron and carbon varying up to 2.0%. The plain or alloyed cast steel is used where castings of improved properties are required over iron or malleable castings. Cast steel is tougher and stronger, weighs less for the same strength of stiffness and has a higher endurance limit than cast iron. They are used for machine members of intricate shape that require high strength and impact resistance, such as locomotive frames, large internal combustion engine frames, gears, wheels and many small and intricate highly stressed machine parts. Steel castings are more difficult to produce than iron castings and are more expensive. Corrosion resistance can be improved by the use of alloys or protective coatings. Alloy-steel castings have also been developed to meet the demands of industry for greater strength and reliability of cast machine members.

2.5.6. Some Important Terms Used in Steel Industry

1. Killed Steel. Steel that has been deoxidized with a strong deoxidizing agent, such as Si or Al, in order to eliminate a reaction between C and O_2 during solidification. Ingots of killed steel are sounder, containing fewer gas holes and more homogeneous than non-killed steel. These are desirable characteristics for forgings and heavy rolled section.

2. Semi-killed Steel. These steels are partially deoxidized and are suitable for applications where great structural uniformity is not needed, as in many steels used for construction purposes.

3. Rimmed Steel. Rimmed steel or unkilled steel is a steel which gives out gases during cooling and freezing, because it has not been deoxidized.

2.6. HEAT TREATMENT OF STEELS

1. Annealing. The definition of annealing process and its aims have already been given under article 2.4. The steel workpiece is heated to about 30 to 50°C above the upper critical temperature, (for Hypoeutectoid steels) and Ac_1 (for Hypereutectoid steels) (Line GSK in Fig. 2.3), then holding it at that temperature for a sufficient time to enable the required changes to take place throughout the work piece, and finally cooling slowly with the furnace. The slow cooling can also be done in abed of sand, lime, or fine ashes.

The holding time in the furnace at the annealing temperature usually ranges from 30 to 60 minutes per tonne of charge. The cooling rate from 150 to 200°C per hour is a regular practice, depending upon the amount of carbon and other elements in the steel. The annealing temperatures for steels of different carbon contents are given below :

Carbon content, %	Annealing temperature °C
< 0.12	875 – 925
0.12 to 0.25	840 – 870
0.30 to 0.50	815 – 840
0.50 to 0.90	780 – 810
0.90 to 1.30 (tool steels)	760 – 780

The above process of annealing in which the metal is heated above the upper critical temperature, is held there until the temperature of the work piece is uniform throughout, and finally cooling the work piece at a slowly controlled rate so that the temperature of the surface and that of the centre of the workpiece is approximately the same, is called "Full annealing". The name is so given because the process wipes out all traces of the previous structure, refines the crystalline structure, softens the metal and relieves the internal stresses previously set up in the metal. Many authors term heating above Ac_3 and then slow cooling as "Full annealing" because the structure gets completely changed to austenite. Heating above and then slow cooling is not termed full annealing because there is only a partial change in the structure. All of the pearlite changes into austenite but only a part of the cementite changes to austenite.

Process annealing. If the steel has been subjected to cold working to increase the tensile strength and yield point, it becomes work hardened and brittle. The metal can be softened by process annealing or "recrystallization". Its purpose is to reduce the distortions of the crystal lattice produced by cold working.

Recrystallization annealing consists in heating the steel to the recrystallization temperature, i.e., to a temperature somewhat below the lower critical temperature, holding at this temperature for a prolonged period and slow cooling. The recrystallization temperature is defined as the lowest temperature which will accomplish complete recrystallization for a particular metal under specific conditions. Recrystallization temperature can be determined from the formula

$$T_{rc} = 0.4 \times \text{melting temperature of the given metal}$$

For steels, it ranges from about 600 to 700°C.

This treatment transforms the grains of steel, broken up or distorted in the process of deformation, back into their normal state (by recrystallization) thus removing work hardening and relieving internal stresses. The process is frequently applied in the production of cold-rolled steel strip, in deep drawing and in wire drawing operations as an intermediate process with the aim of increasing the plasticity of the steel.

Isothermal annealing. In many cases, the ordinary annealing process is incapable of reducing the hardness of many grades of alloy steel to a sufficient degree. In such cases, isothermal annealing is employed. The process consists of two steps. First, the steel is heated above the upper (or only the lower) critical point and held for some time at this temperature. At this stage, austenite is formed in the metal. Then the steel is rapidly cooled to a temperature 50 to 100°C below point A_1, that is 600 – 700°C, and is held at this new temperature until the austenite is completely decomposed to form pearlite. Finally, the steel is cooled in still air. Since the decomposition of austenite takes place at constant temperature, hence the name-isothermal annealing. A more homogeneous structure of the metal is obtained and the results of annealing are more stable. Also, the cycle of heat treatment is substantially reduced in isothermal annealing.

Diffusion annealing. Considerable inhomogeneity is always observed in steel castings and ingots. It is due to the development of dendritic or zonal segregations in the metal. This inhomogeneity can be eliminated or reduced by "Diffusion annealing" or "Homogenising".

In this process the work piece is heated to a high temperature (1000°C – 1100°C) and is held there for a prolonged period (10 to 15 h) and is then cooled with the furnace to 800° – 850°C and finally is further cooled in still air. The composition of the metal becomes more uniform, but the structure becomes coarse grained. Due to this, the steel castings and ingots are subjected to a second full annealing treatment after homogenising.

2. Normalizing. This process has essentially the same purposes as conventional annealing but in differs from full annealing in two respects (*i*) all steels are heated to above either A_3 or Acm lines so as to fall within the austenite region, (*ii*) the cooling is done out in the open in still air (instead of in the furnace) which makes the rate of cooling slightly faster than in full annealing.

Heating all steels to the austenite region helps to homogenize them and the result after normalizing is a stronger pearlite with a finer grain size. This results in higher yield point, tensile strength and impact strength as compared to full annealing. However, the ductility will be some what lower due to slightly increased rate of cooling.

Since normalizing requires less time than conventional annealing, it is extensively replacing the latter in treating low-and medium carbon steels. High-carbon steels undergo normalizing to eliminate the cementite (carbide) net work.

After working (rolling, forging or stamping) certain grades of alloy steel are subjected to normalizing to improve their structure, that is, to bring the grains to their normal condition and to relieve harmful internal stresses in the metal.

Normalizing is particularly important for steel forgings that are to be subsequently heat treated. Sometimes, annealing for machinability is preceded by normalizing. This combined treatment, frequently called a "double anneal" produces a result superior to a simple anneal.

3. Spheroidizing. Spheroidizing may be defined as any heat treatment process that produces a rounded or globular form of carbide. Low carbon steels are spheroidized to meet certain strength requirements before subsequent heat treatment. High carbon steels are spheroidized to improve machinability, especially in continuous cutting operations, such as with lathes and screw machines. Tool steels may also be spheroidized. This is done by heating them to slightly above the critical temperature, holding them at this temperature for a period of time, and then letting them cool in the furnace. The process also tends to improve abrasion resistance and is desirable when the material is to be severely cold worked (for example, extruding, bending, drawing, or cold upsetting).

The difference between the different annealing processes is made clear in Fig. 2.9, a diagram between temperature and time.

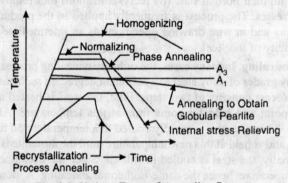

Fig. 2.9. Various Types of Annealing Process.

4. Hardening and Tempering of steel. The heat treating process employed to impart hardness to steel to improve its mechanical properties and to retain its ductility consists of two operations– hardening and tempering.

(*a*) **Hardening.** Hardening consists in heating steel to a temperature from 30 to 50°C above point Ac_3 for Hypoeutectoid steels or above point Ac_1 for Hypereutectoid steels, holding at this temperature until the phase transformations are completed that is, crystal structure is changed from *b.c.c.* at room temperature to *f.c.c.* This is called the austenizing operation, because the other name of *f.c.c.* phase is austenite and then quenching (rapid cooling). After quenching, a martensite structure or martensite + troostite structure is obtained, which is very hard. Hardening of steel is also accompanied by development of high internal stresses and brittleness in steel. So, hardening is followed by tempering to relieve internal stresses and to reduce brittleness. After hardening and tempering, the steel acquires higher strength, hardness and ductility.

Structural steel is hardened and tempered to increase its strength and hardness, and to obtain sufficiently high ductility and toughness, and for many kinds of machine components to provide high wear resistance as well. Tool steel is hardened and tempered mainly to increase its hardness, wear resistance and strength.

The structure (phase) to which austenite will decompose will depend upon the rate of cooling :–

Sorbite, Troostite, Bainite and Martensite. As already discussed, if austenite is obtained in steel and then the heated metal is slowly cooled, the austenite will decompose below line PSK (Fig. 2.4) to form the mechanical mixture of ferrite and cementite called pearlite.

An increased rate of cooling of the steel, corresponding to an increase in the degree of supercooling of the austenite in reference to line PSK, leads to the formation of a finely dispersed pearlite, known as "sorbite" (at about 600°C).

If the steel is cooled at a faster rate, an even finer structure of austenite decomposition is obtained (at 500°C – 550°C) which is called "troostite".

Since the cementite in sorbite and troostite is in a finely divided (dispersed) state, these two structures are harder than pearlite (B.H.N. of pearlite is 180, of sorbite 350 and of troostite 450).

If the temperature is lowered from 550°C to 220°C, acicular (needle like) troostite is formed, which is known as "bainite".

Steel can be cooled from the high-temperature region at a rate so high that the austenite does not have sufficient time to decompose into sorbite or troostite. In this case, the austenite is transformed into a new structural constituent of acicular form, called "martensite". Martensite is ferro-magnetic, very hard and brittle. Its B.H.N. ranges from 650 to 750.

This is explained in Fig. 2.10.

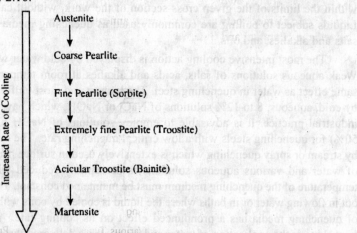

Austenite

Coarse Pearlite

Fine Pearlite (Sorbite)

Extremely fine Pearlite (Troostite)

Acicular Troostite (Bainite)

Martensite

Increased Rate of Cooling

Fig. 2.10. Effect of Rate of Cooling.

Critical Rate of Cooling : It is defined as the minimum rate of cooling at which the austenite is transformed into martensite alone.

Spheroidite : If pearlite is heated just below the eutectoid temperature (say 700°C) and held at this temperature for a day or so, the cementite lamelle in pearlite get transformed to spherical shape. The structure is called "spheroidite". This structure is less conducive to stress concentration because of spherical grains, as compared to cementite (lamelle structure). This, spheroidite is more tough but less hard as compared to pearlite. Due to this, this structure (ductile ferrite + rounded cementite) can be conveniently cold worked.

Heating methods. There are three types of furnaces used for heating the steels for hardening :

(i) **Flame furnaces.** These furnaces are fired with oil, gas or coal and the metal is in direct contact with the flame.

(ii) **Muffle furnaces.** In these furnaces, the metal parts are held in a compartment heated from the outside by flame or electric current.

(iii) **Bath type furnaces.** Here, the parts are heated by immersing in molten salt or lead.

Workpieces should be heated to the prescribed temperature gradually and uniformly to avoid the development of internal stresses in the metal. The more carbon and alloying element in the steel and the more complex the shape of the metal part, the slower it should be heated. Heat transfer to the work is slower in muffle furnaces than in the flame or bath types. The metal is more rapidly and uniformly heated in molten lead or salt baths. Less decarburisation and oxidation is observed in such furnaces. To avoid these two drawbacks, some furnaces work under controlled or protective atmospheres. After the workpieces are heated in such furnaces, their surfaces are clean and bright. The controlled or protective atmospheres are provided by dried gaseous products of the incomplete combustion of fuels, purified nitrogen or other gases.

The heating rate in steel hardening and the holding time in the furnace depend upon the chemical composition of the metal and the shape and cross-section of the workpiece. The heating rates can be in the range given below, per mm of work section :

1.5 to 2 min in an electric furnace, 1 min in an internally fired furnace 0.5 min in a salt bath and 0.1 to 0.15 min in a lead bath

The isothermal time at the given temperature for machine parts is often taken from 15 to 25% of the through heating time.

Quenching Media. Quenching in hardening should enable a martensite structure to be obtained within the limits of the given cross-section of the work, without causing any hardening defects : Liquids subject to boiling are commonly used as quenching media : water, aqueous solutions of salts and alkalies, and oils.

The most intensive cooling action is displayed by cold water which cools steel at a high rate. Weak aqueous solutions of salts, acids and alkalies at room temperature have approximately the same effect as water in quenching steel. The highest and most uniform cooling power is possessed by cold, aqueous, 8 to 12% solutions of NaCl or NaOH, which have proved their worth in regular industrial practice. It is advisable to employ solutions of NaOH of higher concentration (30 to 50%) for quenching steels with a low critical quenching rate. The cooling power can be increased by stream or spray quenching which is extensively used in surface hardening. The quenching power of water and various aqueous solutions is perceptibly reduced when they are heated. So, the temperature of the quenching medium must be maintained constant. This is why quenching is carried out in flowing water or in baths where the liquid is cooled by coils with cold flowing water. Agitation of quenching media has a pronounced effect on its cooling rate. Another method of improving quenching is the application of water and air mixtures delivered through a nozzle. By changing the air-to-water ratio and the pressure of the mixture, the quenching rate can be varied in a range from that corresponding to air to values considerably higher than rates obtained with water. Water and air media are used for heavy forgings, rails, pipes etc. Some alloy steels, notably those containing tungsten, harden when slowly cooled in air.

Quenching media with less intensive action are mineral and vegetable oils. The lower cooling rate prevents quenching cracks caused by rapid contraction of the object being treated. The disadvantage of oil quenching include : the high inflammability, insufficient stability and higher cost. Dies or special fixtures are oil quenched to reduce the warping of work of intricate shape.

Molten salts of potassium and sodium ($NaNO_3$, KNO_3, NaOH, KOH), (their melting points : 130 to 220°C) as well as molten lead, have the lowest heat-extracting power of the liquid quenching media employed in steel hardening.

Comparative cooling rates are :- Agitated (voilent) brine; 5, still brine: 1.2 to 1.3; still water: 1, Agitated water: 4, still oil: 0.3, cold gas: 0.1, still air : 0.02.

Hardening Methods

(*i*) **Conventional hardening.** In conventional hardening, also called continuous hardening or simply quench hardening, quenching is done in a single medium, by immersing the part in it where the part is cooled to room temperature.

This is the most extensively used method. However, in many cases, especially for work of intricate shape, and when it is necessary to reduce distortion, other hardening methods are employed.

(*ii*) **Quenching in two media.** Steel is rapidly cooled (quenched) in the first liquid, usually water, to a temperature from 300° to 400°C, and then is quickly transferred to a quench bath of less severity (oil, as a rule) where it is held until it is completely cooled. This procedure relieves internal stresses in the metal. It is most frequently employed for the heat treatment of tools made of carbon steels.

(*iii*) **Stepped quenching.** This is also done in two stages. The heated steel is first immersed in a quenching medium having a temperature from 150 to 300°C above at the point at which austenite begins to transform into martensite. The part is held until it reaches the temperature of the medium (usually molten salt bath) throughout its whole cross-section. Then the part is transferred to an oil bath where it cools to room temperature.

Comparatively low internal stresses are developed in stepped quenching but is mainly used with parts of smaller cross-section.

(*iv*) **Interrupted quenching or Martempering.** It is a modification of stepped quenching method. Here, after cooling (quenching) in a liquid medium and holding for a definite time, the work is removed from the bath still hot and allowed to cool further in still air to room temperature. The martensitic transformation takes place under conditions of a lower cooling rate and, therefore, the internal stresses are reduced to a still greater extent.

(*v*) **Isothermal quenching or Austempering.** This hardening process is basically the same as the martempering, but has a longer holding time above the martensitic transformation temperature.

The heated steel is quenched in a medium having a temperature from 300°C to 250°C where it is held for as long a time as is needed for the isothermal transformation of the austenite. The main advantages of austempering are that the residual stresses in the metal are substantially reduced, there is less danger of hardening cracks being formed and less warpage. Salt and alkali quenching baths are common for martempering and austempering.

The steps in executing these operations are listed below :

Martempering : Quench steel from the austenizing temperature to a bath just above Ms. Hold it in the quenching medium until the temperature of steel becomes uniform throughout the cross-section. Cool it in air to produce martensite. Temper the martensite as desired. Since, austenite transforms to martensite simultaneously throughout the steel, the distortion in quenching is minimized. This induces greater toughness in the steel.

Austempering : Quench austenized steel to a temperature above that used for martempering. Hold it isothermally to produce "Bainite". The steel possesses greater ductility and toughness than the one quenched and temperature in the conventional manner to give the same hardness.

Difference Between Austempering and Martempering

The difference between the two operations is as under :–

1. In Martempering operation, the austenized steel is quenched to (Ms + 150 to 300°C), then held isothermally and finally cooled to room temperature, whereas in Austempering operation, the austenized steel is quenched to a higher temperature before holding it isothermally at that temperature and finally cooling to room temperature.

2. Holding isothermally is for a much longer period for austempering as compared to martempering.

3. The product after isothermal holding is "Bainite" in the case of austempering, whereas it is "Martensite" in the case of martempering. Bainite being more tough and stress free as compared to Martensite, no tempering is necessary with bainite, whereas martensite formed in Martempering is then tempered as usual.

The difference is illustrated in Fig. 2.11.

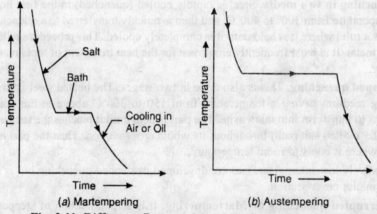

Fig. 2.11. Difference Between Martempering and Austempering.

(*vi*) **Surface hardening.** Parts subjected to heavy impact and fatigue loads (gears, worms, spindles and campshafts etc.) must have a hard, wear resistant surface and a soft tought core. For this, the heat treatment process of surface hardening is used. It is a selective heat treatment in which high hardness is imparted to the surface layers of the work, whilst the tough core is retained. The procedure adotped will depend upon the percentage of carbon in steel. Low carbon steels having upto about 0.2% C are subjected to chemical heat treatment (Casehardening) processes such as carburising, Nitriding, cyaniding and carbo-nitriding etc (discussed ahead). However, parts made of steels including alloy steels, high enough in C (0.4 to 0.7%) to quench harden, may be given a suitable heat treatment which results in only surface hardening or slight penetration hardening of the job. Only the surface layers of the work are heated to the hardening temperature and it is then quenched in water or in some other medium. Two of the methods in widest use are :-

1. Electric induction heating of the work surface followed by quenching.

2. Local heating of the work surface with a hot flame followed by quenching.

Electric Induction Surface Hardening Process :- The job is heated either in an electric furnace or by means of an inductor block or coil. Coil is limited to round jobs only, specially, when only a part of a round job (tooth hardening of a gear or pinion shaft) is to be hardened. The inductor block or coil surrounds the surface to be hardened, but removed from actual contact with it. To ensure uniform heating, the job should be properly centred with the coil.

The working of the inductor block or coil is based on the principle of a transformer. A high voltage current is passed through the coils which form the primary of the transformer. A low voltage and high amperage current is induced in the surface of the job (that forms the secondary) which rapidly heats the metal to any temperature desired. With proper control of the high frequency current and the time of exposure, the temperature indicated may be that required for hardening. After that, the electric circuit is opened and the heated surface of the metal is rapidly quenched by a fine spray of water supplied from a water jacket which is conveniently located inside or outside the inductor block or coil. The time required for performance of the steps of the hardening cycle is only a few seconds. Many Carbon and alloy steels may be successfully surface hardened by the induction method, provided they contain a reasonable percentage of carbon to be properly quench hardened. The depth of penetration decreases as the frequency of the current increases. So, the surface hardening of thin walled sections requires high frequency.

The process is efficient and economical only when large quantities of identical parts are to be surface hardened, since, the equipment consists of expensive inductor block or coils, which must be designed to suit each product. Also, automatic timing device has to be arranged to said the particular job

In induction hardening, a thickness of hardened layer may be 1.5 to 3 mm for parts subjected only to wear or to fatigue. For high contact loads, it can be increased to 4 or 5 mm. For especially high contact loads (mill rolls for cold rolling), the hardened layer may reach 10 or 15 mm or even more.

For induction hardening of crank shaft, high frequency current of about 1000 to 10,000 c/s is passed through the copper coil block, which acts as a primary coil of the transformer. Heat of this induced current is used for induction hardening. Crankshaft is held between the coil block and is rotated. After the completion of the heating time, it is immediately quenched. Hardening of pins/bearings is done in a definite sequence to avoid bending of the shaft. Heating temperature is 800 to 850°C.

Product Applications :- Crankshaft bearings and similar bearing surfaces, such as transmission shafts, can shafts, connecting rods, gears, spindles and cylinders etc.

Advantages :- Our other hardening processes :-
1. Short time cycle
2. Close control of the heating zone
3. Uniformity of the surface hardness achieved.
4. The small amount of distortion produced in the heating cycle.

Flame Hardening :- This is a surface hardening process which imparts to the treated parts those hardening properties that would be difficult and expensive to secure by other heat treating processes. For example, it is impractical to surface harden grey C.I. machine parts by heating them in a furnace and then quenching them, bacause, when this is done, warpage, distortion or fracture is likely to occur. For the same reason, it is difficult to surface harden large C.I. or steel sections by usual methods. Flame hardening, however, can be successfully applied to surface harden such parts.

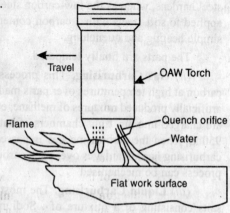

Fig. 2.12. Flame Hardening.

The process consists of applying heat to the metal surface by use of an oxy-acetylene flame, only a thin layer of the heated surface being affected and brought to the hardening temperature.

The torch is moved slowly forward along the part recieving treatment. A stream of water follows the path of the flame, quenching and hardening the surface as rapidly as it is heated, Fig. 2.12 : The depth of hardness is controlled by adjusting the speed of the moving torch. In flame hardening, the hardened layer is usually 2 to 4 mm thick. Both in electric induction hardening and flame hardening, proper heat control and rapid quenching insure a surface hardness that gradually blends into the soft core not touched by the heat. As a result, there is no danger of the surface layer chipping out.

The process of flame hardening depends upon the shape and size of the job. Small parts may be heated individually and then quenched. Parts of cylindrical shape may be slowly rotated and heated by exposing their surfaces to the flame of the torch.

Product applications :- Machine tool beds, rail ends, gear teeth, cams and cam shafts, Castings, forgings and rolled sections irrespective of their size.

Chemical heat treatment of Steel (Case-hardening). The purpose of case-hardening is to increase the surface hardness of steel, its wear resistance etc. This is done by saturating the surface of steel with certain elements from the surrounding medium by their diffusion at high temperatures. The common case hardening methods are discussed below :

1. Carburising :

Here, the parts are carburised hardened and tempered.

It is the process of saturating the surface layer of low-carbon steels at $850° - 950°C$ with carbon from a carbonaceous source capable of giving up its carbon to the metal. The depth of carbon penetration in carburising steel ranges from 0.5 to 2 mm and the carbon content in the surface layer is increased to 0.75 to 1.2%.

An energizer is added to the carbonaceous material to promote reaction. Surface not to be carburised should be copper plated or covered with asbestos powder mixed in fireclay cement.

$$\text{Heating time for Carburising} = \left(\frac{\text{Carburising depth in mm}}{0.2} + 3 \right) \text{ Hours.}$$ There are three methods of carburising :

(*i*) **Solid or pack Carburising.** It is a process of hardening the outer portion of the metal by prolonged heating free from contact with air while packed in carbon in the form of bone char, leather scraps or charcoal or barium carbonate. The outer material absorbs carbon depending upon the composition of part, time and temperature. When the hot metal is quenched this high-carbon steel hardens, whereas the low-carbon steel of the core remains soft and ductile. Case-hardening is applied to soft steels with a carbon content of 0.2 per cent or less which cannot be hardened by simple heating and quenching.

The parts are finally tempered.

(*ii*) **Gas Carburising.** This process consists in passing gases capable of forming atomic carbon at high temperatures over parts made of mild steel. The gases include : natural gas, city gas, artificially produced mixtures of methane, ethane, propane and other gases. The parts to be carburised are charged into air- tight chambers of batch-type or continuous furnaces and are heated to 900 – 950°C. Then the carburising gas is passed through the chamber for a period of 6 to 10 h. Gas carburising has advantages over pack carburising : takes less time, control is more accurate and the process can be mechanised.

(*iii*) **Liquid Carburising.** The most suitable liquid carburising medium is a bath of molten salts consisting of a mixture of : Sodium carbonate (80%), Sodium chloride (10 to 15%) and silicon carbide (6 to 10%). The reaction in the bath is

$$2Na_2CO_3 + SiC = Na_2SiO_3 + Na_2O + 2CO + C$$

This saturates the metal with carbon. The bath is replenished from time to time. Parts immersed in the bath at a temperature from 870° – 900°C acquire a carburised layer 0.2 mm deep in 40 to 50 min. Liquid carburising results in uniform heating of the work and there is the possibility of quenching direct from the bath.

2. Nitriding. Nitriding is a surface hardening process in which the surface of steel is saturated with nitrogen. It consists in heating the part to a temperature of 480° to 650°C inside a chamber through which a stream of NH_3 is passed. Ammonia gets dissociated :

$$2\,NH_3 = 2N + 3H_2$$

The atomic nitrogen so formed diffused into α-iron and saturates the metal. After nitriding, the work is cooled down to 200°C in a stream of ammonia.

The nitrided parts acquire a very high surface hardness (730 to 1100 BHN). Nitriding increases the wear resistance, fatigue limit and corrosion resistance in air, water and water vapour.

Nitriding is usually applied to medium carbon and alloy steels containing Al, Cr, Mo and other elements capable of forming nitrides (nitralloys). Prior to nitriding, parts should be hardened, tempered and undergo the complete sequence of machining operations, including grinding. Only finish grinding or lapping is done after nitriding. The nitrided case is usually from 0.2 to 0.4 mm thick.

Nitriding is done at low temperatures as compared to hardening and carburising, so it requires more time. But, since no quenching is necessary as the high hardness is obtained directly after the operation. This feature enables hardening defects to be avoided.

Nitriding of Guide Ways :- In the machine tool industry, components like guideways, spindles, bushes and boring bars have been nitrided extensively. Guideways have been nitrided because of their outstanding sliding and running properties, together with extreme wear resistance of the surface. Rigidity of the machine tool is also ensured as the steel before nitriding undergoes a tougheing treatment. Also, siezing or corrosion does not occur in case of lubrication failures.

Nitriding : is a surface hardening process for ferrous metals (materials) which is heated in a gaseous atmosphere enriched with atomic nitriding (gas nitriding).

Factors affecting the Gas Nitriding Process

Gas nitriding consists of introducing ammonia gas into the furnace containing the charge at temperatures above 450°C, when it splits up into atomic nitrogen and hydrogen. The atomic nitrogen diffuses into the ferrous material to form a hard, were resistant nitrided layer. The usual range of temperature employed for nitriding is between 490 and 550°C. Temp. is the factor which decides the hardness of the nitrided layer (case) and higher the temp., lower is the surface hardness and deeper is the case.

Nitriding is a thermo-diffusion process and time also plays an important role in deciding the case depth. The usual time of nitriding varies from 20 to 80 hours. As the time of nitriding increases, the depth of the nitrided layer increases, but the maximum surface hardness obtained is decreased due to diffusion.

The degree of dissociation of NH_3 during nitriding must be maintained between 20 to 40% by maintaining suitable rate of flow of the gas.

Another important consideration in nitriding is the microstructure of steel to be nitrided. Before nitriding, the steel must be in a quenched and tempered condition. The temperature of hardening should be accurately controlled to get the optimum prior structure for nitriding. High temperature coarsens the grain structure, thereby reducing the toughness of the core as well as the quality of the nitrided layer.

Reactions in the Gas Nitriding Process :- Ammonia gas dissociates into atomic nitrogen and hydrogen above 450°C, according to the following reaction :

$$2\,NH_3 \longrightarrow 2N + 3H_2$$

This atomic nitrogen will participate in nitriding of the job and part of it will be absorbed. There are two steps in the nitriding reaction :

1. The dissociation of ammonia
2. Absorption of atomic nitrogen by the steel.

The unabsorbed atomic nitrogen immediately changes to molecular nitrogen, which does not help nitriding, and hence must be flushed out of the furnace, under pressure, together with superfluous hydrogen and the undissociated ammonia. Thus, the dissociation % age of $N\dot{H}_3$ is a measure of control of the process.

Advantages :- Nitriding of steel guideways has the advantage over induction hardening and through hardening processes, because of the inherent qualities of the process, like, minimum distortion (since temp. employed is low and no quenching is involved) and the available higher hardness.

Advantages of Nitriding Process :

1. It is simple and has a low cost.
2. There is no quenching, hence, no stresses or distortion are caused.
3. The surfaces are extremely hard.
4. Dimensional changes caused during the process are smaller as compared to other case hardening process.
5. It is possible to mask surfaces, which are to remain soft.

3. Cyaniding. In this process of surface hardening, both carbon and nitrogen are added to the surface layer of steel. The process is based on the decomposition of cyanide compounds that easily release the cyan group (CN). Since the cyan group contains carbon and nitrogen atoms, iron is saturated with both at the same time. Cyaniding produces a thin (0.1 to 0.2 mm) but very hard case in a very short time. The process is most commonly applied to steels containing from 0.2 to 0.4% C. It is especailly effective for medium and small parts, such as, screws, clamps, washers, gears, piston pins, small shafts etc. Cyaniding involves heating the steel in a liquid or solid medium.

(*i*) **Pack Cyaniding.** The powdery mixture for this process consists of : 60 to 80% charcoal, 40 to 20% potassium ferrocyanide $K_4 Fe (CN)_6$. The cyaniding temperature is from 540° to 560°C and the holding time is from 1.5 to 3h. The method is mainly used to improve the cutting properties of tools.

(*ii*) **Liquid Cyaniding.** is more widely used. The bath consists of molten neutral salts ($Na_2 CO_3$, NaCl, etc.) in which various cyanide compounds, such as NaCN, Ca $(CN)_2$, etc. are dissolved. Liquid cyaniding may be classified into three groups :-

Low-temperature Cyaniding. The bath contains : 25 to 40% NaCN, 20 to 45% Na_2CO_3 and 10 to 20% NaCl. The cyaniding temperature is 550° to 600°C and the holding time ranges from 5 to 30 min. The case depth is 0.02 to 0.04 mm and is very hard having good wear resistance and low friction in machining. The process is employed mainly for treating high speed steel tools as it increases tool life considerably.

Medium-temperature Cyaniding. The bath consists of : 20 to 25% NaCN, 25 to 50% NaCl and 25 to 50% Na_2CO_3. The cyaniding temperature is 800 – 850°C and the holding time is from 5 min to 1.5 h depending upon the case depth required. The case depth varies from 0.075 to 0.50 mm. The process is followed by quenching and tempering. The process is mainly used for parts made of medium-carbon steels, such as bolts, nuts, small gears etc.

High-temperature Cyaniding. is carried out at 900° – 950°C in baths consisting of 6 to 10% NaCN, 80 to 84% $BaCl_2$ and upto 10% Nacl. The holding time is upto 1.6 h and the case depth is form 0.5 to 1.5 mm. The process is followed by quenching and low-temperature tempering (160° – 180°C).

4. Carbonitriding. When the cyaniding process is carried out in a gas atmosphere, it is called carbonitriding. The gas mixture consists of natural (or city) gas, 70 to 80% and ammonia (20 to 30%). The process temperature is 850° to 930°C. The process is slower than the liquid cyaniding.

5. Chapmanizing :- It is a heat treatment process which differs somewhat from cyaniding. It employs NH_3 gas in addition to the molten cyanide bath. The dissociated NH_3 gas is bubbled through the molten cyanide bath, thus, increasing the amount of N_2 gas present.

6. Boronizing :- It is a surface hardening heat treatment process. The element added to the surface of the part is boron. For this, the part is heated using boron containing gas or solid in contact with the part. Extremely hard and wear resistant surface is obtained. The case depth ranges from 0.025 mm to 0.075 mm. Common materials hardened by the method are tool steels. Typical product applications are : Tool and Die steels.

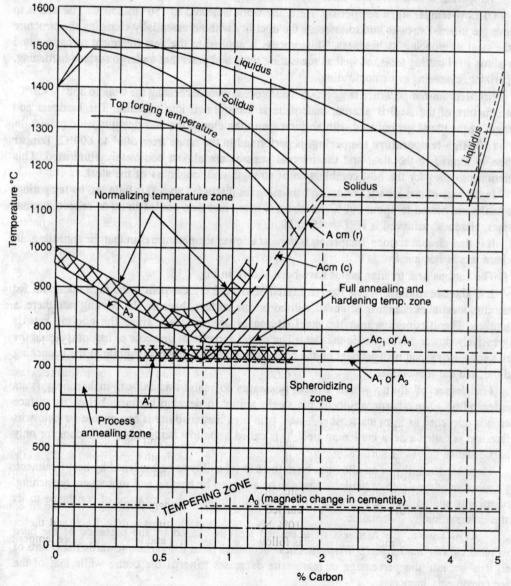

Fig. 2.13. Heat Treating Zones.

Typical product applications are : Tool and Die steels.

(b) **Tempering**

Tempering or Drawing. When a steel specimen has been fully hardened it is very hard and brittle and has high residual stresses. The steel is unstable and tends to contract on aging. These internal stresses can be relieved by an additional heating process which softens the material and toughens it. This heating process is called tempering or drawing. After the specimen has been fully hardened by being quenched from above the critical temperature, it is reheated to some temperature below the critical temperature for a certain period of time and then allowed to cool in still air. The temperature to which it is reheated depends upon the composition and the degree of hardness or toughness desired. Tempering reduces the elastic limit and ultimate strength, slightly, but they are still higher than they were before drawing.

Tempering is classified into three types according to the heating temperatures :

(i) **Low-temperature tempering.** Here, the work is heated to 150° to 250°C. The aim is to relieve the internal stresses and to increase the ductility without essentially changing the structure of the steel or reducing its hardness. This process is applied to the heat treatment of carbon and low-allow steel cutting tools, as well as measuring tools and parts that undergo surface hardening, carburizing, cyaniding or carbonitriding.

(ii) **Medium-temperature tempering.** This process involves heating the work to 350° – 450°C. The structure of the steel is altered, maternsite is transformed into troostite. The hardness and strength of the metal get reduced with an increase in the elongation and ductility.

(iii) **High-temperature tempering.** is performed in the range from 500° to 600°C. Temper sorbite is formed in the steel and the internal stresses are almost completely eliminated. This operation provides for the best combination of strength and toughness of the steel.

In the case of crankshafts, induction hardening (as discussed above) is followed by tempering. The shafts are heated to about 300°C for about 6 hours and then cooled in air to relieve internal stresses. Hardness achieved is HRC = 45 to 50.

It is thus clear that since Tempering is done at a lower temperature than that for annealing, all the hardness is not lost.

The various heat treating zones have been shown in Fig. 2.13.

2.7. Hardenability : When steel is heated above the critical points and then quenched for hardening, maximum hardness achieved will be on the surface, because the cooling rate there is maximum. The hardness within the steel decreases progressively since the cooling rate is progressively slower further inside the steel. The extent and rate of decrease of hardness inside the steel, varies widely and is dependent on the composition of steel, the cooling rate of the quenching medium, and the section size.

The degree of ability which a steel possesses to resist this fall-off in hardness is its "Hardenability". Thus, hardenability is the steel's ability to develop hardness below its surface when it is quenched to form martensite. A steel with high hardenability is hardenable far below its surface and is called a deep hardening steel. It is called a shallow hardening if it hardens for only a short distance below its surface.

Thus, hardenability of an alloy can be defined as its ability to be hardened by heat treatment. It is a measure of the depth of hardness that can be achieved by heating and subsequent quenching. Hardenability should into be confused with hardness. Hardness is a measure of resistance to its plastic deformation by indentation.

As is known, the hardness of quenched steel is caused by the presence of the hard constituent called "martensite". When hardness decreases from the surface towards the centre of steel, it is because the percentage of martensite decreases towards the centre while that of the softer consituents increases.

In industry, the depth of hardening is usually taken as the distance from the surface to the semi-martensitic zone, that is, 50% martensite and 50% pearlite. This zone is also called as the 50% martensite zone. In Industry, 50% martensite is considered the minimum percentage that should exist, even at the centre of a specimen of consistently reproducible properties are to be developed in heat treating. Full hardening of carbon steels is observed in specimen of diameter or thickness upto 20 mm.

Variables Affecting Hardenability :– The factors that affect the hardenability of steel are :

(*i*) The composition of steel, that is, the carbon content and the alloying elements present in the material.

(*ii*) Grain size of austenite.

(*iii*) Cooling rate.

The maximum hardness of a steel is a function of its C-content. It increases as the percentage of carbon increases. Hardenability further improves with the addition of alloying elements. Alloying elements such as Cr, Mn, Ni and V increase the rate at which the martensite transformation occurs and thus the depth to which full hardness can be achieved. Cobalt is the only known alloying element which decreases hardenability. W, Mo, and Ti, Si, P, B, Al are equally effective for increasing the hardenability of steels.

When austenite is first formed, that is, when steel is heated through its critical range, 732°C to 870°C, the grains are small, but they grow in size as the temperature above the critical range is increased, and to a limited extent, as the time is increased. Fine grain steels do not harden as deeply as coarse grained steels. Coarse grained steels harden better.

Hardenability is directly proportional to the rate of cooling.

The presence of impurities in steel (non-metallic inclusions and undissolved carbides) tends to reduce the hardenability. Again, homogenisation increases hardenability.

Determination of Hardenability: The standard test for determining the hardenability of steel is the Jominy test. In the test, the specimen (a round 100 mm long test bar) made from the particular alloy, Fig. 2.14 is first austenised in a protective atmosphere, that is, heated to the proper temperature to form 100% austenite. It is then quenched at one end with a stream of water at 24°C.

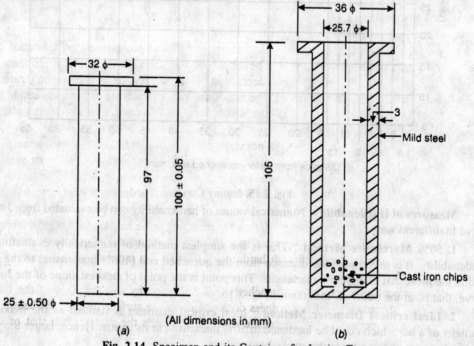

(All dimensions in mm)

(a)   (b)

Fig. 2.14. Specimen and its Container for Jominy Test.

In this way, the quenched end is cooled very rapidly while rest of the specimen is cooled more slowly the farther away it is from the wetted end. The cooling rate thus varies throughout the length of the piece, being highest at the end which is in contact with water. After the specimen is quenched, the hardness is measured along its length at various distances from the quenched end. The curve plotted from hardness measurements is called a Jominy curve or a Hardenability curve, Fig. 2.15.

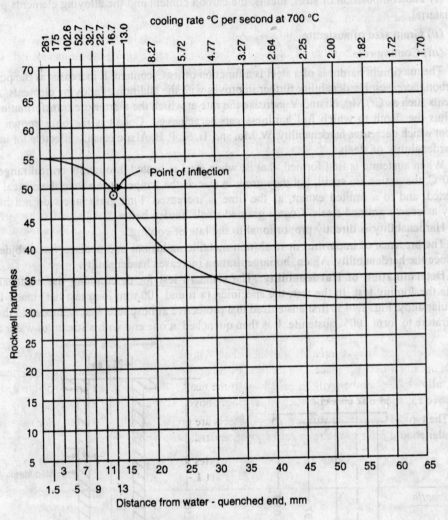

Fig. 2.15. Jominy Curve.

Measures of Hardenability: Numerical values of hardenability can be evaluated from Jominy curve in different ways:

1. 50% Martensite Method : This is the simplest method of numerically evaluating the hardenability. It is in terms of the distance from the quenched end (100% martensite) to the point within the piece that is just 50% martensite. This point is the point of steepest slope of the Jominy curve, that is, at the point of 'inflection', Fig. 2.15.

2. Ideal critical Diameter Method : Ideal critical diameter is defined as the maximum diameter of a bar which could be hardened to 50% martensite at its centre. Hence, larger the value of this diameter, the greater is the steel's hardenability.

3. Specified Hardness Method : In this method, the hardenability of steel is expressed in terms of the distance from the quenched end of the specimen to the point having a specified hardness, Rockwell C, for example, Rockwell C 40.

2.8. DESIGNATION OF STEEL, (INDIAN STANDARD)

Two systems of notation are recommended by IS :

(*a*) Based on ultimate tensile strength.

(*b*) Based on chemical composition.

(*a*) **Based on Ultimate Tensile Strength.** This is applicable to carbon and low alloy steels. The symbol consists of the letter St followed by the number representing the ultimate tensile strength in kgf/mm^2, for example, St 32. The new coding consists of the letter Fe followed by the number representing the ultimate tensile strength in N/mm^2, for example, Fe 410.

(*b*) **Based on Chemical Composition.** This type of designation is preferred if subsequent heat treatment is carried out.

1. Plain Carbon Steels. These are designated by letter C followed by a number representing the average percentage carbon content, for example,

C 14 - carbon steel with 0.14% C.

Its new designation is 14 C4.

Here, the first figure indicates 100 times the average of Carbon content, then letter C, and the last figure indicates 10 times the average percentage of Mn content rounded off to the next integer.

2. Alloy Steels. Here the letter C is omitted and the numbers representing the carbon content are followed by chemical symbols for one or more of the predominant alloying elements followed by numbers indicating their average contents, for example,

15 Cr <u>65</u> - chromium steel with 0.15% C and 0.65% Cr.

20 Cr 18 Ni 2 - Nickel - chromium steel with 0.2% C, 18% Cr and 2% Ni.

The coding of the alloy steels is given below :-

The average alloy content upto 1 per cent, Alloy index number will be : - Average alloy content upto two decimal places, underlined by a bar. For average alloy content one per cent and above, alloy index number will be : rounded to the nearest whole number upto 0.5 rounded down and above rounded up. This coding is clear from above.

The typical uses of the various types of steels are given in Tables 2.2 to 2.6. For more details, the reader should refer to the relevant Indian Standard.

Table 2.2. Tensile Properties and Applications
(IS : 1570 (Part I - 1978)

Designation		Typical uses
Old	New	
St 30	Fe 290	Structural steels sheets for plain drawn or enamelled parts, tubes for oil well casing, steam, water and air passages, cycle, motorcycle and automobile tubes, rivet bars and wires.
St 32	Fe 310	Steels for loco, carriage and car structures, screw stock and other general engineering purposes.
St 34	Fe 330	Structural steel for chemical pressure vessels and other general engineering
St 37	Fe 360	purposes.
St 42	Fe 410	Structural steel for bridges and building construction.

St 50	Fe 490	Structural steel for mines, forgings for marine engines, sheet pilling and machine parts.
St 55	Fe 540	High tensile steel for locomotives carriage, wagon and tramway axles, arches for mines, bolts and seamless welded tubes.
St 63	Fe 620	High tensile steel for tramway axles and seamless tubes.
St 78	Fe 770	High tensile steel for locomotive, carriage and wagon wheels and tyres and machine parts for heavy loading.
St 88	Fe 870	High tensile steel for locomotive, carriage and wagon wheels and tyres.

Table 2.3. Carbon Steels (Unalloyed), IS : 1570 (Part II) - 1979

Steel designation		Typical uses
Old	New	
C 04	4 C 4	Dead soft steel generally used in electrical industry.
C 10	10 C 4	Case-hardening steel used for making camshafts, cams, light duty gears, worms, gudgeon pins, selector forks, spindles, bowls, ratchets, chain wheels, tappets, etc.
C 15	15 C 4	Used for lightly stressed parts. The material, although easily machinable, is not designated specifically for rapid cutting, but is suitable where cold web, such as bending and riveting may be necessary.
C 30	30 C 8	Used for making certain types of cold formed parts, such as shift and brake levers. After suitable case-hardening or hardening and tempering, this steel is also made use of in making parts, such as socket, tie rod, yolk adjustable control levercable, shaft fork and rear hub, 2-wheeler and 3-wheeler lambretta parts, such as sprocket, lever, hubs for forks, cams, rocker arms and bushes are made of this steel. Tubes for aircraft, automobiles, bicycle and furniture are also made of this steel.
C 40	40 C 8	Steel for crankshafts, shafts, spindles, automobile axle beams, push rods
C 45	45 C 8	Steel for spindles of machine tools, bigger gears, bolts and shafts.
C 50	50 C 4	Steel for making keys, shafts, cylinders, machine components requiring moderate wear resistance. In surface hardened condition it is also suitable for large pitch worms and gears.
C 55 and C 55 Mn 75	55 C 4 and 55 C 8	Steel used for making gears, cylinders, cams, keys, crank shafts, sprockets, and machine parts requiring moderate wear resistance for which toughness is not of primary importance.

**Table. 2.4 Carbon and Carbon-Manganese Free Cutting Steels
IS : 1570 (Part III) - 1979**

Designation		Typical Uses
Old	New	
10 S 11	10 C 8 S 10	Low duty bolts, nuts and studs
14 Mn 1 S 14	14 C 14 S 14	Case-hardening steel for camshafts, Tappet rollers, Lightly stressed gears, Gudgeon pins and all relatively lightly stressed and general details requiring high wear hardness.
25 Mn 1 S 14	25 C 12 S 14	Welded parts, may be substituted for C 30 and C 35 steels where deeper hardening with improved machining and higher physical properties are required.

| 40 S 18 | 40 C 10 S 18 | Bolts and Machine details in general |
| 40 Mn 2 S 12 | 40 C 15 S 12 | Bolts and Machine details in general; these are basically oil hardening steels and may be substituted for C 45 and C 50 steels where improved machining, deeper hardening and higher physical properties are required. |

Table 2.5. Alloy Steels (excluding Stainless and Heat Resisting Steels), IS : 1570 (Part IV) - 1978

Designation	Typical uses
20 Mn 2 and 27 Mn 2	Used for welded structures, crank shafts, steering levers, shafting spindles, etc.
35 Mn 2- Mo 28	Used for making general engineering components, such as crank shafts, connecting rods, axle shafts, levers, bolts, etc.
12 Cr 65	Used for roller bearings, measuring instruments, piston pins, and differential pipes.
17 Mn 1 Cr 95	Used for small gear wheels and shafts, carbon joints and steering regulators.
20 Mn 1 Cr 1	Used for medium size gear wheels, and shafts of vehicles.
40 Cr 1 Mo 28	Used for making axle shafts, crankshafts, connecting rods, gears, high tensile bolts and studs, propeller shaft joints, etc.
16 Ni 1 Cr 80	Used for gear box and transmission components, cams, camshafts, etc.
40 Ni 2 Cr 1-Mo 28	Used for high strength machine parts, collets, spindles, screws, high tensile bolts and studs, gears, pinions, axle shafts, tappets, crankshafts, connecting rods, boring bars, arbours, etc.

Table 2.6. Stainless and Heat Resisting Steels (IS : 1570 (Part V) - 1972

Designation	Typical uses
07 Cr 17	oil burner rings, Cold headed fasteners, Nitric acid storage tanks, Annealing baskets, Decorative trim etc.
20 Cr 18 Ni 2	Wind-shield wiper arms, bolting materials, paper machinery etc.
07 Cr 19 Ni 9	Autowheel covers, Refrigerator trays, tubular furniture
04 Cr 19 Ni 9 Ti 20	Air craft engine manifolds, expansion joints, Collector rings, High temperature chemical handling equipment.
07 Cr 19 Ni 9 Mo 2	Acid resistant parts and equipment for chemical industry.
22 Cr 13 S 28	Carburettor parts
45 Cr 9 Si 4	Heat resisting outlet valves in oil engines, lorries, cars
80 Cr 20 Si 2 Nil	Highly stressed outlet valves in high speed and heavy oil engines.
40 Cr Ni 14 W 3 S 12	Inlet and exhaust valves for Aero-engines.

Note. Tool steels have been discussed in chapter 7. The relevant Indian Standard is : IS : 1570 (Part VI) - 1978

2.9. NON-FERROUS METALS AND ALLOYS

Non-ferrous metals are those which do not contain iron as base. Their melting points are generally lower than that of ferrous metals. They generally suffer from hot-shortness, possess lower strength at high temperature, and their shrinkage is generally more than that of ferrous metals. Non-ferrous metals are used for the following reasons :

1. Low density.
2. Attractive colours.
3. Softness and facility of cold working.
4. Good formability.
5. Resistance to corrosion.
6. Special electrical and magnetic properties.
7. Fusibility and easy of casting.

The principal non-ferrous metals used for engineering purposes are : Aluminium, Copper, Tin, Zinc, Nickel, Titanium, Magnesium, etc. and their alloys.

2.9.1. Aluminium and its Alloys. Aluminium is silvery white in colour. The most important advantages of aluminium are :

(*i*) its low specific gravity (2.7)

(*ii*) high electrical and thermal conductivities

(*iii*) high ductility

(*iv*) corrosion resistance in various media.

Due to its above properties, aluminium is extensively used where a light non-corrosive metal is necessary as in aircraft, missile and automobile components, where the saving of weight is an important advantage. Due to its good electrical conductivity, it is used for electrical wires and overhead cables. The high resistance to corrosion and its non-toxicity makes it a useful metal for cooking utensils. Under ordinary conditions, water and air have practically no effect on it. It has the property of being beaten into foil and this Aluminium foil is now widely used as silver foil. Aluminium metal of high purity has high light reflectivity and is, therefore, widely used for reflectors, mirrors and telescopes. The melting point of aluminium is 658°C.

Aluminium Alloys. In its pure state, aluminium is weak and soft and so has few applications. Aluminium finds its widest uses when alloyed with small amounts of other metals and then it becomes hard and strong, while still retaining its light weight. In its alloyed state, it can be blanked, formed, drawn, forged and cast, welded or brazed. The most useful alloying elements for aluminium are : copper, silicon, manganese, magnesium, iron, zinc and nickel. The effects of copper as an alloying element are to raise the ultimate strength and endurance limit and to improve the casting characteristics and machinability, but its resistance to corrosion gets somewhat lowered. Aluminium copper alloys are used in such applications as crank cases, transmission housings and fittings. Manganese also increases the strength and corrosion resistance of the metal. The aluminium silicon alloys have better corrosion resistance and mechanical properties but poorer machinability than aluminium-copper alloys. They are suitable for marine castings, water jackets, housings and castings where a minimum of machining is needed. Magnesium is added to improve the ductility and resistance to impact.

Aluminium alloys can be classified as : cast or wrought.

Casting alloys are employed in foundary practice and wrought alloys are used to make a great variety of articles by rolling (sheets, plates), forming, drawing (wire, rod, tube), forging and pressworking.

Wrought Aluminium Alloys have a high mechanical strength (comparable to steel). The ductility of these alloys, as well as their cold and hot workability, has found them extensive applications in all branches of industry. Wrought aluminium alloys are further classified as : non-heat- treatable and heat-treatable alloys.

Non-heat-treatable wrought Aluminium alloys, that is, those which do not respond to heat treatment, include the Al-Mn alloy, containing about 1.3% Mn, and Al-Mn-Mg alloys, containing about 2.5% Mg and 0.3% Mn. These alloys possess sufficiently high mechanical strength, and ductility, as well as corrosion resistance and weldability. They are most frequently available in the form of sheets and other shapes.

Heat treatable wrought aluminium alloys include complex alloys of aluminium with copper, nickel, iron, silicon and other alloying elements.

Aluminium alloys harden and attain a high strength by heat treatment in a manner different from that of steels. The aluminium alloy is first 'solution heat treated', then quenched and finally 'age hardened'. In contrast to steel, which becomes hard on quenching, aluminium alloys become soft and ductile. They become hard and strong by 'age hardening'. This process precipitates some of the hardening elements (mainly copper, assisted by magnesium, manganese, and sometimes silicon and nickel) throughout the alloy structure. Some alloys age-harden at room temperature; others age harden more quickly with the application of heat. The application of heat to aluminium alloys is called 'artificial aging'.

An important and interesting wrought aluminium alloy is 'Duralumin' which belongs to Al-Cu-Mg system to which Mn has been, added, to increase the strength and corrosion resistance of the metal, and which includes silicon and iron as inevitable minor constituents. Typical duralumin alloys contain : 2.2 to 5.2% Cu, upto 1.75% Mg, upto 1% Mn, upto 1% Si and upto 1% Fe.

Duralumin is suitable for parts that require severe working, and it has good strength and corrosion resistance. It is widely used in the wrought condition for forgings, stampings, bars, sheets, plates, tubes, wires and extruded sections. The plates/sheets can be spot-welded and are widely used in aircraft construction. It is hardened by allowing it to age for 3 or 4 days. In the heat treated and aged condition, duralumin may have a tensile strength upto 400 N/mm^2.

Aluminium forging alloys (used in smith and closed die forging processes) contain : 1.9 to 5% Cu, 0.4 to 1.8% Mg, upto 0.2% Mn, 0.5 to 1.2% Si and 1 to 2.3% Ni. Forgings of these alloys are heated to 510° – 520°C, quenched in water and then artificially aged for 12 to 18 hours at 150° – 160°C. These alloys are used in the manufacture of pistons, vanes, screws, housings, motors and pump impellers, as well as rings, covers, disks and other parts.

Aluminium - base Casting Alloys. These aluminium alloys contain silicon, copper, magnesium and zinc as the alloying elements. Aluminium alloys containing from 8 to 14% Si are called 'Silumin alloys'. Alloys containing from 10 to 13% Si, and 0.8% Cu, and alloys containing from 8 to 10% Si, 0.3% Mg and upto 0.5% Mn, possess good casting properties, and ample ductility and corrosion resistance. The strength of silumin alloys can be substantially changed by adding certain amounts of manganese, copper and zinc. Their strength can also be increased, if they are modified in the molten condition with a small amount of sodium.

Aluminium alloys castings made in sand moulds, permanent metal moulds, and die casting machines are generally stronger than the poorer grades of cast iron. Better surface finish, closer dimensional tolerances, and better mechanical properties, together with the savings in machining and finishing costs, make the use of permanent moulds and die castings desirable when the quantity justifies the extra cost of equipment.

Another alloy containing Cu, Ni and Mg and which may be cast or wrought is known as 'Y-alloy'. The alloy contains : 3.5 to 4.5% Cu, 1.8 to 2.3% Ni and 1.2 to 1.7% Mg. The alloy retains good strength at high temperature. Y-alloy is, therefore, useful for pistons, and other components in aero engines. It is also largely used in the form of sheet and strip and after proper heat treatment may be brought to a minimum tensile strength of about 350 N/mm^2.

Table 2.7 and Table 2.8 show some of the common aluminium alloys with their properties and uses.

Table 2.7. Characteristics of Some Aluminium Alloys

Sr. No.	Normal composition %, remainder aluminium	Outstanding characteristics	Typical uses
1.	5.0 Si	Excellent casting characteristics and pressure tightness, good weld-ability and very good corrosion resistance.	Carburettor bodies, refrigerator shelf brackets and fittings, cooking utensils, general purpose casting of thin sections.
2.	4.5 Cu - 5.5 Si	Good casting characteristics and pressure tightness good weld-ability.	Ornamental grills, reflectors and general purpose castings, used for castings requiring leak tightness and moderate strength.
3.	7.0 Cu - 1.7 Zn	Good casting characteristics and machining property.	Vacuum cleaner housings, general purpose strength.
4.	7.0 Cu - 2.0 Si 1.7 Zn and 7.0 Cu - 3.5 Si	Provides better pressure tightness, modification alloy-3.	Washing machine agitators, hydraulic brake pistons, diesel cylinder, head covers, general purpose castings with pressure requirements.
5.	10.0 Cu - 0.2 Mg	Retains strength at elevated temperatures, good hardness	Machinability and wear resistance.
6.	0.8 Cu - 0.8 Fe - 12.0 Si - 1.0 Mg - 2.5 Ni	Good high temperature properties, low co-efficient of expansion and machinability and weldability.	Pulleys and sheaves
7.	3.5 Cu, 9.0 Si - 0.8 Mg - 0.8 Ni	Similar to 6 but with improved casting characteristics.	Pulleys and sheaves, automotive and diesel pistons.
8.	10.0 Cu - 0.2 Mg - 0.8 Si	Hard in cast condition, good casting and machinability.	Sole plates for electric hand irons.
9.	4.0 Cu - 1.5 Mg - 2.0 Ni	Good strength at elevated temperature.	Aircraft generator housings, motor cycle, diesel and aircraft pistons, air cooled heads.
10.	7.0 Cu - 5.5 Si - 0.3 Mg	Good casting characteristics with good machinability.	Pistons.
11.	4.5 Cu - 2.5 Si	Good casting characteristics with good machinability and weldability.	Aircraft fittings, aircraft gun control parts, aircraft wheels, railroad car seat frames, compressor connecting rods, fuel pump bodies, aircraft gear housings.
12.	3.8 Mg - 1.8 Zn	Good resistance to corrosion and tarnishing.	Cooking utensils.
13.	3.8 Mg - 1.8 Si	Improved foundary characteristics, but reduced mechanical properties, excellent resistance to corrosion.	Cooking utensils and pipefitting for marine as well as general use.
14.	3.5 Cu - 6.3 Si.	Excellent casting characteristics with good mechanical properties.	Type writers, frames, engine parts, water cooled cylinder heads.
15.	3.5 Cu - 9.0 Si	Low co-efficient of thermal expansion, therefore suitable for high temperature applicatons.	Gas meters and regular parts internal combustion engine cylinder heads.

16. 5.0 Si - 0.5 Mg - 1.3 Cu.	Very good casting characteristics and pressure tightness.	Aircraft supper charge cover
17. 7.0 Si - 0.5 Mg.	Good casting and weld-ability, good pressure tightness and resistance to corrosion.	Machine parts, handwheels, aircraft pump parts.
18. 6.5 Si - 1.0 Cu - 1.0 Ni.	Excellent bearing qualities with good compressive yield strength.	Bearings

Table 2.8. Composition and Properties of Some Aluminium Alloys

Per cent of alloy					General information
Cu	Si	Mn	Mg	Ni	
4.5	1.5	0.3	-	-	Structural casting requiring high strength and *shock resistance*.
4	0.7	0.3	1.5	2.0	Air cooled cylinder heads, pistons of high accuracy I.C. engines.
1.3	5.0	0.5	-	-	General use for high strength and pressure tightness.
0.6	5.0	0.3	-	-	Intricate casting with thin sections, corrosion resistance.
0.9	12.0	0.1	1.1	2.5	Piston in I.C. engines low heat expansion.
4.5	2.5	-	0.3	0.3	Structural casting requiring high strength and shock resistance, modified for use in permanent moulds.
0.6	12.0	0.3	-	-	Excellent casting characteristics.
3.5	8.5	0.5	0.1	0.5	Good mechanical properties.
1.0	-	Sn 6.5	-	1.0	Bearing alloy.
4.5	0.5	0.6	1.5	-	Sheets, plates, tubes rivets with high strength.
4.4	0.8	0.8	0.4	-	Highly stressed forgings.
4.5	1.0	-	0.6	-	Complicated shapes.
0.9	12.5	0.2	1.1	0.9	Press forged pistons I.C. engines.
1.0	1.5	-	-	0.5	Bearing alloy.

2.9.2. Magnesium and its Alloys. Magnesium is the lightest metal (specific gravity = 1.74) that is used for engineering purposes. It is very inflammable and burns with a dazzling flame, developing a great deal of heat. Its melting point is 650°C The mechanical properties of pure magnesium are very low, prohibiting its use in engineering. However, the alloys of magnesium possess much better mechanical properties which ensure their sufficient wide application.

The principal alloying elements added to pure magnesium are : aluminium, zinc and manganese. Aluminium (added in amounts upto 11%), increases the hardness, tensile strength and fluidity of the alloy. Zinc (upto 2%) improves the ductility and castability of the metal. Manganese (0.1 to 0.5%) enhances the corrosion resistance of the alloy. Small amounts of cerium, zirconium and beryllium result in : fine-grained structure, increased ductility and oxidation resistance of the alloys at elevated temperatures.

Magnesium alloys are classified into :

Wrought alloys and Casting alloys.

Wrought Alloys. The common compositions of wrought magnesium alloys are :

(*i*) upto 0.3% Al, 1.3 to 2.5% Mn, Remainder Mg.

(*ii*) upto 3 - 4% Al, 0.6% Zn, 0.5% Mn, Remainder Mg.

These alloys are chiefly used for hot smith and closed-die forged machine parts. They are less frequently used as sheets, tubes or bar stock. The tensile strength of these alloys ranges from 200 to 250 N/mm^2.

Casting Alloys. The common compositions of magnesium casting alloys are :

(*i*) 5 to 7% Al, 2 to 3% Zn, upto 0.5% Mn, Remainder Mg.

(*ii*) 8% Al, 0.6% Zn, upto 0.5% Mn, Remainder Mg.

The castability of these alloys is inferior to that of aluminium base alloys. Their mechanical properties can be considerably increased by heat treatment. This consists in heating the first alloy upto 380°C and the second alloy to 415°C, cooling in air, and aging for 15 to 16 hours at a temperature of 175°C. With this, the heat treatment raises the tensile strength from 160 -- 170 N/mm^2 to 250 N/mm^2.

Uses of Mg Alloys. Magnesium alloys are readily machinable and are virtually adaptable to all forms of metal working and joining such as casting, forging, extruding, inert gas-arc welding, resistance welding and riveting. These alloys show good resistance to atmospheric exposure. However, salt water will attack them unless protected by surface finishing. They have also good resistance to attack by chromic and hydrofluoric acids, alkalies, solvents and most organic compounds such as hydro-carbons, aldehydes, alcohols, phenols, amines, esters and oils.

Magnesium alloys have a high strength-to-weight ratio and are ideal for intermediate stage aircraft and missile components, for example, frame and skin stiffeners, fairings, bulkheads, engine parts, wheels and so on; trucks and ordnance vehicles, for example, crank cases, transmission housings, fuel pumps, roof rails etc.; materials handling equipment, for example dockboards, hand trucks, gravity conveyors, platform trucks and so on ; hand tools, optical equipment, office equipment and die-cast components.

2.9.3. Copper and Copper Alloys. Copper is a valuable metal. It is distinguished from all other metals on account of its red colour. Commercial copper is a tough, ductile and malleable metal containing less than 5% of such impurities as tin, lead, nickel, bismuth, arsenic and antimony. Because of its high electrical conductivity, it is used extensively for wire and cable, and all parts of electrical and electronics apparatus which must conduct the current. Copper is also a good conductor of heat and is highly resistant to corrosion by liquids. For this reason, it is used in locomotive fire boxes, water heating apparatus, water pipes, vessels in brewery, chemical and petroleum plants, and power generating industries (for example, in heat transfer equipment) and condenser tubes. For its high heat conduction, it is used for soldering iron bits.

The alloys of copper form an important group of materials with a wide variety of properties. Some have high strengths, some are excellent bearing materials, some retain their strength at high temperature, and others are valuable for their corrosion resistance. Three groups of copper alloys are used in industry. These are : brasses, bronzes and monel metal. Copper is also used as an alloy in steel to increase its resistance to corrosion. In all, there are about 250 copper alloys. Copper as well as most copper alloys can not be heat treated. The mechanical properties are altered and strengthened by cold working. However, beryllium copper is an exception because it is hardenable.

1. Alloys of Copper and Zinc (Brass). An important use of zinc is for alloying with copper to give the various classes of brass. The alloys are of importance in view of the great variety of mechanical properties that may be obtained, the wide range of production processes to which they lend themselves and their resistance to atmospheric effects and corrosion. Suitable types of brass lend themselves to casting, hot forging, cold rolling, into sheets, drawing into wire and being extruded through dies to give special shaped products of bar type. The brasses also good bearing materials.

By adding small quantities of other elements (aluminium, iron, manganese and tin), the strength of brass may be greatly increased from its normal strength 300 – 375 N/mm^2 and a range of "high tensile" brasses is available having ultimate strengths as high as 600 N/mm^2.

The melting point of brass varies according to its composition, but most of the brasses in the common range liquify between temperatures of 850°C and 960°C. Hard brass may be softened by heating to about 750°C.

To improve the machinability of brass, 1 or 2% of lead is often added, as in its ordinary condition the metal is soft and ductile and tends to drag under the tool. Small amounts of tin are sometimes added to brass to increase its hardness and to increase its resistance against the corrosive action of sea water. These alloys are called, respectively, leaded brass and tin brass (for example, admiralty, naval, and tobin brass). Some of the chief brasses with their applications are given in Table 2.9.

Table 2.9. Properties and Uses of Brasses

Cu	Zn	Properties and Uses
90	10	Forgings, rivets, jewellery applications
85	15	Gilding metal, cheap jewellery
80	20	Drawing and forming operations
75	25	Brazing brass. Used where parts must be brazed or silver soldered. Steam condenser tubes.
70	30	Great ductility and strength. Drawing into tubes and Cartridge cases, Drawing into wires cold rolling into strip, cold pressing.
70	29 Sn = 1	Condenser tubes exposed to salt water (high corrosion resistance).
66	34	Casts well and may be rolled, stamped and drawn.
60	40	Muntz metal. A yellow brass which is stronger
60	39 Sn = 1	As above, but possesses increased corrosion resistance. It is called "Naval brass".
60	38 Sn = 1 Al = 1	Brazing alloy for naval brasses
62	32 Al = 4 Fe = 1.5 Mn = 2.25	High tensile brass.
50	50	Low melting point, do not work well, Brazing spelter.

2. Alloys of Copper with Tin (Bronze). Bronze is principally an alloy of copper and tin. The useful range of composition is 5 to 25% Sn and 75 to 95% Cu. As the tin increases upto 8%, the strength and ductility increase rapidly. More than 8% Sn increases the strength but the ductility drops off. Tin bronzes are divided into two groups : wrought bronzes containing upto 8% Sn, and Casting bronzes contain over 8% Sn.

Tin bronze is comparatively hard, resists surface wear and can be cast into shape or rolled into wire, rods and sheets very easily. In Corrosion resistant properties, bronzes are superior to brasses. It is used in hydraulic fittings, pump linings, in making utensils, bearings, bushes, sheets, rods, wires, and many other stamped and drawn articles. The bronzes are more costly than the brasses, and hence are used only when the cheaper alloys do not prove to be satisfactory. They are used in the highest quality thermo-static bellows and other parts that require resistance to severe stretching together with good tensile and elastic strength.

There are some alloys classified as bronzes that contain little or no tin. Many of these alloys are classified as bronzes because they have a colour similar to that of bronze. The principal bronze alloys are : Phosphor bronze, silicon bronze, aluminium bronze, manganese bronze and beryllium bronze.

(*i*) **Phosphor-bronze.** When bronze contains phosphorus, it is called phosphor-bronze. The composition of the metal varies according to whether it is to be forged and wrought or whether made into castings. The percentage of constituents may vary as under :

Cu = 80 to 90%; Sn = 10 to 20%, P = 1% (max.)

A common type of wrought phosphor-bronze has copper 93.7%, tin 6% and phosphorus 0.3%. Phosphorus increases the strength, ductility and soundness of castings. The alloy possesses good wearing quality, good fatigue properties, corrosion resistance and high elasticity.

Phosphor-bronze is used for all average bearings in which wearing qualities are desired. Pump parts, linings, and propellers are examples of cast manufacture. A variety of phosphor-bronze suitable for casting contains 11% Sn, 0.3% P, and remainder Cu. This is used for bearings which must carry heavy loads, worm gears, gears, nuts for machine lead screws and so on. Phosphor-bronze is also useful for making springs due to its high elastic limit and creep resistance at room temperature.

(*ii*) **Silicon-bronze.** Silicon-bronze has the good general corrosion resistance of copper, combined with higher strength and antifriction properties, and in addition can be cast, rolled, stamped, forged, and pressed either hot or cold and can be welded by all the usual methods.

Silicon-bronze has an average composition of 96% Cu, 3% Si, and 1% Mn or Zn. Additions of Mn, Zn, Ni and Pb enable silicon bronzes to be employed as substitutes for tin bronzes in the most critical applications. The alloy finds application in parts for boilers, tanks, stoves, or wherever high strength and good corrosion resistance are required.

(*iii*) **Manganese-bronze.** Manganese-bronze is an alloy of copper, zinc, lead and a little percentage of manganese. It is highly resistant to corrosion. It is stronger and harder than phosphor-bronze. The metal is generally used for making bushes, plungers and feed pump rods etc. Worm gears are frequently made from this metal.

(*iv*) **Gun metal.** Gun metal contains 88% Copper, 10% tin and 2% Zinc. The Zinc is added to cleanse the metal and increase its fluidity. The metal is used chiefly for castings which must be strong and resistant to corrosion by water and atmosphere. Gun metal is not suitable for cold working but may be forged at about 600°C. Another common bronze is made of 5% Zinc, 5% lead and 85% copper.

Originally, gun metal was made for casting guns. It is used extensively for casting boiler fittings, bushes, bearings, glands etc.

(*v*) **Bell metal.** It contains 20% tin and the remainder is copper. It is hard and resistant to surface wear. The metal is used for making bells, gongs, utensils, etc.

(*vi*) **Aluminium-bronze.** Aluminium-bronze is copper with 4 to 11% aluminium. The high mechanical properties and corrosion resistance of these bronzes considerably surpass those of tin bronzes and brasses. The aluminium gives the alloy lightness. A 10% aluminium-bronze is used in cast and hot worked condition for parts requiring high tensile strength and resistance to corrosion and wear. Iron upto 0.5% increases the strength and hardness without reducing the ductility appreciably. An alloy containing 11% Al, 5% Ni, 5% Fe and 79% Cu has extreme hardness and wear resistance at high temperatures, a quality essential in aircraft engine valve seats. In general, the aluminium bronzes are much used in aircraft for bushings, gears, bearing, valve guides, shock absorber, pistons and similar parts.

The 6% aluminium alloy has a fine gold colour, being used for imitation jewellery and decorative purposes.

(*vii*) **Beryllium-bronze.** Beryllium-bronzes contain 1.5 to 2.5% beryllium. These alloys are characterised by high mechanical strength, endurance and hardness through cold working and heat treatment (precipitation hardening). They also possess high corrosion resistance, antifriction properties and good ductility. Other advantageous features are their high electrical and thermal conductivity. The main use of this alloy in machinery is for springs of electrical contacts and watch movements, as well as diaphragms and other elastic parts and also in internal combustion engines, high duty gear, valve sleeves and valve seats.

2.9.4. Other Copper Alloys. When a brass contains a relatively large percentage of nickel (no more than 20%) it is known as "Nickel silver". When a brass contains no more than 2.75% lead and no more than 12% nickel, it is known as "leaded nickel silver". There is also a brass called "cupronickel" that contains no zinc at all; in stead it is an alloy of copper and nickel (30% cupronickel also contains a small quantity of iron). In cupronickels, the percentage of nickel is less than 50%. All these alloys are silver in appearance and tarnish very little under atmospheric conditions. They are malleable and can be worked without annealing. A 75% Cu, 25% Ni, cupronickel is used to make coins, rifle bullets and condenser tubes. A 50% Cu and 50% Ni alloy is called "Constantan" and it is used as the standard resistance. Table 2.10 gives the compositions and uses of the common copper alloys. Nickel silver is used for making dairy and laundry equipment.

Table 2.10. Composition and Uses of Copper Alloys

Name	Per cent of metal						Uses
	Cu	Zn	Sn	Pb	Al	Ni	
Admiral metal	71	28	1.0	-	-	-	Steam condenser tubes
Aluminium brass	76	22	-	-	2.0	-	High strength brass
Aluminium bronze	79	-	-	5.0 (Fe)	11.0	5.0	Bushings, gears, bearings, valve guides, pistons, Shock absorbers.
Ambrac	65	5	-	-	-	30	
Brass red	84	10.0	3.0	3.0	-	-	Sheet, Wire shapes, tubes, valve bodies, plumbing parts, pipe fittings.
Brass yellow	62	35	1.0	2.0	-	-	Spur gears, bear-ings, screw down nuts
Beryllium copper	98	-	-	-	-	2.0 bery-llium	Diaphragms, high duty gears, valve sleeves, valve vents, Springs of electrical contacts and watch movements.

Gear bronze	86.5	-	-	3.3 (Fe)	10.2	-	Gears of high strength
Gun metal	88	2.0	10.0	-	-	-	Boiler fittings, bushes, bearings, glands
Manganese bronze	90	5.8	-	2.0	2.0 (Fe)		Bushes, plungers, feed pump rods, worm gears
Monel metal	30	-	-	-	-	67	Steam turbine blades, high temperature valves, impeller of centrifugal pump, springs.
K - monel	29.0	-	-	-	2.75	66	-do-
Muntz metal	60.0	40.0	-	-	-	-	Water fittings, condenser tubes, household articles
Phosphor bronze	80 -90	-	20 -10	1.0 (P)	-	-	Bearings, pump parts, worm gears, springs

Note. Red brass may contain only Cu (90%) and Zn (10%). This brass is used for hardware. Leaded red brass : Cu : 85%, Sn : 5%, Zn : 5% and Pb : 5%, is used for castings and machinery Similarly Yellow brass may contain only Cu (70%) and Zn (30%). This brass is used for making cartridges and tubes.

Leaded yellow brass : Cu, 72%, Zn : 24%, Sn : 1% and Pb : 3% is used for plumbing fixtures.

2.9.5. Anti-friction Alloys. Antifriction alloys are used mainly for lining (babbitting) bearings and, for this reason, they are also called as "Bearing Metals". It has been found by experience that to give an efficient bearing combination, the following conditions are necessary:

1. The shaft and bearing be dissimilar in their natures with bearings softer than the shaft. In general, a metal consisting of one uniform constituent does not serve well as a bearing.

2. The most efficient bearing metal is one consisting of small pieces of a comparatively hard metal embedded in the softer body of an other metal.

The other requirements of a good bearing material are :

3. The co-efficient of friction between the journal (shaft) and lining must be as low as possible when they actually come in contact, as for example, when a shaft is starting or stopping.

4. The metal must be such as to prevent excessive wear or heating of the friction surfaces.

5. It must with stand high specific loads, retain sufficient strength and hardness when heated to elevated temperatures.

6. It should be capable of being rapidly run in with the shaft and promote the formation of an oil film on the lining surfaces when the bearing is lubricated.

Bearing materials may be classified as :

　(i) Tin base bearing metals
　(ii) Lead base bearing metals
　(iii) Copper base bearing metals, that is, antifriction bronzes.
　(iv) Cadmium base bearing metals
　(v) Anti-friction cast irons
　(vi) Aluminium alloys
　(vii) Silver bearings
　(viii) Non-metallic bearing materials.

(*i*) **Tin base and Lead base Alloys.** Tin is a brilliant white metal with a yellowish tinge. Its melting point is 232°C. Soft, ductile and malleable, it can be rolled into very thin sheets. Tin does not corrode in wet and dry conditions, making it useful as a protective coating for iron and steel. It is also used for tinning copper wire before the latter is made into cables.

An alloy containing 25% tin, 25% lead and 50% bismuth is called as "Fusible Metal" and is used to make fusible plugs for boilers.

Lead is the heaviest of the common metals. It has a bluish-grey colour and a dull, metallic lustre, but this is lost on exposure to air, surface becoming a dull grey. Lead is a very soft, malleable and ductile metal and can be rolled easily. It is resistant to corrosion and many acids have no chemical action on it. Because of this, it is used for water pipes, roof coverings, the sheathing of electric cable and for construction materials of chemical plants. Its melting point is 327°C.

Lead alloyed with tin forms solders and alloyed with other metals make bearing metals. Alloyed with small percentage of arsenic it is used to produce shots for munitions.

The bearing alloys in which tin, lead and cadmium are predominating elements are designated as : "White metals". They have the property of high plasticity combined with low hardness and comparatively low melting point which facilitates the formation of bearings by casting the metal directly in place and usually require no machining.

Tin-base white metals are used where bearings are subjected to high pressure and load, whereas for light loads and pressure, lead base alloys are used. Table 2.11, gives the composition and uses of the common white bearing metals. Tin base white metals (that is, alloys of tin, lead, copper and antimony) are called as "Babbitt metals". The base of babbitts used in industry is lead or other metals capable of substituting for more expensive tin. Babbitt metal is probably the most common bearing material. However, for pressures above $7N/mm^2$, babbitt should not be used. A lead-bismuth alloy (80% lead, 20% bismuth) is also used as bearing lining.

A calcium babbitt is used as the standard bearing metal for railway rolling stock. Besides lead, it contains 0.8 to 1.1% Ca and 0.75 to 1.0% Na.

Table 2.11. Common Babbitt Metals

Composition				Uses
Tin	*Antimony*	*Copper*	*Lead*	
93	3.5	3.5	-	Big end bearings, motor and aero engines
86	10.5	3.5	-	Main bearings, motor and aero engines
80	11	3	6	Bearings for heavy loads and high speeds
60	10	1.5	28.5	Bearings for engines and electric machines, railways and tram ways.
40	10	1.5	48.5	Heavy pressure and bearing speed
20	15	1.5	63.5	Medium pressure and speed
5	15	-	80	Long bearings with medium load.

(*ii*) **Copper-base bearing Metals (Anti-friction Bronzes).** Bearing bronzes are used in plain bearings and other mechanisms with friction surfaces subject to a high specific load. Tin-lead bronzes containing from 4 to 16% lead, are used for this purpose. Lately, from 2 to 7% Zn is being added to tin-lead bronzes. Straight tin and other types of antifriction bronzes are also extensively used.

These bearing metals are generally stronger, have a greater load capacity, have good fatigue strength, are harder, but less score resistant than babbitt bearings.

(*iii*) **Aluminium Alloys.** These bearing metals are widely used in internal combustion engines because of their : load carrying capacity, fatigue strength, thermal conductivity, corrosion resistance and low cost. Their disadvantages are that they require hardened journals and have poor compatibility (good antiweld and antiscoring properties), conformability (ability to adjust to misalignment or other geometric errors) and embeddability (that is the material is soft enough to absorb foreign materials that are too large to pass through the oil film). When a thin layer of babbitt is placed inside an aluminium bearing, the antiscoring and embeddability properties are improved.

(*iv*) **Silver bearing.** Silver bearings are extremely useful for heavy duty applications. These are made by electrodepositing silver on a steel backing with an overlay of lead 0.025 to 0.125 mm thick. A thin layer of indium is then deposited on the lead to provide corrosion protection. These bearings are used in some aeroplane engines.

(*v*) **Cadmium base Alloys.** The cadmium-nickel-silver and the cadmium-silver-copper alloys allow much higher operating temperatures than are safe with babbitts and do not require the extremely hard journals necessary with bronzes. Their compressive strength is greater than babbitts. Cadmium fuses directly into the steel backing, and since no solder or tin is used to make the bond, the bearing can be operated at temperature approaching the softening point of the alloy.

Cadmium-silver bearings are used in some air-plane engines.

(*vi*) **Anti-friction cast iron bearings.** These bearings are suitable for plain bearings operating under high specific pressures but at low shaft speeds. High quality grey-cast irons are used as materials for the liners or shells of bearings. They contain 3.2 to 3.6% C, 2.2 to 2.4% Si, and 0.6 to 0.9% Mn. However, because of poor embeddability and conformability, these bearings require very good alignment and lubrication and freedom from foreign matter.

(*vii*) **Non-metallic materials.** Recently, various non-metallic anti-friction materials have been developed for industrial applications. They include laminated fabric, viozite, plasticised wood and others.

The compositions and properties of the various bearing materials are given in Table 2.12.

2.9.6. Zinc and its Alloys. Zinc is a fairly heavy, bluish white metal used principally because of its low cost, corrosion resistance, and alloying properties. Its melting point is 419°C.

The protection of iron and steel from corrosion is done more often with Zinc that with any other metal coating. The oldest and the most important methods of applying the Zinc are called as "galvanizing". When rolled into sheets, Zinc is used for roof covering and for providing a damp-proof non-corrosive lining to containers etc. Zinc casts well and forms the base of various die-casting alloys.

2.9.7. Nickel and its Alloys. Pure nickel is a tough, silver coloured metal, rather harder than copper and of about the same strength, but possessing somewhat less ductility. It is malleable and weldable and perceptibly magnetic. It is little affected by dilute acids and is far less readily oxidisable, and deteriorates much less rapidly under atmospheric influences. For these reasons, nickel is used where corrosion resistance and oxidation resistance are important requirements. Articles of iron and steel are frequently nickel-plated to protect them from rusting. Nickel is much used for cooking utensils, and other vessels for heating and boiling. Nickel enters as a constituent into a large number of ferrous and non-ferrous alloys, and frequently finds application as a catalyst in important industrial processes. The melting point of nickel is 1435°C.

Nickel Alloys. Some nickel alloys are extremely tough so that they can be used at temperatures as high as about 1100°C as ultra high strength and super alloy structural materials. Other nickel alloys are excellent for cryogenic applications and are strong, tough, and ductile even at temperatures as low as –220°C.

Wrought nickel alloys have good manufacturing characteristics. They are readily machinable,

Table 2.12. Properties of Bearing Metals

Metal	Percentage of Ingredients				Compressive elastic limit (MN/m²)	Brinell Hardness at (27.5°C)	Class of use
	Copper	Lead	Tin	Miscellaneous			
Bronze	91 – 92	-	8 – 9	P = 0.5	260.0	150 – 200	High shock load
Bronze	91 – 92	-	8 – 9	P = 0.5	105.0	80 – 90	High shock load
Bronze	86 – 89	0.2	9 – 11	Zn = 0.3	84.0	60	Shaft bearings
Phosphor bronze	80 – 82	9 – 10	9 – 11	P = 0.7	105.0	55 – 80	Shock load
Aluminium Nickel bronze	80	Al = 10	5	Ni = 5.0	315.0	180	High shock load
Aluminium alloy	1.0	Al = 91.0	6.5	Ni = 1.5	59.5	35 – 50	Severe loads
Aluminium alloy	1.0	Al = 90.5	6.5	Ni = 1.5	105.0	40 – 50	General automotive
Plastic bronze	65	30	5	-	24.5	30	Crank pin bearing
Allan red metal	50	50	-	-	17.5	13.5	Crank pin bearing
Babbit metal	4.5	0.35	90 – 92	Sb = 4.5	9.1	17	Light loads
Babbit metal	2.75 –3.25	25	60 – 62	Sb = 10.5	9.1	22	Moderate loads
Babbit metal	-	75	10	Sb = 15	84.0	-	Crank pin bearing
Person's white brass	2.5 – 5	0.2	64 – 65	Zn = 33	105.0	18	Light load
Lumen brass	10		Zn = 86	Al = 4	260.0	116	Light load, high speed

cut, sheared, punched, cold worked, hot worked and weldable. The casting alloys can be machined, ground, welded and brazed.

Nickel alloys are more costly than steel and aluminium but are less costly than refractory metals (W, Mo, Ti etc.) for solving severe temperature strength problems. Also, they display magnetic, magneto-strictive, electrical and thermal properties that are important for particular applications.

Nickel alloys which are particularly useful for general industrial purposes are described below :

(*i*) **Monel Metal.** Monel metals are the most important nickel-copper alloys, having high strength and toughness and excellent corrosion resistance. Monel metal contains 67% Ni, 30% Cu, with small amounts of iron, manganese, silicon and carbon. It is a white, tough, and ductile metal that can be easily machined and welded and can be heat treated. It is used in the form of rod, sheet, wire and welded tubing. It is widely employed for structural and machine parts which must have a very high resistance to corrosion and have high strength at elevated temperatures, for example, steam turbine blades, high temperature valves, impeller of centrifugal pump, and for springs subjected to temperatures above 200°C.

(*ii*) **K-Monel.** This alloy contains 66% Ni, 29% Cu, 2.57% Al, and small quantities of iron, manganese and carbon. Addition of aluminium increases the strength and hardness above that of Monel and also makes it susceptible to hardening by heat treatment K-monel has the same corrosion-resisting and high temperature properties as Monel and is wholly non-magnetic.

(*iii*) **German Silver.** An alloy of copper (50%), nickel (20%) and Zinc (30%) is known as german silver. Sometimes, tin and lead are also added.

This alloy is hard, white and ductile. It has good mechanical and corrosion resisting properties. German silver is used for making utensils, resistances in electrical work, shop and house fittings and ornamental work of cars.

(*iv*) **Invar.** Invar is an alloy of iron (70%) with 30% nickel. It has a very low co-efficient of heat expansion, making it useful for measuring instruments, for example, surveying tapes, compensation collars etc.

(*v*) **Nichrome.** It is an alloy of nickel (80%) with chromium (20%) and is used widely as resistance wire for electrical appliances.

(*vi*) **Inconel.** Inconel contains 79.5% Ni, 0.2% Cu, 13% Cr, 6.5% iron, and a small amount of silicon and manganese. It has the corrosion resistant properties of Monel but has better resistance to sulphur at higher temperatures. It retains its strength at extremely high temperatures and can be used at 1150°C. Its creep properties are very good. It is non-magnetic at all temperatures above −22°C.

(*vii*) **Nimonics.** A new type of nickel alloys called "nimonics" are being developed, which by proper heat treatment attain excellent properties for very high temperature service. Their common composition is :

Cr (15 to 18%), Co (15 to 18%), 3.5 to 5% Mo, 1.2 to 4% Ti, 1.2 to 5.0% Al, and the remainder Ni.

2.9.8. Alloys for High Temperature Service. Many components in jet and rocket engines, and in nuclear equipments have to with stand temperatures above 1100°C. This has resulted in the development of a number of highly specialised alloys. These alloys have nickel or cobalt (melting point 1495°C) as the base metals. Their yield strength is above 700 N/mm^2 and hardness is 250 to 370 BHN at room temperature. Some typical high-temperature alloys are :

(*i*) **Inconel.** Discussed above

(*ii*) **Nimonics.** Discussed above

(*iii*) **Incoloy 910.** Ni (12%), Cr (13%), Ti (2.4%), Mo (6%), C (0.04%), Iron, remainder.

(*iv*) **Hastealloy.** Ni (45%), Cr (22%), Co (1.5%), W (0.5%), Mo (9%), C (0.15%), Balance Iron.

(*v*) **Vitallium.** Ni (2.5%), Cr (25%), Co (62%), Iron (1.7%), Mo (5.5%) and C (0.28%).

2.9.9. Titanium Alloys. Titanium is a silvery white metal with melting point of 1670°C and a specific gravity of 4.505. Titanium can be alloyed to give high elevated-temperature combined with low weight and corrosion resistance. Industrial titanium alloys contain vanadium, molybdenum, chromium, manganese, aluminium, tin, iron or other metals, singly or in various combinations. These alloys respond to heat treatment, case-hardening and work hardening techniques. However, due to the great affinity of Ti to oxygen, the high melting point and low fluidity, special skills are needed for its casting. Properties of castings can be greatly improved by HIP (Hot Isostatic Pressing).

Because of their corrosion resistance, titanium and its alloys, in the form of sheets and tubes, are extensively used in chemical plants. A combination of high mechanical properties (due to heat treatment) with a low specific weight and excellent corrosion resistance, make the titanium alloys indispensable for critical aircraft components in subsonic and, especially in supersonic aircraft.

2.9.10. Refractory Metals. Refractory metals are those metals which are resistant to heat and difficult to melt. The most important refractory metals are : tungsten (melting point 3410°C), molybdenum (2610°C) and niobium, also called columbium (2470°C). These metals oxidise extremely rapidly, therefore, special (vacuum are or electron beam) melting and casting techniques are required. For the same reason, they must be processed (by metal forming techniques) in vacuum or protective atmosphere. Tungsten is used extensively in the form of wire in incandescent wire lamps. The refractory metals are indispensable in some applications such as rocket motor nozzles.

2.9.11. Metals for Nuclear Energy. In nuclear energy power plants, the various metals used for construction have to with stand very stringent conditions. As a result, some metals, previously considered rare are being widely used in this field. The metals which are used for nuclear engineering purposes are : uranium, plutonium, zirconium, beryllium, niobium and their alloys. They are used as raw fuel materials, moderators, reflectors, fuel elements, fuel canning materials, control elements and pressure vessel materials.

1. Uranium. This metal is found in nature and is the most important metal used for nuclear engineering purposes. Its isotope U_{235} is used as the nuclear fuel. The metal is radioactive, easily oxidised, has a poor resistance to corrosion and needs to be protected for use as fuel elements by roll cladding it in a thin aluminium or zirconium jacket. Pure uranium is weak and is susceptible to severs irradiation damage and growth in the reactor environment. Addition of some alloying elements such as chromium, molybdenum, plutonium and zirconium make the metal highly suitable for nuclear energy applications.

Uranium compounds, such as UO_2 as a dispersion in cermets or as ceramic slugs, have been found to give better results. Uranium oxide is highly refractory, shows no phase change in an inert atmosphere, is highly corrosion resistant and possesses a good strength. But it has low thermal shock resistance, poor thermal conductivity and a high co-efficient of expansion.

2. Thorium. Thorium is also available in nature. It is a fertile nuclear fuel. It can be converted into fissile nuclear fuel, U_{233}, by neutron absorption and beta decay. In pure state, the metal is soft and weak. Its mechanical properties are drastically changed by small addition of impurities. Its tensile strength is raised from 140 to 380 N/mm^2 by the addition of only 0.2% C. Addition of uranium also increases its strength. But small additions of titanium, zirconium and niobium decrease the strength and hardness of the metal.

Like uranium, thorium is also radioactive, but is less susceptible to irradiation damage.

3. Plutonium. This metal does not occur in nature. It is produced from an isotope of uranium, U_{238}, through neutron absorption and subsequent beta decays. The metal is then used as fissile nuclear fuel. It is extremely toxic and emits alpha rays. The metal is chemically more reactive than uranium and has a poor resistance to corrosion. It is used as a fissile nuclear fuel in fast breeder reactors and also for making atomic weapons.

4. Zirconium. Zirconium minerals contain 0.5 to 2% hafnium which is a strong absorber of neutrons and, therefore, must be removed. The main use of the metal is for cladding fuel elements and for structural components in water cooled systems. So, it must have increased corrosion resistance. Zircaloy-2 containing 1.5 Zn, 0.1 Fe, 0.5 Ni and 0.1 Cr which provide better corrosion resistance are generally used in water-cooled reactors. Zirconium has a relatively poor resistance to CO_2 at elevated temperatures, but this is improved by the addition of 0.5 Cu, 0.5 Mo with an increase of tensile strength to 510 N/mm^2 and improved creep resistance at 450°C. This Zirconium is specially useful in gas cooled reactors.

5. Beryllium. It is a light metal with melting point of about 1280°C. The metal is very reactive and forms compounds with furnace atmospheres and refractories. Therefore, vacuum or inert gas is necessary during its melting. The cast metal is usually coarse grained and brittle. Due to this, powder metallurgy methods are employed for its fabrication. The metal is used as a moderator, reflector and neutron source.

6. Niobium. Niobium, Nb, also called as columbium, Cb, is a refractory metal. The metal has good hot strength, ductility and corrosion resistance, especially to liquid sodium coolants. Its oxidation resistance above 400°C is greatly improved by alloying.

2.9.12. Stellite. Stellite is cobalt base metal alloyed with various proportion of chromium (35), cobalt (45) and tungsten (15) with iron, manganese and silicon present only as impurities. The most notable property of these alloys is high red hardness. They have high abrasive resistance, non-tarnishing, corrosion resistance and nonmagnetic properties. These properties make it excellent cutting tool for various machine operations on cast iron and malleable iron and on some steels. Because of the cost of stellite, the larger tools are made of steel with stellite tips welded on it. Coatings of stellite, applied by welding, are used for surface protection against wear and abrasion on such items as oil-well pits, cement-mill grinding rigs, and for some bearing surfaces whose lubrication is impossible or unreliable. The co-efficient of friction on dry metals varies from 0.15 to 0.24 with an average of 0.18. Mechanical properties of various stellite materials are given in table 2.13.

Table 2.13. Mechanical Properties of Stellite

Material	Ultimate strength			Brinell hardness	Properties and Uses
	Tension (MN/m²)	Comp. (MN/m²)	Tension at 500°C (MN/m²)		
Welded	265.0	1792.0	168.0	512	Not machinable, grind
Cast	265.0	2177.0	175.0	600	
cast	600.0	1540.0	126.0	402	
Forged	938.0	1800.0	164.0		Can be rolled, forged and punched at 1000°C.
Welded	462.0	1350.0	133.0	444	Hard-surfacing weld rod, not used for cutting tools.

2.9.13. Non-metallic Materials. The commonly used non-metallic materials are wood, glass, rubber, leather, carbon and plastics.

Wood. Wood has some uses in machine members. It is used where light weight parts subjected to moderate shock loading are required, *e.g.*, in circuit breaker operating rods where non-metallic bearing material is desirable.

Glass. It is usually thought of as a weak brittle material. The greatly improved mechanical properties of the newer glass compositions justify their consideration in design problems. Glass parts can be moulded by heat and pressure or by heating and blowing. They can be finished and cut by grinding and can be machined by carbide tools, but the surface will be too rough for ordinary uses. Glass is used for all parts of centrifugal pumps for acids, piping for mechanical processes, pipe fittings, exchangers and lining for tanks and fittings.

The tensile strength of glass ranges from 42.0 to 84.0 MN/m^2 with small surface scratches reducing the strength by 50 per cent. Compressive strength of glass is over 700 MN/m^2. The modulus of elasticity varies from 45 GN/m^2 to 70×10^6 GN/m^2. Allowable design stresses range from 3.5 to 7.0 MN/m^2.

Rubber. Rubber and similar synthetic materials such as Neoprene have a variety of application in machinery. Rubber should be protected from high temperature, oil and sunlight. It is an excellent material for seats and diaphragms, for water lubricated bearings, for parts subjected to vibrations (such as vibration mountings, flexible couplings and flexible bearing) and for tubes and hose. In industry, hard rubber is used for electric insulation, switch handles, bearings, etc. Table 2.14 gives the different properties of rubber.

Leather. Leather is very flexible and will stand considerable wear under suitable conditions. Modulus of elasticity varies according to load. It is used in belt drives and as a packing or a washers.

Table 2.14. Properties of Rubber and Rubber Like Materials

Material	Form	Compressive Strength (MN/m^2)	Tensile Strength (MN/m^2)	Shear Strength (MN/m^2)	Max. temp. for use(°C)	Effect of heat
Duprene	-	-	1.4 – 28.0	-	150	Stifens slightly
Kore seal	Hard	-	14.0 – 63.0	-	100	Softens
Kore seal	Soft	-	3.5 – 17.5	-	85	Softens
Pilo form	Plastic	60.0 – 77.0	28.0 – 35.0	49.0 – 63.0	70 – 120	Softens
Rubber	Hard	14.0 – 105.0	7.0 – 70.0	63.0 – 105.0	55 – 70	Softens
Rubber	Soft	-	3.5 – 4.2	-	60 – 90	Softens
Rubber	Linings	-	–	-	85	Softens

Carbon. Since long carbon has been used in electrical insulations and it has not been generally used in mechanical insulations. Use of carbon gives low friction losses, low wear rates when operating against metals and is used in chemical handling equipment. Pump rotors, vanes and gears of carbon have been used with good results to replace similar parts of bronze and laminated plastics. Clutch plates and rings of metal and cork have been replaced by carbon parts. The properties of carbon are given in table 2.15. Graphite, a form of carbon, has long been used in bronze bearings as a lubricant, but now bearings made entirely of carbon are being used with operating pressure as high as 7.0 MN/m^2 at low speed.

Table 2.15. Properties of Carbon

Strength MN/m^2

Compression	14.0 – 175.0
Tension	2.8 – 26.5
Shear	22.4
Modulus of elasticity	9.31 – 17 GN/m^2

Maximum operating temperature 450°C.

Co-efficient of friction

Carbon on hard steel, unlubricated	0.18 – 0.3
Well lubricated	0.04 – 0.08
Carbon on glass, unlubricated	0.17

Plastics. These are difficult to define because any acceptable definition usually gives too many exceptions. Common usage has applied the term to a class of materials familiar to everyone in such products as buttons, fountain pens, telephones, dials, knobs, etc. The word plastic was used originally to indicate a material that could be formed or moulded by pressure at moderately elevated temperature. Some of the plastics are available as thin sheets, foams, coatings, petroleum laminates and filaments for weaving. Raw materials are mainly derived from petroleum and agriculture. Plastic moulding is one of the high volume, low cost production methods with products that are replacing those formerly made from wood, glass or metal.

Plastic materials when used have the following advantages :

1. Good accuracy, light, smooth surfaces, low thermal conductivity, pleasing appearance, self lubrication characteristics, resistance to corrosion, and good dielectric strength.

2. Compared to metal, plastics have better resistance to shock and vibration and higher abrasion and wear resistance.

3. They can be either transparent or opaque and can be made in desired colour.

4. No finishing is required after removal from the mould.

5. Although the moulds are expensive, but are long lasting and capable of producing many thousands of parts.

The use of the most of the plastics is limited due to the following reasons :

1. Low strength and rigidity, low heat resistance, and sometimes low dimensional stability.

2. Small loads at room temperatures will induce a continuous type of creep behaviour. This effect is intensified at higher temperatures.

3. The thermal expansion of plastics usually runs from five to ten times that of metal.

4. Embrittlement with age is another disadvantage.

5. The cost of plastic materials is high, but has been decreasing, while other materials have been increasing in price.

Types of Plastics

Plastic materials can be broadly classified as (1) Thermoplasts or thermoplastic materials (2) Thermosets or thermosetting materials.

Thermoplastics, when moulded, undergo no chemical change. Although rigid at room temperature, heating beyond softening point will cause the material to assume a viscous or liquid state. Thermoplastics are sold under such trade name as Celluloid, Nitron, Pyralin, Fibestos, Nixonite and Tenite.

Thermosets, undergo a chemical change when heated. This change is permanent and the material cannot be softened by heating. Thermosets cannot be extruded or calendared. Thermosetting plastics are sold under trade names such as Bakelite, Durite, Textolite, Bakelite uses, Beetle and Plaskon.

The chemistry of plastic materials is very involved. Many hundreds of such materials are available and the number is continuously increasing. The most widely used moulding plastics are given in tables 2.16 and 2.17. The table also indicates the common trade names, characteristic properties and typical applications.

Table 2.16. Names, Characteristics and Uses of Thermoplastics

Chemical Classiffication	Trade name	Characteristics	Typical Applications
1. Callulose acetate	Tenite 1 plastacel Fibestos Lumarith	Nonflammable, good dielectric, good toughness, high impact strength, moulding and fabricating versatility, available in wide range of colours, dimensional stability may not be good.	Machine guards and covers, tool and cutlery handles, toys and knobs. Brush backs, Jewellery, Electrical insulation.
2. Cellulose	Celluloid pyralin Nitron Pyroxylin	Flammable, but otherwise same as cellulose acetate. Oldest commercial plastic.	Toilet articles, moviefilm. Drawing instruments. Piano and typewriter keys.
3. Methyl	Lucite plexiglass Crystalite	Light weight, weather resistant, Best of plastics for light piping, transmission and edge illumination effects.	Aircraft cockpits and windows outdoor signs
4. Polyamide	Nylon zytel	Low co-efficient of friction. Dimensional stability. Good electrical properties. Not affected by gasoline or hydraulic fluids. Bearings can operate without lubricant. Abrasion resistance.	Small moulded gear and bushings, brush bristles fuel container coatings.
5. Polyethylene	Alathon Polythene	Flexible and tough. Excellent dielectric properties. Flammable but slow burning. Dimensional variaions difficult to predict.	Automotive parts, House wares, containers, electrical cable jacketing, tubing, Squeeze bottles.
6. Polystyrene	Lystrex Styron Cerex	Resistant to acids and alkalies. Good dimensional stability Good electrical properties.	Electrical insulation, containers and closures. Instrument panels, knobs, wall tile, radio cabinets.
7. Polytetra-fluoro Ethylene (PTFE)	Teflon	Low co-efficient of friction. Resistance to chemical attack. Tough at low temperature. Bushings can operate without lubricant in presence of abrasives.	Gaskets, packings, seals bushings, lining for pipe and vessels. Non stick surfacing. Electrical insulation.
8. Polyvinyl Chloride	Vinylite Q Koroseal Tygon Geen	Flame resistant Resistant to chemicals, oils, and solvents. Abrasion resistant. Sound and vibration deadening	Automotive panels, parts for vacuum cleaners and refrigerators, floor coverings; pipe fittings, tanks, balls and floats.

Table 2.17. Names, Characteristics and Uses of Thermosets

Chemical Classification	Trade name	Characteristics	Typical Applications
1. Epoxy	Araldite Oxiron	Good toughness. Resistant to acids, alkalies and solvents. Excellent adhesion to metal, glass and wood.	Adhesive and coatings, tools and dies, filament wound vessels, laminates for aircraft, patching compound for metal and plastics.
2. Melamine-formal-	Melmae Resimeve	Good for application requiring cycling between wet and dry	Table-wate, electric insulation, automotive ignition parts, cutlery

		conditions. Hard and abrasion resistant. Good dielectric Does not impart taste to food.	handles, jars and bowls.
3. Phenol-formal-dehyde	Bakelite Marblette Durez Catalin	Good dimensional stability Excellent insulating qualities. Inert to most solvents and weak acids. Good strength around inserts.	Industrial electrical parts. automotive electrical components, paper impregnated battery separators.
4. Phenol-furfural	Durite	Similar to Phenolformaldehyde.	Electrical insulation. Mechanical parts. Housings and containers.
5. Alkyd (Modified polyester)	Glyptal Duraplex Beckosol Teglac Rezly	Can be made flexible, resilient or rigid. Can resist acids but not alkalies, with glass fibre reinforcement resists salt water and fungus growth.	Boats, Tanks, Trailer and Tractor components. Ducts, shrouds. Vaulting poles.

2.9.14. Cemented Carbides. These are cutting tool alloys. These are made of a powdery mixture of tungsten and titanium (and also of tantalum) carbides and cobalt which is first compacted and then sintered. Cemented carbides are extremely hard and they retain their hardness at temperatures upto 1000°C. These cutting tool materials will be discussed in detail in chapter 7.

PROBLEMS

1. Classify the materials of construction.
2. What is malleable iron ? What advantages has this form over white or grey cast iron ?
3. How does carbon content affect cast iron, wrought iron, and steel with reference to hardness and toughness ?
4. What is the chief reason for the use of alloy steels in machine parts ?
5. Explain the difference between malleable cast iron and grey cast iron.
6. Differentiate between hot and cold working.
7. Under what circumstances alloys of cast iron are used ?
8. Explain in detail the effects of nickel, copper, chromium and molybdenum as alloying elements in cast iron.
9. When the cast steels are preferred over cast iron ?
10. Enlist the properties of 0.2% carbon steel.
11. Name the steel alloys used for high temperature service.
12. List the alloying materials of aluminium.
13. What alloy steel is suitable for springs ?
14. What are the copper alloys ?
15. List the advantages and disadvantages of bronze over brass for industrial uses.
16. What is the composition of red brass and yellow brass and where these are commonly used ?
17. Differentiate between the tin base and lead base alloys.
18. What are the constituents of Muntz metal and monel metal ?
19. What are the constituents of Babbit metal ?
20. What are the constituents of stellite and where it is commonly used ?
21. List the important non-metallic materials of construction.
22. Explain clearly the use of wood and glass in place of steel in machine design.

23. Enumerate the advantages and disadvantages of plastic materials over metallic materials.

24. Give the trade names of plastic items used in daily life.

25. Give the materials which are commonly used for the following parts of a steam engine.

    (a) Cylinder head and cylinder   (b) Connecting rod

    (c) D-slide valve   (d) Crankshaft

    (e) Piston   (f) Piston rings

26. What are cupronickels or nickel silver alloys ?

27. Discuss the materials of the following :

    (a) Rivets used in a boiler   (b) gears of a lathe

    (c) Connecting rod of an I.C. Engine   (d) Valve of a safety valve

    (e) body of a safety valve   (f) Steam pipe

    (g) Water pipe

28. Give two typical applications of each of the following alloys :

    (a) 70/30 Copper zinc alloy   (b) monel metal

    (c) babbit metal   (d) Copper-aluminium alloy

    (e) 92/8 Copper lead alloy.

29. What is the difference between cast iron and wrought steel ?

30. Name the four types of cast irons. Indicate the advantages and disadvantages of each.

31. Define the following : (a) hypoeutectoid steel, (b) hypereutectoid steel, (c) eutectoid steel.

32. What are the constituents of the following : austenite, ferrite, cementite, pearlite, and martensite ?

33. Plain carbon steels are divided into three groups. Name these groups and write some typical applications of each.

34. Distinguish between annealing and normalizing. What is the purpose of these processes ?

35. What is meant by tempering of Steel, and why is this process employed?

36. Describe martempering and austempering.

37. Distinguish between hardness and hardenability.

38. How does surface hardening differ from through hardening ? What is its purpose ? Name the various surface hardening methods.

39. What are the advantages of nitriding over carburizing and cyaniding ?

40. Differentiate between age hardening and precipitation hardening. What is artificial aging ?

41. List the three grades of stainless steels. What constituents in stainless steels make them particularly resistant to corrosion ? Write some typical product applications of each.

42. What two methods are used to harden aluminium alloys ?

43. For most atmospheres, aluminium is known to resist corrosion. Explain why.

44. What is the difference between brass and bronze ?

45. List the metals used for high temperature requirements.

46. What is the difference between rimmed steel and killed steel ?

47. What are the two ways in which white cast iron can be obtained ?

48. What is the difference between "Full annealing" and "Isothermal annealing" ?

49. Define critical points in heat treatment of steels.

50. Explain the principle of heat treatment.

51. What is Flame hardening ?

52. What is Induction hardening ?
53. Explain Iron-carbon diagram. Also, discuss the various transformations which are taking place at different temperatures.
54. Explain Eutectic and Eutectoid reactions.
55. Explain nitriding process of case-hardening.
56. What information may be obtained from equilibrium diagram ?
57. What information may be obtained from TTT curves.
58. What is Martensite ? How does it appear under microscope ?
59. Compare martempering and austempering.
60. What are the principal advantages of austempering as compared to conventional hardening and temper methods ?
61. Define hardenability. How it can be measured ? Explain the variables affecting hardenability.
62. List various objectives of heat treatment.
63. List various objectives of hardening heat treatment process.
64. What are: Sorbite, Troostite and Bainite ?
65. What are: Process annealing, homogenizing and spheroidising heat treatment processes ?
66. Write on the various quenching media used in hardening process.
67. Explain the various carburising methods.
68. Explain cyaniding process.
69. Explain Carbo-nitriding process.
70. Write on three types of tempering processes.
71. What is stepped quenching ?
72. Discuss the importance of cooling rate in hardening process.
73. What is the "critical cooling rate"?
74. What is meant by "Soaking time"?
75. Which methods may be used to localize case-hardening?
76. Draw the cooling curve for pure iron and explain the charactersitics.
77. Draw the Iron-Carbon phase diagram.
78. Why is it called as "Equilibrium diagram"?
79. Identify the various phases of iron-carbon phase diagram.
80. Explain the above phase diagram.
81. Identify the constituents of steel from the iron-carbon diagram.
82. Explain the effect of slow cooling for various compositions.
83. What are : Hypo-eutectic cast irons, Hyper-eutectic cast iron and eutectic cast irons ?
84. Explain the TTT diagram.
85. Why is it called as Non-equilibrium diagram ?
86. Draw and write on cooling curves for Pure metals and for alloys.
87. What is the major purpose of tempering steel after hardening it ?
88. Why must hardening of steel always precede tempering ?
89. What property is sacrified in order to get benefits of tempering ?
90. Why is steel always tempered after hardening ?
91. Why is steel not tempered without hardening ?

92. Apart from effect on hardness, what is the major advantage of an oil-quenching steel ?

93. What is the effect of quenching a water-hardening steel in oil ?

94. What is the effect of quenching an oil-hardening steel in water ?

95. Define an air-hardening steel.

96. What is the objective of case-hardening ?

97. Why should the specimens be heated to as high as 930°C during carburization ?

98. What is the function of the carbonate compounds in the carburizer ?

99. What is the mechanism of carburization ?

100. Why does further heat treatment usually follow carburizing ?

101. What type of steel is best suited to carburizing ?

102. What is the difference between case-hardening and case-carburizing ?

103. Which steel has the highest hardenability ?

104. Why is hardenability an important property ?

105. Why is hardenability a property of steel and not of brass or aluminium ?

106. Define 'ideal critical diameter'.

107. On a Jominy curve, where is the point which represents the microstructure condition of 50% martensite and 50% softer constituents ?

108. How can relative hardenability be judged directly from two Jominy curves, each of a different steel ?

109. Define recrystallization annealing.

110. What is "Boronizing" ?

111. What is Chapmanizing ?

112. Which one of the following is not a compound ?

    (a) Chalk   (b) Acetylene   (c) Calcium   (d) Sulphuric acid   (**Ans. :** c) (*AMIE, I.Mech.E.*)

113. Brittle fracture in a metal can be the result of :

    (a) High temperature during service

    (b) Low temperature during service

    (c) Excessive loading during service

    (d) Reduction of ductility during service.   [**Ans. :** b] (*A.M.I.E., L.U.*)

114. How annealing is related to cold working ?

115. Describe the process of Normalizing.   (*D.U., L.U.*)

116. When a steel suffers hot shortness, it is mostly due to the presence of : —

    (a) S   (b) P   (c) Si   (d) Mn   (*B.T.E., A.M.I.E., U.P.S.C.*) (**Ans. :** a)

117. When a steel is subjected to a form of heat treatment known as tempering after it has been hardened, the process is one of :—

    (a) Heating without quenching   (b) Heating and quenching

    (c) Heating and cooling slowly   (d) Heating and hammering.   ₍**Ans. :** c₎

118. Discuss the effect of carbon on steel.

119. What are the effects of heat on the steel structure ?

120. Write briefly about the different heat treatments given to steel to obtain desired properties.

                                                                        (*L.U.*)

121. Which one of the following properties is related to C.I. ?

    (a) Ductility   (b) Malleability   (c) Plasticity   (d) Brittleness   (**Ans. :** d)

122. Which one of the following metals is used when producing a magnetic field ?

    (a) Lead   (b) Sn   (c) Zn   (d) Iron   (**Ans. :** d)

123. What is meant by Stress relieving ?

124. Describe the process of Stress relieving.

125. Is the range of temperature used in the relief of stress :

    (a) Below the recrystallisation temperature

    (b) Above the recrystallisation temperature

    (c) At the recrystallisation temperature

    (d) At the solidification temperature.   [**Ans. :** b]

126. Write a short note on: Nickel Maraging Steels. These are extra strength steels, having very low C-content ($\leq$ 0.03%). Because of the presence of Ni, these steels can be air cooled from a temperature of 800°C to set soft distortion free martensite. High hardness (HRC = 52-54) and high strength can be produced by aging treatment, that is, keeping this steel at 480°C for 3 hours and then air cooling.

    The three grades of this steel, widely used are:-

	Ni	Co	Mo	Ti	Max. stress, N/mm^2
1.	18	8.5	3	0.2	1400
2.	18	8	5	0.4	1750
3.	18	9	5	0.6	2000

    Advantages:-

    1. Ultra high strength, high yield strength, and high temp. strength.

    2. High notch toughness.

    3. High toughness and ductility.

    4. Simple heat treatment and dimensional stability.

    5. Properties of good machinability and weldability.

    6. Can be nitrided.

    7. Low Co-efficient of thermal expansion.

    Applications:- Best suitable for Al die casting dies, Precision plastic moulds, forging dies, carbide die holders, wear resisting index plates.

127. Describe the following properties of metals : ductility, plasticity, elasticity.

128. When a metal regains its original shape and size while the stress acting upon it is removed, the metal in said to have :

    (a) Ductility   (b) Plasticity   (c) Malleability   (d) Elasticity

                                                                              (Ans : d)

129. Percentage elongation of a metal undergoing a tensite test is a measure of :

    (a) Elasticity   (b) Plasticity   (c) Ductility   (d) Malleability

                                                                              (Ans : c)

130. Name some of the common alloying elements present in alloy steels and describe their effects on the properties of these steels.

131. Name the elements usually present in plain Carbon steels and describe their effects on the properties of this steel.

Chapter

3

The Casting Process

3.1. GENERAL

Casting is probably one of the most ancient processes of manufacturing metallic components. Also, with few exceptions, it is the first step in the manufacture of metallic components. The process involves the following basic steps :

1. Melting the metal.

2. Pouring it into a previously made mould or cavity which conforms to the shape of the desired component.

3. Allowing the molten metal to cool and solidify in the mould.

4. Removing the solidified component from the mould, cleaning it and subjecting it to further treatment, if necessary.

The solidified piece of metal, which is taken out of the mould, is called as "Casting". A plant where the castings are made is called a "Foundary". It is a collection of necessary materials, tools and equipment to produce a casting. The casting process is also called as "Founding". The word "Foundry" is derived from Latin word "fundere" meaning "melting and pouring".

Types of Foundries. All the foundries are basically of two types :

(*i*) **Jobbing Foundries.** These foundries are mostly independently owned. They produce castings on contract, within their capacity.

(*ii*) **Captive Foundries.** Such foundries are usually a department of a big manufacturing company. They produce castings exclusively for the parent company. Some captive foundries which achieve high production, sell a part of their output.

3.1.1. Advantages of Casting Process

1. Parts (both small and large) of intricate shapes can be produced.

2. Almost all the metals and alloys and some plastics can be cast.

3. A part can be made almost to the finished shape before any machining is done.

4. Good mechanical and service properties.

5. Mechanical and automated casting processes help decrease the cost of castings.

6. The number of castings can vary from very few to several thousands.

However, casting imposes severe problems from the points of view of material properties and accuracy. Also, a complicated sequence of operations is required for metal casting. Again, the geometric complexity of the final product may be such that this process is of no use.

3.1.2.Applications

There is hardly any machine or equipment which does not have one or more cast components. The list is very long, for example, automobile engine blocks, cylinder blocks of automobile and

73

airplane engines, pistons and piston rings, Machine tool beds and frames, mill rolls, Wheels and housings of steam and hydraulic turbines, Turbine vanes and aircraft jet engine blades, Water supply and sewer pipes, Sanitary fittings and agricultural parts etc. In machine tools, internal combustion engines, compressors and other machines, the mass of castings may be as great as 70 to 85% of the product's total mass.

3.1.3. Classification of Casting Process

The list of the various casting processes is very long. However, there is one convenient way of classifying these processes. It is according to whether the moulds, patterns (used to make mould cavities) and cores (used to produce internal details in a component) are permanent or expendable (disposable).

1. Expendable Mould Casting. In this process, the mould cavity is obtained by consolidating a refractory material (moulding material) around a pattern. The mould has to be broken to take out the casting from the mould cavity. So, such moulds are *one casting moulds*. The moulding material can be sand or some other refractory material. The main drawback of sand mould casting process is that the dimensional accuracy and surface finish of the castings do not satisfy in many cases the requirements of modern machine building and instrument making industry. However, if the moulding material is used in the form of slurry (Slurry moulding), better surface finish and dimensional accuracy can be obtained.

The pattern used in this process can be permanent pattern (which can be used again and again and is made of wood, metal or plastic) or expendable pattern (Full mould process, lost wax method).

2. Permanent Mould Casting. In this process, the mould is used repeatedly and is not destroyed after the solidification of the casting. The moulds are adaptable to the production of tens and thousands of castings. Generally, *the process is practical for making parts of small and medium mass from light non-ferrous alloys. The castings produced by this method have smooth surface and increased accuracy of dimensions*. Due to the high cost of permanent moulds, the use of this method is limited to mass or quantity production.

3. Semi-permanent Mould Casting. These moulds are prepared from high refractory materials, for example, based on graphite. These moulds are not as durable as permanent moulds. So, these can not be used for mass or quantity production, but for only a few tens of castings.

In all the above three methods, the cores used may be permanent (metallic) or expendable (made of core sand or of some other suitable material).

An iron foundry may have the following six prominent sections :

(a) Moulding and core making.   (b) Metal melting.
(c) Metal handling and pouring.   (d) Knockout.
(e) Fettling.
(f) Miscellaneous.

3.2. SAND-MOULD CASTING

This process accounts for about 80% of the total output of cast products. As mentioned above, the sand moulds are single-casting moulds and are completely destroyed for taking out the casting, after the metal has solidified in the mould cavity. The moulding material is sand, which is mixed with small amounts of other materials (binders and additives) and water to improve the cohesive strength and mouldability of sand. For making the mould, the moulding material will have to be consolidated and contained around the pattern. The metallic container is called as *flask*. There can be one flask or more than one flasks. The most common design is two flask system. In the assembled position the upper flask is called "Cope" and the bottom one "Drag". In three flask system, the central flask is called "Cheek". One flask design is used in 'Full mould process' or in 'Pit moulding', where it is used as cope, the pit acting as the drag.

Depending upon the type of pattern used, the sand mould casting process is of two types :

1. Permanent or Removable pattern process. Here, the pattern is removed from the mould cavity, before the molten metal is poured into the mould cavity. This is the most common sand mould casting process.

2. Expendable or Disposable pattern process. Here, the pattern is not removed from the mould cavity, before the molten metal is poured into the mould cavity. It gets melted and forms a part of the final casting. This process will be discussed later.

3.2.1. Steps in making a casting by the expendable mould, "removable pattern sand moulding process".

1. Make the pattern. The material of the pattern can be : wood, metal or plastic.
2. With the help of patterns, prepare the mould and necessary cores.
3. Clamp the mould properly with cores placed properly in the mould cavity.
4. Melt the metal or alloy to be cast.
5. Pour the molten metal/alloy into the mould cavity.
6. Allow the molten metal to cool and solidify. Remove the casting from the mould. This operation is called "Shake out".
7. Clean and finish the casting. The operation is called as "fettling".
8. Test and inspect the casting.
9. Remove the defects if any and if possible (Salvaging the casting).
10. Stress relieve the casting by heat treatment.
11. Again inspect the casting.
12. The casting is ready for use.

3.2.2. Types of Sand Mould Casting Process

Sand moulds can either be made by hand or on moulding machines. Hand moulding is done for piece and small lot production, whereas machine moulding is employed in large lot and mass production.

Depending upon the nature of the work place, hand moulding process can be classified as:

1. Bench Moulding. This is done only for small work.

2. Floor Moulding. This process is done on the foundary floor and is employed for medium sized and large castings.

3. Pit Moulding. This method is used for very large castings and is done on the foundary floor. However, a pit dug in the floor acts as the lower flask (drag) and the top flask (cope) is placed over the pit to complete the assembly. The walls of the pit are brick-lined and plastered with loam sand and allowed to dry. Sometimes, for large and tall castings, the bottom of the pit is rammed with a 50 to 80 mm layer of coke to improve the permeability of the mould. Vent pipes are run from this layer to the surface (at the sides) and the coke is covered with blacking sand.

In "Machine Moulding", the operations done ordinarily by hand, are done by machine. The operations include : Compacting the sand, rolling the mould over and drawing the pattern from the mould etc.

3.2.3. Types of Sand Moulds

As already discussed, a mould is an assembly of two or more flasks (metallic) or bonded refractory particles, with a primary cavity which is a negative of the desired part. It contains secondary cavities (pouring basin, sprue, runners and gates) for pouring and channeling the liquid metal into the primary cavity. If necessary, it also has a large cylindrical cavity for storing the molten metal (riser or feeding head) for feeding into the primary cavity to compensate for the shrinkage of molten metal in the primary cavity, on cooling and solidification.

According to the material used in their construction, the moulds are of following types :

1. Green Sand Moulds. A green sand mould is composed of a mixture of sand (silica sand, SiO_2), clay (which acts as binder) and water. The word "green" is associated with the condition of wetness or freshness and because the mould is left in the damp condition, hence the name "green sand mould". This type of mould is the cheapest and has the advantage that used sand is readily reclaimed. But, the mould being in the damp condition, is weak and can not be stored for a longer period. Hence, such moulds are used for small and medium sized castings.

2. Dry Sand Moulds. Dry sand moulds are basically green sand moulds with two essential differences : the sand used for dry sand moulds contains 1 to 2% cereal flour and 1 to 2% pitch, whereas the sand mixture for green sand moulds may not contain these additives. Also, the prepared moulds are baked in an oven at 110 to 260°C for several hours. The additives increase the hot strength due to evaporation of water as well as by the oxidation and polymerization of the pitch. So, dry sand moulds can be used for large castings. They give better surface finish and also reduce the incidence of the casting defects such as gas holes, blows or porosity that may occur as a result of steam generation in the mould (when the molten metal is poured into the green sand mould cavity). However, due to the greater strength of these moulds, tearing may occur in hot-short materials.

3. Skin - dry Sand Moulds. Here, after the mould is prepared, instead of entirely drying it out, the mould is partially dried around the cavity (to a depth of about 25 mm). This can be done in two ways :

(*i*) About 12.5 mm around the pattern, the proper moulding sand (as described under dry sand moulds) is used, the remaining mould contains ordinary green sand.

(*ii*) The entire mould is made of green sand and then the surface of the cavity is coated with a spray or wash of linseed oil, gelatinized starch or molasses water etc. The advantages and limitations of such moulds are the same as of the dry sand moulds.

4. Loam Sand Moulds. Loam sand consists of fine sand plus finely ground refractories, clay, graphite and fibrous reinforcements. It differs from ordinary moulding sand in that the percentage of clay in it is very high (of the order of 50%). This sand is used in pit moulding process for making moulds for very heavy and large parts (engine bodies, machine tool beds and frames etc.).

5. Cemented - bonded Moulds. Here, the moulding sand contains 10 to 15% of cement as the binder. Such a mould is stronger and harder. Such moulds are made in the pit moulding process and develop their strength by air drying and are used for large steel castings. However, it is very difficult to break away the sand from the casting.

6. CO_2 Moulds. The CO_2 moulding process is a sand moulding process in which sodium silicate ($Na_2O . x Si O_2$), that is, water glass is used as a binder, rather than clay. After the mould is made, CO_2 gas is made to flow through the mould, the sand mixture hardens due to the following reaction.

$$Na_2O . x Si O_2 + n H_2O + CO_2 \longrightarrow Na_2CO_3 \ x.Si O_2 . n (H_2O)$$
$$\text{Stiff gel.}$$

here, $x = 1.6$ to 4, most often 2.

This reaction is very rapid and takes about 1 minute, which is very much less than the several hours needed to produce a dry sand mould. Such moulds can be used for producing very smooth and intricate castings., because the sand mix has a very high flowability to fill up corners and intricate contours.

7. Resin-bonded Sand Moulds. Here, the green sand mixture is mixed with thermosetting resins (polymers) or an oil, such as, linseed oil or soyabean oil. During baking of the mould, the resin or oil oxidises and polymerizes around the sand particles, thus bonding them together. The strength of the polymerized resin is greater than that of pitch used in dry sand moulds. So, the moulds produced are stronger. Such a sand mixture is commonly used for making cores.

Baking is usually needed to make strong moulds or cores. Many times, the required strength of moulds is obtained without baking. These moulds are known as "Furan-no bake" moulds, "oil-no bake" moulds etc. Furan is a generic term denoting the basic structure of a class of chemical compounds. The resins used in the "no-bake" systems are compounds of furfuryl alcohols, urea and formaldehyde. A very low water content (less than 1%) is used in the above moulds. The synthetic liquid resin is mixed with sand and the mixture hardens at room temperature.

8. Dry Sand Core Moulds. When the moulding flasks are too large to fit in an oven (for baking) or when it costs too much to dry a large mass of sand, moulds are made from assemblies of sand cores. A sand core is usually prepared from core sand mixtures (discussed later) and is baked at 175 to 230°C for 4 to 24 h, depending upon sand preparation and mass.

9. Cold-box Mould Process. Here, various organic and inorganic binders are blended into sand to bond the grains chemically, imparting greater strengths to the mould. These moulds are dimensionally more accurate than green sand moulds, but are more expensive.

10. Composite Moulds. These moulds are made of two or more different materials, such as shells, plaster, sand with binder and graphite. These moulds combine the advantages of each material. They are used in shell moulding and other casting processes, generally for casting complex shapes, such as turbine impellers. These moulds result in : increased mould strength, improved dimensional accuracy and surface finish of castings and reduced overall costs and processing times.

The above mentioned types of moulds are compared in Table 3.1.

Table. 3.1. Comparison of Moulds

Type of Mould	Advantages	Disadvantages
(a) **Green Sand Mould**	1. Least expensive	1. Sand control is more critical than in dry sand moulds.
	2. Less distortion than in dry sand moulds, because no baking is required.	2. Erosion of mould is more common in the production of large castings.
	3. Flasks are ready for reuse in minimum time	3. Surface finish and dimensional accuracy deteriorate as the weight of the casting increases
	4. Dimensional accuracy is good across the parting line.	
	5. Less danger of hot tearing of Casting than in other types of castings.	
(b) **Dry Sand Mould**	1. Stronger than green sand moulds, thus are less prone to damage in handling.	1. Castings are more prone to hot tearing.
	2. Overall dimensional accuracy is better than for green sand moulds.	2. Distortion is greater than for green sand mould because of baking.

		3. More flask equipment is needed to produce the same number of finished pieces because processing cycles are longer than for green sand moulds.
	3. Surface finish of castings is better, mainly because dry sand moulds are coated with a wash.	
		4. Production is slower than for green sand moulds.
(c) **Dry Sand Core Moulds**	1. Exceptionally good dimensional accuracy can be maintained.	1. Extreme care must be taken in setting the cores.
	2. Dry sand core moulding is adaptable to greens and foundaries that do not have large drying facilities.	
(d) **Furan, oil, CO_2 Moulds**	1. Sands are free flowing, therefore, ramming is eliminated or reduced.	1. Sands must be used immediately
	2. Tensile strengths of moulds are higher than those of conventional moulds. This permits reduction of mould weight and easier handling of large moulds.	
	3. Moulds can be made without flasks.	
	4. Production rates are high.	
	5. Most of these moulds can produce castings to closer tolerances than are obtainable in green sand moulds.	

Note. 1. More than 85% of all metal castings are poured in sand moulds, the balance are made in ceramic shell or metal moulds.

2. Majority of castings are poured in green sand moulds.

3. In a foundry, upto 90% of the moulding sand can be reprocessed to make new moulds.

3.2.4. Preparing a Sand Mould. The sequence of operations performed in the making of a sand mould is outlined below. For this, a green sand mould and a split pattern have been chosen.

The appropriate split pattern is made which is split into two equal parts at the parting plane and joined together with dowel pins. We will use a two flask system, (Fig. 3.1).

(A) Hand Moulding Process

1. The drag half of the pattern, that is, the half with dowel holes rather than dowel pins, is placed with the flat parting plane on a flat board called "Moulding board".

2. The drag is placed over the moulding board with the alignment or locating pins downwards.

3. A parting material is dusted over the pattern and the moulding board to facilitate both the removal of the pattern from the mould and the separation of the two mould halves.

4. The drag is filled with moulding sand and it is packed and rammed around the pattern. The ramming is done manually with hands and with hand rammers (wooden or iron). The sand should be properly rammed, that is, neither too hard nor too soft. If it is too soft, the mould will fall apart during handling or during pouring and if it is too hard, gases produced on pouring will not be able to leave it. Pneumatic ramming or mechanical ramming can be used for large moulds.

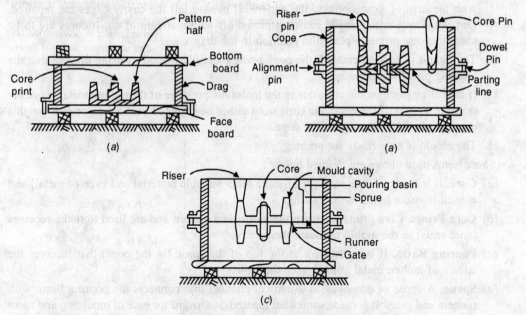

Fig. 3.1. A Green Sand Mould.

5. After the ramming, the excess sand is scrapped off with a straight bar called a "strike rod".

6. Vent holes are pierced in the sand (within 15 to 20 mm of the pattern surface) with "vent wires", for the gases to escape through.

7. A second moulding board is placed on the moulded drag half and clamped if the mould is too heavy to be turned over conveniently by hand. The mould is then turned over 180° and the original moulding board is removed.

8. The cope is mounted onto the drag and the two halves are properly aligned with the help of alignment pins.

9. The cope half of the pattern is properly positioned over the drag half of the pattern with help of dowel pins and dowel holes.

10. For making the sprue and riser, the sprue pin and riser pin are placed approximately 25 mm on either side of the pattern (usually along the parting line passing through the alignment pins).

11. Steps 3 to 6 are repeated.

12. A pouring basin is cut adjacent to the sprue and then the sprue and riser pins are with drawn.

13. The cope is carefully lifted off the temporarily separated from the drag and placed on one side.

14. To take out the split pattern from the drag, "draw spikes" are drawn into the pattern and the pattern is loosened from the sand by rapping them lightly in all directions with a wooden hammer called a "mallet". Then the pattern is lifted off with the help of draw spike. Before with drawing the pattern, the sand around it is moistened with a "Swab" so that the edges of the mould remain firm when the pattern is withdrawn.

15. The gate and runner are cut in the drag or both cope and drag, connecting the mould cavity and the sprue opening. Sometimes, the gate and runner are automatically made

with the help of extensions on the pattern. If needed, all the cavity edges are repaired. Dirt remaining in the mould cavity is blown off with a stream of air. If cores are to be used, they are properly placed in position in the drag.

16. The mould is now assembled, the cope being carefully placed over the drag so that the locating pins fit into the holes.

17. If the lifting force on the cope due to the hydraulic pressure of the molten metal is greater than the weight of the cope, the cope must either be clamped to the drag or else weights must be placed on the top of the cope.

18. The mould is now ready for pouring.

Some terms used above are defined below :

(a) **Core.** It is made of core sand (or of some other suitable material and even of metal) and is used to make holes in the casting.

(b) **Core Prints.** Core prints are the projections on a pattern and are used to make recesses (core seats) in the mould to locate the core.

(c) **Pouring Basin.** It is a reservoir at the top of the sprue (in the cope) that receives the stream of molten metal poured from the ladle.

(d) **Sprue.** A sprue or downgate is a vertical channel that connects the pouring basin with runners and gates. It is made somewhat tapered downward for ease of moulding and more importantly to have a decreasing cross-sectional area corresponding to the increase in velocity of the molten metal as it flows down the sprue hole. This prevents turbulent flow and hence the drawing in of air alongwith the liquid into the mould cavity.

(e) **Sprue base or Well.** It is a reservoir at the bottom end of the sprue. It prevents excessive sand erosion when the molten metal strikes the runner at the sprue base. Also, there is considerable loss of velocity in the well.

(f) **Runner.** The runner is generally a horizontal channel whose functions are to trap slag and connect the sprue base with the gates (ingates), thus allowing the molten metal to enter the mould cavity.

(g) **Gates.** The gates (ingates) are the channels through which the incoming metal directly enters the mould cavity.

(h) **Risers.** The risers or feed heads are a part of the feeding system. These are reservoirs of molten metal that feed the metal in the casting proper as it solidifies, to prevent shrinkage cavities in the casting.

Bars and Gaggers. With large cope flasks, added support is normally required to keep the moulding sand from sagging or falling out when the cope is raised to remove the pattern. This support is provided by two elements, namely bars and gaggers. The bars subdivide the large cope flask areas into smaller areas which are able to support themselves, (Fig. 3.2). The bars should extend downward to within 25 to 50 mm of the pattern or parting surface. If added support is needed, gaggers should also be used. A gagger is a L-shaped steel rod (6.35 to 12.5 mm in diameter). Gaggers extend vertically downward from the top of the bar to within 25 to 50 mm of the pattern or parting surface. The gaggers are generally dipped in a clay slurry to improve the bonding of the mould sand to the gagger. Or their surfaces should be rough to help them obtain a better grip in the sand. They are placed in position after a depth of about 25 to 50 mm of rammed sand is placed over the pattern and parting surface. Their lower ends are then pressed into the first layer of moulding sand with their upright portions against bars for support. The function of 'skim bob' in the figure is to trap foreign matter and slag in the molten metal, so that these do not enter the mould cavity. The portion of the skim bob in the cope traps lighter impurities and the heavier impurities are trapped is the portion in the drag.

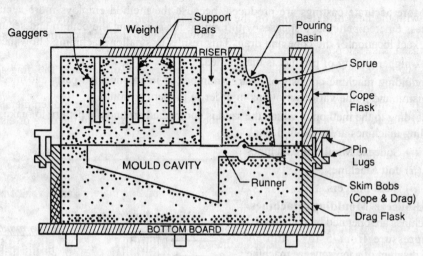

Fig. 3.2. Bars and Gaggers.

Soldiers. In some cases, additional support may be secured by the use of nails or soldiers. Soldiers are wooden or steel pins with rough surfaces. These are placed in the moulding sand, as it is rammed, where reinforcement of the mould is needed.

Three Flask Mould. Sometimes a casting has re-entrant sections which make it more convenient to use a three or more flask mould rather than a two flask mould. The flasks between the cope and drag flasks are referred to as "cheeks". Fig. 3.3 illustrates the use of a cheek to cast a wheel having a groove in the rim (for example a V-belt pulley or a rope pulley).

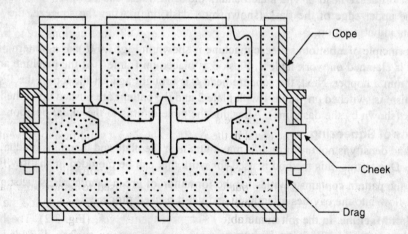

Fig. 3.3. Three Flask Mould.

(B) Machine Moulding. The hand moulding process discussed above is suitable only when the number of moulds to be made is small. But, when large quantities of castings are to be produced, the moulding is done on a machine. Moulding machines pack the sand and draw the pattern from the mould. The use of a moulding machine results in the following advantages:

1. The time required to make a mould is greatly reduced. This reduces the overall costs.
2. The labour productivity is greatly increased, owing to the mechanization of laborious operations of sand ramming and pattern removal.

3. More accurate castings are produced, because the method employs more accurate and less tapered patterns, dispenses with rapping for removing the pattern and secures more exact location of the cope and drag. This results in smaller machining allowances.

4. A higher quality of product is maintained.

A moulding machine consists of a large number of interconnected parts and mechanisms, which transmit and guide various motions in order to prepare a mould.

According to the method in which the sand is compacted around the pattern to make a mould, the moulding machines are classified as :

      (*i*) Squeeze Moulding Machines.

      (*ii*) Jolt Machines

      (*iii*) Sand Slingers

(*a*) **Squeeze Moulding Machines.** These machines are operated by compressed air at a pressure from 5 to 7 atm. A schematic diagram of a top squeeze machine is shown in Fig. 3.4 (*a*). The pattern plate with pattern 2 is clamped on the work table 1 and flask 3 is placed on the plate. Then the sand frame 4 is placed on flask 3. The flask and frame are filled with moulding sand from a hopper located above the machine. Next the table lift mechanism is switched on and the flask together with the sand frame and pattern is lifted up against platen 5 of the stationary squeeze head 6. The platen enters the sand frame and compacts the moulding sand down to the upper edge of the flask (shown by a dash line). After the squeeze, the work table returns to its initial position.

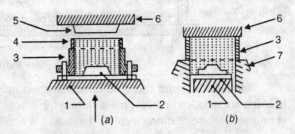

Fig. 3.4. Squeeze Moulding Machines.

The principle of a bottom squeeze machine is shown in Fig. 3.4 (*b*). The pattern plate 2 with the pattern is clamped on work table 1. Flask 3 is placed on frame 7 of the machine and is filled with sand from a hopper. Next, the squeeze head 6 is brought against the top of the flask and the lift mechanism is switched on. Table 1 with plate 2 and the pattern are pushed up to the lower edge of the flask (shown by the dash line). After this the table returns to the initial position.

Limitations of Squeezing

1. Sand density is not uniform. It is maximum near the plate and then falls gradually towards the pattern. Due to this, this method is used for work that can be moulded in shallow flasks.

2. If the pattern contains cavities for the formation of green sand cores, squeezing does not make sand flow into the cavities effectively and get it packed properly.

(*b*) **Jolt Machine.** In the jolt moulding machine, the pattern and flask are mounted on a mould plate and the flask is filled with sand. The entire assembly is raised a small amount by means of an air cylinder and is then dropped against a fixed stop. The compacting of sand is achieved by the decelerating forces acting on it.

The working of a jolt moulding machine is shown in Fig. 3.5. The table 1 with moulding sand, is lifted by plunger 4 to a definite height (about 5 cm) when compressed

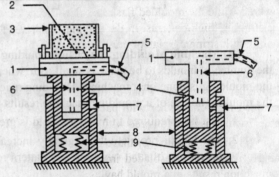

Fig. 3.5. Jolt Moulding Machine.

air is admitted through pipe 5 and channels 6. Next the table drops since the air is released through hole 7. In falling, the table strikes the stationary guiding cylinder 8 and this impact packs the moulding sand in the flask. Springs 9, by cushioning the table blows, reduced noise and prevent destruction of the mechanism and the foundation. About 20 to 50 drops are needed to compact the sand, and the average machine operates at about 200 strokes per minute.

The drawback of the method is that the density of the sand in the mould is not uniform. It is greatest in the layers next to the pattern plate and lowest near the top of the mould, because in the course of impact, every upper layer acts on the lower layer. Also, there is high level of noise produced by the jolt machines in operation and there is considerable load on the foundation.

(c) **Jolt Squeeze Machine.** This machine is similar in appearance to a jolt machine. In addition, it has a vertical column rising above and behind the table to which is fastened a rigid support that overhangs the table. Also, the base contains two concentric air cylinders ; the smaller one to provide the jolting and the larger one to squeeze the mould against the overhead support. On this machine, the pattern can be attached to the match plate. The jolt squeeze method is free of the basic limitations of the squeeze method, that is, weak compaction near the bottom of the mould and that of the jolting method-weak compaction near the top of the mould. The method combines jolting with squeezing, which gives the mould a high and uniform density and increased strength and enables the production of accurate castings of high quality. Jolt squeeze machine now find most widespread use in the foundary practice.

(d) **Jolt Squeeze Strip Machine.** The jolt squeeze strip or jolt squeeze vibrate machine is similar to the jolt squeeze machine except that it has an air hose attached to the match plate so that the pattern can be vibrated while it is being with drawn from the mould. In this machine, both the cope and drag halves of the mould are made on one machine. First the drag half of the mould is completed and then the cope half is made with the match plate (with its attached air hose) is assembled between the cope and drag. The operator raises and turns over the mould halves by hand.

(e) **Jolt Squeeze Roll-over Machine.** The jolt squeeze roll over draw-type of moulding machine is used when the size of the mould is too large to be turned over by hand. Only a half of the mould is made at one time on this machine.

The mould is compacted by jolting on the table in the foreground to which it is clamped. The table is raised and the mould is rolled over the centre column onto the roller table in back of the column. The pattern is stripped from the mould and returned to the jolting table while the completed mould is rolled onto a conveyer that transports it to the assembly and pouring area.

Drawing or Stripping the pattern from the mould halves. There are various methods employed to draw or strip the pattern from the mould half, (Fig. 3.6). In Fig. 3.6 (a), the rammed half mould 2 is raised by stripping fins 4 while the pattern 1 with pattern plate remains on the table 5. In Fig. 3.6 (b), the pattern is drawn through a stripping plate. Pattern 1 with pattern plate 3 is lowered while the moulded flask and the stripping plate 4 remain stationary. This method is used for stripping high patterns. In the stripping plate procedure shown in Fig. 3.6(c), the finished half mould with stripping plate 4 are lifted by pins 6. The pattern drawing principle incorporated in a roll over moulding machine is shown in Fig. 3.6 (d). The moulded flask 2 together with pattern 1 and work table 5 is rotated 180° about their approximate centre of gravity and then pins 6 lift table 5 together with pattern 1 out of the mould. In rock-over pattern draw method, Fig. 3.6 (e), the moulded flask 2 together with pattern 1 and table 5 is swung over by the arm onto the drawing table 7 which is then lowered with the mould away from the pattern.

(f) **Sand Slingers.** In these machines, the sand is thrown out by centrifugal force from a rapidly rotating single bladed impeller and directed over the pattern in the flask. This type of compaction results in a mould having a more uniform density throughout, than does the squeezing or jolting method. These machines can fill flasks of any size, but are generally used only in the making of large moulds. They can be efficiently employed in both mass and piece production. These machines operate with a high output ; one sand slinger can fill flasks, packing the sand, at a rate of 60 m^3 per hour. The disadvantage of the machine is that it does not draw the pattern or handle the mould in any may.

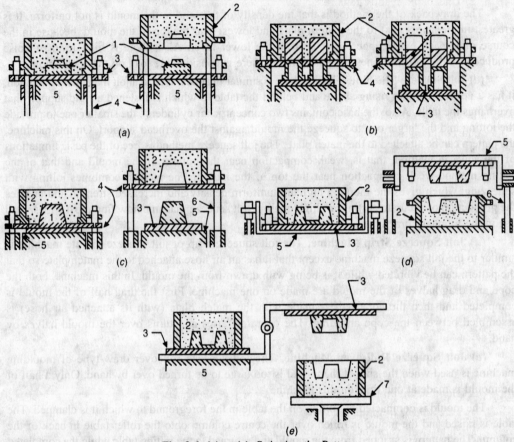

(a)

(b)

(c)

(d)

(e)

Fig. 3.6. (a) to (e). Stripping the Pattern.

The principle of operation of the impeller head on the sand slinger is shown in Fig. 3.7. The head consists of housing in which blade rotates rapidly. Moulding sand is fed by a belt conveyer to opening in the end face of the housing where it is picked up by blade and thrown in separate portions at a high speed through outlet down into the flask under the head.

3.3. PATTERNS

A pattern is an element used for making cavities in the mould, into which molten metal is poured to produce a casting. It is not an exact replica of the casting desired. There are certain essential differences. It is slightly larger than the desired casting, due to the various allowances (shrinkage allowance, machining allowance etc.) and it may

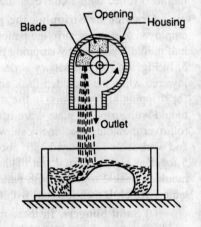

Fig. 3.7. Sand Slinger.

have several projections or bosses called core prints. It may also have extensions to produce runners and gates during the moulding process.

3.3.1. Pattern Materials. The requirements of a good pattern are :

1. Secure the desired shape and size of the casting.
2. Cheap and readily repairable.
3. Simple in design for ease of manufacture.
4. Light in mass and convenient to handle.
5. Have high strength and long life in order to make as many moulds as required.
6. Retain its dimensions and rigidity during the definite service life
7. Its surface should be smooth and wear resistant.
8. Able to withstand rough handling.

The common materials used in pattern making include "wood, metal, plastic and quick setting compounds. Each material has its own advantages, limitations and field of application. Also, the required accuracy, strength and life of a pattern depend on the quantity of castings to be produced. Based on the above factors, we can choose the pattern material as follows:

(*i*) *Piece and short run production.* Wood

(*ii*) *Large scale and mass production.* Metal, being more durable than wood, though costlier.

(*iii*) *Batch production.* Plastics, for example, epoxy resins and also from gypsum and cement.

(*a*) **Wood.** The wood used for pattern making should be properly dried and seasoned. It should not contain more than 10% moisture to avoid warping and distortion during subsequent drying. It should be straight grained and free from knots.

Advantages

1. Light in weight.
2. Comparatively inexpensive.
3. Good workability.
4. Lends itself to gluing and joining.
5. Holds well varnishes and paints.
6. Can be repaired easily.

Limitations

1. Inherently non uniform in structure.
2. Posses poor wear and abrasion resistance.
3. Can not withstand rough handling.
4. Absorbs and gives off moisture, so that it varies in volume, warps and thus changes its mechanical properties. These drawbacks, however, can be remedied by drying and seasoning it and then giving coats of water proof varnishes and paints.

The following types of wood are commonly used for pattern making:

(*i*) **White Pine.** It is the most widely used wood, because of its straight grain and light weight and because it is soft, easy to work and unlikely to warp.

(*ii*) **Mahogany.** It is harder and more durable than white pine. Can be worked easily if straight grained. It is less likely to warp than some of other woods.

(*iii*) **Maple, Birch and Cherry.** It woods are harder and heavier than white pine. They tend to warp in large sections, so should be used for small patterns only. They should be carefully treated, because, they pick up moisture readily.

The other common wood materials are : Teak, Shisham, Kail and Deodar.

(*b*) **Metal.** A metal pattern can be either cast from a master wooden pattern or may be machined by the usual methods of machining. Metal patterns are usually used in machine moulding.

Advantages

1. More durable and accurate in size than wooden patterns.
2. Have a smooth surface
3. Do not deform in storage.
4. Are resistant to wear, abrasion, corrosion and swelling.
5. Can withstand rough handling.

Limitations

1. Expensive as compared to wood.
2. Not easily repaired.
3. Heavier than wooden patterns.
4. Ferrous patterns can get rusted.

The common metals used for pattern making are :

(*i*) **C.I.** With fine grain can be used as a pattern material. It has low corrosion resistance unless protected. Heavier and difficult to work. However it is cheaper and more durable than other metals.

(*ii*) **Brass.** May be easily worked and built up by soldering or brazing. It has a smooth, closed pore structure. It is expensive, therefore, generally used for small cast parts.

(*iii*) **Aluminium.** It is the best pattern material, because it is easily worked, light in weight and is corrosion resistant. It is, however, subject to shrinkage and wear by abrasive action.

(*iv*) **White Metal.** It has low shrinkage, can be cast easily, has low melting point, is light in weight and may be built up by soldering. However, it is subject to wear by abrasive action of sand.

(*c*) **Plastics.** The use of plastics for pattern material results in following advantages :

1. Facilitates the production process.
2. Makes it more economical in cost and labour.
3. Plastic patterns are highly resistant to corrosion, lighter and stronger than wood patterns.
4. Moulding sand sticks less to plastics than to wood.
5. No moisture absorption.
6. Smooth surface of patterns.
7. Strong and dimensionally stable.

Various plastics make good materials for the production of patterns. These are the compositions based on epoxy, phenol formaldehyde and polyester resins ; polyacrylates, polyethylene, polyvinylchloride, and others. In most wide use are cold-curing plastics based on epoxy resins and acrylates.

Plastic patterns are made by one of the following methods :

(*i*) By injecting a plastic material into a die.

(*ii*) Utilizing laminated construction by building up successive layers of resin and glass fibre.

(*iii*) By pouring a plastic material into a plaster mould.

Laminated plastic patterns with surface as smooth as glass are more durable than wood patterns. They draw more easily, are not prone to wear and scratches in service, and can be repaired quickly when damaged. A laminated fibre glass core box can resist tremendous pressures and rough treatments in foundry practice. Various combinations of apoxys, often with lay-on fibre glass for added strength, are employed. Metal grains are also added to the resin, to provide added strength to those areas likely to be abused by foundry methods. The polyurethanes exhibit outstanding resistance to damage, both from abrasion and indentation.

Gypsum patterns are capable of producing castings with intricate details and to very close tolerances. The two main types of gypsum are soft "plaster of paris" and hard metal casting plaster. However, soft plaster does not have the strength of hard plaster. Gypsum can be easily formed, has plasticity and can be easily repaired.

Patterns are also made of a combination of materials used for special purposes. To improve wear qualities and strength, metal inserts are often used, as well as resin-impregnated materials.

Practically, all aluminium match plates and cope and drag plates are cast in plaster moulds. This results in smooth pattern surfaces and accurate reproduction of fine details in the pattern. Due to this castings will have close dimensional tolerances.

Soft wood patterns : upto 50 pieces of medium size castings.

Hard wood patterns : for 50 to 200 castings.

Metal patterns with hardened steel wear plates : 200 to 5000 castings.

Note. Sometimes, if a pattern is first made in wood and then in some other metal by casting, double shrinkages allowances are provided.

3.3.2. Finishing of Patterns. After the patterns are made, they should be finished by sanding so that tool marks and other irregularities are erased. Then they should be applied with 2 to 3 coats of shellac. Shellac fills up the pores and imparts a smooth finish.

The finish of the casting depends on the finish of the pattern. If the pattern is to be preserved for a long period and if a colour scheme is to be used, a good quality enamel paint should be selected to spray or brush paint it.

3.3.3. Pattern Allowances. The difference in the dimensions of the casting and the pattern is due to the various allowances considered while designing a pattern for a casting. These allowances are discussed below :

1. Shrinkage Allowance. Since metal shrinks on solidification and contracts further on cooling to room temperature, linear dimensions of patterns are increased in respect of those of the finished casting to be obtained. This is called the "shrinkage allowance". It is given as mm/m. Typical values of shrinkage allowance for various metals are given below:

C.I., Malleable iron	= 10 mm/m
Brass, Cu, Al	= 15 mm/m
Steel	= 20 mm/m
Zinc, Lead	= 25 mm/m

While laying out a pattern, the dimensions are taken from a Pattern maker's rule, called "Shrink scale", which is longer than a standard scale by the shrinkage value for the appropriate metal.

2. Machining Allowance. Machining allowance or finish allowance indicates how much larger the rough casting should be over the finished casting to allow sufficient material to insure that machining will "clean up" the surfaces. This machining allowance is added to all surfaces that are to be machined.

The amount of finish allowance depends on the material of the casting, its size, volume of production, method of moulding, configuration of the casting, the position the wall surface occupies in the mould and during pouring. Machining allowance is larger for hand moulding as compared to machine moulding. The largest allowances are taken for the surfaces located in the cope half of the mould, since they are liable to contamination due to slag. Typical machining allowances for sand casting are given in Table 3.2. The allowances are in mm per side. For internal surfaces such as bores, the allowance is about 0.8 mm greater and is negative.

Table 3.2. Typical Machining Allowances for Sand Casting

Material Cast	Over all length of external surfaces, cm			
	0 to 30	30 to 60	60 to 105	105 to 150
Al alloys	1.6	3.2	3.0	4.8
Brass, Bronze	1.6	3.2	3.0	4.8
C.I.	2.4	3.2	4.8	6.4
C.S.	3.2	4.8	6.0	9.6

3. Pattern draft or Taper. Pattern draft, also termed "draw", is the taper placed on the pattern surfaces that are parallel to the direction in which the pattern is withdrawn from the mould (that is perpendicular to the parting plane), to allow removal of the pattern without damaging the mould cavity, Fig. 3.8 (a). The draft depends upon the method of moulding, the sand mixture used, the design and economic restrictions imposed on the casting. The common draft is 1° to 3° After applying the draft, the largest cross-section of the pattern will be at the parting line for external surfaces and reverse will be for internal surfaces, (Fig. 3.8 (b).)

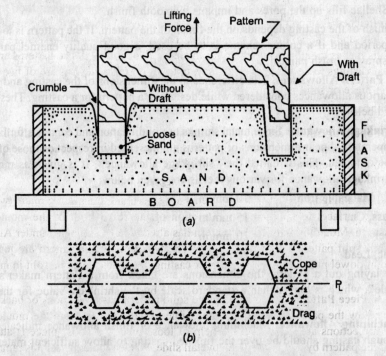

Fig. 3.8. Pattern Taper.

4. Corners and Fillets. The intersection of surfaces in castings must be smooth and form no sharp angles. For this, the external and internal corners of patterns are suitably rounded. They are called rounded corners and fillets respectively. Fillets facilitate the removal of the pattern from the mould, prevent the formation of cracks and shrink holes in the casting. The radius of a fillet is given as $= \dfrac{1}{5}$ to $\dfrac{1}{3}$ (arithmetic mean of the thickness of the two walls that form the angle in the pattern).

5. Rapping or Shake Allowance. To take the pattern out of the mould cavity it is slightly rapped to detach it from the mould cavity. Due to this, the cavity in the mould increases slightly. So, the pattern is made slightly smaller.

6. Distortion Allowance. This allowance is considered only for castings of irregular shape which are distorted in the process of cooling because of metal shrinkage.

3.3.4 Types of Patterns. Patterns may be classified as temporary and permanent patterns, depending upon the material used for the pattern. Temporary patterns of soft wood are easily made. However, they soon wear, warp or crack and so have a short life. Hardwood patterns are used more than any other type of patterns. The portions that wear may be protected by sheet metal. Permanent patterns are made of metals (usually Al or brass) or plastics that are easily cast and machined. Patterns may be classified from their utility point of view. The following factors affect the choice of a pattern.

(*i*) Number of castings to be produced.

(*ii*) Size and complexity of the shape and size of casting.

(*iii*) Type of moulding method to be used.

The common types of patterns are discussed below :

1. **Loose Pattern.** A loose pattern is simply a replica of the desired casting. It is slightly larger than the casting (due to the allowances discussed above) and it may have several projections called core prints that the resulting casting does not have. Loose patterns get their name because they are not attached or mounted on a plate or frame. These patterns may be made of wood or metal depending upon the volume of production. The gates, runners and risers are added during moulding. This makes mould slow and labour intensive. Due to this, loose patterns are used when the number of castings to be made is small, say, upto 100. Loose patterns are of two types :

(*a*) One piece or solid pattern

(*b*) Split pattern

(*a*) **One Piece or Solid Pattern.** This is the simplest type of pattern, exactly like the desired casting. For making a mould, the pattern is accommodated either in cope or drag. The moulding process is quite inconvenient and time consuming. So, such patterns are used for producing a few large castings, for example, stuffing box of steam engine.

(*b*) **Split or Parted Pattern.** These patterns are split along the parting plane (which may be flat or irregular surface) to facilitate the extraction of the pattern out of the mould before the pouring operation. Moulding with a split pattern has already been explained under Art. 3.2.4. Fig. 3.9 (*a*) shows a split pattern for casting a bush. The two parts of the pattern are joined together with the help of dowel pins. For a more complex casting, the pattern may be split in more than two parts.

2. **Loose Piece Pattern.** When a one piece solid pattern has projections or backdrafts which lie above or below the parting plane, it is impossible to with draw it from the mould. With such patterns, the projections are made with the help of loose pieces. A loose piece is attached to the main body of the pattern by a pin or with a dovetail slide. While moulding, sand is rammed securely

around the loose piece. Then the pins are removed. The sand is then packed and rammed around the total pattern. When the main pattern is drawn, the loose pieces remain in the mould. These are then carefully rapped and drawn as shown in Fig. 3.9 (b). One drawback of loose pieces is that their shifting is possible during ramming.

Drawbacks. Another technique to make a mould with a one piece solid pattern (with projections) is the use of drawbacks. A drawback is a portion of the mould, which can be drawn back horizontally in order to allow removal of the pattern. It may be rammed around a rigid support called an "arbor" to facilitate moving it, (Fig. 3.9 (c).)

3. Gated Patterns. A gated pattern is simply one or more loose patterns having attached gates and runners, (Fig. 3.9 (d)). Since the gates and runners are not to be cut by hand, gated patterns reduce the moulding time somewhat. Because of their higher cost, these patterns are used for producing small castings in mass production systems and on moulding machines.

4. Match Plate Pattern. A match plate pattern is a split pattern having the cope and drag portions mounted on opposite sides of a plate (usually metallic), called the "match plate" that conforms to the contour of the parting surface. The gates and runners are also mounted on the match plate, (Fig. 3.9 (e)), so that very little hand work is required. This results in higher productivity. This type of pattern is used for a large number of castings. Several patterns can be mounted on one match plate if the size of the casting is small. The patterns need not all be for the same casting. When match plate patterns are used, the moulding is generally done on a moulding machine. Piston rings of I.C. engines are produced by this process.

5. Cope and Drag Pattern. A cope and drag pattern is a split pattern having the cope and drag portions each mounted on separate match plates. These patterns are used when in the production of large castings, the complete moulds are too heavy and unwieldy to be handled by a single worker. The patterns are accurately located on the plates, so that when the two separately made mould halves are assembled together, the mould cavity is properly formed. For a higher rate of production, each half of the pattern is mounted on a separate moulding machine, one operator working on the cope part of the mould and the other on the drag part of the mould.

6. Sweep Patterns. A sweep is a section or board (wooden) of proper contour that is rotated about one edge to shape mould cavities having shapes of rotational symmetry, (Fig. 3.9 (f)). This type of pattern is used when a casting of large size is to be produced in a short time. A complete pattern is not necessary and would be very expensive for a very large casting where the tolerances are large. The moulds are made manually, either in a pit or on the foundary floor. Thus, this type of moulding is referred to as pit and floor moulding. The moulding sand used is the "loam sand". A framework of brick or wood supports the loam. Once the mould is ready, the sweep pattern and the post about which it rotates, are removed before pouring the mould cavity. Large kettles of C.I. are made by sweep patterns.

7. Skeleton Patterns. For large castings having simple geometrical shapes, skeleton patterns are used. Just like sweep patterns, these are simple wooden frames that outline the shape of the part to be cast and are also used as guides by the moulder in the hand shaping of the mould. This type of pattern is also used in pit or floor moulding process. Again, a complete pattern is not necessary and would be quite expensive for a very large casting where the tolerances are large, and when only a small number of castings is to be made.

Fig. 3.9 (g) shows a skeleton pattern for casting a pipe. It is a ribbed construction of wood which forms an outline of the pattern to be made. The frame work is filled with loam sand and rammed. The sand must be true and smooth. Hence, a strike off board known as a "Strickle board" is used to shape the sand according to the desired shape of the skeleton pattern. For round shapes, the pattern is made in two halves which are joined together by means of screws or with glue etc. This type of pattern is used for casting water pipes, turbine casings etc.

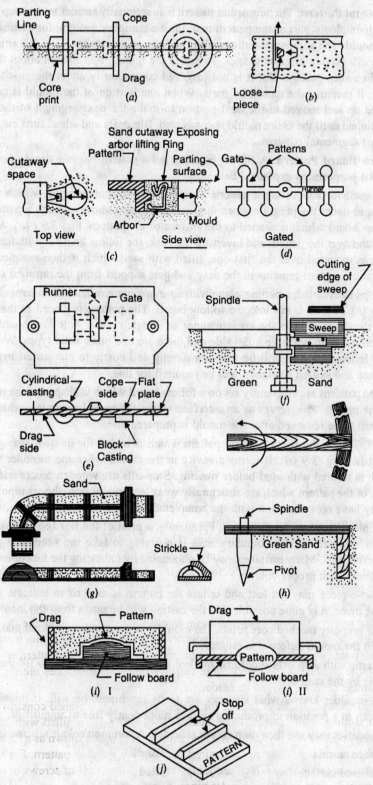

Fig. 3.9. Types of Patterns.

8. Segmental Pattern. The segmental pattern is functionally similar to a sweep pattern in the sense, that both employ a part of the pattern instead of a complete pattern, for getting the required shape of the mould. The segmental pattern is in the form of a segment, (Fig. 3.9 (*h*)), and is used for moulding parts having circular shapes. To create the mould, it is rotated about the post in the same way as in sweep pattern. But it is not revolved continuously about the post to prepare the mould. Rather, it prepares the mould by parts. When one portion of the mould is completed, the pattern is lifted up and moved to the next portion to make the next segment of the mould. This process is continued until the entire mould is completed. Big gears and wheel rims etc. are produced with the help of segmental patterns.

9. Follow Board Pattern. A follow board is not a pattern but is a device (wooden board) used for various purposes as explained below :

(*i*) It is used for supporting a pattern which is very thin and fragile, which may break or collapse under the pressure when the sand is rammed above it. Such a pattern is set on a follow board which is shaped to the surface of the pattern, Fig. 3.9 *i* (*a*). After ramming the sand over the pattern and inverting the flask, the follow board is withdrawn. The other flask is mounted over the first one, filled with sand which is then rammed. During this operation, pattern remains in the drag and gets support from the rammed sand under it.

(*ii*) It helps to establish a parting plane with ease in a pattern that has an irregular shape, Fig. 3.9 *i* (*b*). A hole is cut into the follow board. The pattern is placed in the follow board and then it is used in the same manner as a match plate. A follow board is used with patterns that do not have a flat side and these are one piece solid types. Without the help of a follow board, it will be time consuming and costly to cut out an irregular parting surface and skilled workmen will be required for this.

(*iii*) Gated patterns are frequently set on a follow board which is shaped to the parting surface of the mould. This serves as an interface where the mould separates, which enables the pattern to be removed after the mould is prepared.

Stop-off. This is the portion of the pattern which is added for its own strength only if the pattern is fragile, (Fig. 3.9 (*j*)). It forms a cavity in the mould when the moulder withdraws the pattern, which is refilled with sand before pouring. Stop-offs are wooden pieces used to reinforce some portions of the pattern which are structurally weak, especially from the standpoint of repeated handling. They have no connection with the completed casting.

3.3.5. Colour Scheme for Patterns. Frequently, a print of the finished part is not furnished with a pattern. As a result, the foundary man is not able to take the necessary precautions to produce the best results. Many mistakes may be eliminated by indicating the functions of the various parts of he pattern with proper colours :

(*a*) A loose piece may get lost and unless the pattern is marked to indicate the seat of the loose piece, it is quite possible that the casting will be made from the incomplete pattern.

(*b*) With properly marked core prints, the moulder is constantly reminded that cores must be set in the mould before it is closed.

(*c*) Patterns with stop offs should be marked to remind the moulder to fill the mould cavity made by the stop off.

(*d*) If a moulder knows what surfaces are to be machined, he will, if possible mould the pattern in a position to produce a surface more nearly free of impurities.

The foundaries may use their own colour schemes. A common colour scheme is given below :

1. Surface as cast   Black
2. Machined surface   Red

3. Core prints and seats   :   Yellow

4. Loose pieces   :   Yellow/Red diagonal stripes

5. Stop-off   :   Yellow/Black diagonal stripes

As per Indian Standards, the colour scheme is given in: IS 1513 - 1971

3.3.6. Stack Moulding. Stack moulding is used to make small castings. An advantage of this process is that it requires much less floor space in the foundary. An upright stack moulding process is shown in Fig. 3.10. From 10 to 12 flask sections are arranged one above the other, having a common sprue through which all the moulds are poured.

3.4. MOULDING MATERIALS

Various types of materials are used in foundaries for the manufacture of casting moulds and cores. These materials are divided into two groups : Basic and Auxiliary. Basic moulding materials include : Silica sands, which form the base and the various binders. The auxiliary group includes various additives which impart desired properties to the moulding and core sands.

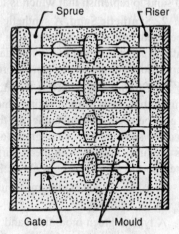

Fig. 3.10. Stack Moulding.

The essential constituents of a moulding sand are : Silica sand, Binder, Additives and water. Silica sand as the widely used moulding material has the following advantages :

1. It is cheap, plentiful and easily available.

2. It is characterised by a high softening temperature and thermal stability, that is, highly refractory.

3. Easily moulded, reusable and capable of giving good details.

Silica sand forms the bulk of the moulding sand.

Binder (most common is clay) may be present in natural sand or added to silica sand separately. In combination with water, it is the bonding agent in a green sand. Although moist sand particles do adhere to one another slightly, but coating with moist clay, the strength (tensile and shear) of the sand mix is increased about three fold. Clay imparts cohesiveness and plasticity to the moulding sand in the moist state and increases its strength after drying. When the moulding sand has the proper amount of water added to it to give a high strength with sufficient plasticity, the sand is said to be "at temper" or "tempered".

Additives impart to the moulding sand special properties (strength, thermal stability, permeability, refractoriness, thermal expansion etc.)

Sand. According to the amount of clayey matter they contain, the moulding sands are classified as :

1. Silica Sand : Upto 2% clay.

2. Lean or weak sand : 2 to 10% clay

3. Moderately strong sand : 10 to 20% clay

4. Strong sand : Upto 30% clay

5. Extra Strong sand (Loam sand) : Upto 50% clay.

There are three types of sand used for making moulds : natural, synthetic and chemically coated.

1. Natural Sand. A natural sand is the one which is available from natural deposits. Only additives and water need be added to it to make it satisfactory for moulding. The clay content of most natural sands is slightly higher than desired so that new sand can be continuously added to the used sand to replenish that which is lost.

2. Synthetic Sand. A synthetic sand is prepared by mixing a relatively clay free sand having a specified type of sand grain, with a specified type of clay binder as well as water and other additives. All are mixed in the foundary. This sand has the advantage that sand grains of specified composition and properties can be prepared on the basis of the metal being cast.

3. Chemically Coated Sand. Clean silica grains are sometimes coated with a non-thermosetting hydrocarbon resin, which acts as a binder. An additional binder in the form of clay can also be used. The advantage of this sand is that the carbon in the resin which is an excellent refractory surrounds the sand grains and does not allow the molten metal to reach the sand grains. This produces casting with clean surfaces as the sand does not get fused in them. The moisture content in this sand is kept to above 3%.

Moulding sands exhibit maximum strength at a moisture content of 4% for lean sands and of 6 to 7% for loam sands.

A typical green moulding sand for gray iron moulding are given below :

Silica sand	=	68 to 86%
Clay	=	10 to 20%
Water	=	3 to 6%
Additives	=	1 to 6%

Binders. Binders used in a foundary are : Inorganic and Organic binders. Organic binders are mainly used for core making and will be discussed later.

Clay binders are the most common inorganic binders. Clays are formed by the weathering and decomposition of rocks. The common types of clay used in moulding sand are : Fireclay, Kaolinite, Illite and Bentonite. Kaolinite and Bentonite clays are most popular, because, they have high thermochemical stability.

1. Fire - clay. Fire clay is a refractory clay usually found in the coal measures.

2. Kaolinite. Its general composition is Al_2O_3 . $2SiO_2$. $2H_2O$. it is one of the decomposition products of the slow weathering of the granite and basalt (a kind of black rock). It is the main constituent of China fire clay. Its melting point is 1750 to 1787°C.

3. Illite. This clay has the approximate composition :

K_2O . Al_2O_3 . SiO_2 . H_2O. It is formed from the weathering of mica rocks. Its particle size is about the same as the kaolinite clay and has similar moulding properties.

4. Bentonite. Its general composition is MgO . Al_2O_3 . SiO_2 . H_2O. It is formed from the weathering of volcanic or igneous rocks. It is creamy white powder. Its melting point is 1250 – 1300°C.

The basic constituent which gives refractoriness to a clay is alumina, Al_2O_3. Of all clays, bentonite is the most commonly used clay. It needs smaller amount of water to obtain a given degree of plasticity. This will result in less steam generation when the molten metal is poured into the mould, permitting a lower permeability in the moulding sand.

Other binders can be : Portland cement and Sodium silicate.

The percentage of binder in the moulding sand is of great importance. The bond must be strong enough to with stand the pressure of and erosion by the melt, yet it must be sufficiently weakened by the heat of metal to allow shrinkage of the casting and finally removal of the sand without damage to the solid casting. However, bond must not destroy the permeability of the sand so that gases present in the melt or produced by the heat of the melt in the binder itself can escape.

Organic Binders. These binders are most frequently used in core making. Cereal binders are obtained from wheat, corn or rye; Resins; Drying oils, for example, linseed oil, fishoil, soyabean oil, and some mineral oils; pitch and molasses.

Additives. Additives are the materials added in small quantities to the moulding sand in order to enhance its existing properties and to impart to it special properties. These additives may be necessary to give a good surface finish to the casting or to eliminate casting defects that arise from either the expansion of the moulding sand as it is heated or the contraction of the casting as it cools in the mould. There may be some overlapping between an additive and a binder, because many people include organic binders also in the category of additives.

Metal penetration or burning-on is penetration of metal between sand grains and also strong adhesion of the fused or sintered sand to the metal of the casting surface. The burnt-on sand involves difficulty in cleaning operations and is responsible for rapid wear of cutting tools used to machine the castings. Some common additives used to prevent the above mentioned defects and to improve the quality of the casting, are discussed below :

1. Sea Coal. Sea coal or coal dust is finely ground soft coal (pulverised coal). It is added to moulding sand used to make ferrous castings. It tends to obtain smoother and cleaner surfaces of castings and also reduces the adherence of sand particles to the casting. It also increases the strength of the moulding sand. It is added upto 8%. Also, when molten metal fills the mould, coal dust burns and gives off volatile substances containing the gases CO and CO_2 which form a gas spacing between the mould walls and metal. This "gas jacket" not only prevents interaction between the metal of the casting and the sand and thus prevents the metal penetration into the sand, but also makes the mould more collapsible when the metal shrinks.

Other carbon rich materials which are sometimes substituted for Sea coal are : finely ground coke, Pitch and Asphalt (2%), Graphite (0.2 to 2%).

2. Cereals. Foundary cereal is finely ground corn flour or corn starch. It (0.25 - 2%) increases the green and dry strengths of the moulding sand. Since the cereal is organic, it is "burned out" when hot metal comes in contact with it. This gives rise to space for accommodating the expansion of silica sand at the surfaces of mould cavity, without buckling these. Because of their low density, about 1% is generally sufficient.

3. Saw Dust. It increases the gas permeability and deformability of moulds and cores. It must be dry. Instead of saw dust, one can use peat that contains about 70 - 73% volatile substance, not over 5 or 6% ash and upto 25 to 30% moisture.

4. Wood Flour. It is ground wood particles or other cellulose materials such as grain hulls. They serve the same purpose as cereals except that they do not increase green strength as much. When required, about 1% is added.

5. Silica Flour. It is a very fine ground silica. It is generally mixed with about twice as much conventional moulding sand to make a "facing sand" and is used to surround the pattern. It thus improves the surface finish of the casting, and because of its purity, it increases the hot strength of the mould face. It also resists metal penetration and minimizes sand expansion defects.

Some other common additives are :

(*i*) **Fuel Oil.** It improves the mouldability of sand.

(*ii*) **Iron Oxide.** It develops hot strength.

(*iii*) **Dextrin.** It increases air setting strength, toughness and collapsibility and prevents sand from drying rapidly. During pouring of molten metal, it gasifies, thus producing extra space between the grains without any grain distortion.

(*iv*) **Molasses.** It is the by product of sugar industry. It enhances the bench life of sand and imparts high dry strength and collapsibility to moulds and cores. Due to high temperature in the mould; it develops CO_2 which sets up an hardening action of the mould.

Facing Materials. These materials when added to the moulding sand tend to obtain smoother and cleaner surfaces of castings, help easy peeling of sand from the casting surface during shake out and prevent metal penetration. Sea coal, pitch (distilled from soft coals), asphalt, graphite and silica flour discussed above, act as facing materials.

Cushion Materials. These materials when added to the moulding sand burn and form gases when the molten metal is poured into the mould cavity. This gives rise to space for accommodating the expansion of the sand at the mould cavity surfaces. Wood flour, cereals, cereal hulls and cellulose etc. discussed above are called as 'Cushion materials'.

3.4.1. Other types of Moulding Sands

1. Facing Sand. This sand is used directly next to the surface of the pattern and comes into contact with the molten metal when the mould is poured. As a result, it is subjected to the severest conditions and must possess, therefore, high strength and refractoriness. This sand also provides a smoother casting surface and should be of fine texture. It is made of silica sand and clay, and some additives without the addition of used sand. The layer of facing sand in a mould usually ranges from 25 to 50 mm.

2. Backing Sand. This is the sand which is used to back up the facing sand and to fill the whole volume of the flask. Old, repeatedly used moulding sand is mainly employed for this purpose.

3. System Sand. In mechanised foundries, where machine moulding is employed a so called "system sand" is used to fill the whole flask. Since the whole mould is made up of this system sand, the strength, the permeability and refractoriness of the sand must be higher than that of backing sand.

Facing sand is always used to make dry sand moulds while system sand is frequently used for green sand moulding.

4. Parting Sand. This sand is used to prevent adhering of two halves of mould surfaces in each moulding box when they are separated. Thus, to ensure good parting, the mould surface (at contact of cope and Drag) should be treated with parting sand or some other parting material. It is also sprinkled or applied on the pattern surface (before the moulding sand is put over it) to avoid its sticking and permit its easy withdrawal from the mould. The parting sand is fine dry sand. There are other parting materials also used in foundary.

Dry parting materials. These are applied by dusting. These include: charcoal, ground bone and limestone, lycopodium (a yellow vegetable matter), tripolite (a silicate rock), ground nut shells, Talc (Magnesium silicate, $3MgO, 4SiO_2.H_2O$) and Calcium phosphate.

Wet parting materials. These are not used with wooden patterns, but are used mostly in machine moulding when metal patterns are used. They are wax based preparations, petroleum jelly mixed with oil, paraffin and stearic acid.

3.4.2. Mould Surface Coatings. Mould surfaces are coated (after the pattern is drawn out) with certain materials possessing high refractoriness. It eliminates the possibility of burn-on and enables castings with smooth surface to be obtained. However, the permeability of the mould gets reduced. Therefore, the Coatings should not contain gas forming materials. Mould surface coatings which are also known as facings, dressings, washes, blackings or whitening, may be applied dry (by dusting) or wet in the form of thin cream. The various mould surface coating materials include : Coal dust, pitch, graphite, china clay, Zircon flour or French chalk (Calcium oxide).

3.4.3. Moulding Sand for Non-ferrous Castings. The melting point of non-ferrous metals is much lower than that of ferrous metals. Therefore, the moulding sands for non-ferrous castings may be less refractory and permeable. Also, a smooth surface is desirable on non-ferrous castings. Due to all this, the moulding sands for non-ferrous casting contain a considerable amount of clay and are fine grained.

3.4.4. Typical Moulding Sand Composition (By Weight) :

1. For Steel Castings

    (*a*) *Green Sand Moulding Facing Sand :*

                  Silica Sand = 95%

                  Bentonite = 4%

        Cereal type binder = 1%

                     Water = 3 to 4%

    (*b*) *Green Sand Moulding Backing Sand*

                  Floor Sand = 95%

                  Bentonite = 5%

                     Water = 2.5 to 4%

    (*c*) Dry Sand Moulding Facing Sand :

        (*i*) *For Heavy Section Castings :*

                  Silica Sand = 70%

                  Silica Flour = 23%

                  Bentonite = 5.5%

                  Mollases = 1.5%

                     Water = 6 to 7%

        (*ii*) *For Light Section Castings :*

                  Silica Sand = 75%

                  Silica Flour = 20%

                  Bentonite = 4%

                  Mollases = 1%

                     Water = 6 to 7%

2. For Iron Castings :

    (*a*) *Green Sand Moulding Facing Sand :*

                Old Silica Sand = 60%

            New Silica Sand = 34 to 37%

                  Bentonite = 1 to 4%

                  Coal dust = 2%

                     Water = 3 to 4%

Typical Core Sand Composition :

1. For Steel Castings :

    (*a*) *For Light section castings :*

                  Silica Sand = 90%

                  Silica Flour = 6%

                  Core oil = 2%

Bentonite   = 1%

Cereal binder = 1%

(b) *For Heavy Section Castings* :

Silica Sand   = 43.5%

Silica Flour = 48.5%

Core Oil   = 4%

Bentonite   = 4%

(c) *Small cores in Average Metal Sections*

Silica Sand   = 80%

Silica Flour = 16%

Core Oil   = 2.5%

Bentonite   = 1.5%

2. For Iron-Castings :

(a) *For Average Castings* :

Silica Sand   = 93%

Core Oil   = 5%

Bentonite   = 2%

(b) *For Heavy Section Castings* :

Silica Sand   = 83%

Silica Flour = 9.5%

Core Oil   = 5%

Bentonite   = 2.5%

A typical composition of core sand used with CO_2 method, when water glass (sodium silicate) is used as a binder is :

Silica Sand   = 80 to 90 kg

Sodium Silicate = 9 to 11 kg

Wood Flour   = 1.5 to 2.5 kg

Coal Dust   = 3.5 to 4 kg

3.4.5. Properties of Moulding Sand

The success of the casting process depends to a large extent on the making of a satisfactory mould. For this, the moulding properties of the sand have to be controlled. These properties include : Porosity or Permeability, Strength, Refractoriness, Plasticity, Collapsibility and Adhesiveness etc. These properties are influenced, not only by the chemical composition, but also by the amount of binder in the sand, by its moisture content and by the shape and size of the silica sand grains. Often, the above variables affect the properties of moulding sand in contradictory manner. For example, the strength and plasticity increase with percentage of clay but this will reduce the porosity of the sand, and so on. The various variables are decided so as to get optimum moulding properties of the sand for a given situation. The properties of the moulding sand are briefly discussed below :

1. Permeability. Permeability or porosity of the moulding sand is the measure of its ability to permit air to flow through it.

Molten metal always contains a certain amount of dissolved gases which try to leave it when the metal solidifies. Also, when the mould is poured, water vapours and other gases are generated when the molten metal comes in contact with the moulding sand and the cores. If all these gases and vapours are not able to escape completely through the walls of the mould, they may penetrate the liquid metal where, after solidification, they form gas holes and pores. To avoid these defects, the moulding sand should have good gas permeability.

Permeability of the moulding sand is influenced by : quality and quantity of clays and quartz in the mixture, moisture content, degree of compaction etc. The higher the percentage of silica content of a moulding sand mixture (that is lower clay content), the better its permeability and vice versa. The larger the grain size, the better its permeability and vice versa. The distribution of grain size in a particular sand mix, greatly influences the permeability. If all the sand particles in a mix are of the same size, then the bulk density is low and the permeability is higher because of the voids between the sand particles. Angular grains that are randomly oriented will have a lower bulk density than spherical grains and thus higher permeability. A sand mixture containing grains of all sizes, from the largest that can be used to the smallest ones, will have a bulk density approaching the true density of the sand. In this case, the permeability of the mixture will be very low, because the smaller particles will fill up the interspaces of bigger grains.

Again, higher the silt content of sand, the lower its gas permeability. If the mould is rammed too hand, its permeability will decrease and vice versa.

2. Strength or Cohesiveness. It is defined as the property of holding together of sand grains. A moulding sand should have ample strength so that the mould does not collapse or get partially destroyed during conveying, turning over or closing. This property also enables the pattern to be removed without breaking the mould and to stand the flow of molten metal when it rushes inside the mould. Also, when the mould cavity is filled with molten metal, its bottom and walls are subjected to a high metallostatic pressure. If the sand is not strong enough to resist this pressure, the mould cavity gets enlarged and the castings obtained are oversize.

Strength of the moulding sand depends on the grain size and shape of sand particles, moisture content and density which varies with the content of clay binders in the sand mixture. The strength of the moulding sand grows with density, clay content of the mix and decreased size of sand grains. So, it is clear that as the strength of the moulding sand increases, its porosity decreases.

3. Refractoriness. It is the ability of the moulding sand mixture to withstand the heat of melt without showing any signs of softening or fusion. This property is greatly influenced by the purity of the sand particles and their size. It increases with the grain size of sand and its content and with the diminished amount of impurities and silt.

4. Plasticity or Flowability. It is the measure of the moulding sand to flow around and over a pattern during ramming and to uniformly fill the flask. This property may be enhanced by adding clay and water to the silica sand.

5. Collapsibility. This is the ability of the moulding sand to decrease in volume to some extent under the compressive forces developed by the shrinkage of metal during freezing and subsequent cooling. This property is especially important for cores. This property permits the moulding sand to collapse easily during shake out and permits of the core to collapse easily during its knockout from the cooled casting. Lack of collapsibility in the moulding sand and core may result in the formation of cracks in the casting. This property depends on the amount of quartz sand and binders and their type.

6. Adhesiveness. This is the property of sand mixture to adhere to another body (here, the moulding flasks). The moulding sand should cling to the sides of the moulding boxes so that it does not fall out when the flasks are lifted and turned over. This property depends on the type and amount of binder used in the sand mix.

7. Co-efficient of Expansion. The sand should have low co-efficient of expansion.

3.4.6. Other Refractory Materials. In addition to silica sand, some other refractory materials which are used for special purposes are :

1. Zircon : Zr Si O_4 2. Chromite : Fe Cr_2 O_4

3. Olivine : $((Mg\ Fe)_2\ Si\ O_4)$

3.4.7. Sand Testing :– Moulding sands should be of proper quality to meet the required level of accuracy and surface finish of castings. Proper quality of the moulding sand will result in sound castings that will decrease the cost/unit and increase the production.

The following tests have been recommended by B.I.S.

1. Moisture content test
2. Clay content test
3. Permeability test
4. Fineness test or Sand grain size test (Sieve analysis)
5. Strength test
6. Mould hardness test.

Sand Rammer : It is the apparatus to make specimens of moulding sand/core sand, for tests such as —Permeable test, the various strength tests, and shatter test etc.

A sand rammer is shown in Fig. 3.11. It consists of a C.I. body with base. A weight is carried at the upper end of the rammer rod. The weight is made to fall by operating the rammer lever attached to a cam. To make a sand specimen, the specimen ram tube is filled with a specified amount of sand. The ram head is moved up by means of weight lever attached to an eccentric disc and the ram tube is placed on the ram tube stand.

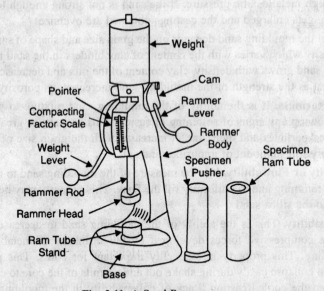

Fig. 3.11. A Sand Rammer.

Three blows are given to the sand by dropping the weight by means of rammer lever. This will result in the production of cylindrical sand specimen 50.8 mm ϕ × 50.8 mm long. As a check, it should be ensured that after 3 blows, a mark on the rammer rod should fall between the marks provided on the rammer stand for this purpose. After this, the specimen ram tube is removed from the stand and the sand specimen is ejected out with the help of specimen pusher.

1. Moisture content test: Moisture is an important constituent of moulding sand. Its content in the moulding sand can be estimated as given below:–

(*a*) **By the loss of weight after evaporation:** Test sample is carefully weighed 50 gm of moulding sand. It is heated for 2 hours at 105°C to 110°C. It is then allowed to cool to room temperature on a desicator, after which it is reweighed. The difference in weight divided by the weight of the sample (50 gm) and multiplied by 100 gives the percentage moisture content.

(*b*) **By Moisture teller :** Ä In this method, the sample is placed on the teller pan which has 500 mesh screen in the bottom. Hot air is blown through the sand. Moisture gets removed in only about 5 minutes and so the method is quite fast. The sand sample is weighed directly in the teller pan, and the loss in weight is accordingly determined.

(*c*) **By moisture teller based on chemical reaction :** In this method, a measured weight of sand (10 gm) in a cap is placed in the moisture teller alongwith a container containing a measured amount of CaC_2 (Sand and CaC_2 should not come into contact with each other). The reactions of CaC_2 with moisture in the sand will produce C_2H_2,

$$CaC_2 + 2H_2O \longrightarrow C_2H_2 + Ca(OH)_2$$

The amount of C_2H_2 produced is proportional to the content of moisture in the sand. The moisture content is directly measured from a calibrated scale on the instrument.

2. Clay content test : Under this test, the clay content is measured by washing it off the sand sample. The standard dried sand sample (50 gm) is put in a mixing device along with distilled water and 1% NaOH solution. The mixture is stirred for 5 minutes and is then allowed to settle for 10 minutes. The sand settles down at the bottom. The dirty water is siphoned off from the top. The operation is repeated until the water above the sand in the mixer is clean. This water is drained off. The sand is dried and weighed. The loss of weight gives the clay content.

$$\text{Clay Content} = \frac{\text{Loss of weight of sand sample, } g \times 100 \%}{50}$$

3. Permeability test : As already defined, permeability or porosity of the moulding sand is the measure of its ability to permit air to flow through it. It is measured in terms of "Permeability number." In this test, a test specimen of moulding sand (50.8 mm dia. × 50.8 mm long) is placed in a tube. Time taken for 2000 cm^3 of air at a pressure of 10 g/cm^2 to pass through the specimen is noted. Then, the permeability number is given as:

$$P = \frac{V \times h}{p \times A \times t}$$

Where,

P = Permeability number
V = Volume of air passing through test specimen
h = Height of specimen
p = Pressure of air
A = Cross-sectional area of specimen
t = time taken by air to flow through the specimen

Understandard conditions, the formula becomes

$$P = \frac{2000 \times 5.08}{10 \times \frac{\pi}{4} \times (5.08)^2 \times t}$$

$$= \frac{50.128}{t} \quad (t \text{ is in minutes})$$

or

$$P = \frac{501.28}{p \times t}$$

4. Fineness Test : Fineness test of the sand specimen determines the size of grains and the distribution of gains of different sizes in the moulding sand. Their effect on the properties of moulding sand has been discussed in Art.3.4.5. The test is performed on completely dry and clay free sand. The test apparatus consists of a set of graded sieves placed one above the other, with the coarsest sieve at the top and the finest sieve at the bottom, next to the pan. The sand is put in the top sieve and the set of sieve is shaken continuously for 15 minutes with the help of an electric motor. At the end of the shaking operation, the sieves are taken out and the sand retained on each is carefully weighed. Each weight is converted to a percentage basis. Each percentage is multiplied by a weighting factor and these are added to get the sum of products. Then the grain fineness number (GFN) is given as,

$$GFN = \frac{Sum\ of\ products}{Sum\ of\ percentages\ of\ sand\ retained\ on\ each\ sieve\ and\ pan}$$

As per AFS (American Foundrymen's Society), the various sievemesh numbers and the corresponding weighting factors (multiplying factors) are given below:

Sieve number	6	12	20	30	40	50	70	100	140	200	270	pan
Weightage factor	3	5	10	20	30	40	50	70	100	140	200	300

Example: Let the weight retained on each sieve are given as :

0.5, 1.0, 1.5, 2.0, 2.5, 4.5, 10, 15, 7.5, 3.5, 1.5 and 0.5 g. GFN is calculated as explained below:

Sieve number	Retained Sample (gm) Fi	Retained percentage Pi	Weightage factor Wi	WiFi	WiPi
6	0.5	1	3	1.5	3
12	1.0	2	5	5.0	10
20	1.5	3	10	15.0	30
30	2.0	4	20	40	80
40	2.5	5	30	75	150
50	4.5	9	40	180	360
70	10	20	50	500	1000
100	15	30	70	1050	2100
140	7.5	15	100	750	1500
200	3.5	7	140	490	980
270	1.5	3	200	300	600
Pan	0.5	1	300	150	300
	$\Sigma = 50$	$\Sigma = 100$		$\Sigma 3556.5$	$\Sigma 7113$

$$\therefore \quad GFN = \frac{3556.5}{50} = 71.13$$

or

$$GFN = \frac{7113}{100} = 71.13$$

5. Strength Tests : These tests are carried out to check the holding powers of various binders used in Green moulding sand, dry moulding sand and core sand. These tests are performed on a U.T.M. The various tests carried out include:-

(*i*) Compressive strength test

(*ii*) Shear strength test

(*iii*) Tensile strength test

(*iv*) Bending strength test

Out of these, compressive strength test is most important.

The test specimen is 5.08 cm $\phi \times$ 5.08 cm long. The test is performed by applying a uniformly increasing load on sand specimen until it breaks. The compressive strength is read directly on the scale of the machine. The other tests are also similarly carried out by using suitable jaws.

The green strength of moulding sands ranges from 30 to 160 k Pa

The dry strength of moulding sands ranges from 140 to 1800 k Pa

The green shear of moulding sands ranges from 10 to 50 k Pa

6. Hardness Test : The hardness of the prepared mould surface is tested to check the ramming density of the sand. The instrument resembles a dial indicator, and carries a spring loaded steel ball of 5 mm . The ball is pressed into the rammed surface. The depth of penetration of the ball is indicated on the dial of the indicator (which is divided into 100 parts) in terms of hardness units. The values of hardness units for sands rammed to different degrees are approximately:–

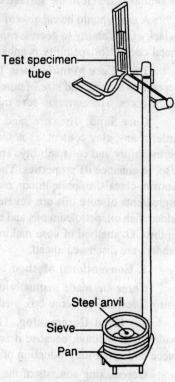

Test specimen tube

> 40 for lightly rammed sand
>
> 50 for medium rammed sand
>
> and 70 for hard rammed sand

7. Shatter Test : This test is a measure of toughness of the moulding sand. It indicates the capacity of the moulding sand to with stand rough handling during the moulding process and also the strain during pattern withdrawl from the mould.

The test is carried out as follows : A standard test specimen of the moulding sand (prepared on the sand rammer) is made to drop through a specified height on to a steel anvil, Fig. 3.12. The complete broken mass of the sand is then put on a 12 mm mesh sieve. Part of it (finer mass) will pass through the sieve. Then the shatter index is given as : Shatter Index (% age) =

Steel anvil

Sieve

Pan

Fig. 3.12. Shatter Index Tester.

$$\frac{\text{Weight of broken moulding sand specimen left on sieve}}{\text{Total weight of the moulding sand}}$$

8. Compactibility Test : This test indicates the decrease in height of a mass of sand in a specimen tube with respect to its original height, under the action of blows. The test is important for sands used in moulding machines. The test is carried out on the sand rammer. The loose riddled sand is filled in the specimen tube. The sand is then compacted on the sand rammer by 3 blows of the weight. The percentage decrease in height is read on the scale.

3.5. CORES

3.5.1. Definition. A core is a body made of refractory material (sand or metal, metal cores being less frequently used), which is set into the prepared mould before closing and pouring it, for forming through holes, recesses, projections, undercuts and internal cavities.

3.5.2. Essential Qualities of a Core. The cores are subject to much more severe thermal and mechanical effects than the mould, because, they are surrounded on all sides (except for the ends) by molten metal. Consequently, core sands should meet more stringent requirements. The dry strength and surface strength of a core must be higher than that of a mould. Core sands must have high refractoriness, good permeability and sufficient collapsibility.

The strength of a core will depend on the kind of sand and binding material used. Their bond strength must be greater to allow handling. Also, because they generally are subjected to bending forces produced by the hydrostatic pressure of the liquid trying to lift the core. The bond strength can be increased by using sand with sharper grains which bond together better.

As already discussed, permeability will depend on grain size and distribution of grains in the core sand mix. It will also depend upon the type and content of the binder.

Refractoriness or thermal stability of core can be increased by giving a thin coating of graphite or similar material to the surface of core.

A core should be capable of collapsing shortly after the molten metal has solidified around it. A lack of this ability to decrease in volume may lead to the formation of cracks in the casting as the metal cools. Collapsibility is enhanced by using oil binding materials.

3.5.3. Core Manufacture. The various methods employed for the manufacture of cores will depend on : shape and size of core, type of the binder used and the technique of imparting strength to the cores. The common core making methods are discussed below :

Core Sand: The core sand mainly consists of silica sand and an organic binder, with very little, if any, clay content, as noted under Art 3.4.4. The presence of clay in core sand reduces its permeability and collapsibility. The core sand may contain small percentages of other constituents also, to enhance its properties. The common organic binders used in core sands include: core oils, dextrin, cereals, sulphite liquor, mollases, resins and other commercial binding materials. The main ingredients of core oils are vegetable oils, for example linseed oil and corn oil. To these may be added: fish oil, petroleum oils and coal tar. Core oils impart sufficient strength and good collapsibility. In the CO_2 method of core making, water glass (sodium silicate) is used as the binder. The resin binders are discussed ahead.

1. Conventional Method :–

Cores are made manually or with machines. Cores are made by hand in core boxes or by using sweeps ; only core box methods are used for machine coremaking.

(A) Hand Coremaking. The manual method of making cores in core boxes is the most widespread method, because it is rather simple and effective. However, the method is useful for piece and small-lot production of castings only.

Coremaking consists of the following sequence of operations :

      (*i*) Moulding a green core

      (*ii*) Baking or curing

      (*iii*) Finishing

      (*iv*) Coating

For moulding a green core, usually a split wooden core box is used, Fig. 3.13. If a core is made of two or more pieces, they are assembled together after baking by pasting or other methods. Refer to Fig. 3.13. The two halves of the core box are fastened together with clamps or dowel pins and the box is placed vertically on the bench. The operator then rams the sand, layer by layer, into the box, trims it off level along the top face.

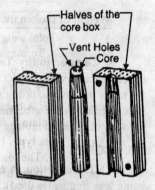

Fig. 3.13. Core Box.

Reinforcement of Cores. Some cores require internal reinforcing within the sand to increase their strength. This is done by embedding wires, rods or arbors within the core sections while they are being moulded.

Reinforcement (core irons) is most often made of annealed low carbon steel wire upto 8 mm in diameter. Heavy cores with a large cross section may be reinforced with cast iron grids. It is important to properly locate the core iron in the core. It should never be too close to the surface, otherwise a thin layer of sand may break off.

Core Venting. While pouring the mould with molten metal, mould walls and cores heat up rapidly and give off a large volume of gases. These gases must be vented out through core prints in order to prevent casting defects such as "Blow holes". Vent holes may be made :

(*i*) By piercing the sand with a wire from the core print end after the sand has been rammed into the core box.

(*ii*) Additional vent holes are made with steel rods or pipes moulded into the cores and subsequently removing these after core moulding, leaving straight vent holes.

(*iii*) By inserting wicks, which form holes after wax melting and chord removal.

(*iv*) In two part cores, before they are pasted together, vent channels are cut along the parting surface.

(*v*) Large cores (round cores over 500 mm long and of a diameter upto 60 mm and more) are made hollow by using sweeps or templates or with cinder or coke filled centres to help provide proper venting.

After the core has been reinforced and vented, the core maker gently knocks on the box with a mallet to facilitate the core removal. The core box is laid in a horizontal position. The clamps or dowel pins are loosened, one box is lifted off and the core is withdrawn from the other half.

Core Dryer. The cores must have adeqeuate support while in the green state before they are baked or cured. For this, the cores are placed on a drying board or plate known as 'Core dryer', (Fig. 3.14), for transporting the cores to the oven. If a shaped core dryer is not available for a core of complex configuration, a sand bed can do well.

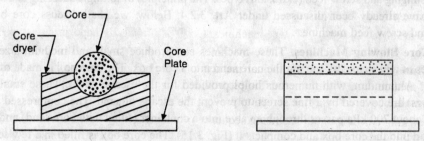

Fig. 3.14. Core Dryer.

Core Baking. To impart proper strength to the cores, these are baked or cured in gas, oil or electric ovens. the curing operation drives off the moisture and hardens core binders.

Core Ovens are of Two Types :

(*i*) **Batch type.** A batch of cores on the drying plate are placed in the oven. When they are cured, the plate is taken out and next batch of cores is placed in the oven.

(*ii*) **Continuous type.** Here, the cores on the drying plate move slowly through the oven, on a conveyer. The loading and unloading is continuous and the curing time is controlled by the rate of travel of the conveyor.

Curing temperature is in the range of 230°C, which should be closely controlled by suitable controlling instruments.

Dielectric Core Baking. This method of core baking is used for materials which are non conductors of electricity. An A.C. field is establishes between two parallel plates (conductors) which function as an electric condenser. The material to be heated (here cores) is placed between these two conductors. When the high frequency A.C. (15 MHz) is switched on, heat is created within the molecules of the cores. A great advantage of the method is that the cores are heated uniformly throughout. Linseed oil (which requires oxidation for imparting strength to the cores) is not suitable for this method. The thermosetting synthetic-resin binders which do not need oxidation and cure at about 110°C are well suited for this method. Small sized cores can be baked only in a few seconds, while the larger ones will take only a few minutes for complete curing.

Plastic or Synthetic Resin Core Binders. These binders have got some important advantages : Approximately half the baking time as compared to linseed oil binders, and excellent collapsibility which will reduce casting defects like hot tears and also reduce the core knockout effort. Urea formaldehyde binders burn out faster and, therefore, collapse at lower temperature as compared to phenol formaldehyde binders. Thus, urea formaldehyde binders are used with low melting point metals such as Aluminium, Magnesium and thin section brass or bronze castings. On the other hand, phenol formaldehyde binders are used for cast iron, steel and thicker section brass and bronze castings.

(B) Machine Core Making. In the mass and large lot production of castings, cores are made on core making machines, which at present are progressively introduced into foundaries producing castings in small lots.

Coremaking machines increase the productivity of labour, make easier the work of operators, and produce cores of high accuracy, largely from sands of lowered green strength, which flow readily into deep pockets of the core box.

There are various types of core making machines used in the foundary : core blowing, jolting, squeezing, slinging and screw feed (extrusion) types. The principles of jolting, squeezing and slinging machines have already been discussed under Art. 3.2.4. Below, we shall discuss core blowing machines and screw feed machine.

(*a*) **Core Blowing Machines.** These machines can produce small and medium sized high quality cores of any shape, by forcing the core sand into a core box. The core box is made of metal, desirably of Aluminium, with numerous holes provided for the escape of air. These small holes (vented plugs) are covered by a fine screen to prevent the escape of sand. The compressed air at a pressure of about 700 kPa passes through a valve into a container (filled with core sand) and forces the core sand into the core box and compacts it (Fig. 3.15). The core box is filled in a few seconds. The drawback of the method is that the core sand has to be of low green strength, which involves difficulties in core transportation, removal of cores from boxes and so on.

In Fig. 3.15, the core box is placed on the table, located and pressed up against the blow plate. Then the compressed air is introduced above the sand in the reservoir. The core box is filled and rammed in less than a second, and it is then lowered and removed from the machine.

(*b*) **Extrusion Machines.** These machines, (Fig. 3.16), produce small cores of any uniform cross section. The core sand is extruded by a screw or piston through a replaceable die (the section of the die will depend on the section of the core) onto a plate. The sand goes out in the form of a continuous core which is cut to the required length after baking. The core prints are then ground if necessary. The machines are simple in design, reliable in operation, and highly productive.

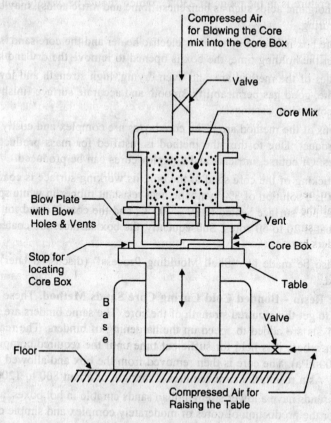

Fig. 3.15. Core Blowing Machine.

The machine produced cores are then cured as usual.

2. Hot Core Box Method. The main drawback of the conventional method of coremaking is that baking or curing of the cores is needed to impart strength to them. This lengthens the production process and lowers the operating efficiency of the foundry.

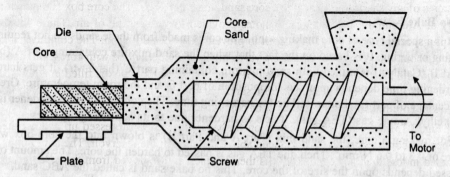

Fig. 3.16. Core Extrusion.

The procedure of core drying in ovens is eliminated by the process of production of cores from quick-set synthetic resins- bonded core sands. These binders (phenol formaldehyde, Urea formaldehyde, Phenolic alcohols and Furan-base binders) are capable of hardening at $230 - 250°C$ in a short time (2 or 3 min to 30 - 50 s, depending on the composition and size of cores). Catalysts (both organic and inorganic acids such as benzenesulfonic and nitric acids), may be added to speed up the process of curing.

The metal core box is heated by a gas or electric heater and the core sand is forced into it by a core blower. After the holding time, the box is opened to remove the dry and strong core.

The advantages of the method are : no oven drying, high strength and low crumbleness of cores in the dry state, good gas permeability, smooth and accurate surface finish and provides for easy shake out of cores from castings.

The limitations of the method are : The core boxes are complex and costly which add to the cost of finished product. Due to this, the method is justified for mass production of small and medium-sized cores. Of course, intricate and complex cores can be produced.

To prevent sticking of the core sand to the box, its working surface is coated with a parting composition which is a solution of 3% synthetic heat resistant rubber in white spirit. The solution is sprayed on to the box surface heated to 80 – 100°C, and the coat is dried for 10 - 15 min. The durability of the coat is 20 to 50 cores. Subsequently, the box surfaces are coated at the operating temperature.

Cores can also be made by "Shell Moulding Process" (discussed later), where a heated match plate is used.

3. Synthetic Resin - Bonded Cold Curing Core Sands Method. These sands do not call for heat treatment to get the required strength of the core. The same binders are used as in the hot box method. Catalysts are added to speed up the hardening of binders. The ready mix is poured into the core boxes where it is held for sufficient time until the required compressive strength is reached (300 to 500 kPa). The core is then removed from the box and allowed to stand in the air for 30 to 120 min. As a result, the core acquires a strength of about 800 to 1200 kPa.

Cold curing sands have a lower strength than sands curable in hot boxes, and therefore, they are largely used for the production of cores of moderately complex and simple configuration. The total hardening time may reach a few hours.

The advantages of the method are :

Core boxes of wood, plastic and metal can be used ; core production process can be mechanized, improves the quality of castings and increases the output. The method has found the widest application in the batch production of moderate sized and large-sized castings from iron and steel.

No Bake Sand :

It is a special type of core making sand. The cores made from these sands do not require heat for baking or curing. It is based on the fact that when the sand mixture containing part A (binder) and part B (Catalyst) is mixed with sand mixture containing part C (hardener), it gets hardened. The hardening time depends upon the composition of part C and the room temperature. Greater is the percentage of part C, shorter will be the hardening time. The commonly used hardener is Tetra (or Tri) ethyl Amine gas (TEA gas). It acts as hardener due to its addesive properties.

For making a core, the sand mix (Part A and Part B) is blown into the core-box with air pressure of 0.3 to 0.6 N/mm². Then, the TEA gas is passed to harden the core. The amount of TEA gas passed depends upon the size of the core. This no bake sand is called the ABC sand.

In Furan no-bake core sand

Furan no-bake resin = 2%

Activator (phosphoric acid) = 40%

4. Cold Curing CO_2 process. The CO_2 process has already been discussed for the drying and hardening of moulding boxes. The sand mixture includes : pure silica sand (without clay) and sodium silicate liquid base binder (water glass). These two are mixed in a muller for about 3 to 4 min. The moisture content should not exceed 3%. Sawdust (about 1.5%) and asbestos powder (upto 5%) make the cores more deformable and collapsible. The prepared mixture is packed in the core box for core making manually or by machines. After this, CO_2 gas is forced through the core sand under a pressure of about 140 kPa. This CO_2 reacts with sodium silicate to form 'silica gel' which binds the sand grains together to provide strength and hardness to the core. The chemical reaction is as follows :

$$Na_2O . x\,SiO_2 + n\,H_2O + CO_2 \longrightarrow Na_2CO_3 + x . SiO_2 . n\,(H_2O)$$
$$\text{Stiff gel}$$

x is usually 2.

The gassing process lasts for about 15 to 30s only. Immediately after gassing, the core is ready for use.

This method is used in the piece and batch production of steel and iron castings. To improve the strength of these cores, they are dried at $200 - 250°C$.

3.5.4. Finishing and Coating of Cores. Before the cores are transported to the stores, they are subjected to additional treatment : burr trimming, sealing for correcting small defects, and so on. The cores are trimmed off with an emery stone, file, wire, hard rubber and emery paper. The grinding process is done to give smooth surface finish and accurate dimension to the core.

The coatings on the core surface prevent metal penetration, increase the surface strength, decrease the crumbleness of core and provide clean and smooth appearance. The coatings consists of refractory materials alongwith binding materials. The choice of coating depends on the kind of metal cast, mass of the casting and the moulding method. For large iron castings, the coating may consist of black lead, bentonite and binders. For small and medium sized castings, the coating may be of graphite or of silica flour mixed with coal and ground coke. For steel castings, the coating consists of silica flour or Zirconium silicate mixed with some binders.

3.5.5. Types of Cores. The cores can be classified in many ways :

(*a*) **According to state of Core**

    (*i*) Green sand core

    (*ii*) Dry sand core

A green sand core is formed by the pattern itself when it is being rammed [Fig. 3.17 (a)]. the core is made of the same sand as the moulding sand. Such cores are weak and can be used only for light castings.

Dry sand cores are made separately (as explained above) and then positioned in the mould, after the pattern is taken out and before the mould is closed. These are the cores most commonly used.

(*b*) **According to the position of the Core in the Mould**

    (*i*) **Horizontal Core.** This core is placed horizontally in the mould and is very common in foundaries. It is usually positioned along the parting line of the mould.

    (*ii*) **Vertical Core.** These cores are positioned vertically in the mould, [see Fig. 3.17 (*b*)]. The two ends of the core rest on core seats in cope and drag. The maximum portion of the core is supported in the drag.

    (*iii*) **Balanced Core.** [Fig. 3.17 (*c*).] These cores are used when blind holes along a horizontal axis are to be produced. Since the core is supported only at one end, the core seat should be of sufficient length to prevent its falling into the mould.

(*iv*) **Hanging Core.** [Fig. 3.17 (*d*).] These cores are used when a cored casting is to be completely moulded in the drag, with the help of a single piece solid pattern. The core is supported above and hangs into the mould. A hole in the upper part of the core is provided for the metal to reach the mould cavity.

(*v*) **Drop Core.** [Fig. 3.17 (*e*).] This core is used when a hole which is not in line with the parting surface is to be produced at a lower level.

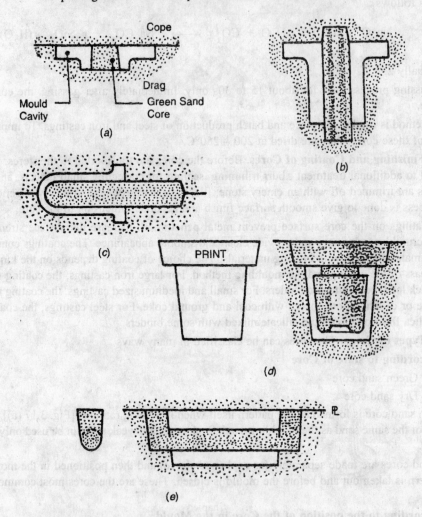

Fig. 3.17. Types of Core.

3.5.6. Chaplets. Sometimes it is not possible to provide sufficient support for a core in the mould being poured, particularly if the cores are very big in size. In such cases, the core is supported with rigid metal pieces, called "Chaplets", [Fig. 3.18 (*a*)], placed between the core and the mould face. The material of the chaplet must conform to the molten metal or alloy being cast in order to effect proper fusion. For iron or steel castings, the chaplets are made of tin plate and low-carbon steel.

The surface of the chaplets must be clean, without any trace of corrosion, moisture or oil.

Chaplets are shot peened (to increase their compressive strength) and then tinned before use. Clean chaplets fuse well with the metal and do not cause the formation of holes and discontinuities. It is, however, undesirable and even, sometimes, impermissible to use chaplets for castings to be used as pressure vessels.

Fig. 3.18 (b) shows the various forms of chaplets used in the foundry.

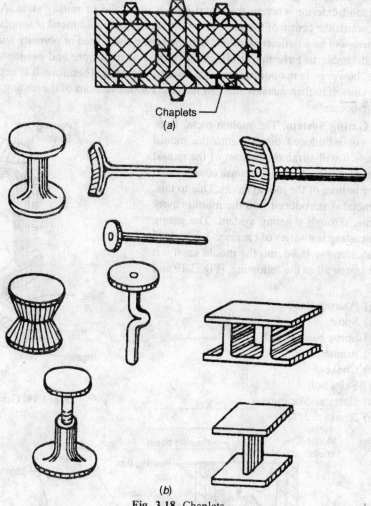

Chaplets
(a)

(b)

Fig. 3.18. Chaplets.

3.6. GATES AND RISERS

3.6.1. General. After the mould has been prepared, the molten metal is to be poured or injected into the mould cavity. The problem of introducing the molten metal into the mould cavity so as to obtain a sound casting, is one that exists in connection with all casting processes. Unfortunately, because of the large number of variables present, the problem has not been solved completely by scientific analysis. Therefore, differences exist as to the correct procedures to use and the solution in a particular case usually depends on the application of previous knowledge and trial and error, guided by an understanding of certain basic factors.

The problem basically is one of introducing the molten metal into the mould cavity in a manner which does not erode the mould, fills the mould completely without entrapping gases and permits cooling and solidification to progress in such a way that the accompanying shrinkage may take place without resulting in voids, cracks or porosity within the casting.

As the molten metal cools, solidifies and further cools, shrinkage occurs in connection with each step. Normally, the metal adjacent to the walls of the mould solidifies first, resulting in a shell of solid metal. The centre of the section remains liquid while there is a zone between the liquid interior and solid exterior wherein the metal is in a semisolid or mushy state. As solidification progresses towards the centre of the section, unless additional liquid metal is supplied to offset this shrinkage, there will be a deficiency of metal at the centre and a void or porosity will result. Ideally it would be desirable to have the solidification started at the centre and progressed towards the outside. This, however, is not normal and is difficult to achieve. Therefore, it is necessary to try to provide reservoirs of molten metal which can feed the various sections of the casting as solidification and shrinkage occurs.

3.6.2. Gating System. The molten metal from the ladle is not introduced directly into the mould cavity, because it will strike the bottom of the mould cavity with a great velocity and can cause considerable erosion of the bottom of the mould cavity. Due to this, the molten metal is introduced into the mould cavity from the ladle, through a gating system. The gating system for a casting is a series of channels which lead molten metal from the ladle into the mould cavity. It may include any or all of the following, [Fig. 3.19 and 3.20] :

(*i*) Pouring Basin

(*ii*) Sprue

(*iii*) Sprue base or well

(*iv*) Runner

(*v*) Choke

(*vi*) Skim bob

(*vii*) Gates and/or ingates.

(*viii*) Riser

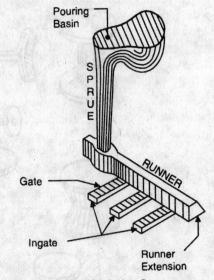

Fig. 3.19. Gating System.

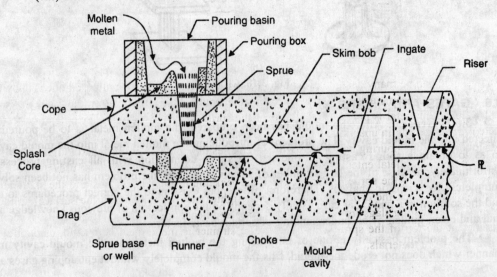

Fig. 3.20. Gating System.

1. Pouring Basin. A pouring basin or cup is a reservoir at the top of the sprue that receives the stream of molten metal poured from the ladle. Sometimes, the metal is directly poured into the top of the sprue, which is made with a funnel shaped opening. However, better results are usually obtained with the use of a pouring basin.

The pouring basin may be moulded into the cope at the top of the sprue, or it may be made of core sand and placed on the cope above the sprue. It may also be made from C.I. for non-ferrous alloys, if chilling is not a problem, or it may be lined with core sand to reduce the chilling effect. Such pouring basins are also placed on the cope above the sprue.

The pouring basin is filled quickly at the start of the pour and it should remain full of molten metal during pouring. Thus, dross consisting of oxides and slags which float, may be kept from entering the sprue. If the depth of metal in the cup is insufficient, a funnel is likely to form above the sprue entrance, through which air and slag may get into the sprue and then into the mould cavity. The depth of the pouring basin is a function of sprue entrance diameter. This will prevent the formation of a vortex at the top of the sprue and hence the drawing in of air and dross into the sprue.

Experience has shown that liquid metal depth above the sprue entrance should be 2.5 times the sprue entrance diameter to prevent the formation of a vortex.

To prevent the slag from flowing down the sprue (at the start of the pour), it is sometimes useful to close the sprue entrance with a plug, (Fig. 3.21 (*a*)), or tin plates and allow the molten metal to fill the basin. The plug is then lifted off. The tin plates melt.

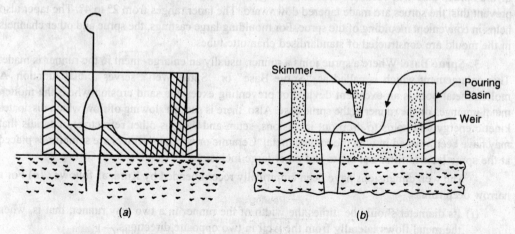

(*a*)   (*b*)

Fig. 3.21

There can be many designs of pouring basins, but the most commonly used one is shown in Fig. 3.21 (*b*). The metal must be poured into the pouring basin that is remote from the sprue entrance. If the metal is poured directly down the sprue entrance, lot of vortexing and turbulence take place, resulting in unsound and defective casting. However, when the metal is poured into the far low side of the pouring basin, a dam effect enables the operator to reach and optimum pouring speed before any metal enters the sprue. This condition must be maintained, to prevent dross and slag from entering the sprue.The weir will hold back the heavier inclusions and the skimmer or dam will hold back the dross (oxides and other lighter inclusions rising to the surface). Another means of preventing slags from entering the sprue and hence the mould cavity, is to use a ceramic strainer at the top of the sprue, (Fig. 3.22). The strainer is made from core sand, chamotte and refractory fibre materials.

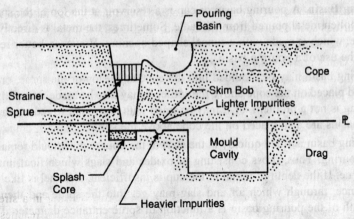

Fig. 3.22. Use of Strainer.

2. Sprue. From the pouring basin, the molten metal is transported down into the mould cavity by means of the sprue or downgate. It is a vertical channel that connects the pouring basin with runners and gates.

As the metal flows down the sprue, its velocity increases. Hence the section of the sprue should decrease, otherwise the sprue will not remain full of metal with the metal leaving the walls of the sprue. This will result in aspiration of gases through the surrounding moulding sand. To prevent this, the sprues are made tapered downward. The taper ranges from 2° to 4°. The taper also helps in convenient moulding of the sprue. For moulding large castings, the sprue and other channels in the mould are constructed of standardised chamotte tubes.

3. Sprue Base. Where a sprue joins a runner, usually an enlarge- ment in the runner is made. This enlargement which is called as "Sprue Base" or "Sprue Well" serves a dual function. A molten metal pool is an excellent device for preventing excessive sand erosion where the molten metal impinges on the runner at the sprue base. Also, there is sudden slowing of flow which dissipates kinetic energy and helps to drop out inclusions, scum and various other refractory materials that may have been washed in with the molten metal. Ceramic or wiremesh filters are sometimes placed at the sprue base to filter out dross and other large inclusions.

The well dimensions have been empirically recommended by Kura, as follows : (*a*) For a narrow deep runner:–

(*i*) Its diameter should be times the width of the runner in a two way runner, that is, when the metal flows laterally from the well in two opposite directions.

(*ii*) Base diameter = 2 × width of runner in a one runner system.

(*b*) For square, round or wide shallow runners, the well should have a cross-sectional area

$$= 5 \times \text{area of the sprue bottom}$$

and,   depth = 2 × that of the runner.

Splash Core. This is a piece of ceramic or baked sand core inserted in the mould directly beneath the sprue. Its function, (Fig. 3.19), is to prevent the erosion of the mould sand where the molten metal strikes it at the base of the sprue.

4. Runners. A runner is commonly a horizontal channel which connects the sprue with gates, thus allowing the molten metal to enter the mould cavity. The runners are of larger cross-section and often streamlined to slow down and smooth out the flow, and are designed to provide approximately uniform flow rates to the various parts of the mould cavity. Runners are commonly made trapezoidal in cross-section.

Skim - bob. A skim bob is an enlargement along the runner, whose function is to trap heavier and lighter impurities such as dross or eroded sand, (Fig. 3.22). It, thus, prevents these impurities from going into the mould cavity.

5. Gates. Gates are channels which connect the runners to the mould cavity and through which the incoming metal directly enters into the mould cavity. The gates should break off easily from the casting after solidification. For this, at the junction to the cavity, the gates are much reduced in thickness. This will also choke the flow of metal and ensure its quiet entrance into the mould cavity. From experience, the best cross- section for gates is a trapezoidal one that smoothly passes into a rectangular section at the junction of the cavity.

Ingate. This is the end of the gate where it joins the mould cavity and through which the molten metal will be introduced into the mould cavity.

Runner extension. The leading edge of the molten metal flowing in a stream follows the path of least resistance and continues to build up kinetic energy until it reaches the end of the runner. If a runner extension is used, the kinetic energy may be absorbed, thus causing a smoother flow of metal in the runners and into the mould cavity. It also serves as a trap for inclusions carried into the runner by the first metal.

Gate Ratio. It is defined as the ratio of sprue base area, followed by the total runner area and the total ingate area. The sprue base area is taken as unity.

Choke. The choke is that part of the gating system which has the smallest cross-sectional area. Its function is to control the rate of metal flow to help lower the flow velocity in the runner, to hold back slag and foreign material and float these in the cope side of the runner and to minimize sand erosion in the runner. Depending upon its location, the gating system may be classified as :

(*i*) Pressurised or chocked system.

(*ii*) Unpressurised or free system.

Pressurised gating system. In this system, the ingates serve as the choke. This system maintains a back pressure and causes the entire gating system to become pressurised. It is usual to cut runners in the cope and gates in the drag. And since in the pressurised system, the runner flows full, the slag will remain in the runner while floating up to its upper section. The system will flow full even if a straight sprue is used once the flow has been established. The full flow system will minimize aspiration and oxidation in the gating system. However, the molten metal will enter the mould cavity with relatively high velocity, causing turbulence. This will cause erosion and oxidation in the mould cavity. But, in this system the molten metal will enter the mould cavity uniformly through all the gates. A typical gating ratio in this system can be : 1 : 0.75 : 0.50.

Gating ratio is defined as : Sprue area : Runner area : Ingate area.

Unpressurised gating system. In this system, the sprue base serves as the choke. Typical gating ratios in this system can be :

$$1 : 2 : 4 \qquad \text{or} \qquad 1 : 4 : 4.$$

This system reduces velocity and turbulence and hence minimizes erosion and oxidation in the mould cavity. But, since the system will not flow full, it may favour absorption of gases and oxidation of metal in the gating system. Also, the slag will not float up and will get access to the mould cavity. This system must have tapered sprues, sprue base wells and pouring basins. This system can deliver metal uniformly to multiple gates only if the runner is reduced after each gate.

For casting alloys such as light metals and Manganese bronze, usually the unpressurised system is used. In contrast, for casting heavy and ferrous metals, pressurised system has been used. However, according to Briggs, for high quality steel castings, a gating ratio of 1 : 2 : 2 or 1 : 2 ; 1.5 will produce castings nearly free from erosion, will minimize oxidation, and will produce uniform flow. But a gating ratio of 1 : 4 : 4 might favour the formation of oxidation defects. Heine suggests a typical gating system for Malleable iron using a four hole strainer and tapered sprue as : 1 : 2 : 9.5, that is, an unpressurised system.

6. Riser. Risers or feed heads are a part of the feeding system. These are reservoirs of molten metal that feed the melt in the casting proper as it solidifies. The riser thus provides the feed metal which flows from the riser to the casting to make up for the shrinkage which takes place in the casting metal as it changes from liquid to solid. The riser is a passage of sand made in the mould during ramming. The molten metal rises in the riser after the mould cavity is filled up.

Risers find use in castings of heavy sections or of high shrinkage alloys.

To understand the functions of risers, the mechanism of solidification of the casting has to be understood. when the casting solidifies, it shrinks or constracts in size. This shrinkage occurs in three stages :

(i) **Liquid Contraction or Shrinkage.** This shrinkage occurs when the metal is liquid. It occurs when the molten metal cools from the temperature at which it is poured to the temperature at which solidification occurs.

(ii) **Solidification Shrinkage.** This occurs when the metal looses its latent heat, that is, during the time the metal changes from the liquid state to the solid state.

(iii) **Solid Shrinkage.** This occurs when the metal cools from the freezing temperature to the room temperature.

Only the first two shrinkages are considered for risering purposes, since the third is accounted for by the Pattern maker's contraction allowance. Liquid shrinkage is generally negligible, but solidification shrinkage can be substantial (12 to 15%).

Gray C.I. with a carbon equivalent of 4.3% has negative shrinkage, that is, it actually expands upto 2.5% because of graphite precipitation. So, for this, no risering is needed.

Solidification shrinkage for other ferrous metals varies from 2.5 to 4%.

Solidification shrinkage for non-ferrous metals is even more, for example,

For pure aluminium it is 6.6% and for copper, it is 4.9%. Solidification shrinkage in case of their alloys is somewhat less.

As already discussed, when the mould cavity is filled with molten metal, the metal adjacent to the walls of the mould cools and solidifies first. This results in a shell of solid metal, with the centre of the section remaining liquid, while there is a zone between the liquid interior and solid exterior wherein the metal is in a semisolid or mushy state. The solidification then proceeds inwards towards the centre of the section. This solidification is called as "Lateral or Progressive solidification". Longitudinal solidification occurs at right angles to the lateral solidification at the centre line, (Fig. 3.23). The gating should be designed in such a manner that it permits solidification and cooling to progress in such a way that the accompanying shrinkage may take place without resulting in voids, cracks, or porosity within the casting, so as to obtain a sound casting. This type of solidification is called "Directional Solidification". For this to occur, the following two conditions should be satisfied :

(a) The longitudinal solidification must progress from the thinnest faster cooling sections to the heavier hotter sections.

(b) The temperature gradient, in addition to being properly directed, must be sufficiently steep so that the liquid metal can pass through the wedge shaped channel to compensate for shrinkage as it occurs at the centre line. It implies that the progressive solidification is controlled in such a way that no portion of the casting is isolated from liquid metal feeding channels, during the complete solidification cycle.

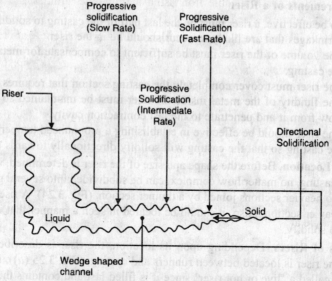

Fig. 3.23. Directional Solidification.

If the depth of a section is quite large as compared to its cross-section, then the progressive solidification rate will exceed the longitudinal solidification and result in fine center line porosity or even a larger or series of large cavities. To prevent such defects, the cross-section of the casting should increase towards the hotter sections.

When it is discovered in the foundary that progressive solidification of a casting is uncertain or impossible because of unique sections or isolated masses, three remedies may be available :

(*i*) The foundary-man can add a riser to feed the remote thick sections.

(*ii*) The designer can thicken (pad) the thin sections that serve as feed paths to the heavier remote sections.

(*iii*) The designer can reduce the mass of the remote thick sections or increase their rate of cooling (with the help of chills).

In riser system, the effective directional solidification is one which starts in those parts of the mould which are farthest from the risers and proceeds through the casting towards the risers.

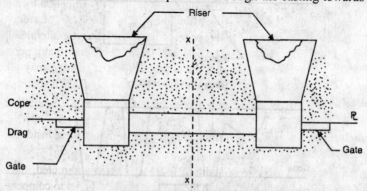

Fig. 3.24. Riser Location.

In addition to promoting directional solidification, the riser performs the following functions :

(*a*) It permits the escape of air and gases as the mould cavity is filled up with molten metal.

(*b*) A riser full of molten metal indicates that the mould cavity has already been completely filled up.

(*A*) **Requirements of a Riser**

   (*i*) To be effective, a riser must be the last part of the casting to solidify, such that all the shrinkages that are likely to occur should be in the riser.

   (*ii*) The volume of the riser must be sufficient to compensate for metal shrinkage within the casting.

   (*iii*) The riser must cover completely the casting section that requires feeding.

   (*iv*) The fluidity of the metal inside the riser must be maintained so that the metal can flow from it and penetrate to the last contraction cavity.

   (*v*) The riser should be effective in establishing a pronounced temperature gradient with the casting so that the casting will solidify directionally towards the riser.

   (*B*) **Riser Location.** Before the shape and size of the riser is determined, its location must be specified. Any casting, no matter how complex, can be subdivided into several geometrical shapes, consisting of two heavier sections joined by a thinner section, (Fig. 3.24). A riser should be located close to each heavier section. Also, it should be located in such a manner that it is the last portion of the casting to solidify.

   (*C*) **Types of Risers.** Depending upon its location, the riser is described as 'Top riser' or 'Side riser'. If the riser is located between runners and casting, (Fig. 3.25 (*a*)), it is known as 'side riser'. It is also called a 'live or hot riser' since it is filled last and contains the hottest metal. If a riser must be placed at the top of the casting, (Fig. 3.25 (*b*)), then it is called as 'Top riser' or 'dead or cold riser'. These types of risers fill up with the coldest metal and are likely to solidify before casting. The side riser receives the molten metal directly from the runner before it enters the mould cavity and is more effective than the top riser. Even though with a top riser, there is a little saving of material as compared to a side riser, but, a deeper mould has to be made with the top riser. A riser is called as "End Riser", Fig. 3.25 (*b*), if it is located at the end of the mould cavity. This is also a cold riser. A riser may either be an "Open riser" or a "Blind riser".

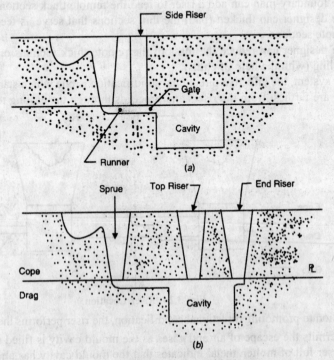

Fig. 3.25. Types of Risers.

(*I*) **Open Risers.** These risers open to the atmosphere at the top surface of the mould, (Fig. 3.25). Such risers have the following advantages:

      (*i*) It can be easily moulded.

      (*ii*) As it is open to atmosphere, it will not draw metal from the casting as a result of partial vacuum in the riser.

      (*iii*) These risers serve as collectors of nonmetallic inclusions floating up to the surface.

The limitations to the usefulness of open risers are as follows :

    (*a*) They can be moulded only in the cope (either at the top of the mould cavity or on the side at the parting line).

    (*b*) They should have the height commensurate with the height of the cope. This reduces the 'yield' of the casting. The 'yield' is the percentage of total metal poured into a mould which actually ends up in the casting.

    (*c*) Open risers are holes through which foreign matter may get into the mould cavity.

    (*d*) Since the top of the riser is open to the atmosphere, the molten metal in it starts loosing heat to the atmosphere. To assure that it does remain molten a sufficient length of time, the following means are used :

    (*i*) *Use of Exothermic Materials.* These materials (which are a mixture of the oxide of the metal to be cast and Aluminium metal in powder form) may be added to the surface of the molten metal in the riser just after the pouring. Due to its contact with molten metal, chemical reaction takes place, producing substantial heat. The metal in the riser thus gets superheated and remains molten for a longer time. It also forms a refractory insulating top on the riser to conserve this heat. Exothermic materials may also be mixed with moulding sand in the riser walls.

Another common method is to mix some binding agents with the exothermic material, enabling it to be moulded into convenient shapes, such as hollow cylinders or sleeves, suitable for lining riser cavities. When it is desired to use a sleeve in contact with the casting, it is necessary to provide a base of core sand, one half of the sleeve wall thickness, to avoid burning on.

This method of "exothermic feeding" has the following advantages :

    1. Smaller risers can be employed.

    2. Shallower moulding boxes can often be used, with a consequent savings in sand and moulding costs.

    3. A greater yield of castings per melt, thus reducing component costs.

    4. Melting costs are reduced for any given casting.

    5. Because of the smaller sizes of risers, fettling and grinding costs are reduced.

    6. Exothermic liners (risers) can be used with the majority of foundary metals and alloys.

    (*ii*) The riser may be insulated by a simple asbestos shield on top of the riser.

    (*iii*) By using insulating material for the riser whole.

    (*iv*) By supplying heat at riser top by a torch.

    (*v*) Pouring molten metal in riser at the end.

All the above methods help in attaining directional solidification.

An open riser should preferably be cylindrical to have a minimum of surface area in contact with the mould, to reduce the loss of heat to sand by conduction.

    (*II*) **Blind Risers.** A riser which does not break to the top of the cope and is entirely surrounded by moulding sand is known as 'Blind Riser' (Fig. 3.26). Blind risers are set up in high moulding boxes, where the use of open risers would entail a large consumption of molten metal. The advantages of blind risers are :

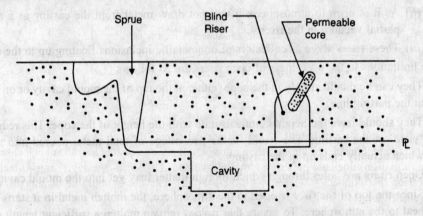

Fig. 3.26. Blind Riser.

(*i*) Considerable latitude or flexibility is allowed for positioning the riser, either in a cope or in drag.

(*ii*) It is surrounded on all sides by moulding sand. Thus it looses heat slowly which helps in better directional solidification of the casting.

(*iii*) A blind riser can be smaller than a comparable open riser, therefore, more yield is obtained.

(*iv*) A blind riser can be removed more easily from the casting than an open riser.

The main drawback of a blind riser is that when the metal in it cools, metal skins may quickly form on its walls. This will result in a vacuum in the riser and the riser will not feed and may actually draw metal from the casting. To avoid this, a permeable dry sand core is inserted into the riser cavity, connecting it to the mould sand layers. Through these sand layers air passes into the riser interior. The riser thus operates under atmospheric pressure.

Blind risers are often made rounded at the top to effect metal savings, because a hemi-spherical shape has the smallest surface area to volume ratio.

(*III*) **Shape and Size of Riser.** The risers are designed to solidify last so as to feed enough metal to heavy sections of the casting to make up for the shrinkage before and during solidification. For this, they should loose heat at a slower rate. Amount of heat content is proportional to the volume and the rate of heat dissipation depends upon the surface area of the riser. Thus, the risers should be designed with a high V/A (Volume/Surface Area) ratio, for a given size. This will minimize the loss of heat, so that the riser will remain hot and the metal in the molten state as long as possible. This condition can be met when the riser is spherical in shape so that its surface area is minimum. The next best practical shape is a cylinder. Rectangular sections are very inefficient and must be avoided as far as possible. As risers of ideal spherical shape are difficult to mould, consequently, the cylinder is probably the best shape to employ for general run of casting.

The riser size for a given application depends primarily on the metal poured, but numerous other factors are also important, for example, gray C.I. requires little or no risering to compensate for solidification contraction because the precipitation of flake graphites causes compensating expansion. Steel, white iron and many non-ferrous alloys which have long freezing ranges, may produce sound castings only with the best application of foundary engineering and experience.

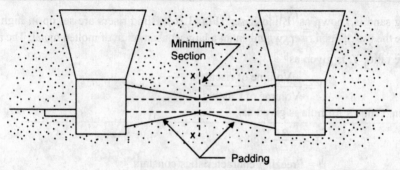

Fig. 3.27. Use of Padding.

As regards the correct height of the cylindrical risers, there is as yet no one opinion. The general points to be considered are that they must be tall enough so that any shrinkage cavity in the riser (pipe formation) does not penetrate into the castings. The shrinkage cavity must lie above the neck (a portion that connects the riser with the casting). The neck should be as short as possible and also solidify longer than the casting. In general,

[Height of Cylindrical Riser = 1.5 × Diameter of Riser]

Riser Size : As has been noted above, the freezing time or solidification time of a casting (Riser is also a casting) depends upon the amount of heat in a casting (directly) and depends (inversely) upon the surface area of the casting. Based on these facts, many relations have been suggested for determining the riser size

1. Chvorinov'rule :–

Solidification time or Freezing time

$$t = C.\left(\frac{V}{SA}\right)^2$$

where V = Volume of Casting

SA = Surface area of casting

C = Constant of proportionately that depends upon composition/properties of cast metal (including its latent heat). pouring temperature, mould material etc,

Since, the metal in the riser must be the last to solidify, to achieve directional solidification.

$$\left(\frac{V}{SA}\right)_{Riser} > \left(\frac{V}{SA}\right)_{Casting}$$

In practice,

$$\left(\frac{V}{SA}\right)_{Riser} = (1.10 \text{ to } 1.15)\left(\frac{V}{SA}\right)_{Casting}$$

Since V and SA for the casting are known, $(V/SA)_{riser}$ can be determined, Assuming height to diameter ratio for the cylindrical riser, the riser size can be determined.

Chvorinov's formula is not very accurate, because, it does not take into account the solidification contraction or shinkage. The method is valid for calculating the proper riser size for short frezing-range alloys such as steel and pure metals. There is no satisfactory relationship for determining riser size for non-ferrous alloys.

2. Caine's Formula : Caine's method of determining riser size is based on an experimentally determined hyperbolic relationship between relative freezing times and volumes of the casting and the riser.

Relative freezing time or Freezing ratio is defined as

$$X = \frac{(SA/V)_{Casting}}{(SA/V)_{Riser}}$$

Volume ratio, Y, is given as

$$Y = \frac{\text{Volume of riser}}{\text{Volume of Casting}}$$

Then, Caine's formula is given as,

$$X = \frac{a}{Y-b} + c$$

where a = Freezing characteristics constant

b = Liquid – solid solidification contraction

c = Relative freezing rate of riser and casting

Typical values of a, b and c for commonly used cast metals are given below :–

Cast Metals	a	b	c
Steel	0.12	0.05	1.00
Aluminium	0.10	0.06	1.08
Gray Cast Iron	0.33	0.03	1.00
Cast Iron, Brass	0.04	0.017	1.00
Aluminium Bronze	0.24	0.017	1.00
Silicon Bronze	0.24	0.017	1.00

A typical Caines hyperbolic curve is shown in Fig. 3.28

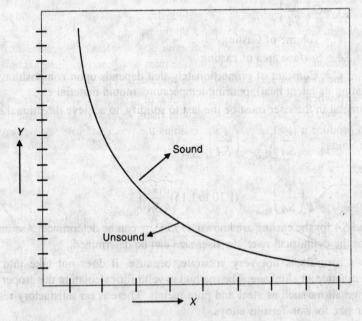

Fig. 3.28. Caines Hyperpolic Curve.

Such curves for different cast metals are available in Handbooks. To find the riser size for a given casting, the riser diameter and height are assumed. Then knowing the values of a, b and c, the values of X and Y are Calculated. These values of X and Y are plotted on the hyperbolic curve figure. If the values of X and Y meet above the curve, the assumed riser size is satisfactory. Otherwise, a new assumption is made.

(*IV*) **Use of Padding.** The casting in Fig. 3.24 is symmetrical about axis X - X. The two thick portions of the casting have been provided with risers. The cooling of this casting will initiate from the section X - X and move towards the heavier sections. As already discussed, for the production of a sound casting, the temperature gradients should be such that no part of the casting remains without metal during the full solidification cycle. For this, the thinner section should be tapered towards heavier sections to change the progressive solidification to directional solidification, (Fig. 3.27). This tapering of thinner section towards thicker section is known as 'padding'. However, this will require extra material. If padding is not provided, centre line shrinkage or porosity will result in the thinner section.

'Insulating Sleeves' may also be used around the thinner sections to retard their rate of cooling, so that the metal in them remains in the liquid state for a longer period, Fig. 3.29.

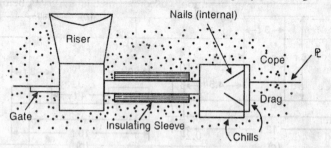

Fig. 3.29. Use of Insulating Sleeves.

(*V*) **Use of Chills.** Chills are massive metal inserts of increased heat capacity and thermal conductivity, which are placed in the mould to induce directional solidification and help over-come the effect of shrinkage. Chills are used to speed up the process of cooling of thick sections of the casting. Owing to chills, heat removal from the massive portion of a casting proceeds more intensely than from the thin portion. This aids in equalising the rates of freezing of the thick and thin sections, decreasing the volume of a shrinkage cavity, or in some case, eliminating this defect completely.

Chills are used when it may be either impractical or impossible to use riser on thick sections of the casting. However, they can be used alongwith risers if possible. Chills and risers placed on massive portions produce a joint effect which enables the production of castings completely free from contraction voids.

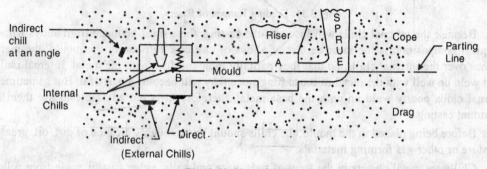

Fig. 3.30. Use of Chills.

The use of chills is illustrated in Fig. 3.30. The casting is gated at A in order to put the coldest metal in portion B of the casting. If the casting were gated at B, the chills will absorb heat from the hot metal and become saturated with heat, thereby, loosing much of their chilling ability.

Also, cooled metal will flow into the thin section of the casting, which is not desirable from the point of view of directional solidification.

The chills can be either external or internal chills. The external chills are rammed up in the mould walls, whereas the internal chills are inserted in the mould cavity, (Fig. 3.30). The external chills may be direct or indirect chills. External chills are made of iron or steel. Of course, the most effective chills will be made of copper, because of its high heat conductivity. External chills are coated with red lead or moulding sand to keep them from welding upto the casting. External chills can be used again and again.

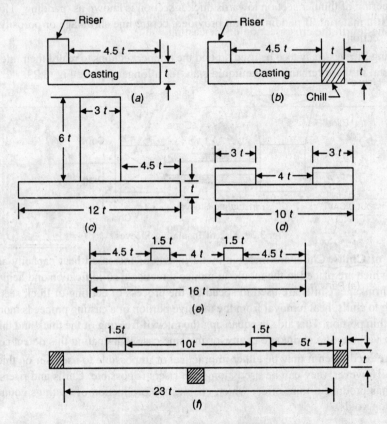

Fig. 3.31. Feeding Ranges of Risers.

Because the internal chills will fuse into the casting, these must be made from alloys whose chemical composition is the same as that of alloys of castings. In pouring the mould, the metal washes over the internal chills, so that they partially melt and fuse with the metal. Internal chills must weld up well with the metal of the casting since they will become a part of it. But sometimes, internal chills poorly weld up with the base metal, therefore, it is not advisable to use them in important casting.

Before being placed in the mould, the chills should be thoroughly cleaned of dirt, oil, grease, moisture or other gas forming materials.

Chills are metal objects in the form of rods, wire and nails, either cast or made from rolled stock.

(*VI*) **Risering versus Padding and Chilling.** Because risers add to the cost of a casting in several ways (time is consumed in providing them, they reduce the yield of the metal poured and time is required for their removal), every effort should be made to design castings so that the number of risers is minimised. Padding is one method of doing this.

(*VII*) **Flow-offs.** Flow-offs are vertical channels, just like sprue, made in the mould Fig. 3.32 (*a*). They serve many purposes in a casting process. In the case of castings, where risers are not needed or where blind risers are used, they permit the escape of gases from the mould cavity. They also decrease the dynamic pressure of the metal on the mould and point to the end of pouring. They can also feed the castings just like risers but are of much reduced size as compared to risers. They usually taper off from top to bottom just like sprues. The mould can have one or several flow offs depending on its size. The cross-section of a flow-off at the base is generally taken to be equal to one-half or one-fourth the cross-section of the casting wall.

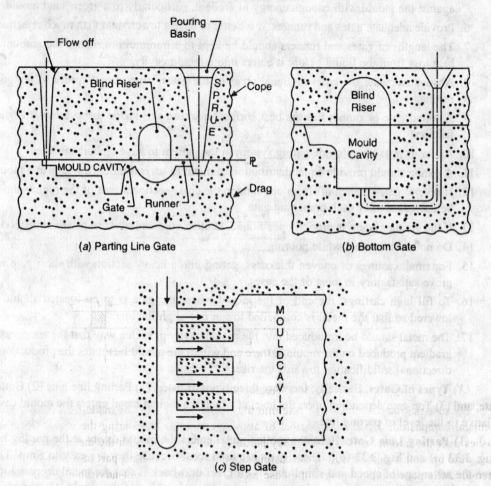

(a) Parting Line Gate   (b) Bottom Gate

(c) Step Gate

Fig. 3.32. Types of Gates.

(*VIII*) **Feeding Range of Risers.** It has been seen that for steel castings, an adequate riser will provide complete sounding of the casting upto a length equal to 4.5 times the minimum thickness of the casting. A metal chill of minimum section equal to the cross section of the casting will, when placed at the end of the casting, merely adds a distance equal to the thickness of the casting. However, the same chill placed in-between two risers will permit them to be 2t further apart without impairing soundness. It has also been seen that a riser in the centre of a casting has a much greater feeding range that at the end of a casting. Fig. 3.31 illustrates the feeding ranges of risers.

(*IX*) **Requirements of Gating System.** From the above discussions, it is clear that the following design considerations should be given a weightage while designing a gating system :

1. The metal should flow with a minimum of turbulence and aspiration of mould gases.

2. The metal must be rapidly poured into the mould cavity or else it will solidify before completely filling the mould.

3. The use of higher superheat of metal is undesirable since the amount of gas dissolved in the liquid metal increases with an increase in superheat.

4. Loose sand, slag or oxides should be prevented from entering the mould cavity.

5. Erosion of the mould surface should be avoided. For this, the metal must not impinge against the mould with enough energy to erode it, particularly in a green sand mould.

6. Provide adequate gates and runners. It is better to have a lower yield than much rejections.

7. The lengths of gates and runners should be kept to a minimum to reduce the amount of heat loss from the liquid before it enters into a mould cavity.

8. Always calculate the cross-sectional areas of the gates, runners and sprues to get good results.

9. A round gate or runner has the best surface area, use this shape to have lower surface friction.

10. As far as possible, provide gating system in the pattern to have smooth surface.

11. A gating should provide equal distribution of metal to several mould cavities in a mould.

12. If several gates branch off from one runner, the cross-sectional area of the runner should be decreased after each branching gate.

13. If the gating system is properly positioned, strainer core and other traps are unnecessary.

14. Do no tilt the mould white pouring.

15. For small castings of uneven thickness, gating into a heavy section with short gate will prove satisfactory in most of the cases.

16. To fill high castings, the end of the mould where the gate is to be located should be lowered so that the metal is compelled to run in a slight incline.

17. The metal should be introduced into the mould cavity in such a way that the temperature gradient produced on the mould surface and within the mould facilitates the production of directional solidification towards the riser.

(*X*) **Types of Gates.** Basically, there are three types of gates, (1) Parting line gate (2) Bottom gate, and (3) Top gate depending upon the level at which the molten metal enters the mould cavity relative to the level of parting line.

(1) **Parting Line Gate.** Here, the molten metal enters the mould cavity at the parting line, [Fig. 3.32 (*a*) and Fig. 3.32 (*b*)]. These gates are used most because they are easy to form. They have the advantage of speed and simplicity. Their chief drawback is that the metal drops into the mould cavity and for deep cavities, it may cause erosion or washing of the mould. In case of non ferrous metals, this drop aggravates the dross and entraps air in the metal, which make for inferior castings.

(*i*) It is a general practice to cut runners in the cope and ingates in the drag. The main reason for this is to trap the slag and dross, which are lighter and thus trapped in the upper portions of the runners.

(*ii*) Whenever possible, surfaces to be machined should be cast in the drag side of the mould. This helps to provide a cleaner casting surface on the bottom, while dross, oxides and other impurities float to the top. Any shrinkage would also be on the top surface and not on the surface to be machined. If finished surfaces must be cast in the cope side of the mould, an extra allowance should be made.

(2) **Bottom Gate.** For deep cavities, bottom gating may be employed. Here, the metal enters the mould cavity at or near the bottom of the mould cavity, (Fig. 3.32 (b)). This offers a smooth flow of metal into the cavity with a minimum of mould core erosion and the turbulence of metal. However, these gates are difficult to make and require extra skill to mould. Many times, these gates use a core gating system. Also, their main drawback is that in castings which are bottom gated and fed by top risers, an unfavourable temperature gradient is created in the casting. Hottest metal enters the cavity and the coldest metal will be in the riser. This drawback sometimes can be partially or completely corrected by special casting techniques discussed earlier, that is,

(a) Use of exothermic materials in the making of the riser or spreading these at the top of the riser.

(b) Radiation shielding on top risers reduces radiant heat loss.

(c) Insulating riser sleeves help maintain riser heat.

(d) Chills can promote directional solidification or deduce undesirable heat concentration.

(e) Pouring the risers last with fresh metal places the hottest metal there.

Another technique to minimise the drawbacks of bottom gating is to use a 'Step gate', (Fig. 3.32 (c)). The sizes of ingates are normally increased from top to bottom such that the metal enters the mould cavity from the bottom most gate and then progressively moves to the higher gates. This ensures a gradual filling of the mould without any mould erosion and produce a sound casting. However, a difficulty with step gating is that most of the metal will continue to enter through the bottom most gate.

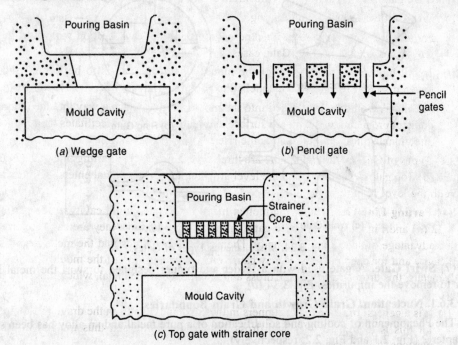

(a) Wedge gate   (b) Pencil gate

Fig. 3.33. Top Gates.

(3) **Top Gate.** In this type of gating, the metal enters the mould cavity above the level of the parting line. Its main advantage is that it is conducive to a favourable temperature gradient. The

pouring basin and gates themselves may serve as risers, (Fig. 3.33). However, its big disadvantage is mould erosion, lot of turbulence and excessive aspiration of air and gases. It is not recommended for metals which oxidise easily, for example, Aluminium and Magnesium, since such metals have a tendency to form excessive dross when agitated and produce unsound castings. Top gates are at times used for gray castings of simple design, for example thin, flat plates. The different designs of top gates are shown in Fig. 3.33.

Pencil Gate. (Fig. 3.33 (*b*)). A series of small round gates enter the mould cavity from above and come from a common pouring basin. This gate is employed to reduce the rate of flow of metal and to control the inclusions of sand, slag or dross. However, excessive turbulence is still present.

Use of a strainer (to trap sand, slag or dross) in a top gate is shown in Fig. 3.33 (*c*)

Other types of Gates. The three main types of gates are sometimes modified to meet certain specific conditions. Some of these gates are discussed below :

(4) **Branch Gate.** (Fig. 3.34 (*a*)). Two or more gates leading into the casting cavity. It is designed either to feed a single casting at several points or a number of individual castings. Also, see Fig. 3.17.

(5) **Ring Gate.** (Fig. 3.34 (*b*)). A gate so formed that the number of small gates conduct the metal from a circular runner to a mould in the centre.

(6) **Whirl Gate.** (Fig. 3.34 (*c*)). A gate and sprue arrangement which tangentially introduces metal into a riser so that the centrifugal action forces dirt or slag to the centre of the riser and away from the riser connection as the metal enters the mould cavity. It thus prevents dirt and slag from entering the gate and the mould cavity.

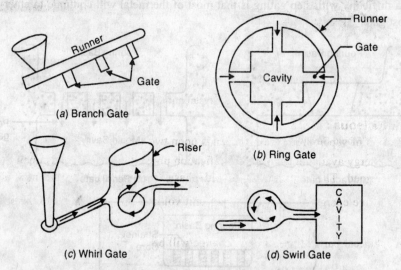

Fig. 3.34. Miscellaneous Types of Gates.

(7) **Swirl Gate.** A gate used with a feeder and runner designed to swirl the metal in the feeder to remove the impurities. Fig. 3.34 (*d*).

3.6.1. Nucleation, Grain Growth and Grain Boundaries:

The Phenomenon of cooling and solidification of a pure metal and an alloy has been shown in Chapter 2 (Fig. 2.1 and Fig. 2.2, respectively).

When a molten metal begins to cool and solidify individual crystals will begin to form independent of one another, with random orientations and at various locations within the molten mass. "**Nucleation**" is the process of formation of first stable tiny particle (a crystal) when a mass of molten metal begins to solidify. With passage of time, these crystals grow in size. Thus, "Grain growth" is the process of increase in the sizes of these crystals. The pattern of grain/crystal growth is in the shape of radial arms which begin to develop from the various crystal nuclei. With passage of time, secondary arms (branches) develop at right angles to the radial arms. The shape of the grain looks like a "fir tree" (crystal formation is always in three dimensions). This type of grain is called a "Dendrite", Fig. 3.35 (*a*). Dendrite (from Greek) is derived from Dendron (meaning akin to) and drys (meaning tree).

As the process of cooling and solidification progresses, the dendrites will grow in size until the primary and secondary arms (radial arms and branches) eventually interlock with other similiar growths. This process continues, until a grain is eventually formed without a trace of the original skeleton structure. The individual grains interfere and impinge on one another. The surfaces that separate the individual grains are called "Grain Boundaries",Fig. 3.35(*b*).

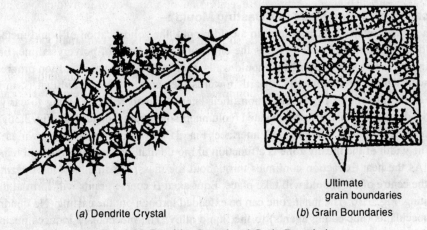

(*a*) Dendrite Crystal   Ultimate grain boundaries   (*b*) Grain Boundaries

Fig. 3.35. Dendrite Crystal and Grain Boundaries.

Radius of Nucleous :

Nucleation of supercooled grains depends upon two factors:-

1. Free energy available from the solidification process, which depends upon the volume of the particle formed. The replacement of old phase (molten state) by the new phase (solid) accompanies a free energy decrease, ΔF_v per unit vol. and this contributes to the stability of the new phase.

For a spherical particle, free energy change will be

$$-\frac{4}{3}\pi r^3 \cdot \Delta F_v \qquad (-ve \text{ as it decreases}), \ r = \text{radius of sphere}$$

2. Energy required to form a liquid-solid interface. Particles formed in the melt have some surface area. Solid-liquid phases possess a surface in between the two. Such a surface has a +ve free energy σ per unit area, associated with it. Creation of new interface results in free energy increase which is $= \sigma . 4\pi r^2$

∴   Free energy change

$$\Delta F = -\frac{4}{3}\pi r^3 \Delta F_v + \sigma.4\pi r^2$$

critical radius, r_c of particle is

$$\frac{\partial \Delta F}{\partial r} = 0$$

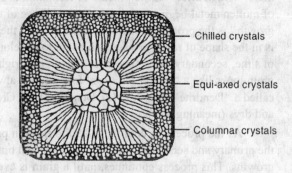

$$\therefore \quad r_c = \frac{2.\sigma}{\Delta F_v}$$

$$\Delta F = \frac{16}{3} \cdot \frac{\pi \sigma^3}{(\Delta F_v)^2}$$

Fig. 3.36. Crystal Formation in Cast Structure.

Solidification of Molten Metal in a Casting Mould :–

When the molten metal is poured in a cold mould, the solidification of liquid metal will be very rapid along the mould walls. This is the chill zone and a layer of polycrystalline, fine, equi-axed grains will be produced along the mould walls, Fig. 3.36. As the solidification progresses, the grain growth will be predominantly inwards towards the centre of the mould that is, in opposite direction to the direction of heat extraction, their lateral growth reduced owing to early contact made with adjacent crystals. These elongated (columner) solid grains (dendrites), Fig. 3.36, protrude into the unaffected liquid - Solid (L-S) interface, Fig. 3.37 and form what is known as "Mushy Zone". The width of the mushy zone is a function of mould material, cooling rate and temperature gradient. As the heat extraction continues throughout the mass, the simultaneous freezing of the metal at the centre of the mould will take place. Equi-axed B coarse grains will form at the centre of the casting, Fig. 3.36. The inner zone can be extended through out the casting (No dendrites), by adding inocculants (nucleating agents) to the liquid alloy. The inocculant induces nucleation of grains throughout the liquid metal. Common inocculants are: - Ferro-silicon, Ferro-manganese, Ferro-chromium, Ferro-silicon-chromium, Ferro-silicon-cadmium and so on.

Segregation :– When a liquid alloy metal cools and solidifies, the separating out of the constituent elements with different freezing temperatures, is termed as "Segregation". There are many types of segregations, as given below :

1. **Micro-segregation :-** The "Cored dendrites" formed, Fig. 3.37, have higher concentration of alloying elements at the surface than at the core of the dendrite. This is due to solute rejection from the core towards the surface during solidification of the' dendrite. This is known as "Micro-segregation".

2. **Macro-segregation:** An alloy contains elements with different freezing temperatures. When a liquid alloy is poured into a mould, the higher freezing point metal will form the first crystal. As cooling progresses, the lower freezing point metals will start nucleating. In a casting mould, the cooling and solidification starts from the mould walls and progresses inwards towards the centre of the mould. Thus, the outer surface of the casting will be richer in higher freezing point elements and the central zone of the casting 'will be richer is lower freezing point constituents. Due to this, the casting will not be homogeneous in properties and will contain different composition from crust to core. This is termed as "Macro segregation". This can be avoided by rapid cooling of the melt or by keeping the melt in motion as long as possible. In existing castings, it can be remedied by annealing heat treatment process.

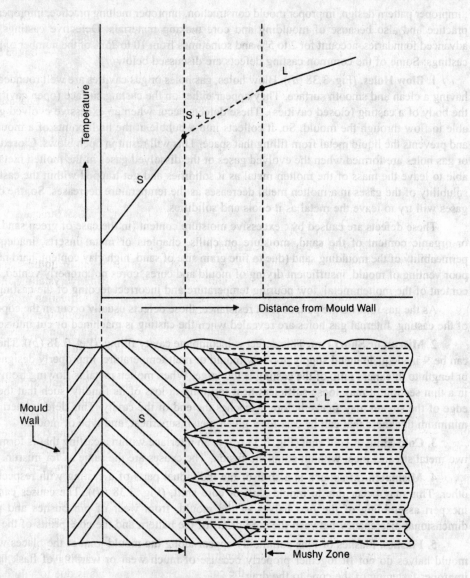

Fig. 3.37. Solidification of a Liquid Metal.

3. **Normal segregation :** This type of segregation occurs, when the solidification moves away from the mould walls as a plane front (no formation of dendrites). Lower freezing point constituents of the alloy are driven to the centre of the resultant casting.

4. **Gravity segregation :** This type of segregation takes place due to gravity. Higher density elements will sink to the bottom of the mould and ligher elements will float to the surface. This will result in a casting richer in higher density elements at the lower part and the upper part will be richer in lighter elements.

3.7. SAND CASTING DEFECTS

A properly designed casting, a properly prepared mould and correctly melted metal should result in a defect free casting. However, if proper control is not exercised in the foundary-sometimes it is too expensive – a variety of defects may result in a casting. These defects may be the result of

: improper pattern design, improper mould construction, improper melting practice, improper pouring practice and also because of moulding and core making materials. Defective castings, even at advanced foundaries, account for 2 to 5% and sometimes from 10 to 25% of the number of produced castings. Some of the common casting defects are discussed below :

1. **Blow Holes.** (Fig. 3.38 (a)). Blow holes, gas holes or gas cavities are well rounded cavities having a clean and smooth surface. They appear either on the casting surface (open cavities) or in the body of a casting (closed cavities). These defects occur when an excessive evolved gas is not able to flow through the mould. So, it collects into a bubble at the high points of a mould cavity and prevents the liquid metal from filling that space. This will result in open blows. Closed. cavities or gas holes are formed when the evolved gases or the dissolved gases in the molten metal are not able to leave the mass of the molten metal as it solidifies and get trapped within the casting. The solubility of the gases in a molten metal decreases as the temperature decreases. So, the dissolved gases will try to leave the metal as it cools and solidifies.

These defects are caused by : excessive moisture content (in the case of green sand moulds) or organic content of the sand, moisture on chills, chaplets or metal inserts, inadequate gas permeability of the moulding sand (due to fine grain size of sand, high clay content, hard ramming), poor venting of mould, insufficient drying of mould and cores, cores not properly vented, high gas content of the molten metal, low pouring temperature and incorrect feeding of the casting etc.

As the gas follows the path of least resistance, these defects usually occur in the cope portion of the casting. Internal gas holes are revealed when the casting is machined or cut into sections.

2. **Misrun or Short run.** This defect is incomplete cavity filling, (Fig. 3.38 (b)). The reasons can be :- inadequate metal supply, too low mould or melt temperature, improperly designed gates, or length to thickness ratio of the casting is too large. When molten metal is flowing from one side in a thin section, it may loose sufficient heat resulting in loss of its fluidity, such that the leading edge of the stream may freeze before it reaches the end of the cavity. This defect determines the minimum thickness that can be cast for a given metal, superheat, and type of mould.

3. **Cold Shut.** A cold shut (Fig. 3.38 (c)) is an interface within a casting that is formed when two metal streams meet without complete fusion. The causes are the same as for misrun.

4. **Mismatch.** Mismatch is a shift of the individual parts of a casting with respect to each other. This may occur due to mould shift or core shift, (Fig. 3.38 (d)). The causes can be—an inexpert assembling of the two halves of the mould, from wear of pin bushes and pins and dimensional discrepancy between the core prints of the pattern and the core prints of the core.

5. **Flashes.** Flashes or Fins commonly appear along the mould joint at the places where the mould halves do not fit together properly because of much wear or warping of flask halves, or improper fastening of the cope to the drag.

6. **Metal Penetration.** or burnt on sand is a strong crust of fused sand on the surface of a casting which results from insufficient refractoriness of moulding materials, a large content of impurities, inadequate mould packing and poor quality of mould washes. When the molten metal is poured into the mould cavity, at those places when the sand packing is inadequate, some metal will flow between the sand particles for a distance into the mould wall and get solidified. When the casting is removed, this lump of metal remains attached to the casting. Of course, it can be removed afterwards by chipping or grinding.

7. **Drop.** Drop or crush in a mould is an irregularly shaped projections on the cope surface of a casting (Fig. 3.38 (e)). This defect is caused by the break-away of a part of mould sand as a result of weak packing of the mould, low strength of the moulding sand, malfunctioning of moulding equipment, strong jolts and strikes at the flask when assembling the mould. The loose sand that falls into the cavity will also cause a dirty casting surface, either on the top or bottom surface of the casting, depending upon the relative densities of the sand and the liquid.

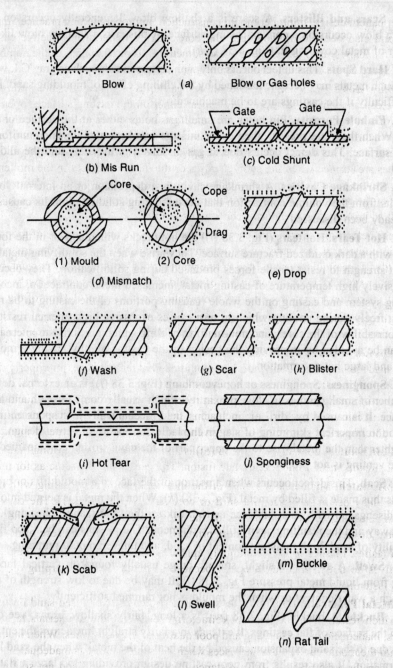

Fig. 3.38. Casting Defects.

8. **Run out.** Run out is the defect of metal leaking out of the mould during pouring. This defect occurs due to faulty moulding and faulty flask equipment.

9. **Cut or Wash.** A cut or wash is a low projection on the drag face of a casting that extends along the surface, decreasing in height as it extends from one side of the casting to the other end. It usually occurs with bottomgating castings in which the moulding sand has insufficient hot strength, and when too much metal is made to flow through one gate into the mould cavity, (Fig. 3.38 (*f*)).

10. Scars and Blisters. A scare is a shallow blow. It generally occurs on a flat surface, whereas a blow occurs on a convex casting surface. A blister is a shallow blow like a scar with a thin layer of metal covering it, (Fig. 3.38 (g,h)).

11. Hard Spots. This defect occurs only with certain metals such as gray C.I. with insufficient silicon. Such metals may become hardened by the chilling effect of moulding sand. Hard spots will cause difficulty if the castings are to be machined.

12. Pinhole Porosity. Pin holes are small gas holes either at the surface or just below the surface. When these are present, they occur in large numbers and are fairly uniformly dispersed over the surface. This defect occurs due to gas dissolved in the alloy and the alloy not properly degassed.

13. Shrinkage Cavities. A shrinkage cavity is a depression or an internal void in a casting that results from the volume contraction that occurs during solidification. Its causes and remedies have already been discussed.

14. Hot Tears. Hot tears (Fig. 3.38 (i)) are hot cracks which appear in the form of irregular crevices with a dark oxidized fracture surface. They arise when the solidifying metal does not have sufficient strength to resist tensile forces produced during solidification. They occur chiefly from an excessively high temperature of casting metal, increased metal contraction, incorrect design of the gating system and casting on the whole (causing portions of the casting to be restrained from shrinking freely during cooling which in turn causes excessive high internal resistance stresses), poor deformability of the cores, and non-uniform cooling which gives rise to internal stresses. This defect can be avoided by improving the design of the casting and by having a mould of low hot strength and large hot deformation.

15. Sponginess. Sponginess or honeycombing (Fig. 3.38 (j)) is an external defect, consisting of a number of small cavities in close proximity, which usually come through and are apparent on the surface. It is caused by 'dirt' or 'inclusions' held mechanically in suspension in molten metal and is due to imperfect skimming of slag in the ladle and incorrect gating design. The impurities being lighter than the metal, rise to the upper part of the cavity, often accompanied by bubbles of gas if the venting is not proper.

16. Scab. This defect occurs when a portion of the face of a mould lifts or breaks down and the recess thus made is filled by metal (Fig. 3.38) (k). When the metal is poured into the cavity, gas may be disengaged with such violence as to break up the sand (sand upheaving), which is then washed away and the resulting cavity filled with metal. The reasons can be :- too fine a sand, low permeability of sand, high moisture content of sand, and uneven mould ramming.

17. Swell. A swell is a slight, smooth bulge usually found on vertical faces of castings, resulting from liquid metal pressure Fig. 3.38 (l). It may be due to low strength of mould because of too high a water content or when the mould is not rammed sufficiently.

18. Buckle. A buckle (Fig. 3.38 (m)) is a long, fairly shallow, broad, vee depression that occurs in the surface of flat castings. It extends in a fairly straight line across the entire flat surface. It results due to the sand expansion caused by the heat of the metal, when the sand has insufficient hot deformation. It also results from poor casting design providing too large a flat surface in the mould cavity.

Buckling is prevented by mixing cereal or wood flour to sand. When the molten metal is poured into the mould cavity, these organic particles are oxidised and burnt. They leave the mould as a gas. This results in small void spaces for the expanding sand particles to move into without inducing severe compressive stresses in the mould.

19. Rat - tail. A rat tail is a long, shallow, angular depression in the surface of a flat casting and resembles a buckle except that it is not shaped like a broad vee. The difference between a buckle and a rat-tail are shown in Fig. 3.38 (n). The reasons for this defect are the same as for buckle.

3.8. DESIGN OF CASTINGS

A cast part must have such a design as to ensure a high level of its working characteristics (strength, rigidity, stiffness, tightness, and corrosion resistance) at a given mass and shape of the part. Proper attention to design details can minimize casting problems and lower costs. For this, a close collaboration between the designer and the foundry engineer is important.

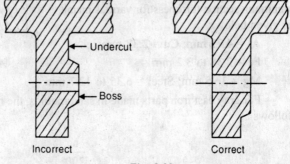

The main feature of the casting process is that the molten metal poured into the mould contracts as it cools and solidifies. The main consideration is that the shape of the casting should allow for directional solidification. Some of the important design considerations are discussed below:

1. The shape of the castings should be as simple as possible. That helps to reduce the cost of patterns, cores and moulds.

Fig. 3.39

2. Castings should be made as compact as possible. Large steel castings of complex shape are divided into two or more castings, which can be easily cast, and then joined by welding to produce a 'cast-weld' construction.

3. Projecting details (bosses, lugs etc.) or undercuts should be avoided. Or, the pattern elements for them should be made so that they do not hinder the removal of pattern from the mould, (Fig. 3.39).

4. To facilitate removal, provision should be made for draft on the castings vertical surfaces. The draft is greater for the inside surfaces than for the exterior surfaces.

5. Wherever possible, avoid complex parting lines on the pattern, because these increase the cost of moulding operations. Parting lines should be in a single plane, if practicable, (Fig. 3.40). The design (b) is better, not only because the lines are simpler and the pattern is less costly bat also because a plane parting can be used in the process of moulding.

6. Avoid concentration of metal so that no shrinkage cavities are formed. For this reason, bosses, lugs, pads should be avoided unless absolutely necessary. Metal section is too heavy at bosses which is difficult to feed solid, (Fig. 3.41).

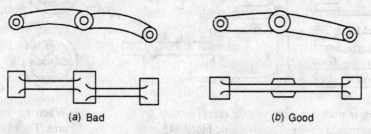

(a) Bad   (b) Good

Fig. 3.40

7. The position of the casting's surfaces during metal pouring must be taken into account, since gas blow holes may form on the casting's upper horizontal surfaces. Critical surfaces of castings should lie at the bottom part of the mould.

8. **Minimum Section Thickness.** The thickness of the casting walls is determined depending on the size and mass of the casting, its material and the casting method. Except for cast iron, the minimum section thickness depends mainly upon the fluidity of the molten metal. If a casting section is too thin, or if it is relatively thin and extends too far, a misrun or cold shut defect will occur. The minimum section thickness for various metals is given below :

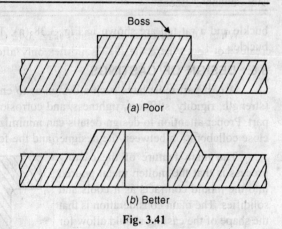

(a) Poor

(b) Better

Fig. 3.41

    Al = 4.75 mm; Cu = 2.38 mm;

    Fe = 2.38 to 3.2 mm

    Mg = 3.95 mm; Steel = 6.35 to 12.7 mm.

For gray cast iron parts made in sand moulds, the minimum wall thickness can be obtained as follows :

$$t = \frac{L}{200} + 4 \text{ mm}$$

where L = greatest dimension of the casting.

Inner sections of the castings, resulting from complex cores, cool much slower than outer sections and cause variations in strength properties. Due to this, the internal walls should be 10 to 20% thinner than the external walls.

9. Whenever feasible, the castings should be designed with uniform section thickness, because shrinkage defects (porosities, cracks) may arise in the thickened portions. Where it is not possible, the difference in thickness of adjoining sections should not exceed 2 to 1 and the two sections must be joined gradually with the help of large fillets, (Fig. 3.42 (a)). An abrupt change in section and sharp corners act as stress raisers in the finished casting, create turbulence during pouring and hinder proper feeding of the casting.

10. Sharp corners, (Fig. 3.42 (b)), in addition to creating troubles discussed under point 9, cause local heavy sections. The sharp corners are eliminated with a radius at the corner from one-half to one-third of the section thickness.

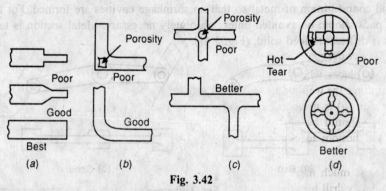

Fig. 3.42

11. Ribs are used for two purposes : (i) to increase stiffness (ii) to reduce weight

Too shallow in depth and too widely spaced ribs prove in effectual. Thickness of rib should be 0.8 times the casting thickness. Ribs should be rounded at edges and correctly filleted. Avoid complex ribs. Wide and low ribs are safer than thin and high ones.

When two ribs cross each other, (Fig. 3.42 (c)), localized heavy cross sections result. This creates hot spot where the melt solidifies only after adjacent zones have solidified, resulting in shrinkage cavities. This can be avoided by offsetting the ribs.

The staggered ribs, (Fig. 3.43 (a)) cause less distortion than the regularly spaced ribs, (Fig. 3.43 (b)).

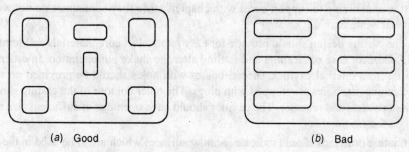

(a) Good (b) Bad

Fig. 3.43

Ribs should be used chiefly for static loads. These should be avoided where impact loads are expected since these increase the rigidity of the parts.

12. Due to the same reasons as for cross ribs, bring or join minimum number of sections together.

13. Inside diameter of a cylinder or bushing should be greater than the wall thickness of the casting. If it is less, it is better to cast solid. Holes can be produced by cheaper and safer methods than by coring.

14. A material that has a large solidification shrinkage will result in hot-shortness (hot tears) if the moulding material does not collapse sufficiently to allow shrinkage or the moulds should be of simple shape so as not to develop tensile stress during solidification. If possible, the casting design should be changed to allow deformation without moving large mould masses. For example, in Fig. 3.42 (d), the straight arms can result in hot tears, but S-shaped arms can straighten a little to accommodate the required shortening on and after solidification.

15. Don't use iron castings for impact and shock loading.

16. Don't use cast iron at temperature above 300°C, since its strength decreases after 300°C.

17. Load the iron castings in compression, as far as possible. Tensile and bending stresses can be eliminated or minimised by proper design.

18. Provide places where holes are to be drilled, to reinforce the walls of the casting, (Fig. 3.44). Design (a) is not good, because the drilled holes should be normal to the surfaces, top and bottom to eliminate drill breakage.

Design (b) is much more satisfactory because it eliminates drill breakage, reduces drilling time and saves lot of material.

19. The casting shape should allow easy cut-off of the gating system elements and removal of cores.

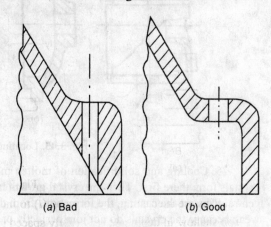

(a) Bad (b) Good

Fig. 3.44

20. It is preferable to dispose the entire casting in the drag if the casting construction permits doing so. This helps rule out mismatch.

21. The mould should have a minimum number of cores or no cores at all, if possible. It is advisable to use projection cods.

22. The cavities in castings should have extensions roomy enough to receive the core prints of cores. It is undesirable to support cores with chaplets since they sometimes do not weld enough with the metal being cast.

23. The casting design should provide for easy removal of core materials and reinforcements and should make for ease of cleaning and fettling after the shake out operation. In order to remove core material from internal cavities, special bosses with holes should be provided on the casting. After the cleaning, the holes are stopped with plugs. The outer contour of the casting should be free of deep blind pockets and recesses. The cavities should have openings of sufficient size to facilitate stripping.

24. Casting drawings should indicate locating surfaces which are to be used in the machining of the castings and also in the checking of the castings. The locating surfaces should be formed by the pattern and should lie in the same mould half, so that relative displacements of mould parts and the cores do not affect accuracy of these surfaces. These locating surfaces are not needed for part functioning and can be removed after machining when necessary.

Examples of locating surfaces are :

(*i*) Centre holes on shafts.

(*ii*) Centring recess 1 and end face 2 on the skirt of an automotive engine piston, (Fig. 3.45 (*a*)).

(*iii*) Flats 1 of bosses 2 on cast blanks, provided for their proper loading and clamping., (Fig. 3.45 (*b*)).

(*iv*) Bosses 1 on turbine blade blanks, (Fig. 3.45 (*c*)).

(*v*) Two locating holes 1 on housing-type castings (Fig. 3.45 (*d*)).

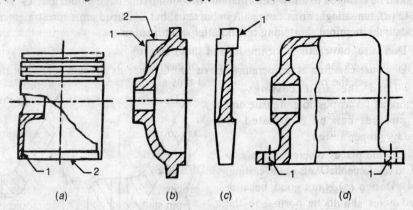

Fig. 3.45. Locating Surfaces Types.

25. Cooling and solidification of molten metal start at the surface of the mould cavity and crystals form there first. Then the crystal growth takes place inwards, normal to all surfaces. At the central plane of the casting, the formations from different sides intersect. The metal in this plane is weak because the crystals do not join perfectly or even porosity may result there. In a casting with sharp corners, (Fig. 3.46 (*a*)), a plane of weakness extends from corner to corner, exactly where the stresses are apt to be maximum. In castings with corners rounded off, (Fig. 3.46 (*b*)), the plane of

weakness runs uniformly throughout the centre, where the stresses are extremely low. Also, the heat flows propagating normally to the corner walls intersect and develop a 'hot zone' within the corner inner area. The corner walls here are made 20 to 25% thinner than those in the areas farther from the corner.

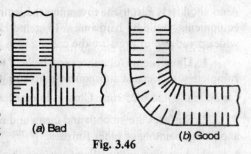

(a) Bad

(b) Good

Fig. 3.46

26. The design of a cast part must take into account the casting properties of the alloy being cast.

Gray iron has good casting properties. The structure of gray iron is more affected by the rate of cooling than other grades. A change in the iron structure affects the mechanical properties of iron, its machinability, durability, corrosion resistance, and other working properties. If the metal cools fast, all the carbon in the thin walls of castings, proves to be in the bound state, forming he cementite, Fe_3C. This structure is of high hardness and is not amenable to machining. This defect in gray-iron castings is called hard spots. In the thick walls of the same casting, metal solidifies slowly resulting in a structure of low strength. So, the need for the uniform wall thickness in gray-iron castings acquires a particular importance.

High strength grades of iron show decreased fluidity and enhanced shrinkage. These factors should be properly considered while designing castings.

The low fluidity of steel causes difficulties in producing thin-walled long castings. High shrinkage of steel may result in blows, cracks and porosities in the thickened sections of castings, at the junction of walls and in bosses. Risers placed at these locations help eliminate these defects. Special reinforcing ribs are provided at the junctions of various thickness, to exclude the formation of cracks in the castings. The ribs are afterwards cut off in the fettling operation.

Aluminium alloys are rather fluid materials; but they are not free of such defects as gas holes and shrinkage porosities, especially in massive members. For this reason, it is advisable to produce aluminium castings with thin walls of uniform thickness.

Magnesium alloys are inferior to Aluminium alloys in casting properties. They are subject to porosities, and therefore, the thick sections show poorer mechanical properties than thin members.

Tin bronzes have satisfactory fluidity. But they solidify long, so the metals develop shrinkage voids which lowers the plasticity and tightness of castings. A decrease in the wall thickness of the castings increases the rate of solidification and thus aids in improving the properties of castings.

Tin free bronzes show enhanced shrinkage. Due to this, the casting design should provide for risering of castings.

27. Shot blast the parts whenever necessary to increase the endurance strength particularly of thin castings.

3.9. MISCELLANEOUS CASTING PROCESSES

3.9.1. Die Casting. In the die casting process, the mould used for making a casting is permanent, called a die. It is thus quite different from sand casting where the mould is expendable and must be broken in order to obtain the casting. If the molten metal is poured into the permanent (metallic) mould under a gravity head (as is done in sand casting) the process is called as ``Gravity die casting" or "Permanent mould casting". However, if the molten metal is forced into a metallic die under external pressure, the process is known as "Pressure die casting" or simply "Die casting". So, Pressure die casting can be defined as a process by which a casting is made by injecting molten metal under high pressure into a permanent (metallic) mould, called a die.

Pressure die casting is a widely used process—it is difficult to name a product or appliance where die castings are not used for at least some of the component parts. In every industry there is a steadily rising demand for high quality die castings. Pressure die cast parts are used in Automobile,

Auto ancilliary, Electrical equipments, Electrical motors. Business machines, Telecommunication equipments, Building hardwares, Toys and Home appliances and so on. The main reasons for the wide spread use of pressure die casting as a production process are listed below:–

1. Dimensional tolerances can be held to remarkably close limits which reduces or sometimes completely eliminates subsequent machining operations. For small castings, the tolerance range can be ±0.03 to 0.25 mm. Closest tolerances are obtained, when Zinc alloys are die Cast.

2. Surfaces are smooth and clean and require a minimum of preparation for chrome plating. anodising, painting or other finishes.

3. A casting with walls of varying thickness can be produced.

4. Intricate castings (with thin walls) with high tensile strength can be obtained, resulting in reduced raw material input. They are superior to stampings in this regard.

5. The production rate is rapid which lowers the conversion cost.

6. Cored holes down to 0.75 mm diameter at accurate locations are possible.

7. Inserts of any metal can be successfully embedded into a die casting, which largely eliminates secondary operations such as drilling and certain types of threading.

8. Die casting dies retain their usefulness and accuracy over a very long time of production.

9. The sprue, runners and gates can be remelted, resulting in low scrap loss.

The metals most widely used for die casting are non-ferrous and include: Lead, Tin, Zinc alloys, Aluminium alloys, Magnesium alloys and copper base alloys (Brass). Because of its many desirable properties (high dimensional accuracy, high castability and long die life), Zinc accounts for over $\frac{2}{3}$rd of all die castings. Because of its light weight, the use of Aluminium as a die casting material is increasing. Magnesium die castings have superior vibration absorbing properties. Other main characteristics of Magnesium are :— lightness $\left(\frac{2}{3} \text{ weight of Aluminium}\right)$, excellent machineability, dimensional stability, shorter solidification time, less lubrication problems and little tendency to solder to the die. Although, Brass has high strength and resistance to corrosion, the high melting temperature has a serious effect in reducing the die life.

3.9.1.1. Product Applications

1. **Household Equipment:** Decorative parts and mechanical parts for mixers, fans, dishwashers, vacuum cleaners, washing machines, refrigerators, meat slicers, can openers and stoves.

2. **Business Equipment:** Components for offset duplicating machines, pencil sharpeners, staplers, typewriters, data processing machines and so on.

3. **Hard ware:** Cabinet handles, knobs, catches, latches, bathroom fixtures, electrical fixtures; Taps, valves, fittings, burners (of brass) etc.

4. **Industrial Equipment:** Motor housings, parts for hoisting equipment, motors, switches, rotor fan, Impeller wheel (Pump industry), electrical terminal sockets and so on.

5. **Automotive:** Windshield frames, window channels, bodies of fuel pumps and carburettor (of Zinc), instrument panel housings, handles, rear view mirror parts, switch housings, stearing wheel hubs, brake shoe (Al), clutch housing (Al), handle bar top, crank case cover etc.

6. **Music and Communications:** Components for micro phones, fire alarm systems, Telephones, Television sets, speakers, drums, clarinets, record players and so on.

7. **Toys:** Pistols, electric trains, model aircraft, automobiles, game equipment and so on.

3.9.1.2. Limitations of Die Castings

1. Only small parts can be made. The maximum practical weight for a die casting is about 200 newton for zinc, 100 newton for Aluminium and 80 newton for Magnesium. The minimum weight can be as low as 0.05 newtons.

2. Only non-ferrous metals and alloys can be commercially cast. For ferrous metals (C.I. and steel), the chief drawback to their use is the lack of suitable and strong die materials for withstanding the high pouring temperatures.

3. Because of the high cost of equipment and dies, the process is economical only for mass production where the number of parts produced is 1000 or more. The dies will retain their size and shape over long periods of production during which many thousands of identical castings have been made. In general, the dies are heat treated and water cooled when in operation. The die life can be:

> 600,000 pieces of zinc
>
> 150,000 to 200,000 pieces for Aluminium or Magnesium,

and   40,000 to 50,000 pieces for Brass.

4. Because of some entrapped air (due to intensive stirring of metal with air under a rapid filling of the die), the die castings are usually porous, resulting in reduced mechanical properties. However, this drawback can be overcome by some methods discussed later.

3.9.1.3. Die-Casting Machines

A die-casting machine consists of four main parts:—

1. The frame
2. The die
3. The mechanism for opening and closing the dies.
4. Apparatus for injecting the molten metal into the die, along with source of molten metal.

The frame must be rigid and strong to support the weight of the dies, since often the weight of an assembled die may exceed several tonnes. The machine frame incorporates a stationary platen and a movable platen to which the die halves are attached (Die is made in 2 halves to facilitate removal of the casting). Die casting machine frames generally are four bar *presses*, although the solid one piece frame has gained wide acceptance for small machines.

The basic function of a casting machine is to open and close the die and to hold the two die halves together against the pressure of the molten metal developed by the injection system. The locking force must ensure leak proof clamping at the die parting. In some modern die-casting machines, locking forces may approach 10 MN, depending on the die size and the molten-metal pressure employed. The maximum force tending to open a die will be equal to the maximum molten metal pressure times the total projected area of the mould cavity and gating.

The opening and closing mechanism, which actuates the movable platen can be — Pneumatic, Hydraulic, Mechanical or a combination of these. In straight hydraulic method, live pressure backs up the die at all times, when it is closed. The most common method is the combination of hydraulic with mechanical system, where compound toggles are used with the force supplied by the hydraulic cylinder. Such machines have a fixed stroke, beyond which there is no force. In a toggle system, the full locking force is generated only when the toggle system is fully extended. Hence to accommodate dies of various thicknesses, the locking system is capable of sliding along the machine base. The die opening stroke is therefore independent of the die thickness. Fig. 3.47 shows the important features of such a system, (minus the molten metal injection system). The die is closed when the piston in the hydraulic cylinder moves to the right. This causes the toggle links to be straightened so that they close the die with great force. Due to the inherent kinematic properties of the toggle system, the movable platen moves slow in the beginning of the stroke, moves fast subsequently and finally slows down towards the end of the stroke. This serves as a built-in safety even if no other safety is provided. Double toggle system ensures parallel motion of all parts of the die throughout the stroke even with heavy dies.

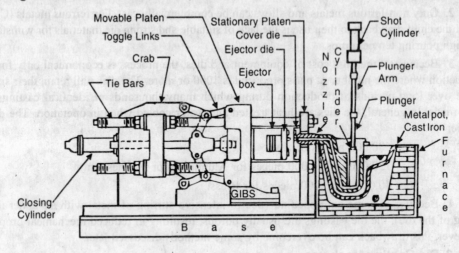

Fig. 3.47. A Die-Casting Machine.

The toggle system is self-locking and will not snap back even if there is a power failure. The system is, flexible and the closing speed can be infinitely variable and the locking force can be adjusted to suit the requirements by adjusting the toggle nuts. The other closing systems can be : wedge-lock hydraulic, cam lock hydraulic. Die casting machines are normally rated by the magnitude of the clamping force. Another method specifies the shot-weight capacity of the *injection* system. Machine capacities range from 50 kN to 25 MN.

The steps involved in the production of a die-casting are :—

1. Closing and locking the two halves of the die.
2. Forcing the molten metal into the die cavity under pressure.
3. Maintaining the pressure for a short time, and permitting the metal to solidify.
4. Opening the die halves.
5. Ejecting the casting with its assembly of sprue, runners and gates, by pins, and the above cycle is repeated.

After the casting has been ejected, the parting lines and gates are removed by trimming the excess metal from them. The casting is then ready for the finishing operations.

To obtain uniformity of die castings and maximum speed of operation, a predetermined and automatically controlled time cycle must be employed. A machine cycle is started by pushing a button and from then onwards the cycle continues automatically, stopping at the end of one complete cycle.

3.9.1.4. Molten Metal Injection Systems. Die-casting machines can either be hot chamber machines or cold chamber machines. In hot chamber machines, the metal pot and furnace are an integral part of the machine. The injection ram (plunger) and cylinder are submerged in molten metal. In cold chamber system, the molten metal is contained in a separate holding furnace. It is ladled into the cold chamber or shot sleeve and then forced into the die by a ram or plunger.

In hot chamber machine, the melting pot is usually made of steel. So, this method is not suitable for casting high melting point metals and alloys such as Aluminium, Magnesium and Copper-base alloys, to avoid wear and erosion of the melting pot, injection ram and cylinder. Molten aluminium readily reacts or alloys with the solid steel. Thus, it takes in iron from any steel with which it comes in contact. So, hot chamber system is used for casting Zinc, Lead, Tin and low melting point alloys. Cold chamber method is used for higher melting point non-ferrous metals and alloys such as Aluminium, Magnesium and Copper-base alloys. Since molten aluminium contact with the cold chamber and plunger is only momentary, pick up of iron by aluminium is held to a minimum. The lower melting point alloys (Zinc, Lead, Tin etc.) can be cast in cold chamber machines, but they are more economically cast in the faster operating hot chamber machines. Cold chamber system is slower than the hot chamber system, since hand ladling is used. However, hand ladling can be eliminated by employing electromagnetic pumping to bring the correct amount of metal into the cold chamber. With this, the production rate of a cold chamber machine can be increased by 25 per cent. Also, better castings are obtained since cleaner metal is pumped from below the surface of the metal in the furnace.

The metal injection pressure in hot chamber system is generally below 14 N/mm^2, whereas in cold chamber system, it may range from 35 to 175 N/mm^2 depending upon the size and type of castings to be made. However in some hot chamber machines, the injection pressure may be upto 40 MPa, that is, 40 N/mm^2.

Note. Aluminium alloys can be cast with hot chamber system by using ceramic pumps, but there are still some problems with the durability of the pumps.

Small to medium size castings can be made at a cycle rate of 100 to 800 (even upto 1000) die fillings or shots per hour.

3.9.1.5. Hot Chambers Machines. There are two designs of such machines:

(i) Submerged Plunger Machine

(ii) Air-blown system (employing "gooseneck" machine).

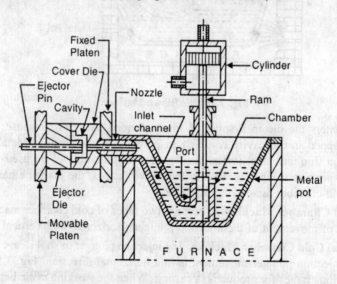

Fig. 3.48. Submerged Plunger Machine.

1. Submerged Plunger Machine. Fig. 3.48 shows the submerged-plunger type hot chamber machine. The ram or plunger is submerged below the surface of the molten metal, and operates with in a cylinder. The working medium can be pneumatic or hydraulic. The casting cycle consists of the steps already explained. The dies are locked together. When the ram is raised, it uncovers a part in the chamber wall, through which molten metal enters and fills the chamber. In operation, the plunger is forced downward closing the port, and then forcing the confined metal up through an inlet channel and nozzle into the die cavity. After a present time interval, the ram (plunger) is again raised, allowing the molten metal in the channel and nozzle to drop pack into the metal pot. Then, the die is opened and the solidified casting is ejected by ejector pins. Metal injection speeds and pressures can be controlled to suit different metals and castings.

    2. Air-blown Machine:— In this machine, also known as the "direct air-injection machine", there is a closed pot or chamber often called a "gooseneck", Fig. 3.49. This container is supported above a larger metal pot from which the container is filled by dipping below the metal level (by lowering the container with the help of operating links). The container is then raised above and its nozzle is locked against the die. Air under pressure (usually 2 to 4 MPa) is admitted through a valve and forces metal through the nozzle (spout) into the die. Next, the is closed, air above the metal is released and exhausted, and the gooseneck is lowered to be refilled, breaking away at the end of the sprue where the spout is kept hot by a flame. After the casting formed in the die solidifies, the die is unlocked and opened and the casting is ejected. After, relocking the die, the cycle is repeated.

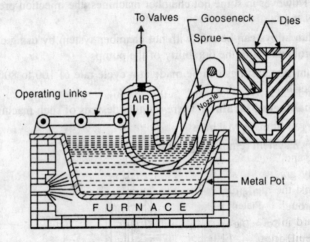

Fig. 3.49. Air Blown Machine.

    The metal enters the die in a spray of finely divided particles. Because of this spraying action, air is entrapped in the cavity resulting in porosity in the casting. Metals which have a dissolving effect on iron and steel (material of gooseneck) should not be used. The machine is rather slow and expensive to operate. Due to the above factors, the machine has been gradually replaced by the cold-chamber die-casting machine.

    3.9.1.6. Cold Chamber Machines. There are two types of cold chamber machines depending upon the direction of movement of the injection plunger: Horizontal and Vertical.

    1. Horizontal Cold Chamber Machine. The injection plunger or shot sleeve is in a horizontal position and the injection plunger movement is in a horizontal direction. Fig. 3.50 shows such a machine in the various stages for producing a casting. When the working cycle begins (Fig. 3.50a), the two die halves are closed with the core being in the working position. The injection plunger is in the extreme right hand position. Melt of a quantity sufficient for one shot is transferred (often mechanically) to the injection cylinder or shot sleeve. The plunger moves to the left and forces the molten metal into the cavity of the die (Fig. 3.50b). After a sufficient time for solidification the die automatically opens and the movable die half (left one) moves away from the fixed die half (the right one)carrying the casting (Fig. 3.50c) with it. The plunger goes on moving to the left and

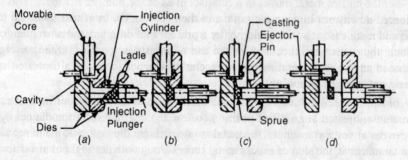

Fig. 3.50. Horizontal Cold Chamber Machine.

pushes out the sprue, connected with the casting, out of the fixed die. The movable core is then removed from the casting by a special device (not shown in the figure (Fig. 3.50d): The movable die stops and ejector pin extends from it to eject the casting. The injection plunger then returns to the right, into its initial position. The working cycle is now over and starts again to produce the next casting. These machines are fully hydraulic and semi-automatic. After the metal is poured, the remaining operations are automatic. Main disadvantages of a cold chamber machine are:—

1. The need for an auxiliary method of feeding metal.

2. Longer cycle time as compared to hot chamber method.

3. The possibility of metal defects due to loss of superheat.

2. Vertical Cold Chamber Machine. In this machine, the injection cylinder (shot sleeve) is in a vertical position and so the injecting plunger moves in a vertical direction. Fig. 3.51 shows a vertical cold chamber machine for producing a casting. At the start of the working cycle, the injecting plunger is up and the molten metal is poured into the chamber from a ladle. The return piston is held up by the spring and shuts the opening of sprue adapter. This prevents the metal from getting into the die cavity by gravity flow, under no external pressure. When descending, the injection plunger presses against the metal and moves the return piston downward, forcing a shot of metal into the die cavity through the sprue channels (Fig. 3.51b). After the holding period, the injection plunger moves upward into its initial position, the return piston actuated by the pusher removes excessive metal (biscuit) from the chamber. The casting is ejected out of the die by ejector pins when the movable die goes to the left (Fig. 3.51c). The advantage of this machine is that in a

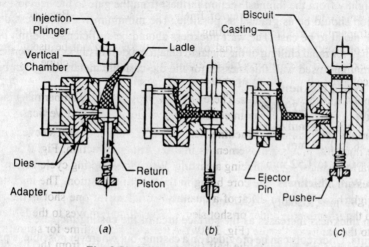

Fig. 3.51. Vertical Cold Chamber Machine.

vertical chamber the molten metal moves in a compact mass as the plunger advances. This minimises metal turbulence and ensures low porosity in the castings produced. In general, vertical machine is restricted to producing castings that could not be made as well on a horizontal machine - notably, parts for which high density is specified, or the use of inserts is required. One drawback of this machine is that in having two operating plungers, one of which also acts as a trimmer (lower one), it requires frequent maintenance work.

It is clear from Figs. 3.50 and Fig. 3.51 that in the case of horizontal cold chamber machine, the molten metal is injected at an offset position (below the centre line of the die cavity) into the die cavity, whereas in vertical machine, the metal is injected into the centre of the die cavity. Again, in the horizontal machine, the slug of excess metal comes along with casting, but in vertical machine it is rejected at the chamber.

Horizontal Chamber Machine Vs Vertical Machine

Machines with horizontal cold chambers have some advantages as compared to the vertical chamber machines in the following respects:—

1. Shorter working cycle since there is no need to remove excess metal, the latter is pushed out along with the casting when the die opens. So, production rate on horizontal machines is higher compared to vertical machines.

2. Short travel of the metal from the chamber into the die cavity with no turn at right angle, resulting in less pressure drop and velocity drop in horizontal machines than in vertical machines. This allows the metal to fill up the die cavity under higher pressure resulting in better overall strength of the castings.

3. More complex articles can be cast in horizontal machines.

4. Metal consumption per shot is lesser in horizontal machines.

Offset Injection Vs. Central Injection. The die design in the case of offset injection (as in hot chamber system and horizontal cold chamber machine) is simpler and therefore, manufacture and maintenance of dies are easier and less time consuming. However, there are certain parts that can best be made with centre gating (vertical machine), that is, parts having thick centre hubs and thin outer sections, for example, wheels and blower impellers etc.

3.9.1.7. Die Casting Design. Some of the factors to be kept in mind while designing a casting to be made by casting method are discussed below:—

1. Minimum Wall Thickness. Keep wall thickness of the casting as uniform as possible or one that tapers slightly from the thinnest section farthest from the gate to the heaviest section at the gate. The transition should be as gradual as possible. The minimum wall thickness depends upon the fluidity of the metal to be cast. The wall thickness should be sufficient to permit proper filling but sufficiently small for rapid chilling of the metal to obtain maximum physical properties (maximum density). The commonly used wall thicknesses for the die-castable metals are given below:

Minimum Wall Thickness

(a) Cu, Mg = 1.27 to 2.29 mm

(b) Al = 0.76 to 2.03 mm

(c) Zn = 0.38 to 1.29 mm

(d) Pb, Sn = 0.76 to 1.52 mm

Maximum Wall Thickness

Preferably 7.93 mm, Usually < 12.7 mm

The section thickness increases as the surface area of the casting increases.

2. Undercuts. Undercuts can be provided on a casting, but wherever possible, a part should be redesigned to eliminate undercuts, since these result in large added cost and reduced production rate.

3. **Ribs.** Ribs may be employed to increase strength and stiffness of the casting. These reduce the weight of the casting and makes for better distribution of metal within the die.

Height of ribs $\not> 5 \times$ wall thickness

Draft and fillets should be ample to obtains a smooth transition into the thinner section.

4. **Inserts.** Inserts such as bearings, wear plates, bushings, shafts and screws can be incorporated in die castings. They must be easily and precisely located in the die. The surrounding material must shrink on to the insert so that it does not come loose. Inserts, however, result in reduced production rate.

5. **Cored Holes.** Holes vertical to the die parting line can be readily cast with stationary core pins. Holes in planes not perpendicular to the die parting plane require special core pulls. The cored holes may be round or of any other desired shape. The following data may be used for cored holes:—

(a) *For Al and Mg:*

Minimum: 3mm diameter × 5 mm deep, advancing proportionately to: 3 diameter deep at 6 mm diameter and above.

(b) *Zn:*

Minimum: 1.5 mm diameter × 2.5 mm deep, increasing proportionately to: 6 diameter deep at 6 mm diameter and above.

6. **Corner radii and fillets.** Avoid sharp corners in all castings. Corners must be given proper radii. Die casting permits the smallest corner radii as compared with other casting processes, because the metal is injected into the die under high pressure. For low melting point alloys,

$$\text{Fillet radius} = \frac{1}{2} \times \text{wall thickness}$$

To avoid an undesirable concentration of metal at a corner, the fillet radius should not be greater than wall thickness.

7. **Draft.** The amount and location of draft on a casting will depend upon its location in the die and whether it is an external surface or a cored hole. Draft on the die surfaces normal to the parting line permits the casting to be ejected without excessive wear on the die cavity. Draft allowance may be taken as follows:—

(a) On Al and Mg: 1 in 100

(b) On Zn: 1 in 200

(c) On Cu alloys: 1 in 80

Taper in cored holes:—

(a) For Al and Mg: 1°upto 10 mm diameter increasing to 2° on diameters over 25 mm.

(b) For Zn: Half the above values

8. **Other characteristics:**

   (a) *Dimensional Tolerance:—*

   0.025 to 0.178 mm upto first 25 mm size.

   and 0.025 to 0.050 mm for additional 25 mm size.

   (b) *Machine finish allowance:—* 0.79 to 0.40 mm

   (c) *Surface Roughness:—* 1.02 to 2.54 µm

   (d) *Overall size:—*

      Maximum:—

          Zn = 34 kg,   Al = 45kg,   Mg = 20 kg

          Cu = 2.3 kg,   Sn = 4.5 kg,   Pb = 6.8 kg

      Minimum:— < 0.028 kg.

      (*e*) *Optimum Lot Size:*— *1000 to 100,000.*

      (*f*) *Cost:*—

          (*i*) Tooling Cost: High

          (*ii*) Direct labour cost, finishing cost, Scrap loss: Low

3.9.1.8. Design of Die-Casting Dies

    Types of Die-Casting Dies. Depending upon the number of cavities in the die and their function, the die-casting dies are of the following types:—

    1. Single-cavity Dies. These dies contain only one die cavity and produce only one casting at a time. Such dies are used for large or complex castings.

    2. Multiple-cavity Dies. If the quantity of castings to be produced is large and they are relatively small in size, a multiple-cavity die can be used. In such a die all the cavities are identical.

    3. Combination Die. It is again a multiple-cavity die but the cavities are not alike. Such dies are often used to produce several parts of the same assembly. They are frequently made of insert blocks that can be removed so that other die blocks can be substituted.

    4. Unit Dies. Results achieved by multi-cavity and combination dies are sometimes also achieved by using a group of unit dies. Unit dies are separate small dies having usually one or more cavities, that are inserted in a common master holding die, and are connected by runners to a common opening or sprue hole, so that all dies in the group are filled simultaneously. When this is done, units can be arranged in various combinations and different unit dies may be interchanged in the master die. This results in the production of a variety of castings with one master die. Unit dies are commonly low in cost and often are employed with high economy.

    3.9.1.9. Die-Design. When designing a new die, the aim must be a simplest possible die design. A die casting die must be designed to facilitate ease of ejection of the casting from the die, readily. For this, the dies are nearly always made in at least two halves (as already discussed). Fig 3.52 shows the elements (sectional view) of a typical die-casting die. The ejector die is attached to the movable platen and the cover die is attached to the fixed platen of the machine. Between the ejector die and the movable platen is a box (usually of C.I), having a recess for an ejector plate and often a core plate and means for moving them relative to the box and to the ejector die. The following factors must be kept in mind while designing a die:

    (1) The joint between the two die halves is called the "parting line" and is commonly in a plane normal to the direction in which the ejector half of the die moves. When planning a new die, it is important to decide where the parting is to be located and how the die cavity or cavities are to be arranged with respect to the parting plane. A flat parting in a single plane is highly desirable. However, often an irregular parting will be required to permit removal of the casting from the die. The location of the parting line must ensure that on opening of the die, the casting will pull away from the cover die and remain in the ejector half. When a casting does not have interior contours, then, in general most if not all, of the die cavity is in the ejector portion die, any remainder being in the cover half.

    However, when shapes having interior contours are to be cast, as much of the cavity as possible is located in the cover die half. Castings shrink away from the die walls and onto the protruding ejector half and core pins which form the interior surfaces of the casting. Thus, when the die is opened, the casting will be in the ejector half of the die, from which it can be ejected with the help of ejector pins carried in the ejector plate. The number of ejector pins must be sufficient to prevent the hot casting from distorting. As the die is opened, the ends of ejector pins move outward together. This pushes the die casting with its gating from the ejector die surface without distortion. The location of the pins in the ejector plate should be such that their contact marks with the casting will not be detrimental to the appearance of the casting. When the casting is removed and the die is closed for the next cycle, surface pins (safety or return pins) attached to the ejector plate return this plate to its casting position, thus withdrawing the ejector pins from the cavity.

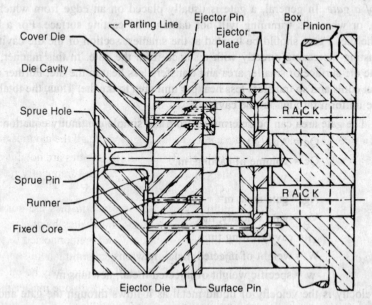

Fig. 3.52. Section Through a Typical Die-Casting Die.

The two halves of the die are equipped with heavy dowel or guide pins to maintain the two halves in proper alignment.

The side walls of the die, as well as the core pins, are given a slight taper or draft so that the casting will come free of them readily. Some machines have the ejection mechanism as an integral part of the machine, that is, with integral rack—and pinion ejection (Fig. 3.51).

(2) Sprues, Runners and Gates

A sprue is a passage in the cover die through which the molten metal enters the die assembly to fill the die cavity. It is aligned with the injector nozzle of a hot chamber machine or with the shot chamber of a cold chamber machine. A sprue is joined by passages called runners, to the gates where the runners admit molten metal to the cavity or cavities.

Sprue holes are tapered, the small end being outward where the sprue breaks off when the die is opened. Opposite the sprue holes, a sprue pin, which acts as a core to make the sprue hollow and deflects the metal entering the die into runners, is provided. The hollow sprue also decreases the metal to be remelted.

Gating System. Gates are narrow passages that join runners to the die cavity. A gating system should be designed to provide the required fill rate and a minimum amount of gas inclusions in the casting. The design of a gating system is predicated upon the experience of the designer and the performing of dies successful in the production of similar parts, because there are many conflicting conditions to be satisfied. For example, the gates should be thin to facilitate trimming and cleaning. On the other hand, gates should be large enough so that metal will enter the die cavity as a smooth solid stream, rather than being sprayed into the die cavity. In gating and venting design, two conflicting requirements for cavity filling must be combined in a reasonable compromise. These requirements are:—

1. Cavity fill should be as slow as possible, for optimum venting.

2. Cavity fill must be fast enough to be completed before the compression phase of the machine cycle sets in and before solidification of metal can take place in the most remote and thinnest section of a given casting.

Locating of a gate. In general, a gate is usually placed on an edge from which it can be cleanly trimmed, or where its trimming will not damage the casting surface. For a better heat balance within the die, a gate should be located at the smallest section of the die cavity with the surface of the casting increasing directly with distance from the gate. In this manner, the hotter metal contacts the die surface of smaller area and transfers less heat to the die. Further away from the gate, the metal cools and so transfers less heat per unit area to the die. Thus, the total heat input to the die is more uniform throughout the cavity.

Gate Area. The gate area can be determined from the simple continuity equation:—

$$Qc = Ag.Vg.t$$

where
Qc = volume of casting, m^3

$= W/w$

Ag = gate area, m^2

Vg = gate velocity, m/s

t = cavity fitting time, s

W = weight of injected metal, newtons

w = specific weight of injected metal, newtons/m^3.

The gate velocity is the velocity of liquid metal as it flows through the gate and it greatly influences the gate design, but it is difficult to establish it. However, experience has shown that metal turbulence can be greatly reduced by increasing the gate area and thereby lowering the gate velocity without changing the fill time. Conversely, decreasing gate area and increasing gate velocity, without changing fill time serves to overcome premature solidification in remote areas of thin-wall castings. The cavity fill time is a part of the total optimum cycle time which is established on the basis of past experience and a trial production run.

The following gate velocities can be taken, which are based on past experience:

(*a*) For Aluminium, Vg = 48 to 33 m/s as the minimum wall thickness varies from 0.762 mm to 6.35 mm.

(*b*) For Zinc, the corresponding values of Vg = 45 to 30 m/s.

Gate Thickness. Selection of gate thickness from a calculated area for a given casting is often governed by the size of the die parting surface available for a required width of gate. The gate thickness may be taken from Table 3.3, which is based on past experience.

Table 3.3 Gate Thickness

Wall Thickness	Gate Thickness, mm	
	Al	Zn
Very thin	0.813	0.711
Thin	1.270	0.864
Medium	1.600	1.372
Thick	2.032	1.676

A single large gate is usually preferable to multiple gates which cause increased turbulence when two metal streams meet. The gate is usually wide, relatively thin and so directed that the metal travels across the longer dimension of the cavity if cores or other features of the geometry do not dictate another arrangement.

Runner Design. To obtain "gate controlled fill" of the die cavity the cross-sectional area of a runner must be larger than that of the gate. However, for minimum heat loss, metal velocity in the runner feeding a gate must be as high as possible. For these reasons, a runner to gate area ratio of 1.15:1 to 1.5:1 is generally used. Runners should have a reasonably smooth surface finish.

Shapes of runner cross sections vary from round to trapezoidal to elliptical, from wide and flat to narrow and thick. A thick runner (of square a round section) will not solidify fast enough for the cycling rates generally used. A thin, flat runner will cause the metal to lose too much heat before it enters the gate. As a compromise, a standard width-to-depth ratio of 1.6:1 to 1.8:1 is generally used. This ration provides for reasonably fast cooling without excessive heat loss during cavity filling.

Runners can be placed in either half of the die and can be carried over slides. In most dies, the runner is machined entirely in the ejector half and the cover half forms only the flat side of the runner, so that it comes free of the die with the casting.

(3) **Vents.** Since the die material is not permeable, vents must be provided which serve as outlets through which air can escape from the die cavity, permitting complete filling by the metal. Air, that is present in the cavity when molten metal enters must be expelled to the largest extent possible to produce sound castings. Vents about 0.125 mm deep, cut in the parting surfaces will help the escape of air. Vents often lead into overflow wells, which are themselves vented. Overflow wells are small cavities cut into the parting surface adjacent to and outside of certain portions of the die cavity. The first metal to pass through a die cavity entraps most air and it carries this air on through the vents into the overflow wells. The vent passages are partly filled by metal that forms flash. This is so thin that the metal freezes almost instantaneously and prevents liquid metal from squirting through the die opening. The flash metal found at the sectional mating surface must be trimmed off in the finishing operations

Venting is also provided by clearance between the die surfaces and movable cores, ejector pins and slides. The total of the cross-sectional areas of vents should be at least 50% of the gate area.

(4) **Cores.** Cores are used to form holes and depressions in the casting. The simplest cores are projections, permanently fastened to either die half. Adequate draft must be provided to permit their withdrawal from the die castings as the die is opened or when the castings are ejected.

Cores used in die-casting dies may be either fixed (stationary) or movable. Economy and the particular application are the guides to the type of core to be used. Cores that extend parallel with the die movement and that, therefore, do not have to be removed before ejection of the casting are called "fixed cores". The ejector pins force the casting from fixed cores as the casting is pushed out of the die cavity. "Movable cores" are used to form holes and cavities which extend in various directions not in the line of die opening. They move in or out along these desired directions. For this, the die is provided with core pulls which can be manual, semi-automatic or automatic. Such cores should be withdrawn before the casting is removed from the die. Movable cores permit the production of complicated die castings, which would otherwise not be possible.

Collapsible Cores may also be used to cast internal threads or other complex internal contours in places inaccessible for both the stationary and movable cores. They are ejected from the die with the casting, then separated from it outside the machine by pulling devices and placed in the die again prior to metal pouring. As is clear, cores are also made of metal (usually alloy steel).

(5) **Slides.** Slides are the movable die parts needed to build up die surfaces. These are used when it is impossible to avoid undercuts in a casting. The part of the die cavity wall that forms the

undercut portion is made on the face of a slide that is accurately fitted in a guide cut in the die block. The slide must be retracted before the casting can be ejected. A separate locking mechanism must be provided for each slide. The use of slides adds considerably to die cost.

(6) **Cooling.** The die casting process is a hot process and there is hot metal in the die cavity during a large portion of each cycle and cycle frequency is rapid. Due to this, heat is dissipated to and retained by dies, especially around the sprue and around heavy cross-sections in the casting. To prevent overheating of a die, and for rapid production, sections of the die are cooled to a controlled temperature by water circulating through passages drilled in these sections. Temperature control is achieved by control of amount of water in circulation.

(7) **Shrinkage allowance.** The shape and size of a die cavity and also of cores must correspond to the dimensions of the part, plus draft or taper to facilitate *ejection*, plus machining allowance and plus an allowance for shrinkage, of the casting metal. For close toleranced parts, allowance must also be made for thermal expansion of die cavity.

The shrinkage allowance normally used are:—

For Zn alloys: 5 mm/m

For Al alloys: 6mm/m

For Mg alloys: 7 mm/m

For Cu alloys: 8 mm to 18 mm/m

3.9.1.10. Die-Materials. Since the die casting is accomplished at elevated temperatures and alternating heating and cooling, the die material is subject to heavy working conditions. The die material should possess the following properties:

1. Sufficiently high melting point to withstand erosion by the hot liquid metal.

2. High enough strength so as not to deform in repeated use.

3. A high thermal fatigue strength to resist premature crazing, that is, the formation of thermal fatigue cracks.

4. Resistance to softening, that is, material should retain hardness at elevated temperature.

5. Low thermal expansion co-efficient.

6. Low adhesion to melt to prevent welding of part to the die.

The performance of die materials is directly related to the injection temperature of the molten alloy, the thermal gradients within the die, the production cycle and the production quantities. The die material may be close grained C.I., although alloy steels are the most widely used. Alloy steels of increasing alloy content are required as the injection temperature of the molten metal and the thermal gradients within the die increases and the production cycle becomes shorter. For casting higher melting point alloys (brasses and ferrous metals), the die steel must contain large proportions of stable carbides so that strength is retained at higher temperatures. Composition of die-casting die-steels is given in Table 3.4.

Table 3.4 Die—casting Die-Steels

Type of Steel	Composition, %							Casting Metal
	C	Cr	Mo	W	V	Co	Ni	
Hot work Tool Steel:								
H11	0.35	5.00	1.50	—	0.50	—	—	Zn
H12	0.35	5.00	1.50	1.50	0.40	—	—	Al
H13	0.35	5.00	1.50	—	1.00	—	—	Al

H19	0.40	4.25	—	4.25	2.00	4.25	—	Cu alloys
H20	0.35	2.00	—	9.00	—	—	—	Cu alloys
H21	0.35	3.50	—	9.00	—	—	—	Cu alloys
Mould Steel P2	0.30	1.70	0.40	—	—	—	—	Zn
Maraging Steel:								
250 grade	—	—	5.00	—	—	8.00	18.00	Cu alloys
300 grade	—	—	5.00	—	—	9.00	18.00	Cu alloys

The die material is heat treated to minimum hardness of 35 Rc for Zinc. It will be higher for Mg, Al and Cu alloys and lower for lead and tin alloys.

Recent work with refractory materials-particularly Mo, W and their alloys-has greatly improved die life for casting copper alloys.

Materials for Cores and Slides :
   (i) For Zn alloys :— H11, H12, H13
   (ii) For Al or Mg alloys : H11, H12, H13
   (iii) Copper alloys :— H20, H21

Materials for Pins :
   (i) For Zn alloys :— H11, H12 nitriding steel, H13
   (ii) For Al or Mg alloys :— H11, H12 nitriding steel, H13
   (iii) For Cu alloys :— H20, H21

Note. Sliding components, except those used with dies for casting copper alloys are nitrided for improved wear resistance.

3.9.1.11. Die-Manufacture. The dies used for die-casting may be either wrought or cast. The cavities in the wrought die blocks are made by the conventional machining methods including die sinkers (special purpose milling machines). The unconventional machining methods such as ECM, EDM, and USM have gained wide applications in making complex dies.

Advantages of Wrought Dies
1. More economical whenever a single cavity or core is required with relatively shallow machining.
2. More economical whenever cavities can be hobbed with simple hobs and where production requirements are low enough to make the hobbing of steels economical.
3. More economical to machine for low production requirements and for dies with simple configurations that can be sunk in low cost steels.
4. Are usually more economical with conventional machining and engraving whenever engraving is to be raised on the casting.
5. They are generally more economical whenever EDM can be used in shallow impressions and whenever EDM electrode configuration is simple and few in number. Whenever, extremely close tolerance is required, this method is superior, especially on prehardened blocks.
6. They are necessary for the production of refractory material dies, which can not be precision cast at present.
7. Have the advantage in applications where cores are long and fragile.

Advantages of Cast Dies

1. Give improved service life.

2. Their production requires no additional costs to form complex die parting line.

3. This method cheaply, rapidly and accurately produces cavities and cores after patterns are made.

4. Casting of dies permits these to cycle at higher speeds, because cores, waterways etc. may be cast directly into the dies.

5. Eliminate difficult metal removal problems when cores are deep and complex.

6. Better and more economical when textures must be die cast or when engravings must be sunk into the die castings.

7. With the use of reversed patterns, casting allows simplified production of many dies which would be difficult to machine.

3.9.1.12. Die Lubrication and Coatings. In all die casting processes, it is essential to apply a die lubricant to the die surfaces in between each shot. Lubrication prevents a casting from adhering to the die and provides the casting with a better finish. The lubricant is usually graphite or MoS_2 in an oily carrier, which is then dispersed in water. Evaporation of water aids cooling.

A coating or dressing is applied to the die and core surfaces to serve as a barrier between the molten metal and the surfaces while a skin of solidified metal is formed. A coating is applied for the following purposes:

1. To protect the die and reduce heat transfer, thereby minimising thermal shock to the die material.

2. To prevent soldering of molten metal to the die, reduce adhesion and facilitate ejection of the casting.

3. To revent premature freezing of the molten metal.

4. To control the rate and direction of solidification of the casting and thus its soundness and structure.

Coatings or dressings are composed of refractory powder in a suspending material. Refractory coatings (graphite, silicone) are sometimes built upto thicker layers for the purpose of reducing temperature fluctuations on the die surface. Coatings are an important element in the system and their uniform application is most important.

3.9.1.13. Preheating of Dies. The die casting dies work as heat exchangers. At the start of the production cycle, the dies must be preheated to the desired temperature. This is done to produce sound castings. The molten metal can fill the thinnest and remotest sections of the casting. Also, it facilitates the application of mould coatings/ lubricant to the die surfaces. During steady state production of castings, heat given off by the molten metal while solidifying, is removed by means of radiating pins or fins or circulating water. The die faces are also cooled by the evaporation of water from lubricants and coatings. The typical temperatures to which the dies must be preheated are:—

(1) For Zn: 150 to 200°C

(2) For Al: 225 to 330°C

(3) For Mg: 250 to 275°C

(4) For Cu alloys:300 to 700°C

3.9.1.14. Vacuum Die Castings. In this method, a vacuum is applied to remove all air from the die cavity before a shot of molten metal is forced into the die cavity. This csompletely removes porosity from the casting. However, application of vacuum is not a suitable substitute for good die practices.

3.9.1.15. Defects in Die Castings

Die-casting defects, basically can be divided into three categories:

1. *Defects due to the cooling of the die :*

   The possible defects under this category are:

   (*a*) Non-filling of die cavities   (*b*) Cold shut

   (*c*) Severe chill   (*d*) Chill

   (*e*) Flow line

2. *Defects due to the heating up of the die or the metal: These defects include :*

   (*a*) Soldering   (*b*) Crack

   (*c*) Bent part   (*d*) Broken parts

3. *Defects due to one or the other reasons :*

   These defects include:

   (*a*) Scaling   (*b*) Blister

   (*c*) Porosity   (*d*) Mechanical defects

Below, we discuss the possible causes and the remedies for these defects:

(*i*) *Non-filling of die-cavities*: The causes are :

— Quantity of metal is less than needed

— Cooling of the die or the metal

— Less period of the metal shot

The remedies to avoid the occurrence of this defect are:

— Required quantity of metal should be used. Do not allow the metal or the die to be cooled, that is, avoid any delay in completing the operation. Heat the metal to the required temperature and do pre-heating of the die if needed.

— Apply the shot with the proper speed

(*ii*) *Cold shut/Mis-run* :

This defect is the same as in sand mould casting. The reasons and remedies are also similar. The reasons are:

— Cooling of die or loss of plasticity of the metal

— Shot speed less

— Air-vent or overflow is closed

The remedies are:

— The metal should be heated to the required temperature. Die should be pre-heated if needed. The thickness of the casting should not be less than the minimum recommended design thickness.

— Shot speed should be proper.

— Air vent should be opened.

(*iii*) *Severe chill :* This defect is similar to the defect of cold shut/mis-run, with the difference that whereas, mis-run/cold shut is a localised phenomenon, severe chill covers a large portion of the casting. The reasons and remedies are the same as mentioned under the cold shut/mis-run defect.

(*iv*) *Flow-Line :* This defect is similar to cold shut/mis-run and chill defects. The causes, thus, are:

— Low temperature of the metal or die

— Excess of die lubricant

The remedies are:

— Keep the optimum temperature of the metal and the die

— Do not use excess of lubricant.

(v) *Soldering :* This defect pertains to the sticking of the cast metal to the die. This results in certain other defects like cracks, porosity etc.

The causes are :

— high temperature of the metal or the die.

— excess of die-lubricant

— roughness of the die surface

— content of iron is less in the metal

The remedies are:

— Keep the temperature of the metal and die, optimum.

— Do not use excess of lubricant.

— Smoothen the die surface

— Use the metal with proper iron content.

(vi) *Broken part* : Sometimes, during ejection of the casting from the die cavity, the total casting does not come out of the die-cavity. Some part of the casting remains sticking with the die.

The causes are :

— Soldering

— Die-lubricant.

The remedies are :

Avoid soldering as discussed under point (v)

Use proper die-lubricant.

(vii) *Heat mark* : Heat mark is a prominant line on the surface of the metal. Sometimes, due to the closure of the air vent or overflow, some gas is entrapped inside the die. Due to this, the size of the heat mark gets increased.

The causes of this defect are:

— improper die steel

— improper die cooling

— production done with the cooled die

The remedies are:

—Use proper die steel

— Proper cooling time should be given

— Production should not be done with the cooled die

(viii) *Scaling* : Due to chemical reaction and oxide scale formation, an irregular surface appears on the surface of the die.

The remedies are :

— Use Caustic solution

— Polish the Casting

— only adequate use of lubricant.

3.9.1.16. Recent trends in Die-Castings process:

(1) *Die Casting of Ferrous metals.* Because steel cannot withstand the temperatures of molten

C.I. and steel, it has not been feasible to use die casting method for Ferrous metals. However, advances in the use of W and Mo as die materials has increased interest in the die casting of C.I. and steel. More recently, refractory metal alloys, particularly the precipitation-hardenable molybdenum alloy TZM (0.015% C, 0.5% Ti, 0.08%Zr), have found increasing application. Graphite dies can also be used for steel, but only for relatively simple shapes. These materials have got the following advantages for ferrous die casting:

   (*i*) High melting point

   (*ii*) Low co-efficient of thermal expansion.

   (*iii*) High thermal conductivity. This causes rapid solidification of the castings, in as little as tenths of a second in several cases, resulting in fine grained structure and rapid cycle time. Fine grained steels and C.I. exhibit strength values that approach the properties of forged steel.

   (*iv*) Unusual resistance to thermal fatigue.

Characteristics of Ferrous Die-Castings

   (*a*) Good dimensional accuracy.

   (*b*) Tolerance $= \pm 0.05$ mm across parting line of 19 mm thick casting. Closer tolerances are possible within die cavities.

   (*c*) Wall thickness upto 3.2 mm.

   (*d*) Surface roughness = 0.8 to 1.6 µm Ra.

   (*e*) Draft can be held to a minimum if the casting is removed from the die while it is hot. No draft is necessary in internal die cavities and 3° to 5° draft can be for long diameter, short cores.

   (*f*) Certain refractory dies last as long as 15000 cycles.

 (2) *Reduction of porosity in Casting:*

   (*i*) A recent trend is to keep the injection pressure at medium level, followed by much higher pressure after the casting has startedto solidify. This tends to improve the density and reduce porosity.

   (*ii*) In the method known as "Squeeze Casting" or "Melt forging", also known as "Liquid forging", typical forging dies are used. A pre measured amount of molten metal is poured into a die. When the casting has cooled to the forging temperature, the dies are closed and solidification is completed. This method which is a transition between die casting and conventional hot forging has been discussed in Chapter 4. The method produces a highly refined grain structure and is also used for producing Al alloy parts such as diesel engine pistons reinforced with Al_2O_3 fibres.

 (3) *Use of Robots.* Programmable robots can perform the repetitive tasks involved in die casting, for example, opening and closing the die, removing and quenching the casting, insertion into a trim press and also application of coatings. Some of the newer die casting machines use indexing turrets to move the casting through trimming and minor machining operations.

3.9.1.17. Permanent Mould Castings

As already explained, a permanent mould is the one which can be used repeatedly. In permanent mould casting, also known as "gravity die casting", the molten metal is gravity fed to the mould cavity. No external pressure is applied except that obtained from the head of metal in the mould. The discussion on permanent mould casting follows the same pattern as was followed for die casting.

The method is basically used for non-ferrous metals (Al, Mg, Zn, Cu-alloys, Sn, Pb), although smaller C.I. and steel castings can also be made. A permanent mould is made up of at least two parts one of which is stationary and the other movable to facilitate removal of the casting from the mould cavity. The casting machine is basically a bed that supports these two halves of the mould. The two common designs of a mould are:—

1. *Hinged type or Book Mould*. This is the simplest design where the two halves are hinged at one end as pages in a book, with provision for clamping the two halves together at the other end, Fig 3.53.

2. *Straight line retractable type*. Fig 3.54. It is used more by industry because it can be adapted to automatic or semi-automatic production lines.

The two halves of the mould should be securely clamped together before pouring, in order to resist the fluid pressure of the molten metal and any tendency of the mould to warp out of shape due to heat. Smaller moulds in manually operated machines are usually clamped together by simple hand operated latches, screw clamps and toggle clamps. Large permanent moulds in mechanised machines have pneumatic or hydraulic actuators.

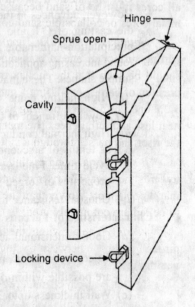

Fig. 3.53. Book Mould.

When the two halves of the mould are clamped together at the parting line, the mould cavity with its necessary gating is formed. The thickness of the mould usually varies from 25 mm to 50 mm. Moulds less than 25 mm thick have a comparatively short life because of their susceptibility to cracking and warping. Moulds that are too heavy require too much time to bring to temperature and are awkward to handle. Interior mould thickness can be 3.2 mm for Al and 4 mm for Mg. The mould

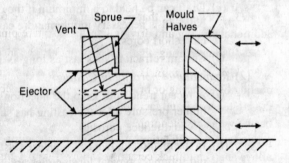

Fig. 3.54. Straight Line Retractable Type Mould.

thickness is larger, opposite thicker sections of the casting. This helps in removing greater amounts of heat from the castings and achieving a uniform temperature for the mould cavity surfaces and the desired chilling effect. Cooling fins and other projections may be placed on the outside of a permanent mould where faster cooling is desired.

Mould Material. The same factors influence the selection of material for a permanent mould as for the die-casting die (See Art. 3.9.1.10). The mould material is selected on the basis of: *material cost, expected number of pours required and the casting alloy. The mould material may be: dense, fine grained, heat resistant C.I., alloy steels, graphite or other suitable refractories (See Art. 3.9.1.10).*

Cores. Both metal and dry sand cores can be used. Metal cores (usually made of alloy steel) are used when they can be extracted conveniently from the casting. A metal core should be extracted as soon as possible after solidification of castings, otherwise a casting will shrink around a metal core making its extraction difficult.

If metal cores cannot be withdrawn easily from the casting, then dry sand cores are used and the process is called "Semi-permanent mould casting". These cores are located and supported in core prints. For better surface finish, gypsum cores may be used. For C.I. permanent mould casting, all cores must be of sand because of the higher temperatures involved. In conjunction with split metal cores or collapsible sand cores, the process is very versatile.

Gating, Risering and Venting. The sprue, risers, runners, gates and vents are cut into the parting surface of one or both mould halves. Most moulds are bottom poured. The gating design should be such that the molten metal can enter at the bottom by gravity without turbulence or creation of hard spots. Using a gating ratio (sprue base area: total runner area: total ingate area) of 1:2:2 or 1:2:1.5 with a pouring basin, conical sprue and sprue base, will give faster flow with least heat loss and turbulence. The metal flows from the sprue base well along the runner bottom, feeds the riser and passes through a slot gate into the mould cavity.

Risers. For a sound casting, there must be directional solidification from thin remote sections towards the riser. The riser is last fed with hot metal and has low surface area to volume ratio so that it cools more slowly than the casting. Blind risers, located about 6.35 mm above the sections to be fed are commonly used.

Venting. The air within the mould cavity should escape as fast as the metal enters the mould, through the space between parting surfaces. This natural venting is usually inadequate. Additional venting may be achieved by :

1. Cutting vent channels about 0.13 mm deep into a parting surface.

2. Drilling small cluster of holes 0.20 to 0.25 mm diameter in the mould wall at the location where venting is needed.

3. Pin venting, that is, drilling one or more 6.35 mm diameter holes into the area requiring additional venting and driving into them square pins 6.35 mm across the corners.

4. Plug venting, that is, drilling holes and inserting slotted plugs.

Mould Coatings. Before operation, the surfaces of cavity, gate and riser are given a suitable coating by spraying or brushing. The coating protects the surfaces from heat and erosive action of the molten metal and facilitates casting removal. This is applied after the mould surfaces have been heated with suitable torches. The insulating effect of the coating may be used to help obtain proper progressive solidification. A lubricant type coating is used for Al and Mg alloys and for Cu-based alloys and C.I. a thick ceramic coating of upto 1-mm is used. The common coating for Al and Mg alloys consists of French chalk (Calcium oxide) suspended in water glass (sodium silicate). The coatings are usually given once each shift. Also read Art. 3.9.1.12

3.9.1.18. Permanent Mould Operation. The casting cycle consists of the following steps:

1. Preheating the mould surfaces (after setting the cores if needed) only initially before operation. The moulds are then main- tained at a fairly uniform temperature-usually by controlling the casting rate-to avoid rapid chilling of the casting.

2. Applying the coating on all the mould surfaces etc.

3. Closing and locking the two halves of the mould.

4. Pouring the molten metal into the mould cavity.

5. Allowing the casting to cool and solidify.

6. Ejecting the casting. Considerable force is required to eject castings from moulds properly. Hydraulic and air operated mechanisms (ejector pins) are helpful. Manual devices use race and pinion.

7. Blowing out the hot moulds.

3.9.1.19. Advantages and Limitations

Advantages

1. Good grain structure. In some cases, mechanical properties can be improved by heat treatment

2. Good surface finish and better appearance.

Surface roughness = 2.54 to 6.35 μm.

3. High dimensional accuracy. Usual tolerances are: 0.015 mm/mm for first 25 mm. Add 0.025 to 0.050 mm for each additional 25 mm. May be cut to 0.25 mm total.

4. Repeated use of moulds (upto 25000).

5. Rapid production rate. Usually 15 to 30 mould castings can be poured per mould each hour.

6. Low Scrap loss.

7. Low porosity.

8. Lesser floor space is required.

9. Smaller-cored holes (4.76 to 6.35 mm diameter, minimum) can be obtained with metal cores.

10. Inserts (metal pieces) can be readily cast in place.

Limitations:

1. High initial cost of moulds and equipment and the cost of mould maintenance. So economically used for large lot production only:

3000 to 10,000 castings for C.I.

10,000 to 25,000 castings for Al.

2. Shape size and intricacy limitations.

Overall size:

Maximum = 0.5 to 225 kg

45 kg common in Al.

Minimum = several 0.1 kg

Section Thickness:

Maximum = 50.00 mm

Minimum = 4.76 mm for C.I.

2.38 to 3.18 mm for Al

3.96 mm for Mg

2.38 to 7.94 mm for Cu.

3. Mainly used for low melting point non-ferrous alloys. High melting metals such as steel unsuitable.

3.9.1.20. Product Application

Automotive aluminium alloy pistons using multiple movable cores, and cylinder heads, aircraft and missile castings, pump bodies, cooking utensils, refrigerator compressor cylinder blocks, heads and connecting rod, flat iron sole plates, kitchenware, and typewriter parts of aluminium, washing machine gear blanks of C.I.

3.9.1.21. Casting Design. The design of permanent mould castings follows the main general rules which apply to sand castings (see Art. 3.8) and die-castings (Art. 3.9.1.7), regarding uniform wall thickness, minimum wall thickness, minimum cored hole diameter, tolerances etc. (discussed in the last article). Other factors are discussed below:—

1. *Fillet radii:* To avoid sharp corners,

   Inner fillet radius = Average wall thickness

   Outer fillet radius = 3 × Average wall thickness

2. *Draft:*

   On cavity: Minimum 2° on each side.

   Usual range = 2° to 3°.

   In recesses = 5°, desirable

On metal cores = minimum 3°, preferably 5°, to facilitate their removal.

3. *Machine finish allowance:*

   = 0.79 mm for parts upto 100 mm

   = 1.58 mm for parts > 100 mm.

4. *Bosses: yes, with small added cost.*

5. *Undercuts:* yes, large added costs, reduced production rate. Undercuts can be made in a casting by using a core made in two or more pieces. To remove such a core, the key piece should be pulled first. This enables the other pieces to be moved laterally, clear of undercuts, so they can be extracted. Such cores are expensive and it slows down the casting cycle, but there is saving in both metal and machining costs.

6. *Inserts:* yes, no difficulty.

3.9.1.22. Production of Permanent Moulds. As discussed in Art. 3.9.1.11, permanent moulds can either be machined or cast. Production by machining involves high cost of machining. In casting, the mould is cast to size, then the cavities are polished and mating surface machined. If casting tolerances are critical, this practice can't be followed and the entire mould must be machined to size.

3.9.1.23. Turntable Moulding Machine. This is a large quantity production machine. It consists of a turntable which revolves constantly from 2 to 7 rev/min. Upon the turn table, a suitable number of permanent moulds are mounted. They can produce same castings or similar castings with equal cycle time. The cycle time may be varied by varying the rotational speed of the turnable. Usually, the centre of the turntable has a cooling station that blows cool air over the moulds. As the turntable rotates, the moulds automatically open and close at predetermined work stations. One operator is required for pouring and another for removing the castings. Another worker will be needed if sand cores are to be set in the mould. If a 12 station turntable rotates one complete revolution in 3 minutes, then a mould is poured every 15 s.

3.9.1.24. Variants of Permanent Mould Casting

1. *Slush Casting, Fig 3.55.* This is a special form of permanent mould casting in which hollow castings are produced without the used of cores. The mould is filled with molten metal and waiting for some time, during which an outer metal shell is sufficiently solidified, the mould is turned over to drain off most of the melt. This leaves behind in the mould a hollow thin walled casting with a good outer surface but very rough inner surface. The method is used mainly to produce non structural, decorative parts such as hollow lamp bases, candle sticks, statuettes,

ornamental objects, toys and other novelties. The parts are then either finished or painted to represent more expensive metals such as silver, bronze etc. The metals used for casting the parts in this method are: Lead, Zinc and other low melting alloys. Die costs are relatively low and that is an advantage for small quantity production.

2. *Low - Pressure Permanent - Mould Casting*. In this method, Fig. 3.56, the permanent mould is mounted directly above the melting or holding furnace. The molten metal is forced by air or inert gas pressure (approximately 1 atm) up a riser tube, into the mould cavity. The Air/gas pressure is released as soon as the cavity is filled with solidified metal. The metal in the riser tube drops back into the sealed crucible. The casting is ejected from the cavity. The cavity is then recoated with a refractory and the process is repeated. Sometimes, a vacuum is created in the mould cavity to ensure a more dense structure and faster filling.

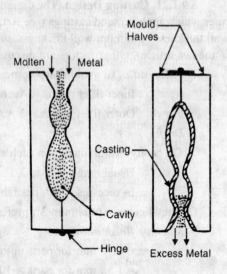

Fig. 3.55. Slush Casting.

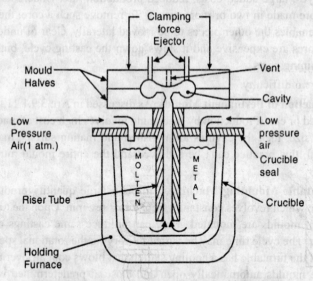

Fig. 3.56. Low Pressure Permanent Mould Casting.

Advantages

1. The riser tube extends close to the bottom of the crucible, so, only clean metal is forced up through the riser tube into the cavity. So, the castings will be free from inclusions and have better surface appearance and dimensional accuracy as compared to the castings made by permanent mould casting process.

2. Castings are more sound and more homogeneous in structure as compared to the castings made by permanent mould casting process, since the solidification is directed from the top downward.

3. The process is easy to automate.

4. Low scrap loss, usually less than 10% and can be as low as 2%.

The process finds wider applications to aluminium alloys and is economically feasible for annual production rates of from 5000 to 50,000. The weight of the casting can be upto 300 newtons.

3.9.2.Centrifugal Casting. Centrifugal casting is the method of producing castings by pouring the molten metal into a rapidly rotating mould. The metal is thrown out towards the mould face by the centrifugal force under considerable pressure. This results in better mould filling and a casting with a denser grain structure, which is virtually free of porosity. The mechanical properties of most metals are improved by 10 to 20%. The method is chiefly used for casting parts having the shape of bodies of revolutions. According to the shape of the mould, the centrifugal casting method can be classified as :

1. True - Centrifugal Casting   2. Semi - Centrifugal Casting

3. Centrifuge Casting.

3.9.2.1. True - Centrifugal Casting. True centrifugal castings are produced by pouring molten metal into the cavity of a rapidly rotating metal mould to whose walls the metal is thrown by centrifugal force and where it solidifies in the form of a hollow casting. Thus the distinguishing feature of true-centrifugal casting is the production of hollow casting by the centrifugal force alone and without the aid of a central core.

The centrifugal casting machines used to spin the mould may have either a horizontal or a vertical axis of rotation. For short castings, that is, when diameter to length ratio is rather large (bronze bushings, worm wheels and piston ring blanks), the rotational axis is vertical. Long parts, that is, castings with relatively long length in relation to their diameters (C.I. water supply and sewerage pipes, steel gun barrels etc.) are made in horizontal axis machines.

The principle of the vertical axis machine is shown in Fig. 3.57 (a). As is clear, the central hole will not be completely cylindrical, but will be slightly paraboloidal, which will need machining after the casting is made. However, nearly cylindrical holes can be made by employing higher spinning speeds. The moulds may be permanent moulds made of metal or graphite or may be sand lined.

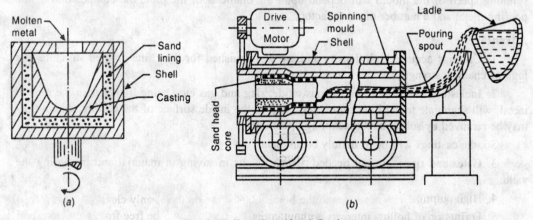

Fig. 3.57. True Centrifugal Casting.

There are two types of horizontal axis centrifugal casting machines which differ in the way the metal is distributed along the length of the mould during pouring : In one, the pouring trough (ladle or spout) travels horizontally, while the spinning mould is stationary. In the other type, the ladle is stationary and the mould travels. The mould or flask is made of steel or graphite. The metal mould can be used as it or its inner surface may be lined with green sand or dry-sand. The choice depends upon the geometrical dimensions of a casting, its material and the production volume.

Metal moulds are preferred for the production of a large number of single-type parts which show no retarded shrinkage and have an outer shape allowing easy extraction of the casting from the mould. Sand-lined moulds are preferred for castings in which retarded shrinkage takes place and the outer surface of these castings causes difficulties in removing them from the moulds. Such moulds are used to advantage for the production of a small lot of cast iron pipes without chilling. These pipes will not require annealing heat treatment, as will be needed for similar pipes made in metal moulds, since the cooling rate will be slow because of sand lining. The sand lining also protects the metal mould from the intense heat of the molten metal and, increases its durability.

The method of casting pipes in which the ladle is stationary and the mould travels is called as "The deLavaud Process". This is explained with the help of the following steps, (see Fig. 3.57 (b)),:

1. The machine consists of an accurately machined metal mould surrounded by water. Dry heat-insulating coats (refractory mould wash of materials such as quartz sand and phosphate flour) are applied to the inner surface of the mould to secure stable thermal conditions, increase its durability and produce iron castings free of chill. The machine is mounted on wheel so that it can be moved lengthwise on a track.

2. The metal mould is heated to 150 – 200°C before pouring. After pouring, the mould is cooled to by circulating water through the surrounding shell.

3. The long pouring spout is inserted to the far extremity of the mould.

4. As pouring proceeds, the rotating mould, that is, the machine is moved slowly on the track, leftwards.

5. At the end of the process, the machine will be at the lower end of its track, with the mould spinning continuously till the pipe has solidified.

6. The cast pipe is then extracted from the mould by inserting a piper puller.

The use of the sand head core is to form the inside contour of the bell end of the pipe. If desired, the outer contour of the casting can be varied, while the inside remains cylindrical. The spinning speed of the mould will depend upon the diameter of the pipe, the composition of the pouring metal and a number of other factors.

Advantages

1. Castings acquire high density and are distinguished for their fine-grained structure and high mechanical strength.

2. Inclusions and impurities such as oxide, slag and gas etc., being lighter than the molten metal, will segregate toward the centre and cling to the inside surface of the casting, where they may be removed by subsequent machining operations.

So, the castings will be of mainly clean metal.

3. Gates and risers are not needed, which results in saving in material and increasing the yield.

4. High output.

5. Formation of hollow interiors without cores.

6. The castings are less subject to directional variations than static castings.

Disadvantages

1. Contaminations of inner surface of the casting with segregates and non-metallic inclusions, which make it necessary to increase finishing allowance for subsequent machining of inner surfaces.

2. An inaccurate diameter of the inner surface of a casting.

3. Not all the alloys can be cast by this method due to the increased segregation of alloy constituents during pouring under centrifugal forces.

Product applications. Parts with rotational symmetry : C.I. water supply and sewerage pipes, steel gun barrels, pump components, rolls, liners, hollow shaftings, bearings, sleeves, hydraulic jack cylinders and air cylinders, large propeller shaft sleeves and stern tubes, chemical reactor vessels, heat exchanger bodies, refinery and. petrochemical applications ; pressure vessel bodies, reactor tubes and pressure piping for nuclear power plants ; paper mill rolls, textile rolls, steel mill rolls and machinery drive rolls and street lamp posts etc.

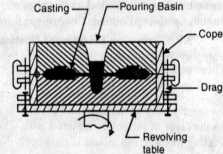

Fig. 3.58. Semi-centrifugal Casting.

3.9.2.2. Semi - centrifugal Casting. When the moulds prepared by any of the techniques under expendable or permanent moulds are rotated about the central vertical axis and the casting is symmetrical about the axis of rotating (that is the axis of the casting coincides with the axis of rotation), the process is called as "Semi-centrifugal casting". The centrifugal force aids the flow of the molten metal from a central feeding sprue and can thereby produce a somewhat more dense structure as compared to conventional sand casting, (Fig. 3.58). Casting shapes can be more complicated than true centrifugal casting. Cores are used if central hole is needed, the spinning speed being considerably less than that for true centrifugal casting. An advantage of the process is that stack moulding can be used to cast many parts at the same time.

Product applications. Disk shaped parts : wheels, rings, rollers, sheaves, pulleys, flywheels, gear blanks, Turbo-Supercharger diaphragm disks and steel railroad wheels etc.

3.9.2.3. Centrifuge Casting. When a group of small moulds are arranged in a circle (to balance each other) around the central vertical axis of the flask and the flask is rotated about the vertical axis, the process is called as "centrifuge casting", [Fig. 3.59]. It is clear that the moulds are not symmetrical about the axis of rotation, that is, the axes of the castings and the axis of rotation do not coincide with one another. Here again, the centrifugal force is used to obtain higher pressure on the metal and get more dense castings. The molten metal will flow to all the moulds under centrifugal force from a central feeding sprue. The process is again adaptable to stack moulding.

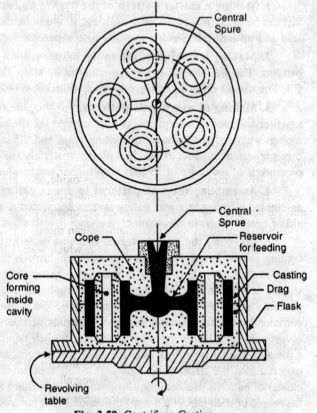

Fig. 3.59. Centrifuge Casting.

Product applications. Products may be irregular or non- symmetrical: valve bodies, plugs, valve bonnets, pillow blocks and yokes etc. Jewelery is centrifugally cast by spinning the investment moulding during pouring. Centrifugal force transfers the metal and ensures good mould filling.

3.9.3. Precision Investment Casting. The two common and widely used methods under this category are :

1. Lost - wax method   2. Shell - moulding method.

These methods are called as "precision" because the castings obtained by these methods have very smooth surfaces and possess high dimensional accuracy. The term "investment" refers to the layer of refractory material with which the pattern is covered to make the mould. Like sand casting method, the mould is destroyed everytime a casting is made.

The difference between lost-wax method and shell moulding method is that in the former, the pattern is made of either wax or a plastic material, whereas in the latter method, it is made of a metal.

3.9.3.1. Lost - wax method. The Lost-wax method, sometimes, also called simply as 'precision-investment casting' has been used for many years by jewelers and dentists. Since world-war-II, the method has been adapted to the production of small and precise industrial castings. Basically, the method involves the use of expendable (heat disposable) pattern surrounded with a shell of refractory material to form the casting mould. Castings are formed by pouring molten metal in the mould cavities created by melting out the pattern. Since the pattern made of wax is melted out and gets destroyed, that is, why the name "lost - wax method".

The steps involved in this method are explained below :

1. Making a master pattern of the part to be cast. The pattern is usually made of a metal that can be easily machined, such as, brass, aluminium alloy or steel, or a fusible alloy (alloy of tin, lead and bismuth). It is made oversize to compensate for wax and metal shrinkage.

2. Making a composite die to the master pattern (by casting) for casting the wax/plastic patterns. The die-material is a low melting-point alloy like bismuth alloys or even aluminium and C.I. The master dies can be directly made from die-blocks of steel by machining the cavities.

3. Making of wax/plastic patterns. For this, the two halves of the master die are clamped together and molten wax/plastic is injected into the die cavity under pressure, (Fig. 3.60 (a)). The molten wax is slightly above its melting point and the injection pressure is about 4 bars with the dies preheated to about 65°C. For plastic materials (polystyrene, polythenes etc.), the injection pressure is of the order of 35 bars with higher temperature.

4. Assembling the wax patterns to a wax gating system. Several small wax patterns are assembled together to a wax gating system connected to a central sprue, by wax welding with the aid of heated tools. In this manner, a cluster or "tree" of wax patterns is formed, (Fig. 3.60(b)).

5. Investing the wax patterns. The wax patterns are invested in two stages. Firstly, a thin coating (about 1 mm) of primary investment slurry is made around the wax patterns by dipping these in the slurry. This slurry is made by mixing extremely fine silica sand with a water/ethyl silicate or gypsum solution. This slurry coating being in direct contact with the surfaces of the wax patterns, will determine the surface quality of the castings. After this primary coating has dried sufficiently, the final investment layer consists of coarser and less expensive slurry. The final investment moulds may be either solid type or shell type. A solid type mould is formed by placing a metal container type flask over the cluster of patterns and then pouring a hard- setting moulding material into the flask, (Fig. 3.60 (c)). Shell type investment moulds are made by dipping the cluster of patterns in a ceramic slurry and the procedure is repeated until the required thickness of the mould or shell (about 6.5 mm) is obtained. The common refractory used for investment material is silica. The binder is gypsum or water-based sodium silicate.

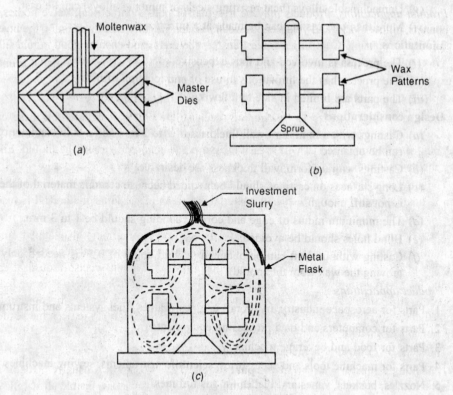

Fig. 3.60. Lost-wax Method.

6. Melting out the wax patterns and baking the mould. The finished mould is dried in air for 2 to 3 hours and then baked in an oven for 2 hours to melt out the wax. At a temperature of 100 to 120°C, the wax melts and the moulds are inverted so that all or most of the wax will run out of the sprue.

7. Melting the metal and pouring the mould. The mould or flask is transferred to a drying furnace where it is first held at 150°C and then gradually heated to 800 to 900°C. This will vaporize any remaining wax in the mould. The preheated mould also ensures that the molten metal will completely fill the mould cavity. The preheated mould is poured with molten metal which fills the cavity and is allowed to cool and solidify. Another way to fill the cavity is to place the mould on a vacuum table and drawing a vacuum through the slurry which will help suck the metal right into the mould or by placing the mould in a centrifugal casting machine and pouring the metal in this manner.

8. Shaking out the castings, removing gates and feeders. After cooling, the fragile mould material is broken away freeing the castings. The gates and runners are removed in the normal way.

9. Cleaning and inspecting the casting

Advantages of Lost - wax method:

    (*i*) Intricate details can be cast.

    (*ii*) Undercuts and other shapes, which would not allow the withdrawal of a normal pattern, are easily obtained.

    (*iii*) The surface is very smooth (1.5 to 2.25 µm Ra) and there is no parting line.

    (*iv*) High accuracy can be obtained (tolerances of the order of ± 0.003 mm/mmcan be obtained) so that much of complicated and costly machining can be eliminated.

(v) Unmachinable alloys (heat resisting steels or nimonic alloys) can be cast.

(vi) More than one casting can be made at a time.

Limitations

(i) The process is involved and thus expensive.

(ii) The process has the limitations in use of and location of holes.

(iii) The parts are limited in size to a few kg.

Design considerations

(a) Castings with a minimum wall thickness of 1 to 2 mm and a hole diameter of 2 mm can be obtained.

(b) Castings with uniform wall thickness are desirable.

(c) Long surfaces on castings should be avoided because ceramic material of the mould is not stiff enough.

(d) The minimum radius of edge and corner rounding should be 1 to 3 mm.

(e) Blind holes should be avoided.

(f) Casting without draft can be obtained (a draft angle of 0.5° is needed only for removing the wax from the mould).

Product applications.

1. Parts for aerospace industry, in aircraft engines, frames, fuel systems and instruments.

2. Parts for computers and data processing equipment.

3. Parts for food and beverage machinery.

4. Parts for machine tools and accessories, scientific instruments, sewing machines.

5. Nozzles, buckets, vanes and blades for gas turbines.

6. Costume jewellery.

7. Rock drill thread chaser holder blocks.

8. Dentures and special metal implants for orthopedic surgery.

9. Parts for movie cameras and projectors.

10. Radar wave guides.

11. Parts such as reciprocating slides for cloth cutting machines.

Precision investment casting is used, when :

1. Forging of the component material is very difficult.

2. Pressure die-castings are too expensive.

3. Non-machinable materials are preferred for the component.

4. Frequent design changes are required.

5. The volume of production is too small to justify much tooling.

6. The machining operations call for expensive tools.

7. The design of the component calls for intricate machining operations.

8. Assembly costs can be eliminated by redesigning and making a single casting.

3.9.3.2. Shell Moulding. The process involves the use of match plate patterns similar to cope and drag patterns which are used for green sand casting. The process is based on the capability of a thermosetting resin and sand mixture to assume the shape of a preheated metal pattern and to form a dense, quickly hardened shell mould. The two matching shell halves (made from cope and drag parts of the pattern) are clamped or glued together to form the mould cavity. Castings are obtained by pouring molten metal into this mould cavity. The shell thickness varies from 5 to 8 mm. As in sand casting process, the mould is expendable and must be broken away to facilitate the removal of the solidified casting.

Shell moulding process involves the following steps.

1. Preparation of the metal match plate cope and drag type patterns. The patterns are machined from copper alloys, C.I., Al or Steel depending upon the life of the pattern. They are given the usual shrinkage and draft allowances, are polished and then attached to the metal match plates.

2. Mix the investment material. The investment material consists of dry, fine and thoroughly washed silica and 5 to 10% of thermosetting phenolic resin (phenol formaldehyde) which acts as a binder. The two are thoroughly mixed together.

3. Heat the pattern. The pattern plate is heated to about 200 to 300°C for investing it. To prevent/minimize the mould adhesion of the investment material and to make the removal of the shell convenient, a release agent containing a silicone is next sprayed over the hot pattern plate surface.

4. Invest the pattern. For this, the investing material is placed in a container called ":dump box" (about one-third full) and the heated pattern plate is clamped to it, with the pattern surface inwards. The dump box is then quickly inverted on its trunnions. The investing material falls over the surface of the heated pattern. The heat penetrates the mixture, softens the binder making it effective. This will result in the formation of a uniform shell around the pattern surface after the binder thermosets. The shell thickness will depend upon the time of contact of the mixture with the heated pattern. In about 30 to 45 s, we can get a normal shell thickness of 5 to 8 mm. The dump box is then rotated back to its normal position. The loose and unaffected investing mixture will fall down, leaving the shell adhering closely to the pattern.

5. Curing the Shell. For this, that is, to cure or harden the shell, the pattern plate is removed from the dump box and transferred to an oven and cured for about 1 to 3 minutes at a temperature of about 250 to 450°C.

6. Remove the Shell. The shell is then stripped from the pattern plate with the help of a number of ejector pins which pass through the plate. When these ejector pins are pressed simultaneously, the tops of these pins at the pattern plate surface, more upward and strip the shell from the pattern plate.

7. Repeat the steps 2 to 6 for the other half of the metal match plate pattern to produce the other half of the shell.

8. Assemble the Shells. The two halves of the cured shells are securely assembled by clamping or bonding them together at the parting line with a quick-acting thermosetting resin adhesive such as phenol-formaldehyde.

9. Pour the Mould. It is done in the same manner as for Lost- wax method, that is static pouring or vacuum pouring or centrifugal pouring.

10. Remove the Casting. After cooling and solidification, the shells are broken or shaken away from the castings in the usual way. The steps are clear in Fig. 3.61.

Advantages

1. A high precision/accuracy of castings with tolerances of ± 0.002 to 0.005 mm/mm, is possible.

2. Smooth surface finish and reduced machining allowances possible. Many shell mould castings require almost no subsequent machining. The common value of surface roughness is in the range of about 3.2 μm Ra.

3. Complex parts can be made by this method, even of difficult to machine metals and alloys.

4. The moulds can be stored until required, because the used resins are not hygroscopic.

5. Less sand is used as compared to sand casting.

6. Permeability of the thin shell moulds is higher compared with other types of moulds, so the gases escape easily through the walls. Also, thin shell does not have as great a chilling effect as a sand mould. Due to the above two factors, a better quality of the casting is assured.

7. The process enables foundary automation to be introduced.

8. Cleaning is considerably reduced and in some cases eliminated.

9. Saving of metal through use of smaller gates, sprues and risers, resulting in increased yield.

Disadvantages:

1. Due to the higher cost of match plate patterns and the cost of binder, the process is economical for mass/batch production.

2. Size of the casting is limited - 10 to 13.5 kg.

3. Serious dust and fume problems during sand and resin mixing.

4. Carbon pick up in the case of steels.

Design considerations:

1. A single parting line should be provided for the mould.

2. Detachable pattern parts and cores should be avoided.

3. The casting walls of uniform thickness are desirable, the minimum wall thickness being 2 to 2.5 mm.

4. Draft angles of no less than 1° and rounding radii of 2.5 to 3 mm should be used.

Product applications. For making cores, small pulleys, motor housing, mixers, fan blades and valve bodies etc. Other parts include : Bomb casings, brake drums and bushings, cams, camshafts, pistons and piston rings, permanent-magnet pole pieces, pinions, impellers, pipe bends, air-compressor crank cases and cylinders, conveyor rollers and so on.

Core - making by Shell Moulding Method. Hollow cores to very close limits are made by this process. Fine sand and upto 6% resin are thoroughly mixed. The halves of the metal core box are heated upto 160°C and are coated with stripping or parting solution and are then assembled. The sand-resin mixture is poured into the heated core-box. The box is then either vibrated or the sand is joggled to fill all the core-box cavities. After about 10 to 20 s, the loose sand is poured out of the box. The assembly is then placed in an oven for curing, for about 20 s.or intricate cores, multiple-piece core boxes can be used. Cores for steel castings have an oil bond and in some cases, Zircon flour, alcohol and other agents are added to the mixture.

Shell moulded cores are used to increase dimensional accuracy of the normal green-sand mouldings for such items as manifolds and cylinder blocks.

3.9.3.3. The Mercast Process. This process is a variant of "Lost-wax method" where mercury is used in place of wax, as the pattern material. The steps are similar. The mercury patterns are made by injecting it into a die and are then frozen (at − 40°C). The frozen mercury patterns are invested and the mercury is then reclaimed by allowing the mould/flask to come to the room temperature so that mercury flows out of the mould cavity. Then the flask undergoes the heating, curing and pouring steps. The use of mercury has the advantage that superior accuracy (surface/dimensional) is obtained as compared to 'Lost- wax process'. Also, mercury changes size little on melting and is not as likely to crack a thin/weak would as is wax or plastic. Again, recovery of mercury is more than that of wax. The co-efficient of expansion of mercury is about $\frac{1}{3}$ of that for wax. So, thinner walls may be used for the shell. Mercury has low creep properties so that mould dimensions are more consistently produced. Frozen mercury has a high state of self- diffusion, so that two surfaces will adhere immediately they contact each other. This is known technically as 'booking' and facilitates the assembly of intricate patterns.

However, initial cost of mercury is high and the vapours of both mercury and acetone (needed for obtaining low temperature) are poisonous and call for special means of extraction.

3.9.3.4. Plaster - Mould Casting. If the sand casting process is changed so that a finer-grained refractory made into a slurry with water is poured around the pattern, the process is called "Slurry moulding." The slurry will flow around all details of the pattern, resulting in improved surface conditions/and dimensional control. In plaster-mould casting, we use a plaster of Paris slurry (Gypsum, $CaSO_4$. $2H_2O$). Talc, silica flour, asbestos fibre and other substances are added to the slurry to control setting time and expansion and to improve strength and permeability. The slurry is poured over a pattern (which has been coated with a thin film of oil) and allowed to harden. The mould is dried to remove water and prevent the formation of steam upon exposure to hot metal.

Since the plaster is not permeable of its own, therefore, for the success of the process, the plaster should be made permeable so that the gases could escape from the mould. The following ways are used for this :

(*i*) Using excess water in the slurry. It helps because it is driven off when the mould is dried and baked and leaves pores.

(*ii*) One variant of the process uses a large proportion of sand with only enough gypsum as a binder.

(*iii*) The plaster slurry is added to an agent that is first beaten to a foam. The mould is dried below 200°C. The walls of the foam bubbles break as the slurry sets.

(*iv*) In the "Shaw process" two slurries that gel when mixed, are used. On heating, the volatile agents in the mass are ignited leaving behind a microcrazed structure in the mould, which is finally dried in the oven.

(*v*) In an other variant, 'Antioch Process', steam pressure treatment is applied to produce intergranular air passages.

Since gypsum is destroyed at 1200°C, it is not suitable for ferrous castings. Metals most commonly used for casting are : Yellow brass, manganese and aluminium bronzes, aluminium, magnesium and their alloys. Typical products made by plaster mould casting are : Aluminium pistons, locks, propellers, aircraft parts, plumbing fixture fittings, ornaments, and tire and plastic moulds. Patterns are mainly made of brass and phenolic resin plastics because of their ability to resist the corrosive effects of plaster.

The rate of cooling of the melt is slow and uniform due to low heat conductivity of plaster. This results in coarse-grain structure of the castings. Due to this, the castings of some metals have lower strength as compared to castings made in sand or metal moulds. However, castings can be made in intricate shapes with varying sections and particularly with extremely thin walls (1.6 to 6.5 mm).

Advantages

(*i*) More accurate and smooth surfaces and more faithful reproduction of details than sand casting.

(*ii*) In some cases, machining and finishing operations are completely eliminated.

(*iii*) Very close tolerances can be obtained : as close as ± 0.003 mm/mm. More common

values are : ± 0.005 mm/mm on one side and ± 0.010 mm/mm across parting lines.

(*iv*) Surface roughness obtainable is : 0.75 to 3 μm Ra.

Disadvantage

(*i*) The process is expensive due to the cost and care of patterns. Also, it takes about 20 to 24 hours for the moulds to dry and bake.

(*ii*) Not suitable for ferrous castings.

3.9.3.5. Ceramic - mould Casting. In this process, the slurry is made up of fine-grained refractory powders of zircon (Zr Si O_4), alumina (Al$_2$ O_3), or fused silica (Si O_2) together with patented bonding agents. The slurry is applied as a thin coating to the pattern and is backed by a less expensive fire clay. The mould is baked at 1000°C and the melt is poured while the mould is still hot. This process is suitable for all materials due to the use of better ingredients for the slurry.

3.9.4. Full - mould Casting. The process "Full-mould casting" also called as "Cavity less casting" or "Evaporative casting" or "disposable pattern casting" is a variant of sand casting in the sense that the process utilizes an expendable pattern, which instead of being removed from the mould gets burnt and evaporated when the molten metal is poured into the mould. The pattern material is expanded polystyrene foam. Very complex parts can be built up by shaping large blocks or sheets of expanded foam, and then runners etc. are attached with rubber cement or hot melt-resins. The process has the advantages : it requires less time, no rapping and draft allowances are required on the pattern since it is not to be taken out of the mould (this results in material saving). Also, there is no need of cores, core boxes and parting lines etc. However, the pattern being delicate, the process is not suitable for machine moulding. Since the pattern gets destroyed in the process, the method is mainly used for product research in foundary industry and for one-of-a-kind complex casting. The method is also known as "Lost Foam" process.

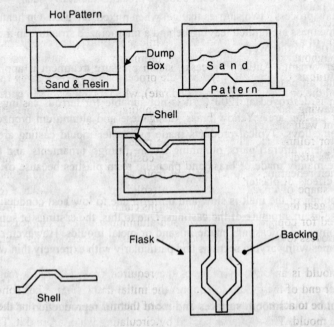

Fig. 3.61. Shell Moulding Process.

Advantages

1. It requires less time, no rapping and draft allowances are required on the pattern since it is not to be taken out of the mould. This results in material saving.

2. It is relatively a simple process because there is no need of cores, core boxes, parting lines or riser systems.

3. The process has design flexibility.

4. The product needs minimum cleaning and finishing operations.

5. Inexpensive moulding flasks are sufficient for the process.

6. Polystyrene is inexpensive and it can be easily fabricated into patterns having very complex shapes and fine surface details.

7. The process can be automated.

8. The process is economical for long production runs. A major factor is the cost of dies needed for expanding polystyrene beads to fabricate the pattern.

Drawbacks

1. The pattern being delicate, the process is not suitable for machine moulding.

2. Since the pattern gets destroyed in the process, the process is mainly used for product research in foundry industry and for one- of-a-kind complex casting.

Product Applications

1. Cylinder heads, crankshafts, brake components, machine bases and manifolds for automobiles.

2. In a variant of lost-wax process and a modification of evaporative-pattern method, the polystyrene pattern is surrounded by a ceramic shell. It is burned out before mould pouring. Its advantage over lost wax process before mould pouring. Its advantage over lost wax process is that carbon pick up into the metal is completely avoided.

3. Recently, polymethy-lmethacrylate (PMMA) and polyalkaline carbonate have been used as the pattern materials for ferrous castings.

4. Production of metal-matrix composites. While moulding polymer pattern, particles or fibres are embedded throughout. These fibres or particles ultimately become an integral part of the product.

3.9.5. Continuous Casting. In essential, the process consists of pouring molten metal into a short vertical metal die or mould (at a controlled rate), which is open at both ends, cooling the melt rapidly and withdrawing the solidified product in a continuous length from the bottom of the mould at a rate consistent with that of pouring. Fig. 3.62. The process is used for producing blooms, billets and slabs for rolling structural shapes. The process (a German invention perfected in the early 1960's) allows steel producers to bypass the costly process of pouring molten metal (steel) into ingots and then reheating them for milling (roll) and finishing. This is cheaper than rolling from ingots. Any shape of uniform cross-section (solid or hollow) such as : round, rectangular, square, hexagonal, gear toothed and many other forms can be produced by the process. The process is mainly employed for copper, brass, bronze and aluminium and also increasingly with C.I. and steel. Again, the process to quite a considerable extent, has replaced the batch methods of producing ingot castings.

Since the mould is an open cylinder of the required cross-section, a metal block must be placed at the lower end of the mould to support the initial metal until it has solidified. The object of the process must be to achieve such a steady state of thermal equilibrium that the casting solidifies before leaving the mould. The mould is cooled by circulating water around it. The solidi- fication zone is localized in the water cooled mould when casting non-ferrous metals. However, ferrous metals conduct heat comparatively slowly, freeze only skin deep while in the mould. They are further cooled with water sprays throughout after leaving the mould. The solidified casting is withdrawn gradually from the bottom end of the mould at a controlled speed by the withdrawing rolls, typically at speeds of 25 mm/s.

Theoretically, the process may go on almost indefinitely. In that case, the required lengths of billet, bloom or slab are cut up during their movement with a flying saw or torch. In the "semi continuous casting process", the required lengths of billets, blooms and slabs or ingots are obtained by successively pouring sufficient molten metal for each length and the process is interrupted periodically to remove the casting. Large diameter and long iron water pipes with flanged ends are also cast by the semi-continuous process with a separate charge of molten metal for each pipe.

Moulds are made of graphite or copper (particularly for casting of steels due to its high-heat conductivity). To prevent the adhesion and welding of the melt to the mould, its surface is given a coating of ceramic powder for

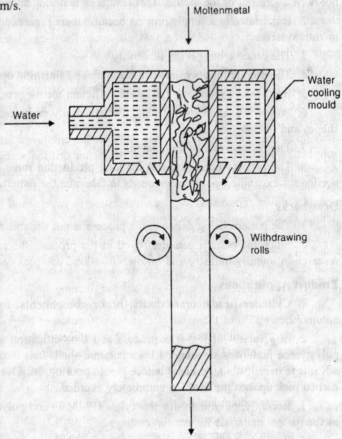

Fig. 3.62. Continuous Casting.

steel castings or of a lubricating type parting compound often containing graphite or molybdenum disulphide. Some systems employ vibrating or reciprocating mould to keep the casting from sticking.

Continuous casting process has many advantages : High quality metal can be obtained because it is protected from contamination while melting and being poured. Its yield in rolled shapes is about 10% more as compared to that from ingots. The physical properties and surface qualities are comparable to those obtained in other permanent mould processes. Ease of automation, Reduced energy consumption, Fueleconomy, Less installation and operating costs and safety.

Fig. 3.62 shows the principle of continuous casting of steel. The system contains water cooling mould as well as secondary cooling Zone where the sprays of water brings the ingot to complete solidification. As it passes through the withdrawal-roll set, the ingot enters the carriage of a cutting device moving together with the hot ingot. A gas cutter cuts off the ingots into billets. Roller conveyers then carry the billets for rolling.

3.10. CLEANING AND FINISHING OF CASTINGS

After a casting has solidified and cooled down sufficiently in an expendable mould, the first step is freeing the casting from the mould. This operation is called as the "Shake out operation". Since a great deal of heat and dust are involved in this operation, the operation is usually mechanised.

Shake out is usually done by means of vibratory knockouts, jolting grids and vibraters. The mould is intensively jolted and broken up.

After shaking the casting out of the mould, it is conveyed to the fettling (dressing) shop for cleaning and finishing. The fettling process (cleaning and finishing) consists of the following operations : Decoring or core removal, cleaning of surfaces, removal of gates, risers and fins etc., repair of defective castings if possible and heat treatment.

Before starting the fettling process, the castings are examined for obvious defects such as misrun, drop, cold laps and coldshuts etc. Defective castings are set aside and are not cleaned.

1. Core Removal or Core knockout. Due to the reasons mentioned under "shake out operation", this operation is also done mechanically. Hammering and vibrating will loosen and break up cores. Stationary or portable vibrators are employed for this purpose. To knockout cores from heavy castings, it is advantageous to use air drills. Removal of cores by hydro blasting is more sanitary process keeping in view the dust problems. The operation consists of breaking up and washing out the cores with a jet of water delivered at a pressure of 25 to 100 atm. A recent method for core removal is hydro sand blasting in which sand is mixed with the water jet. This method results in a sufficiently clean surface.

2. Cleaning of Surfaces. This operation involves the removal of all adhering sand and oxide scale and produce a uniformly smooth surface. Mechanical methods are employed for this purpose, since cleaning by hand with wire brush is tedious and costly. These methods include :

(*i*) **Tumbling.** This method is used for cleaning small and light castings. The castings are loaded into a tumbler or a barrel alongwith white iron picks (jack stars) (in an amount of 20 to 35% of the mass of castings). Rotation of the barrel causes the castings and jack stars to tumble. Jack stars abrade the surfaces of the castings and also the castings abrade one another. This operation removes the adhered sand and oxide scale from the surface of the castings. The rotational speed of the barrel is 30 rev/min.

(*ii*) **Sand Blasting and Shot-Blasting.** These methods are widely used to clean surfaces of light, medium and heavy castings. In these machines, dry sand or shots (white C.I. shot, steel shot) or grit of white C.I. or steel (grit is made by crushing shot) is blown by a stream of compressed air against the surfaces of the casting. The impact of the abrasive particles traveling at a high speed, on the surface removes the adhering sand and oxide scale. Velocity of the abrasive particles leaving the nozzle of the machine is in the range of 35 to 75 m/s and the air pressure is in the range of 0.7 MPa.

(*iii*) **Airless Shot Blasting.** In airless shot blasting of mechanical impact cleaning, shots are hurled on the surface of a casting by a fast rotating paddle wheel. For harder castings, the shots are made of white iron, malleable iron or steel, whereas for softer non-ferrous castings, these are made of copper, bronze, glass or mild steel. The wheel rotates at 1800 to 2500 rev/min. The velocity of shots striking the casting surface is about 60 to 72 m/s.

This method offers the following advantages : a high output (10 times the output of a pneumatic shot blasting machine), low power consumption, shot jet speed regulation by changing the speed of the rotor, and better working conditions. The drawbacks of the method are : rapid wear of rotor blades and poor cleaning of shaped castings with intricate cavities.

(*iv*) **Hydroblasting.** This is the most effective surface cleaning method. Here two operations are accomplished simultaneously : Core knockout and surface cleaning. Castings are placed on a rotary or stationary table and high velocity jets containing about 15% sand and 85% water, under a pressure of 10 to 20 MPa, are directed at the casting surface. The jet velocity can be upto 100 m/s. The method produces no dust but consumes lot of water.

3. Removal of Gates and Risers. Gates, runners, risers and sprue can be removed before or after cleaning operations. In brittle materials, these are simply broken off from the castings. In more ductile materials, the following methods are used to remove them : power hacksaws, band saws, disk type cutting benches, Abrasive cut off wheels, flame cutting with an oxyacetylene cutting torch and arc cutting for heat-resistant and acid-resistant steels which are not amenable to gas cutting. The surface of cut becomes rough and needs additional treatment.

Fins or flash (that forms when melt flows into gaps between two mould halves or at cores), ends of nails and other unwanted projections are removed by : chipping, sawing, flame cutting, flame gouging and grinding.

Powder Cutting. Powder cutting is a process by which large risers and gates can be rapidly removed from castings made of oxidation resistant alloys. Preheated iron powder is introduced into an oxygen stream. This burning iron then attacks the metal riser or gate by a process of fluxing and oxidation.

4. Some minor defects detected may sometimes be repaired by welding without affecting the function of the finished casting.

5. The finished castings are sometimes subjected to various heat treatments to modify mechanical properties or reduce residual stresses.

3.11. INSPECTION AND TESTING OF CASTINGS

The aims of inspection and testing of castings (that is quality control) are to prevent defective castings being supplied from the foundary and to reduce the percentage of inevitable processing rejects.

The various inspection and testing procedures may be classed as follows :

1. Visual Inspection. Visual inspection of castings can reveal many of the common surface defects such as misrun, cracks and warping etc. This method is very common and is applicable both in piece and mass production of castings. The inspection is carried out in two steps : prior to cleaning and annealing and then after the final finishing operation.

2. Dimensional Inspection. Geometric dimensions of castings are checked by means of measuring tools such as plug and snap gauges, template gauges, marked-out plates and special alliances, to establish whether the dimensions of the casting conform to the drawing or not and to make certain that the pattern and core boxes are correct. The deviations of dimensions should not exceed the permissible limits.

3. Metallurgical Control. Under this the chemical composition and the mechanical and other properties are determined in a laboratory.

The chemical composition of castings is checked by the methods of chemical and spectral analysis. For this, the test pieces are commonly cast-on test bars, that is, cast integral with the casting, or separately cast test specimens prepared for checking strength properties.

The strength or mechanical tests include test in : bending, tension, hardness, compression, shear and creep.

4. Pressure Testing. This test is carried out on those castings to be used for conveying liquids or gases. The castings are checked for pressure tightness or impermeability and leakage. The tests include : water or air-pressure tests.

In water pressure test, the casting is held under a certain pressure of water, the test pressure depends on the conditions under which the casting has to function. The outer surface of the casting must be dry, otherwise it will not be possible to detect the traces of leakage, if any.

In the air-pressure test, a soap solution is applied to the surface of the casting. When the casting is subjected to air-pressure testing, bubbles will appear on the surface showing the place of leakage, if any.

5. Radio-graphical Testing. Internal defects in a casting such as cracks, voids, cavities and porosity etc., as well as surface cracks can be revealed by radio-graphic inspection using X-rays and γ-rays.

In X-ray testing, (Fig. 3.63) short wave length rays from an X-ray tube are passed through a casting and recorded on a special film held against the opposite face of the casting. If the casting has an internal defect, the density of the material at that spot will be less as compared to the surrounding material. This area will allow more penetration of the rays, that is, the sections of the casting with cracks cavities will absorb a smaller amount of X- rays as compared to fully dense material. This will result in the appearance of a dark shadow on the X-ray film reproducing the contour of the defect. The power source used for X-ray tube is a high-voltage source: 200 kV for casting thickness upto 50 mm and 1 million volts for thickness form 50 to 180 mm.

γ – ray testing is used for checking heavy-walled castings since these rays are more penetrating and less scattering as compared to X-rays. γ – rays radiate from Radium or its salts contained in a capsule. Another source can be radio-active element Co^{60}.

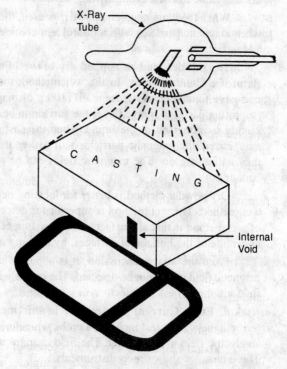

Fig. 3.63. X-Ray Testing.

6. Magnetic Testing. In this method, the casting to be tested is magnetised and then placed between the poles of an electro-magnet or in the magnetic field of a solenoid coil. The energized coil is now moved along the casting. If the coil comes across a defect on its way, the magnetic flux changes its direction and induces an emf in the coil turns, the value of which shows up on the galvanometer.

The method can detect defects (cracks) on the surface or slightly below the surface of a casting. Thus, it supplements the radio-graphical methods which ordinarily can not detect small cracks. However, the method can be applied to castings made from ferro-magnetic metals.

7. Magnetic Particle Testing: This method of inspection is a procedure used to determine the presence of defects at or near the surface of ferro-magnetic castings.

The method is based on the principle that, if an object is magnetised, surface cracks and voids in the material, which are at an angle to the magnetic lines of force, interrupts the magnetic field which gets distorted. That is, there is an abrupt change in the path of a magnetic flux flowing through the casting normal to the surface defect. This results in a local flux leakage field and hence interference with the magnetic lines of force. The magnetic lines spread out in order to detour around the interruptions, Fig. 3.64. This interference is detected and hence the shape and size of the crack or void is revealed, by the application of a fine powder of magnetic material, which tends to pile up around and bridge over the discontinuities. A surface crack is indicated by a line of the fine particles following the outline of the crack.

The magnetic powder may consist of fine iron filings, but Fe_2O_3 is preferred which is ground to pass a 100-mesh sieve. A variation of the method is that the magnetic particles are prepared with a fluorescent coating. Inspection will be carried out under U.V. light to intensify the effect. Every crack will be marked by a glowing indication.

When the plain magnetic powder is used, the trade name of the method is "Magna-flux", but when magnetic particles with a fluorescent coating are used, the method is called "Magnaflow" or "Magnaglo".

The powder may be applied dry or wet. For the dry method, the powder is applied in the form of a cloud or spray. In the wet method, the powder is suspended in a low viscosity, non-corrosive fluid such as kerosene oil (100 g of magnetic powder in about 5 l of K.oil). This liquid (supraflux paste) is sprayed over the surface to be tested, by hydraulically operated machine or the casting is immersed in the liquid. Then the casting is allowed to dry. Now, when the casting is magnetised, the magnetic particles will gather around the crack and in the "Magnaglo" method, they will also glow. The magnetic fields can be generated either with D.C. or A.C., using yokes, bars or coils.

Dry powder method is better for locating near surface defects and is also less messy than the wet method. The wet method is superior for detecting fine surface defects. Another big advantage of wet method is that all surfaces of the casting can be reached, including vertical surfaces and the underside of the horizontal surfaces, by housing or by immersion in the liquid.

From the above discussion, it is apparent that cracks that are in a direction parallel to the magnetic field would not be detected. The cracks which are perpendicular to the direction of magnetic field are the easiest to detect.

8. Eddy Current Inspection. In this method, the material of the casting need not be ferromagnetic. The test includes a probe which is supplied with a high frequency current. It induces an electric field in the casting. The field changes in the presence of surface or near-surface defects. These changes show up on instruments.

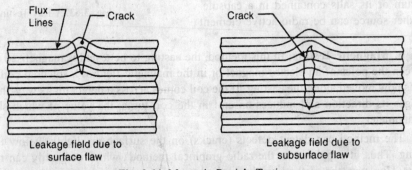

Fig. 3.64. Magnetic Particle Testing.

9. Liquid - penetrant Inspection. This method can reveal surface defects only but can be used for any material. The surface of the casting is thoroughly cleaned and dried. Then the liquid penetrants are applied as sprays or by immersion. The penetrant liquid contains either a material which will fluoresce under black light or a dye that can be visually detected. The liquid penetrant will be readily drawn into extremely small surface cracks. The surface is cleaned and dried. Then, a powder material called a "developer" is sprayed on the surface. The penetrant trapped in defects bleeds out due to blotting action and delineate defects during development. The extent of the discontinuity in the casting surface will be proportional to the amount of penetrant bleeding out. If a fluorescent penetrant is used, defects show up as glowing yellow green dots or lines against a dark back ground. In dye penetrants, defects are revealed as red dots or lines against a white background.

10. Ultrasonic Testing. This test is based on the fact that a beam of ultrasonic waves (frequency 20,000 Hz) passes through a solid (dense) material with little loss but is partially reflected from surfaces. Therefore, this method can detect voids, cracks and porosity within a casting.

The ultrasonic waves are produced by the application of reverse Piezo-electric effect. That is, if an electric potential is applied across the flat ends of a crystal (quartz crystal), it will either contract or elongate in the normal direction. The crystal is held against a smooth surface of the casting with the help of a coupling fluid. A high frequency A.C. (1 million c/s) is impressed across the faces of the crystal with the help of an oscillator. The sound waves produced travel through the casting. These will get reflected from the other end of the casting and the signals are measured with a C.R.O. If the casting has same flaws within it, some of the sound waves will be reflected back and will return to the instrument earlier. The location of the defect from the testing surface may be readily obtained by measuring the relative position of the flaw "pip" between the two "pips" representing the metal thickness, (Fig. 3.65).

The method is not very suitable for a material with a high damping capacity e.g. C.I., because in such a case, the signal gets considerable weakend over some distance.

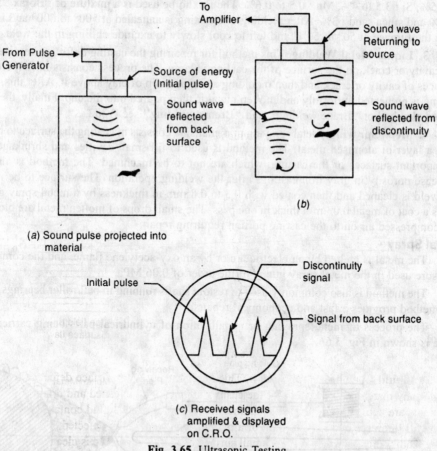

(a) Sound pulse projected into
material

(b)

(c) Received signals
amplified & displayed
on C.R.O.

Fig. 3.65. Ultrasonic Testing.

The tests for determining the mechanical properties of the castings are called as "Destructive testing" since the castings or cast test specimens which undergo these tests, become unserviceable. All other tests discussed above are called as "Non Destructive Testing", that is, "NDT", since the casting after the test can be used in the usual way, if found suitable.

3.12. REPAIRING AND SALVAGING DEFECTIVE CASTINGS

Minor defects on the unimportant surfaces of a casting can be repaired and the casting salvaged. The methods used for repairing the defects of castings are :Ä (1) Cold welding (2) Hot welding (3) Liquid metal welding (4) Metal spraying (5) Luting and impregnation

1. Cold Welding. This method is employed to rectify cracks and cavities only on surfaces which are not to be subsequently machined. Both gas welding or electric arc welding can be used for this. Various filler materials used are : Steel, copper, steel-sheathed copper, copper nickel. These are used in the form of long rods 5 to 6 mm in diameter. Defective areas to be repaired are grooved with pneumatic chippers or drilled out. Cracks should be cut out to the entire depth.

2. Hot Welding. Hot welding is used to repair large cavities, holes and cracks. Before welding, a casting is preheated to 500° to 600°C to preclude the appearance of cracks, stresses and chilling of the casting metal. The casting is held at this temperature for 45 to 60 minutes. After this, the defects can be repaired either with an OAW flame or electric arc welding. OAW with preheating is a suitable method for rectifying the defects in gray iron castings of complex configuration, whose sections sharply vary in thickness. The filler rods used are of the following composition :- C : 3.2 to 3.5%, Si : 3.5 to 4%, Mn : 0.5 to 0.6%. The flux to be used is a mixture of : Borax : 50%, soda : 47% and silica sand : 3%. After welding, the casting is annealed at 500° to 600° and is removed from the furnace at 50° to 60°C and left to cool slowly to exclude chilling in the weld.

3. Liquid Metal Welding. This method for repairing the casting defects is resorted to when the cavity or crack on the surface of the casting is large. The process consists in first cleaning the surfaces of cavity or crack and then moulding a cup or basin of clay above it. After this, the whole casting is preheated uniformly and molten metal is then poured into the cup. Finally, the casting is cooled slowly. For "Braze welding" and "Bronze welding" see P 382.

4. Metal Spraying. Metal spraying or metallising consists in coating the surface to be repaired with a layer of atomised metal. The method is used to fill small cavities and shrinkage pores on unimportant surfaces of the casting, which are not to be machined. The method is also used to decrease porosity in gray iron castings after the welding operation. The surface to be repaired or the weld is cleaned and then coated with 0.3 to 0.8 mm in thickness by a metal spray gun, which gives a coat of metal 0.03 mm thick in one pass. The small drops of molten metal are blown out by the compressed air on to the casting portion requiring repair.

Metal Spray

The metal is melted by an electric arc or by an oxy-acetylene flame, and the compressed air pressure used in the metal spray gun is of the order of 0.06 MPa.

The method is also commonly used to restore shafts running in ball/roller bearings, for which the method provides a fast and economical repairs.

The process of metal spraying or metallization of cylindrical parts being carried out on a lathe is shown in Fig. 3.66.

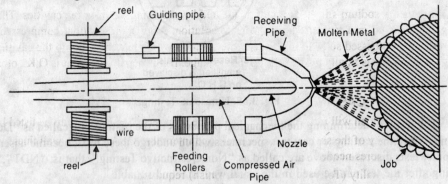

Fig. 3.66. Metallization

The method involves the following steps :—

1. The surface to be metallized is first prepared (made rough) by knurling or by sand blasting or by cutting rough threads.

2. The surface is now cleaned of oil and dirt.

3. The job is then held in the chuck or between centres and the metallizing device is mounted on the lathe carriage.

4. It is preferable to preheat the surface to be metallized to about 200°C by rotating it while mounted in the lathe, locally by oxy-acetylene flame. Preheated surface takes better deposition.

5. The welding wires from the reels are fed by the rollers through the guiding pipes and the receiving pipes. The arc is struck at the meeting ends of the wires, which melts the metal. The molten metal is sprayed on the surface to be metallized by means of compressed air entering through the compressed air pipe and the nozzle.

6. Welding wires of different materials can be fed from the two sides and the composition can be varied by adjusting different rates of feed of the two wires.

7. The sections to be protected against metal spraying (keyways etc.) are plugged with a wooden key.

Advantage :— In this process, the parts get heated upto a much lower temperature than in welding. Thus, there is a less chance of distortion of the part.

5. Luting and Impregnation. In these methods, the defects in the castings are repaired with the help of sealing agents.

Lutes or putties are plastic substances prepared from epoxy resins. These are used for smoothing out surface imperfections on castings and improving the appearance of the finish. After the defective surface is sealed with a lute and its solidification, the repaired surface is trimmed and the casting is made ready for machining. The lute in the solidified state possesses high strength and readily lends itself to machining and grinding.

If the casting is found to be positive for pressure leakage, then the salvaging operation called "impregnation" is carried out. The pressure leakage is due to some "micro-defects" in the casting. Air gets entrapped in these minute cavities. The operation consists in sealing the micro-cavities with liquid sealing agents. The operation is carried out by forcing the sealing compound into the micro-cavities under pressure alone or by a combination of pressure and vacuum treatment. The sealing compound is finally cured either by air drying or by baking. The commonly used sealing compounds are: Synthetic resins, linseed oil, sodium silicate etc. The most common is: phenol form aldehyde lacquer. For impregnating the casting, the lacquer at about 200°C is used under pressure of about 10 to 30 bar. On slow solidification, it becomes impervious to water, petrol and oil.

While using sodium silicate, vaccum is created by removing air from the cavities. Then, the casting is immersed in a tank of sodium silicate solution. After impregnation, compressed air at about 4 to 5 bar is passed so as to dry and set the solution which has entered into the cavities. The impregnated casting is finally tested for pressure leakage. If it is negative, then it is O.K., otherwise the casting is a scrap.

3.13. CHOICE OF CASTING METHOD

The factors which will influence the choice of the proper casting method can be listed below :

1. Complexity of the shape, that is, external and internal shape, minimum wall thickness and types of cores needed.

2. Surface quality (Tolerance and surface finish) required.

3. Volume of Castings required.

4. Cost of the pattern or die.

5. Weight

6. Working characteristics (strength, rigidity, stiffness, tightness, corrosion resistance etc.) required.

Because of the many factors involved, it is difficult to say just which casting method will be best for making a given part. However, the qualitative information of Table 3.5 (Pages 183-184) can often be used in deciding on a suitable casting method in a particular instance.

3.14. COMPARISON OF CASTING PROCESS WITH OTHER PROCESSES

The casting process has the following plus points, as compared to the other manufacturing processes :

1. The process is particularly suited to the parts which contain internal details that are too complex, too large or inaccessible, to be easily produced by the machining process.

2. The process (die-casting) is advantageous to cast complex parts in large numbers, especially of non-ferrous metals and their alloys.

3. For producing one of a kind part, in a variety of materials.

4. For processing precious metals, since there is little or no loss of material (Lost Wax Method).

5. Parts made by casting process are isotropic, which can be an important characteristic in some applications.

However, the casting process is not viable for producing parts of metals, with high melting points, such as tungsten etc. Casting is not economical, when parts can be made by sheet metal working processes. Also for many parts, particularly of lower melting point, non-ferrous alloys, the extrusion process may be preferrable to casting process.

3.15. CUPOLA

The cupola is the most widely used furnace in the foundary for melting ferrous and nonferrous metals and alloys. A cross-section of a cupola is shown in Fig. 3.67. A cupola is a shaft furnace of cylindrical shape erected on legs or columns. The cupola shell is made of steel plate 8 or 10 mm thick. The interior is lined with refractory bricks to protect the shell from getting over-heated. The charge for the cupola consists of metallic materials, fuel and fluxes. The metallic part of the charge is made up of definite quantities of pig iron of various grades, cast iron and steel scrap, foundary scrap (gating, splashes and spills, rejects and chips) and a small amount of ferroalloys. Foundary coke and, sometimes, anthracite are used as fuel for melting the metallic charge. Fluxes used in melting both grey iron and steel may be limestone, dolomite (Ca CO_3 and $MgCO_3$), fluorspar (CaF_2) and CaC_2 etc. The fluxes melt and react with contaminants and non-metallic elements and inclusions, the resulting slag (Calcium silicate) floats to the surface of the melt. By definition, a flux is a substance which reacts with a slag (accumulation of oxides and other unwanted materials) to lower its melting point. Fluxes used in melting non-ferrous metals are usually chlorous and fluoric salts of alkali and alkaline-earth metals.

The solid materials (metal, coke, flux) are charged into the cupola from the charging floor through charging hole (door). Charging is mechanised in large foundaries where drop bottom buckets are employed. Air for combustion of the fuel is delivered from a blower and enters a chamber called the wind box. The wind box completely encircles the cupola. Its purpose is to supply air evenly to all the tuyers, which are the openings which extend through the steel shell and refractory wall to the combustion zone. The tuyers are arranged above the cupola well (the lower part of the cupola from sand bottom to tuyers is called the well). The products of combustion (flue gases) pass

Casting Methods
Table 3.5. Design Considerations

S. No.	Methode of Casting	Material choice	Complexity of Part	Casting mass, tonnes, t	Minimum wall Thickness, mm	Precision and tolerance	Surface Smoothness	Surface Details	Mechanical Properties	Remarks
1.	Sand Casting	Wide	Considerable	-Unlimited (100 t and over)	3	± 0.6 to 0.3 mm/mm	Poor	Poor	Fair to High	Usually require machining before use
2.	Shell Mould Casting	Wide	Moderate	Best for Smaller parts	1.5	± 0.003 to 0.005 mm/mm	Good	Good	Good	Best for low costing methods
3.	Permanent Mould Casting	Restricted : Al, Brass, Bronze,	Limited	Moderate, 250 newtons For Al.	2.5	± 0.06 mm/mm	Good	Good	Fair	Economical for Mass production only
4.	Machine Moulding	Wide	Considerable	3 to 5	3	± 0.125 to 0.125 mm	Good	Good	Fair to High	Well machanized
5.	Casting in Cored Moulds	-do-	-do-	Unlimited	3	-do-	-do-	-do-	Good	Same
6.	Plaster Mould Casting	Narrow : Brass, Bronze, Al	Considerable	Moderate, upto 80 newtons	0.75	æ 0.25 to 0.125 mm	Good	Good	Fair	Little finishing required
7.	Investment Casting	Wide : includes materials hard to forge and Machine	Considerable	Moderate, Best for parts under 10 newtons	0.75	æ 0.125 mm/mm	Excellent	Excellent	Good	Best for too complicated parts
8.	Diecasting	Narrow : Nonferrous	Considerable	300 newtons for Al; 1000 newtons for Zinc	0.06	0.025 mm/mm	Good	Good	Fair to Good	Most economical where application
9.	Centrifugal Casting	Wide	Considerable	0.01 to 0.10 t	5 to 8	0.6 mm/mm	Good	Good	Good	Exonomical for Mass production
10.	Full mould	Steel C.I.	Considerable	upto 15 t	6 to 8	± 0.003	Excellent	Excellent	Good	Casting cycle is Shortened

Casting Method
Cost Considerations

S.No.	Method of Casting	Raw Materials Cost	Tool and Die costs	Direct Labour Cost	Finishing Cost	Scrap Loss	Optimum Lot Size
1.	Sand Casting	Low to Medium depending on metal	Low	High	High	Moderate	Side range, From a few pieces to large quantities
2.	Shell Mould Casting	Low to Medium	Low to Moderate	Relatively	Low	Low	From few to Quantity depending upon complexity
3.	Permanent Mould Casting	Medium	Medium	Moderate	Low to Medium	Low	Large-in thousands
4.	Plaster Mould Casting	Medium	Medium operators necessary	High-Skilled	Low	Low	100-2000 best range
5.	Investment Casting	High	Low to Moderate	High	Low	Low	Wide-although best for Small Quantities
6.	Die Casting	Medium	High	Low to Medium	Low	Low	Large-1000 to hundreds of thousands
7.	Centrifugal Casting	Medium	Medium	Moderate	Lot to Moderate	Low	Large-in thousands

out through stack and spark arrester. The function of spark arrester is to catch the incandescent dust carried with the flue gases and thereby prevent fires. The bottom of the cupola is rammed of weak moulding sand possessing high refractoriness. After each heat the bottom is dropped. A taphole is provided at the lower part of the sand bottom to let the molten metal into a forehearth or a ladle. A forehearth is a metal receiver in front of a cupola. It may perform the following functions :

1. Mix the molten metal collected over a period of time thus ensuring a more uniform metal.

2. Hold the molten metal in temporary storage.

3. Permit an intermediate metallurgical treatment of the metal such as desulphurising or adding of inocculants (Ferrosilicon, ferromanganese, ferro-chromium, ferro silicon-chromium, ferro silicon-cadmium and others). Slagging is done, as required, through a slag spout.

Dimensions of a Cupola. The cross-sectional area of a cupola depends upon the designed hourly output and is determined from the following formula :

$$A_C = \frac{\pi}{4} d^2 = \frac{Q}{Q_1} \, m^2$$

where d = Clear diameter of the cupola, m

   Q = designed cupola output, t/h.

   Q_1 = specific output of the cupola in tonnes per sq m of cross sectional area per hour.

As a rule Q_1 = 6 to 8.

The useful height of a cupola (distance from the axis of the tuyers to the lower edge of the charging door), is taken as 3 to 5 times the diameter of the cupola. The cupola height directly affects the melting rate, fuel consumption and the temperature and the quality of the molten. If the cupola height is too much, the coke may be crushed as the charge drops. If it is too low, the metal is not heated to the desired level, the drought is reduced and the cupola output is decreased. The common dimensions of a cupola are :

   (*i*) Outside diameter : 900 to 2700 mm

   (*ii*) Inside diameter : 500 to 2100 mm

   (*iii*) Height : upto 12 m.

The cupola *tuyers* should deliver a uniform blast sufficient for complete combustion of fuel. This requires that their total cross-sectional area should be in a definite relation to the cupola cross section. Cupola output and the temperature and quality of the metal depends upon the tuyer design.

Total cross-sectional area of the tuyers

$$= \left(\frac{1}{5} \text{ to } \frac{1}{6} \right) \text{ of the area of the cupola in the clear}$$

Usually, the tuyer size is : 50 × 150 or 100 × 300 mm.

The tuyers of the receiver cupola (cupola with a forehearth) should be as near as possible to the sand bottom. In cupolas without receivers, the position of the tuyers above the bottom is determined by the amount of molten metal that it is necessary to accumulate in the well before tapping.

   Height of well = 150 to 200 mm for a receiver cupola

               = upto 450 mm for a cupola without receiver

Cupola Operation. A newly built cupola (or one after inspection and repairs if any) should be thoroughly dried before firing. The bottom doors are then closed and held shut by means of a vertical prop. A layer of sand about 150 mm thick is placed over the doors and sloped towards the tap hole. In firing a cupola, fire of kindling wood is started on the sand bottom. Coke is then added in several portions to a level slightly above the tuyers and the air blast is turned on at a lower than normal blowing rate. This intensifies coke combustion. Then new portions of coke are charged into the cupola to reach a height of 700 to 800 mm above the tuyers. This layer of coke is called "Coke bed". The height of the coke bed is very important to the cupola process. It affects the temperature, melting rate and chemical composition of the grey iron tapped from the cupola. As soon as the coke bed is thoroughly ignited, alternate charges of limestone, iron and coke are added in weighted portions until level with the charging door.

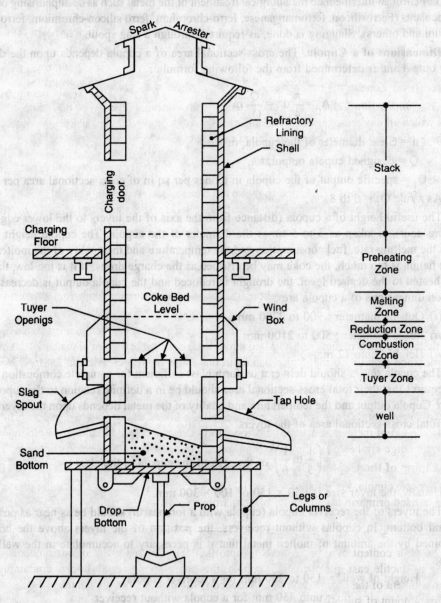

Fig. 3.67. Cross-section of a Cupola.

Limestone = 2 to 4% by weight of metal charge

Coke = 8 to 12% of the metal charge.

Full blast, delivered to the tuyers from the blower is turned on after completely charging the cupola. The first molten metal would appear at the tap hole within 5 to 10 minutes. When the well or the crucible becomes full, the slag is first drained off through the slag spout. For intermittent tapping (cupola without a receiver), the tap hole is closed with a suitable lump of sand and clay called a "bot". For tapping, the bot is punctured with a long bar and the cast iron flows out the tap spout into a holding ladle. When the crucible is emptied of cast iron, another bot is rammed into the tap hole to accumulate another melt. As the cupola is operated, additional charges of limestone iron and coke are charged through the charging door when there is sufficient room for them.

Various zones in a cupola are

1. Well or crucible.

2. Tuyer Zone.

3. Combustion Zone. This zone extends from the top of the tuyers to a surface boundary below which all oxygen of air blast is consumed by combustion of coke. The reaction is exothermic and the highest temperatures are developed in this Zone, which may reach 1600° to 1700°C.

$$C + O_2 \longrightarrow CO_2 + Heat$$

4. Reducing Zone. This zone is above the combustion zone upto a height of initial coke bed charge. The CO_2 flowing upward through this zone reacts with hot coke and the reaction is endothermic :

$$CO_2 + C\,(Coke) \longrightarrow 2CO - Heat$$

Because of this reaction, the temperature in the reducing zone gets reduced to about 1200°C. However, due to the reducing atmosphere, this zone protects the metal charge above from getting oxidised.

5. Melting Zone. This zone includes the first layer of iron above the initial coke bed. In this zone, the charge starts melting and trickling through the coke to the bottom of the cupola. A significant part of carbon pick up by metal also occurs in this Zone according to the following reaction :

$$3Fe + 2CO \longrightarrow Fe_3C + CO_2$$

6. Preheating Zone. This zone includes all the layers of cupola charges above the melting zone to the top of the last charge. In this zone, moisture and volatile matter are evaporated and the layers of charge are heated by the outgoing gases and the temperature here is upto about 1090°C.

Lining of the Cupola. The cupola lining may be basic or acidic.

In basic cupola, the refractory material lining is magnesia bricks or dolomite plaster. A basic cupola is used primarily to eliminate sulphur from iron as,

$$FeS + CaO + C \longrightarrow Fe + CaS + CO$$

Sulphur content may be reduced to upto 0.005%. The main use of basic cupola is for the making of ductile cast iron. In acidic cupola, the lining is of fireclay bricks, containing silicon. Sulphur content of the charge can not be reduced while melting. On the contrary, the metal absorbs a certain amount of sulphur from fuel.

Note. Lining of a cupola with a refractory is being abandoned in favour of water cooled steel jackets.

Output of a Cupola. The output of a cupola is defined as the tonnes of liquid metal obtained per hour of heat. It depends upon the dimensions of the cupola and the intensity of coke combustion which is defined as the tonnes of coke burned per m^2 of the cross-sectional area of the cupola in unit time.

The output of a cupola can be increased by :

1. Oxygen enrichment of the air blast (upto 30 - 35% O_2)

2. Utilisation of the heat of the outgoing gases to preheat the blast upto 180°C – 260°C or higher. Such a cupola is called a "Hot blast cup- ola".

Advantages of a Cupola

1. Its continuous operation

2. Low cost of operation.

3. Easy to operate.

4. Composition of the melt can be controlled.

5. Temperature of the melt can be controlled

3.15.1. Calculation of Cupola Charge : In order to control the specifications of the cast iron produced by the cupola furnace, it is necessary to estimate the proportions of the contents of the charge, which consists of : Pig iron, scrap and returns (gates, risers etc.)

Pig iron is available in five grades depending upon the proportion of Mn & S in it.

Grade	Mn%	P%	S%
A	1.5 – 2	upto 0.4% ⌉	upto 0.05%
B	1.0 – 1.5	upto 0.4%	
C	0.5 – 1.0	upto 0.4% ⎬	
D	— do —	0.40 to 1.0	
E	— do —	1.0 to 1.3 ⌋	

Each of these five grades is subdivided into four sub grades depending upon the % of Si.

Sub-grade	Si%
1.	2.75 – 3.75
2.	2.25 – 2.75
3.	1.75 – 2.25
4.	1.25 – 1.75

The grades have to be suitably combined in a most economical manner to achieve a desired composition of cast iron.

During the melting operation of the charge, there is a loss or gain of the various constituents of Pig iron (C, Mn, S, P & Si).

C : – it is absorbed by the metal during its passage through the cupola. It depends upon : initial C – contents, size of coke, time allowed for the metal to remain in cupola and temperature. There is also loss due to oxidation.

Net gain : upto 0.15%

Si : it has the tendency to get oxidised

Loss : 10%, In exceptional cases : upto 30%

S : tends to increase : 0.03 to 0.05 %

Mn : tends to decrease : Loss → 15 to 20%

P : Small loss : 3 to 4%

Procedure :–

Knowing the % of elements C, Si, Mn, S & P present in each constituent of charge and the loss or gain of each element, the final analysis of iron is estimated. If the final composition of C.I. is not as desired, the % of each constituent is then adjusted by trial and error, till the reqd. % analysis of C.I. is achieved.

Example : A cupola charge weights 1000 kg and is made upto of the constituents of following composition :–

Constituent	Proportion %	Compositon %				
		C	Si	Mn	P	S
Pig iron 1	15	3.5	3	1	0.40	0.02
Pig iron 2	20	3.2	1.5	0.50	0.80	0.01
Scrap	30	3.5	1.8	0.60	0.50	0.08
Returns	35	3.3	2.5	0.65	0.16	0.035

Solution 1. Amount of carbon present in :

Pig iron 1 $\qquad = 1000 \times \dfrac{15}{100} \times 0.035 = 5.25 \text{ kg}$

Pig iron 2 $\qquad = 1000 \times \dfrac{20}{100} \times 0.032 = 6.40 \text{ kg}$

Scrap $\qquad = 1000 \times \dfrac{30}{100} \times 0.035 = 10.50 \text{ kg}$

Returns $\qquad \dfrac{= 1000 \times \dfrac{35}{100} \times 0.033 = 11.55 \text{ kg}}{ 33.70 \text{ kg}}$

C - gain = 0.15 % $\qquad = \dfrac{0.15}{100} \times 33.70 = 0.05 \text{ kg}$

$\therefore$ Total C = 33.75 kg

$\therefore$ Final analysis $\qquad = \dfrac{33.75}{1000} \times 100 = 3.375\%$

2. Silicon

Pig iron 1 $\qquad = 1000 \times \dfrac{15}{100} \times 0.03 = 4.5 \text{ kg}$

Pig iron 2 $\qquad = 1000 \times \dfrac{20}{100} \times 0.015 = 3.0 \text{ kg}$

Scrap $\qquad = 1000 \times \dfrac{30}{100} \times 0.018 = 5.4 \text{ kg}$

Returns $\qquad = \dfrac{1000 \times \dfrac{35}{100} \times 0.025 = 8.75 \text{ kg}}{ 21.65 \text{ kg}}$

	Silicon loss	$= 10\% = 2.165$ kg
	Remaining Si	$= 21.650 - 2.165 = 19.485$ kg
	$\therefore$ Final analysis	$= 1.9485\% \cong 1.95\%$

3. Mn

	Pig iron 1	$= 100 \times \dfrac{15}{100} \times 0.01 = 1.5$ kg
	Pig iron 2	$= 100 \times \dfrac{20}{100} \times 0.005 = 1.0$ kg
	Scrap	$= 1000 \times \dfrac{30}{100} \times 0.006 = 1.8$ kg
	Return	$= 1000 \times \dfrac{35}{100} \times 0.0065 = \dfrac{2.275 \text{ kg}}{6.575 \text{ kg}}$

	Mn loss	$= 15\% = \dfrac{15}{100} \times 6.575 = 0.98625$ kg
	Remaining Mn	$= 5.58875$ kg
	Final Analysis	$= 0.559\ \%$

4. P

	Pig iron 1	$= 100 \times \dfrac{15}{100} \times 0.004 = 0.6$ kg
	Pig iron 2	$= 1000 \times \dfrac{20}{100} \times 0.008 = 1.6$ kg
	Scrap	$= 1000 \times \dfrac{30}{100} \times 0.005 = 1.5$ kg
	Returns	$= 1000 \times \dfrac{35}{100} \times 0.0016 = 0.56$ kg
		$= 4.26$ kg

	Loss	$= 4\% = 0.17$ kg
	Remaining P	$= 4.09$ kg
	Final Analysis	$= 0.409\%$

5. S:

	Pig iron 1	$= 1000 \times \dfrac{15}{100} \times 0.0002 = 0.03$ kg
	Pig iron 2	$= 1000 \times \dfrac{20}{100} \times 0.0001 = 0.02$ kg
	Scrap	$= 1000 \times \dfrac{20}{100} \times 0.0001 = 0.02$ kg
	Returns	$= 1000 \times \dfrac{35}{100} \times 0.00035 = 0.1225$ kg
		$= 0.4125$ kg

$$
\begin{aligned}
\text{gain} &= 0.05\% = 0.005 \times 0.4125 \text{ kg} \\
&= 0.0002 \text{ kg} \\
\text{Total S} &= 0.4127 \text{ kg} \\
\text{Final analysis} &= 0.04127 \%
\end{aligned}
$$

Instead of using the foregoing procedure of trial and error, a quicker and modern method of linear programming can be written to arrive at the exact cupola charge. A numerical method using Simplex technique can be used for the purpose. A computer programme can also be written to get the optimum charge.

3.16. SOME MORE CASTING PROCESSES

1. Graphite Mould Casting. Graphite is a high refractory substance. Graphite moulds are used for casting metals, such as Titanium, that tend to react with many common mould materials. Graphite is used for moulding in much the same manner as plaster. For this, graphite is available in an investment type of mixture, which is obtained by combining powdered graphite with cement, starch and water. This slurry is compacted around a precision machined metal pattern. The pattern is removed and mould is fired at 1000°C producing a solid graphite mould which is then poured. After solidification of the metal, the mould is broken for the removal of the casting. Graphite moulds have an advantage over plaster moulds, because they may be reused. Graphite moulds can also withstand the heat of grey, ductile or malleable metals. However, the size of graphite moulds is limited. It is of the order of 50 × 45 × 25cm. Castings upto a mass of about 23 kg can be produced.

2. Vacuum Moulding Process. Sand can be lodged in place if air is removed from the sand mass. This principle is employed in vacuum moulding process in which no binder and moisture are used. The process involves the following steps : Fig. 3.68.

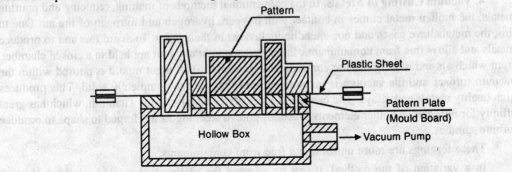

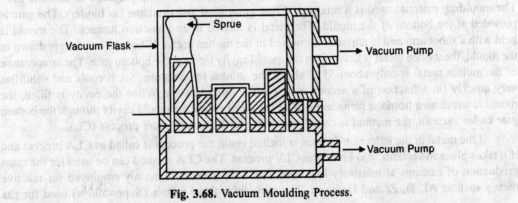

Fig. 3.68. Vacuum Moulding Process.

1. A thin plastic sheet is draped over the pattern (which has holes in it) positioned over the mould board. Vacuum is drawn on the pattern. This makes the plastic sheet to be tightly drawn over the pattern surface.

2. A double walled vacuum flask is placed over the pattern and it is filled with clean unbonded sand. Pouring basin and the sprue are formed and another plastic sheet is placed over the sand.

3. Vacuum is drawn on the sand. This makes the sand very hard.

4. Vacuum is now released on the pattern and the mould stripped.

5. Similarly the second half of the mould is made.

6. The two mould halves are assembled and the molten metal is poured. Vacuum in flasks is maintained during pouring and later till the casting solidifies.

7. The plastic sheet will burn up. When the casting is solidified, vacuum on the flasks is released. The sand collapses and the clean casting is taken out.

The process, also known as V-process, has got the following advantages :

    (*i*) Saving on the binder cost, as no binder is used in the process.

    (*ii*) No defects related to moisture and binder fumes.

    (*iii*) Any sand can be used.

    (*iv*) Easy shakeout. However, the process is quite slow.

3. The EFF-Set Process. In this process, frozen water is used as the binder. The moulding material is sand plus a little clay and frozen water as the binder. The green strength of the mould so formed is quite low. Liquid N_2 is sprayed over the mould suface. Frozen water is converted into ice and the mould becomes quite strong. The two mould halves are assembled and the molten metal is poured. The advantages of the process are : low binding cost and easy shake out.

4. Vacuum Casting of Metals. In the conventional methods of melting, reducing and pouring metals, the molten metal comes in contact with oxygen, hydrogen and nitrogen of the air. Due to this, the metals have gases and non-metallic inclusions in their mass. To avoid this and to produce metals and alloys free from contaminants, the metals made in any unit are held in a closed chamber, from which air and other gases are continuously evacuated. The ingot mould is poured within the vacuum furnace and the vacuum is maintained until the ingot is completely solid. This produces high quality metals and alloys. The process is particularly beneficial for Titanium, which has great affinity for nitrogen and other elements. Vacuum-poured steel ingots are forged to shape to produce turbine spindles.

These forgings are more uniform and free from contaminants.

In a variation of the method, it can be adopted for casting thin walled (about 0.76 mm) complex shapes with uniform properties. For this, the mould cavity is prepared in metallic dies. The moulding material used is a mixture of fine grain sand and urethane (as binder). The gate is provided at the bottom of the mould. The metal is melted in an induction furnace. The mould is held with a robot arm and is partially immersed in the molten metal. When the vacuum is drawn in the mould, the molten metal is drawn into the mould cavity through the bottom gate. The temperature of the molten metal is only about 55°C above the solidus temperature. So, it cools and solidifies very quickly (in a fraction of a second or so) in the mould cavity. When the cavity is filled, the mould is withdrawn from the furnace. Because the metal enters the mould cavity through the bottom gate under vacuum, the method is called: Counter gravity low pressure process (CL).

If the metal in the induction furnace is melted in air, the process is called as CLA process and if it takes place in vacuum, it is known as CLV process. The CLA method can be used for the mass production of castings at relatively low cost. The CLV process is mainly employed for reactive metals such as Al, Ti, Zr and Hafnium. The parts from these metals (Super-alloys) used for gas turbines may be as thin as 0.50 mm. The method can be automated and the production costs are comparable to green sand mould casting.

5. Snap-flask Moulding Process. This process differs from the most widely used process of moulding (flask moulding) in the following respects:

(*i*) The process uses special cope and drag flasks which are tapered from top to bottom on all sides. This construction enables the easy removal of the flasks after closing the mould.

(*ii*) After the mould has been prepared and closed, the flasks are removed from the mould and the mould is held in a steel jacket before it is poured.

The process uses match plate pattern (of aluminium) to obtain an offset parting plane. The offset parting plane avoids shifting of the flasks and prevents molten metal from leaking out through the parting plane during pouring. The process consists of the following steps, which are almost similar to those employed for conventional flask moulding, Art. 3.2.4 :

1. The drag flask is placed over the match plate pattern, which for convenience, rests over the inverted cope flask, [Fig. 3.69 (*a*)].

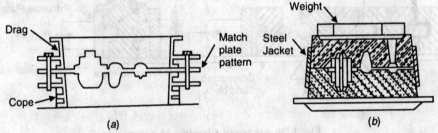

Fig. 3.69. Snap-flask Moulding.

2. The drag is filled with sand and rammed.

3. A board is placed over the top of the drag and the complete assembly is then turned out. The cope is then filled with sand and rammed.

4. The cope is lifted off the match plate, the sprue pin is withdrawn and then the match plate pattern is taken off the drag.

5. The two halves of the mould are repaired and finished by hand. Cores are placed in the mould cavity and the two halves of the mould are assembled.

6. The assembled mould is then delivered to the pouring station. The cope and drag sections of the flask are removed simultaneously from the mould.

7. A steel jacket is slipped around the closed mould, a weight is set on the top, to keep the cope from lifting and then the mould is poured. [Fig. 3.69 (*b*)].

The process, which is also known as "Slip-flask moulding", is extensively used for producing small castings in batches. If offers important advantages; shake out is much easier, economy in the cost of flasks. However, the sand consumption is somewhat higher and the process is labour intensive.

6. Flaskless Moulding Process. When properly bonded and high strength moulding sands, of not less than 186 kPa in green state, are used and the ramming pressures are high enough (around 7 to 14 MPa), the sand acquires sufficient strength to maintain the integrity of the mould, without a supporting flask. This principle is employed in flaskness moulding process.

In automatic flaskless moulding machines, all the moulding operations are performed automatically. The moulding sand is rammed by the method of sand blowing and squeezing. The process has got the following advantages :

1. It fully excludes the manual labour.

2. Costing flasks are not needed.

3. High strength of moulds minimizes wall movement during casting.

4. High quality castings are produced.

5. The process is very effective or mass production, as well as for batch production, 300 to 500 moulds per hour can be prepared and small shaped castings upto about 300 kg can be produced.

The process uses a vertically parted flaskless moulding machine and two pattern plates. One pattern plate is fastened to the pressure plate of the machine and the other to the counter pressure plate, (Fig. 3.70). The process is completed in the following steps :

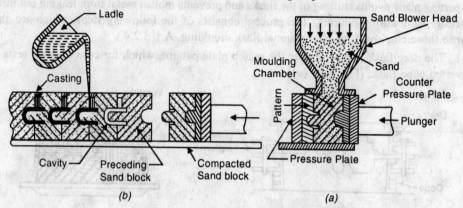

Fig. 3.70. Automatic Flaskless Moulding.

1. In the initial position, [Fig. 3.70 (a)], sand is blown from blower head into the moulding chamber under the action of compressed air.

2. The entrance to the chamber is stopped off and a squeeze plunger moves forward and compacts the sand into about 7-14 MPa.

3. The pressure plate of the machine moves away and turns aside. The plunger then pushes the compacted sand block until it comes into contact with the preceding compacted sand block, thereby forming the mould cavity.

4. In this manner, a continuous row of moulds is produced.

5. The moulds are then poured and shifted to a shake out grid.

6. After castings have cooled and solidified, they are stripped off the sand.

7. The sand is conveyed for reconditioning and reuse, while the castings are delivered to the cleaning and fettling department.

8. The automatic lines are equipped with special mechanisms (automatic core setters) for inserting cores in the moulds.

Product applications can be : brass valve bodies, malleable iron pipe fittings and gas stone grills etc. The process is competitive with die-casting for producing small brass and ferrous parts, of course with a slight inferior surface finish.

7. Electro-magnetic Casting. In this recent casting method, which is a variant of conventional continuous casting method, the molten metal is contained and solidified in an electro-magnetic field instead of in a conventional mould. There is no sliding contact of the molten metal with the mould walls, and the metal can be solidified by direct water impingement. The surface finish of the casting is very good and the process can be automated. The method is being used for obtaining continuous strands of metals.

3.17. Foundry Furnaces: One of the common foundry furnaces, Cupola, which is used mainly for melting cast iron, has been discussed in Art 3.15.. Inspite of its many advantages, the cupola has the following drawbacks :

    (*i*) It is difficult to maintain close temperature control.

    (*ii*) Since the fuel (Coke) and the molten metal come into contact with each other, some of the elements like *Si* are lost and others like S are picked up. This changes the final analysis of the molten metal.

Other common foundry furnaces are discussedc below :

1. Crucible or Pot Furnaces : These are the simplest of all the furnaces used in afoundry. The are used for melting many ferrous and non-ferrous metals. for melting copper-based alloys, the crucibles are made of Chamotte or clay and graphite, while for melting Al and Zinc base alloys these are made of steel or C.I. These are available in convenient shapes and are used as melting pots.

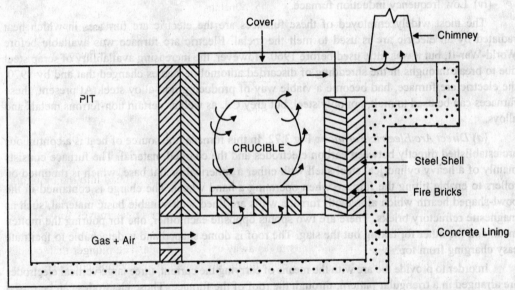

Fig. 3.71. Crucible furnace.

These furnaces are usually installed in a formed pit, Fig. 3.71. They have a refractory lining inside. These furnaces are fired by solid fuel (Coke), pulverised fuel, liquid or gaseous fuel (or natural gas). Both natural or artificial draughts can be used. In coke fired furnaces, the crucible containing metal is placed over the bed of coke. The products of fuel combustion heat the walls of the crucible or pot which transmit the heat to the metal inside. Thus, in most cases, the products of combustion do not come into direct contact with the metal, the metal does not become saturated with flue gases and high quality castings can be made. These furnaces may be stationary, tilting or movable. Tilting-pot furnaces are mounted above the floor level on supports. The furnace is tilted on trunnions to pour the molten metal. The capacity of these furnaces ranges from 30 to 150 kg. The melting time depends upon the metal and the type of fuel used. A disadvantage of these furnaces is the high fuel consumption.

2. *Electric Furnaces* : Electric furnaces are one of the major methods of melting in iron and steel factories. These furnaces are thus finding increasing use in foundries. Since there are no products of combustion in these furnaces, the loss of constituents elements is minimum. This results in the production of high quality metal for foundary purposes. Also, there is higher and accurate metallurgical control in getting proper compositions and temperature for casting intricate high duty alloys having various metallurgical and physical properties. Unlike cupola or air furnaces, electric furnaces possess greater adaptability and flexibility and provide precise control over the temperature of molten metal. The high cost of electric power is a limitation, but this is outweighed by several overwhelming advantages listed above. Also, these furnaces have simple controls. They can be readily started up or stopped.

Electric furnaces are now being used for melting and refining all kinds of steel, including stainless steel and other alloy steels. At times, they are also used for melting plain and alloy cast irons.

Electric furnaces are of four types:

(*i*) Direct arc furnace

(*ii*) Indirect arc furnace

(*iii*) High frequency induction furnace

(*iv*) Low frequency induction furnace.

The most widely employed of these furnaces are the electric arc furnaces in which heat radiated by an electric arc is used to melt the metal. Electric arc furnace was available before World-War-II, but it was little used before 1960. However, the increasing availability of scrap steel due to break throughs in the shredding of discarded automobile bodies changed that and by 1970, the electric arc furnace, had become a viable way of producing non-alloy steel. At present, these furnaces can be used to melt, not only steel, but grey C.I. as well as certain non-ferrous metals and alloys.

(*a*) *Direct Arc Electric Furnace* : Fig 3.72. In this furnace, the source of heat is a continuous arc established directly between carbon electrodes and the charged material. The furnace consists mainly of a heavy cylindrical steel shell with either a spherical or flat base, which is mounted on rollers to enable tilting the furnace when operating a hand wheel. The charge is contained in the bowl-shaped hearth which alongwith furnace walls arc lined with suitable basic material, such as magnesite refractory bricks. There are two spouts opposite each other, one for pouring the molten metal and the other for taking out the slag. The roof is dome shaped and is detachable to facilitate easy charging from top.

In order to provide the arc with the means of carrying the current, three large vertical electrodes are arranged in a triangular pattern, through the roof of the furnace. These electrodes can be raised or lowered automatically by suitable electric or electronically controlled devices or by hydraulic control with the help of servomotors. For 50 t furnace, each electrode carries a current of the order of 25000 A.

The furnace works on the principle that heat is generated when resistance is offered to the flow of electricity. In this case, it is the metal in the charge that provides the resistance to the flow of current. When the metal is molten, the slag offers the resistance to the flow of current. Thus to maintain proper heating even when the metal is molten, the electrodes must be raised so that they just touch the slag layer.

The electrodes should have high electrical and low thermal conductivity, good refractoriness and resistance to oxidation or chemical reaction. They should also possess good mechanical strength at elevated temperature. Out of graphite and amorphous carbon, graphite is preferred as it has higher electrical conductivity and is lighter. The charge consists of scrap plus a small amount of carbon and limestone. The scrap consists of 40% heavy scrap such as heads, risers and bloom heads, 40% medium scrap and 20% light scrap. The charge should be so distributed as to facilitate the formation of a pool under the electrodes. It is sound practice to place on the furnace base a small amount of light scrap topped by heavier scrap. Light scrap or turnings form another layer to reduce the electrode breakage and allow fast melting. The heaviest pieces of scrap are then placed directly below the electrodes, where the heat is the greatest.

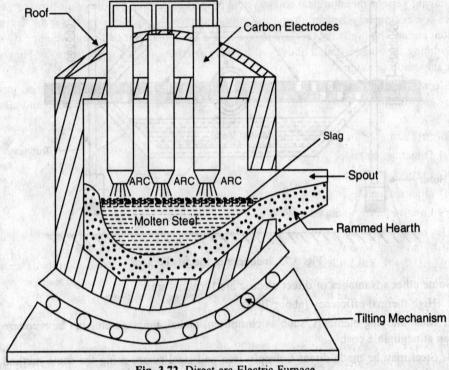

Fig. 3.72. Direct-arc Electric Furnace.

The charge is placed in the furnace through the roof which is lifted up for charging. The roof is then closed and the electrodes are lowered. The power supply is switched on. The three carbon electrodes carry the current to contact the metal charge. Arcs are established between the electrodes and the metal charge. Within about 2 hours, the charge melts. The power supply is switched off. the electrodes are raised and the furnace is tilted to pour the molten metal into a ladle. The electrodes can be upto 750 mm in diameter and 1.5 to 2.5 m in length. Their lengths within the furnace can be adjusted depending upon the amount of charge and the wear of electrodes. The capacity of such furnaces may be upto 50 tonnes. These furnaces operate on 3-phase supply and consume about 600 to 850 kWh of electric energy to produce 1 tonne of steel from a solid charge. The temperature in the furnace can be as high as 1925°C, so as to melt metals with a high concentration of components with high melting points (Chromium, Tungsten, Molybdenum and other admixtures).

(b) *Indirect arc electric furnace* : Here, the arc is struck between two electrodes, Fig. 3.73, instead of between electrode and the metal charge. Such furnaces are commonly used for melting copper base alloys. The furnace consists of a horizontal refractory lined drum. Two graphite or carbon electrodes between which the arc is struck, are inserted in the centres of the end walls. The drum is mounted on trunnions and rollers due to which rocking motion can be given to the furnace. When needed, the furnace is tilted on trunnions and the molten metal is poured into a ladle. The capacity of such a furnace is upto 1000 kg.

As noted above, this furnace is specially designed for non-ferrous metals. However, these furnaces are excellent for melting and refining plain carbon and low alloy and high alloy steels, in addition to non-ferrous metals.

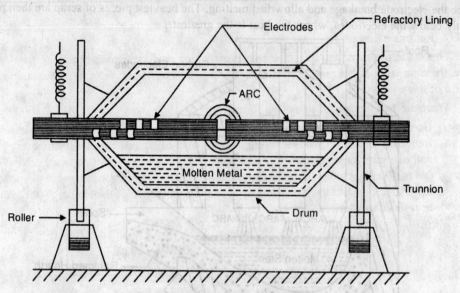

Fig. 3.73. Indirect Arc Electric Furnace.

Some other advantages of direct electric arc furnaces are:

1. High thermal efficiency (about 70%).

2. Most alloying elements, such as chromium, nickel, tungsten etc. can be recovered from the scrap at negligible cost.

3. Steel may be made direct from pig iron and steel scrap, using the same method as for open-hearth furnaces

4. An arc furnace is preferred for it is: quicker ready ness for use, longer hearth life and ease of repair.

Because of high electric energy consumption, these furnaces are recommended for the production of high grade melt of selective quality, where the added expense is warranted. Also, these furnaces have definite economic advantages over the use of cupolas because of high-ash coke in India. Therefore, they are preferred to cupolas for melting C.I.

(c) *Induction Furnaces :* Melting of metal in an induction furnace differs from that in the electric arc furnace in that, instead of the bulk of the heat being generated in an arc and radiated to the charge, all the heat is generated in the charge itself. The furnace contains a refractory lined crucible surrounded by a water cooled copper coil. The furnace works on the principle of transformer. Water cooled copper coil is the primary and the secondary is the metal charge. When A.C. is passed through the copper tubing, a magnetic field is set up. This magnetic field induces eddy currents in the crucible charge, which melts the metal. If ferrous metals show magnetic property, the loss due to hysterises produces extra heat. Very high temperatures can be obtained by this method of melting, the only limitation being the ability of the furnace lining to withstand the temperature developed.

The charge ratio is:

Steel : 40 to 60%

Pig iron : 4 to 7%

Returns : Rest

In case, Pig iron is not available, then, charge ratio is.

Steel : 40 to 65%

Returns : Rest

The induction furnaces are suitable especially for smaller quantities, 50 kg to 10 tonnes. Since, these furnaces do not require electrodes, this prevents carburisation of the metal and simplifies control of the process.

There are two designs of induction furnaces:

(*i*) *Core-less or high frequency induction furnace :* Fig. 3.74, is a cross-section of a high frequency induction furnace. Here, a water-cooled copper coil constituting the primary coil of a transformer completely surrounds the crucible. A high frequency current (10000 cps to 500,000 cps) is passed through the coil. A heavier, secondary current is induced in the charge constituting the secondary coil. The resistance of metal charge will cause it to heat up to the desired temperature.

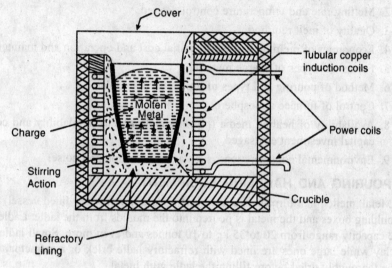

Fig. 3.74. High Frequency Induction Furnace.

(*ii*) *Core or Channel furnace or Low frequency induction furnace:*

Here the coil surrounds only a small portion of the crucible and the A.C. passed through the coil is of low frequency (50 to 60 cps).

The induction furnaces are employed to melt steel, iron, bronze, brass and Al. base alloys. They are especially widely used to melt precision alloys, that is, alloys of exact composition based on iron and other metals. These furnaces have capacities ranging from few kgs to 4 or 6 tonnes.

Advantages

(*i*) *Simple controls.* These furnaces can be readily started or stopped. High rate of melting and can deliver metal at regular intervals.

(*ii*) Metal can be heated to very high temperatures without the danger of localised overheating that is sometimes observed in electric arc furnaces.

(*iii*) Gas atmosphere within the furnace can be controlled or a vacuum may be set up if necessary.

(*iv*) The motor effect of the strong electro-magnetic forces in the bath produces a circulatory motion, that is, automatic stirring or mixing. This facilitates better mixing between metal and slag. This mixing characteristic is excellent for alloying and adding new charge of metal. All this results in more uniform composition of the metal.

(*v*) Automatic mixing and stirring of the metal in the bath also has a favourable effect on its degassification and upon the removal of non-metallic inclusions. Thus high quality metals and alloys free of H_2 and N_2 can be easily produced.

The main drawback of high frequency induction furnace is its high initial cost. The low frequency furnace has better efficiency. Low frequency furnace is commonly used in non-ferrous foundries. It is particularly suitable for super heating (which improves fluidity), holding (keeping the metal temperature constant for a longer time which makes it suitable for die-casting) and duplexing (using two furnaces, melting in one furnace and then transferring to the second).

Choice of Furnace : There are a number of furnaces available which can meet the requirements of melting and casting metals and alloys in foundries. The quality of castings and economics of casting operations will depend upon the furnace selection. Therefore, the following factors should be given careful consideration while selecting a furnace for a job:

1. Capacity of molten metal/alloy required.
2. Melting rate and temperature control desired.
3. Quality of melt required.
4. Economics of melting, that is, the initial cost and operation and maintenance charges.
5. Forms and types of charge material.
6. Method of pouring and types of products contemplated.
7. Control of furnace atmosphere.
8. Availability of heating media (power supply and its availability and cost of fuels), and capital investment envisaged.
9. Environmental considerations, such as air pollution and noise.

3.18. POURING AND HANDLING EQUIPMENT

Metal, melted in a furnace is tapped into a ladle (a refractory lined vessel) which is taken to the moulding boxes and the metal is poured into the moulds from the ladle. Ladles are available in a wide capacity range from 20 to 35 kg to 10 tonnes and even more. Small ladles are luted inside with clay while large ones are lined with refractory ladle brick or a refractory mass. The lining must be thoroughly dried before filling the ladle with metal.

The other pouring and handling equipment includes:— Shanks (Ladle handles), trolleys, monorails, cranes, hand wheels, tilting levers etc.

Types of Ladles: All types of ladles used in foundries are basically of two types:

(*a*) *Large Reservoir or Holding Ladle :* As is clear from the name, these are large capacity ladles. The molten metal is tapped into these ladles from the furnace. As the name implies, these ladles hold or store the metal temporarily. From these ladles, the metal is then taken to the moulds in smaller ladles. So, these bigger ladles receive and distribute the molten metal simultaneously. These ladles are steel shells lined with firebricks. The bottom and sides of the ladle can also be lined with fire sand and clay, which is hardened by baking. These are also employed when there may be a mismatch between the rates of melting and using material.

(*b*) *Crane or Monorail Ladles :* These are also large capacity ladles but smaller in size as compared to holding ladles. These are conveyed with the help of a crane or monorail to the place where the moulds are kept ready for pouring. The capacity of these ladles can range from 350 kg to 100 tonnes (for very big castings).

These ladles are of the following types :

(*i*) *Lip Pouring Ladle :* The action of this ladle is just like that of pouring water out of a jug. To avoid going of slag and other impurities into the mould, the molten metal in the ladle is skimmed with the help of a metal skimming bar before it is poured into the mould. Or a refractory dam can be built in front of the lip to achieve the same results. To pour the metal into the mould, the ladle is tilted by hand wheel or lever.

(ii) *Teapot Ladle :* This ladle resembles a tea pot except that the snout is inside the body of the ladle. Since the metal leaves the ladle near the bottom, it is clean and free of any slag etc. For pouring, the ladle is tilted with the help of a hand wheel.

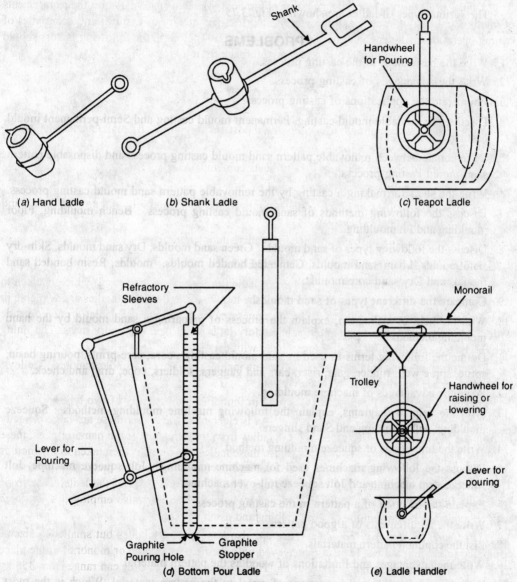

Fig. 3.75. Various Types of Ladles.

(iii) *Bottom Pour Ladle :* In this ladle, the tap hole is at the bottom. The tapping can be stopped with a refractory covered vertical rod stopper. Clean metal goes into the mould.

However, in this ladle, the momentum of the pouring metal is greater as compared to lip and tea pot ladles.

Crane or monorail ladles are employed in case of very heavy castings. A mechanical device called "ladle handler" which hangs from the overhead monorail, enables one man to pour the metal from the ladle. A large handwheel is used for readily raising or lowering the ladle, and the ladle is tipped for pouring by a hand lever.

For small castings hand type ladles are used. A small ladle can be handled by a single person. However, bigger ones (with capacity of 15 kg to 30 kg) are handled by two persons with the help of handle called "Shank".

The various types of ladles are shown in Fig. 3.75.

PROBLEMS

1. Write the basic steps in the casting process.
2. Write the advantages of casting process.
3. Enumerate the applications of casting process.
4. Discuss : Expendable mould casting, Permanent mould casting and Semi-permanent mould casting.
5. Differentiate between removable pattern sand mould casting process and disposable pattern sand mould casting process.
6. Write the steps for making a casting by the removable pattern sand mould casting process.
7. Discuss the following methods of sand mould casting process : Bench moulding, Floor moulding and Pit moulding.
8. Discuss the following types of sand moulds : Green sand moulds, Dry sand moulds, Skin-dry sand moulds, Loam sand moulds, Cemented bonded moulds, moulds, Resin bonded sand moulds and Dry sand core moulds.
9. Compare the different types of sand moulds.
10. With the help of a diagram, explain the process of preparing a sand mould by the hand moulding method.
11. Define the following terms as used in sand mould casting : core, core-prints, pouring basin, sprue, sprue well, runner, gate, riser, bars and gaggers, soldiers, cope, drag and cheek.
12. Write the advantages of machine moulding.
13. With the help of diagrams, explain the following machine moulding methods : Squeeze moulding, Jolt moulding and Sand slingers.
14. Write the limitations of squeeze moulding method.
15. Discuss the following machines used for machine moulding : Jolt squeeze machine, Jolt squeeze strip machine and Jolt squeeze roll-over machine.
16. Explain the function of a pattern in the casting process.
17. Write the requirements of a good pattern.
18. List the common pattern materials.
19. Write the advantages and limitations of wood as the pattern material.
20. Write the advantages and limitations of metal as the pattern material. Which is the most commonly used metal for patterns.
21. Write the advantages of plastics as the pattern material.
22. Write on : finishing of patterns.
23. Discuss the various pattern allowances.

24. What are loose patterns ? What are one piece or solid and split or parted loose patterns ?

25. With the help of diagrams discuss the following types of patterns : Loose piece pattern, Drawback, Gated pattern, Match plate pattern, Cope and drag pattern, Sweep pattern, Skeleton pattern, Segmental pattern and follow board pattern.

26. What is a "Stop-off" ?

27. Why a colour scheme for patterns is needed ? Illustrate a common colour scheme.

28. What is "Stack moulding" ?

29. Name the various moulding materials used in foundary.

30. Name the essential constituents of moulding sand.

31. Write the advantages of silica sand as a moulding material.

32. What are the functions of a binder in moulding sand ?

33. What is meant by sand "at temper" ?

34. What are the functions of additives in moulding sand ?

35. How the moulding sand is classified on the basis of clayey matter it contains ?

36. Discuss: natural sand, synthetic sand and chemically coated sand.

37. Give the composition of a typical green moulding sand.

38. Discuss the various binders used in moulding sand.

39. Discuss the functions of the following additives in moulding sand : Coal dust, cereals, saw dust, wood flour, silica flour, fuel oil, iron oxide and dextrin.

40. What is the function of facing materials in moulding sand ? Name the common facing materials.

41. What is the function of cushion materials in moulding sand ? Name the common cushion materials.

42. Write about the following types of sands : Facing sand, Backing sand, System sand, parting sand.

43. Write on "parting materials" used in sand moulding.

44. Discuss the "mould surface coatings" used in sand mould casting.

45. Write about the moulding sand used for non-ferrous castings.

46. Discuss the various properties of moulding sand.

47. Discuss the essential qualities of a core. What is core sand ?

48. Explain the manual method of core making.

49. What is a core dryer ?

50. Why the cores are reinforced ?

51. What is core venting ?

52. Discuss synthetic resin core binders.

53. With the help of a diagram explain the core-blowing machine method for core making.

54. With the help of a diagram explain the extrusion method of core making.

55. Discuss the "Hot core box method" of core making.

56. Discuss the "Synthetic resin-bonded cold curing core sands method" of core making.

57. Discuss the CO_2 cold curing process of core making.

58. Write on "finishing and coating of cores".

59. With the help of diagrams discuss the various types of cores used in sand mould casting.
60. Explain the function of chaplets. Sketch the various forms of chaplets used in the foundary.
61. Sketch a common gating system. Label it and explain the function of its various elements.
62. Discuss the various methods of preventing the slag from flowing into the mould cavity.
63. Why the section of a Sprue reduces downwards ?
64. Explain the functions of : splash core, skim bob, runner and runner extension.
65. What is "gate ratio" ?
66. What is "choke" ? Discuss the "pressurised gating system" and "unpressurised gating system".
67. What is the function of a riser ? Write the requirements of a good riser.
68. What is "directional solidification" ? Explain it with the help of a diagram.
69. Write about "riser location".
70. Compare top riser and side riser.
71. What are open and blind risers ? Give their advantages and drawbacks.
72. Write the methods of keeping the metal hot and in the molten state in the top riser ?
73. Why the risers should be made with a high volume / surface area ratio.
74. Discuss the various shapes of a riser.
75. Write about the height of risers.
76. With the help of diagrams discuss the use of : (a) padding (b) chills and (c) Sleeves, in achieving directional solidification and thereby obtaining sound castings.
77. What are "flow offs" ?
78. With the help of a diagram, discuss the feeding ranges of risers.
79. Discuss the requirements of a good gating system.
80. Sketch and compare : Parting line gate, top gate and bottom gate.
81. What are : Pencil gate, Wedge gate, Whirl gate, Ring gate, Branch gate and Swirl gate.
82. Sketch the various sand mould casting defects. Give their causes and remedies.
83. With the help of sketches, discuss the various design considerations for designing the sand mould castings.
84. Differentiate between Pressure die Casting and Permanent mould casting.
85. List the main reasons behind the widespread use of pressure die castings process.
86. What are the limitations of Pressure die casting method ?
87. List the product applications of Pressure die casting method.
88. How are the dies opened and locked in die casting.
89. What is meant by the capacity of a die casting machine. Write its usual values.
90. Write the steps for making a casting by die casting process.
91. Why die-casting method is mainly used for non-ferrous metals.
92. Compare Cold-chamber and Hot-chamber methods of die casting.
93. List the metals normally cast by the cold-chamber method and hot chamber method.
94. Compare horizontal die casting machines and vertical die casting machines.
95. Compare off-set and central metal injection techniques.

96. Discuss the various factors for die casting design.
97. Name the various types of die-casting dies.
98. What are the various types of cores used in die-casting ?
99. Discuss in detail the design of gating system for die-casting.
100. Discuss the runner design of a die casting process.
101. Why venting is necessary in die-casting and how it is achieved ?
102. What is the difference between a multiple cavity die and a combination die ?
103. What are unit dies ?
104. Why are ejector pins required in a die-casting ?
105. What factors are important while deciding about the parting line in a die-casting ?
106. What is the use of 'Slides' in die-casting ?
107. Why cooling of dies is necessary during their operation ?
108. List the factors affecting the selection of die material.
109. Discuss some common die materials.
110. How the dies for die casting are manufactured ?
111. List the advantages of wrought dies and cast dies.
112. What is vacuum die-casting ?
113. Can the ferrous metals be cast by die-casting method ? if yes, then how?
114. What is "Squeeze casting" ?
115. What is a "book mould' ?
116. List the materials commonly used to make permanent moulds.
117. What are the major types of cores used in permanent mould casting ?
118. Explain permanent mould venting.
119. Explain permanent mould gating system.
120. Why are risers usually required in permanent mould casting method.
121. Why permanent moulds are preheated before operations ?
122. What metals are cast by permanent mould method.
123. Discuss the mould coatings.
124. List the steps needed for permanent mould casting operation.
125. List the advantages and limitations of permanent mould casting method.
126. Discuss the casting design for a permanent mould casting method.
127. How the permanent moulds are manufactured ?
128. Explain a Turntable moulding machine.
129. Discuss "Slush Casting" and "Low pressure permanent mould casting".
130. Name the products made by Slush casting process.
131. Define the method of centrifugal casting.
132. With the help of diagrams discuss the following casting methods : (a) True-centrifugal casting (b) Semi-centrifugal casting, and (c) Centrifuge casting.
133. Write the advantages, disadvantages and product applications of True-centrifugal casting method.

134. Write the product applications of Semi-centrifugal and centrifuge casting methods.
135. What is meant by "Precision investment casting" ?
136. With the help of diagrams, discuss the "Lost wax method".
137. Write the advantages, limitations and product applications of Lost -wax method.
138. With the help of diagrams, discuss the "Shell moulding" method.
139. Write the advantages, disadvantages and product applications of Shell moulding method.
140. Discuss the following casting methods :
    (a) The Mercast process   (b) Plaster - mould casting
    (c) Ceramic mould Casting   (d) Full - mould casting, and
    (e) Continuous casting.
141. Write the advantages and disadvantages of Plaster - mould Casting.
142. What is "Shake-out operation" ?
143. How the cores are removed from Castings ?
144. Discuss the various methods of cleaning the surfaces of Castings.
145. How the gates and risers are removed from a Casting ?
146. What is the aim of inspection and testing of Castings ?
147. Discuss the following methods of inspection and testing of castings :
    (a) Radio - graphical testing   (b) magnetic testing
    (c) Magnetic particle testing   (d) Eddy current inspection
    (e) Liquid penetrant inspection   (f) Ultrasonic testing.
148. Discuss the various methods of repairing and salvaging defective castings.
149. With the help of a diagram, explain the working of a "Cupola".
150. Write the advantages of a Cupola.
151. What is the necessity of sand testing ?
152. Write brief notes on :-
    (a) Moisture content test   (b) Clay Content test
    (c) Permeable test.   (d) Fineness test
    (e) Hardness test   (f) Strength tests
153. Discuss the "Chvorinov's rule" and "Caines rule" for determining the Riser size.
154. Discuss the various defects in die-castings :their causes and remedies.
155. List the drawbacks of Cupola as the foundry furnace.
156. Sketch and discuss a Crucible or Pot furnace.
157. List the advantages of Electric furnances.
158. List the types of Electric furnance.
159. Sketch and write on Direct arc electric furnace.
160. Sketch and write on Indirect arc electric furnace.
161. List the advantages of Direct arc electric furnaces.
162. What is the principle of Induction furnances.
163. Write on the two types of Induction furnances.
164. Sketch and write on High frequency induction furnance.

165. List the advantages of Induction furnaces.

166. List the main draw back of high frequency induction furnace.

167. List the advantages of Low frequency induction furnance and its applications.

168. Write a brief note on : Choice of furnace.

169. What is a Ladle ?

170. Sketch and discuss the various types of Ladles used in a foundry.

171. What are Jobbing foundries and Captive foundries ?

172. Compare the solidification times for castings of three different shapes of same volume : cubic, cylindrical (with height equal to its diameter) and spherical.

Solution :– From Chvorinov's equation,

$$\text{Solidification time} = C.\left(\frac{\text{Volume of Casting}}{\text{Surface Area of Casting}}\right)^2$$

Since all the three castings have the same volume (Let it be equal to unity),

$$\text{Solidfication time, } t = C.\left(\frac{1}{\text{Surface Area}}\right)^2$$

(a) **Cubic Casting :** – Let 'a' be the side of the cube

$$\therefore V = a^3 = 1 \therefore a = 1$$

Surface Area $= 6a^2 = 6$ units

$$\therefore t = C.\left(\frac{1}{6}\right)^2 = 0.0278C$$

(b) **Cylindrical Casting :** Let r be the radius and h be the height of the cylinder.

$$\therefore \qquad h = 2r \ V = \pi r^2 . h = 2\pi r^3$$

$$\therefore \qquad r = \left(\frac{1}{2\pi}\right)^{\frac{1}{3}}$$

$$\therefore \text{Surface Area} = 2\pi r^2 + 2\pi rh = 6\pi r^2 = 6\pi \cdot \left(\frac{1}{2\pi}\right)^{\frac{2}{3}} = 5.53 \text{ units}$$

$$\therefore t = C\left(\frac{1}{5.53}\right)^2 = 0.0327C$$

(c) **Spherical Casting :** $V = \frac{4}{3}\pi r^3 \qquad \therefore \qquad r = \left(\frac{3}{4\pi}\right)^{\frac{1}{3}}$

$$\therefore \text{Surface Area} = 4\pi r^2 = 4\pi \cdot \left(\frac{3}{4\pi}\right)^{2/3} = 4.83 \text{ units}$$

$$\therefore t = C.\left(\frac{1}{4.83}\right)^2 = 0.0429 \ C$$

∴ Spherical casting has the maximum solidification time (∴ it will solidify the slowest and the cubic casting has the least solidification time (∴ it will solidify fastest)

173. The first type of crystal that is formed upon the solidification of a metal is classified as :

    (*a*) A dendrite crystal   (*b*) A columnar crystal

    (*c*) A chilled crystal   (*c*) An equi-axed crystal

                                                              (*D.U., L.U*) (**Ans. :** *a*)

174. Draw an approximate sketch of a dendritic crystal, what are columnar crystals ?

175. Define : Nucleation, Grain growth, Grain boundaries.

176. Derive an expression for the critical radius of nucleous.

177. Define the term "Segregation". Discuss the various types of segregations during cooling and solidification of metals.

178. Write a brief description of sequence of events taking place in solidification of a pure metal.

                                                    (*UPSC, AMIE, DU*)

179. Which one of the following metals is not suitable for testing with ultrasonics ?

    (*a*) Cu   (*b*) Al   (*c*) C.I.   (*d*) Stainless steel

                                               (*BTE, UPSC, I.Mech-E*) (**Ans. :** *c*)

180. Which one of the following tests is of a destructive nature ?

    (*a*) Ultrasonic testing   (*b*) Radiographic testing

    (*c*) Macroscopic testing   (*d*) Electro-magnetic testing

                                                    (*BTE, UPSC*) (**Ans. :** *c*)

181. Describe the details of magnetic particle test. State one of its limitations.

182. State briefly the ultrasonic test and describe its specialities.

183. Radiography plays a vital role in the body of methods of non-destructive testing. Justify the statement. (*L.U.*)

184. How the calculations of Cupola Charge are done ?

185. A steel rectangular section 100 × 75 × 200 mm is to be cast. Calculate the size of a teakwood pattern if an Al pattern is to be obtained first to be subsequently used for making steel castings.

    Shrinkage allowance for Al = 16 mm/m   (**Ans. :** 103.7 × 77.78 × 207.4 mm)

    Shrinkage allowance for steel = 21 mm/m

186. Figure shows finished dimensions of a brass bushing (in mm) in which the central hole is to be cored. Calculate the dimensions of a teak wood pattern showing shrinkage. Take shrinkage allowance for Brass = 16 mm/m.

187. Calculate the dimensions of the pattern in problem 186, by considering Draft allowance also. Take draft = 5 mm/m.

188. Calculate the size of a cylindrical riser (height and diameter equal) necessary to feed a steel slab casting 25 × 25 × 5 cm with a side riser, casting pouring horizontally into the mould.   (*PTU. Dec. 2004*).

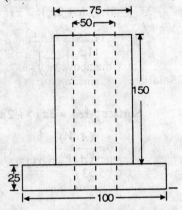

Solution :– Refer Appendix – III, Q 40 of Chapter 3.

Volume of casting = 25 × 25 × 5 = 3125 cm³.

Shrinkage volume = Depending upon metal, this shrinkage volume varies from 2.5% to 7.5% of volume of casting.

For steel, let us assume it to be 3%.

∴ Shrinkage volume = 0.03 × 3125 = 93.75 cm³

A riser should be designed with the minimum possible volume, while having a longer solidfication time than the casting. It is an uneconomical design to have a larger riser volume to ensure greater solidification time.

Now from practice, minimum volume of riser is approximately three times the shrinkage volume.

$\therefore$ Minimum volume of riser, $V_r = 3 \times 93.75 = 281.25$ cm^3

$\therefore \dfrac{\pi}{4} dr^2 \times hr = 281.25$

Now, the optimum ratio of diameter and height of a cylindrical side riser is ,
$hr = dr$

$\therefore dr = 7.1$ cm

$\left(\dfrac{A}{V}\right)_r = \dfrac{6}{dr} = \dfrac{6}{7.1}$

Now, for sound casting, the metal in the riser should be the last to cool, that is, the riser should have a longer solidification time than the casting. So,

$\left(\dfrac{V}{A}\right)_r \geq \left(\dfrac{V}{A}\right)_c$

Now $\left(\dfrac{V}{A}\right)_c = \dfrac{3125}{2(25 \times 25 + 5 \times 25 + 5 \times 25)} = \dfrac{3125}{1750} = 1.786$ cm^{-1}

and $\left(\dfrac{V}{A}\right)_r = \dfrac{7.1}{6} = 1.1833$

As is clear, $\left(\dfrac{V}{A}\right)_r$ is $< \left(\dfrac{V}{A}\right)_c$, which is not desirable

For the condition

$\left(\dfrac{V}{A}\right)_r \geq \left(\dfrac{V}{A}\right)_c$

In practice, $\left(\dfrac{V}{A}\right)_r = (1.05 \text{ to } 1.075)\left(\dfrac{V}{A}\right)_c$

$\dfrac{dr}{6} = (1.05 \text{ to } 1.075) \times 1.786$

or $dr = 11.25$ to 11.52 cm

Let $dr = 11.5$ cm; $\therefore hr = 11.5$ cm. $\therefore Vr = 1194.55$ cm^3

189. Solve the above problem by Caines formula.

Solution :— Caines formula is

$x = \dfrac{a}{y-b} + c$

Now $x = \dfrac{(A/V)_c}{(A/V)_r} = \dfrac{(1/1.786)}{(6/dr)} = \dfrac{dr}{6 \times 1.786}$

$y = \dfrac{V_r}{V_c} = \dfrac{\pi}{4} dr^3 \times \dfrac{1}{3125}$

For steel, $a = 0.12$, $b = 0.05$, $c = 1$

$\therefore \dfrac{dr}{6 \times 1.786} = \dfrac{0.12}{\dfrac{\pi dr^3}{12500} - 0.05} + 1$

$$= \frac{1500}{\pi \, dr^3 - 625} + 1$$

$$\therefore \quad \pi d_r^4 - 625 dr = 6 \times 1.786(\pi d_r^3 + 875) \; = 33.67 d_r^3 + 9376.5$$

$$\therefore \quad \pi d_r^4 - 33.67 \, d_r^3 - 625 \, dr - 9376.5 = 0$$

By trial and error

$$dr \cong 13.2 \; cm.$$

190. Calculate the riser diameter for an annular cylinder of outside dia. 30 cm., inside dia. 10cm and height 30cm.   (*PTU*)

191. A Sample of sand of 50 gm. is weighted after washing and drying and found to weight 41.6 gm. What would be the clay percentage in this sand sample ?   (*PTU* ; **Ans.** 16.8%)

192. Calculate the permeability number of a sand specimen if it takes 1 min. 15 seconds to pass 2000 cm^3 of air at a pressure of 6 gm/cm^2, through the standard specimen.

(*PTU*; **Ans.** $\cong 67$)

193. Calculate the optimum pouring time for a casting whose mass is 20 kg and having an average section thickness of 15 mm. The materials of the casting are gray C.I. and steel. Take the fluidity of iron as 28".   (*PTU*; **Ans.** 7.79*s*, 8.72*s*.)

Note :– The optimum pouring time may be calculated approximately by the following formulas :

1. **Steel Castings :** $t = K\sqrt{m}, s$

    m = mass of casting in kg.

    K = constant, varies from about 1.95 for 45 kg castings to about 0.65 for 45,000 kg castings.
Another relation is : $t = (2.4335 - 0.3953 \log m) \sqrt{m}, s$

2. **Gray Iron Castings :**

    (*a*) $t = K\left[1.44 + \dfrac{T}{14.30}\right]\sqrt{m}, \, s,$ for *m* upto 450 kg

    $\qquad = K\left[1.262 + \dfrac{T}{16.32}\right]\cdot (m)^{\frac{1}{3}}, \, s,$ for *m* > 450 kg

    where T = Average section thickness in mm.

    $$K = \frac{\text{Fluidity Index of Iron in inches}}{40}$$

Fluidity Index :– Fluidity refers to the relative ability of molten metal to fill the mould at a given temperature. Fluidity index is the length of the solidified metal in the spiral passing. The greater the length of the solidified metal, the greater its fluidity.

3. **Light Metal Alloys :**–

    $t = K\sqrt{m}, s$

    K = 0.1 for T < 6 mm = 1.19 for T 6 to 12 mm
       = 2.13 for T > 12 mm

4. **Copper-base alloys, and also for ferrous alloys :**–

    $$t = \left(1.34 + \frac{T}{13.77}\right) \cdot m^{1-p}, s$$

    where *p* = 0.5 for m upto 500 kg
       = 0.67 for m 500 – 5,000 kg

= 0.70 for m > 5000 kg.

194. Determine optimum pouring time for casting C.I. whose mass is 50 kg and a thickness of 50 mm. Fluidity index is 22". (Ans. 19.2 s)

Note :– High pouring rate results in turbulent metal flow in the mould channels and the mould cavity, leading to mould erosion. Low pouring rate may not completely fill the mould cavity, leading to defects like cold shut and misrun. Hence, the significance of optimum pouring time.

195. A casting $200 \times 200 \times 70$ mm^3 size solidifies in 10 mins. Determine the solidification time for $200 \times 100 \times 10$ mm^3 under similar conditions. (Ans. 0.648 min.)

Hint :– $\dfrac{t_1}{t_2} = \left(\dfrac{V_1}{A_1}\right)^2 \Big/ \left(\dfrac{V_2}{A_2}\right)^2$

196. What is choke Area. Write an expression to determine it.

Solution : As explained in Art. 3.6.2, for a pressurized system, ingate is the choke, where as for the unpressurized system, the sprue base is the choke, The expression to determine its area is based on Bernaullis theorem, as :

$$CA = m/c\rho t\sqrt{2gH}, \ mm^2,$$

where m = mass of the Casting, kg

ρ = mass density of metal, kg/m^3

t = Pouring time

c = Efficiency factor and is the function of gating system used

H = Effective head of liquid metal, Refer Fig. 3.76.

= h for top gate

= $h - \dfrac{1}{2} h_m$ for bottom gate, h_m = Total height of mould cavity

= $h - \dfrac{h_c^2}{2h_m}$ for Parting line gate, h_c = Height of mould cavity in cope

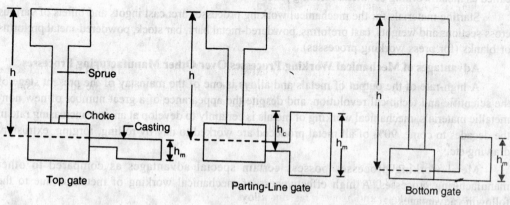

Fig. 3.76. Gates

Chapter
4
Mechanical Working of Metals

4.1. GENERAL

Mechanical working processes are based on permanent changes in the shape of a body, that is, on the plastic deformation under the action of external forces. Mechanical working processes include : rolling, forging, extrusion, drawing and press working (sheet metal working). The stresses induced in the part (due to the application of external forces) are greater than the yield strength and less than the fracture strength of the material, except in shearing, piercing and blanking sheet metal working processes, where the stresses induced in the part are equal to or greater than the fracture strength of the material.

Mechanical working processes exclude the machining (metal cutting) processes, where, even though external forces are used and the stresses induced in the part are equal to or greater than the fracture strength of the material, the part is obtained by removing the material in the form of chips. In mechanical working processes, no chips are produced. In shearing, piercing and blanking sheet metal working processes, even though the part is obtained by cutting it from the sheet metal, no chips are produced. That is why, these processes are also called 'chipless manufacturing processes'. In all other mechanical working processes, the size or shape of a part is obtained by deforming and displacing the material under the action of large external forces. Hence these processes are also called as metal working or 'metal forming processes'.

Starting materials for the mechanical working processes are: cast ingots and billets of various cross-sections and weights, cast preforms, powdered-metal bars, bar stock, powdered-metal preforms or blanks (for press working processes).

Advantages of Mechanical Working Processes Over Other Manufacturing Processes

A high-rate of the output of metals and alloys is one of the mainstay of the present stage of the scientific and technical revolution, and despite the appearance of a great number of new non-metallic materials, mechanical working of metals is certainly to develop at an ever increasing rate in the decades to come. 90% of all metal produced are worked to day by rolling, forging, extrusion, drawing etc.

Metal working processes possess certain special advantages as compared to other manufacturing processes. A high effectiveness of mechanical working of metals is due to the following advantages :

1. Higher productivity, as compared to other manufacturing processes. Modern rolling and forging units fabricate hundreds of tonnes of end products per working shift. Hence these processes are high production rate processes and are most suitable for mass production.

2. The possibility of fabrication items with preset specific physical and mechanical properties and required structure, which, in the final analysis, ensures high-standard quality of fabricated products, one which can not be equalled by any other alternative technique.

This is due to the fact that the fibre lines in the material are not interrupted, but are made to follow the contour of the formed part (The strength of a component is maximum parallel to the direction of the fibre lines, and minimum perpendicular to them). In case of casting, the fibre lines get destroyed on melting of the material. A cast component will have the typical cast dendritic structure resulting in very low mechanical properties. Also, the 'yield' of casting processes varies between 60 to 70%. A machine component has the draw-backs that during manufacture, the fibre lines are also cut and get interrupted resulting in poor mechanical properties of the component. Also, lot of metal is removed to get the final shape of the component, which goes waste in the form of chips. Again, cut fibres are exposed to atmosphere resulting in corrosion of the machined component.

This is best explained by the example of manufacture of a crank shaft. The casting, (Fig. 4.1 (*a*)) has no grain flow and so has the poorest mechanical properties. In (Fig. 4.1 (*b*)), the crank shaft has been produced by machining from a bar stock and the fibre of the metal gets cut and interrupted and for this reason, the mechanical properties of this shaft will be poorer than those of the crank shaft made by forging, (Fig. 4.1 (*c*)), where the fibre of the metal has not been interrupted and continues along the entire length of shaft.

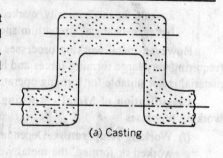

(*a*) Casting

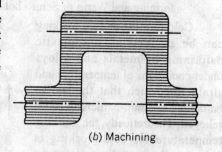

(*b*) Machining

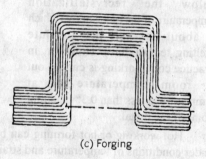

(*c*) Forging

Fig. 4.1. Comparison of Grain Flow.

3. It is clear from the above discussion that the formed components will have higher strength, and better corrosion and wear resistance, as compared to casting and machining processes. Also, formed components have high strength-to-weight ratio.

4. Mechanical working of metals involves minimum waste of metal and, therefore, is used on an ever wider scale in various engineering fields, supplanting machining and other methods that involve loss of metal to chips. etc.

5. High dimensional accuracy and surface finish of the products.

6. By controlling the end forming temperature and the degree of deformation, it is possible to impart any strength to the component within the permissible range. This is a unique advantage of metal working processes as compared to other processes.

7. Many an item can not simply be fabricated by any other alternative means. Extra-thin foil, wire, sheet steel and other products, which are indispensable in modern civilization, originated with the advent and development of mechanical working.

8. During mechanical working of metal, the grains of the material get elongated in the direction of metal flow. so, they would be able to offere more resistance to stresses across them. As

a result, the mechanically, worked metals called wrought products would be able to achieve better mechanical strength in specific orientation, that of the flow direction.

However, metal working processes become impractical when the component is very large (requiring very large forming forces and high tonnage machines), or geometrically complex or the material is not suitable for forming operation.

Classification of Metal - working Processes. There are many ways of classifying metal working processes :

(*i*) **Working Temperature.** Depending upon the temperature at which a material is mechanically worked or formed, the metal working process can be classified as : Cold forming, Hot forming and Warm or Semi - hot forming.

Cold forming or cold working can be defined as the plastic deforming of metals and alloys under conditions of temperature and strain rate, such that the work-hardening or strain-hardening is not relieved. Theoretically, the working temperature for cold working is below the recrystallization temperature of the metal/alloy (which is about one-half the absolute melting temperature). However, in practice cold working is carried out at room temperature or at temperatures less than 0.3 × melting point of the metal.

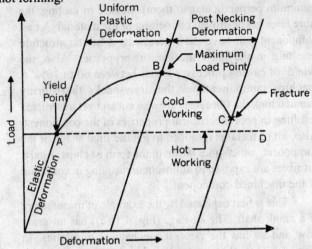

Fig. 4.2. Load Deformation Curve.

Hot working or hot forming can be defined as the plastic deformation of metals and alloys under conditions of temperature and strain rate, such that recovery and recrystallization takes place simultaneously with the deformation. The hot working is carried out above the recrystallization temperature of the material (typically 0.7 to 0.9 times the melting point temperature), and after hot working, a fine refined grained recrystallized structure is obtained.

The recrystallisation temperature is discussed in some detail as below :

Recrystallisation Temperature:

Recrystallisation temperature is very important from the point of view of mechanical working of metals and also regarding process annealing operation.

When a metal is heated and deformed under mechanical force, an energy level will be reached when the old gain structure (which is coarse due to previous cold working) starts disintegrating. Simultaneously, an entirely new grain structure (equi-axed, stress free) with reduced grain size starts forming. This phenomenon is known as "recrystallisation" and the temperature at which this phenomenon starts is called "Recrystallisation temperature". It takes some time for this phenomenon to get completed. According to ASM (American Society of Metals), the recrystallisation temperature is defined as "the approximate minimum temperature at which the complete recrystallisation of a cold worked metal occurs within a specified period of approximately one hour". Recrystallisation decreases the strength and raises the ductility of the metal.

Factors affecting Recrystallisation Temperature:

There are many factors that influence the recrystallisation temperature. These factors are discussed below:

1. Type of Metal : It is lower for pure metals as compared to alloys.

For pure metals, $T_{cr} = 0.3\ T_m$

and For alloys, $T_{cr} \cong 0.5\ T_m$

Where T_m = Melting point of the metal

In practice, Tcr is taken as equal to $\left(\dfrac{1}{3}\ \text{to}\ \dfrac{1}{2}\right) \times T_m$

Recrystallisation temperature of lead and Tin is below room temperature and that for Cadmium and Zinc it is room temperature.

2. *Extent of prior cold work :* Higher the prior cold work, lower will be the recrystallisation temperature.

3. *It is a function of time :* Recrystallisation temperature is a function of time, because the process involves diffusion, that is, movement and exchange of atoms across grain boundaries.

For a constant amount of prior deformation by cold working, the time required for recrystallisation decreases with increasing temperature.

4. Higher the amount of deformation, smaller the grain size becomes during recrystallization.

5. Smaller grain size before cold working, decreases recrystallisation temperature.

6. Increasing the rate of deformation decreases the recrystallization temperature.

7. Presence of second phase particles decreases recrystallisation temperature.

The characteristics of cold working and hot working of metals can be understood from the load deformation curve, (Fig. 4.2). To deform the metal plastically for a permanent change in shape of the work-material, the applied load/stress has to be equal to (atleast) or greater than the yield point of the work material (the elastic deformation being completely recoverable, once the load is taken off). The curve OABC represents the cold working, whereas the curve OAD represents the hot working process. The portion AB represents the uniform plastic deformation region, that is the work hardening or strain hardening region (which means that increasing loads will have to the applied to get increasing deformations). At point 'B' (maximum load point) local neeking of the material starts and the portion BC represents the post necking deformation, ultimately resulting in fracture at point C.

It is clear that in cold working, the force increases with increased deformation, whereas, in hot working, once the forces equals the yield point load, the deformation proceeds at almost constant value of force.

(*a*) **Characteristics of Cold - working.** It is clear from the Fig. 4.2, that due to work hardening, the strength of the metal increases but its ability to deform further (formability or ductility) decreases

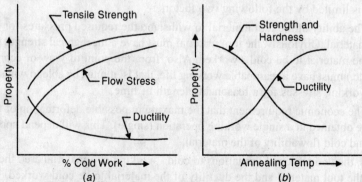

% Cold Work →

(a)

Annealing Temp →

(b)

Fig. 4.3. Effects of Cold Working and Annealing.

with cold working (See Fig. 4.3 (a)). So if the material is excessively deformed, it may fracture before it is formed. To avoid this, large deformations in cold working are obtained in several stages, with intermediate annealing. This will soften the cold worked material and restore its ductility and hence the formability, (Fig. 4.3 (b)).

Advantages of Cold-working :

1. Since cold working is done at room temperature or low temperatures, no oxidation and scaling of the work material occurs. This results in reduced material loss.
2. Surface defects are removed.
3. Excellent surface finish which reduces or completely eliminates subsequent machining resulting in enormous saving in material.
4. High dimensional accuracy.
5. Highly suitable for mass production and automation, because of low working temperatures.
6. Thin gauge sheets can be produced by cold working.
7. Heavy work hardening occurs and so the inherent strength of the material is permanently increased. This makes it possible to use inferior materials whose properties are enhanced by work hardening and preferential flow.
8. The physical properties of metals that do not respond to heat treatment can be improved by cold working.

Draw backs of Cold-working :

1. At low temperatures, the strength of a metal is very high. So, large forces are needed for deformation. For this, high capacity equipment is required which is costly.
2. The ductility / formability of metals is low at low temperatures. Hence for large deformation cold working requires several stages with interstage annealing, which increases the cost of production.
3. Also, due to limited ductility at room temperature, the complexity of shapes that can be readily produced is limited.
4. Since low reductions are required to attain the required parameters, more sensitive controls are needed in cold working than in hot working.
5. Due to very high forces, tool pressures and power requirements are high too. So, the tooling must be specially designed, which increases the tool cost.
6. Severe stresses are set up in the metal during cold working. This requires stress relieving, which again increases the cost.
7. Due to the above factors, normally, only the ductile metals are cold worked.

Materials for Cold-working. In principle, any material can be cold-worked. In practice, however, the choice is limited by the following two factors :-

1. The ability of the tool material to withstand the required pressures for cold -working of a material. Obviously, the tool material must have a mechanical strength greater than that of the material to be cold - worked. Also, from the point of view of economy, the tool (die etc.) must have a reasonable working life, that is, it must be able to withstand the developed working stresses for a reasonable length of time.
2. The economic requirement that the maximum possible deformation of the material should be obtained in a single working operation (single). This will depend upon the cold ductility and cold flowability of the material.

Thus, the two principal limitations to cold - working of a material are : the permissible stress placed on the tool material and the ductility of the material to be cold-worked.

Both cold ductility and cold flowability of a material depend closely on its chemical composition. As for steel, with an increase in the percentage of carbon or alloying constituents, its deformability decreases and the resistance to deformation increases. The maximum limit is usually 0.45% carbon for steels used in cold extrusion and 1.6% carbon for other cold forging operations. Impurities such as S, P, O_2 and N_2, also impair the cold workability of the steel. For cold working, the micro-structure of the material, also plays an important role. Soft annealing known as spheroidize annealing of steel before cold working, improves its cold workability. The grain size is also an important factor. Large grain is easier to cold work, while the parts made from fine grained material are stronger. A good guiding rule for forging steels used to produce forgings is that the stress on the die should not exceed 2500 N/mm^2 and the material must allow at least a 25% deformation in a single step.

As a general rule, the requirements for a material to be cold worked are :

1. Yield stress curve of gentle slope.
2. Early yield point.
3. Then great elongation with pronounced necking before fracture.

The materials commonly used for cold working include : low and medium carbon steel (0.25 to 0.45% C), low alloy steels, copper and light alloys such as Aluminium, Magnesium, Titanium, and Berrylium.

Cold forming is most suitable for axisymmetric components such as shaft components, flanged components, finished gears and bearing races etc.

Characteristics of Hot-working. It is clear from Fig. 4.2 that hot working of the metal occurs at an essentially constant load/flow stress, that is, there is no work-hardening of the metal.

Advantages of Hot-working :

1. The strength of the metals is low at high temperatures. Hence low tonnage equipments are adequate for hot working.
2. Very large workpieces can be deformed with equipment of reasonable size.
3. Because of high ductiliy at high temperatures and absence of work hardening, large deformations can be undertaken in a single stage, and, complex parts can be fabricated.
4. Interstage annealing and stress relieving are not required.
5. Blow holes and porosities are eliminated by welding action at high temperatures and pressure.
6. Grain size can be controlled to be minimum (Fig. 4.4). This makes the metal tougher.

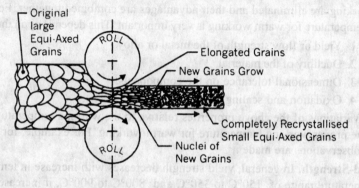

Fig. 4.4. Micro-Structural Changes in a Hot Working Process (Rolling.)

7. Inclusions within the metal are broken up and elongated into fibres or threads with definite orientation. This again makes the metal tougher.

8. Segregation may be reduced or eliminated, since hot working promotes diffusion of constituents.

Typical hot working temperatures are :-

Steels	:	1100 to 1260°C
Cu and its alloys	:	760 to 925°C
Magnesium	:	315°C
Aluminium and its alloys	:	370 to 455°C

Drawbacks of Hot-working :

1. Due to oxidation and scaling, there is heavy material loss. This also results in poor dimensional accuracy and surface finish.

2. Automation is difficult due to high working temperatures.

3. Thin parts (sheets, wires etc.) can not be produced due to loss of ductility because of high rate of loss of heat.

4. High energy costs to heat the metals to high temperature.

5. Surface decarbonisation in steels, reduces strength and hardness on the surface.

6. Due to high working temperatures, these is a serious problem of surface reactions between the metal and the furnace atmosphere, more so in the case of reactive metals like Ti, calling for inert atmosphere.

Note 1. It is clear from the above discussion that hot working is mainly employed to produce large deformations in the material. The final dimensional tolerances accuracy and surface finish are obtained by cold working involving only a small deformation in the material.

2. It should be noted that the difference between cold working and hot working depends only upon the temperature of recrystallization and not on any arbitrary temperature of deformation. Lead, tin and zinc recrystallize rapidly at room temperature (Below 27°C) after large deformations. Hence, the working of these metals at room temperature will constitute their hot working. Similarly working of tungsten at about will be termed its cold working, because it has recrystallization temperature above this value.

However, in every day use, cold working means working at room temperature and hot working means working of a preheated material above its recrystallization temperature.

Warm working or Semi-hot working. It can be defined as plastic deforming of a metal or alloy under conditions of temperature and strain rate, such that the drawbacks of both cold working and hot working are eliminated and their advantages are combined together. For this, the selection of proper temperature for warm working is very important. This depends upon the following factors :

1. Yield or flow strength of the metal or alloy.
2. Ductility of the material.
3. Dimensional tolerance on the components.
4. Oxidation and scaling losses.

The variations of the above properties relative to the working temperature can be studied to arrive at the proper working temperature for warm working. For example, for 0.13% C steel ; the following observations are made :

Yield-Strength. In general, yield strength decreases with increase in temperature. However, in the temperature range of 150°C to 350°C and 800°C to 900°C, it increases with, increases in temperature. The first temperature range is called blue brittleness range of steel and in the second range, structural changes occur in steel. Both these ranges are brittle ranges and if steel is worked in these temperature ranges, it will fracture. So, the best temperature ranges from the yield strength point of view are 400°C to 750°C and above 900°C.

Ductility. In general, the ductility or formability of a material increases with increase in temperature. However, in temperature ranges of 250°C to 350°C and 800°C to 900°C, it decreases with increase in temperature. Thus, from the ductility point of view, the best temperature ranges for the above mentioned steel are : 400°C to 750°C and above 900°.

Dimensional tolerance and Scaling and Oxidation Losses. The dimensional tolerances increase rapidly above 700°C. Similarly, scaling and oxidation losses, which are negligible upto 700°C, increases very rapidly above this temperature.

From the above discussion, it is clear that the best temperature range for working the above-mentioned steel is 400°C to 700°C. Working of steel within this temperature range is called warm working or Semi-hot working.

In general, warm working is done at a temperature of 0.3 T_m to 0.5 T_m, where T_m is the melting point of the material.

(*ii*) **Type of Stress applied to the Workpiece.** On the basis of the type of stress applied to the workpiece as it is formed into shape, the processes can be classified as :

1. Direct compression-type processes.

2. Tension type processes.

3. Combined stress (tension and compression) type processes.

4. Bending type processes.

5. Shear Stress type processes.

Processes in which the material is subjected principally to compressive stress are : forging, rolling, extrusion, coining, spin forging, swaging and kneading etc. The metal flows at right angles to the direction of the applied stress. These processes are also called as "Squeezing processes".

Processes involving the use of pure tensile stresses are : Stretch forming, vacuum forming and creep forming.

In combined stress type processes, the primary applied forces are frequently tensile with the indirect compressive stresses coming into play due to the reaction of the work piece with the die. The processes include: Drawing processes (wire, rod and tube), deep drawing and embossing etc.

Bending involves the application of bending moments to the sheet. The processes include : straight bending or flanging, V-bending, stretch flanging (concave flanging), shrink flanging (convex flanging) and seaming etc.

Processes involving shear stresses refer to the application of shear forces of sufficient magnitude to rupture the metal in the plane of shear (chipless forming). The processes include : Piercing, blanking, press shearing and cutting off, notching and nibbling etc. Fig. 4.5 shows typical metal working operations.

(*iii*) **Steady or Non-steady State Forming.** In steady state processes, the zone in which plastic deformation is enforced, remains fixed in shape and size and does not alter with time. Examples are : drawing processes (wire, rod, tube) and rolling. In non-steady processes, the geometry and zone of plastic deformation continuously change, for example, forging process. Extrusion process is transitory, that is, the deformation is nonsteady at the beginning and end but acquires steady state conditions while the greater part of the billet is extruded.

(*iv*) **Primary and Secondary Metal Forming Processes.** Primary metal working processes are involved in the initial breakdown of the original material (ingot, bloom, billet) to shapes that are then processed for the final product, for example, rolling, forging, extrusion.

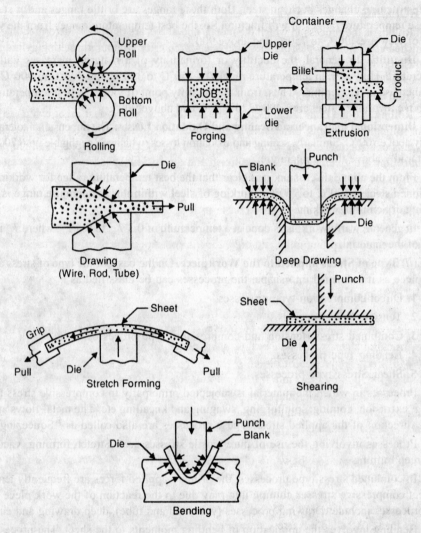

Fig. 4.5. Typical Metal Working Processes.

Secondary processes are those which take the products of some primary processes and change their geometry and properties to the semi-finished or finished stage, for example, drawing processes, spinning, swaging, coining, embossing, stretching, bending, deep drawing, rubber forming and sheet metal forming etc.

(*v*) **Extent of Plastic Deformation Zone.** As per this criterion, the metal working processes can be classified as : Bulk deformation processes and Sheet metal working processes.

In bulk deformation processes, the thickness (diameter or other major dimension) of the workpiece is substantially reduced (changed). These may be steady state or non-steady state processes, for example, forging, extrusion, rolling, drawing etc.

In sheet metal working processes, any change in sheet thickness is fairly limited. But the starting material, that is the sheet, is the product of a bulk deformation process, that is, rolling.

(*vi*) **According to Low or High Rate of Strain.** Conventional metal working processes and non-conventional (HERF, HVF) processes.

(*vii*) **Shape of Workpiece or Finished Part** (sheet metal, bar stock etc.)

4.2. ROLLING

Rolling is the process in which the metals and alloys are plastically deformed into semifinished or finished condition, by passing these between circular or contoured rotating cylinders (rolls). the metal is drawn into the opening between the rolls by frictional forces between the metal and the roll surface (see Fig. 4.4). In deforming metal between rolls, the workpiece is subjected to high compressive force from the squeezing action of the rolls.

Rolling is done both hot and cold. The starting material is cast ingot, which is broken down by hot rolling into blooms, billets and slabs, which are further hot rolled into plate, sheet, rod, bar, pipe, rails or structural shapes. Cold rolling is usually a finishing process in which products made by hot rolling are given a good surface finish and dimensional accuracy with increased mechanical strength of the material. Thinner gauges are obtained by cold rolling. The main objective in rolling is to decrease the thickness of the metal. Ordinarily, there is negligible increase in width, so that the decrease in thickness results in an increase in length.

Rolling is a major and a most widely used mechanical working process. About 75% of steel output is treated in rolling mills and only 25% is consumed for forging extrusion and founding.

4.2.1. Terminology for Rolled Products. The various rolled products are given names according to the dimensions, but the terminology is fairly loose and sharp limits with respects to dimensions can not be made.

Bloom. A bloom is the product of the first break down of ingot. It has square or slightly rectangular section, ranging in size from 150 mm × 150 mm to 250 mm × 300 mm. A bloom is used to make structural shapes, that is, I beams, channels etc., by hot rolling.

Billet. A reduction of bloom by hot rolling results in a billet. The size of a billet ranges from 50 mm × 50 mm to 125 mm × 125 mm. It is rolled to make rounds, wires and bars.

Slab. A slab is a product obtained by hot rolling, either from ingot or from bloom. It has a rectangular cross-section, with thickness = 50 to 150 mm and width = 0.6 to 1.5 m. Slabs are further rolled to get plates, sheets, strips, coil and skelp.

Plate. A plate is a finished or semi-finished product with a minimum thickness of 6.35 mm. Its width will be equal to the width of the roll and the length equal to the maximum which can be handled or shipped.

Sheet. A sheet is a thin partner of plate with a maximum thickness of 6.35 mm. A sheet with B/t less than 3 is called a Narrow sheet. For sheet metal working B/t > 3.

Strip. A strip is a narrow sheet and has a maximum width of 600 mm with a maximum thickness of 6.35 mm. Since it is normally handled in coil form, its length can be considerable and is limited only by the manufacturing and handling facilities.

Foil. It is a thin strip with a maximum width of 300 mm and a maximum thickness of 1.5 mm. It is available in coil form.

Bar. It is a long, straight, symmetrical piece of uniform cross-section. It may be round, square, or of another configuration. A circular bar is called a rod.

Wire. A wire is a thin variety of bar, available in coil form and not normally so identified over 9.5 mm cross-section.

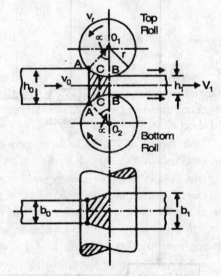

Fig. 4.6. Schematic Diagram of Rolling Process.

Billets are normally further rolled to make rounds, bars and wires. They can also be rolled into flats and sections. These intermediate products are further processed to get final products as shown below. Billets are also hot forged to get final products as shown below:-

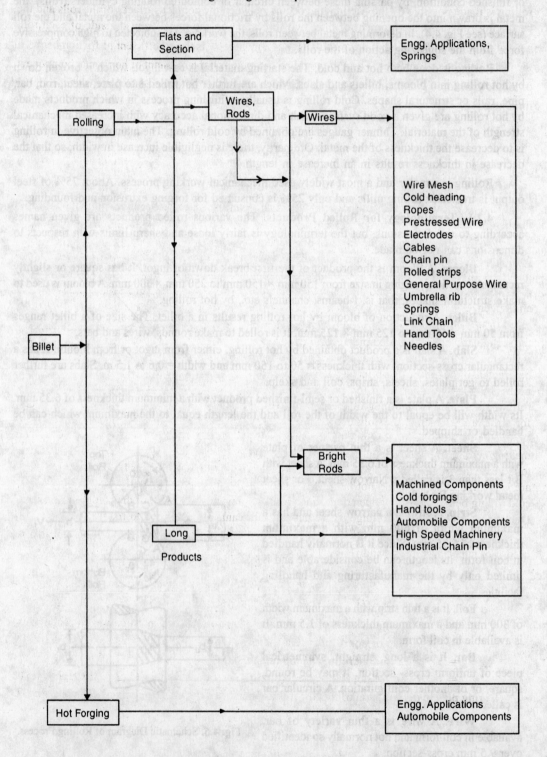

4.2.2. Mechanism of Rolling. Fig. 4.6 shows a schematic diagram of the rolling process. The metal contacts each of the two rolls along the arc AB, which is known as the arc of contact. This arc corresponds to the central angle α, called the "angle of contact or bite". The process of metal rolling is made possible by the friction that occurs between the contact surfaces of the rolls and the part being rolled. At the moment of bite, two forces act on the metal from the side of each roll, normal force P and the tangential force μP (Fig. 4.7) where μ is the co-efficient of friction between the metal and the roll surfaces. The part would be dragged in if the resultant of horizontal component of the normal force P and tangential force (frictional force) μP is directed in that direction. In the limiting case,

$$P \sin \alpha = \mu \, P \cos \alpha$$

$$\mu = \tan \alpha$$

or

$$\alpha = \tan^{-1} \mu.$$

If α is greater than $\tan^{-1} \mu$, the metal would not enter the space between the rolls automatically, that is, unaided.

The maximum permissible angle of bite depends upon the valve of 'μ' which in turn depends upon the materials of the rolls and the job being rolled, the roughness of their surfaces, and the rolling temperature and speed.

In hot rolling, the primary purpose is to reduce the section and hence the maximum possible reduction is desired. so, the value of α and hence of μ should be greater. In hot rolling, lubrication is generally not necessary. On the other hand, on primary reduction rolling mills such as blooming or rough rolling mills for structural elements, the rolls may sometimes be "ragged" to increase μ. Ragging is the process of making certain fine grooves on the surface of the roll to increase the friction. In cold rolling, the rolling loads are very high, hence should not be much. Besides,

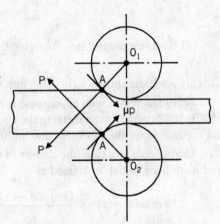

Fig. 4.7. Forces During Rolling.

cold rolling being a finishing operation, rough rolls will impair the surface of the cold rolled product. Due to this, rolls for cold rolling are ground and lubricants are also used to reduce μ.

The usual materials for rolls are : Cast or forged steel. To reduce cast alloyed C.I. can also be used. For superior strength and rigidity, special alloy steels, even though costlier are used.

The usual values of biting angle are :

α = 3° to 4° for cold rolling of steel and other metals with lubri- cation on well-ground rolls.

= 6° to 8° for cold rolling of steel and other metals with lubri- cation on rough rolls.

= 18° to 22° for hot rolling steel sheets

= 20° to 22° for hot rolling aluminium at 350°C

= 28° to 30° for hot rolling steel (blooms and billets) in ragged or well-roughed rolls.

During plastic deformation of metals, it is assumed that the volume remains constant, that is,

$$V_0 \, h_0 \, b_0 = V_1 \, h_1 \, b_1$$

Since

$$b_0 \gtrsim b_1$$

$$V_1 = V_0 \cdot \frac{h_0}{h_1}$$

Now $h_1 < h_0$, $\therefore$ $V_1 > V_0$, and so we have

$V_1 > V_r > V_0$, V_r is the velocity of the roll.

Hence, the speed at which the metal is delivered by the rolls, V_1 is higher and the metal entrance speed V_0 is lower than the peripheral speed of the rolls V_r. At a section C - C in the deformation zone (shown hatched), the velocity of metal will equal the velocity of rolls. This section is called "neutral or no slip section". To the left of neutral section, the deformation Zone is called "Lagging Zone" ($V_0 < V_r$) and to the right of the section, it is called "Leading Zone", ($V_1 > V_r$). We have two definitions,

$$\text{Forward slip} = \frac{V_1 - V_r}{V_r} \times 100; \quad \text{Backward slip} = \frac{V_r - V_0}{V_r} \times 100$$

(i) Absolute draught $\Delta h = (h_0 - h_1)$ mm; relative draught $= \dfrac{\Delta h}{h_0} \times 100$

(ii) Absolute elongation, $\Delta l = (l_1 - l_0)$ mm; Co-efficient of elongation $= \dfrac{l_1}{l_0}$

(iii) Absolute spread $= (b_1 - b_0)$ mm

Spread increases with an increase in roll diameter and co-efficient of friction, as well as with a fall in temperature of the metal in the course of hot rolling. Spread is proportional to the draught and depends upon the thickness and width of the job.

During cold working, the change in the properties of metals depend upon the percentage of cold work used, which is defined as

$$\% \text{ of cold work} = \frac{\text{Original area of cross section} - \text{Final area of cross section}}{\text{original area of cross section}} \times 100$$

$$= \frac{A_0 - A_f}{A_0} \times 100$$

$\therefore$ For cold rolling of sheets, % of cold working $= \dfrac{h_0 b_0 - h_1 b_1}{h_0 b_0} \times 100$

$$= \frac{h_0 - h_1}{h_0} \times 100 = \left(1 - \frac{h_1}{h_0}\right) \times 100 \qquad (b_0 \cong b_1)$$

4.2.3. Rolling mills and their Classification. A rolling mill is a complex of machines for deforming metal in rotary rolls and performing auxiliary operations such as transportation of stock to rolls, disposal after rolling, cutting, cooling, melting, piling or coiling etc. A set of rolls in their massive housing is called a "stand". Rolling mills are classified according to the number of rolls in the working stand, the product rolled, arrangement of stands etc.

1. **Classification Based on Number of Rolls in the Stand.** According to this criteria, rolling mills are of the following types :

    (*i*) two high rolling mill ;   (*ii*) three high rolling mill

    (*iii*) four high rolling mill;   (*iv*) multi-roll rolling mill;

    (*v*) universal rolling mill

    (*i*) **Two High Rolling Mill.** As the name implies, it has two rolls with a constant direction of rotation about the horizontal axes, (Fig. 4.8(*a*)). For successive reductions, the stock is returned to the entrance of the rolls by hand carrying or by means of a platform which can be raised to pass the stock over the rolls.

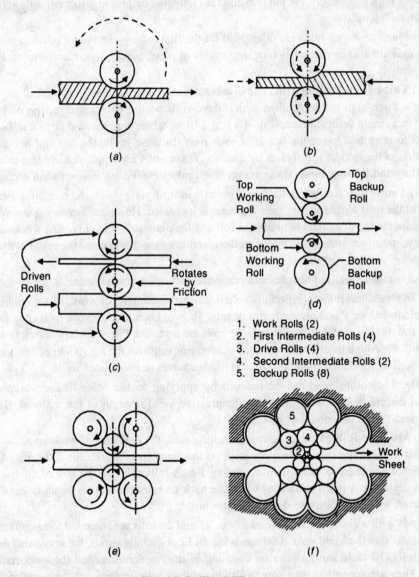

Fig. 4.8. Rolling Mills.

1. Work Rolls (2)
2. First Intermediate Rolls (4)
3. Drive Rolls (4)
4. Second Intermediate Rolls (2)
5. Bockup Rolls (8)

The upper roll may be raised or lowered to change the distance between the rolls. This method of successive reductions slows down the process. The faster method is to pass the stock through a series of rolls for successive reduction, but this method requires more investment in equipment. The alternative procedure is to use "two high reversing" rolling mill, (Fig. 4.8 (b)), where the direction of rotation of the rolls is reversed after each pass. The rolls are brought closer together after each pass and the bar or plate reciprocates many times between the rolls before the final thickness is obtained. This design is limited by the length that can be rolled and by the inertial forces that must be over come each time a reversal is made. Also, much more power is consumed as compared to simple two high stand. Some time is also lost in reversing the mill.

A two high non-reversing mills are the most common for both hot and cold rolling since they are least expensive. Such stands are widely used in mills through which the bar passes only once (continuous mills). Normally, the job movemet is facilitated by providig support rolls at the etry and exit of the rolling mill.

Two high reversing mills are often used for the first rolling of an ingot into blooms and slabs. These stands are also employed as roughing stands of plate, universal, rail and structural and other mills.

(*ii*) **Three High Rolling Mill.** The disadvantages of a two high reversing mill are over come by using a three-high rolling mill in which three rolls with a constant direction of rotation are arranged in a single vertical plane, (Fig. 4.8 (c)). Lifting tables are provided on one or both sides of the stand to raise and lower the bar after each pass. In these mills, the top and bottom rolls are drive rolls and the middle roll rotates by friction. These mills are employed as blooming mills, for billet rolling and finish rolling. These stands also find extensive use in open-train section mills.

(*iii*) **Four-High Rolling Mill.** For a given width of plate/sheet and reduction per pass, the bending of the rolls will be less as their diameter is increased. However, increasing the roll diameter will increase the arc of contact between the roll and the plate/sheet (see Fig. 4.6). This will result in an increase in roll separating force (due to the reaction of the metal on to the rolls), which is given as,

P = mean specific pressure between metal and roll × contact area.

∴ In plate/sheet rolling (especially cold rolling), the diameter of work rolls should be as small as possible to reduce P and power requirements. To avoid bending of work rolls (due to their low strength and rigidity), large diameter back up rolls are installed, Fig. 4.8 (d) resulting in a four-high rolling mill. Four-high rolling mills are used in reversing mills for the hot rolling of armour and other plate, as well as for the hot and cold rolling of sheet steel in continuous mills.

Note. The rolling load can be reduced by applying tensile force to the workpiece in the horizontal direction. This will lower the compressive yield strength of the material. Both "back tension" and "front tension" can be applied.

(*iv*) **Multiple-Roll Mills.** In four-high rolling mill, the diameter of back up rolls can not be greater than 2 to 3 times that of the work rolls. As the diameter of work rolls is decreased more and more to accommodate processes with exceedingly high rolling loads, the size of the back up rolls must also decrease. A point is reached when the back up rolls themselves begin to bend and must be supported, hence the ultimate-design- cluster mill.

Stands with a cluster of six (Fig. 4.8 (e)), 12 and 20 rolls are intended to manufacture strips down to 0.001 mm thick and upto 2000 mm wide. In 12 or 20 rolls stands, the very small diameter of working rolls (10 to 30 mm) allows no coupling of driving spindles, and the work rolls are idle running. They are supported by a row of driving rolls which, in turn, are supported by a row of back up rolls. The work rolls are thus rotated by friction against the driving intermediate back up rolls.

Sendzimir mill. This mill is a modification of the cluster mill with 20 rolls which is very well adapted to rolling thin sheet or foil from high-Strength alloys (*e.g.* Stainless Steel). Only the outer rolls are driven. The remaining rolls get the motion due to friction, from the back up rolls, (Fig. 4.8 (*f*)). High C-steel sheets of 5 to 50 μm can be made to an accuracy of 1 to 5 μm. This type of mill has been set up in Salem Stainless Steel Complex in Tamil Nadu.

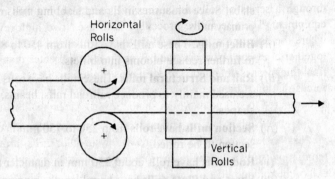

Fig. 4.9. Universal Rolling Mill.

(*v*) **Universal Rolling Mill.** In this rolling mill, the metal is reduced by both horizontal and vertical rolls, (Fig. 4.9). The vertical rolls roll the edges of the bar even and smooth. Vertical rolls are mounted either on one side (front or back) or on both sides fo the horizontal roll stand. The horizontal rolls may be either two-, three-, or four-high arrangement. These mills are used for rolling wide strip, sheets, plates and slabs that require rolled edges and also for rolling of beams and H-sections.

Planetary Rolling Mill. This mill consists of a pair of heavy backing rolls surrounded by a large number of small planetary rolls, Fig. 4.10. The main feature of this mill is that it hot reduces a slab to coiled strip in a single pass. Each pair of planetary rolls gives an almost constant reduction to the slab as it sweeps out a circular path between the slab and the backing roll. The total reduction is the sum of a series of such small reductions following each other in rapid succession. The feed rolls push the slab through a guide into planetary rolls. On its exit side, a 2- or 4-high planishing mill is installed to improve the surface finish and is followed by a coiler.

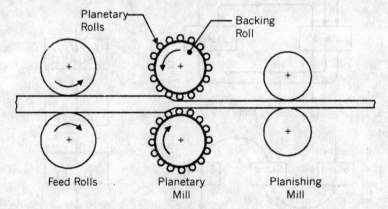

Fig. 4.10. Planetary Rolling Mill.

Steckel rolling. In all the above methods, the rolls are powered and the job is pulled in due to the frictional force between the metal and the roll surface. In steckel rolling, the strip is drawn through idler rollers by front tension only, the torque on the rolls being zero.

2. Classification Based on the Products Rolled. According to the products rolled, the rolling mills may be classified as follows :

      (*i*) **Blooming and slabbing mills.** These are heavy mills with rolls from 800 to 1400 mm in diameter. They are designed to roll ingots (2 to 25 tonnes in weight) into blooms and slabs. Since blooming mills and slabbing mills are quite similar, these are called as primary mills.

(*ii*) **Billet mills.** These mills have rolls from 450 to 850 mm in diameter and are designed to further reduce blooms into billets.

(*iii*) **Rail and Structural mills.** These mills have rolls from 750 to 800 mm in diameter and are used mainly to produce railroad rails, beams, channels and other heavy structural shapes.

(*iv*) **Section mills** have rolls from 250 to 750 mm in diameter, depending upon shape and section to be rolled.

(*v*) **Rod mills** have rolls about 250 mm in diameter and are used to produce wire rod.

(*vi*) **Sheet and Plate mills** have barrel lengths ranging from 800 to 5000 mm for hot rolling and from 300 to 2800 mm for cold rolling.

(*vii*) **Seamless Tube mills** produce seamless tubes as discussed later.

(*viii*) **Tyre and Wheel mills** are used to manufacture rail-road wheels and tyres.

3. Arrangement of Rolling Stands. Single stand mills are used singly or in various floor-layout combinations for rolling metals.

(*i*) **Looping Mill.** (Fig. 4.11 *a*). The products are looped from one mill stand to another by arranging the stands in a "train" in which the rolls of one mill stand are driven from the ends of the rolls in the adjacent stand.

(*ii*) **Cross-country Mill.** , (Fig. 4.11 *b*). It consists of individual roll stands placed some distance apart so that the workpiece must leave one set of rolls before it enters the next set. To save space and avoid complicating the mill drive mechanism, the roll stands are generally arranged in one or more parallel lines. Transfer and skid tables are used to reverse the direction of travel of the workpiece and to convey it from set of roll stands to another.

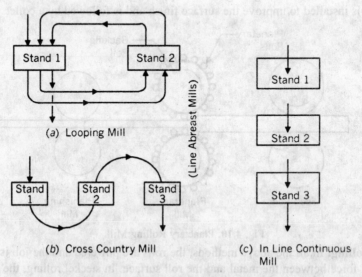

(*a*) Looping Mill

(Line Abreast Mills)

(*b*) Cross Country Mill

(*c*) In Line Continuous Mill

Fig. 4.11. Arrangement of Rolling Stands.

(*iii*) **Continuous Mill.,** (Fig. 4.11 *c*). It employs a number of individual roll stands arranged one behind the other in a straight line (in tandem). The work pieces continuously pass through the various roll stands and emerge from the last roll stand as a finished shape. The rolls of each successive stand must turn faster than those of the preceding one by a precise amount so as to accommodate the increased length which accompanies each successive reduction in thickness.

All the above three mills require a large capital outlay and are only justified for mass production. Looping and cross country mills require the work piece to be bent or turned between the stands and are, therefore, used for rolling rods, rails or sections. Continuous mills are used for plates, strips or sheets. Looping mills and cross-country mills are also called as "Line abreast continuous mills" and continuous mills are called as "In- line continuous mills".

4.2.4. Roll Pass Design. As already discussed, because of the limitations in the equipment and workability of the metal, rolling is accomplished progressively in many steps. Plate, sheet and strip are rolled between rolls having a smooth, cylindrical, slightly cambered (convex) or concave working surface. Bars, rods and special purpose shapes (I-beams, channels and rails etc.) are rolled between grooved rolls. The shape cut into one roll is called the "groove". The shape formed when the grooves of the mating rolls are matched together is called the "pass". By rolling the metal consecutively through the passes, the initial square or rectangular cross-section of the ingot (bloom or billet) can be gradually changed to obtain a bar of the final required shape.

According to their designation, passes fall into the following groups:

(1) Breakdown or roll down or roughing passes.

(2) Leader passes.

(3) Finishing passes.

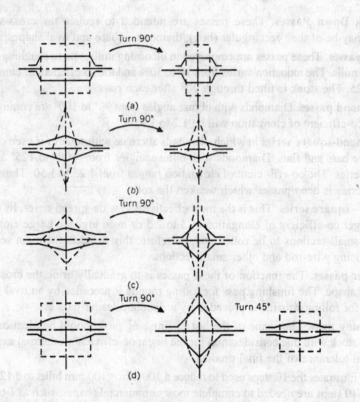

Fig. 4.12. Breakdown Passes.

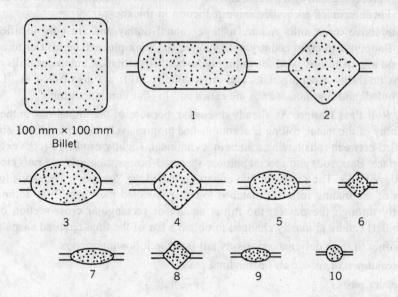

Fig. 4.13. Reduction of a Billet to a Rod.

1. Break Down Passes. These passes are intended to reduce the cross-sectional areas. These passes may be of the : rectangular (box), diamond, square and oval shapes, (Fig. 4.12).

   (*i*) **Box passes.** These passes are employed in blooming mills, and in roughing and continuous billet mills. The reduction varies from 10 to 30% and the co-efficient of elongation from 1.1 to 1.25. The stock is tilted through 90° after each pass.

  (*ii*) **Diamond passes.** Diamonds with obtuse angles from 90° to 100° are commonly employed. The co-efficient of elongation will be 1.2 to 1.4.

 (*iii*) **Diamond-square series** in which diamonds alternate with squares is used chiefly in rolling square bars and flats. Diamonds with obtuse angles from 100° to 125° are employed in this series. The co-effi- cient of elongation ranges from 1.25 to 1.50. The short coming of the series is deep passes which weaken the rolls.

 (*iv*) **Oval - square series.** This is the most effective and wide-spread series. Its chief advantage is larger co-efficient of elongation (1.5 to 2.5 or even higher). Large elongations enable very small sections to be rolled and, therefore, this series is the main sequence used in producing wire-rod and other small sections.

2. Leader passes. The function of these passes is to gradually bring the cross section of the bar to the final shape. The finishing pass for rolling rounds is preceded by an oval leader pass, the finishing pass for rolling squares is preceded by a diamond leader pass etc.

3. Finishing pass. The shape of the last or finishing pass should be identical to that of the finished rolled stock with due consideration for the linear co-efficient of thermal expansion and for the dimensional tolerance of the final product.

Fig. 4.13 illustrates the 10 steps used to reduce a 100 mm × 100 mm billet to a 12.7 mm diameter rod. From 8 to 10 steps are needed to complete most commercial shapes, such as I-beams, channels and rails from blooms.

4.2.5. Ring Rolling. So far we have discussed flat rolling and shape rolling. Seamless rings are used as steel tyres of railway car wheels, as rotating rings of jet engines and as races of ball bearings. The starting material for ring rolling is a pierced billet to form a thick walled ring. This ring is placed between rolls A and B, (Fig. 4.14). The driving roll A is fixed but free to rotate on its axis. The pressure roll B is made to approach A so as to grip the ring between A and B. When the ring is gripped, it is caused to rotate, at the same time the ring is gripped, it is caused to rotate, at the same time being continuously reduced in thickness. If there is no transverse spread, the circumference of the ring steadily increases, until the required diameter is obtained. In order to ensure that a circular ring is rolled, a pair of guide rolls, correctly positioned, must be used. Larger rings are hot rolled, but smaller rings, especially those of small cross-sectional area are frequently cold rolled. In addition to simple rectangular profile, rings of a fairly complex cross sectional profile may be rolled.

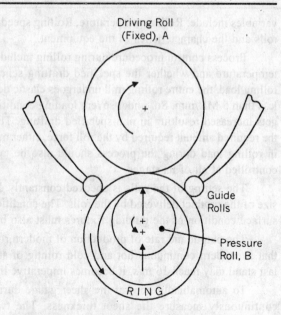

Fig. 4.14. Ring Rolling.

4.2.6. Cold Rolling. Hot rolled products have a relatively rough surface finish and lack dimensional accuracy and certain desired physical properties. However, hot-rolled plate, over 6 mm thick and 1800 to 5000 mm wide, is an important starting material in ship building, boiler making, and high-rise welded machine structures. Hot rolled sheet, 0.8 to 6 mm thick and upto 2300 mm wide is in an important starting material (in coil form) for the cold pressing of structural parts of vehicles, heavy equipment, and machinery and also for making welded tube.

Thinner gauges, better surface finish and tighter tolerances are obtained by cold rolling. Bars of all shapes, rods, sheets and strips produced by hot rolling are commonly finished by cold rolling. Cold rolled sheets and strips make up an important part of total steel production. Cold rolling gives *springiness* to sheets. These sheets are major raw material for some high- production consumer goods industries, such as for household appliances. Machinability of steel is improved by cold rolling and for this reason, cold rolled stock is widely used for fast automatic machining operations. Sheet steel less than 1.25 mm thick is cold rolled because it cools too rapidly for practical hot rolling. Actually, shapes with wall thickness less than 3 mm are very difficult to be hot rolled. Prior to cold rolling, steel is pickled to clean the surface and remove scale.

Large quantities of steel are rolled to about 0.75 mm for automotive and appliance bodies and down to 0.15 mm for food and beverage cans. Copper is rolled to various gauges for roofing, containers, cooking vessels and down to 0.075 mm for radiator fin stock. Aluminium alloy sheet of about 1.0 mm thickness is extensively used in aircraft fuselages, automotive components, and trailer construction. Aluminium foil of down to 0.8 μm gauge is used in large quantities for packaging. Foils of down to 0.3 thickness are produced on special mills in all materials.

Rolling speed may range upto 25 m/s for coldrolling. It can be higher with highly automated and computer controlled facilities.

4.2.7. Rolling Mill Control : As with any metal working process, the rolling process also involves a large number of process and material variables, which have to be controlled to get a product of the desired properties and quality (surface finish and dimensional accuracy). these variables include: Rolling temperature, Rolling speed, Roll gap, lubrication and other conditions of rolls and the characteristics of the equipment.

Process control procedure during rolling includes the checking of the initial and final rolling temperature and whether the specified drafting scheme is being maintained. Under the imposed rolling load, the entire rolling mill undergoes elastic deformation. The mill elastic constant is usually less than 5 MN/mm. So, under severe loading conditions (Cold rolling of thin sheets), the roll gap gets increased resulting in non-specified drafting. Therefore, the roll gap should be decreased by the required amount required by the roll force, either manually or by automatic control. Any variation in rolling load during the process should also be taken care of likewise. The rolling process is controlled at all of its stages.

The setting of the rolls is checked constantly during rolling by inspection of the shape and size of the product delivered by the rolls. The condition of the roll passes as well as the setting and surface condition of the guiding fixtures must also be inspected frequently.

The output and rate of production of modern rolling mills is so high and also due to the fact that in modern continuous hot and cold rolling of strips, the speed of the strip/sheet leaving the last stand may reach 16 m/s, it becomes imperative that these mills are controlled automatically.

To automatically control the sheet gauge during rolling, on-line sensors are employed to continuously measure the sheet thickness. The two commonly used instruments are: flying micrometer and X-ray or isotope gauges. Measurement of thickness by the X-ray gauge depends upon the amount of radiation transmitted through the sheet.

Cold-rolled sheet and strip are produced to very close tolerances as dictated by the subsequent processing and to avoid economic wastage if the sheet/strip is not of the specified dimensions. The most common method of automatic control is to adjust the roll gap. The thickness after the first stand is measured by an X-ray gauge (which has very rapid response). The error signal is fed back to the rolling mill serews of the first stand to adjust the roll gap. This method is quite effective for thick gauges. It is, however, less effective for thin gauges and high speeds of sheet/strip. As the strip becomes thinner and harder, the gauge becomes less responsive to screwdown.

For thin sheets, the more effective method is to adjust the tension in the strip. It is a more sensitive and more rapid technique. For single stand mills, the signal from the sensor is fed to the motor of the coiler, to adjust the speed. In multistand steel strip mills, the interestand tension is adjusted by altering the relative speed of the rolls in the successive stand or the coiler speed.

In continuous hot strip rolling, the sheet thickness is controlled indirectly. The rolling load is monitored and by using the characteristic curve of the mill (Between rolling load and strip thickness showing the elastic curve of the mill structure and plastic deformation curve of the strip), the correct thickness is established by adjusting the roll gap.

4.2.8. Rolling Defects

There are two types of defects which can be observed in rolled products:

1. Surface defects

2. Internal structural defects

1. *Surface defects :* These defects include defects such as: Scale, rust, scratches, cracks, pits and gouges etc. These defects occur due to the impurities and inclusions in the original cast material or various other conditions related to material preparation and rolling operation.

2. *Internal structural depicts :* These defects include defects like:

(a) Wavy edges	(b) Zipper cracks	(c) Edge cracks
(d) Alligatoring	(e) Folds	(f) Lamitations

Defects due to bending of Rolls : The defects of wavy edges and zipper cracks occur due to bending of rolls as explain below:

Rolls act as straight beams loaded transversely (due to rolling loads) and so undergo deflection, Fig. 4.15 (*a*). Due to this, the edges of the job get compressed more than the central portion, that is, the edges are thinner than the central portion, giving the sheet a "Crown". Since the reduction in thickness is converted into increase in length of the strip, the strip elongates more at the edges relative to the centre. However, the material is continuous and to maintain this continuity, strains within the material adjust. There are compressive strains on the edges and tensile strains at the centre, Fig. 4.15 (*b*). Because the edges are restrained from expanding freely in the longitudinal direction wavy edges on the sheet result, Fig. 4.15 (*c*). Under other conditions of the ratio of the mean thickness to the length of the deformation zone, the strain distribution might lead to cracks in the centre of the sheet (known as zipper cracks), Fig. 4.15 (*d*), Zipper cracks can also occur due to poor material ductility at the rolling temperature.

The remedy is to provide a "Camber" to the rolls, that is, their diameter is made slightly larger at the centre than at the edges, Fig. 4.15 (*e*). When under load, the rolls will get flattened along the containing surface and will provide a straight uniform gap to the strip, Fig. 4.15 (*f*).

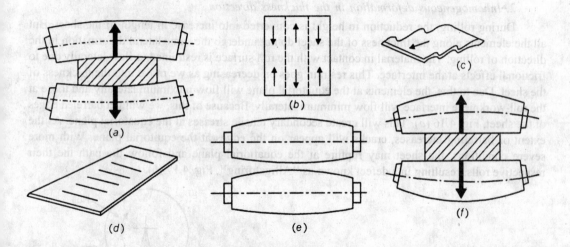

Fig. 4.15. Rolling Defects.

Defects Due to Inhomogenous Deformation

1. *Inhomogeneous deformation of elements across the width :* As the workpiece passes through the rolls, the decrease in height is converted into increase in its length. However, there is a tendency for lateral spread also (in the transverse direction to the rolling direction). This outword lateral spread is countered by the inward shear/frictional forces. Due to friction hill, these forces are maximum towards the centre of the sheet. So, for the elements near the centre of sheet, the lateral spread will be less than for the elements near the edges. Hence, the decrease in thickness for the elements near the centre will be mainly converted into increase in length. But for the elements near the edges, part of the decrease in thickness is converted into lateral spread, so the increase in length will be less than for the elements near the centre. This will result in rounding of the ends of the sheet in the direction of rolling, Fig. 4.16 (*a*). However, due to continuity of material elements, the elements near the edges will be under tension and the elements near the centre will be under compression. Such a situation can lead to edge cracks, Fig. 4.16 (*b*). If the conditions are very severe, the sheet might split along the centre (Centre Split), Fig. 4.16 (*c*).

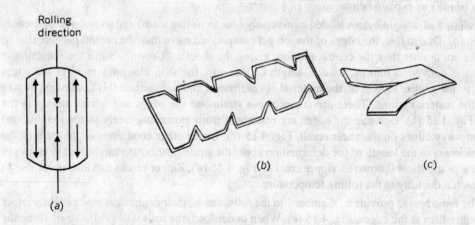

Fig. 4.16. Rolling Defect.

2. *Inhomogeneous deformation in the thickness direction :*

During rolling, the reduction in height is converted into increase in length of the sheet. But all the elements along the thickness of the sheet do not undergo the same lateral deformation in the direction of rolling. The material in contact with the roll surface is restrained to flow laterally due to frictional effects at the interface. This restrain goes on decreasing as we move into the thickness of the sheet. Due to this, the elements at the equatorial plane will flow maximum laterally and those at the roll-workpiece interface will flow minimum laterally. Because of this, we will get barreled edges of the sheet, Fig. 4.16 (*a*). This will create secondary tensile stresses at the equatorial plane. As the extent of barreling increases, cracks will appear on the edges at the equitorial plane. With more severe conditions, the sheet may rupture at the equatorial plane and follow the path the their respective rolls, resulting in a defect known as "Alligatoring", Fig. 4.17 (*b*).

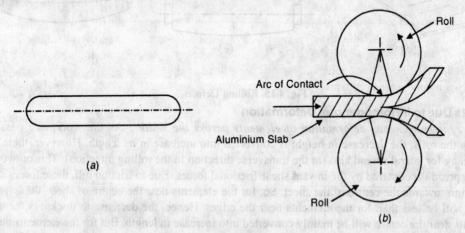

Fig. 4.17.

Folds: these defects are encountered during plate rolling if the reduction per pass is very small.

Laminations : Internal defects such as fissures are encountered due to incomplete welding of pipe and blow-holes during the rolling process. Some defects like longitudinal stringes of non-metallic inclusions are introduced at the time of ingot productions. Under severe reduction, these defects can result into small cracks or laminations along the thickness direction. Due to this, the strength along the thickness direction can get drastically reduced.

4.2.9. Main Process Variables in Rolling Process

The rolling load can be calculated as,

$$P = l.b. \, p_m$$

Where l = Roll-strip contact length

            b = width of sheet

            p_m = mean specific pressure

As is clear from Fig. 4.6, l depends on roll diameter and angle of bite. It is approximately given as

$$l \cong \sqrt{R . \Delta h}$$

Where R = Roll diameter,

and Δh = draft = h0 – h1 (See Fig. 4.6)

p_m depends upon R, h0, h1, and yield strength of the work material.

∴ Main process variables in Rolling process are:—

1. Roll diameter

2. Angle of bite

3. Temperature

4. Strength of work material

5. Speed of rolling

6. Roll gap or draft (h0 – h1)

7. Co. efficient of friction (that is lubrication).

8. Dimensions of sheet, i.e., h0, h1 and b.

4.3. FORGING

Forging may be defined as a metal working process by which metals and alloys are plastically deformed (reduced) to the desired shapes by the application of a compressive force. Forging may be done either hot or cold. However, forging is always understood to be hot working, unless stated other wise. It differs from rolling process which also employs compressive force to deform the metal, in that the pressure is applied intermittently instead of continuous pressure as in rolling. The products generally are discreet pieces rather than a flowing mass as in rolling. Again, the dies used to apply pressure to the material is not a cylindrical roll (as in rolling process) but usually a rectangular block of certain thickness. Also, the dies have a linear working motion instead of rotary motion of rolls in rolling.

Depending upon the mode of application of compressive force, the forging equipment used may be grouped under two main categories :

1. Hammers. Hammers impart stress on the material by impact and they operate in a vertical position.

2. Forging Presses and Forging Machines (Upsetters). In these equipments, the compressive force is applied continuously and the material is gradually pressed or squeezed into shape. The forging press operates in a vertical position like a hammer. The forging machines or the upsetters operate in horizontal position.

Forgings may be produced in either open or closed dies. Dies are made in pairs. In open die forging, the material is struck or pressed between two flat surfaces and the compressive force is progressively applied locally on different parts of the metal stock. In closed-die forging process the force is applied to the entire surface, causing the metal to flow into a die cavity that has been cut to a specific shape. Open-dies are less costly than closed dies and are more economical for a few parts but can be used for simple shapes parts only. On the other hand, for more complex and accurate parts and with increased production rates, closed-dies are employed. Also, less skill is required with closed-dies than with open dies. Most hammers and presses may be used for open or closed-die forgings.

Both types of forging equipment mentioned above have their advantages and limitations with respect to the shapes to be produced and the materials to be used. Open-die hammers are used for production of simple shaped components and for low outputs where the cost of complex impression or closed dies will not be justified. Closed-die hammers are used for production of close- tolerance parts where the quantity of production is comparatively small (upto 2000 parts per die run). For close limit forgings and for large quantity production (5000 to 6000 forgings per die run), presses are employed. Presses are used for large jobs of symmetrical shape, whereas hammers and forging machines are used for smaller parts. When there is a decrease in section, hammer is employed and when there is an increase in section, forging machine or upsetter is used.

In general, the forging process has got the following advantages and drawbacks as compared to other manufacturing processes.

Advantages

1. Impurities in the metal in the form of inclusions are broken up and distributed throughout the metal, resulting in structural homogeneity.
2. Porosity, voids and blowholes in the metal are largely eliminated, resulting in internal soundness.
3. Coarse or columnar grains are refined, resulting in increase in yield and ultimate strengths.
4. Better mechanical properties, especially if the fibre flow lines are properly directed.
5. Greater strength per unit of cross-sectional area under static loads, that is, minimum weight per unit strength; and better resistance to shock.
6. Ability of the forging to withstand unpredictable loads.
7. Superior machining qualities. The uniform structure permits higher machining speeds; the freedom from imbedded impurities allows longer tool life and fewer grindings; and homogeneity reduces machining scrap. Quality of parts is uniform.
8. Minimum metal removal in machining.
9. Relatively smooth surface of the forging.
10. Forgings can be held to within fairly close tolerances.
11. Rapid duplication of components.
12. Wide range of forgeable metals is available.
13. Forgings are easily welded.

Drawbacks

1. In hot forging, due to high temperature of metal, there is rapid oxidation or scaling of the surface resulting in poor surface finish.
2. Tooling and handling costs are high.
3. High tool maintenance.
4. Limitations in space and size.
5. Many intricate and cored shapes possible by casting process cannot be forged.
6. Usually, forgings cost more than castings.

The forging temperatures for hot forging of various metals are as given below :-

Ferrous metals = 930 to 1375°C

Copper, Brasses, Bronzes = 595 to 930°C

Aluminium and Magnesium alloys = 345 to 485°C

The conventional forging processes described in this chapter are intended to apply only to hot forging methods.

4.3.1. Basic Forging Operations

1. **Upsetting.** When a piece of stock is worked in such a way that its length is shortened and either or both its thickness and width (or diameter of a circular stock) increased, the piece is said to be upset and the operation is known as upsetting.

2. **Heading.** When the upsetting is done in such a way that the section of the stock is increased only on one end of the stock, the operation is called heading.

3. **Fullering.** It is the operation of reducing the stock between the two ends of the stock at a central place, so as to increase its length. The inclined surfaces of the die prevents material movement in the width direction (spread) because there is a pressure component acting in the direction of material flow. Repeated strokes, with the work piece rotated around its axis between strokes, allow substantial material redistribution.

4. **Edging.** The function of edging or rolling operation is to distribute the metal longitudinally by moving metal from the portion of the stock where it is in excess to the portion which is deficient in metal. For example, for forging a connecting rod from a bar stock, the metal will have to be moved longitudinally since the section of the rod varies along its length. This is an important operation in closed die forging.

5. **Drawing down.** Drawing down or "Cogging" is an operation similar to fullering with the difference that the stock is reduced at only one end (and its length increased) instead of at a central place as in fullering.

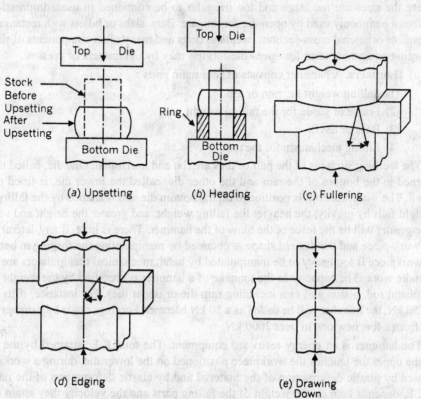

(a) Upsetting   (b) Heading   (c) Fullering

(d) Edging   (e) Drawing Down

Fig. 4.18. Basic Forging Operations.

6. **Bending.** Bending operation makes the longitudinal axis of the stock in two or more places. This operation is done after the stock has been edged or fullered and edged so that the stock is brought into a proper relation with the shape of the finishing impression (in closed die forging) where such a section is of non-symmetrical section.

7. **Flattening.** This operation is used to flatten the stock so that it fits properly into the finishing impression of a closed die.

8. **Blocking.** It is a forging operation which imparts to the forging its general but not exact or final shape. This operation is done just prior to finishing operation.

9. **Cut-off.** A pair of blades, either milled in the corner of a pair of forging dies, or inserted in the dies, used to cut away a forging from the bar after the finishing blow.

10. **Piercing.** Piercing is the operation done with the help of a punch to obtain blind or through holes in the metal. The pierced billet is further processed.

11. **Punching.** This is the operation of shearing out a slug in a forging to produce a hole.

12. **Swaging.** It is the operation of reducing or changing the cross-section area of diameters by revolving the stock under fast impact blows.

13. **Coining.** It is a cold closed die forging operation (no flash) to obtain closer tolerances and smoother surfaces.

4.3.2. Forging Processes. Forging processes may be grouped under two headings : open die forging and closed or impression die forging :

4.3.2.1. Open-Die Forging. In open-die forging which is also called 'Hammer forging' or 'Flat-die forging', the work piece is struck or pressed between two flat surfaces. Open-die forging is used where number of components to be forged is too small to justify the cost of impression-dies or where the sizes are too large and too irregular to be contained in usual impression dies. The shapes most commonly used by open-die forging are: Bars, slabs or billets with rectangular, circular, hexagonal or octagonal cross-sections, weldless rings and many other components of simple shapes. The forging equipment used for open- die forging may by : Hammers or presses.

(*a*) **Hammers.** A hammer consists of four main parts :

(1) Falling weight *i.e.* ram or top

(2) Frame or guide for the falling weight.

(3) Base or anvil.

(4) Lifting mechanism for the ram.

The working surfaces of the pair of dies are flat and horizontal. One die, called the upper die, is fastened to the bottom of the ram and the other die, called the lower die, is fitted on the top of the anvil. The work-material is positioned on the bottom die and is shaped by the falling weight. As the weight falls by gravity, the heavier the falling weight, and greater the height and velocity of the fall, the greater will be the force of the blow of the hammer. There is little, if any, lateral confinement of the work-piece and the desired shape is obtained by manipulating the forging in between blows. If the workpiece is too heavy to be manipulated by hand, mechanical manipulators are used to hold and handle work. The capacity or the tonnage of a hammer is specified by the weight of its falling parts (piston rod, piston and ram including ram die or upper die). For instance, if its falling parts weigh 50 kN, the hammer will be called as a 50 kN hammer. Forgings made by hammer forging may weigh from a few newtons to over 2000 kN.

The hammer is an energy-restricted equipment. The total K.E. attained by the falling parts when the upper die touches the workpiece positioned on the lower die, during a working stroke, is dissipated by plastic deformation of the material and by elastic deformation of the ram and anvil. This K.E. depends both on the weight of the falling parts and the velocity they attain at the end of the downward stroke $\left(\text{K.E.} = \dfrac{1}{2}mv^2 \right)$. Again, v, depends upon the stroke of the hammer

($v = \sqrt{2gh}$, $h = stroke$). Therefore, it is necessary to rate the capacities of the hammers in terms of kinetic energy, *e.g.*, metre-kilograms or metre- tonnes. The practice of specifying a hammer by its falling weight is not useful. That can be regarded only as a specification and not the capacity of the hammer.

We know that in hammer forging, the hammer is lifted up to a certain height and then it is allowed to fall by gravity. Depending upon the lifting mechanism, the hammers may be classified as : Spring hammers, Pneumatic hammers and steam-and- air hammers. Steam and air hammers are most widely used in forging practice and they operate either on steam or on compressed air. Steam and air hammers are of two types : single acting and double acting. In single acting hammer, the steam or air pressure is used only to lift the ram which then falls by gravity. In double acting hammer, the steam or air is employed both for raising the ram and for increasing the force of its impact on its downward stroke. In 'single acting steam-air hammer', steam or compressed air is delivered to the cylinder through inlet port (Fig. 4.19), thus raising the piston and the ram connected to it. The force necessary to ensure quick lift up of the ram can be 3 to 5 times the ram weight. When the ram has been lifted to a sufficient height, the steam or air is cut off which escapes through the inlet port. The ram drops down under its own weight and strikes the workpiece positioned on the anvil block. In order to slow down the speed of the piston as it reaches its upper position, several ports are provided in the upper section of the cylinder. As these ports are covered by the piston on its

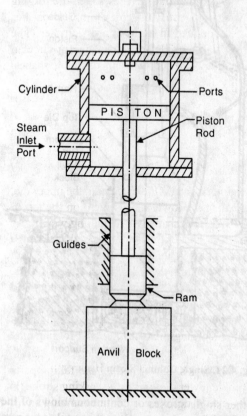

Fig. 4.19. Single Acting Steam Hammer.

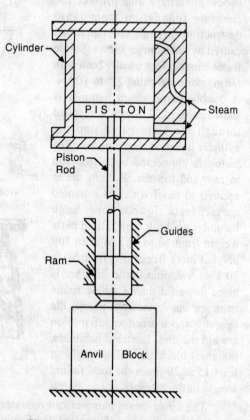

Fig. 4.20. Double Acting Steam Hammer.

upward travel, the air in the cylinder above the piston cannot escape and will start getting compressed. This compressed air will act as a buffer and slow down the upward motion of the piston. Single acting steam-air hammers are seldom used now.

In double acting steam hammer (Fig. 4.20), ports are provided both at the upper section and lower section of the cylinder. On the down ward stroke of the ram, steam enters the cylinder from the upper port and acts on the piston to increase the impact force of the ram. For lifting the ram, steam enters the cylinder from the bottom port. As the ram moves upward, the steam above the piston escapes through the upper port. Steam or air pressure em- ployed ranges from 7 to 9 atm., gauge pressure. Steam hammers are built with ram weight upto 100 kN, and the stroke is 0.9 m to 1.2 m.

By design of columns, steam-air hammers are divided into Single column or frame hammer and double column (frame) hammer. A single frame steam hammer is shown in Fig. 4.21. The hammer is installed on a concrete foundation. The anvil block is mounted on its own foundation separate from the frame. Both are installed on separate wooden beams. These wooden supports act as shock absorbers and protect the concrete foundation from rapid destruction through the vibrations caused by the hammer blows. Single frame hammers are usually built with falling parts weighing 2.5 to 10 kN. A double frame steam hammer is shown in Fig. 4.22. Steam is supplied through the slide valve into the cylinder under or above piston. The piston is connected by piston rod to ram and top die. Bottom die is secured to anvil which is mounted on separate foundation. Such hammers are built with falling parts weight from 10 to 50 and even 100 kN, but more frequently, from 30 to 50 kN. A double frame hammer is more powerful than a single frame hammer, but it does not permit the operator more freedom of motion around the dies. In steam hammers, the anvil block normally weighs at least 15 to 20 times the total falling weight of the hammer.

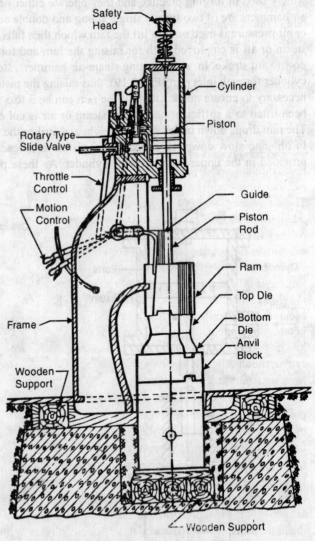

Fig. 4.21. Single Column Steam Hammer.

The air-or-steam hammer can operate with either single strokes or continuous blows of the ram die on the forging. If required, the forging can be held down (squeezed) to the anvil or the ram can be held up. The single acting hammers are also called as "Steam/air lift, gravity drop hammers" and double acting hammers are called as "Steam/Air lift, Steam/Air drop hammers".

Pneumatic Hammer. Pneumatic power forging hammers are usually used to smith forge small parts. In these hammers, the weight of Anvil is equal to (15 to 20) times the falling weight. A pneumatic forging hammer, (Fig. 4.23), has two cylinders : a compressor cylinder and a ram cylinder. Air is compressed on both upward and downward strokes of the piston in the compressor cylinder and is delivered to the ram cylinder where it actuates the ram of the ram cylinder, delivering the forging blows to the work. The reciprocation of the compressor piston is obtained from a crank drive which is powered from on electric motor through a reducing gear.

The distribution of air bet- ween compressor cylinder and ram cylinder is controlled by means of two rotary valves with ports through which air passes into the ram cylinder, below and above the ram, alternately. The valves are actuated by depressing foot treadle or operating a hand lever. By cont- rolling air distribution the required ram movement can be attained : either continuous blows are deli- vered to the forging, or the forging is held down on the anvil, or the ram is held in its upper position. The upper die is secured to the bottom of the ram and the bottom die is secured to a steel cap by means of taper keys in a dovetail joint. The steel cap is mounted on a heavy anvil which is separate from the hammer frame.

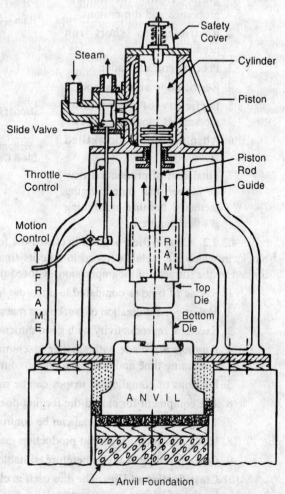

Fig. 4.22. Double Column Steam Hammer.

The size of the pneumatic hammer, *i.e.*, the weight of its falling parts (weight of the ram piston, ram and upper die) usually varies from 0.5 to 10 kN. Such hammers operate at 80 to 200 blows per minute. In these hammers, the ram falls not only under its own weight but the downward force is also increased by the action of compressed air above the ram.

(*b*) **Hydraulic Presses.** For the fabri- cation of heavy forgings, hydraulic presses are employed. In presses, the material is worked upto a greater depth as compared to hammers. The action of a press is opposite to that of the hammer. In hammer forging, the maximum amount of energy is available at the instant the upper die touches the work-piece and is gradually reduced to zero as the metal deforms. But in press, the force builds up from minimum at the start of stroke to maximum at the bottom of press stroke. Hydraulic presses are rated according to the maximum force they can exert. They range in size from 5 to 500 MN. For open-die forging, their size ranges from 2 to 150 MN.

Limitations of Open-Die Forging

1. Less control in determining grain flow, mechanical properties and dimensions.

2. Restricted to short run production.

3. Poor material utilization.

4. Restricted to simple shapes.

5. Difficulty of maintaining moderately close tolerances.

6. Absolute need for skilled labour.

7. Final cost of production may be higher than other forging methods, because machining is often required.

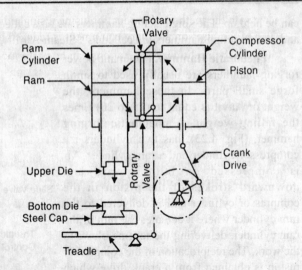

Fig. 4.23. Pneumatic Hammer.

4.3.2.2. Closed-Die Forging. In closed-die forging, cavities or impressions are cut in the die block, in which the metal is forced to take its final shape and dimensions. The flow of metal is limited by the surfaces of the impressions. Closed-die forgings have the following characteristics :-

1. Saving of time as compared to open-die forging.

2. Makes good utilization of workpiece materials.

3. Excellent reproductivity with good dimensional accuracy.

4. Forgings are made with smaller machining allowances, thus reducing considerably the machining time and the consumption of metal required for the forging.

5. Forgings of complicated shapes can be made.

6. The equipment for closed-die forging does not require highly skilled workers.

7. The grain flow of the metal can be controlled ensuring high mechanical properties.

8. Method is suited for rapid production rate.

9. Cost of tooling is high, therefore, suitable for large production runs.

(*a*) **Classification of Dies.** The dies used in closed-die forging or impression-die forging may be classified into two groups :

    (*i*) **Single Impression Die.** This die contains only one cavity or impression which is the finishing impression. The preliminary forging operations are done by hand or on forge hammers, forging rolls etc., and only final finishing operation is done in the die-cavity.

    (*ii*) **Multi - Impression Die.** This die contains finishing operation and one or more auxiliary impressions for preliminary forging operations. The final shape of a part is progressively developed over a series of steps from one die impression to the next. Generally, multi-impression dies are very expensive to make and are employed only when the quantity to be made is sufficiently large.

Advantages of Multi-Impression Die

(1) Complete sequence of forging operations can be carried out on one equipment only, avoiding the use of auxiliary forging equipment.

(2) Use of multi-impression dies is particularly suited for production of small and medium sized forgings in large quantities as this method gives 2 to 3 times the production compared

with the method of production using a single die. This is because the time of preparation of the 'use' on auxiliary equipment is reduced or eliminated.

(3) All the preliminary operations can be performed on these dies with good ease. The 'use' can be prepared to fairly accurate dimensions. Besides this more accurate forgings are prepared.

(4) Wastage of forging metal is reduced.

(5) 'Use' may not be reheated for the finishing impression.

(6) Initial die cost becomes insignificant in case of high output.

(7) Finishing impression lasts long, because, much of the load is taken by blocking impression.

(*b*) **Classification of Closed-Die Forging.** Closed-die forging is of three types :

    (*i*) **Drop Forging.** In this process, the forging is made by hammering a heated bar or billet into aligned die cavities. The forging equipment used for this is 'Drop Hammer'. Drop hammers are very similar in design and arrangement to the steam hammers already described. They have the added provision of larger and more accurate guides for the vertical movement of the ram, so that the top die meets the bottom die in close alignment. Also the frame of a drop forging hammer is secured to the anvil block and the total hammer structure is mounted on single foundation. This is to keep upper and lower dies aligned. The two most commonly used drop forging hammers are : Steam-Air-drop hammer and Board drop hammer.

Steam-Air Drop Hammer. Steam-air drop hammer has two column frame which is secured to the anvil block by spring loaded bolts, which dampen impacts. A steam drop hammer is not truly a drop hammer, since steam pressure is used to raise the ram as well as to control the strike force. A steam hammer ranges in capacities from 2.25 to 225 kN. It works rapidly and can deliver upto 300 blows per minute. The steam or air pressure used ranges from 7 to 9 gauge atmospheres. The impact of the striking blow can be varied from a light tap to full blow. The operation is controlled by a foot treadle. The control diagram of a steam drop hammer is shown in Fig. 4.24. The treadle is used to deliver the striking blow by controlling the throttle valves. The treadle must be depressed for each blow that is delivered by the steam drop hammer. The magnitude of the blow is dependent on the speed and distance the treadle is depressed. When the treadle is pressed down, the throttle valve becomes wide open and steam enters through the inlet to the centre of the slide valve and flows to the top of the piston to exert pressure. When the treadle is released, steam enters at the bottom portion of the cylinder and lifts the piston and ram. As the ram moves upward, there is a slight movement of the cam which raises the slide valve

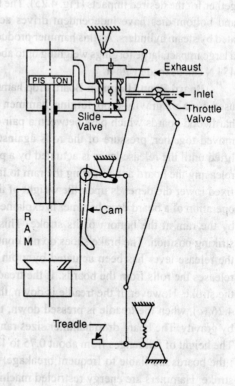

Fig. 4.24. Steam Drop Hammer.

slightly. Due to this, a small amount of steam is admitted to the upper side of the piston, which exhausts from the lower side. As the ram travels further up, the slide valve moves slightly downward. Due to this action of cam when the treadle is up, ram oscillates in the idling position, thus ensuring a constant supply of steam through the cylinder and avoiding the possibility of condensation.

A variation of the hammer discussed above is the 'gravity drop hammer'. In this design, the steam or air that is used to lift the ram is suddenly released to allow the ram to fall freely under gravity. The chief drawback of steam-air drop hammer is a need for large foundations, and despite the precaution, appreciable vibration of soil and of production shop building. This trouble is eliminated by using a 'Counterblow Steam Hammer'. This hammer has two opposed vertically moving rams, which move in opposite directions and meet together for the desired impacts (Fig. 4.25). The top and bottom dies have independent drives actuated by steam cylinders. As this hammer produces a large impact, large forgings weighing upto about 45 kN can be made with it.

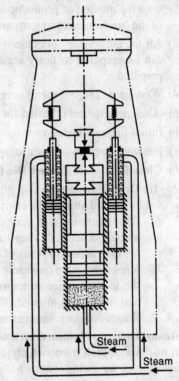

Fig. 4.25. Counter Blow Steam Hammer.

Board Drop Hammer. Board drop hammer is a gravity drop hammer. It is the most commonly used type of gravity-drop forging hammer. The ram carrying the upper die is fastened to the hardwood boards which pass between a pair of steel rolls which rotate continually. These rolls are moved together, pressure of the rolls against the boards raises the ram. The ram continues to be lifted until the release lever is actuated by a pin on the ram. This causes the rolls to move outward, releasing the board and allowing the ram to fall freely by gravity. The force of the blow against the fixed lower die depends upon the weight of the falling ram and the height to which it is lifted. The operation of a board drop hammer is explained in Fig. 4.26 (a), the knock off dog has been actuated by the ram at the bottom of its stroke. This causes the rolls to engage the ram and lift it to its striking position. The brake shoes do not contact the boards as the treadle is down. In Fig. 4.26 (b), the release lever has been actuated by a pin on the ram. This raises the front rod upward, which releases the rolls from the boards. If the treadle is up, the break shoes hold the boards at the top of the stroke. However, if the treadle is down, the blows of the ram are repeated automatically. In Fig. 4.26 (c), when the treadle is pressed down, the brake shoes disengage the board and the ram falls by gravity. The board drop hammer sizes range from about 900 to about 45000 kN. falling weight. The height of fall ranges from about 0.75 to 1.5 m. The disadvantages of the board drop hammer are : the boards are liable to frequent breakage, the intensity of blow cannot be controlled during the stroke. Hammers are energy restricted machines since the deformation results from dissipating the kinetic energy of the ram.

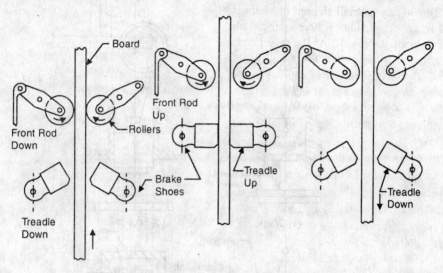

Fig. 4.26. Board Drop Hammer.

The other types of drop hammers employed in modern forge shops are :

1. **Belt Drop Hammers.** In these hammers, the ram is suspended from a belt. The mechanism of belt drop hammers is operated by 5 to 15 hp electric motors. Generally, these hammers are made with ram weights ranging from 1 kN to 1.5 kN. The main disadvantage of these hammers is the rapid wear of the belts which are in constant touch with rotating pulley.

2. **Rope Drop Hammers.** Here the ram is suspended from a rope.

3. **Chain Drop Hammers.** Here, the ram is suspended from a chain.

(*ii*) **Press Forging.** Like drop forging, press forging also uses impression dies but the parts are made by plastically deforming a metal blank into die-cavities by a slow squeezing action. The forging pressure builds up from the start to the end of stroke, resulting in maximum penetration and in improved grain flow throughout the entire forging. Completed forgings are ejected manually or mechanically from the die cavities.

The presses used for press forging are : Mechanical Presses (crank, eccentric, knuckle or screw type) and upright hydraulic presses (see Fig.4.27). The power flow diagram of a crank type mechanical press is shown in Fig. 4.28. An electric motor drives the flywheel mounted on the counter shaft by means of a belt drive. Torque from the counter shaft is transmitted to the crankshaft through gearing. From the crankshaft, reciprocating motion is given to the ram with the help of a connecting rod. The bottom die is locked in position by means of a wedge mechanism. Disk clutch is used to start and stop motion of ram which is brought to a gradual stop by means of a brake. Mechanical presses are faster than hydraulic presses and operate at about 25 to 100 strokes per minute. Their capacities range from 900 kN 110 MN and they are generally employed for non-ferrous alloys weighting up to about 135N. Hydrau- lic presses are larger having capacities upto 450 MN.

The initial cost of a hydraulic press is higher than that of a mechanical press of equivalent capacity. However, in a hydraulic press, pressure can be changed as desired at any point in the stroke by adjusting the pressure control valve. This will help in controlling the rates of deformation according to the metals being forged. But in hydraulic presses, the contact time between the workpiece and the dies is more as compared to a mechanical press. Due to this the die life in hydraulic presses is sometimes shortened because of heat transfer from hot workpiece to the dies.

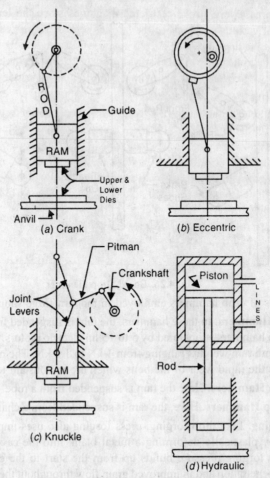

Fig. 4.27. Presses.

Hydraulic presses are of two types :

1. **Direct-drive hydraulic presses.** These presses usually employ hydraulic oil or water as the working medium which is pressurised directly by high pressure pumps.

2. **Accumulator-driven hydraulic presses.** These presses usually employ a water oil emulsion as the working fluid supplied from accumulators which are in turn pressurized by high pressure pumps.

The larger presses (10,000 to 50,000 t) are of this type. The accumulator drive is more economical if one accumulator system can be used by several presses, that is, multiple ram forging, thereby, leading to enhanced production rates.

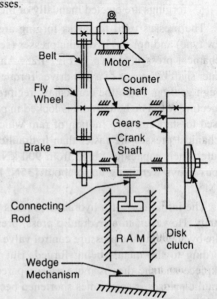

Fig. 4.28. Crank Type Mechanical Press.

Mechanical presses are stroke-restricted machines since the length of the press stroke and the available load at various positions of the strokes represent their capabilities. Hydraulic presses are load-restricted machines because their capacity to do a forging process depends upon their maximum rating. The ram stroke in mechanical presses (the most commonly used is eccentric press) is shorter than in a forging hammer or hydraulic press, therefore, these presses are best suited for low profile forgings.

It may be of interest that every 10 MN of crank mechanicalpress approximately to 1 tonne of falling parts of a hammer. The cost of a crank-type press is higher than that of an equivalent hammer. However, crank type presses are economically advantageous even in low volume production runs, provided equipment is utilized to no less than 35 to 40%. Hydraulic presses are used to produce slender forgings and forgings from poorly plastic alloys and to effect operations requiring large- stroke tools. This technique is applicable to the manufacture of large levers, flanges, toothed wheels, hollow bodies, railway wheel disks, crankshafts, tank bottoms, propellers, ribbed panels and other parts of aircraft and rocket bodies.

In friction screw presses, the blow is midway between that of a hammer and mechanical hydraulic press. These machines are used extensively for hot brass work, but can also be used for steel drop-forging of small sizes.

Advantages of Press Forging over Drop Forging

Die forging presses were introduced in the early thirties, for large scale production of die forgings. These forging presses have been replacing the drop forging hammers and today are widely used through out the die forging industry. The special advantages of die forging presses are as given below:

(1) Press forging is considerably quieter operation than drop forging.

(2) Press forging is normally faster than drop forging since only one squeeze is needed at each die impression.

(3) Alignment of the two die halves can be more easily maintained than with hammering.

(4) Structural quality of the product is superior to drop forging.

(5) With ejectors in the top and bottom dies, it is possible to handle reduced die drafts. Forgings obtained will thus be more accurate. Also, reduced die drafts reduce the weight of the charge and subsequent machining of the workpiece.

(6) High longitudinal and transverse stability of the press contri- butes to fine accuracies and this results in uniform forgings with exacting tolerances and low machining allowances.

(7) The number of strokes and ram speed are high (for mechanical press) and the ejectors release the forgings from the dies immediately after the deformation has taken place. The shorter contact periods, thus obtainable in mechanical die forging presses, increase die life.

(8) Simple handling enables high output even with unskilled operators.

(9) Mechanisation of workpiece transfer further increases pro- ductivity.

(10) Low susceptibility to failure and simple maintenance.

(11) Die forging presses are ecologically safer than forging hammers and screw presses.

A multi impression die and the forging sequence for a connecting rod is shown in Fig. 4.29. The heated forging stock is first placed into the fullering impression 1 where it is reduced by the blows of the hammer with an increase in its length. The next operation "edging", 2, redistributes the metal, the cross-section is increased at certain places and reduced at others as required to fill the cavities of the die. After this, the bending operation is done on the stock to give it proper shape, in bender 4.

Before being forged in the finish impression 3, the stock is processed in the blocking (semifinish) impression 5. By giving the forging its general shape, the blocking operation reduces the wear of the finishing operation. The finish impression, imparts the final shape to the forging. The flash gutter 6 (to collect the excess metal) is provided only around the finish impression. Forging in the blocking and finishing impressions is done in one (less frequently) or several blows of the hammer ram. Fig. 4.29 (a) is the part drawing, Fig. 4.29 (b) is the bottom half of the die and Fig. 4.29 (c) illustrates the forging sequence.

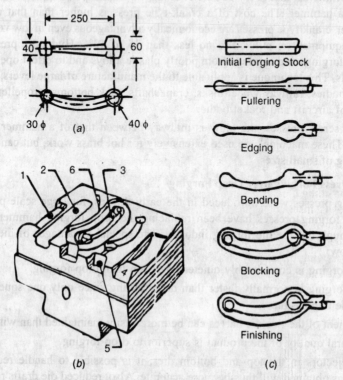

Fig. 4.29. Multi-Impression Forging Die.

(iii) **Machine Forging (Upset Forging).** Like press forging, in machine forging also, the material is plastically deformed by squeeze pressure into the shape provided by the dies in the forging machine. But unlike press forging, it operates in horizontal direction. It is the forging method which is often selected when certain parts are required with an increased volume of metal at the centre or only at one end. The automatic forging machines are employed for the mass production of nuts, bolts, rivets, wood screws, roller and ball bearing balls, gear blanks, valve stems, axles, couplings and other axially symmetrical items. The initial blanks are standard rolled stock, such as sections or rods cut to required lengths. The forging machine consists of a heavy cast steel body in which its three main components, stationary die, moving die and heading tool are properly secured. The operation of the machine can be explained with the help of Fig. 4.30. Fig. 4.30 (a) shows the parts to be forged. For this purpose, barstock of the correct size is selected, one of its ends heated and stock placed in position in the stationary die and pushed forward until it contacts the stock gauge. As the lever is pressed down, the moving or gripper die closes against the stationary die so that the stock is tightly gripped. At the same time, automatic stock-gauge moves aside, as shown in Fig. 4.30 (c). Then header slide moves forward and forces the heading tool against the projecting plastic stock, moving the stock into the cavities of the dies (Fig.4.30 (d)). After the metal completely fills the die impression, both the moving die and the heading tool start moving back to their original positions, as shown in Fig. 4.30 (e). Horizontal forging machines are specified or rated for size by the diameter of the largest bar size they could handle. These machines can handle bar stock ranging in diameter from 6.35 mm. to 254 mm. with a maximum metal deforming pressure ranging from 500 kN to 30 MN.

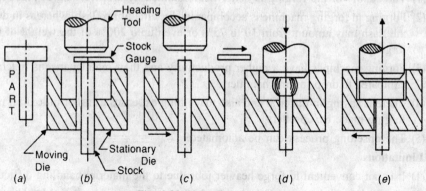

Fig. 4.30. Upset Forging.

The power flow diagram of a forging machine is shown in Fig. 4.31. An electric motor rotates flywheel which is mounted on a drive shaft. This shaft, through a system of gears. rotates crank shaft, connected to sliding block through connecting rod. Sliding block carries heading tool slide in which heading tool is inserted. Connecting rod connects the sliding block only when the foot treadle is pressed down. The free end of the connecting rod then enters the recess of the sliding block, thereby actuating the latter. Through levers and with the aid of eccentrics, lateral sliding block actuates the moving die slide which carries the moving die. The stationary die is secured in stationary die holder. The movements of sliding block and moving die slide are adjusted so that the

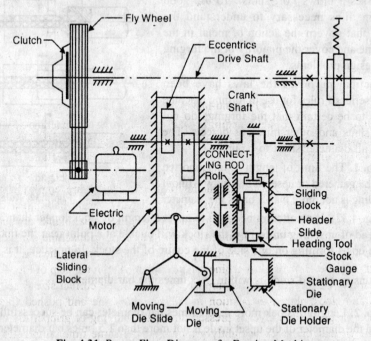

Fig. 4.31. Power Flow Diagram of a Forging Machine.

stock to be upset, when inserted in the machine upto stock gauge, is gripped between the moving die and the stationary die and only after this does the heading tool, secured in he heading tool sli|e, commences to move. Stock gauge is now withdrawn from the range of travel of the slide by the roll. During its return stroke, the heading tool releases the work.

Advantages of Machine Forging

(1) The quality of the forging is better than obtained by drop forging or press forging.

(2) Forging in forging machine is accompanied by little or no flash, whereas in drop forging, the flash may amount from 10 to 75% or even upto 200% of the weight of the finished forging.

(3) Forging machines have a higher productivity and their maintenance is much cheaper as compared to drop forging hammers.

(4) There is saving in material and also machining expenses as no or little draft is needed on forging made by upsetters.

(5) The upsetting process can be automated.

Limitations

(1) It is not convenient to forge heavier jobs due to the material handling difficulties.

(2) The maximum diameter of the stock which can be upset is limited (Max about 25 cm).

(3) Intricate, nonsymmetric and heavy jobs are difficult to be forged on a forging machine.

(4) The tooling cost may be high.

Rules for Machine Forging

In completing a forging in the forging machine, one or more steps comprise the sequence so that metal may not fold upon itself producing a cold shut or cracks in the forgings. These steps are commonly termed as 'passes', 'blows'; or 'shots'. To use good forging design, it is necessary to understand the practical laws that govern the action of metal in the forging machine and cover the majority of the forging machine die design problems.

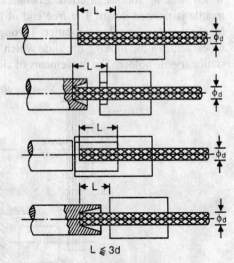

$L \leqslant 3d$

Fig. 4.32. Rule 1.

For practical purposes the laws have been translated into series of rules for use in forging machine practice so as to be certain that the forgings do not develop cold shuts and other injurious defects. The rules apply to all diameter stock to be upset.

Rule No. 1. The limit of length of unsupported stock that can be gathered or upset in one blow without injurious buckling is not more than 3 times the diameter of the bar, (Fig. 4.32). If an attempt be made to upset a length of stock longer than 3 times the bar diameter, instead of upsetting uniformly, the stock will buckle at a point near the middle and result in more of the upset forming on one side of the centre of the stock. In practice, it is better that the length of the unsup- ported stock is within $2\frac{1}{2}$ times the bar diameter.

Rule No. 2. Length of stock more than 3 times bar diameter can be successfully upset in one blow, provided the diameter of the upset made is not more than 1.5 times bar diameter. If this is kept more than 1.5d, the buckling will be excessive and the stock will fold in. In practice, it is advisable not to exceed 1.3 times bar diameter (Fig. 4.33).

Rule No. 3. In an upset requiring more than 3d

in length then the diameter of the upset is $1.5d$, the amount of unsupported stock beyond the face of the die must not exceed one diameter of bar, (Fig. 4.34). However if the diameter of the hole in the die is reduced below $1\frac{1}{2}d$, then the length of unsupported stock beyond face of the die can be correspondingly increased.

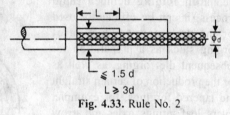

Fig. 4.33. Rule No. 2

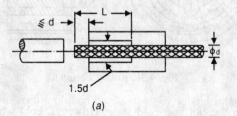

(a)

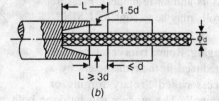

(b)

Fig. 4.34. Rule No. 3.

Speed Range of Forging Equipment :—

Equipment	Speed range, m/s
Hydraulic Prass	0.06 — 0.30
Mechanical Press	0.06 — 1.50
Screw Press	0.6 — 1.20
Gravity drop hammer	3.6 — 4.8
Power drop hammer	3.0 — 9.0
Counter blow hammer	4.5 — 9.0

4.3.3. Roll Forging. A variety of shapes having straight or tapered reduced sections may be forged with the aid of rolls. Here, the rolls are not completely cylindrical but are sector shaped to permit the stock to enter between the rolls. These roll segments have one or more sets of grooves to impart a desired shape to the piece being forged. When the rolls are in the open position, the heated stock is advanced upto a stop, (Fig. 4.35). As the rolls rotate, they grip and roll down the stock. The stock is transferred to a second set of grooves. The rolls turn again and so on until the piece is finished. Like this, the bar stock can be increased in length, reduced in diameter and changed in section as desired.

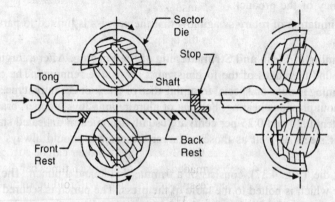

Fig. 4.35. Roll Forging.

Roll forging being a rapid process, it can be efficiently used for the preliminary reduction of forging stock as a preparation for subsequent die forging, as well as for the production of certain straight and tapered forgings, for example, levers, leaf springs, axles and arrow and spear type parts (cutlery and scissors and knife blades). Pressure on rolls may be as high as 1 MN.

4.3.4. Rotary Forging or Swaging. Round bars or tubings can be reduced in their diameters by a process called "rotary forging or

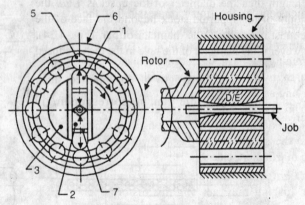

Fig. 4.36. Rotary Forging.

swaging". The process can be done both in the hot and cold state. However, cold working is preferable because of the greater ease of handling and better surface finish obtained. Fig. 4.36 schematically illustrates the rotary forging process. Small rams 1 with dies 2 inside the spindle head 3 slot are brought together to reduce the work- piece and separate again under the action of centrifugal force or springs. The spindle head is housed inside cage 4 with rollers 5 which rest from the outside on annular ring 6. As the spindle rotates, the small rams run against the rollers and so strike blows from various directions upon the job fed axially which is reduced in diameter by drawing out process.

Reduction is controlled by means of liners 7. The other applications of this process are fabrication of stepped and tapered shafts, pipes with forged out ends etc. Capacity of hot reduction is 150 mm in terms of rod diameter, and 300 mm in terms of pipe diameter. Forgings are accurate to within 0.1 to 0.3 mm and the surface quality is as good as that in machining.

The other advantages of this process are :

1. Low initial investment.
2. Easy maintenance.
3. Low tool cost
4. Low labour cost (semi-skilled labour).
5. Rapid production.
6. Consistency of the product.

The major limitation of rotary swaging is that the process is limited to parts of symmetrical cross-section only.

4.3.5. Trimming of Flash and Straightening of the Forging. After a forging is produced in dies, the flash around the edges of the forging, must always be removed. The operation of flash removal, *i.e.*, trimming is done on special trimming dies of crank or eccentric type. Trimming can be done with or without previous heating. Forging of aluminium alloys, copper, brass, bronze and of mild steel (C-content 0.20 and 0.25 per cent) are usually trimmed in unheated state. However, the forgings of harder steels as well as those of larger dimensions should always be heated before trimming.

A trimming die, (Fig. 4.37), consists of a trimmer blade and a punch. The trimmer blade is fastened to a shoe which is bolted to the table of the press. The punch is secured to the press slide by means of its dovetail. The blade is made of tool steel and has a cavity both in contour and dimensions to the finish impression of the forging die. The clearance bet- ween the trimmer blade and punch is 0.5 to 1 mm. For trimming the flash, the forging is placed over the cavity in the trimmer blade, the flash serving as the support for the forging. When the press is started, punch travels downwards and cut off the flash. The forging falls down into the shoe and the flash remains on the top of trimmer blade.

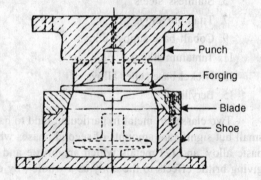

Fig. 4.37. Trimming Die.

Straightening. After the trimming operation, the forging may get slightly distorted or deformed, and must be straightened. This operation is done on a hammer or in a special press immediately after the trimming operation. Straightening can be done cold or hot as the case may be. Straightening under the hammer is done with one light blow in the finish forging impression of the die or in a special straighting impression.

4.3.6. Forgeability : It is a metallugical fact that not all metals can be successfully forged. The term "forgeability" is the word used to express this forging ability (or lack of it) both qualitatively and quantitatively. These is no simple way, of defining this term. Howerver, the forgeability of a metal can be defined as the metal's tolerance or relative ability to deform before cracks appear in the metal. A metal's forgeability may be excellent, zero or some what in-between. Many metals can be forged a little, or in certain ways such as in the closed-die forging process, or at room temperature. These same metals may crack under continued forging or when unconfined or when hot forged or cold forged. The degree of forgeability of a metal depends upon the crystallographic structure, metallurgical factors (purity phases present and grain size) and such factors as : the melting point, the yield strength, strain rate and die friction. These factors are discussed below :

1. Crystallographic Structure

(a) F.C.C. metals are the most forgeable, followed by B.C.C. and hexagonal close packed.

(b) Forgerbility increases with billet temperature upto the point at which a second phase appears or where there is incipient melting of grain boundaries or grain growth becomes excessive.

2. Purity :– The forgeability of a metal is lowered by the impurities present, specially when they are segregated in groups or in grain boundaries.

3. Phases present :– The forgeability is affected by the number, amount and composition of phases and their location in the structure. Alloys which are present in the solid solution form at the forging temperature, generally possess good forgeability.

4. Grain Size :– Generally, smaller the grain size the better the forgeability.

5. Melting point :– Higher the melting point of a metal, the lower its forgeability.

6. Yield strength :– Higher the yield strength of a metal, the lower its forgeability.

7. Strain rote :–

(i) Metals that have low ductility have reduced forgeability at higher strain rate.

(ii) Highly ductile materials are not so strongly affected by increasing strain rate.

8. Die friction :– The forgeability of a metal decreases as the die-friction increases.

The following is a list of materials in order of decreasing forgeability in terms of such considerations as : ductility, friction, temperature, strength and quality of forging :

1. Aluminium alloys
2. Magnesium alloys
3. Copper alloys
4. Carbon and low alloy steels

5. Stainless steels   6. Nickel alloys
7. Titanium alloys   8. Iron-base super alloys
9. Cobalt-base supper alloys   10. Columbium alloys
11. Tantalum alloys   12. Molybdenum alloys
13. Nickel-base super alloys   14. Tungsten alloys
15. Beryllium

Two classes of metal in particular, tend to have poor forgeability. These are : (1) metals with small but significant amounts of second phases which melt at the usual forging temperature of the basic alloy, and (2) metals which are brittle and tend to segregate in the grain boundaries thus giving brittle effects to the alloy as a whole , by estabilishing a semi-continuous brittle phase.

An example of the first of these two categories is leaaded free cutting copper alloys in which the lead remains in the elemental form as a separate phase even when heated to the usual forging temperature range for copper alloys. During the forging of such an alloy, tremendously high local hydraulic pressures are developed in the melted lead liquid phase. these pressures tend to cause the breaking open of channels between greains as the high pressure liquid seeks to force its way outward to relieve the high pressure gradient. These channels are really creacks. Oddly, somewhat lesser, but still significant amounts of lead may improve forgeability to the point of providing an alloy with the benefits from forging, and yet retain the excellent machining qualities given by the lead.

Some metals which exhibit poor forgeability when processed without lateral restriction to confine the spreading metal, such as a hammer forging, become relatively forgeable when used in the closed-die processes of forging. This is due to the fact that ductility of a metal increases by isostatic compression (metal being confined in the die-cavity).

It is important to distinguish between forgeability and ease of forging. As previously stated, forgeability refers to the property of being deformable by forging without cracking. Ease of forging, on the other hand, refers to the power or force requirement for accomplishing the deformation. Usually when commonly forged metal is heated into its forging temperature range, it exhibits both higher forgeability and greater ease of forging than at lower temperatures.

4.3.7. Defects in Forgings. Forging defects may result from the following causes : poor quality of the stock, incorrect die design, improper heating, incorrect forging conditions, wrong forging methods, uneven cooling of stock after forging etc. The common defects in forgings are discussed below :

1. Cold shuts or laps. Cold shuts or laps are short cracks which usually occur at corners and at right angles to the surface. They are caused by metal surface folding against itself during forging. Sharp corners in dies can result in hindered metal flow which can produce laps.

2. Pitting. Pitting of the forging surface is caused by scale, which if not removed thoroughly from the die cavities is worked into the surface of forging. When this scale is cleaned from the forging, depressions remain which are known as 'scale pits'. Pitting should be avoided as much as possible during manufacture of forging by proper control of furnace and frequent cleaning of dies.

3. Die shift. Die shift is caused by misalignment between the top and bottom forging dies. This may be caused due to loose wedges.

4. Incomplete filling of dies. This defect may be caused by : wrong amount of metal, insufficient number of blows during forging, forging the stock at too low a temperature when it has practically lost its plasticity, poor forging design or incorrect die design.

5. Dimension of forging do not correspond to those specified in the drawing. The causes can be : worn out dies, ir.correct dies or as a result of a mismatched forging.

6. Dents. Dents re the result of careless work.

7. Burnt and overheated metal. This defect is caused by improper heating conditions and soaking the metal too long.

8. Fins and rags. Fins and rags are small projections or loose metal driven into the surface of the forging.

9. Ruptured Fibre structure. This is a discontinuity in the flow lines of the forging which is revealed only when observing the macrostructure. This defect is caused by : working some of the alloys too rapidly during the forging operation, inadequate stock size or improper die design.

10. Cracks. Cracks which occur on the forging surface may be longitudinal or transverse. Their occurrence may be due to : bad quality of ingot, improper heating, forging at low temperature or incorrect cooling of alloy steel forgings.

11. Hair Cracks. These are very fine surface cracks not exceeding a fraction of a millimetre in width. These can occur due to : defects in metal ingot or too rapid cooling of the forging.

12. Slags, Sand and Porosity. These defects may occur either on the surface of, or inside the forging. These defects may be due to defects in the ingots or incomplete discard of the ingot head.

13. Internal cracks. Internal cracks in forgings can result from too drastic a change in shape of the raw stock at too fast a rate.

14. Flakes. Flakes are internal breaks or ruptures occurring in some grades of alloy steel. These are caused by too rapid a cooling from forging temperature.

15. Decarburization. If the raw stock is subjected to too high a temperature for too long a period, it can produce decarburized surface on the forgings, particularly in high carbon steels.

The chief defects mentioned above may be divided into two groups :

(*a*) **Irremovable defects.** Such as deep cracks, cavities, burnt metal and decarburization.

(*b*) **Removable defects.** Shallow cracks, overheating, coarse grained structure, internal stresses and distortion.

Defects in forgings can be remedied as follows :

(*i*) Surface cracks and decarburized areas are removed from important forging by grinding on special machines.

(*ii*) Shallow cracks and cavities can be removed by chipping out of the cold forgings with pneumatic chisels or with hot sets during the forging process.

(*iii*) Distorted forgings are straightened in presses.

(*iv*) The mechanical properties of the forging can be improved and internal stresses removed by annealing or normalising.

4.3.8. Cleaning and Finishing of Forgings

1. Removal of Oxide scale. A thin layer of scale (iron oxide) which is caused by contact of heated steel with air, is formed on the surface of steel forgings. Amount of scale depends upon the forging temperature and length of time of the operation. The simple way to remove the scale is by employing steam or compressed air to blow away the scale, from the surface of the forging as well as from the die cavities.

2. Cleaning by pickling. Pickling process is used to remove hard scale from the surface of the forgings. It consists of immersing the forgings in a tank filled with an acid solution, which is 12 to 15% concentrate of sulphuric acid in water. The solution acts to loosen the hard scale from the forging surface and remove it. The acid solution should not react with the clean metal while removing the scale. For this, an inhibitor agent is added to the acid solution.

3. Tumbling process. Tumbling process is used to remove scale and for the general cleaning of the forgings. The forgings along with some abrasive materials such as coarse sand or small metallic particles are placed in a barrel. The tilted barrel is rotated at low speeds. The forgings and the abrasives roll over themselves. This action loosens the scale from the surface of the forgings and removes it alongwith affecting a general cleaning of the forgings.

4. Blast cleaning. Blast cleaning process consists of directing a jet of sand, grit or metallic shots against the forgings. The blasting force is obtained from compressed air or centrifugal force through suitably designed apparatus. By this process the scale is removed and a smooth surface finish is imparted to the forging.

4.3.9. Heat Treatment of Forgings

After their manufacture, forgings are heat treated before and after machining. The initial treatment is done to improve the grain structure and also to make the machining of the forging easier. The final treatment is done to impart certain properties to the forgings for the service intended. For example to make the forging hard and tough, it is hardened and tempered. So the heat treatment of the forgings is done for the following purposes :

(1) To relieve the forgings of stresses set up during forging and subsequent cooling.

(2) To improve the mechanical properties of the product.

(3) To equalise the structure of the metal of the forging.

(4) To impart that degree of hardness to the forging which makes it most easy to machine.

Annealing. Annealing is a form of treatment which is used to accomplish the following results : remove internal stresses, improve mechanical properties, make the metal softer for machining or grinding. The annealing process consists in heating the forging in an annealing furnace upto or beyond the critical temperature of metal. For steel forgings, this temperature ranges from 750 to 900° depending upon the carbon content of steel. The forging is then allowed to cool slowly in he furnace.

Normalising. Normalising consists in heating the forging as in annealing and then allowing the forging to cool in air at atmospheric temperature. The following results are achieved by normalising : a fine grade structure better than obtained in annealing, improved mechanical properties-increased tensile strength and ductility and removal of internal stresses.

Hardening. Hardening heat treatment process consists in heating the forgings slightly above the critical temperature of the metal and cooling it rapidly. The cooling medium is usually water, brine or oil.

Tempering. During hardening process. severe stresses are set up in the forging due to rapid cooling. These stresses must be removed, otherwise the forging may crack. This is done by tempering. Tempering consists in heating the hardened forging to a temperature between room temperature and the critical temperature of the metal. The forging is kept at this temperature for a definite period and then the forging is allowed to cool in air.

4.3.10. Metallurgy of Forging.
The reason of high strength-to-weight ratio of forged parts is that these have fibrous structure and the grain structure or the flow lines of the metal are not interrupted but are made to follow the contour of the forged part. The main objective of good forging design is to control the lines of metal grain flow so that a part with greatest strength and resistance of fracture is produced. This is clear if we compare the three methods of manufacturing crankshaft : casting, machining and forging (Fig.4.38). The crankshaft produced by casting (Fig. 4.38 *a*) has no grain flow and so has the poorest mechanical properties. In Fig. 4.38 (*b*), the crankshaft has been made by machining from a bar stock and the fibre of the metal gets interrupted and for this reason the mechanical properties of this shaft will be poorer than those of the crankshaft

made by forging [Fig. 4.38 (*c*)], where the fibre of the metal has not been interrupted and continues along the entire length of the shaft.

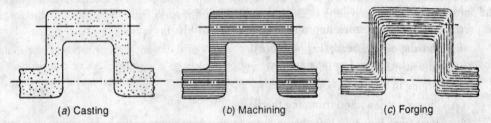

(*a*) Casting   (*b*) Machining   (*c*) Forging

Fig. 4.38. Comparison of Grain Flow.

It is clear from Fig. 4.38 (*c*), that the effect of flow lines is to produce marked directional properties in the material and here (in the case of crankshaft), these qualities add toughness to the webs and where they join the round parts of the shaft. Controlling the directions of fibrous structure within forgings will develop the maximum mechanical properties for applications where shock and fatigue are encountered. For static loads, the direction of these fibre lines is not so important. Below, we will explain how flow lines are used to advantage in forging typical components.

(*i*) **Gear Blank.** Flat forgings of gear blanks are usually made by upsetting the bar stock. The pattern of the flow lines in the bar stock (which has been produced through forging or rolling) is shown in Fig. 4.39 (*a*). When this bar stock is upset on ends (that is, the bar stock is placed in dies such that the flow lines are vertical), the grain pattern produced will be radial and the gear blank will have flow lines concentrated where they will give greatest strength to the teeth, Fig. 4.39 (*b*), and all the teeth will be equally strong. This is desired because each tooth can be considered as a cantilever beam and the fibre flow lines will be parallel with the expected tensile and compressive stresses along the face of the gear teeth. However, if the bar stock is placed in the dies for upsetting in such a manner that its flow lines are horizontal, then the grain pattern produced with be as shown in Fig. 4.39 (*c*). The teeth cut on such a blank will not be of the same strength. Teeth 1 and 2 in Fig. 4.39 (*c*) will withstand less stress than teeth 3 and 4, because they have fibres running perpendicular to the expected stresses.

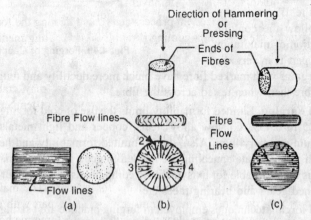

Fig. 4.39. Forging of Gear Blank.

(*ii*) **Coupling Hooks.** Coupling hooks are subjected to severe service conditions and the safety of the railway traffic depends upon the strength of the hook. Therefore, the coupling hooks should be forged in such a manner that : (*i*) due consideration is given to the direction of the fibre of the material (*ii*) the fibre of the material is not severed during the forging process. Also, it must be ensured that the highest possible tensile strength is developed in the hook. Below, we compare the two methods of forging a coupling hook:

Method A. In this method, (Fig. 4.40-I), the sequence of operations is as follows :

(*i*) Cutting the bar stock to proper length, (Fig. 4.40 I(*a*)).

(*ii*) Drawing out the head, (Fig. 4.40 I(*b*)).

(*iii*) flattening the head, (Fig. 4.40 I(*c*)).

(*iv*) Forging in dies, (Fig. 4.40 I(*d*)).

(*v*) Cutting out jaws and trimming the flash.

It is clear from Fig. 4.40 I(*d*), that in order to give bent shape to the hook, the metal is cut and the flow lines are severed at the nose of the hook which is the most dangerous section. Since the tractive force is directed along and not across the flow lines, there is danger that failure will occur at this section.

Method B. In this method, (Fig. 4.40. - II), after drawing out the head of the hook, the material is bent and then forged in dies. In this way the flow lines will follow the contour of the hook which will result in maximum tensile strength of the hook. The mechanical properties of the hook produced by this method will be much higher than of the hook produced by the first method.

It is clear from above that while designing a forging and forging tools, it must be ensured that : the fibre flow lines of the material are not severed during the process of forging and the fibres in the forging should follow the contour or lie in the direction of maximum stresses when the part is in service,

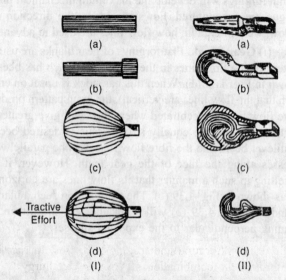

Fig. 4.40. Forging of Coupling Hook.

since the metal forgings with marked fibre have much more ductility and toughness when tested in the direction of fibre than when tested across the fibre.

4.3.11. Cold Forging. Limited formability limits the use of cold forging to : low and medium carbon steels (0.25 to 0.45% C), low alloy steels, copper and light metals such as aluminium, magnesium, titanium and beryllium. Also, due to limited formability and heavy work hardening, several stages with intermediate annealing are needed to get a large deformation, which increases cost. The process is most suitable for axisymmetric components such as shaft components, flanged components, finished gears and bearing races etc.

Various cold forging techniques employed in forging practice are : sizing, coining and heading etc. The aim of sizing operation is to obtain closer dimensional tolerances on portions of a forging. In plane sizing, the forging is pressed between two flat dies. The operation straightens the forging, enables accurate dimensions to be obtained and improves the surface finish. Three dimensional sizing imparts the final size to the whole forging in impression dies with the formation of flash which is subsequently trimmed. If the sizing operation is such that the metal flow is restricted in a space confined by the die impression (that is no flash is formed), the sizing operation is called "coining'".

Sizing and coining operations are commonly done on knuckle joint presses, (Fig. 4.27 (c)). The crankshaft driven by motor reciprocates the ram (slide) by means of a linkage consisting of the pitman and two knuckle joint levers. The upper die is fastened to the slide. This arrangement enables a high tonnage to be exerted at the bottom of the stroke with a comparatively low torque on the drive shaft. Coining presses range in ratings from 0.1 MN to 8 MN and even more.

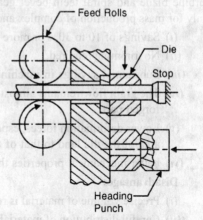

Fig. 4.41. Cold Heading.

The "cold heading" process was first introduced for the cold forming of heads on rivets, bolts and screws. At present, the process has found widespread application in the mass production of small parts and fastenings: bolts, screws, rivets, nuts, nails, links and pins etc. The process is also well suited to the production of small steel balls for use as ball bearings and rollers for use as roller bearings. The stock for these parts is wire or cold drawn bars from 0.6 to 40 mm in diameter of carbon steel, non ferrous metals and their alloys.

A cold heading operation sequence is shown in Fig. 4.41. The stock is fed through a die to a stop with the help of rolls. Next, the die is shifted to cut off the blank and to carry it over to the heading line where the required head is formed by a blow of a punch mounted on the heading gate. Cold heading in one or several strokes is done chiefly in automatic cold headers in which all operations including wire (or bar) feed, cut off, carry over and ejection of the finished parts are completely automatic. These machines have an output from 20 to 250 pieces per minute.

4.3.12. New Trends in Forging Technology. The development of advanced forging techniques have come from the aerospace industry and its rapid development over the past 40 years. The need to manufacture highly stressed airframe and engine parts led very rapidly to the combination of specific primary forming and forging processes. In particular, spectacular advances have been made through the combination of Powder Metallurgy (P/M) and forging processes. This trend found applications also in automobile and machine tool manufacture due to the following reason:

The cost of the finished components has been increasing due to increase in cost of raw materials, power and labour. This has focussed attention of cost reduction by better utilization of raw materials and production of close tolerances components necessitating minimum finish machining.

The above mentioned factors have resulted in the development of new forging technologies which will be discussed below :-

1. Precision and High Precision forging (No draft forging).

2. Closed-die forging without flash.

'No draft forging' also called 'precision' or 'close-tolerance forging' is a special variation of conventional press forging. As the name implies, the die walls have little or no draft. The part produced by this method can be used "as forged" or after a very little amount of machining. For this, the following factors are of prime requirement :

(*i*) The accurately sized blank is prepared after an extensive sequence of preforming steps.

(*ii*) The die cavity is made to exacting standards.

(*iii*) There is increased control over preheating both the dies and blank, descaling of die surfaces, lubrication, die material and use of special die inserts punches, pins etc.

No draft forging is currently used for aluminium, copper and magnesium. Its use is being extended to some steels and titanium. Examples of parts made by this process are : complex shaped turbine blade and spiral teeth bevel gears. Because of high tooling cost, this method is justified only for mass production of complex and close tolerance parts. The advantages of this method are :

(*i*) Savings of 10 to 30% or more in weight of material used.

(*ii*) No trimming required.

(*iii*) Substantial savings in machining costs.

(*iv*) The grain flow remains almost undisturbed as no or very little machining is needed of the forged part.

(*v*) Lower deformation forces, especially in the case of smaller forgings where the ratio of the area of the die land to that of the die itself is large.

(*vi*) better mechanical properties through the elimination of residual flash.

Disadvantages

(*i*) Precise volume of material is required.

(*ii*) Careful distribution of material required.

(*iii*) Workpiece requires very exact positioning in die cavity.

(*vi*) Tendency towards end face flash formation.

(*v*) Variations in wall thickness.

3. Warm Forging. As discussed earlier, the aim of warm forging is to combine the advantages of both hot and cold forging. The forging temperature affects both the behaviour of the material during deformation as the properties of the finished part. In comparison to hot forging, warm forging requires higher forces because of greater flow stress, thus making increased demands on the forging tools and equipment. On the other hand, greater part accuracy in terms of both dimensions and surface finish can be achieved. The optional temperature for a particular warm forging operation always represents a compromise. Its lower limit is set by the force which can be produced by the forging press and by the forgeability of the material, the upper limit is determined by the amount of oxidation and thus the amount of scale which can be tolerated.

4. Hot Die Forging. In conventional forging, the workpiece tends to cool during the process because the dies are at a lower temperature as compared to that of the workpiece (the difference in temperature between workpiece and die may be upto 1000° and more). This seriously inhibits the complete filling of the dies. In drop forging, the die forging is also adversely affected by higher resistance to deformation since higher strain rates are involved. These difficulties can be overcome by reducing the temperature difference between the workpiece and the die (hot die forging) or by keeping the workpiece and the die at the same temperature (isothermal forging). Dies are preheated to the desired temperature by flame, induction or resistance heating. However, induction heating is more popular as it gives more flexibility for using different coil sizes with the same power source.

In hot die process, the difference in temperature is only about 200°C. This method was developed in order to be able to use Ni-based material for die manufacture. At operating temperatures of 750 to 850°C, these alloys require no vacuum or inert gas atmosphere. Ti alloys are forged at temperatures of about 950°C. The process may be seen as a compromise between isothermal and conventional forging, although in fact it is more closely related to isothermal forging.

5. Isothermal Forging. This process is a further development of hot die forging. Here, both the dies and the forging stock are kept at the same temperature (forging temperature) during the forging process. The forging stock for this process can be either as used in conventional forging or a preform obtained by P/M. The materials most used are Ti and high temperature resistant Ni base alloys which because of their high flow stress are difficult to forge. Parts made of these materials have been forged by this process, for the automotive and aircraft industry. The process can be used economically for batch sizes between 100 and 1000 parts. This process requires control over the deformation and, therefore, hydraulic presses are employed for isothermal forging. The heated billet is placed in the bottom die and the load exerted by the press is maintained at a preselected low value. The downward speed of the press slide is automatically controlled by the resistance of the work piece to deformation. The die materials depend upon the level of temperature required. The material should possess the following properties : toughness, high hot hardness, high temperature strength and resistance to wear and thermal fatigue. The die material most commonly used for forging Ti alloys (generally without a surrounding inert gas atmosphere) is the Ni-base alloy. Ti alloys are generally forged at 950°C. When higher temperatures are required such as for components of Ni-base alloys, Molybdenum base die materials are needed. Since Mo reacts strongly with O_2 at high temperature, it is necessary to protect the dies from the surrounding air by either an inert atmosphere or a vacuum, otherwise they would be oxidised to pieces in a few minutes.

Isothermal forging offers the following advantages.

(i) Complex and close tolerance parts can be produced from comparatively simple preforms, generally in a single stroke of the press and a single die set.

(ii) Greater material utilization and less machining.

(iii) Uniform wrought properties of the product.

(vi) The speed of the press slide especially towards the end of the forging stroke is quite lower as compared to conventional forging and consequently lower forging loads are needed in isothermal forging, about of that required for conven- tional forging of the same material.

(v) Lower production cost due to reduced number of forging operations.

(vi) Reductions in cross-section of upto 80% can be achieved in single forging operation, thus facilitating the forging of parts with fins and ribs.

6. Powder Forging. Powder forging also called powder metal forging (P/M forging) or hot forming combines the conventional forging and powder metallurgy processes. In conventional forging, a major limitation is to obtain a uniform flow of the raw solid material within a forging die. This limits the complexity of the forging or requires more steps in the forging process, with resulting multiple and costly dies or substantial post forging machining. Therefore, the more nearly the raw material shape conforms to the shape of the forging, the easier it is to obtain a desired product. In P/M forging, the preforms closely resembling the forging, made by P/M method are hot forged in close impression dies, often in a single forging step. The steps in the process can be written as :-

1. Powder
2. Compacting the preform
3. Sintering the preform
4. Finish forge

The powder forging method thus combines dimensional precision, weight control and high material utilization of powder metallurgy with the mechanical properties of conventional forging, at reasonable production cost. This technology is being widely employed for aluminium, steels, titanium, nickel base and many other structural alloys. The automotive industry is the principal user of this process. Examples of powder-forged production parts include : gears and pinions, bearings, pistons, connecting rods, crankshaft, camshaft, cylinder liners, piston rings, clutch discs and plates and clutch knobs etc. This technique can be used either with conventional forging or isothermal forging or hot die forging.

The material structure of sinter forged parts is very fine grained and homogeneous. The mechanical properties are thus largely isotropic (non-directional grain flow), which in some cases has a positive effect on the fatigue strength of sinter- forged parts making them superior to conventionally forged parts. While the fatigue strength of conventionally forged parts (steel) differs by about 100% in the longitudinal and transversal directions, the corresponding values for powder-forged steel are the same in whatever direction they are measured. This isotropic property is a great advantage in many components for example, increased fatigue strength of powder forged connecting rods and the reduction in the tendency of teeth to fail in fatigue tests on powder forged gear wheels. These are just two examples of part families for which powder forging offers advantages over traditional methods, particularly in the case of components which have to withstand high dynamic stresses. When in addition to stresses, the design of the parts poses problems of material distribution, powder forging is almost unrivalled. The only alternative methods of manufacture are either expensive mechanical machining or casting techniques, whereby in the later case the parts are seldom able to withstand very high dynamic stresses.

The precision powder forged parts have the following advantages over the wrought counterparts :

(i) Almost 100 per cent material utilization.

(ii) Better surface finish, of the order of 5 to 10 μ m.

(iii) Material homogeneity and fine grain size.

(vi) Almost complete elimination of machining.

(v) Close dimensional tolerances in the range of qualities IT8 to IT10.

(vi) Density increases upto about 99%.

The main drawback of this process is that the preform contains about 15 to 30 per cent porosity. This reduces the ductility of the preform during the forging operation. Also, due to internal gaps the preform is susceptible to internal oxidation and decarburization at the forming temperature.

7. Liquid Metal Forging (Squeeze Casting). The liquid metal forging process is hybrid between conventional casting and forging methods and produces complex shaped components from molten metal in a single step. The various stages in liquid metal forging process are :

(a) Pouring the molten metal into the bottom forging die.

(b) Allowing the metal to solidify partially.

(c) Closing the upper and bottom dies, applying pressure and maintaining it for a fixed time until solidification is completed.

(d) Opening the dies and ejecting the forged component from the bottom die.

The metal may be poured manually into the bottom die for small forgings (upto 10 kgs) and for heavier parts, it is poured mechanically. The dies are kept at a temperature of 100 to 250°C. The successful production of a forging by this process depends upon the proper selection of the following variables : Pouring temperature of metal, Temperature of dies, Delay time to apply pressure, Press speed, Pressure level, Period of pressure application, metal volume and die coatings for facilitating the ejection of the forging. The liquid metal forging process has the following advantages over conventional casting and forging processes :

(i) Ability to produce thinner and more complex components as compared to those produced by either casting or forging.

(ii) There are no gas and shrinkage porosities. These get closed up during the process.

(iii) Pressure needed is quite less as compared to conventional forging. Therefore, low capacity presses are needed for this process.

(*iv*) Production rates are higher as compared with any conventional casting process. However, the rate would be lower than that for conventional forging. But this difference can be made up by the lower machining requirements of squeeze castings.

(*v*) Both cast and wrought alloys such as cast iron, aluminium and supper alloys can be used.

(*vi*) The process is economical from the material point of view. There is better material utilization and also scrap can be used. Gates and risers are not needed. So, yield is higher in comparison to sand castings.

(*vii*) Mechanical properties of the product are comparable to those by conventional forging. And they are considerably better than sand castings.

(*viii*) The tooling and equipment needed are basically simple, low cost and readily available.

Like any other process, the liquid forging process has got the following limitations :-

(*i*) All the component shapes cannot be obtained by this process.

(*ii*) If there is a large difference in the dimensions of thinnest and thickest sections of the component, the pressure distribution will not be uniform and also there will be chances of shrinkage porosity and cracking of the component as the thinner sections will solidify first.

(*iii*) cooling rates being faster, the effect on microstructure of the component will be different as compared to casting or forging. This may necessitate different heat treatments for liquid forged parts.

8. Gatorizing. This new forging technique involves the following steps :

(*i*) The forging stock is preconditioned in inert atmosphere to obtain a temporary condition of fine grained microstructure resulting in low strength and high ductility. For this, the work-piece is mechanically worked at temperature slightly below the recrystallization temperature of the material.

(*ii*) After preconditioning, the isothermal forging operation is carried out at slightly below the recrystallization temperature of the material.

(*iii*) Lastly, certain heat treatment operations are done on the forgings to get normal high strength and hardness.

At present, this method is being used for making aircraft components of nickel and titanium based alloys.

9. Orbital Forging. Orbital forging or rotaforming is a cold forming process. In this method, the pressure of the upper die of the work-piece is concentrated on a small area at any time, and not on the total workpiece area as in conventional forging. The upper die is slightly inclined to the vertical axis of the machine and it imparts a high frequency circular rocking motion across the top surface of the workpiece (Fig. 4.42). At the same time, the workpiece is slowly moved hydraulically upward and pressed against the orbiting upper die. The forging operation get completed when the hydraulic ram touches a preset stop. The ram is then lowered and the hydraulically operated ejector ejects the forging from the lower die. All the metals that can be cold worked can be forged by orbital forging. Examples of parts produced by this process include : parts flanged with indented or crown shapes and disks etc. To avoid tilting of the workpiece due to orbital forging, its height to diameter ratio should be less than 2. The advantages of orbital forging are :

(*i*) Press capacity requirements are only 5 to 10% of that needed by conventional forging, because only a small portion of die actually contacts the workpiece

(*ii*) Better surface finish.

(*iii*) The method requires smaller and lower cost equipment.

The method has the limitation in that the forging is obtained by filling the lower die and so the bottom surface of the upper die should be flat and smooth.

10. Hot Isostatic Pressing (HIP). In this method the metal powder is sealed in a metal or ceramic container that has the shape of the desired part. The container is placed in a special pressure vessel that has the capability of simultaneously heating the container and subjecting it to a hydrostatic pressure (gas). The powder is compacted, densified and sintered in one step. Upon removal of the container, a finished part close to the final shape is obtained. The H.I.P. method is particularly suited to producing parts from high temperature alloys that are difficult to forge and machine. For nickel based alloys, the pressure and temperature employed are 100 MPa and 1260°C respectively. For pressurisation, both helium and argon have been used. This method can also produce preforms for subsequent forging. At present, this method is being tried to forge exotic materials for aircraft industry. A 35% saving in the material needed to make a gas turbine disk has been reported for the HIP process.

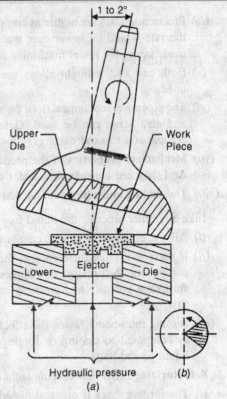

Fig. 4.42. Orbital Forging.

11. Incremental Forging. In this method, very big forgings are made by working different areas of the forging into shape, one at a time. Since only a limited area is worked at any time, the forging equipment can be much smaller in capacity as compared to conventional forging. This makes it possible to forge huge parts on presses of modest capacity. This method is particularly suited to aircraft industry. A major drawback of this method is that the workpiece tends to cool below the forging temperature as it moves from incremental step to step. Reheating the part to its original forging temperature may destroy the thermomechanical work already done on it in the case of many alloys. This can be prevented by two methods : The workpiece is progressively reheated to a lower temperature after its temperature falls below the forging temperature. Secondly, insulating blankets and other coatings are used to cover the billet so as to minimize the heat loss.

12. Super-Plastic Forging. This process is carried out at even lower strain rates than isothermal forging. This is accompanied by an increase in the pressure contact time and a further reduction in the deformation force. The preconditions for super plastic behaviour of a material are :-

   (i) Very fine structure with grain size of just a few m. Changes in structure due to grain growth during forging are not permissible.

   (ii) The forging temperature must lie above $T_m/2$.

   (iii) Strain rates must be very small to 10^{-1} to $10^{-5} s^{-1}$.

Super plasticity occurs in principle with all pure metals. However, preference is generally given to eutectic or eutectoid alloys since they also usually fulfill the first precondition, namely, that of a fine grain structure. The temperatures required for super plastic forging of high-temperature resistant Ni-and Ti-based alloys between 800 and 1150°C. In this range, due to high thermal and long term stresses, it is necessary to make dies from Mo based alloys. Super-plastic forging is mainly used to manufacture high temperature resistant engine components (impeller wheel etc.) of Ni-base alloys.

4.4. EXTRUSION

Extrusion may be defined as the manufacturing process in which a block of metal enclosed in a container is forced to flow through the opening of a die. The metal is subjected to plastic deformation and it undergoes reduction and elongation during extrusion. The section of the product will depend upon the shape of the die opening. This process could well be considered an adaptation of closed die forging, the difference being that in a forging, the main body of the metal is the product and flash is cut away and discarded ; in extrusion, the flash (metal flowing out of the die) is the product and the slug remaining in the die is not used.

Extrusion is more widely used in the manufacture of solid and hollow sections from non-ferrous metals and their alloys (aluminium alloys, copper, brass and bronze etc.), but steel and other ferrous alloys can also be success fully processed with the development of molten-glass lubricants. The initial material in extrusion is cast or rolled billets. The range of extruded items is very wide : rods from 3 to 250 mm in diameter, pipes of 20 to 400 mm in diameter and wall thickness of 1 mm and above, and more complicated shapes which can not be obtained by other mechanical working methods, (Fig. 4.43).

Fig. 4.43. Type of Extrusions.

Extrusion may be done hot as well as cold. The two methods employed for extrusion are : Direct or forward extrusion and Indirect or backward extrusion. In direct extrusion, the product emerges from the die in the same direction as the direction of application of pressure, whereas in indirect extrusion, the product travels against the direction of application of pressure.

4.4.1. Hot Extrusion. Fig. 4.44 illustrates the hot extrusion methods for producing solid and hollow products by forward extrusion (Fig. 4.44 *a*) and by backward extrusion (Fig. 4.44 *b*)).

Direct Extrusion. In Fig. 4.44 *a* (*i*), the heated billet is placed in the container. It is pushed by a ram towards the die. The metal is subjected to plastic deformation, slides along the walls of the container and is forced to flow through the die opening. At the end of the extruding operation a small piece of metal, called butt-end scrap, remains in the container and can not be extruded. To obtain a hollow section, a hollow billet is often used around a mandrel. In some instances, the billet is solid and is pierced by the mandrel or an axial hole is drilled in it by means of a drilling machine before the extrusion cycle begins. The mandrel may be fastened to the ram. As the ram moves in the direction towards the die, the metal is forced out through the annular clearance and form a tube, (Fig. 4.44 *a* (*ii*)). With a modern extrusion press, the piercing mandrel is actuated by a separate hydraulic cylinder from the one which operates the ram, (Fig. 4.44 *a* (*iii*)). The billet is first upset with the ram with the piercing mandrel with drawn. Next the billet is pierced with the pointed mandrel ejecting a plug through the die. Then the ram advances and extrudes the billet over the mandrel to produce a tube. The outside diameter of the extruded tube equals the diameter of the die hole and the inside diameter equals that of the steel mandrel. This method is called as "Tubular extrusion".

Indirect Extrusion. For the production of a solid part, the die is mounted on the end of a hollow ram and enters the container, (Fig. 4.44 $b(i)$) the other end of container being closed by a closure plate. As the ram travels, the die applies pressure on the billet and the deformed metal flows through the die opening in the direction opposite to the ram motions, and the product is extruded through the hollow ram. Hollow section is extruded inside an annular gap between the container and the ram, (Fig. 4.44 b (ii)). In indirect extrusion, there is practically no slip of billet with respect to the container walls.

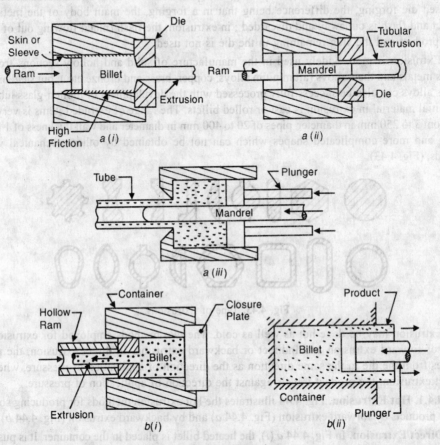

Fig. 4.44. Hot Extrusion.

Comparison of Direct and Indirect Extrusion. The direct extrusion, is the simplest, but it is limited by the fact that as the ram moves, the billet must slide or shear at the interface between billet and container. These large friction forces must be overcome by very high ram forces, which produce very high residual stresses on the container. In the indirect method (also called reverse, back or inverted), the billet proper does not move relative to the container, instead the die moves. The friction involved is only between the die and container and this is independent of the billet length. The friction forces are lower and the power required for extrusion is less than for direct extrusion. Extruding force is 25 to 30% less than in direct extrusion. However, a long hollow ram is required and this limits the loads which can be applied. Due to this, and complex design of tools, the indirect extrusion finds only limited application. The scrap or the process waste which is equal to the poorly shaped leading end of the section plus the unextruded butt is 18 to 20% of billet weight in direct extrusion, whereas it is only 5 to 6% of billet weight in the cast of indirect extrusion.

Extrusion ratio. The extrusion ratio is defined as the ratio of the cross-sectional area of the billet to the cross-sectional area of the product. It reaches about 40 : 1 for hot extrusion of steel and may be as high as 400:1 for aluminium.

Machines for extrusion. Both mechanical and hydraulic presses can be used for extrusion provided they possess high kinetic energy and long ram guides. Hydraulic presses with either vertical or horizontal plungers are most commonly used. Mechanical presses are used to a lesser extent. The pressure of the working fluid (water or emulsion) may reach 400 atm in hydraulic presses and produce a force of 300 MN. The plunger transmits the pressure to the ram and the pressure plate which force the metal through the die. To reduce the friction between the metal and the container walls and to achieve a more uniform flow of the metal, lubricants are used. Lubricants include a mixture of machine oil and graphite, molten glass (for steel) and other lubricating materials.

Extrusion speed is of the order of 0.5 m/s for light alloys and of the order of 4.5 m/s for Cu alloys.

4.4.2. Cold Extrusion. This process is similar to hot extrusion except that the metals worked possess the plasticity necessary for successful forming without heating them. Usually, these metals have a high degree of ductility. Cold extrusion is also done to improve the physical properties of a metal and to produce a finished part (sizing operating). The widely employed cold extrusion methods are : The Hooker or extrusion down method, the impact or extrusion up method and hydrostatic extrusion. Cold extrusion is done mostly on vertical mechanical presses because they are fast and simple. The method is fast, wastes no or little material and gives higher accuracy and tolerances.

1. The Hooker Method. In the Hooker or extrusion down method, the ram/punch has a shoulder and acts as a mandrel, [Fig. 4.45 (*a*)]. A flat blank of specified diameter and thickness is placed in a suitable die and is forced through the opening of the die with the punch, when the punch starts downward movement.

Pressure is exerted by the shoulder of the punch, the metal being forced to flow through the restricted annular space between the punch and the opening in the bottom of the die. If the tube sticks to the punch on its upward stroke, a stripper [see Fig. 4.45 (*c*)] will strip it from the punch. Small copper tubes and cartridge cases are extruded by this method. In place of a flat solid blank, a hollow slug can also be used.

2. Cold Impact Extrusion. The cold impact extrusion method consists in placing a flat blank of specified diameter with a small hole punched in the centre, in the die cavity and striking it by a punch with a powerful blow. The material gets heated up and becomes plastic and is forced to squirt up around the punch, [Fig. 4.45 (*b*)]. Thin walled tubes of low flow strength materials (tin, lead, aluminium etc.) are rapidly formed by this method. The end of the tube will correspond to the shape of the die cavity and also of the punch. The outside diameter of the tube takes the shape of the die and the wall thickness is equal to the clearance between the punch and the die. The operation is fully automatic and the production rate is as high as 50 tubes or more per minute. When the punch is on its upward stroke, the tube sticks to it. To effect release, either a stripper [See Fig. 4.45 (*c*)] or compressed air is directed against the tube, thus stripping it from the punch. Threads may be formed at the end of these collapsible tubes by retractable die portions or by other methods. The tubes are them trimmed, enamelled and printed. These collapsible tubes are used for cosmetics (cream, shaving cream), tooth paste, grease etc.

Other product applications include : Cans, fire extinguisher cases, radio shields, food containers, boxes for condensers and cigarette lighter cases (if symmetrical).

A variation of the method where a flat solid blank or slug (that is, without a hole) is used in the die cavity (the bottom of the die cavity is closed) is shown in Fig. 4.45 (*c*). The method is also being employed to make thick walled products such as paint-spray-gun containers and grease-gun containers, by using large presses.

Impact extruxion speed is 100 to 350 mm/s

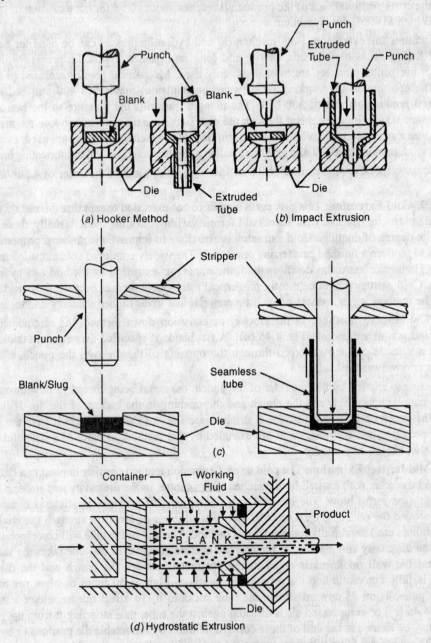

(a) Hooker Method   (b) Impact Extrusion

(c)

(d) Hydrostatic Extrusion

Fig. 4.45. Cold Extrusion.

3. Hydrostatic Extrusion. In hydrostatic extrusion, [Fig. 4.45 (d)], a high pressure liquid medium is used for the transmission of the force to the billet/blank. The liquid completely envelops the blank and enters die canals. Due to the hydrostatic pressure, the ductility of the material is increased. Even brittle materials like tungsten, cast iron and stainless steel etc. can be extruded. This also permits the extrusion of very long billets or even wire, accompanied by large reductions. There is no container friction and the pressurised fluid also acts as a lubricant and because of this, the extruded product has a good surface finish and dimensional accuracy. However, the absence of container friction combined with reduced die friction can increase the tendency to internal crack formation. The pressure transmitting fluids commonly used for hydrostatic extrusion are : Glycerin, Ethylglycol, SAE 30 mineral lubricating oil, castor oil with 10 per cent alcohol and isopentane. The hydrostatic pressure ranges from 1100 to 3150 N/mm^2. The main commercial applications of this process are : Cladding of metals, making wires of less ductile materiats and extrusion of nuclear reactor fuel rods.

4.4.3. ADVANTAGES OF EXTRUSION

1. The range of extruded items is very wide. Cross-sectional shapes not possible by rolling can be extruded, such as those with re-entrant sections.

2. No time is lost when changing shapes since the dies may be readily removed and replaced.

3. Dimensional accuracy of extruded parts is generally superior to that of rolled ones.

4. In extrusion, the ductility of the metals is higher as the metal in the container is in composite compression, this advantage being of particular importance in working poorly plastic metals and alloys.

5. Very large reductions are possible as compared to rolling, for which the reduction per pass is generally ≤ 2.

6. Automation in extrusion is simpler as items are produced in a single passing.

7. Small parts in large quantities can be made. For example, to produce a simple pump gear, a long gear is extruded and then sliced into a number of individual gears.

8. Extrusions are lighter, more sound and stronger than castings.

9. They do not need draft or flash to trim and needless machining as they are more accurate than forgings.

4.4.4. DRAWBACKS OF EXTRUSIONS

1. Process waste in extrusion is higher than in rolling, where it is only 1 to 3%.

2. Inhomogeneity in structure and properties of an extruded product is greater due to different flows of the axial and the outer layers of blanks.

3. Service life of extrusion tooling is shorter because of high contact stresses and slip rates.

4. Relatively high tooling costs, being made from costly alloy steels. ·

5. In productivity, extrusion is much inferior to rolling, particularly to its continuous varieties.

6. Costs of extrusion are generally greater as compared to other techniques.

7. Only the shapes with constant cross-section (die outlet cross-section) can be produced.

Due to the above factors, the main fields of application of extrusion process are :-

(*a*) working of poorly plastic and non ferrous metals and alloys.

(*b*) manufacture of sections and pipes of complex configuration.

(*c*) medium and small batch production.

(*d*) manufacture of parts of high dimensional accuracy.

4.4.5 Main Process Variable in Extrusion Process

Total extrusion pressure is given as,

$$pt = \sigma_{x_0} + p_f$$

Where σ_{x_0} = extrusion pressure to deform the material

$$= \frac{\sigma_0 (1 + B)}{B} [1 - R^B]$$

and p_f = ram pressure required by container friction.

$$= \frac{4\tau_i L}{D}$$

Now σ_0 = yield strength of work material

R = extrusion ratio

$B = \mu \cot \alpha$

μ = Co-efficient of friction

α = half Die angle

τ_i = Interface shear between billet and container wall.

L = Length of billet in container

D = Internal diameter of container

∴ Main process variables in Extrusion process are:

1. Strength of billet material
2. Extrusion ratio
3. Co-efficient of friction/lubrication
4. Die-angle
5. Size of billet (Length and diameter)
6. Temperature
7. Speed of extrusion

4.4.6. Some Other Extrusion Processes

1. Side Extrusion. In this process, which is also known as "Lateral extrusion", the material flows at right angle to the direction of ram motion. The method can be : solid side extrusion and hollow side extrusion. In solid side extrusion, a solid body, with a solid protrusion of any profile is extruded. In hollow side extrusion, a workpiece with a hollow protrusion of any profile, is extruded. The tool opening is determined by the split die and the mandrel.

The extrusion force required in this process is very high. Due to this, the method is mainly used for non-ferrous metals and highly plastic materials, like lead. Fig. 4.46 shows the principle of side extrusion process for cable sheathing.

2. Continuous Extrusion. In conventional extrusion process, we start with a finite length of billet and get a finite-length product. However, in continuous extrusion process, continuous feed stock is converted to continuous product. This is achieved by applying the extrusion

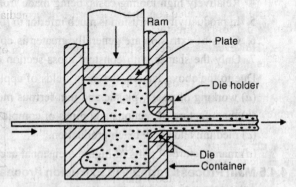

Fig. 4.46. Principle of Side Extrusion.

pressure on the periphery of the feedstock, instead of on the back, as in conventional extrusion. Again, whereas in conventional extrusion, there is a need to reduce friction between the billet and the container, in continuous extrusion, it is the friction force which provides the driving force for the extrusion. The impetus for the development of continuous extrusion process has been the need for the production of large tonnage of products continuously.

The most successful technique of continuous extrusion is the "Conform process" illustrated in Fig. 4.47. Continuous feedstock in the form of rod is inserted between the grooved extrusion wheel and the mating die shoe. As the wheel rotates, the rod is carried round the wheel by friction and is finally pressed against a stationary block, known as the abutmen. It gets upset to conform to the container (space between the wheel groove and the mating die shoe). Enough pressure is built up to force the material to extrude through a die opening.

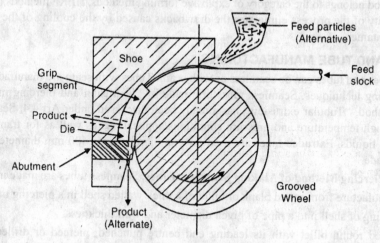

Fig. 4.47. Continuous Extrusion.

The process has the followng advantages :

(*i*) The process is truly continuous.

(*ii*) Raw stock, in the form of rod, powder or machined swarf, can be used.

(*iii*) Metallic and non-metallic powders can be intimately mixed and extruded.

(*iv*) Polymeric materials and even fibre reinforced plastics can be extruded.

(*v*) Low capital and operating costs.

(*vi*) If the process is run fast, enough heat is generated due to friction and the product emerges in an annealed condition. No further intermediate heat treatment is needed and the product can be put to use directly.

However, the process is limited to the extrusion of non-ferrous metals, mainly copper alloys and aluminium.

3. Helical Extrusion. It is a novel technique for the production of wire or tube. The technique more closely resembles machining process. A conical punch is driven slowly into the end of a copper billet, to form a short tube with an annular face. This is then steadily deformed by a tool (resembling a negative rake cutting tool) that rotates about the axes of the built and slowly advances in a helical path. The swarf, so produced, is not wasted but is trapped in a small chamber, from which it is forced to escape through an orifice, as a wire. The technique has the following advantages :

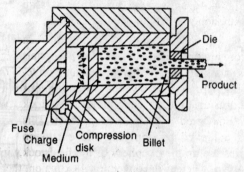

Fig. 4.48. Explosive Extrusion.

(*i*) The forces are low due to two factors : only a small volume of metal is deformed at a given instant and the yield stress gets reduced, because of severe local heating.

(*ii*) Very large reductions in cross-section are possible (upto about 150 times in diameter).

4. Explosive Extrusion : The method, illustrated schematically in Fig. 4.48, has been introduced industrially. When the explosive is detonated by igniting the fuse, pressure shock waves are generated. These are transmitted to the billet with the help of pressure waves transmitting medium (Here Air) and a compression disk. This forces the billet material out of the container through the die. The method belongs to the category of explosive forming methods, HERF methods (See Chapter 9). The rapidity of the process eliminates the drawbacks caused by the cooling of the billet inside a massive container.

4.5. PIPE AND TUBE MANUFACTURING

The pipes and tubes can be seamless or with seam. Tubes with seam are manufactured by the various welding techniques. Seamless tubes are made by : extrusion and piercing methods. The extrusion method, "Tubular extrusion" has already been discussed under Art 4.4. Seamless tubes are used in high temperature and pressure conditions/applications as well as for transporting gas and chemical liquids. Extruded tubes are used for gun barrels. Upto 400 mm diameter steel pipes have been made.

4.5.1. Piercing Method of Making Seamless Tubes. Seamless tubes are made in two stages:

1. Manufacture from round blank or billet of a thick walled shell in a piercing mill.

2. Rolling of shell into a pipe of given diameter and wall thickness.

A heated round billet with its leading end centre punched, pierced or drilled, is pushed longitudinally in between two large convex shaped (tapered) rolls that revolve in the same direction, their axes being inclined at opposite angles of about 6° from the axis of the billet, Fig. 4.49 (*a*). The clearance between the rolls is less than the diameter of the billet. As the billet is caught by the rolls and rotated, their inclination causes the billet to be drawn forward into them. The reduced clearance between the rolls forces the billet to deform into an elliptical shape. As the billet tries to rotate under high compressive forces created by the rolls, secondary tensile stresses are set up at 90° to the compressive forces at the centre of the billet. The punched hole at the centre of the billet

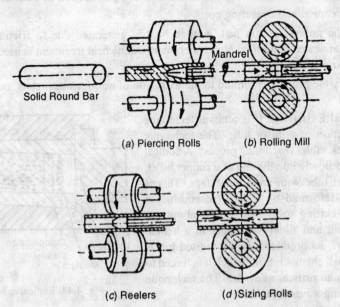

(*a*) Piercing Rolls   (*b*) Rolling Mill

(*c*) Reelers   (*d*) Sizing Rolls

Fig. 4.49. Piercing Methods.

will tear open. The mandrel assists this action. As the billet rotates and feed towards the mandrel, the tearing action is propagated along the length of the billet forming a seamless shell (roughly formed tube). Upon completion of the operation, the mandrel is forced out of the shell. This piercing of the billet to form a rough tube is called "Mannesmann process".

The pierced shell is further processed in a "plug rolling mill", (Fig.4.49 (b)), which is a two-high reversing stand with a series of round passes in the rolls. A short mandrel (plug) is held in the centre of the pass by a long bar. The clearance between the mandrel and the pass determines the wall thickness of the rolled tube. This operation elongates the tube and reduces the wall thickness. The outside diameter of the tube is only approximate, however. The tube is still in a rough state. Therefore, another operation, called "reeling" is performed between reelers and over a mandrel as shown in Fig. 4.49 (c). The reeling operation improves the finish of the inside and outside surfaces, eliminates irregularities, scratches and out of roundness, and decreases the differences in wall thickness. Finally, a sizing operation is performed between sizing rolls without use of a mandrel, (Fig. 4.49 (d)) The final operations of reeling and sizing are often conducted on cooled tubes in order to improve their finish and size.

Continuous Seamless Tube Mill. A most effective and advanced method for pipe rolling is the manufacture of thick walled shells in a piercing mill and then subsequent rolling in several continuous mills. These mills consist of several stands located one after another, the pipe being reduced in grooves and the direction of reduction changing by 90° in the adjacent stands. Rolling speeds can be adjusted in stands by means of electric motors, this allowing tension rolling and so increasing the reduction per passing and so thinning out pipe wall.

A typical continuous mill for manufacturing pipes from carbon and alloy steels in diameters from 30 to 102 mm and wall thickness of 1.75 to 8 mm from blanks 140 mm in diameter, consists of: furnace for rapid heating of blanks/billets, a piercing mill, multi-stand (7 to 9) mill for rolling rough pipes on a long mandrel, a device for extracting the mandrel, an induction furnace for heating rough pipes prior to subsequent rolling, an 11-stand continuous reducing mill in which the pipe is rolled without the use of a mandrel but with tension (when wall thickness is to be reduced) or without tension (when no change in wall thickness is desired) and a 19-stand continuous reducing mill for rolling with high tension in order to sharply reduce the diameter and the wall thickness of the pipe. After rolling, pipes are cut by saws and finished in continuous automated production lines.

Extensively used are automatic varieties of mills. An automatic mill is a standard non-reversible two-high stand with grooved rolls. Pipes from 57 to 425 mm in dia. with wall thickness of 3 to 30 mm can be rolled on these mills.

4.5.2. Welded Steel Tubing. Welded pipes are made in two steps : forming a strip into a circular section and then joining strip edges by welding. Welded pipes are much cheaper than seamless one, and their output increases from year to year. Their short comings are : poor strength and corrosion resistance of seams. However, these short comings are minimized by cold rolling.

1. Furnace Butt Welded Pipe. In this method, the skelp with one end trimmed is heated to 1300 to 1350° in a furnace. The hot skelp is drawn out of the furnace by grasping its trimmed end with tongs, over the handles of which a welding bell is slipped, (Fig. 4.50). The tong is pulled by a draw chain. This pulls the skelp through the welding bell which bends and folds the skelp along its longitudinal axis to circular shape, forcing the edges into contact. At the point of contact, the butt edges are welded together due to pressure exerted by the bell. The welded pipe is now transferred to the sizing rolls similar to Fig. 4.49 (d).

These rolls give the pipe a fairly correct outside diameter. Next, the pipe undergoes final sizing operation in a series of cross-rolls. This finally corrects the outside diameter of the pipe to the dimension specified and its surface appearance is improved, owing to the fact that the scale is removed in the final sizing operation. After this, the pipe is straightened in straightening rolls.

Finally, the pipe is washed in water, and its ends trimmed and threaded. This method is suitable for rapid production. 300 pipes of 0.6 m length each may be produced per hour. In a similar manner, pipes may be produced by lap welding instead of butt welding, with the edges overlapping. Tubes from 75 to 100 mm dia. are produced by this method.

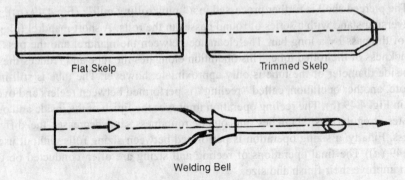

Fig. 4.50. Furnace Butt Welding Process.

The furnace butt-welded pipes are used for structural purposes, posts, and for carrying water, gas and wastes. Butt-welded pipes vary from 3 mm to 75 mm in diameter. Lap welded pipes are used primarily for large sizes from about 50 mm to 400 mm diameter.

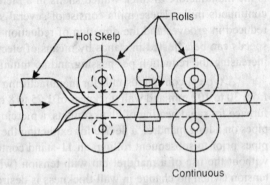

Fig. 4.51. Continuous Butt Welding.

Continuous Furnace Butt-welding. Continuous furnace butt-welding is used for water and gas pipes of 13.5 to 114 mm in dia. and wall thickness of 2 to 4 mm. A coiled strip is uncoiled in a continuous device, then heated in a furnace to 1300 to 1350°C. From the furnace, the strip (skelp) passes through a series of grooved rolls and is formed into a pipe, Fig. 4.51. Finally the pipes are finished in a reducing mill, then cut to standard lengths by a flying saw.

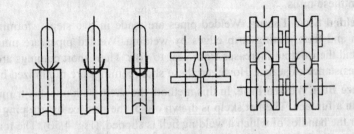

Fig. 4.52. Roll Forming of Pipe.

2. Electric Resistance Welding. This technique enables tubing of higher quality to be obtained than by the furnace welding process. Tubing from 6 to 630 mm in dia and with a wall thickness of 0.5 to 20 mm is produced by this method. The initial material for making the pipe is bright cold-rolled strip in coils, or sheet steel (for large- diameter tubing), which is preliminarily cleaned from scale and rust by pickling or shot blasting.

The flat strip or sheet is gradually roll formed into a tubular shape in a continuous mill of 5 to 12 stands, Fig. 4.52. The formed stock is inserted beneath the electrodes, Fig. 4.53, and the edges are heated by electric current. The heated edges are forced together by side pressure rolls and bottom pressure roll. A welded joint is formed by this action. External and internal flashes are removed by a cutter tool. After welding, pipes are sized or shaped into proper size, in a continuous mill, then cut to standard lengths by saws and transferred to a finishing department. Electric welded pipes are used primarily for pipe line conveying petroleum products and water.

Electric resistance welding is the most widely used process in tube production, but other electric welding methods are also employed. For example, SAW is used for thick walled tubes of medium size of carbon and alloy steels and large-size tubes of carbon steels. Atomic-hydrogen welding is used for tubes upto 200 mm in diameter with walls from 2 to 12 mm thick of alloy steels. Argon-arc welding is used for welding thin walled tubing of a diameter upto 450 mm with a wall thickness from 0.6 to 5 mm made of high-alloy austenitic steel, or of non-ferrous metals and alloys.

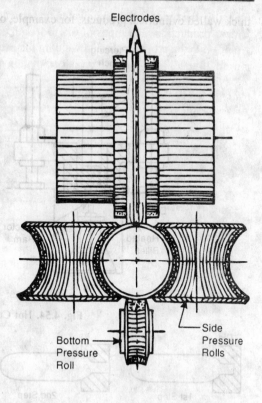

Fig. 4.53. Electric Butt Welded Pipe.

4.6. HOT DRAWING AND CUPPING

This is another technique of producing seamless cylinders and tubes. The heated billet or bloom is first pierced on a vertical hydraulic press, (Fig. 4.54 (a)). As the plunger, on its downward stroke, pierces the billet/bloom, confined in a die, the plastic metal is displaced and is moved upward and around the space between the plunger and die to produce a thick walled closed end shell. Upon completion of the downward stroke, the plunger moves upwards and the shell is pushed out of the die with the help of an ejector ram. This hot piercing method is followed by hot drawing. The formed shell is reheated and forced through a series of annular dies (of decreasing dia- meter), built on a push bench, (Fig.4.54(b)), with the help of a hydraulically operated plunger. The cup shaped piece is reduced in diameter and increased in length. To obtain long thin walled cylinders/ tubes, repeated heating and drawing may be necessary. If the final product is to be a tube, then the closed end is cut off and the tube under goes sizing and finishing operations as in piercing method of making seamless tubes. If the final product is to be a cylinder (for storing O_2 etc.), the open end is swaged to form a neck, (Fig. 4.55). Swaging involves hammering or forcing a tube or rod into a confining die to reduce its diameter, the die often playing the role of a hammer. Repeated blows cause the metal to flow inward and take the internal form of the die.

Seamless cylinders and tubes can also be made by hot drawing or cuppling, (Fig. 4.56). A thick metal blank (usually 8 or 10 mm thick) of circular shape is placed over a cylindrical die. The plunger of the hydraulically operated press forces the heated blank through the die to form a cup shaped product. The thickness of the cup is reduced and its length increased by drawing it through a series of dies having reduced clearance between the die and the punch. The same result can be obtained by drawing on a bench, (Fig. 4.54 (b)). This process is used primarily for forming thick walled cylindrical products, for example, oxygen tanks, and artillery shells etc.

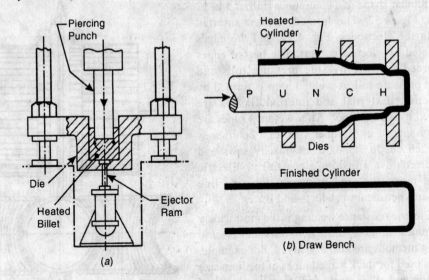

Fig. 4.54. Hot Cupping and Drawing.

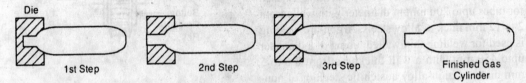

Fig. 4.55. Swaging the Open End of a Cylinder.

4.6.1. Other Methods of Tube Manufacture

As discussed before, the manufacture of seamless tubes consists of four stages :

      (*i*) Reduction of billets and blooms.

      (*ii*) Production of hollows.

      (*iii*) Hot finishing.

      (*iv*) Cold finishing.

The two methods of making hollows have been discussed : Mannesmann process (Art. 4.5.1) and Hot cupping (Art. 4.6). These two processes do not provide sufficiently large wall reduction and elongation to produce hot-worked tubes. Two methods of hot reduction of both diameter and wall thickness of hollow shells have already been discussed : Plug rolling mill [Fig. 4.49 (*b*)] and Drawing [Fig. 4.54 (*b*)]. The other methods employed for the same purpose are :

1. The Assel Elongator. In this technique, three conical driven rolls of special design, all inclined to the tube axis are used. This method has been widely adopted.

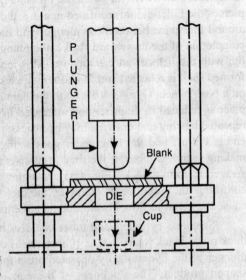

Fig. 4.56. Hot Drawing and Cupping.

2. Three-Roll Piercing Machines. The Assel elongator led to the development of three-roll piercing mill, (Fig. 4.57).

This rolling mill produces more concentric tubes with smoother inside and outside surface than the old Mannes-Mann mill.

3. Pilgering. A widely used method for hot reduction of both diameter and wall thickness of thick-walled shell is known as the "Pilger Process". A Pilger rolling mill, (Fig. 4.58) has two rolls, with pass grooves of varying profile. Thus, when the rolls rotate, the dimensions of the pass change continuously and, therefore, the form of the pass is variable during one revolution of the rolls. At maximum diameter of the

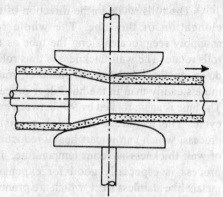

Fig. 4.57. Three-Roll Piercing Mill.

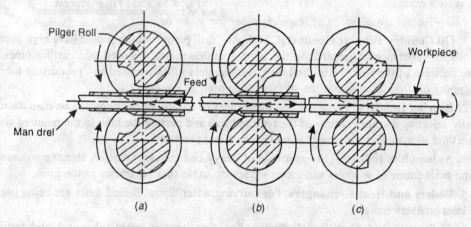

Fig. 4.58. The Pilger Rolling Mill.

pass grooves, the rolls form an idle pass (Position *a*) whose dimensions are larger than the outer diameter of the shell. At this moment, the shell, together with the inserted mandrel, is automatically fed into the gap between the rolls by the amount of feed. Upon further rotation of the rolls, the dimensions of the pass are gradually decreased due to its varying form. The rolls bite the shell and roll the hollow shell on to the central mandrel. The shell is reduced in thickness and diameter, (Position *b*), this reduction being increased with the decrease in the pass groove diameter. The rolls force the gripped portion of the shell in the direction of rolls rotation, so that the shell and mandrel are made to move backwards, that is, opposite to the direction they were fed by the feeder (Position *c*). When the rolls have rotated through 360°, they return to the position (*a*) and the feeder again advances the shell between the rolls. The shell is turned 90° as it is being fed forward, to maintain uniform walls. Hence, in the Pilgering process, the thick hollow shell is reduced both in diameter and thickness and hence elongated in a series of discontinuous steps, two steps forward and one step backward. After rolling the shell, the mandrel is removed from the tube. The next shell is rolled on a new mandrel, while the first one is cooled, lubricated and prepared for further use. Very high reductions (upto about 70%) can be achieved by Pilgering process.

After hot finishing, the last stage in the Tube manufacture is cold finishing. This is done by Reelers and Sizing rolls [Fig. 4.49 (*c*) and (*d*)] and by Tube drawing (Art. 4.7.2). Another method of Cold-reducing or cold-finishing resem- bles the Pilger hot process, (Fig. 4.59). Two rolls are used with a tapered semi-circular groove in each. The maximum size of the groove is equal to the outside diameter of the ingoing tube and minimum size equal to the outer diameter of the outgoing tube.

The rolls rotate in the direction of the elongation of the tube. The whole roll assembly reciprocates along the tube as the rolls rotate. The wall thickness is thus rolled down on the fixed tapered mandrel, much more steadily than in the hot Pilger process. The tube is again rotated by 90° between each cycle. The technique is a high precision process, which can impart heavy reductions of wall thickness at room temperature. The process is especially good for expensive metals like stainless steel, which are prone to pickup trouble in drawing. Interfacial sliding is much less than in drawing and lubricating is relatively simple.

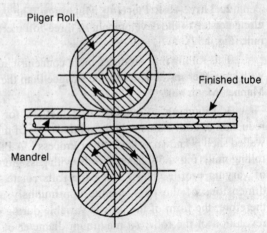

Fig. 4.59. Cold Pilger Process.

The principal applications of seamless tubes are given below :

1. **Oil Country Tubular Goods (OCTG).** As "drill pipes" which should have high strength and collapse resistance. After drilling the bore, seamless tubes are used as "casting pipes" to prevent collapse of the bore wells. And then, the seamless tubes are used as "production tubing" for pumping oil from oil wells to the surface. Also used as a water drill.

2. **Bearing Industry.** The outer and inner races of ball/roller bearings can be manufactured easily by selecting a seamless tube of the required size and parting the tube to the required width. This method of manufacturing races is inexpensive and preferred.

3. **Automobile Industry.** For rear axle of heavy commercial vehicles, steering columns of cars and main frame of scooters and motor cycles etc. Also small diameter piston pins.

4. **Boilers and Heat Exchangers.** For carrying water. Spiral finned tubes are being used in waste heat recovery boilers.

5. **Refineries and Fertilizer Industry.** For pipe lines in petro-chemical and fertilizer complexes. Also in sugar industry.

6. **Mechanical Tubing.** Seamless tubes are used where structural integrity is of paramount importance, *e.g.*, for hydraulic cylinders, gas cylinders etc. High pressure gas cylinders are used for storage of gases such as O_2, N_2 and C_2H_2 etc. Oxygen and acetylene cylinders are extensively used for gas welding.

7. **Speciality Tubes.** Such as fine capillary tubes, clad tubes, dual tubes etc. for special applications in electronics, instrumentation, medical, air craft, nuclear industries, etc.

4.7. DRAWING OF WIRE, ROD AND TUBE

Drawing is a cold working process in which the workpiece (wire, rod or tube) is pulled through a tapered hole in a die so as to reduce its diameter. The process imparts accurate dimensions, specified cross-section and a clean and excellent quality of surface to the work. The process may appreciably increase the strength and hardness of metal.

Round, rectangular, square, hexagonal and other shapes of bars upto about 10 cm, across or in diameter, wire of all sizes, and tubes are commonly finished by cold drawing. Wire can not be hot rolled commercially/economically smaller than about 5 mm dia. and is reduced to smaller sizes by cold drawing. In addition to direct applications such as electrical wiring, wire is the starting material for many products, such as wire-frame structures (coat hangers, shopping carts etc.), nails, screws, bolts, rivets and wire fencing wiremesh, wire ropes, electrodes, chain pin, umbrella ribs, springs, link chain, handtools and needles etc. Seamless tubes are made by a variety of hot working techniques (extrusion, piercing, hot drawing and cupping etc.), but below a minimum size (less than 3 mm thick), they must be further reduced by cold drawing. Cold drawn tubes perform important functions in hydraulic systems of vehicles, aeroplanes, ships, industrial machinery, water distribution systems and as hypodermic tubes (needles).

The starting materials for drawing are in the form of rolled or extruded rods of 5 to 9 mm in dia., rolled or formed sections of 5 to 150 mm in dia., welded pipes of 6 to 200 mm in dia., seamless rolled pipes of 40 to 200 mm in dia., and non-ferrous extruded pipes of 20 to 400 mm in dia. Drawing is used to fabricate wire from 0.008 to 6 mm in diameter, pipes of 1 to 360 mm in outside dia. and wall thickness of 0.1 to 10 mm, etc.

4.7.1. Wire and Rod drawing. Fig. 4.60 (*a*) shows a section of a typical circular draw die. The die geometry is typified by a bell mouthed entrance Zone (angle β is usually about 40°), a conical working zone with half die angle α (usually 6° to 12°) and a short sizing land. The entrance zone allows the introduction of lubricant into the working zone and also it protects the work material against scoring by the die edges. The actual reduction takes place in the conical working zone. The land (a few mm long) serves to guide the wire or rod as it comes out of the working zone of the die. It ensures accuracy of dimensions and of sections shape. The exit zone prevents damage to die bearing and scoring of finished product. Very large dies (for drawing rods and tubes of large cross-section) are made of high carbon or high-speed steel, the moderate-size dies of tungsten carbide, and the dies for the finest wires (down to 0.05 mm dia.) are made of diamond. The deformation force is supplied by the pulling action but the material is deformed in compression due to the reaction of the die on the material. Therefore, drawing is often called indirect compression deformation process.

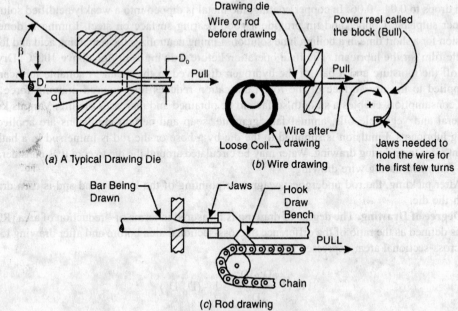

(a) A Typical Drawing Die

(b) Wire drawing

(c) Rod drawing

Fig. 4.60. Wire and Rod Drawing.

1. Wire drawing. Materials below about 16 mm diameter are handled in coil form. At the start of wire drawing, the end of the rod or wire to be drawn is pointed (by swaging etc.) so that it freely enters the die orifice and sticks out behind the die. This end is gripped by the jaws of the plier, or carriage which pulls the rod through all zones of the die hole where it undergoes deformation, that is, reduction and elongation. The wire is pulled sufficiently so that its end can be attached to the power reel. After that, the power reel rotates at the proper speed and pulls the wire through the die with the wire getting continuously wound on the reel, (Fig. 4.60 (*b*)). For fine wire, the material may be passed through a number of dies, receiving successive reductions in diameter, before being coiled. Such successive drawing in general requires driving rolls between the dies. The drawing arrangement used in wire drawing is called "Bull-block drawbench". The diameter of the drawing block in machines of various sizes may vary from 150 to 1000 mm and the available power ranges from 5 kW to 110 kW.

2. Rod drawing. In rod or bar drawing, the product must remain straight. The maximum length of the rod which can be drawn depends upon the maximum travel of the carriage which pulls it through the die (it may be 15 m to 30 m). The front pointed end of the rod protruding from the die is gripped by the jaws of the plier (drawing Carriage) and the hook is lowered to engage the moving chain. This drawing arrangement used in rod drawing is called "chain drawbench". The pull capacity of the drawbench, (Fig. 4.60 (*c*)), ranges from 10 kN to 1500 kN.

Drawing speed may be 0.15 m/s for the largest size rods and 1.5 m/s for small rods and coils and upto 25 m/s for very fine wires.

Preparing the metal for drawing. Before drawing, the rod is cleaned of scale. Descaling is commonly done by pickling in acid solutions. Steel rods are pickled in sulphuric or hydrochloric acid, or a mixture of acids ; copper and brass are treated in sulphuric acid ; nickel and its alloys, in a mixture of sulphuric acid and potassium bichromate.

After pickling, the metal is washed to remove all remains of acid and sludge from its surface. The metal surface is then conditioned by sulling, coppering, phosphating and liming.

In sulling or yellowing, the blank is given a thin coating of iron hydroxide, $Fe(OH)_3$, which combines with lime to serve as a filler for the lubricant. Phosphating consists of applying a film of phosphates of Mn, Fe or Zn. Lubricant sticks well to the phosphate coating, and the co-efficient of friction drops to 0.04 - 0.06. In copper coating, the metal is dipped into a weakly acidified solution of copper sulphate. Copper and tin provide a good bearing surface on steel. Liming is done by immersion for a short time in a boiling lime solution. Liming neutralizes the remaining acid and forms a vehicle film for the lubricant. The final operation before drawing is drying above 100°C. Drying drives off the moisture and a part of the hydrogen dissolved in the metal. A suitable lubricant is then applied to the dry surface of the rod. Lubrication reduces the required drawing force and energy consumption, enables a smooth surface to be obtained and increases die life. Various kinds of mineral and vegetable oils, animal fats, graphite, soap and certain emulsions are applied as drawing lubricants. Emulsion is supplied to the die by a hose or the rod is immersed in a bath of lubricant prior to or during drawing. Water may be circulated around the die to cool it as considerable heat is generated during wire drawing.

After pickling, the rod undergoes swaging or pointing of the leading end and is then drawn through the die.

Degree of Drawing. The degree of drawing is measured in terms of "reduction of area (RA)" which is defined as the ratio of the difference in cross-sectional area before and after drawing to the initial cross-sectional area, expressed in per cent :

$$RA = \frac{D_i^2 - D_o^2}{D_i^2} = 1 - (D_0/D_i)^2$$

For fine wires, the reduction per pass of 15 to 25% is used, while for coarse wires this value per pass may be 30 to 35 per cent. For rods, the value can be upto 40 per cent.

4.7.2. Hydrostatic Wire Extrusion. Hydrostatic wire extrusion is now well established and is particularly suitable for brittle materials and composites. In hydrostatic extrusion, it is not necessary that the billet be straight or cylindrical and it need not have a constant cross- sectional area along its entire length. Thus, for example specially bent billets or even a coiled wire or multi-stepped workpiece can be extruded. Since there is no friction in the billet chamber, the billet length is dependent only on the dimensions of the pressure chamber. Thus, in hydrostatic wire extrusion, a wire coil placed in the pressure chamber, (Fig. 4.61) can be extruded upto a ratio of raw-wire length to raw-wire diameter of the order of 105. By applying a front tension, an efficient and well controlled extrusion-drawing process is available.

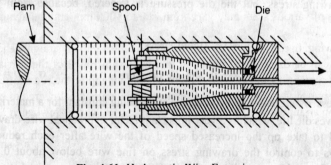

Fig. 4.61. Hydrostatic Wire Extrusion.

4.7.3. Tandem Wire Drawing. It is clear that for fine wire, (below 10 mm φ), the drawing involves passage through several dies in series, especially for copper wire, which is very ductile.

This is called multi-stage or tandem or continuous wire drawing. The wire is passed through several dies in series (3 to 12), Fig. 4.61A, each held in water-cooled die- blocks. In this way, a higher deformation ratio can be achieved and the surface temperature of the wire is also

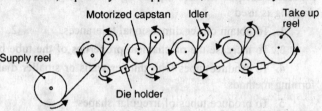

Fig. 4.61A. The continuous wire drawing machine.

reduced. The temperature gradients between the wire surface and the interior are reduced during the period the wire is between two dies. Additional cooling can also be used. If extensive deformation is required, intermediate anneals must be performed between the various stages of drawing.

Below, are shown the various stages of copper-wire drawing from 8 mm φ to 1.42 mm φ and then fine copper-wire drawing from 1.42 mm φ to 0285/0.295 mm φ.

Copper-Wire drawing :–

8 mm $\xrightarrow{\text{to}}$ 6.4 mm $\xrightarrow{\text{to}}$ 5.4 mm $\xrightarrow{\text{to}}$ 4.55 mm $\xrightarrow{\text{to}}$ 3.80 mm $\xrightarrow{\text{to}}$

3.30 mm $\xrightarrow{\text{to}}$ 2.90 mm $\xrightarrow{\text{to}}$ 2.55 mm $\xrightarrow{\text{to}}$ 2.25 mm $\xrightarrow{\text{to}}$ 2 mm

$\downarrow$ to

1.42 mm $\xleftarrow{\text{to}}$ 1.6 mm $\xleftarrow{\text{to}}$ 1.8 mm

Fine-Copper-Wire drawing :–

1.42 mm $\xrightarrow{\text{to}}$ 1.34 mm $\xrightarrow{\text{to}}$ 1.20 $\xrightarrow{\text{to}}$ 1.05 mm $\xrightarrow{\text{to}}$ 0.96 mm

$\downarrow$ to

0.57 mm $\xleftarrow{\text{to}}$ 0.63 mm $\xleftarrow{\text{to}}$ 0.70 mm $\xleftarrow{\text{to}}$ 0.78 mm $\xleftarrow{}$ 0.86 mm

$\downarrow$ to

0.51 mm $\xrightarrow{\text{to}}$ 0.46 mm $\xrightarrow{\text{to}}$ 0.42 mm $\xrightarrow{\text{to}}$ 0.38 mm $\xrightarrow{\text{to}}$ 0.31 mm

$\downarrow$ to

0.285/0.295 mmφ

To avoid excessive tension on the drawn wire, it is usual to wind one or two turns round a capstan between each pair of dies. The capstans are driven at carefully regulated speeds, so that there is a frictional drag at the capstan surface, which pulls the wire through the die, and the capstan also provides small back tension on the wire entering the next die. This back tension increases the drawing stress, but the die pressure is lowered, because from the conditions of yielding,

$$\sigma_1 - \sigma_2 = \sigma_0 \quad \text{(yield stress)}$$

Now $\qquad \sigma_2 = -p$, the die pressure $\qquad \therefore \quad \sigma_1 + p = \sigma_0$

if the drawing stress σ_1 increases, p will decrease (σ_0 being constant for a material). This reduction in pressure improves die life, which is a very important factor in practical wire-drawing. The capstans are synchronized to take up the increased speed of the wire after each reduction. The use of tentioning pulleys to control the drawing stress on fine wire below about 0.1 mm ϕ, enables drawing speeds of upto 15 m/s to be used.

4.7.4. Tube Drawing. Hollow cylinders and tubes or pipes which are made by hot-working processes such as extrusion, piercing and rolling, often are cold finished by drawing. Cold tube drawing is used :

    1. To obtain closer dimensional tolerances.   2.   To produce better surface finish.

    3. To increase the mechanical properties of the tube by strain hardening.

    4. To produce tubes with thinner walls or smaller diameters than can be obtained with hot forming methods.

    5. To produce tubes of irregular shapes.

Like bar drawing, tube drawing is done in most cases with the use of a "drawbench".

The three common methods of tube drawing are : Tube sinking. Tube drawing with a plug and Tube drawing with a moving mandrel, the last two methods being more widely used because in tube sinking, (Fig. 4.62 (a)), the inside of the tube is not supported and so during drawing operation,

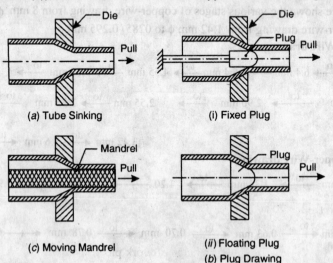

(a) Tube Sinking   (i) Fixed Plug

(c) Moving Mandrel   (ii) Floating Plug
                                          (b) Plug Drawing

Fig. 4.62. Tube Drawing.

the inner surface becomes uneven and there will be tendency for the wall thickness to increase slightly. In plug drawing and movable mandrel drawing, both the inner and outer surfaces of the tube are controlled and we get tubes of better dimensional accuracy as compared to Tube sinking.

In plug drawing, the plug (which may be either cylindrical or conical) can either be fixed, (Fig. 4.62 *b* (*i*)), or floating, (Fig. 4.62 *b*(*ii*)). The friction with a fixed plug will be more than with a floating plug, so the reduction in area seldom exceeds 30% in this method. With a floating plug, this figure can be approximately 45% or with the same reduction, the drawing loads will be less with floating plug than with a fixed plug. The friction is minimized in Tube drawing with a movable mandrel [Eq. 4.62 (*c*)]. However, after tube drawing, the mandrel has to be removed by rolling which results in slightly increased tube diameter and reduced dimensional tolerances.

Tube sinking is used to only reduce the outside diameter of tube. If the wall thickness of the tube is also to be reduced, an internal die is also needed, which may be in the form of a plug or a mandrel. Mandrels are used for tubes from about 12.7 mm to 250 mm in diameter. Heavy walled tubes and those with less than 12.7 mm dia. are drawn without a mandrel. This is the procedure used for drawing hypodermic needles (starting from a 50 mm dia. tube) with outside diameter less than 0.02 mm and with inside diameter half of the outside diameter.

A number of high-tech industries such as electro-medical, bio- medical, orthodonitics, semi-conductors etc. use specially processed tubes such as hypodermic needles, hermetic seals, connectors, mercury weighted switches, silicon controlled rectifiers, electronic auto-ignition and speed control devices, photographic cartridges, numeric readout units etc. Dual tubes consisting of two concentric seamless tubes are used in the semi- conductor industry to handle hazardous gases such as Arsine, Phosphine, Silane, Diborane etc. Special shapes such as oval, rectangular and combinations thereoff are produced for instrumentation industry, bourdon tubing etc. The capillary tubes with OD of 4.5 mm and ID about 1.5 mm are used for transmission of pressure over long distances. They are used for liquid chromography. The seamless tubes are used extensively in aircraft hydraulic systems.

These special tubes are produced by drawing of seamless hollows. These tubes have to meet the following requirements :

    (*i*) Very close dimensional tolerances.

    (*ii*) Extremely good external and internal surface finishes.

    (*iii*) Freedom from any chemical or other impurities.

    (*iv*) Close tolerances on mechanical properties.

4.7.5. Main Process Variables in Drawing Process

Drawing stress is given as:

$$\sigma_d = \frac{\sigma_0(1+B)}{B}\left[1 - \left(\frac{r_1}{r_0}\right)^{2B}\right]$$

where σ_0 = yield strength of metarial

                                $B = \mu \cot \alpha$

                                μ = co-efficient of friction

                                α = half die-angle

                                r_1 = radius of work piece at exist

                                r_0 = raidus of work piece at entry.

∴ Main process variables of Drawing Process are :

1. Strength of work material   2. Temperature

3. Speed of drawing   4. Co-efficient of friction/lubrication

5. Die-angle   6. Reduction of area

4.8. SHEET METAL WORKING OR PRESS WORKING OF SHEET METALS

Press working may be defined as a chipless manufacturing process by which various components are made from sheet metal. This process is also termed as cold stamping. The main features of a press are : A frame which supports a ram or a slide and a bed, a source of mechanism for operating the ram in line with and normal to the bed. The ram is equipped with suitable punch/ punches and a die block is attached to the bed. A stamping is produced by the downward stroke of the ram when the punch moves towards and into the die block. The punch and die block assembly is generally termed as a "die set" or simply as the "die". Press working operations are usually done at room temperature.

In this process, the wall thickness of the parts remain almost constant and differs only slightly from the thickness of the initial sheet metal. The process has got the following advantages:

1. Small weight of fabricated parts.

2. High productivity of labour (upto 30,000 to 40,000 pieces per 8 hour working shift).

3. High efficiency of technique as regards the fabrication of items of diversified shapes, both simple and complex, such as washers, bushings, retainers (cages) of ball bearings, tanks and car bodies etc.

4. The parts obtained by cold sheet metal working are distinguished for their size accuracy (narrow tolerances with a high surface finish). In many cases, they require no subsequent machining and are delivered to the assembly shop.

All the above advantages have made sheet stamping very attractive to a host of industries, particularly, to automotive, air craft, electrical engineering and others.

The initial material in cold press working is : low carbon steels, ductile alloy steels, copper and its alloys (brass, bronze), aluminium and its alloys, as well as, other ductile materials from tenth of a mm to about 6 or 8 mm thick. As discussed under cold rolling and wire drawing, the metal must be free from scale before sheet metal working. Scale is removed by pickling and other operations already discussed.

4.8.1. Elastic recovery or Springback. We know that in metal working processes, the total deformation imparted to a work piece will be the sum of elastic deformation and plastic deformation. We also know that elastic deformation is recoverable whereas plastic deformation is permanent. So, at the end of a metal working operation, when the pressure on the metal is released, there is an elastic recovery by the material and the total deformation will get reduced a little. This phenomenon is called as "Springback". This phenomenon is of more importance in cold working operations, especially in forming operations such as bending etc. Springback depends upon the yield point strength of a metal. The higher the yield point strength of a metal, the greater the springback. The amount of springback for a forming operation is difficult to predict and cut- and try methods are most satisfactory to account for it. To compensate for springback, the cold deformation must always be carried beyond the desired limit by an amount equal to the springback.

4.8.2. Press operations. The sheet metal operations done on a press may be grouped into two categories, cutting operations and forming operations. In cutting operations, the workpiece is stressed beyond its ultimate strength. The stresses caused in the metal by the applied forces will be shearing stresses. In forming operations, the stresses are below the ultimate strength of the metal. In this operation, there is no cutting of the metal but only the contour of the workpiece is changed to get the desired product. The cutting operations include : blanking, punching, notching, perforating, trimming, shaving, slitting and lancing etc. The forming operations include : bending, drawing, redrawing and squeezing. The stresses induced in the metal during bending and drawing operations are tensile and compressive and during the squeezing operation these are compressive.

Below we give the definitions of the various press operations :

(*a*) *Blanking.* Blanking is the operation of cutting a flat shape from sheet metal. The article punched out is called the 'blank' and is the required product of the operation. The hole and metal left behind is discarded as waste. It is usually the first step of series of operations, (Fig. 4.63 (*a*)).

Plain blanking is explained in Fig. 4.64.

(*b*) *Punching (Piercing).* It is a cutting operation by which various shaped holes are made in sheet metal. Punching is similar to blanking except that in punching, the hole is the desired product, the material punched out to form the hole being waste (Fig. 4.63 (*b*)).

(*c*) *Notching.* This is cutting operation by which metal pieces are cut from the edge of a sheet, strip or blank.

(*d*) *Perforating.* This is a process by which multiple holes which are very small and close together are cut in flat work material.

(*e*) *Trimming.* This operation consists of cutting unwanted excess material from the periphery of a previously formed component.

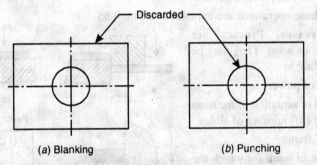

(*a*) Blanking   (*b*) Punching

Fig. 4.63. Blanking and Punching.

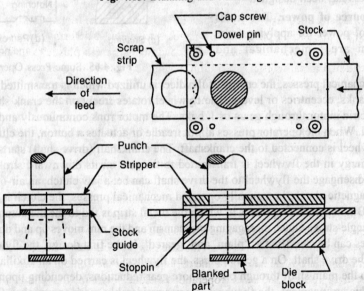

Fig. 4.64. Plain Blanking.

(*f*) *Shaving.* The edges of a blanked part are generally rough, uneven and unsquare. Accurate dimensions of the part are obtained by removing a thin strip of metal along the edges. This operation is termed as shaving.

(g) *Slitting*. It refers to the operation of making incomplete holes in a workpiece.

(h) *Lancing*. This is a cutting operation in which a hole is partially cut and then one side is bent down to form a sort of tab or louver. Since no metal is actually removed, there will be no scrap.

(i) *Nibbling*. The nibbling operation which is used for only small quantities of components, is designed for cutting out flat parts from sheet metal. The flat parts range from simple to complex contours. This operation is generally substituted for blanking. The part is usually moved and guided by and as the continuously operating punch cuts away at the edge of the desired contour.

(j) *Bending*. In this operation, the material in the form of flat sheet or strip, is uniformly strained around a linear axis which lies in the neutral plane and perpendicular to the lengthwise direction of the sheet or metal.

(k) *Drawing*. This is a process of a forming a flat workpiece into a hollow shape by means of a punch which causes the blank to flow into a die cavity.

(j) *Squeezing*. Under this operation, the metal is caused to flow to all portions of a die cavity under the action of compressive forces.

Some of these operations are explained in Fig. 4.65.

4.8.3. Presses. Presses are classified in various ways. They may be classified according to :

(i) source of power

(ii) method of actuation of the rams (slides) (iii) number of slides

(iv) type of frame

(v) the type of work for which the press has been designed

(a) **Source of power.** Two kinds of sources of power for applying force to the ram are : mechanical and hydraulic.

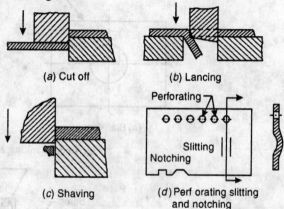

(a) Cut off   (b) Lancing

(c) Shaving   (d) Perf orating slitting and notching

Fig. 4.65. Some Press Operations.

In mechanical presses, the energy of flywheel is utilized which is transmitted to the workpiece by gears, cranks, eccentrics or levers. The flywheel rotates freely on the crank shaft and is driven from an electric motor through gears or V belts. The motor runs continuously and stores energy in the flywheel. When the operator presses a foot treadle or actuates a button, the clutch gets engaged and the flywheel is connected to the crankshaft. The crankshaft (drive shaft) starts rotating and the stored up energy in the flywheel is transmitted to the ram on its downward stroke. The clutch to engage and disengage the flywheel to the drive shaft can be: a jaw clutch, an air-operated clutch or an electromagnetic clutch. In manually operated mechanical presses, the clutch is disengaged after each cycle. But in automatic presses in which the metal strip is fed to the die automatically, there is no need of single-stroke clutch disengaging mechanism and the ram moves up and down continuously. These presses can be classified as 'plain' and 'geared'. In the first design, the flywheel is mounted directly on the drive shaft. On a geared press, the flywheel is carried on an auxiliary shaft which is connected to the main shaft through one or more gear reductions, depending upon size and energy needed. In this arrangement, the flywheel stores considerably more energy than the plain drive as its speed is higher than the main drive shaft, (Fig. 4.66.)

In hydraulic press, the ram is actuated by oil pressure on a piston in a cylinder.

Mechanical presses have following advantages over the hydraulic presses :-

(1) run faster (2) lower maintenance cost (3) lower capital cost.

Advantages of hydraulic presses are : (1) More versatile and easier to operate. (2) Tonnage adjustable from zero to maximum. (3) Constant pressure can be maintained throughout the stroke. (4) Force and speed can be adjusted throughout the stroke. (5) More powerful than mechanical presses. (6) Safe as it will stop at a pressure setting. The main disadvantage of hydraulic press is that it is slower than a mechanical press.

A press is rated in tonnes of force, it is able to apply without undue strain. To keep the deflections small, it is a usual practice to choose a press rated 50 to 100% higher than the force required for an operation.

(*b*) **Method of actuation of slides.** The various methods used for transmitting power to the ram or slide are shown in Fig. 4.67. The drive (Fig. 4.67 *h*) is for hydraulic presses in which the ram is actuated from a piston by means of a connecting rod. The remaining arrangements are for mechanical presses. The most common drive is crankshaft. Crankshafts are used for longer strokes. For shorter strokes, eccentric drive is employed. Cam drive is similar to eccentric drive except that at the bottom of the stroke dwell is obtained. Rack and pinion drive is used where a very long stroke is required. In this drive, the movement of the slide is uniform and much slow as compared to crank drive.

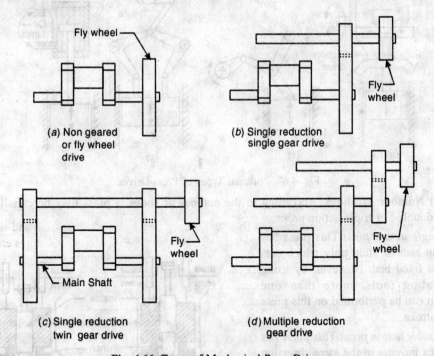

(*a*) Non geared or fly wheel drive

(*b*) Single reduction single gear drive

(*c*) Single reduction twin gear drive

(*d*) Multiple reduction gear drive

Fig. 4.66. Types of Mechanical Press Drives.

In the screw drive, the slide is attached to the flywheel through a screw. As the flywheel is rotated by a friction drive, it moves down and the slide motion is continuously accelerated. At the bottom of the stroke, the entire energy stored in the flywheel is consumed by the work. The knuckle joint drive consists of an upper link and a lower link joined together with another horizontal link at the centre. The top end of the upper link is attached to a rigid portion of the frame. The horizontal link is driven by crankshaft. As the crankshaft rotates and completes its cycle, it pulls the horizontal link until the other two links assume a straight line vertical in position. This results in a short powerful movement of the slide with slow motion at the bottom of the stroke. Due to this reason, knuckle joint presses are used for heavy coining, embossing and sizing operations. The toggle drive is primarily used to drive the outer sides of a double action press. For example, in drawing operation, the outer ram should dwell to hold the blank during part of the stroke.

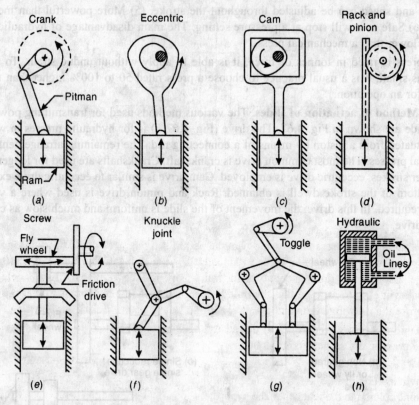

Fig. 4.67. Principal Types of Press-Drives.

(*c*) **Number of Slides.** According to the number of slides, a press may be classified as : single-, double-, or triple-action press.

*Single action press.*This press has one plain ram or slide only which acts against a fixed bed. However, by using combination tools, more than one operation can be performed on this press at each stroke.

*Double action press.*This press has two slides moving in the same direction against a fixed bed. The outer slide is referred to as blankolder slide and the inner slide is called the punch or plunger slide, (Fig. 4.68). They are used chiefly for deep drawing operations.

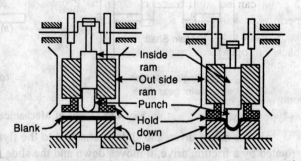

Fig. 4.68. Double Action Press.

*Triple action press.*This press has three slides, two slides moving in the same direction against the fixed bed as in double action press and the third or lower slide moving upward through the fixed bed, (Fig. 4.69). They are used only for large work such as motorcar body panels.

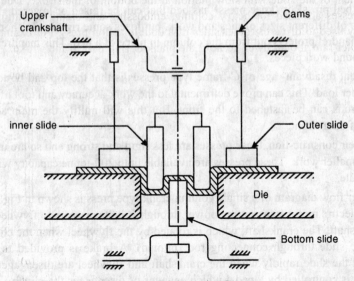

Fig. 4.69. Triple Action Press.

The double action press is known as double action cam press or double action toggle press, depending upon whether the outer slide is actuated by a cam located in the crankshaft or by a toggle drive. Triple action press is cam type for small work and toggle type for large work. The use of cams makes it easy to arrange that the holder descends ahead of the punch so that the blank is gripped before the drawing starts and also to keep the holder at rest during the drawing.

(*d*) **Type of frame.** According to the design of the frame, the presses may be classified as open frame presses and closed frame presses.

Open Frame Press. (Fig. 4.70) This press is also known as 'Gap frame' or 'C' frame press. It has only one column to the rear of the die, whose shape resembles letter *C*. the front or die area is accessible from three sides, front, left side and right side. This speeds up production as the sheet metal can be fed in many ways. The back of such a press can be solid or open. Open back press permits feeding of the sheet metal from front to back or the ejection of the finished parts from the back. For open back frame presses, the frame may be fixed in a vertical position or in a fixed inclined position or it may be of inclinable type. The most common type press is 'open back inclinable *C*-type frame press', commonly known as *OBI* press. Its frame is inclined backward which facilitates the removal of scrap or parts by gravity through the open back. It ranges from a small 1 tonne bench press to floor presses rated upto 150 tonnes. The solid back type press in a fixed vertical position on integral base is more rigid than an inclinable press and has wider bed and arms.

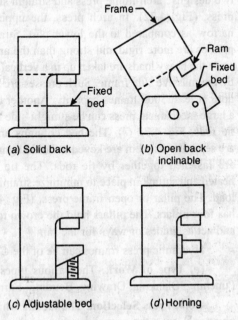

Fig. 4.70. Open Frame Press.

An 'adjustable bed press' or 'knee press' has bed that can be raised or lowered. This permits the accommodation of different sizes of dies and work, but loses some rigidity. In 'horn press', a large round post or mandrel projects out from the column in place of a bed. This mandrel is called 'horn' and supports round workpieces.

An inherent disadvant- age of C-frame type presses is that the top and bottom of the frame swing apart under load. This can prove detrimental to the work accuracy and tool life. To counteract this effect, tie rods can be fastened to the front. But this will nullify the main advantage of the press, that is, of open front.

Due to their construc-tion, these presses are less rigid and strong and so are useful mainly for operations on smaller work. These presses are available upto 200-tonne capacity with strokes of 90 to 120 per minute.

The power flow diagram of a single column crank type press is shown in Fig. 4.71. The drive consists of an electric motor transmitting power through V-belts or gears to flywheel which rotates freely on crankshaft. The crankshaft, which is rotated by the flywheel when the clutch is engaged, reciprocates the slide through connecting rod (pitman). A brake is provided to stop the crank mechanism and the slide rapidly when the crankshaft and flywheel are disengaged by the clutch. Press operation is controlled by a pedal which engages or disengages the clutch.

Closed Frame Press. These presses have two upright columns on each side of the die. They are stronger, more rigid and balanced than C-type frame presses. The design is appropriate for wide beds and long strokes and so is suitable for heavier work. Work is fed either from the front or from the back of the press into the die area. Closed frame presses can be of two designs : arch frame press and straight side frame press, (Fig. 4.72). In arch press, the upper part is narrow as compared to the lower part. Straight-side presses are more rigid and strong than the arch press, since the heavy loads are taken up in a vertical direction by the massive side frame. Such presses are available upto at least 3000 tonnes capacity. Another design of a large mechanical press can be straight-side type with tie rods, Fig. 4.72 (c). The bed columns and crown are separate units but are keyed to hold alignment and are fastened together by tie rods. The tie rods are heated and shrunk in place to minimize straining under load. The pillar or open frame press, (Fig. 4.72 (d)), has four pillars. The pillars hold the crown to the bed and act as guides or ways for the ram.

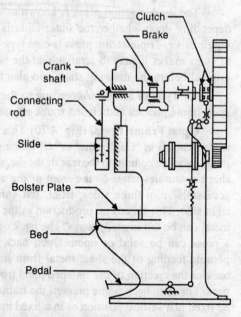

Fig. 4.71. Power Flow of Single Column Crank Press.

Hydraulic press frames can be of the C-type, straight side type with tie rods or of pillar type.

(e) **Type of Work.** The various types of work for which the press may be designed are, Punching, Blanking, Drawing, Bending, Forming, Coining, Embossing etc.

4.8.4. Press Selection. The factors which should be considered while selecting a press for a given job, are : the overall work size, the stock thickness and material, kind of operation to be performed, power required and speed of operation.

For punching, blanking and trimming operations, usually the crank or eccentric type mechanical press is used. This is due to their small working strokes and high production rates. In these operations, there is sudden release of load at the end of the cutting stroke. This sudden release of load is not advisable in hydraulic presses. So, hydraulic presses are not preferred for these operations. If however these are inevitable, then some damping devices are incorporated in the press design. For coining and other squeezing operations, which require very large forces, knuckle joint mechanical press is ideally suited. Hydraulic presses, which are slower and more powerful, can also be used for these operations. Hydraulic presses are also better adapted to pressing, forming and operations, which are basically slower processes.

4.8.5. Press Working Terminology. A simple cutting die used for punching and blanking operations is shown in Fig. 4.73. Below, the definitions of the main components of the die and press are given :

Bed. The bed is the lower part of a press frame that serves as a table to which a bolster plate is mounted.

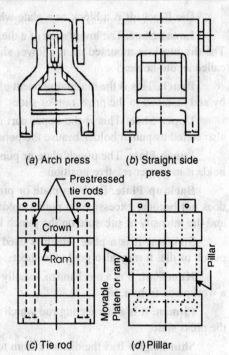

(a) Arch press   (b) Straight side press

(c) Tie rod   (d) Plillar

Fig. 4.72. Closed Frame Presses.

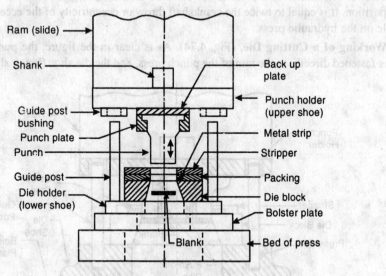

Fig. 4.73. A simple Cutting Die.

Bolster Plate. This is a thick plate secured to the press bed, which is used for locating and supporting the die assembly. It is usually 5 to 12.5 cm thick.

Die Set. It is unit assembly which incorporates a lower and upper shoe, two or more guideposts and guidepost bushings.

Die. The die may be defined as the female part of a complete tool for producing work in a press. It is also referred to a complete tool consisting of a pair of mating members for producing work in a press.

Die Block. It is a block or a plate which contains a die cavity.

Lower Shoe. The lower shoe of a die set is generally mounted on the bolster plate of a press. The die block is mounted on the lower shoe. Also, the guide posts are mounted in it. It is also called as die-holder.

Punch. This is the male component of the die assembly, which is directly or indirectly moved by and fastened to the press ram or slide.

Upper Shoe. This is the upper part of the die set which contains guidepost bushings. It is also called as punch holder beause the punch is mounted on it.

Punch Plate. The punch plate or punch retainer fits closely over the body of the punch and holds it in proper relative position.

Back up Plate. Back up plate or pressure plate is placed so that the intensity of pressure does not become excessive on punch holder. The plate distributes the pressure over a wide area and the intensity of pressure on the punch holder is reduced to avoid crushing.

Stripper. It is a plate which is used to strip the metal strip from a cutting or non-cutting punch or die. It may also guide the sheet.

Knockout. It is a mechanism, usually connected to and operated by the press ram, for freeing a workpiece from a die.

Pitman. It is a connecting rod which is used to transmit motion from the main drive shaft to the press slide.

Shut height. It is the distance from top of the bed to the bottom of the slide, with its stroke down and adjustment up.

Stroke. The stroke of a press is the distance of ram movement from its up position to its down position. It is equal to twice the crankshaft throw or eccentricity of the eccentric drives but is variable on the hydraulic press.

Working of a Cutting Die, (Fig. 4.74). As is clear in the figure, the punch holder (upper shoe) is fastened directly to the ram of the punch press, and the die shoe (lower shoe) is fastened to

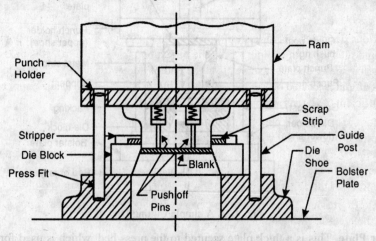

Fig. 4.74. A Cutting Die.

the bolster plate of the press. Guide posts may be used to better align the punch holder with he die shoe. These three main components (punch holder, die shoe and guide posts) constitute what is known as the die set. A die set can be had with two guide posts located at the rear of the die set (known as back posts), diagonally; one at the back and the other in the front of the die set, or with four guide posts, one in each corner of the die set. The lower ends of the guide posts are press fitted into the die shoe. At the upper end, the guide posts have a slip fit with the guide bushings which are press fitted into the punch holder. With this, the guide posts have a free movement in the bushings. The punch is fastened to the punch holder and the die block is fastened to the die-shoe. The punch is aligned with the opening in the die-block. Since, both the punch and die block act as cutting tools, they are hardened.

The cutting action takes place during the downward movement of the punch into the die block. After the cutting action, the elastic recovery in the strip material takes place. Due to this, the size of the blank (cut portion from the strip) increases and that of the hole in the strip decreases. So, at the end of the cutting action, when the punch starts to move upwards, the scrap strip clings to the punch and the blank gets clogged in the die- opening. To remove the scrap strip from the punch surface, a stripper is used. In Fig. 4.74, a simplest type of stripper is used. It strips off the scrap strip from the punch surface when the scrap strip strikes the bottom surface of the stripper during the upward movement of the punch. To avoid clinging of the blank in the die opening, the walls of the die-opening are tapered.

In addition to the two above mentioned troubles, the blank may also adhere to the face of the punch. This usually happens with thin blanks or with blanks which have been treated with a lubricant. To help the blank free itself from the punch face, pushoff pins are provided which are fitted into the punch body, (Fig. 4.74).

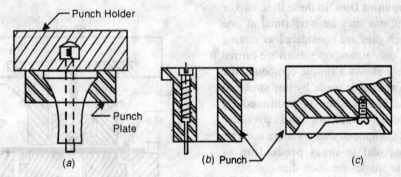

Fig. 4.75. Push-off Pins.

The various basic designs of pushoff pins are shown in Fig. 4.75. The most popular design is a straight, round plunger with a sliding fit in the punch body, Fig. 4.75 (*a*). It is held in place by a light compression spring and a set screw. If at the end of the punch body, a pilot is to be provided, then the push- off pin is located off centre, (Fig. 4.75 (*b*)). When the space available for a compression spring is insufficient, a flat spring may be used, (Fig. 4.75 (*c*)).

In the case of very small punches, no space is left to provide the push-off pin. In such cases, the sticking of the blank to the punch face may be avoided by changing the shape of the punch bottom, (Fig. 4.76). With this, the oil seal or vacuum created by the oil film is broken and tendency of the blank to stick to the punch face is greatly decreased. The drawback of this method is that the blank gets distorted. Due to this, this method is suitable for punching operation only.

4.8.6. Types of Dies. The dies may be classified according to the type of press operation and according to the method of operation.

4.8.6.1 Type of press operation. According to this criterion, the dies may be classified as : cutting dies and forming dies.

Cutting Dies. The dies are used to cut the metal. They utilize the cutting or shearing action. The common cutting dies are : blanking dies, piercing dies, perforating dies, notching, trimming, shaving and nibbling dies etc.

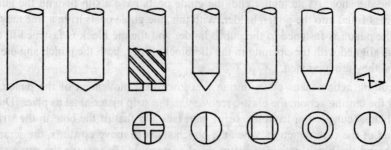

Fig. 4.76. Punch Face Contours to Prevent Blanks from Sticking to Very Small Punches.

Forming Dies. These dies change the appearance of the blank without removsing any stock. These dies include bending dies, drawing dies, squeezing dies etc.

4.8.6.2. Method of operation. According to this criterion, the dies may be classified as : Single-operation dies or simple dies, compound dies, combination dies, progressive dies, transfer dies, and multiple dies.

Simple Dies. Simple dies or single action dies perform single operation for each stroke of the press slide. The operation may be any of the operations listed under cutting or forming dies.

Compound Dies. In these dies, two or more operations may be performed at one station. Such dies are considered as cutting tools since, only cutting operations are carried out. Fig. 4.77 shows a simple compound die in which a washer is made by one stroke of the press. The washer is produced by simultan-eous blanking and piercing operations. Compound dies are more accurate and economical in mass production as compared to single operation dies.

Combination Dies. In this die also, more than one operations may be performed a one station. It differs from compound die in that in this die, a cutting operation is combined with a bending or drawing operation. Fig. 4.78 explains the working of a combination blank and draw die. The die ring which is mounted on the die-shoe, is counterbored at the bottom to allow the flange of a pad to travel up and down. This pad is held flush with the face of the die by a spring. A drawing punch of required shape is fastened to the die shoe. The blanking punch is secured to the punch holder. A spring stripper strips the skeleton from the blanking punch. A knockout extending through the centre opening and through the punch stem ejects the part on the upstroke as it comes in contact with the knockout bar on the press. In operation, the blank holding ring descends as the part is blanked, then the drawing punch contacts and forces the blank into the drawing die which is made in the blanking punch.

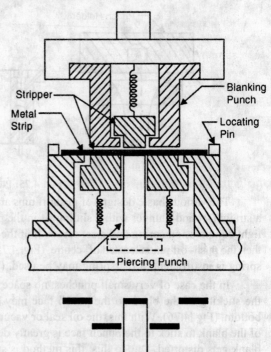

Fig. 4.77. Compound Die.

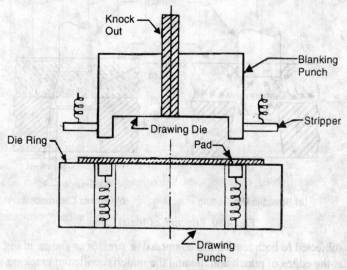

Fig. 4.78. Combination Die.

Fig. 4.78. Combination Die.

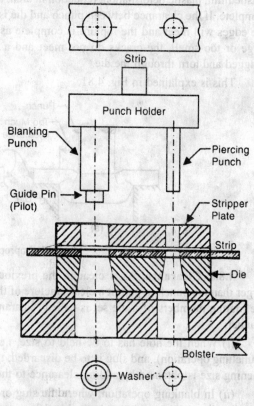

Progressive Dies. A progressive or follow on die has a series of stations. At each station, an operation is performed on a workpiece during a stroke of the press. Between stroke, the piece in the metal strip is transferred to the next station. A finished workpiece is made at each stroke of the press. A progressive die is shown in Fig. 4.79. While the piercing punch blanks out a portion of the metal in which a hole had been pierced at a previous station. Thus after the first stroke, when only a hole will be punched, each stroke of the press produces a finished washer.

Transfer Dies. Unlike the progressive dies where the stock is fed progressively from one station to another, in transfer dies the already cut blanks are fed mechanically from station to station.

Multiple Dies. Multiple or gang dies produce two or more work- pieces at each stroke of the press. A gang or number of simple dies and punches are ganged together to produce two or more parts at each stroke of the press.

Fig. 4.79. Progressive Die.

4.8.7. Principle of Metal Cutting. The cutting of sheet metal in press work is a shearing process. The cutting action is explained with the help of Fig. 4.80. The punch is of the same shape as of the die opening except that it is smaller on each side by an amount known as 'clearance'. As the punch touches the material and travels downward, it pushes the material into the die opening.

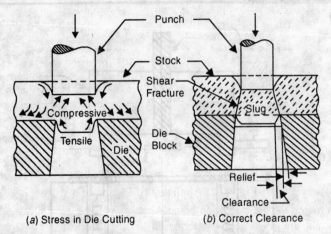

(a) Stress in Die Cutting   (b) Correct Clearance

Fig. 4.80. Principle of Metal Cutting.

The material is subjected to both tensile and compressive stresses as shown in Fig. 4.80 (a). Stresses will be highest at the edges of punch and die and the material will start cracking there. The various steps in the rupture or fracture of the material can be written as : stressing the material beyond its elastic limit, plastic deformation, reduction in area, fracturing starts in the reduced area and becomes complete. If the clearance between punch and die is correct, the cracks starting from the punch and die edges will meet and the rupture is complete as shown in Fig. 4.80 (b). If the clearance is too large or too small, the cracks do not meet and a ragged edge results due to the material being dragged and torn through the die.

This is explained in Fig. 4.81.

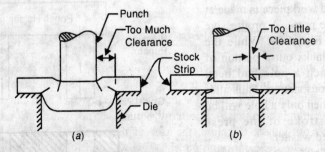

Fig. 4.81. Improper Clearance.

4.8.8. Clearance. As is clear in the previous article, the die opening must be sufficiently larger than the punch to permit a clean fracture of the metal. This difference in dimensions between the mating members of a die set is called 'clearance'. This clearance is applied in the following manner:

(i) When the hole has to be held to size, i.e., the hole in the sheet metal is to be accurate (Punching operation), and slug is to be discarded, the punch is made to the size of hole and the die opening size is obtained by adding clearance to the punch size, (Fig. 4.82 (a)).

(ii) In blanking operation, where the slug or blank is the desired part and has to be held to size, the die opening size equals the blank size and the punch size is obtained by subtracting the clearance from the die-opening size, (Fig. 4.82 (b)).

In Fig. 4.82 c, is the amount of clearance per side of the die opening. The clearance is a function of the kind, thickness and temper of the work material, harder materials requiring larger

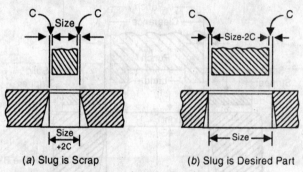

(a) Slug is Scrap   (b) Slug is Desired Part

Fig. 4.82. Applicant of Clearance.

clearance than soft materials, the exception being Aluminium. The usual clearances per side of the die, for various metals, are given below in terms of the stock thickness, t :

For brass and soft steel, c = 5% of t

For medium steel, c = 6% of t

For hard steel, c = 7% of t

For aluminium, c = 10% of t

The total clearance between punch and die size will be twice these figures. These clearances are for blanking and piercing operations.

The clearance may also be determined with the help of the following equation :

$$c = 0.0032t \cdot \sqrt{\tau_s}, \text{mm}$$

where τ_s is the shear strength of the material in N/mm^2.

The reason behind the application of clearance in the manner as given above, is explained below :

The diameter of the blank or punched hole is determined by the burnished area. On the blank, the burnished area is produced by the walls of the die. Therefore, the blank size will be equal to the size of die-opening (neglecting a slight expansion of the blank due to elastic recovery after the cutting operation is completed). Similarly, in punching operation, the burnished area in the hole is produced by the punch, therefore, the size of the hole will be the same as the punch. Therefore, the application of clearance on punch or die will depend on whether the punched hole or the cut blank is the desired product. Hence, in punching operation (where hole in the strip is the desired product), the punch is made to the correct hole size and the die opening is made oversize an amount equal to die clearance. Similarly, if the blank is the desired product, the die opening size is made to the correct blank size and the punch is made smaller an amount equal to die clearance. In other words, punch controls the hole size and die opening controls the blank size.

A section through blanking die is given in Fig. 4.83, showing clearance, land, straight and angular clearance.

Land. It is the flat (usually horizontal) surface contiguous to the cutting of a die which is ground and reground to keep the cutting edges of the punch sharp.

Straight. It is the surface of a cutting die between its cutting edge and the beginning of the angular clearance. This straight portion gives strength to the cutting surface of the die and also provides for sharpening of the die. This straight portion is usually kept at about 3 mm for all materials less than 2 mm thick. For thicker materials, it is taken to be equal to the metal thickness.

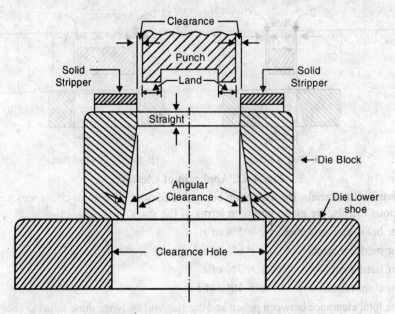

Fig. 4.83. Section Through Blanking Die.

Angular clearance. Angular clearance or relief is provided to enable the slug to clear the

die. It is provided below the straight portion of the die surface. It is usually $\frac{1}{4}^{\circ}$ to $1\frac{1}{2}^{\circ}$ per side but

occasionally as high as 2°, depending mainly on stock thickness and frequency of sharpening.

Punch and Die Clearance After Considering the Elastic Recovery of the Material. It has already been explained that after the cutting operation has been completed, elastic recovery of the strip material takes place. In blanking operation, after the release of blanking pressure, the blank expands slightly. The blanked part is thus actually larger than the die opening that has produced it. Similarly, in punching operation, after the strip is stripped off the punch, the material recovers and the hole contracts. Thus, the hole is actually smaller than the size of the punch which produced it. This difference in size due to elastic recovery will depend upon : blank size, stock thickness and stock material. It may be taken as between 0.0125 mm and 0.075 mm. If the stock thickness is upto 0.25 mm, this difference may be taken as zero. For stock thickness between 0.25 mm and 0.75 mm, it may be taken as equal to 0.025 mm and for stock thickness more than 0.75 mm, it may be taken as 0.050 mm. Thus to produce correct hole and blank sizes, the punch size should be increased and the die opening size should be decreased by an amount as explained above.

4.8.9. Cutting Forces. In cutting operation, as the punch in its downward movement enters the material, it need not penetrate the thickness of the stock in order to affect complete rupture of the part. The distance which the punch enters into the work material to cause rupture to take place is called 'penetration' and is usually given as the percentage of the stock thickness.

The per cent penetration depends on the material being cut and also on the stock thickness. When a hard and strong material is being cut, very little penetration of the punch is necessary to cause fracture. With softer materials, the penetration will be greater. For example, for soft aluminium, it is 60% of 't' ; for 0.15% carbon steel annealed, it is 38% of 't' ; and only 24% of 't' for 0.5 per cent carbon steel annealed. The percentage penetration also depends upon the stock thickness, being smaller for thicker sheets and greater for thinner sheets, as shown in Table 4.1.

Table. 4.1. Penetration

Stock Thick -ness t. mm	25	20	15	12.5	10	8	6	5	3	2.5	1.6	Below 1.6
Penetration % of t	25	31	34	37	44	47	50	56	62	67	70	80

The maximum force F_{max} in newtons needed to cut a material is equal to the area to be sheared times the shearing strength, τ_s in N/m m^2, for the material. For a circular blank of diameter D mm and of thickness t, mm., the cutting force will be given as,

$$F_{max} = \pi Dt \, \tau_s = P.t.\tau_s \, ... \qquad\qquad ... (4.1)$$

where 'P' is the perimeter of the section to be blanked

For rectangular blanks with length L and width b, it is

$$F_{max} = 2\,(L+b)t \cdot \tau_s \, ... \qquad\qquad ...(4.2)$$

The shear strengths of the various metals are given in Table 4.2.

Table 4.2. Shear strengths of various metals

Metal	$\tau_s N / mm^2$
Carbon steels :	
0.10% C	245 to 311
0.20% C	308 to 385
0.30% C	364 to 469
High strength low-alloy steels	315 to 446
Silicon steels	420 to 490
Stainless steels	399 to 903
Aluminium alloys	49 to 322
Copper and bronze	154 to 490
Lead alloys	12.8 to 41
Magnesium alloys	119 to 203
Nickel alloys	245 to 812
Tin alloys	20.5 to 77
Titanium alloys	420 to 490
Zinc alloys	98 to 266

Energy in Press Work :

Energy in press work or the work done to make a cut is given ideally as,

$$E = F_{max} \times \text{punch travel}$$
$$= F_{max} \times K \times t$$

where K = percentage of penetration required to cause rupture.

To allow for energy lost in machine friction and in pushing slugs through the die etc., the above equation gets modified as,

$$E = F_{max} \times K \times t \times C$$

where the factor C accounts for the amount of extra energy required. This depends upon the circumstances in each case. For general purpose, a factor of 1.16 is recommended.

4.8.10. Methods of reducing cutting forces. For calculating the cutting forces in the last article, it has been assumed that the bottom of the punch and the top of the die block lie in parallel planes and that the blank is severed from the sheet metal by shearing it simultaneously along the whole perimeter. This process is characterized by very high punch forces exerted over a very short time, resulting in shock or impulse conditions. It is usual, however, to reduce cutting forces and to smooth out the shock impact of heavy loads. This is achieved by arranging for a gradual cut instead of sudden cut of the stock. For this, two methods are generally used:

(1) Shear. The working faces of the punch or die are ground off so that these don't remain parallel to the horizontal plane but are inclined to it. This angle of inclination is called 'shear'. This has the effect of reducing the area in shear at any one time and the maximum force is much less. It may be reduced by as much as 50%. This is made clear in Fig. 4.84, which shows the relation of cutting forces to amount of shear.

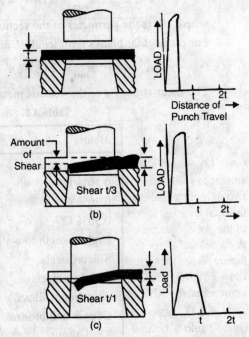

In fig. 4.84 (*a*), the shear is zero, *i.e.*, the cutting edges are parallel. The material is cut at once on the entire perimeter resulting in maximum load. The force diagram shows a steep rise at maximum load and then sudden load release sometimes severe on both press and dies, as the cut is completed. In Fig. 4.84 (*b*), the face of the punch is ground off so that shear = $t/3$. The cutting action will start at the leading edge of the punch and then it will gradually spread to the rest of the punch. With this, only a part of the punch would be cutting at any one instant. While the maximum force will decrease, the energy needed to complete the cut is unchanged. So, the punch travel in this case will be more than in case (*a*). In case 4.84 (*c*), shear = $t/1$. When the leading

Fig. 4.84. Effect of Shear on Cutting Force.

edge has travelled through the stock a distance '*t*', the trailing edge will state making contact with the material. Maximum force would be at this position of the punch and since the cut is complete, the maximum load would be about half of that when shear is zero. The punch travel will be still greater.

The provision of shear distorts the material being cut. When shear is on the face of the punch, the blank cannot be flat and when shear is on the die, the piercing cannot be flat. So, for blanking operation, shear is provided on the die face and for punching or piercing operation shear is provided on the punch face. Fig. 4.85 shows the various methods of applying shear on the punch and die face. Wherever possible, double shear should be used so that the two shear faces neutralise the side thrusts which each sets up.

It is clear from the above analysis that it is advisable to provide shear on punches and dies. The amount of shear to be applied is a matter of compromise. If the shear is quite big, say $2t$ or $3t$, they the cutting edges of the tools will become too acute and liable to break away easily. However, the shear must be at least equal to the percentage penetration.

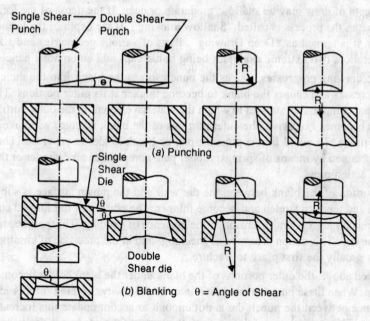

Fig. 4.85. Application of Shear.

(2) Staggering of Punches. An effect similar to shear can be obtained by staggering two or more punches, that is, making them of unequal lengths, that all operate in one stroke of the press. The punches are arranged so that one does not enter the material until the one before it has penetrated through. Like this, the cutting force can be reduced approximately 50%. (Fig. 4.86)

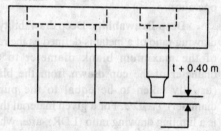

Fig. 4.86. Staggering of Punches.

4.8.11. Deep Drawing. Drawing operation is the process of forming a flat piece of material (blank) into a hollow shape by means of a punch which causes the blank to flow into the die-cavity, Fig. 4.87.

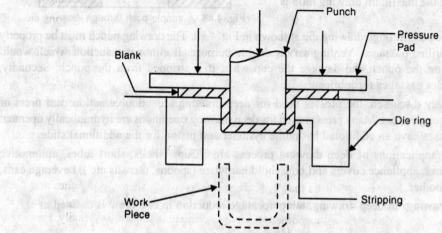

Fig. 4.87. Deep Drawing Operation.

The depth of draw may be shallow, moderate or deep. If the depth of the formed cup is upto half its diameter, the process is called "Shallow drawing". If the depth of the formed cup ex-ceeds the diameter, it is termed as "Deep Drawing". Parts of various geometries and sizes are made by drawing operation, two extreme examples being bottle caps and automobile panels.

As the drawing progresses, *i.e.*, as the punch forces the blank into the die cavity, the blank diameter decreases and causes the blank to become thicker at its outer portions. This is due to the circumferential compressive stresses to which the material element in the outer portions is subjected. If this stress becomes excessive, the outer portions of the blank (flange) will have the tendency to buckle or wrinkle. To avoid this, a pressure pad or blank holder is provided. The holding down pressure is obtained by means of springs, rubber pad, compressed air cylinder or the auxiliary ram on a double action press.

The portion of the blank between the die wall and the punch surface is subjected to nearly pure tension and tends to stretch and become thinner. The portion of the formed cup, which wraps around the punch radius is under tension in the presence of bending. This part becomes the thinnest portion of the cup. This action is termed as 'necking' and in the presence of unsatisfactory drawing operation, is usually the first place to fracture.

As noted above, the outer portions of the blank under the blankholder become thicker during the operation. When these portions are drawn into the die cavity, 'ironing' of this section will occur if the clearance between the punch die is not enough to accommodate this increased thickness of the workpiece. This ironing is useful if uniform thickness of the product is desired after the drawing operation.

Deep Drawability. Deep drawability or drawing ratio of a metal is defined as the ratio of the maximum blank diameter to the diameter of the cup drawn from the blank (usually taken to be equal to the punch diameter), *i.e. D/d*. For a given material there is a limiting drawing ratio (LDR), after which the punch will pierce a hole in the blank instead of drawing the blank. This ratio depends upon many factors, such as type of material, amount of friction present, etc. The usual range of the maximum drawing ratio is 1.6 to 2.3.

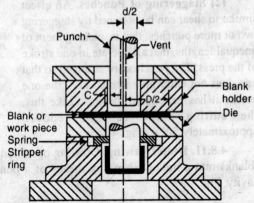

Fig. 4.88. A simple push through drawing die.

A simple push through drawing die is shown in Fig. 4.88. The drawing punch must be properly vented with drilled passages. Venting serves double purpose. It eliminates suction which would hold the cup on the punch and damage the cup when it is stripped from the punch. Secondly, venting provides passages for lubricants.

As already discussed, the presses used for deep drawing are : double action cam press or double action toggle press. Many presses used for deep drawing operations are hydraulically operated and these presses have an additional hydraulic cylinder and piston for the additional slide.

Product applications of deep drawing process are : Cups, shells, short tubes, automotive bodies, gas tanks, appliance covers and household hardware (spoons, utensils etc.), beverage cans, seamless can bodies.

Redrawing. In deep drawing, the percentage reduction in one draw is defined as :

$$\% \text{ reduction} = \frac{D-d}{D} \times 100$$

now $\qquad \dfrac{D}{d} = 1.6 \text{ to } 2.3$

$\therefore \qquad \dfrac{d}{D} = 0.435 \text{ to } 0.625 = 0.50 \text{ (average)}$

$\therefore$ The average reduction in deep drawing

$$= \left(1 - \frac{d}{D}\right) \times 100 = 50\%$$

To make tall cups of smaller diameter (such as cartridge cases and closed-end tubes), it is necessary to use successive drawing operations. Reducing a drawn cup to a smaller diameter and increased height is known as "Redrawing". The two methods used for redrawing are : direct redrawing and indirect or reverse redrawing.

Fig. 4.89 (a and b) are direct redrawing methods. In Fig. 4.89 (a), the metal bends twice inducing high strain hardening in it. In Fig. 4.89 (b), the metal again bends twice, but the angle through which it bends is less than 90°. This reduces strain hardening as compared to Fig. 4.89 (a) and punch load is reduced. But the drawback is that the initial drawn cup must be made with a taper corner.

In reverse drawing, (Fig. 4.89 (c)), the basic phenomenon that a cold-worked material exhibits greater ductility when the deformation direction is reversed in successive operations (strain softening) is made use of.

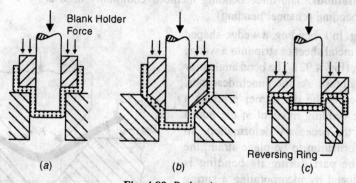

Fig. 4.89. Redrawing.

Redrawing is extensively used for food containers, fountain-pen caps, oil filter housings and shock absorber pistons etc.

Practical reductions in diameter for successive redraws are : 30, 25, 16 and 13%. Metal becomes work-hardened as it is drawn and redrawn and must be annealed to prevent failure before it reaches its limit.

Ironing. It is the process of smoothening or thinning the wall of a shell or cup (cold or hot) by forcing the shell through a die with a punch. If the thickness of the sheet is more than the clearance between the punch and die, the thickness will get reduced. This is known as ironing and it produces cups with thinner walls than the base, Fig. 4.90, as in the case of beverage cans and household saucepans.

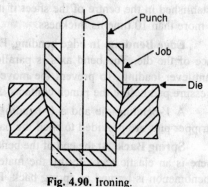

Fig. 4.90. Ironing.

4.8.12. Bending. Bending is the metal working process by which a straight length is transformed into a curved length. It is a very common forming process for changing sheet and plate into channels, drums, tanks etc. During the bending operation, the outer surface of the material is in tension and the inside surface is in compression. The strain in the bent material increases with decreasing radius of curvature. The stretching of the bend causes the neutral axis of the section to move towards the inner surface. In most cases, the distance of the neutral axis from the inside of the bend is 0.3 t to 0.5 t, where 't' is the thickness of the part. Bending terminology is illustrated in Fig. 4.91.

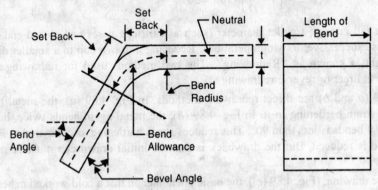

Fig. 4.91. Bending Terminology.

Bending Methods. The three bending methods commonly used are : V- bending, Edge bending, and U-bending (channel bending)

V–Bending. In V-bending, a wedge-shaped punch forces the metal sheet or strip into a wedge shaped die cavity, (Fig. 4.92). The bend angle may be acute, 90° or obtuse. As the punch descends, the contact forces at the die corner produce a sufficiently large bending moment at the punch corner to cause the necessary deformation. To maintain the deformation to be plane-strain, the side creep of the part during its bending is prevented or reduced by incorporating a spring loaded knurled pin in the die. The friction between the pin and the part will help to achieve this, (Fig. 4.93). Plane strain conditions will also be established in the centre of the sheet if its width is more than 10 time its thickness.

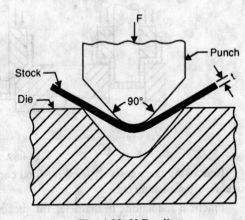

Fig. 4.92. V-Bending.

Edge Bending. In edge bending, Fig. 4.94, a flat punch forces the stock against the vertical face of the die. The bend axis is parallel to the edge of the die and the stock is sub-jected to cantilever loading. To prevent the movement of the stock during bending, it is held down by a pressure pad before the punch contacts it.

A V-bending die and a U-bending die are shown in Fig. 4.95 and Fig. 4.96 respectively. Stripper pins are provided to shed the part from the punch.

Spring Back. At the end of the bending operation, when the pressure on the metal is released, there is an elastic recovery by the material. This causes a decrease in the bend angle and this phenomenon is termed as spring back. For low carbon steel, it can be 1° to 2° and for medium carbon steel, it can be 3° to 4°, for phosphor bronze and spring steel the spring back can be from

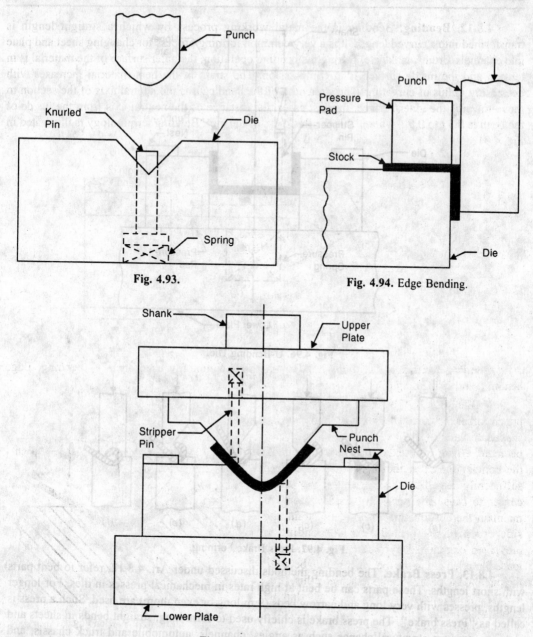

Fig. 4.93.

Fig. 4.94. Edge Bending.

Fig. 4.95. V-Bending Die.

10 to 15°. To compensate for spring back, the wedge-shaped punches and the mating dies are made with included angles somewhat less than required in the formed component. Due to this, the component will be bent to a greater angle than desired, but it will spring back to the desired angle. For other types of bending, the part is overbent by an angle equal to spring-back angle by having the face of the punch undercut or relieved. The values of spring back given above are for 90° bends and are usually greater for greater angles.

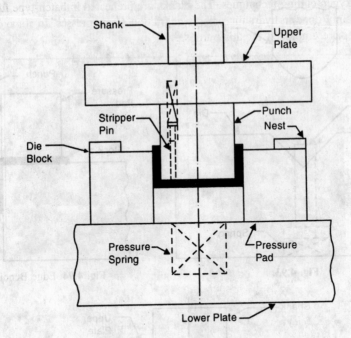

Fig. 4.96. U-Bending Die.

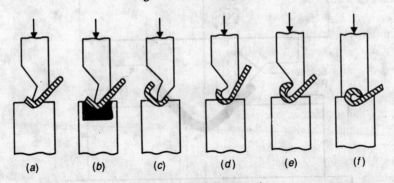

Fig. 4.97. Press Brake Forming.

4.8.13. Press Brake. The bending methods discussed under Art. 4.8.12, refer to bent parts with short lengths. These parts can be bent at high rates in mechanical presses in dies. For longer lengths, presses with very long and narrow beds (9 m long or even more) are used. Such a press is called as "Press brake". The press brake is chiefly used to form long, straight bends in sheets and plates to produce structural shapes such as angles, channels, automobile and truck chassis, and corrugated sheets. The metal is bent between interchangeable dies attached to the bed and the ram. By using different dies, many types of bends may be obtained, (Fig. 4.97).

Fig. 4.98 shows a typical mechanical press brake and a hydraulic press brake constructed by HMT.

4.8.14. Hot Press Working of Metals. Hot press working of metals is resorted to for sheet steel over 6 or 8 mm thick, or even for thinner material of low ductility. Hot press working or hot stamping is employed in the manufacture of ship hull components, bottoms and other parts of tank cars, boilers, chemical machinery and apparatus etc. The plate is usually cut up into the required blanks mainly by oxygen cutting techniques. The blanks are preheated in batch-type furnaces. Hot press working is mainly done in hydraulic presses or friction screw presses. In some cases, crank type forming presses are employed for this purpose.

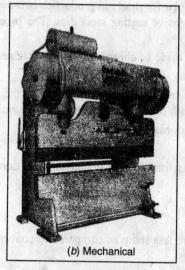

(b) Mechanical

(c) Hydraulic

Fig. 4.98. Press Brakes.

4.8.15. Miscellaneous Forming Operations

1. Roll Forming. On long parts, the punch and die can not be made full length, and forming can be accomplished by "Roll forming", where the material, usually strip stock, is fed through a series of rolls which produce the desired shape, often by a succession of small shape changes. It is a continuous bending operation resulting in long shaped sections such as angles, channels and tubes (see Fig. 4.52). "Roll bending" uses three large rolls arranged in a pyramidal fashion, (Fig. 4.99), to curve metal sheets and plates. This is an important preparation step for making large welded plate structures.

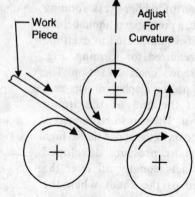

Fig. 4.99. Roll Bending.

2. Rubber Press Forming. Rubber-press forming or Rubber-pad forming is a sheet metal forming (bending and stretching or drawing) operation in which either the punch or the die is a piece of constrained elastomer (rubber or polyurethane). The basic principle of the process is that if a block of rubber or polyurethane is placed in a cylinder and pressure is brought to bear upon it by applying a force by a ram of a press, any such force must develop a resultant reaction on every surface with which the elastomer comes in contact. This resultant reaction force is used for forming sheet metal to the required shape

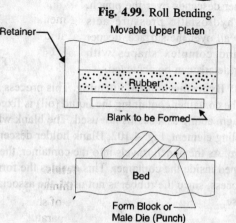

Fig. 4.100. Rubber-press Forming.

using form blocks or punches or dies. Fig. 4.100 shows a schematic view of Rubber-press forming operation. Rubber is restrained from sideward motion and acts as a deformable female die to exert essentially hydrostatic pressure on the workpiece.

This process is becoming increasingly popular for short run production because of its economy since it eliminates the need for the more expensive mating steel dies. The process has got the following advantages:

1. Tools have fewer components and are made of cheap and easy to machine materials.

2. One rubber pad takes the place of many different die shapes.

3. The forming radius decreases progressively during forming unlike the fixed radius on conventional dies, thereby allowing greater depth of draw in one stroke (draw ratio upto 2.7).

4. There is almost no thinning of the work material.

5. Tool setting time is greatly reduced.

6. The variation in sheet thickness is not a limitation as in conventional drawing, since only one tool is used in rubber pad forming.

The limitations of the process are :

1. Rubber pads wear out rapidly.

2. Details of the compo- nents formed are less sharp as compared to conventionally formed components.

3. Rubber Hydroform Process. In this process, which is a variation of rubber-press forming process, a pressurized liquid behind the rubber pad is used to exert the force required for forming. Fig. 4.101 shows one such set up. The rubber pad or diaphragm acts as a seal at the end of the liquid container. The part to be formed is wrapped on to the punch due to high hydrostatic pressure developed which acts equally all over the surface of the sheet when the container descends over the punch. Since hydrostatic pressure acts equally all over the surface, deeper cups and complex shapes with sharper details can be achieved.

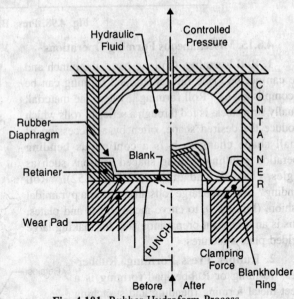

Fig. 4.101. Rubber Hydroform Process.

4. Hydromechanical Forming. This process is a modification of rubber hydroform process. Here, the container containing the liquid (oil) is fixed on the bed of the press and the rubber pad or diaphragm acting as a seal is not used. The blank which is directly placed on the draw ring acts as the sealing element, Fig. 4.102. Blank holder descends on the blank and applies the blank holding pressure. As the punch travels into the container, the cup is formed against the hydrostatic pressure developed inside the container. This enables the formation of deeper cups and complex shapes. In this process, since the rubber is not used, the associated problems of wear and replacement etc. do not arise.

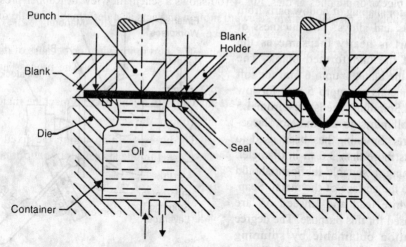

Fig. 4.102. Hydromechanical Forming.

5. Stretch Forming. This method was developed during world war II as a means for producing large accurately contoured sheets for aircraft wing and fuselage parts. Since then, the method has been developing rapidly. Like rubber-press forming, stretch forming uses only the male die or form block. Sheet metal is stretched to the yield point in tension, and then wrapped over and around the form block. This method has the advantage over other forming methods that springback is either greatly reduced or completely eliminated, since direct bending stresses are never introduced. All of the plastic deformation is tensile extension in the direction of pulling. Another advantage of the method is relatively low tooling costs. Male dies or form blocks may be of wood, masonite, zinc alloys or cast iron.

Fig. 4.103 shows two methods of stretch forming. In Fig. 4.103 (a), the grips are stationary and the form block moves upward to provide the necessary tension and motion. In Fig. 4.103 (b), the jaws first stretch the work and then wrap it around the form block. This method avoids most of the friction which somewhat limits the degree of forming obtainable with the moving form block.

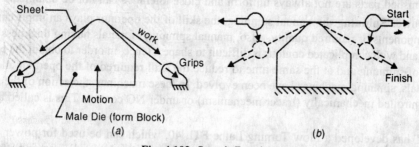

Fig. 4.103. Stretch Forming.

The process is most suitable for low volume production as is typical of air craft industry, for example, for the production of fuselage skins, wing skins and boat hulls etc.

6. Metal Spinning. Spinning is one of the oldest methods of sheet metal forming. Parts that have circular cross-sections can be made by spinning from sheet metal. The method involves the forming of a workpiece over a rotating form block or chuck held in a special lathe, Fig. 4.104. A smooth, hardened, rotating or stationary tool is held by the operator and is pressed against the blank to progressively bend the workpiece to conform to the chuck or mandrel. The mode of deformation of the metal during spinning is a mixture of bending and stretching, making the process most suitable for shaping of hollow parts from ductile metals and alloys. The thickness of the spun part is nearly the same as the thickness of the undeformed blank. The thickness of the blank is upto 6 mm for soft non-ferrous metals and upto 5 mm for low carbon steel. Spinning speeds vary from 1.5 m/s for small parts to 25 m/s for large-diameter parts. Spinning has been used to produce parts more than 3.6 m in diameter. Before spinning, a suitable lubricant should be applied to the surface of the metal. Soap, beeswax, white lead and linseed oil are commonly used for this purpose. The degree of deformation obtainable by spinning depends upon the shape of the finished part, the material, the lubricant, and particularly the skill of the operator.

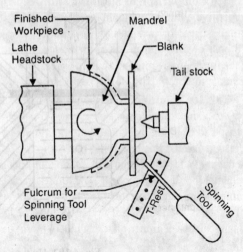

Fig. 4.104. Metal Spinning.

Product applications of spinning are : reflectors, kitchenware, bells on musical instruments, light fixtures, funnels and large processing kettles, radar dishes, roket motor cases.

The special features of metal spinning are :

1. Low equipment cost. The equipment consists of a speed lathe to the chuck of which the form block is attached. The blank is held between the formblock and a tailplate.

2. Low tool costs. The form block may be of plaster, wood or metal.

3. Some complex parts of re-entrant shape (kettles, pitchers) can be very economically produced by spinning.

The drawbacks of the method are :

1. The method depends to a large extent on the skill of the operator.

2. Finished parts are not always uniform and close tolerance can not be obtained.

(*a*) **Power Spinning.** In manual spinning, the skill of the operator plays an important role in getting components of required quality. Also, manual spinning of metals having thickness of more than 1 mm and with complicated contour is difficult to shape. Hence, in order to obtain the economic advantage of spinning and at the same time to reduce the skill required of the operator and to spin thicker metals, spinning machines have been evolved. In these machines, the action of the spinning roller is controlled mechanically (tracer mechanism) or under NC control. This is called as Power spinning.

HMT has developed a Flow Turning Lathe FTL 40, which can be used for power spinning also. It is a semiautomatic spinning and flow turning machine with a hydraulic copying attachment. The forming spinning cycle of the machine is automatic, but the loading and unloading of work pieces is manual. The machine consists of a head stock, a hydraulically operated tailstock, and slides mounted on an auxiliary bed which is fixed to the mainbed. A circular blank is held between the tailstock quill and the spinning mandrel (form block) and the metal is shaped to the required form in a single pass or with a number of successive passes, using a single or multiple templates respectively. There is very little change in the metal thickness and no limitations in the shape of the parts. When the roller control mechanism is set for a particular part, each successive part will then be spun in the same manner.

(b) **Comparison of Spinning and Deep Drawing.** Metal spinning is both supplementary and competitive with drawing in presses. Due to its low tooling and equipment costs, spinning is normally used for low volume production. But drawing is preferred for mass production (due to high cost of dies and presses) to reduce the production cost of the component. Labour costs are higher for manual spinning than for press work. Also, production rates are much less. However, as the size and complexity of the part increase, the spinning process becomes more competitive.

(c) **Hot Spinning.** Hot spinning of metals is used commercially to dish or form thick circular plates to some shape over a revolving form block. A blank of sheet metal is clamped on centre against a form block or chuck, which is revolved on the spindle of a lathe. A rounded stick or roller is pressed against this revolving piece and moved in a series of sweeps. This displaces the metal in several steps to conform to the shape of the chuck. The pressure may be applied by hand or mechanically. A hot spinning machine is a combination of a vertical press and a large vertical spinning lathe which rotates the blank about a vertical axis. Power actuated rollers do the forming, as the part is rotated. Metal upto 150 mm thick is routinely hot spun into dished pressure vessels and tank shapes. Thinner plates of hard to form metals like Titanium are also shaped by hot spinning.

7. Flow turning. This method is used to form axisymmetric, conical, cylindrical, parabolic and hemispherical shapes. Unlike power spinning, where there is no significant change is section thickness of the work material, in flow turning, (Fig. 4.105), the metal in plastically deformed and progressively displaced under the compressive forces of a pressure roller. The metal flow is entirely by shear. The thickness of the blank gets reduced to the required amount, resulting in an increase in length. However, the diameter of the blank remains unchanged. The thickness of the finished part will be given as :

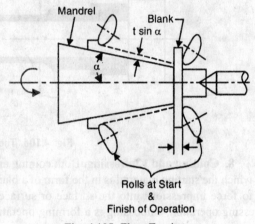

Fig. 4.105. Flow Turning.

For conical parts, thickness of finished part = Thickness of blank × sin α

If α is less than 30°, the part is finished in more than one stages with an anneal between the stages. Upto 80% reduction in metal thickness can be achieved.

The method is also known as "Shear forming", "Shear spinning" or "Spin forging". The method can also be used to reduce the thickness of the tube or to produce tubes of multiples diameters, (Fig. 4.106). Then the method is called as "Tube spinning".

Advantages:

1. Very less or no material wastage

2. Economical, due to lesser tooling and set up costs.

3. Improved metallurgical properties like hardness and tensile strength.

4. Ability to produce heavier flanges or end sections.

5. Possibility of seamless construction.

6. Flexible to adopt to any design changes.

Product Applications. Television tube cones, airframes, aircraft engine parts, Hotel utensils, cooking pots, pressure cookers, pans, Lamp shades, reflectors, dishes, missile noses, cream separator bowls, milk separator components, Monobloc Aluminium Alloy milk cans, thin walled seamless tubing, pesticide bottles, air craft engine parts, pressure vessel components, V-pulleys and brake drums etc.

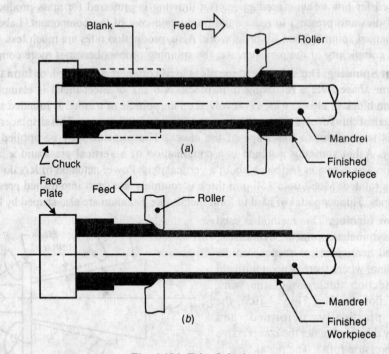

Fig. 4.106. Tube Spinning.

8. Coining and Embossing. Both coining and embossing are cold press working operations in which the starting material is in the form of a blank of sheet metal. The aim of both the operations is to force impressions into the surface or surfaces of the metal. However, whereas coining is a pressing operation, embossing is a forming operation.

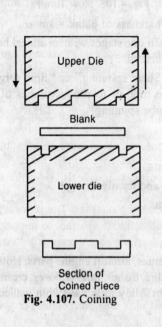

Fig. 4.107. Coining

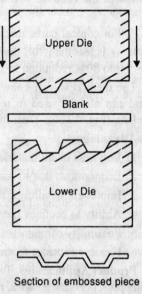

Fig. 4.108. Embossing.

(*a*) **Coining.** Coining is a special type of closed die forging operation is which the lateral surfaces are restrained (metal is completely confined within a set of dies) resulting in a variable thickness and a well defined imprint of the die faces on the metal (Fig. 4.107). Very large pressures are exerted (1200 to 3000 MPa) to cause the metal to flow to all portions of the die cavity. The metal is caused to flow in directions perpendicular to the compressive force along the die surfaces. Usually the two sides of any coined article bear totally different designs. The depth of impression is never very great, rarely exceeding 0.8 mm due to the difficulty of forcing the metal to flow. Only the metal at or near the surface is deformed. Hard currency is probably the best known product of coining operation. Other applications of coining are the manufacture of insignia, medals, badges, piece of art and household hardware.

(*b*) **Embossing.** Embossing is a forming or drawing operation for producing a raised or projected design in relief on the surface of the workpiece. The operation uses matching punch and die with the impressions machined into both surfaces, (Fig. 4.108). The process differs from coining process in that the material thickness remains constant. It is actually a combination of shallow drawing and stretching process rather than a squeezing process. The forces needed are much less than in the coining process. The metal flow is in the direction of the applied force. The entire metal thickness is affected. The product applications of the process are : to obtain various rigidity ribs, functional and ornamental recesses and projections and to manufacture name plates, medallions, identification tags and aesthetic designs on thin sheet metal.

4.9. HOBBING, RIVETING AND STAKING

(*i*) **Hobbing.** Hobbing or hubbing is the process of forming a very smooth, accurately shaped die cavity by pressing a hardened and polished shaped punch (hob) (of tool steel) into a softer metal die block (of mild steel) (Fig. 4.109 (*a*)). The die cavity is formed slowly and carefully and some times in several stages with annealing between stages. A retaining ring helps to keep the die/ mould from spreading out of shape. The method is used for making dies/moulds for the plastic and die casting industries. The main advantage of the process is that many duplicate cavities can be made with a single hob/punch.

(*ii*) **Riveting.** To join two parts permanently by riveting, a rivet is put through the drilled or punched hole in the parts and is placed on the anvil. A riveting punch with a hollowed end mashes the stem of the rivet which is headed by a single squeezing action, (Fig. 4.109 (*b*)).

(*iii*) **Staking.** Staking is again a method of fastening two parts permanently. It is a substitute to drilling/punching and riveting. In this method, a shaped punch is forced into the top of a projection of one of the parts to be fastened. This indentation action of the punch deforms the metal sufficiently to squeeze it tightly against the second component so that they are firmly locked together, Fig. 4.109 (*c*).

4.10. SHOT PEENING

Shot peening is mainly employed to increase the fatigue strength of work pieces subjected to impact and/or fatigue loads (parts made of steel and non-ferrous alloys), and also for strengthening welds. Typical applications include:- Coil springs, leaf springs, gear wheels and other complex parts. The other functions of shot peening are to prevent the cracking of work pieces in corrosive media and to improve the oil retaining properties of the processed surfaces. The process is based on plastic deformation of the surface layer and consists in subjecting the surface to impacts of a jet of shots. Many overlapping indentations are made, causing localized compressive deformation of the surface. Since bulk of the material is not affected, compressive residual stresses are set up. Since fatigue failure occurs due to tensile stresses, the compressive residual stresses greatly offset any tendency to fatigue failure. The surface also gets slightly hardened and strengthened by shot peening (a cold working process). The shots are made of cast iron, steel, aluminium or glass. Cast iron or steel shot is used in peening steel work pieces, and aluminium or glass shot for non ferrous alloys. The depth of the workhardened layer obtained does not usually exceed 2 mm. This depth increases with the diameter of shot (0.4 to 2 mm) and its velocity (60 to 100 m/s), and decreases with an increase in the initial hardness of the workpiece. The efficiency of the process also depends upon the angle between the path of the shot and the surface being peened, and the duration of peening, which is not more than 10 min.

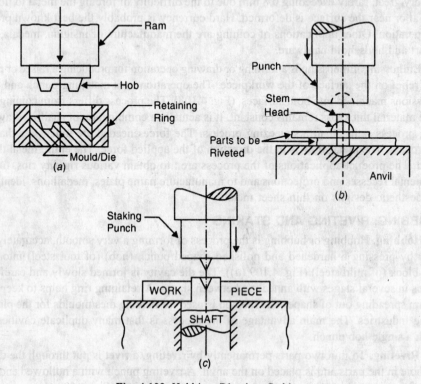

Fig. 4.109. Hobbing, Riveting, Staking.

Shot peening is performed in special equipment consisting of a workpiece chamber and a shot blasting device. The most widely used shot blasting devices are :

1. Air - nozzle
2. Centrifugal - wheel type.

In the air-nozzle device, the shot is thrown by compressed air at a pressure of 6 to 8 atm. from several nozzles simultaneously.

The centrifugal wheel device (airless blast equipment) consists of a work piece chamber with a mechanism for moving the work piece under the jet of shot and a centrifugal wheel. The latter is a rapidly rotating bladed wheel which throws the shot centrifugally in the required direction. This process of shot peening is done on the following types of products :- torsion bars, the tension side of automobile springs, other types of leaf springs, all sorts of shafts and axles (sometimes only in key ways), splines and fillets, gear teeth roots after carburizing and case hardening, oil well drill pipe (inside or outside, or both), and automobile connecting rods and crankshafts etc.

Characteristics of the shot peened surfaces are given below :

Increase in hardness = 20 to 50% over the original

Residual compressive stresses set up in the surface layer = 500 to 800 N/mm2.

Table 4.3 Metal Forming Process—Design Considerations

S.No.	Process	Choice of Materials	Complexity of part	Maximum size	Minimum size	Mechanical Properties
1.	Drop Forging	Medium-many alloy are forgeable	Moderate	Large	Small even fraction of a kg.	High
2.	Press Forgoing	Medium-Best for non-ferrous alloys	Limited, but better than drop forging	Moderate : 0.012 to 0.014 t	Smaller than drop forging	High
3.	Upset Forging	Medium	Limited to cylindrical shapes	Medium 250 mm bar about largest	Moderate	High
4.	Cold Headed Parts.	Narrow-Steel and hightly ductile alloys	Limite-less than forgings	Small-12.5 cm by 1.25 cm diameter usual maximum	Small : 3 mm dia parts	High
5.	Extrusion	Restricted-Light metals, some steels, Cu and Ti.	Limited-can be Complex in Cross-section only	Medium 20 to 25 cm dia maximum	Small-1.25mm sections in Al and Mg	Good
6.	Impact Cold Extrusion	Narrow-Al, Tin, Mg, Lead	Limited-must be concentric	Small-15 cm dia in soft alloys, 10 cm in hard.	Moderate : 18 mm dia smallest	High
7.	Roll Forming	Narrow-Cold rolled steel; Some Al and stainless steel	Restricted to thin sections and uniform cross-section	Large	Sections from 3 mm up	Good
8.	Press Wroking	Wide-Include all workable metals	Limited-many design restrictions	Large	Small sections as thin as 0.075 mm possible	Fair to High
9.	Metal Spinning	Wide-Many sheet metals can be spun	Limited-cylindrical or concentric shapes	Large : Upto several m is dia	Moderate-6 mm in dia in gauges less than 1 mm	Good

Table 4.4 Metal Forming Process-Design Considerations (Cont.)

S.No.	Process	Precision and Tolerance	Special Structural properties	Surface smoothness	Surface Details	Getting into production	Rate of output	Remarks
1.	Drop Forging	±0.25 to 0.75 mm	Grain flow provides toughness	Fair	Fair	Slow-dies require much work	Medium-120 per hour on small parts	Used for high strength
2.	Press Forging	Medium-Better than drop forging	Same	Same	Same	Same	Medium-Slower than drop forging	Greater complexity than drop forging
3.	Upset forging	Medium-comparable to press forging	Toughness	Medium	Medium	Slow	Medium	Best Suited to Small parts
4.	Cold Headed parts	±0.25 mm common æ 0.05 mm possible	Toughness	High	Fair	Fair-dies relatively simple	Extremely high	One of fastest Process
5.	Extrusion	±0.125 to 0.5 mm	Grain flow improves properties	Good	Only as part of Contour	Moderate-dies relatively simple	High	Sometimes used as blanks for other processes
6.	Cold Impact Extrusion	±0.25 mm	Same	Good	Good	Same	High-Upto 2000/h	Can eliminate machining
7.	Roll Forming	±0.05 to 0.4 mm	Cold work improves properties	Good	None	Slow-roll takes long to be made	High	Requires large quantities
8.	Press Working	±0.25 mm common	None	High	Fair	Slow-dies require several weeks	High-Upto Several thousand	Low cost for mass production
9.	Metal Spinning	±0.40 to 1.5 mm	Grain flow and Cold work improves properties	Good	None	Fast-forms can be made quickly	Slow 12 to 30 per h.	Except for large piece best in short runs

Table 4.5. Metal Forming Process-Cost Consideration

S.No.	Process	Raw Material Costs	Tool and die costs	Direct Labour Cost Medium	Finishing Costs	Scrap loss	Optimum lot size
1.	Drop Forging	Low to Moderate	High	Medium	Medium	Moderate	Large, > 1000
2.	Press Forgoing	Low Moderate-equal to drop forging	High, usually less than drop forging	Medium-less than drop forging	Medium	Moderate, usually less than drop forging	Medium to High
3.	Upset Forging	Low to Moderate	High	Medium less than other forging process	Medium-less than other forging process	Medium-lowest of Forging processes	Same
4.	Cold Headed Parts	Low to Moderate-chiefly Steel wire	Medium	Low-almost completely automatic	Low	Low-practically nil	Large, not suited to small quantity
5.	Extrusion	Moderate primarily non-ferrous metals, some alloy steels	Moderate	Moderate	Low	Low	Moderate
6.	Impact Extrusion	Moderate-Primarily Tin, Lead Aluminium	Medium	Low-Little skilled labour needed	Low-often nil	Low-most scrap in blank scrap	Wide, from hundreds to thousands.
7.	Roll Forming	Low to Moderate-mostly low carbon steel sheet	High	Moderate	Low-cutting done	Low	High
8.	Press Forming	Low to Moderatre-ranging from carbon steel to stainless stell	High	Medium	Low-cleaning and	Low to Moderate	Large, > 10,000
9.	Metal Spinning	Low to Moderate	High-skilled operators needed	Low	Low-only cleaning and trimming	Low-practically no scrap	Low

Increase in Fatigue life :

    Gear wheels   = 2.5 times

    Coil springs   = 1.5 to 2 times

    Leaf springs   = 10 to 12 times

Roughness of shot peened surface = 3.2 to 0.8 μm Ra. Finish of originally rough-machined surfaces becomes finer and that of finish machined surfaces coarser.

Another peening method is with pneumatic hammer. It is shaped like a spherical striker, its action results indents on the surface worked. The process is used for cold working of stressed areas in large parts prior to finish machining.

4.11. CHARACTERISTICS OF METAL FORMING PROCESSES

The characteristics of metal forming processes are given in tables 4.3 to 4.5. The greatest extent of automation is typical of 3rd, 4th and 7th methods and to a lesser extent of 1st and 2nd methods. In the die-forging of small parts on forging hammers and presses, upto 1000 parts can be obtained per hour. Open die- forging gives the lowest production rates. The greatest metal utilization factor (0.9) is typical of 3rd method and especially of the 4th method, where this factor is unity. The shortest processing cycle (without cleaning and heat treatment) is provided by the 3rd and 4th methods.

PROBLEMS

1. Define the process of Mechanical working of metals.
2. What is the starting material for mechanical working of metals ?
3. Enumerate the advantages of mechanical working of metals over other manufacturing processes.
4. Differentiate between hot working and cold working of metals. Bring out the advantages and disadvantages of each of these techniques.
5. Discuss "worm working" of metals.
6. Define the Rolling process.
7. What is the difference between a bloom and a billet ?
8. What is the difference between plate, sheet, strip and foil ?
9. What is the difference between wire and rod ?
10. Define "Slab".
11. Why is metal cold worked ?
12. Explain what happens to a metal, when it is cold worked.
13. Why a cold worked metal is annealed ?
14. What is angle of bite in rolling ? On what factors does its value depend?
15. Describe and specify the merits and limitations of the different kinds of rolling mills.
16. Sketch and explain the working of "universal rolling mill" and "Planetary rolling mill".
17. What is "Steckel rolling" ?
18. Why are a number of passes required to roll a steel bar ?
19. Describe what occurs in metal when it is rolled.
20. How is cold rolling done ? What benefits are obtained from cold rolling metal ?
21. Why for cold rolling, a four high rolling mill is usually used ?
22. Define forging process.

23. Give the advantages and drawbacks of forging process.
24. Describe the common types of forging hammers.
25. How the size of a forging hammer is specified ?
26. How are a forging hammer and drop hammer alike and how do they differ ?
27. What is the difference between hammer forging and drop forging ?
28. What is Press forging ? How does it differ from drop forging ?
29. What is upset forging and how it is done ?
30. Discuss the rules which govern the flow of metals in upset forging process.
31. How are the sizes of presses and upset forging machines specified ?
32. What is roll forging and how it is done ?
33. What is rotary forging or swaging and how it is done ?
34. With the help of a suitable sketch, explain the working of "Board drop hammer"
35. Describe the common defects in forgings and write about the causes of each.
36. Describe the various methods for cleaning the forgings.
37. Describe the various methods for heat treatment of steel forgings.
38. What is the purpose of heat treatment of forgings ?
39. Define "Forgeability". On what factors does it depend ?
40. List the advantages and limitations of liquid forging.
41. List the steps of operations in liquid forging process.
42. Write a short note on isothermal forging.
43. Write a short note on Powder metal forging.
44. What is "No-draft forging" ?
45. Write a short note on "Orbital forging".
46. Write a short note on "Hot isostatic pressing".
47. Write short notes on : Incremental forging, Gatorizing and Super-plastic forging.
48. Define extrusion process.
49. Compare extrusion and rolling processes,
50. Describe the common ways of extruding metals.
51. Compare direct extrusion and indirect extrusion.
52. What is Tubular extrusion ?
53. Define "extrusion ratio" and give its common values for various metals.
54. What is impact extrusion ? Give its product applications.
55. What is "The Hooker method" of cold extrusion ?
56. Describe cold hydrostatic extrusion and give its advantages.
57. List the advantages and disadvantages of extrusion process.
58. Compare open and closed die forging.
59. How is seamless tubing pierced ?
60. What are the final operations in producing finished steel tubes ?
61. Describe the three ways of making butt welded pipe.
62. Give the product applications of extruded pipe, pipe made by piercing technique and the welded pipes.

63. Describe the operation of hot drawing and cupping of metals.
64. How the oxygen gas cylinders are made by this method ?
65. Describe wire drawing and rod drawing.
66. Define "Degree of drawing". What are its normal values ?
67. Describe Tube drawing.
68. How the hypodermic tubes are produced ?
69. How the metal is prepared for drawing operation ?
70. What is the material of the dies used for drawing operation ?
71. Give the advantages of Sheet metal working processes.
72. What is elastic recovery or spring back ?
73. What are the basic units of a press and what does each do ?
74. How do hydraulic presses compare with mechanical presses ?
75. What are knuckle joint and toggle process and what is the purpose of each ?
76. What are single action, double action and triple action presses ?
77. Compare open and closed frame presses.
78. Sketch a Blanking die and label it properly. Write the function of each part.
79. With the help of a sketch, describe the working of a Cutting Die.
80. Describe a progressive, a combination and a compound die.
81. Describe what happens when sheet metal is sheared ?
82. Write the formula for calculating the cutting force in shearing operation.
83. How can the cutting force be reduced ?
84. Define "deep drawing process".
85. With the help of a neat diagram, describe a "deep drawing process". Give its product applications.
86. What is LDR ? What is its usual range ?
87. What is "redrawing" ?
88. Explain the "Bending terminology" with the help of a suitable sketch.
89. What are the various methods of bending ? Sketch and describe each.
90. What is "Press brake" ?
91. Describe "Roll forming".
92. Describe : "Rubber press forming", "Rubber hydro forming", and "Hydromechanical forming".
93. Describe "Stretch forming".
94. Describe "Metal spinning". Write its product applications. Differentiate between cold and hot metal spinning.
95. What is "Power spinning" ?
96. What is "Flow turning" ?
97. Differentiate between "coining" and "embossing".
98. Compare "metal spinning" with "deep drawing".
99. What is the difference between "riveting" and "staking" ?
100. What does "hubbing" do ?
101. Describe "shot peening".

102. What is "cold heading" ? What are its uses and advantages ?

103. Name two metals which are hot worked at room temperature.

104. Name six metals or alloys which may be cold worked at rom temperature

105. What are the effects of forging on porosity and segre gation ?

106. What is the effect of forging on grain structure and why is this benefitial to the properties of the metal ?

107. What is the relationship between carbon cantent of a steel and its maximum allowable forging temperature ?

108. What will be the consequences if a steel is forged : (*a*) at too high a temperature ? (*b*) at too low a temperature ?

109. Explain the difference between cold working and hot working of metals. (UPSC, DU)

110. How annealing is related to cold working ?

111. What is the effect of hot working on the structure and mechanical properties of metals?

112. Estimate the blanking force to cut a blank of 25 mm wideand 30 mm long from a 1.5 mm thick metal strip, if the ultimate shear stress of the material is 450 N/mm^2. Also determine the work done if the percentage penetration is 25% of material thickness.

(PTU; Ans.: 74.25kN ; 27.84375 N-m).

Hint : — $F = P.t.\tau_s$ (eq. 4.1 & 4.2); work done = F × Punch travel

Here Punch travel = Percentage penetration = 0.25 × t

Lubrication:

1. **Rolling :** – Hot rolling of ferrous metals is normally done without a lubricant. If need be, graphite can be used. Water-based solutions are used to cool the rolls and to break the scale on the rolled material. For hot rolling of non-ferrous metals, these is a wide choice; a wide variety of compounded oils, emulsions and fatty acids.

   For cold rolling, the common lubricants are : – water-soluble oils, low-viscosity lubricants, such as mineral oils, emulsions, paraffins and fatty acids.

2. **Forging :–** Lubricants gretly influence : friction, wear, deforming forces and flow of material in die-cavities. They act as thermal between how workpiece and the relatively cool dies, thereby, slowing the rate of cooling of the workpiece and improving metal flow. Alsol they serve as parting agents which inhibit the forging from sticking to the dies and so help in its release from the dies.

   For hot forging, the common lubricants are : graphite, MOS_2 and sometimes molten glass. For cold forging, these are : mineral oil and soaps. In hot forging, the lubricant is applied to the dies, but in cold forging, it is applied to the workpiece.

3. **Extrusion :–** For hot extrusino, glass is an excellent lubricant with steels, stainless steels and high temperature metals and alloys. For cold extrusion, lubrication is critical, especially with steels, because of the possibility of sticking (siezure) between the workpiece and the tooling if the lubrication breaks down. Most effective lubricant is : application of a phosphate conversion coating on the workpiece followed by a coating.

113. Explain the difference between elastic and plastic deformation.

114. Which equipment is used for sheet- metal working ?

Chapter

5

The Welding Process

5.1. GENERAL

5.1.1. Definition. There are many definitions of a welding process. But the most comprehensive definition is given below :

Welding is defined as "a localized coalescence of metals, wherein coalescence is obtained by heating to suitable temperature, with or without the application of pressure and with or without the use of filler metal. The filler metal has a melting point approximately the same as the base metals".

The welding process is used to metallurgically join together two metal pieces, to produce essentially a single piece of metal. The process results in what is known as a 'permanent joint'. A good welded joint is as strong as the parent metal. The product is known as 'Weldment'.

5.1.2. Applications. The welding process finds widespread applica-tions in almost all branches of industry and construction. Welding is extensively employed in the fabrication and erection of steel structures in industrial construction and civil engineering, for example, structural members of bridges and buildings etc. ; vessels of welded-plate construction (steel reservoirs, boilers, pressure vessel tanks and pipelines etc.); and concrete reinforcement. It is the chief means of fastening panels and members together into automobile bodies and also in aviation industry. It has taken the place of castings for a large proportion of machine, jig and fixture bases, bodies and frames. The process is also extensively used for the repair of broken parts, in the building of warn surfaces and in the repair of defective castings. In fact, the future of any metal may depend upon how far it would lend itself to fabrication by welding.

5.1.3. Advantages. The widespread use of welding at the present time is due to its following advantages :

1. Welding results in a good saving of material and reduced labour content of production.

2. Low manufacturing costs.

3. Dependability of the medium, that is, the weldments are safer.

4. It gives the designer great latitude in planning and designing.

5. Welding is also useful as a method for repairing broken, worn or defective metal parts. Due to this, the cost of re-investment can be avoided.

6. Without welding techniques, the light weight methods of fabrication, so vital to the automotive and aircraft industries, would be unthinkable.

The welding process has the plus points that it is readily adaptable to streamline structure and the welded joints are very tight. Welded joints are strong, especially under static loading. However, they have poor fatigue resistance due to stress concentration, residual stresses and various weld defects, such as cracks, incomplete fusion, slag inclusions and the like. But, all these drawbacks can be overcome to a large extent.

Advantages of Welded Joints over Riveted Joints

 1. Economy of material and lighter weight of structure owing to :

  (*a*) Better utilization of metal elements (plates, angles) since their working sections are not weakened by the rivet holes, consequently the sections of the welded pieces can be made smaller than the sections of riveted elements, for the same acting forces.

  (*b*) Possibility of a wide use of butt-jointed seams, requiring no additional elements, such as cover straps.

  (*c*) Lighter weight of the joining elements (rivets weight more than the welds). The weight of welds comprises about 1 to 1.5 per cent of work weight, while the weight of rivets is about 3.5 to 4 per cent. The use of welding instead of riveting, saves on an average 10 to 20 per cent in weight.

 2. Greater strength of the joints, due to absence of holes needed for riveting.

 3. Less labour is required, since there is no need for marking out and drilling or punching holes. Riveting consumes much more labour and is a much more complicated and less productive job, than welding, which can be often largely automated.

 4. Possibility of joining curvilinear parts.

 5. Tightness and impermeability of the joint.

 6. Noiselessness (riveting is inevitably accompanied by noise).

Advantages over Casting Process

 1. Lighter weight and saving of material due to :

  (*a*) lesser machining allowances and

  (*b*) the possibility of utilizing smaller sections, since the wall thickness of cast parts, determined in many cases by the casting process, is as a rule 2 to 3 times greater, and sometimes even more than that of welded parts.

The saving of metal in welded machine components, as compared with cast ones, may amount to 40%.

 2. Lower Cost.

 3. Greater strength.

 4. Maximum homogenity.

Whether machine parts should be welded, is decided in each particular case, by design and economy considerations.

The drawbacks of welding can be : Not all the metals are satisfactori- ly weldable and the weldments are less readily machinable, as compared to castings.

 5.1.4. Classification. Welding processes may be classified accord-ing to the source of energy employed for heating the metals and the state of metal at the place being welded. Depending upon the source of heat, the welding processes are classified as :-

 1. Chemical (oxygen + combustible fuel gas, e.g., acetylene, propane, butane, natural gas, hydrogen etc.).

 2. Chemico – Mechanical (Pressure gas welding, Thermit welding)

 3. Electro – chemical (Atomic hydrogen welding)

 4. Electro-Mechanical (Electric resistance welding)

 5. Electric – Arc welding.

These may be divided into two groups as follows :

(a) **Pressure Processes.** In these processes, the parts to be joined are heated to a plastic state (fusion may occur to a limited extent) and forced together with external pressure to make the joint. Some of the more common processes in this group are mentioned below :

1. Forge welding
2. Thermit Pressure welding
3. Pressure Gas welding
4. Electric Resistance welding

(b) **Fusion Processes.** In these processes, the material at the joint is heated to the molten state and allowed to solidify to make the joint, without the application of pressure. Here, some joints may be made without the addition of a filler metal, but, in general, a filler metal must be added to the weld to fill the space between the parts being welded. The filler metal deposited should ordinarily be of the same composition as the base metal.

Some of the common welding processes in this group are listed below :

1. Gas welding
2. Electric Arc welding
3. Thermit Fusion welding

The welding processes can also be classified as :

Autogeneous, Homogeneous and Hetrogeneous

In 'Autogeneous' processes, no filler metal is added to the joint interface, for example, cold and hot pressure welding processes and electric resistance welding.

In 'Homogeneous' processes, filler metal is added and is of the same type as the parent metal, for example, welding of plain low- C steel with a low- C welding rod and welding of 70 - 30 brass with a 70 - 30 brass welding rod etc.

In 'Hetrogeneous' processes, a filler metal is used but is of a different type from the parent metal, for example, brazing and soldering processes. Brazing and Soldering are not strictly the welding processes in view of the definition of welding process given above. However, these processes also belong to the family of welding processes.

The two most widely used welding methods are : Gas welding and Arc welding. The temperature of an electric arc is much higher than that of a gas flame, so the joint zone melts practically instantaneously in arc welding. Gas welding involves long preheating period which raises the metal adjacent to the joint to a high temperature. This exerts an unfavour- able effect on the crystalline structure, which results in considerable stresses being set up. So, gas welding is unsuitable for relatively large cross-sections due to this trouble and the time involved in preheating. Plates above 20 mm thick are, therefore, best welded by arc welding.

5.1.5. Types of Weld Joints. The relative positions of the two pieces being welded determine the type of joint. Welded structures are assembled by five basic types of joints : Butt, Lap, Corner, T and Edge joints, shown in Fig. 5.1. All other possible joints are variations of these basic joints. To make a weld, the two pieces to be joined are located and clamped or held in the correct position.

Butt joints are formed by welding the end surfaces or edges of the members.

In Lap joints, the two members being welded should overlap by an amount from 3 to 5 times their thickness. Edge of each piece is welded to the surface of the other.

T-joint is used to join two pieces whose surfaces are approximately at right angles to each other.

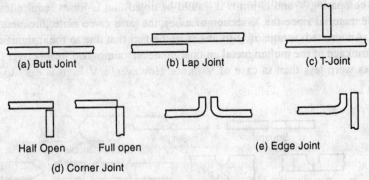

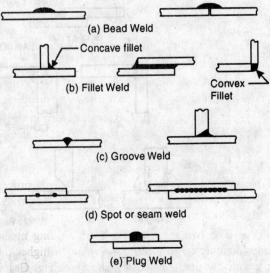

Fig. 5.1. Basic Welded Joints.

Corner joints are used to join the edges of two pieces whose surfaces are approximately at right angles to each other.

Edge joint is used to join the edges of two pieces in which a part of the surface remains parallel to each other.

5.1.6. Types of Welds. Fig. 5.2 shows the various types of welds used in making a joint. A 'bead' weld is one in which the filler metal is deposited at a joint where the two surfaces adjoining the joint are in the same plane. A 'bead' is defined as a single run of weld metal. A 'fillet' weld is one in which the filler metal is deposited at the corner of two intersecting surfaces, such as a T or Lap joint. A 'groove' weld is one in which the filler material is deposited in a groove formed by edge preparation of one member or of both the members. A 'plug' or 'slot' weld is one in which a hole is formed through one of the pieces to be welded and the filler material is then deposited into this hole and fused with the mating part.

Fig. 5.2. Types of Welds

5.1.7. Edge Preparation. The pre-paration of the edges of the pieces to be welded depends upon the thickness of metal being welded. Edge preparation is necessary when thickness increases so that heat would be able to penetrate the entire depth. This ensures formation of sound welds. The edge preparation is done by bevelling the edges of the pieces after the rust, grease, oil or paint are completely removed from their surfaces. The various edge preparations are illustrated in Fig. 5.3. There are five basic types of chamfers put on the mating edges prior to welding : Square, V, Bevel, U and J.

Butt Joints. The straight square butt joints with no special edge preparation is used when the thickness of the two plates to be welded is small so that heat of welding penetrates the full depth of joint. These joints are suitable for thicknesses from 3 to 8 mm. However, if the plate thickness is more than 4.5 mm, edge preparation is recommended.

Single V : For thickness upto 16 mm

Double V : For thickness > 16 mm

Single and Double U : For thickness greater than 20 mm.

When comparing V and U-joints it should be noted that U-joints require less electric power and electrode material since the X-section of a U-joint for a given plate thickness is less than that of a V-joint. Another advantage of U-joint lies in the fact that due to the insignificant bevel of the edges, the shrinkage of the molten metal on cooling occurs almost uniformly over the entire section and the plates warp less than in case of V-joints. However, a V-Joint is easy to make than a U-joint.

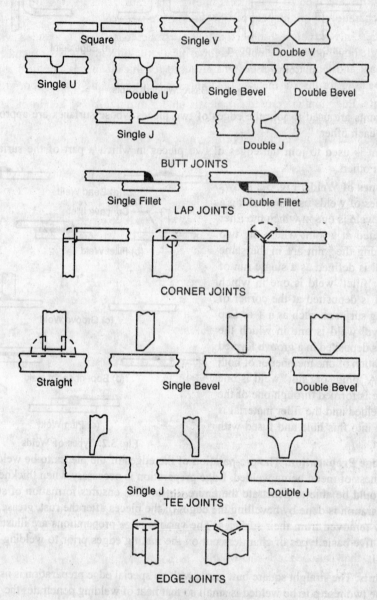

Fig. 5.3. Edge Preparation.

Double V and U-joints are by no means inferior to single V-joints when plates of 12 mm and over are welded because the X-sectional areas of double V and U joints is 30-40 percent less than that of single V-joints at the same bevel angle. The short comings of double V and U-joints accrue from poor penetration liable to accur inside the butt and the greater cost of edge preparation especially in the case of U-joints.

Other edge preparations for a butt joint are : Single bevel, Double bevel, Single J, Double J. Butt joints are made by Bead or Groove welds.

Lap Joints are used to join thin sheets, usually less than 3 mm thick. These joints do not need any special edge preparation. The joint is produced by fillet welds.

Corner Joints are used to join sheets upto 5 mm thick. These joints are welded with or without edge preparation, with the help of fillet and/or groove welds.

Tee Joints. Only structures subjected to low static loads can be welded without edge preparation. Single bevel joints are employed for critical structures in which the members are from 10 to 20 mm thick and Double bevel designs are used for thicker metals. Single J and Double J joints can also be used for thicker metals. Tee joints are made by using fillet and/or groove welds.

Edge Joints. Edge joints are used for metals upto 3 mm thick. The height of flange should be twice the thickness of the sheet. These joints are made by Bead or Groove welds.

Fig. 5.4 gives the various definitions concerning welding joints and welds.

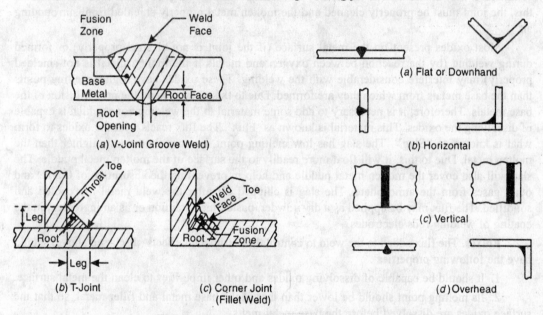

Fig. 5.4. Definitions.   Fig. 5.5. Welding Positions.

5.1.8. Welding positions. The basic welding positions are shown in Fig. 5.5. The flat position is the easiest and quickest for welding. In this position, welding benefits from the force of gravity and maximum deposition rates are obtained resulting in strongest welded joints. Next in ease of welding is the horizontal fillet position in which the force of gravity helps to some extent. However, the major defects that can occur while welding in horizontal position are : undercutting and overlapping of the weld zone.

For welding in these positions, the joint should be level or nearly so when possible. Welding in positions other than flat requires the use of manipulative techniques and welding rods/electrodes that result in faster freezing of the molten metal and slag, to counteract the effect of gravity. In vertical position, the welder can deposit the bead in the uphill or downhill direction. Uphill welding is preferred for thick metals because it produces stronger welds. Downhill welding is faster than the uphill welding and is suited for thin metals.

5.1.9. Cleaning the Joint and Fluxing. The weld area (joint) must be free of oil, dirt, grease, paint or moisture etc. Firstly, these will interfere with the proper fusion on the metal and result in a weak joint. Secondly, gases may evolve from these (under the action of heat) which may be absorbed by molten metal.

For removing oily substances, the cleaning is done by organic solvents like acetone, CCl_4 and trichloro ethylene. For removing foreign substances, cleaning is done with a rag soaked in the solvent. Heavier oxide films may be removed by acid pickling, wire brushing or emery. When organic solvents are used for cleaning, these should be completely evaporated from the interfaces before any welding is attempted. Otherwise, highly poisonous gases such as phosgene may form under intense heat of welding.

In addition to many gases which may evolve if the joint is unclean, gases such as O_2, N_2 and H_2 are present in the atmosphere. Also, water vapours in air, breakdown under intense heat of welding to form O_2 and H_2. All these gases may be absorbed by the molten metal. As the metal cools after welding, its solubility for these gases decreases. The gases try to leave the metal as it solidifies. If they are not able to leave, they will form porosities and gas holes in the weld. To avoid this, the joint must be properly cleaned and the molten metal properly shielded from surrounding air.

Most oxides present on the metal surface (if the joint is not cleaned properly) or formed during welding (by the reaction between oxygen and metals if the molten metal is not shielded properly) may interfere considerable with the welding. These oxides have higher melting points than the base metals from which they are formed. Due to this, they prevent the proper fusion of the base metals. Therefore, it is necessary to add some material to the welding zone, which is capable of dissolving the oxides. This material is known as 'Flux'. The flux reacts with the oxides to form what is known as "Slag". The slag has low melting point, is more fluid and is lighter than the molten metal. Due to this, it will float more readily to the surface of the molten metal puddle. The slag will also cover the molten metal puddle and help in preventing the absorption of O_2, N_2 and other gases from the atmosphere. The slag is chipped off after the weld metal has cooled and solidified. The flux may be applied as a dry powder, paste, thick solution or as an ingredient in the coating of welding rods/electrodes.

Fluxes. The flux added to the weld to control the detrimental effects (discussed above) should have the following properties :

1. It should be capable of dissolving oxides and other impurities to clean the metal surface.

2. Its melting point should be lower than that of the base metal and filler metal, so that the surface oxides are dissolved before the base metal melts.

3. Its specific gravity should be lower than that of the base metal and the filler metal, so that the slag floats readily to the surface of the molten metal puddle.

4. It should control the flowability of the molten metal.

5. It should not affect the base metal adversely.

The type of flux used will depend upon the type of the metals being welded. The common fluxes used are listed below :

(*i*) **For Aluminium and Aluminium Alloys.** Mixture of alkaline fluorides, chlorides and bisulphates, for example, mixtures of chlorides of sodium, potassium, Lithium and Barium, fluorides of calcium (Fluorspar, CaF_2), sodium and potassium and sodium bisulphate.

(*ii*) **Copper and Copper Alloys.** Mixtures of sodium and potassium borates, carbonates, chlorides, sulphates; Borax ($Na_2B_4O_7.10H_2O$) Boric acid (H_3BO_3) and Di-sodium hydrogen phosphate (Na_2HPO_4) are suitable for dissolving oxides called cuprous oxides.

(*iii*) **Ferrous Metals.** For welding C.I., Mixtures of Borax, Sodium carbonate and Potassium carbonate ; Sodium carbonate and Sodium bicarbonate ; Borax, Sodium carbonate and Sodium nitrate or Borax alone are suitable fluxes.

For Carbon steels : Dehydrated borax and calcium oxide dissolved in liquid are common fluxes.

For Alloy steels : Mixture of Boric acid, dehydrated borax and Calcium fluoride.

Borax forms compounds with iron oxide and the carbonates cleans and promotes fluidity.

5.2. GAS WELDING

Gas welding is "a group of welding processes wherein coalescence is produced by heating with a gas flame or flames with or without the application of pressure and with or without the use of filler material".

It may be noted here that out of the various types of gas welding processes, pressure is used only in Pressure Gas Welding (PGW). In all other types of gas welding processes, joint is made without the application of any pressure. The edges or surfaces to be joined are melted (alongwith the filler material when used) by a suitable gas flame and the molten metal is allowed to flow together to form a permanent joint on cooling.

The welding heat is obtained from burning a mixture of oxygen and a combustible gas. The gases are mixed in the proper proportion within a welding torch (also called Blowpipe) which provides control of the welding flame. The mixture is burnt at the blowpipe nozzle or tip. The general name of the method is : Oxy Fuel Gas Welding (OFW).

The common commercial gases used in gas welding include : acetylene, hydrogen, propane and butane. The most common form of gas welding is oxygen-acetylene (oxy-acetylene) welding, OAW. Acetylene (C_2H_2) produces higher temperature (in the range of 3200°C) than other gases, (which produce a flame temperature in the range of 2500°C) because it contains more available carbon and releases heat when its components (C and H) dissociate to combine with O_2 and burn. The cost of production of acetylene is low and the gases (O_2 and C_2H_2) can be stored at high pressure in separate steel cylinders. The main drawback of acetylene is that it is dangerous if not handled carefully.

5.2.1. Oxy-Acetylene Welding (OAW). There are two systems of OAW depending upon the manner in which acetylene is supplied for welding : High pressure system and Low pressure system. Acetylene is supplied either from generators or it may be purchased in metal cylinders. O_2 is always supplied from metal cylinders.

1. High Pressure System. In this system, both O_2 and C_2H_2 are supplied from high pressure cylinders. Oxygen cylinders are charged to a pressure of 120 atm. gauge. Due to the danger of explosion, pure acetylene can not be compressed to a pressure more than 0.1 Pa above atmosphere. Therefore, acetylene is supplied in cylinders in the form known as "Dissolved acetylene". It is stored in cylinders in which it is dissolved in acetone under a pressure of from 16 to 22 atm gauge. At normal pressure, one litre of acetone dissolves about 25 litres of acetylene. For every additional atmosphere of pressure another 25 volumes of acetylene will be dissolved. As a safety measure, the cylinder of acetylene is filled with a porous filler (usually charcoal) forming a system of capillary vessels. It should not be with drawn from cylinder too rapidly, since some acetone may then be with drawn along with acetylene. The maximum recommended pressure when taking acetylene from a cylinder through a rubber hose is 1 bar (1×10^5). In H.P. system, the pressure of acetylene at the welding torch is from 0.06 to 1.0 bar.

2. Low Pressure System. Here, acetylene is produced at the place of welding by the interaction of calcium carbide and water in an acetylene generator, according to the reaction :

$$CaC_2 + 2H_2O \rightarrow Ca(OH)_2 + C_2H_2 + 127.3 \text{ k J per mol.}$$

As is clear from above, a great deal of heat is evolved in this reaction.

The produced acetylene is supplied to the blowpipe at a low pressure from a gas holder incorporated in the generator. Acetylene is cleaned by passing it through a purifier. To prevent the possibility of an explosion by oxygen or air blowing back and entering the generating plant, a back pressure valve is arranged between the blowpipe and the gas holder.

The pressure of acetylene at the torch is upto 0.06 bar

For oxygen, the desired pressure at the welding torch is :

(i) High Pressure System (Welding and Cutting) = 0.1 to 3.5 bar

(ii) Low Pressure System (Welding) = 0.5 to 3.5 bar

5.2.2. Gas Welding Equipment. Equipment required in gas welding includes : cylinders for compressed gases (acetylene generator in place of acetylene cylinder in low pressure system), regulators, blowpipes, Nozzles, Hose and Hose fittings. The assembled basic equipment required for high pressure system is shown in Fig. 5.6.

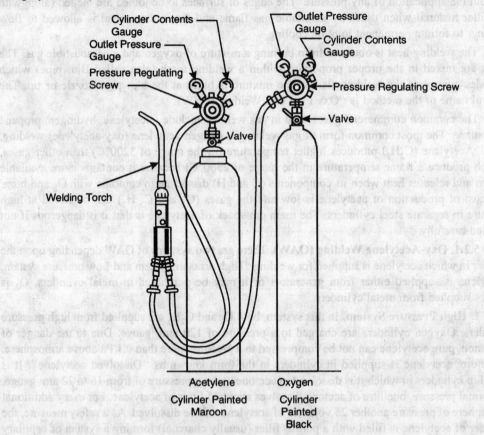

Fig. 5.6. High Pressure Gas Welding Equipment.

1. Cylinders for Compressed Gases. The Oxygen cylinder is painted Black and is made of steel. Acetylene cylinder is painted Maroon and is made of steel. To avoid potentially lethal situations, C_2H_2 cylinders have L.H., threads and O_2 cylinders have R.H. threads. This safety precaution also applies to all valves, connectors and regulators.

2. Pressure Regulators. A pressure regulator or pressure reducing valve, located on the top of both O_2 and C_2H_2 cylinders, serves to reduce the high cylinder pressure of the gas to a suitable working value at the blow pipe and to maintain a constant pressure. The pressure is regulated with the help of a spring loaded diaphragm. Variations of pressure is necessary for different sized nozzles (inside diameter) and the pressure is controlled by a graduated adjusting screw which serves to vary the compression of the spring.

3. Pressure Gauges. Each gas cylinder is provided with two pressure gauges. One gauge indicates the pressure of the gas inside the cylinder and the other indicates the pressure of the gas supplied to the blow pipe.

4. Blow Pipe. The blow pipe or weld-ing torch serves to mix the gases in proper proportion and to deliver the mixture to the nozzle or tip where it is burned. The gases from the cylinders are taken to the blow pipe through reducing valves and with the help of rubber tubes (hoses). On the shank of the blowpipe, two control values (needle type) are provided, one for controlling the flow of acetylene and the other of oxygen, entering a chamber called mixing chamber where the two gases are mixed in a correct proportion. The control knobs of the control valves are usually coloured, red for acetylene and blue for oxygen.

Depending upon the system of OAW, there are two designs of blow pipes: Injector type and High pressure type. A detailed view of the Welding Torch (Blow Pipe) is shown in Fig. 5.7 (c).

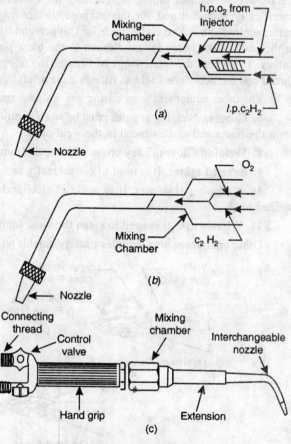

Fig. 5.7. Blow Pipes.

The injector type blow pipe is used in the low pressure system. The low pressure of acetylene is not sufficient to force it through the small passage, into the mixing chamber. To overcome this difficulty, high pressure oxygen at a very high velocity is led through an injector nozzle inside the body of the blow pipe. It produces a vacuum in the acetylene channel, drawing acetylene into the mixing chamber, (Fig. 5.7 (a)). From the mixer, the gas mixture flows to the tip. In the high pressure system, (Fig. 5.7 (b)), both the gases are at high pressure. The gases flow on their own to the mixing chamber and no injector is needed. Under no circumstance, must a high pressure torch be used on a low pressure system, because the absence of injector makes it unsafe. Low pressure blow pipe is expensive than the high pressure blow pipe, because the whole head containing both the nozzle (tip) and injector is to be replaced with every nozzle change.

5. Nozzle or Tip. The nozzle is a device screwed to the end of the blow pipe. It is used to permit the flow of oxyacetylene gas mixture from the mixing chamber of blow pipe to the tip of the nozzle to facilitate burning. In order to vary the size of flame (and heat supply) necessary to weld varying thicknesses of metal, a selection of tips is available for the blow pipe. For this, the nozzles are interchangeable so that the correct nozzle is fitted at the end of the blow pipe. Each nozzle is marked showing its gas consumption in litres/hour and a table supplied with the blowpipe shows which tip should be used to weld any required thickness of metal. The delivery pressure from the regulator must be varied according to the size of the tip used, and instructions are supplied to obtain the correct conditions.

6. Hose and Hose Fittings. The hose connects the outlet of the pressure reducing valve and the blow pipe. Rubber tubing is necessary for flexibility but it should be of the highest quality, specifically manufactured for this purpose. In accordance with International standards, hose is manufactured to a colour code : Blue for Oxygen and Red for acetylene. Hose fittings are provided at the ends of the hoses for attachment to the blow pipe and the outlet of the pressure reducing valves. To prevent the interchange of fittings, the oxygen hose connection nut has a right handed thread and the acetylene fuel gas fittings have a left handed thread.

The other equipment used during gas welding are :

7. Goggles. Welding goggles must be worn to protect the eyes from the heat and light radiated from the flame and molten metal in the weld pool.

8. Welding Gloves. They protect the hands from the heat and metal splashes.

9. Spark Lighter. It is used to conveniently and instantaneously light the blow pipe.

10. Chipping Hammer. It is made of steel and is used to remove metal oxides from the welded bead.

11. Wire-brush. It is used to clean the weld joint before and after welding.

Other equipment also includes : safety shields and protective clothing.

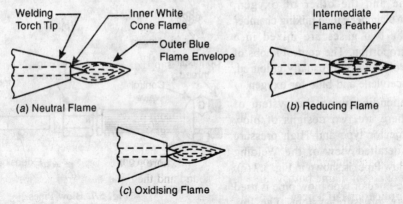

Fig. 5.8. OAW Flame Settings.

5.2.3. Oxy-acetylene Flame Settings. In an oxyacetylene flame, O_2 and C_2H_2 are mixed and burnt to release heat. The complete combustion of acetylene in an atmosphere of oxygen is represented by the following reaction :

$$C_2H_2 + 2.5O_2 = 2CO_2 + H_2O \text{ (vapour)} + 1284.57 \text{ k J/mol}$$

An oxy-acetylene flame can be set to : neutral, carburising or oxidising condition depending upon the metal to be welded and the type of filler metal to be used. In a neutral flame, O_2 and C_2H_2 are mixed in equal amounts. In carburising or reducing flame, the percentage of C_2H_2 is more than that of O_2 and in the oxidising flame, the percentage of O_2 is more than of C_2H_2. These three types of flames are illustrated in Fig. 5.8.

1. Neutral Flame. A neutral flame is obtained when equal amounts of O_2 and C_2H_2 are mixed and burnt in a torch. The flame is recognised by two sharply defined zones, the inner white cone flame and the outer blue flame envelope, (Fig. 5.8 (a)). The reaction at the inner cone for the neutral flame where equal volumes of cylinder oxygen and acetylene are used is,

$$C_2H_2 + O_2 \longrightarrow 2\,CO + H_2$$

This provides the most concentrated heat with the highest tempera- ture for welding at a distance of 3 to 5 mm from the end of the inner cone. It is also apparent that the environment within the outer envelope consists of carbon monoxide and hydrogen and is relatively inert to materials that oxidise readily.

The reactions at the outer envelope are :

$$2\,CO + O_2 \longrightarrow 2\,CO_2$$

$$H_2 + \frac{1}{2}O_2 \longrightarrow H_2O \text{ (vapour)}$$

For these reactions, the oxygen is supplied from the surrounding air. During actual welding, the outer envelope spreads over the surface of the work material and serves as a protective shield from the ordinary atmosphere. Also, since the heat developed is not as concentrated, this outer envelope of flame contributes only to preheat the work material for welding.

2. Carburising Flame. A carburising or reducing flame is obtained when an excess of acetylene is supplied than which is theoretically required ($O_2 : C_2H_2 = 0.85$ to 0.95). A reducing flame is recognised by three distinct sections : the inner cone (which is not sharply defined) and an outer envelope as for the neutral flame. The third zone surrounds the inner cone and extends into the outer enveloping zone. It is whitish in colour and is called "excess acetylene feather". Its length is an indication of the amount of excess acetylene. (Fig. 5.8 (b)).

To obtain a neutral flame, first the reducing flame is obtained. Then the supply of oxygen is gradually increased until the intermediate feather disappears. The resulting flame will be a neutral flame.

3. Oxidising Flame. This flame has an excess of oxygen over that required for a neutral flame ($O_2 : C_2H_2 = 1.15$ to 1.50). To obtain an oxidising flame, the flame is first set to the neutral condition. Then the acetylene valve is turned down gradually to reduce the amount of acetylene, giving an excess of oxygen. The flame resembles the neutral flame except that it acquires a light blue tint and the inner cone is slightly shorter and more pointed than in a neutral flame (Fig. 5.8 (c)). An oxidising flame burns with a harsh sound and the outer envelope is short and narrow.

Applications of Three Types of Flames

(a) **Neutral Flame.** In most welding situations, it is theoretically desirable to use a neutral flame, but in practice it is very difficult to discern whether the flame is neutral or oxidising, either a slightly reducing or a slightly Oxidising flame is used.

If possible, most welding should be done with a neutral flame, since such a flame has a minimum chemical effect upon most heated metals. The flame is widely used for the welding of steel, stainless steel, cast iron, Copper and Aluminium.

(b) **Reducing Flame.** The acetylene being excess in this flame, the available carbon is not completely consumed. With iron and steel, it will form iron carbide (hard and brittle). Therefore, metals that tend to absorb carbon should not be welded with a reducing flame. This flame is used for materials that oxidise rapidly like steel and aluminium. It is suitable for welding low alloy steels, low c-steels and for welding those metals (for example, non-ferrous) that do not tend to absorb carbon. Such flames are also used for welding Monel metal and Nickel and in hard surfacing with high speed steel and cemented carbides.

(c) **Oxidising Flame.** This flame has limited use because the excess oxygen tends to combine with many metals to form hard, brittle, low strength oxides. Also, excess of oxygen causes the weld bead and the surrounding area to have a skummy or dirty appearance. So, this flame is not used for welding steel. It is mainly used when welding materials which are not oxidised readily and which have a high solubility of hydrogen in the molten state and low solubility in the solid state, for example, brasses, bronzes and gold. For these metals the oxidising atmosphere creates a base metal oxide that protects the base metal. For example, in welding brass, Zinc has à tendency to separate and fume away. The formation of a covering copper oxide prevents Zinc from dissipating.

Lighting up the Flame. For lighting up the torch for welding, the following steps should be followed :

1. Open both cylinder valves slowly.

2. Adjust the pressure regulators to the required working pressures.

3. Open the acetylene gas valve on the blow pipe and adjust the pressure regulating screw until the gauge reads correctly.

4. Close the acetylene gas valve on the blow pipe.

5. Repeat steps 3 and 4 for oxygen.

6. Turn on the acetylene gas valve on the blowpipe and allow the gas to flush the system.

7. Using a friction spark-lighter, ignite the gas. This will produce an acetylene flame.

8. Adjust the blowpipe valve until the flame just stops smoking and releasing soot.

9. Gradually open the oxygen control valve on blowpipe and adjust it until the required flame is obtained.

Closing Down Procedure. When closing down :

1. First turn off the acetylene blowpipe control valve.

2. Then turn off the oxygen blowpipe control valve.

3. Close the cylinder supply valves.

4. Purge each hose in turn by opening the control valves on the blow pipe, first for oxygen and then for acetylene.

5. Release the pressure on the two regulators.

6. Finally check that the blow pipe valves are closed.

Power of Blowpipe and Nozzles

The power of a blowpipe is denoted in various ways :

(i) By the bore diameter of the nozzle. The gas consumption and hence the size of the gas flame will depend upon this dimension.

(ii) By the amount of gas flow in litres/hour. Acetylene consump- tion varies from 50 to 2800 litres per hour. Oxygen consumption varies from 50 to 3100 litres/hour.

(iii) By a number which represents the thickness of the plate that can be welded with this blowpipe.

It is thus clear that the power of the blow pipe determines the size of the flame produced and hence the heat available for welding. The power will be influenced by the velocity and the quantity of the gas mixture leaving the nozzle. Both these factors will depend upon the supply pressure of the gases and the size of the orifice of the nozzle.

The velocity of the gas mixture leaving the nozzle orifice ranges from 60 to 200 m/s. The lower velocity flame will burn quietly and is called 'soft flame'. The higher velocity flame burns with a hissing sound. In general, a flame of average velocity will give best results.

5.2.4. Oxy-Acetylene Welding Techniques. A sound welded joint can be obtained by the proper selection of the torch size, filler material, method of moving the torch along the weld and the angle at which the torch is held, as well as proper regulation of the welding flame.

As discussed above, the size of torch required will depend upon the thickness and heat conductivity of the metal being welded. Metals with higher conductivity will require a torch head with a larger gas consumption.

The joint is first heated with the torch until the welding pool is formed. A welding rod (if used) should be held in the flame so that its end melts at about the same time as the base metal and the filler metal is added to the pool.

In OAW, there are two techniques commonly used, called as : Leftward and Rightward techniques. The choice of either technique will depend upon the metal to be welded, its thickness, any test requirements, and total cost. To compare the two techniques, the blow pipe is held in the right hand and the filler rod in the left hand (with a right handed person). The filler rod is carried to the left of the blowpipe.

1. Leftward Welding Technique. In left ward (also called as forward or forehand) welding technique, the torch flame progresses from right to left, (Fig. 5.9 (a)). The angles of blow pipe and filter rod are shown in the figure. The method allows preheating of the plate edges immediately ahead of the molten pool and this is the method more commonly used. The blowpipe is given a very slight side to side movement and with the filler rod is moved progressively along the joint. With the blowpipe movement, the flame moves away from the just welded portion of the joint, which starts loosing heat and cooling starts soon. Due to this, this technique is restricted to welding of mild steel plates upto 5 mm thick, cast iron and non-ferrous metals.

2. Rightward Welding Technique. In the rightward (or back hand or backward) technique, welding commences at the left hand side of the plates and proceeds towards the right, (Fig. 5.9 (b)). The blow-pipe points in the direction of the completed weld with the inner cone of the flame directed towards the bottom of the joint, concentrating the maximum amount of heat into the plates. Due to this, the weld puddle is kept hot for a longer time and a narrow and deeper weld results. Hence, this technique is principally used for welding thick sections (over 5 mm thick).

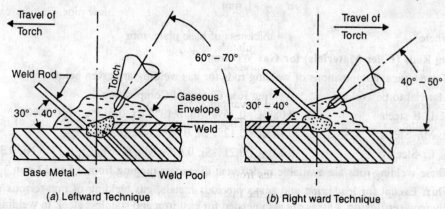

Fig. 5.9. OAW Techniques.

During welding, the blowpipe moves regularly along the weld seam without any lateral movement. On the other hand, the end of the welding wire describes a series of loops instead of moving steadily.

Chief Advantages of Rightward Technique

1. The rightward technique is faster by comparison with the leftward technique. This is because, in the left ward method, the view of the joint edge is interrupted and it is necessary to remove the end of the filler rod to inspect the progress. This action slows down the process. Also, the end of the filler rod becomes oxidised resulting in an unfavourable weld structure.

2. Plates upto 9 mm thick can be welded with square edge preparation, whereas with the leftward technique, plates over 3mm thick will have to have edges bevelled. For this reason, this technique is often limited to materials upto 5 mm thick.

3. The technique consumes less gas and filler material in comparison to left ward technique. On larger thicknesses, this technique requires no or little edge bevelling and therefore, less filler metal is required resulting in corresponding savings in gas and time.

4. The mechanical properties of the weld are better due to the annealing effect of the flame which is directed on the completed weld.

5. The included angle of edges is smaller in right ward technique as compared to leftward technique. The heat remains confined to the weld seam and there is less spread of flame. Due to this, the amount of distortion in the work is minimum.

Note:

    (*i*) Back hand welding is faster by 20 to 25% and from 15 to 25% less acetylene is need in comparison to forehand welding.

    (*ii*) Horizontal and overhead welding are usually done by the backhand technique.

    (*iii*) Vertical joints are welded by the forehand technique.

    (*iv*) The angle at which the torch is inclined to the surface being welded depends upon the thicknessof the metal. Thicker metals require a higher concentration of heat and consequently a largertorch angle.

5.2.5. Filler Material and Fluxes. The welding wire or rod used as filler material in gas welding should have a chemical composition similar to that of the base metal. The diameter of the welding rod is selected to suit the thickness of the base metal. The welding rod diameter d can be approximately determined by the following empirical relation :

$$d = \frac{t}{2} + 1, \text{mm}$$

where t = thickness of base plate, mm

Welding Rods (Filler Materials) for Gas Welding

Some typical compositions of welding rods for gas welding are given below :

Material to be Welded	Welding Rod Chemical Composition
1. L–C steels	0.08%C, 0.36% Mn, 0.13% Cr, 0.013% Ni, 0.20%P
2. Mn–Steels	0.14%C, 0.12% Si, 0.81% Mn, 0.25% Ni
3. Cr-Steel	0.24%C, 0.21%Si, 0.42% Mn, 0.96% Cr, 0.17% Ni, 0.35% S

These welding rods are available in different diameters ranging from 0.3 to 12 mm.

Flux. Except for lead, zinc and some precious metals, gas welding of non-ferrous metals generally requires fluxing. Fluxes are also needed for cast iron and stainless steel. In welding mild steel, the gas flame adequately shields the weld pool and no flux is needed. For C.I., fluxes are required to increase the fluidity of the fusible iron silicate slag, as well as to aid in the removal of slag.

Fluxes compose of borates or boric acid, soda ash and small amounts of other compounds such as sodium chloride, ammonium sulphate and iron oxide. Mixture of equal amounts of boric acid and soda ash, 2% aluminium sulphate and 15% powdered iron makes a satisfactory flux.

Gas welding fluxes must melt at a lower temperature than the metals being welded so that surface oxides will be dissolved before the metal melts.

5.2.6. Advantages and Disadvantages of OAW

Advantages

1. The equipment is low cost, versatile, self-sufficient and usually portable. It requires little maintenance, and can be used with equal facility in the field and in the factory. The oxy-acetylene can be used for welding, brazing, soldering, preheating, postheating and metal cutting etc.

2. It can weld most common materials.

3. The gas flame temperature is lower and easily controllable which is necessary for delicate work. Therefore OAW is extensively used for sheet metal fabrication and repairs.

4. The process is well adapted for short production runs.

For the above reasons, gas welding is used in :

Automotive and aircraft industry, Sheet metal fabrication plants, and in fabrication of industrial pipes.

OAW is best suited for : joining thin sheet metal, thin small tube, small pipe and assemblies with poor fit up and for repairing rough arc welds.

Disadvantages

1. Oxygen and acetylene gases are expensive.

2. There are safety problems involved in their handling and storing.

3. The flame takes considerably longer for the metal to heat up. Due to this, OAW is not suitable for thick sections.

4. Because the flame is not concentrated, considerable areas of the metal are heated and distortion is likely to occur.

5. Flux applications and shielding provided by OA flame are not so effective as in inert gas arc welding.

Metals unsuited for welding with OAW torch are : refractory metals (Columbium, Tantalum, Molybdenum, Tungsten) and the reacting metals such as Titanium and Zirconium.

5.2.7. Other Fuel Gases. As already noted, the other fuel gases which can be used in gas welding are : propane, butane, natural gas or hydrogen. But because of the lower temperature of the flame (about 2500°C) obtained with these gases, these are used particularly for welding lower melting point alloys such as aluminium, zinc, lead and some precious metals.

MAPP Gas. Methyl acetylene propadiene gas is replacing acetylene gas particularly when portability is important, because :

1. It is more dense, thus providing more energy for a given volume.

2. It can be stored safely in ordinary pressure tanks.

5.2.8. Pressure Gas Welding (PGW). In this process, the abutting surfaces of the parts being welded are heated by an Oxy-acetylene flame to a state of fusion or plasticity and then coalescence is produced by the application of pressure and without the use of a filler material. The method is widely employed in butt welding bars, pipes, tubes, railroad rails, tools and rings of low and medium carbon steels and of low and medium alloy steels.

Two methods are used commercially for PGW :

1. Closed-joint Method. In closed joint pressure gas welding, clean square surfaces are butted together under moderate pressure. The surfaces are then heated by a water cooled oxyacetylene torch, Fig. 5.10, until the correct temperature is attained. Then an additional upsetting pressure is applied to complete the joint. For low carbon steel, the initial pressure is less than 10 MPa and the final upsetting pressure may be in the range of 28 MPa. An oscillating motion to each side is imparted to the torch to ensure more uniform heating of the abutting surfaces of the parts.

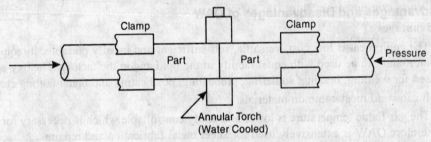

Fig. 5.10. Pressure Gas Welding.

2. Open-joint Method. In this method, the gas flames play directly upon the square weld joint faces, which have been spaced a short distance apart. When the ends of the joint have reached the fusion temperature, they are brought rapidly in contact under pressure to effect welding under upsetting.

Both methods are generally used in partially or fully mechanised set ups.

5.2.9. Oxy-Acetylene Flame Cutting.
Oxy gas cutting is based upon the ability of certain metals to burn in oxygen with the evolution of a great deal of heat thereby melting the metal and forming oxides. The torch for flame cutting is similar to the welding torch, with two exceptions. First, the welding tip contains only one hole in the centre of the tip through which the mixture of C_2H_2 and O_2 gases flow, whereas the flame cutting tip contains a centre hole through which pure oxygen, which does the actual "cutting" flows. There are also several concentric holes around the centre hole through

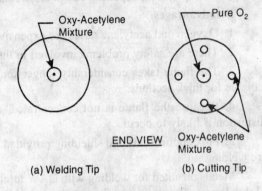

Fig. 5.11. Welding and Cutting Tip.

which mixture of C_2H_2 and O_2 flows and the flame produced by its burning preheats the metal, (Fig. 5.11). Second, the cutting torch has an additional, or third, valve for controlling the flow of pure oxygen.

Flame cutting is done both manually and with motor driven heads. As the metal is burnt and eroded away, the torch is moved steadily, (Fig. 5.12), along the path of cut. A uniformly wide slot called a 'kerf' is cut by the jet of oxygen. The faster the rate of traverse, the more the bottom lags behind the top of the cut. This is known as 'drag' and must be kept small. Thicknesses upto 1.5 m can be cut.

This method is suitable for cutting only those metals which have lower ignition/oxidation temperatures than their melting points and the melting point of the formed oxides is lower than that of the metal itself. Also, the oxides must have fair fluidity. The heat conductivity of the metal must be low so as to concentrate the heat. Nearly all flame cutting is done on steel (carbon steels with a carbon content upto 0.7% and low alloy steels). Cast iron can not be cut effectively since its melting point (1200°C) is lower than its ignition temperature (1350°C) Also, the graphite oxidizes more readily than the ferrous matrix and it simply melts the matrix. Aluminium can not be cut because of its high thermal conductivity. Stainless steel can not be cut because of its oxidation resistance. High - alloy chro- mium and chrome-nickel steels and non-ferrous alloys can not be cut since the melting point of their oxides is higher than that of the base metals.

When iron powder is added to the gas stream (powder oxyfuel cutting or powder metal cutting), oxidation of the metal powder provides the heat to melt oxidation-resistant materials.

Underwater   Cutting. Techniques have been developed for cutting metal underwater in ship building and repair work, construction and repair requirements associated with offshore exploration, drilling and recovery of oil and natural gas.

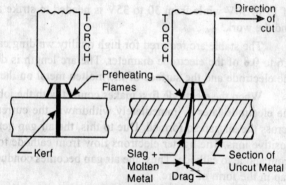

Fig. 5.12. Oxy-Flame Cutting.

A specially designed torch is employed for this purpose. An auxiliary skirt surrounds the main tip of the torch. Compressed air is supplied through the passages in the skirt. The compressed air performs two functions : it expels the water away from the tip area and it provides secondary oxygen and thereby stablises the flame.

For depths upto 7.5 m, oxy-acetylene torch is used but for greater depths, oxy-hydrogen torch is employed, because at such depths, C_2H_2 will have to be used at higher pressure to neutralise the high surrounding pressure created by the depth of water. The use of C_2H_2 at high pressure is very unsafe. But H_2 can be compressed to a higher pressure without any danger.

The torch is either ignited in the conventional manner before it is taken underwater or is ignited by an electric spark device after it is submerged.

5.3. ELECTRIC ARC WELDING

Electric are welding is the most extensively used method of joining components of metallic parts, the source of heat being an electric arc. An electric arc is a continuous stream of electrons flowing through some sort of medium between two conductors of an electric circuit and accompanied by intense heat generation and radiation.

An electric arc for welding is obtained in the following ways :

1. Between a consumable electrode (which also supplies filler metal) and the workpiece.

2. Between a non consumable electrode (carbon, graphite or tungsten etc.) and the workpiece.

3. Between two nonconsumable electrodes.

The most common electric arc welding method is the one in which the arc is struck between an electrode and the work. This is called as 'Direct arc'. The arc struck between two non consumable electrodes adjacent to the parts being welded is called as "Independent or Indirect arc". The metal is heated by the indirect action (by radiation) of the arc. Due to this, the thermal efficiency of the method is poor. Thus it is very rarely used these days. The method is called as "Double or Twin arc method". Atomic hydrogen welding process belongs to this category and is used in a few special applications.

To strike an arc, the electrode is brought in contact with the work at the point where the welding is to be started, after connecting the work to the welding circuit. After a light contact, the electrode is immediately withdrawn to a distance of from 2 to 4 mm from the work. Only a comparatively low potential difference is required between the electrode and the work to strike an arc. From 40 to 45 V is usually sufficient for D.C. and from 50 to 60V for A.C. This voltage available at the output terminals of a welding set, before the arc is struck, is known as open circuit voltage (OCV). The voltage falls after the arc is established which is normally less than half the OCV. A stable arc can be maintained between a metal electrode and the work metal with a voltage of 15 to 30V while from 30 to 35V is needed to strike an arc between non consumable electrode and the work.

The stable arc required for high quality welding can be achieved with an arc length equal to 0.6 to 0.8 of the electrode diameter. The arc length is defined as the distance between the end of the electrode and the surface of the molten metal on the work.

When the electrode first makes contact with the job, a large short circuit current flows. When the electrode later is immediately withdrawn, the current continues to flow in the form of spark across the air gap so formed. Due to this, the air gap gets ionized, that is, splits into electrons and positive ions. The lighter electrons flow from cathode to anode and the heavier positive ions flow from anode to cathode. Thus, the air gap becomes conducting and current is able to flow across the gap in the form of an arc.

When the lighter, high-velocity electrons strike the anode at great velocity, intense heat is generated at the anode. Heat generated at the cathode is much less, because of the low velocity of impinging positive ions.

Thermal and luminous energy is not uniformly evolved in the welding arc. About 43 percent of the total amount of heat is evolved on the anode and about 36 percent on the cathode. The remaining 21 per cent is evolved by the arc.

The temperature of an electric arc depends upon the type of electrodes between which it is struck. It is about 3200°C on the cathode and about 3900°C on the anode for carbon electrodes and 2400°C and 2600°C respectively for metal electrodes. The temperature may reach 6000 to 7000°C in the centre of the arc.

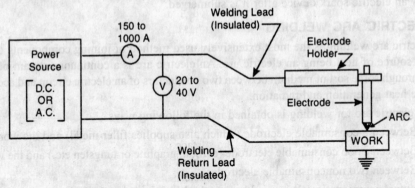

Fig. 5.13. Electric Arc Welding.

Only from 60 to 70% of the heat is utilised in arc welding to heat up and melt the metal. The remaining 30 to 40% is dissipated into the surroundings.

Definition. Electric arc welding is "a welding process wherein coalescence is produced by heating with an arc or arcs, with or without the application of pressure and with or without the use of filler metals."

Electric arc welding is quite versatile and able to weld under many conditions. High quality welds are produced. Metal is deposited rapidly and it is competitive cost wise for many situations.

Fig. 5.13 illustrates an Electric Arc Welding circuit.

5.3.1. Power Sources. Both D.C. and A.C. equipment are employed in arc welding. D.C. arc welding machines are D.C. generators driven by an electric motor or an internal combustion engine. A.C. welding machines are transformers for stepping down the main supply voltage to the voltage (20 to 40V) and current (150 to 1000 A) suitable for arc welding. The two power sources are discussed below :

(a) D.C. Power Source

Advantages :

1. It is known to most operators.

2. It can handle all situations and jobs.

3. It is preferred for difficult task like over head welding.

4. Arc stability is much higher with D.C. than with A.C. The reason is that the arc gap cools when an A.C. arc is periodically extinguished and re-established.

5. One advantage of D.C. welding over A.C. welding that offsets its higher cost is the fact that in D.C. supply, the electrons flow in one direction only. Direction of flow of electrons can be changed by simply reversing the cables at the terminals located on the generator (from electrode to work and vice-versa). This fact can be utilized for obtaining desired penetration of the base metal.

The electrons move from the negative terminal to the positive terminal of an arc, striking it at great speed. Due to this about $\frac{5}{8}$ th of the arc energy goes to the anode surface and about $\frac{3}{8}$ th is liberated at the cathode surface.

DCSP. In D.C. Straight Polarity, work is positive (anode) and elec-trode is cathode, (Fig. 5.14 (a)). Therefore, the work material is heated much faster than the electrode. This is of advantage in welding massive pieces because it puts the heat where needed. This system is preferred on all metals except aluminium, magnesium, copper and beryllium. Its advantages are : deeper penetration, Fig. 5.15 (a), the narrowest heat-affected zone, the fastest travel speed, less electrode consumption and least distortion because of the faster heat input into the work. Also, we can use bare and medium coated electrodes as they require less amount of heat for melting.

DCRP. In D.C. reverse polarity electrode is positive and the work is negative terminal, (Fig. 5.14 (b)). The electrons flow from the workpiece which tends to clean it. But the heat flow is also towards the electrode making its consumption faster and so limiting the current that can be put through an electrode. This system is preferred in welding thin sections such as automobile bodies and non-ferrous metals to prevent the melting or burning of holes in the metal, since only about 38% of the arc energy is liberated at the work surface in this case. Because this system has an inherent ability to scour the oxide film from the surface of the work, it is very useful for welding aluminium and magnesium whose oxides are very hard and brittle. A wide bead (due to shallow penetration) and cleaner work surface are the characteristics of this system, Fig. 5.15 (b).

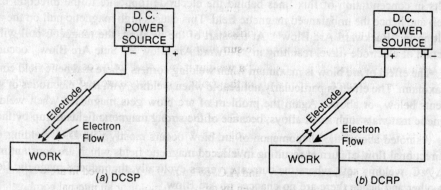

Fig. 5.14. Polarity of D.C. Supply.

In A.C. welding, since the polarity is changing at the rate of 50 c/s, half of the arc energy is liberated at the work surface and half at the electrode. Thus, the penetration of the heat zone in the base metal is approximately midway between the two D.C. types, [Fig. 5.15 (c)].

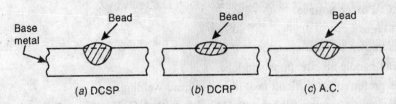

Fig. 5.15. Arc Penetration.

6. Higher power factor of the system (0.6 to 0.7) as compared to A.C. welding (0.3 or 0.4).

7. Bare electrodes are also suitable for welding.

Disadvantages

1. The efficiency of the machine is low (from 0.3 to 0.6).

2. Cost is higher. The equipment is heavier in weight, larger in size and operation and maintenance is difficult because of moving parts.

3. Electric energy consumption per kg of metal deposited is higher (6 to 10 kWh) as compared to A.C. welding (3 to 4 kWh).

4. The chances of "magnetic arc blow" are more in D.C. welding than in A.C. welding. Arc blow is the wandering arc that occurs during the welding of magnetic materials, such as steel with D.C. system when the cross section of the metal being welded is not symmetrical about the electrode. The unbalanced magnetic forces in this situation cause the D.C. arc column to vander from what should be its normal position.

This phenomenon of "arc blow" can be explained as below :

As noted above, arc blow is the deflection of the arc away from the weld point. The electric arc column can be considered as a flexible current carrying conductor and the arc blow is its deflection due to the magnetic fields set up owing to the flow of welding current. When current flows through electrical conductors, magnetic fields are set up around them in planes perpendicular to the direction of flow of current. When the magnetic flux lines surrounding the electrode or the workpiece become unbalanced, they tend to bend the arc away from its intended path resulting in "Arc blow". This effect is more pronounced at the two ends of the workpiece (that is beginning and end of the weld) or when welding corners. When the electrode moves forward along the direction of welding, the magnetic flux lines surrounding it also move with it. When the electrode reaches the end of the workpiece, the flux lines move out of the base metal, which is not possible. This results in concentration of flux lines behind the electrode (opposite to the direction of electrode travel) and hence the unbalanced magnetic field. This causes high magnetic pull on the arc column resulting in "Backward Arc Blow". At the start of the welding, the magnetic pull will be in the direction of electrode travel resulting in "Forward Arc Blow". "Side Arc Blow" occurs rarely.

The effect of arc blow is maximum when welding corners where magnetic field concentration is maximum. The effect is particularly noticeable when welding with bare electrodes or when using currents below or above Again the problem of arc blow gets magnified when welding highly magnetic materials such as Ni alloys, because of the strong magnetic fields set up by these metals.

As noted above, the phenomenon of arc blow occurs mostly with D.C. welding, because of unidirectional flow of current resulting in induced magnetic fields which are constant in direction. With A.C. welding sets, where the current reverses cyclically, the induced magnetic fields cancel each other and hence there are no chances of Arc Blow.

Arc Blow Results in :

Low heat penetration in the weld zone leading to incomplete fusion and to bead porosity. Also, there is excessive weld spatter, that is, throwing out of tiny droplets of weld metal out of the point on to the base metal resulting in tiny dots on base metal plates.

The effects of arc blow can be minimized with D.C. sets by :

1. Shortening the arc column length.

2. Reducing the current used which will reduce the strength of the induced magnetic field.

3. Reducing the rate of travel of the electrode.

4. Putting steel blocks near the ends of the workpiece so that the flux lines flow through them and not through the air.

5. Placing one ground lead at each end of the workpiece.

6. Wrapping the electrode cable a few turns around the workpiece.

(b)**A.C. Power Source**

Advantages

1. Equipment for A.C. welding is considerably less expensive, light in weight, smaller in size and simpler in operation due to the absence of moving parts. This also results in lower maintenance and operating costs.

2. Little "magnetic arc blow".

3. High efficiency of A.C. welding transformers (0.8 to 0.85).

4. Less electric energy consumption per kg of metal deposited as compared to D.C. welding.

Disadvantages

1. Low power factor.

2. Unstable arc. The stability of the arc can be increased by raising the voltage or by increasing the frequency of the alternating current.

3. Only coated electrodes are suitable for welding. In case of A.C. supply, the arc cools at zero current position. This tends to deionize the arc path. However, shielding gas keeps the arc space ionized and, therefore, with A.C., coated electrodes (which contain ionizing agents) are must. Bare electrodes without the use of shielding gas should not be used with A.C. supply. However, bare electrodes can be used satisfactorily with D.C. supply only.

5.3.2. Arc-Welding Electrodes. As noted above, the electrodes used for arc welding are of two types : Non-consumable and Consumable.

Non-consumable Electrodes. These electrodes are made of carbon, Graphite or Tungsten. Carbon and Graphite electrodes are used for D.C. welding only. Tungsten electrodes are used for D.C. as well as A.C. welding. When non-consumable electrodes are used, the filler material is added separately. Since the electrode is virtually not consumed, the arc length remains constant, so that it is stable and easy to maintain.

Consumable Electrodes. The consumable electrode provides the filler material also. These may be made of various metals, but should have the same composition as the material to be welded. During welding, they melt and supply the filler material. Therefore the arc length and the resistance of the arc path vary, as a result of the change in arc length and the presence or absence of metal particles in the path. This requires that the electrode be moved toward or away from the work to maintain the arc and satisfactory welding conditions.

The consumable electrodes are of three kinds : (a) Bare electrodes (b) Fluxed or lightly coated electrodes (c) Coated or extruded / shielded electrodes.

Bare electrodes may be used to weld wrought iron and mild steel. They must be used only with straight polarity. Bare electrodes in the form of sticks or rods are used for hand arc welding. For automatic welding, bare electrode is in the form of continuous wire (coil).

Lightly coated electrodes have a coating layer several tenths of a millimetre thick, the weight of the coating is from 1 to 5 per cent of the electrode weight. The primary purpose of a light coating is to increase arc stability and are also called as ionising coatings. This type of coating contains chalk (80 to 85 parts by weight) and water glass (15 to 20 parts by weight). These electrodes are used in welding only noncritical structures. The welds produced have poor mechanical properties due to the lack of the protection of the molten metal.

Coated electrodes are covered with a relatively high quality covering applied in a layer of from 1 to 3 mm. The weight of such a coating is from 15 to 30% of the electrode rod. The greatest amount of welding is done with coated electrodes. Since the electrode coating is brittle, only straight stick electrodes can be used. This restricts the process to a slow manual operation. If the flux coating is placed inside a long tube, the electrode can be in the form of a bare wire in the form of a coil and then the shielded arc process can be made continuous and automatic.

The stick electrodes are available in the following sizes : 3.2, 4, 5, 6, 8, 9 and 12 mm diameter and lengths of 350 or 450 mm.

Functions of Coatings

1. Improves arc stability by providing certain chemicals which have this ability, by ionizing the path of arc.

2. Provides a protective gaseous atmosphere to prevent O_2, H_2 and N_2 pick-up by the molten metal.

3. Provides a protective slag over hot metal.

4. Provides flux, which helps to remove oxides and other impurities from the molten weld metal.

5. Reduces spatter of weld metal – when coating burns off slower than core.

6. Acts as deoxidizer.

7. Adds alloying elements.

8. Increases deposition efficiency.

9. Slows down the cooling rate of weld (due to protective layer of slag) to prevent hardening.

10. Coatings are normally insulators of electricity and so permit the use of electrodes in narrow grooves etc.

Electrode Coatings

1. Slag Forming Ingredients. asbestos, mica, silica, fluorspar, titanium dioxide, Iron oxide, magnesium carbonate, Calcium carbonate and aluminium oxide.

2. Arc Stablising Ingredients. or ionizing agents : potassium silicate, Ti O_2 + Zr O_2 (Rutile), Mica, Calcium oxide, sodium oxide, magnesium oxide, feldspar (KAl Si$_3$ O$_8$).

The major types of feldspars are :-

(i) Potash feldspar, K_2O . Al_2O_3 . $6SiO_2$

(ii) Sodium feldspar, Na_2O . Al_2O_3 . $6SiO_2$

(iii) Lime feldspar, CaO . Al_2O_3 . $6SiO_2$

3. Deoxidizing Ingredients. Cellulose, Calcium carbonate, dolo- mite, starch, dextrin, wood flour, graphite, aluminium, ferromanganese.

4. Binding Materials. Sodium silicate, potassium silicate, asbestos.

5. Alloying Constituents to Improve Strength of Weld

6. Ti O_2 and potassium compounds increase the melting rate of the base metal for better penetration.

7. Iron powder provides higher deposition rate.

Types of Electrode Coatings

There are four main types of coatings which are most commonly used in practice :–

1. Cellulosic coating
2. Rutile coating
3. Iron oxide coating
4. Basic or low H_2 coating.

The first two coatings are almost identical but with one difference. The percentage of Titanium dioxide, TiO_2 (rutile) is somewhat more in rutile coating than in cellulosic coating. When the cellulose bruns, it results in the evolution of a mixture of gases. H_2 and CO. These gases provide a protective shield to the molten base metal.

With the same thickness of the work, a cellulosic coating results in deeper penetration as compared to rutile coating. Since the rate of evolution of H_2 gas is high, there is a danger of hydrogen embrittlement of the base metal, with these two coatings.

In iron oxide coating, the evolution of H_2 gas is less as compared to the first two coatings. Therefore, protection to the molten base metal is mainly provided by slag.

In basic coating, the major constituents are calcium carbonate and fluospar (CaF_2). When this coating burns, it results in the evolution of a mixture of CO and CO_2 gases. This mixture provides protection to the molten base metal. This coating has certain adventages over the other coatings : There is no danger of hydrogen embrittlement of the welded joint. The mixture (CO + CO_2) is less reducing than H_2 gas. So, a shorter arc length is maintained for complete shielding of molten base metal.

The thickness of the coating will depend upon the size of the job. Thicker coating results in narrower and deeper penetration.

It should be noted that with A.C. supply, the arc goes off after every half cycle when cycle crosses the zero current line. No such thing happens with D.C. supply. So, with A.C. supply, the arc must reignite after every half cycle. The reignition voltage is higher than the normal arc voltage. However, the process of reignition is facilitated by the presence of ions of low ionization potential, in the gap. Now, pottasium has low ionization potential (4.3V) as compared to sodium (5.1V). Hence, with A.C. supply, the electrode coating has pottasium silicate as the binder, and with D.C. supply, it is sodium silicate.

Coding of Electrodes.

There is no standard code designation used to classify the bare electrodes. Although, the composition of the electrode is basically the same as the base metal, small amounts of special additives, such as deoxidizers, are included by many manufacturers to improve the weld quality.

There is a code designation for coated stick electrodes for metal arc welding, for selecting a correct electrode for a specific application IS : 815 -1974 :

The coding for an electrode shall consist of a prefix letter, a code number of six digits in numerals and in some cases one or more suffix letters, each indicating a specific property or characteristic or both of the electrode.

1. Prefix letter indicates the method of manufacturing, of code.

Prefix letter	Method of manufacturing
E	Solid extrusion
R	Extruded with reinforcement

2. **First Digit.** The first digit of the code indicates the type of covering.

Digit	Type of covering
1.	Having a high cellulose content
2.	Having a high content of titania and producing a fairly viscous slag.
3.	contains appreciable amount of titania and producing a fludi slag.
4.	contains a high content of oxides and / or silicates or iron and manganese and producing an inflated slag.
5.	contains a high content of iron oxides and/or silicates and produce a heavy solid slag.
6.	having a high content of calcium carbonate and fluoride.
7.	A covering of any other type not classified above.

3. **Second Digit.** The second digit of code number indicates the welding position or positions in which the electrode may be used.

Digit	Welding Positions
0	F, H, V, D, O
1	F, H, V, O
2	F, H
3	F
4	F, H_f(H_f – horizontal fillet)
9	Any other welding position not classified above.

where

F stands for flat

H stands for horizontal-vertical

V stands for vertical-up

D stands for vertical-down

O stands for over-head

4. **Third Digit.** The third digit of the code number indicates the welding current conditions recommended by the manufacturer of the electrode, as follows :

Digit	Welding Current condition
0	D +
1	D +, A90
2	D –, A70
3	D –, A50
4	D +, A70
5	D ±, A90
6	D ±, A70
7	D ±, A50
9	Any other current conditions not classified above

The notations are as follows :

D +   DC with electrode positive

D –   DC with electrode negative

D±	DC with electrode positive or negative
A90	AC with an open circuit voltage not less than 90V
A70	AC with an open circuit voltage not less than 70V
A50	AC with an open circuit voltage not less than 50V

Note 1 : The electrodes may not function satisfactorily at a lower voltage than that for which it is classified but a higher voltage may be used in service with advantage.

2 : The open circuit voltage necessary for striking the arc varies according to the core diameter of the electrode. The reference core wire diameter for coding is 4 or 5 mm. Within the range of sizes 2.5 mm to 8 mm, the open-circuit voltage necessary may be expected to vary approximately as follows :

Code voltage	Variation in voltage
90	100 to 70
70	80 to 55
50	60 to 40

The higher voltages are associated with 2.5 mm electrodes and the lower voltages with 8 mm electrodes.

5. Fourth and Fifth Digits. Fourth and fifth digits indicate mechanical properties such as tensile strength and the appropriate yield stress. The range of tensile strength 410 to 510 N/mm^2 is indicated by the digit 41 and the digit 51 indicates the range 510 to 610 N/mm^2. The minimum yield stress for the strength range of 410 to 510 N/mm^2 is 330 N/mm^2 and for the strength range of 510 to 610 N/mm^2, it is 360 N/mm^2.

6. Sixth Digit. The sixth digit of code number indicates the percentage elongation in combination with impact value of the deposited metal.

Digit	Strength code number	Minimum elongation in % of guage value	Temp. for min. impact value of 47.J,°C
0	41	–	–
1	41	20	+ 27
2	41	22	0
3	41	24	– 20
4	41	24	– 30
5	41	24	– 40
0	51	–	0
1	51	18	+ 27
2	51	18	0
3	51	20	– 20
4	51	20	– 30
5	51	20	– 40

7. Suffix Letters. The suffix letters indicate the special properties/ characteristics or both of the electrode, as following :

Suffix Letters	Special properties/characteristics
H	Hydrogen controlled electrodes
J	Iron powder covering, giving a metal recovery of 110 to 130%.
K	Iron powder covering, giving a metal recovery of 130 to 150%.
L	Iron powder covering, giving a metal recovery of over 150%.
P	Deep penetration

A typical electrode coding will be written as follows :

D 426 - 513 H

Selection of Electrodes

The selection of a proper electrode for electric are welding is very important to obtain a sound welded joint of proper strength. The various factors affecting the selection of electrodes have been discussed above. It is clear that these factors are :

1. Power Source : A.C. or D.C.
2. Composition of the base metal.
3. Thickness of base metal
4. Welding position
5. Welding current conditions recommended by the manufacturer of the electrodes.
6. Mechanical properties desired in the joint.
7. Extent of penetration required in welding and lastly,
8. Economic considerations.

The diameter of the electrode, current and voltage requirements are basically related to the thickness of the metal to be joined. However, the Table 5.1. below is a good guide for selecting a proper electrode (Also see Art 5.3.3 for SMAW) :

Table 5.1 : Selection of Electrode

Metal Thickness mm	Electrode Diameter, mm	Electrode diameter (SWG)	Current range, A	Voltage across arc, V
Upto 1.5	2.0	14	50 – 70	15
1.5 – 3	2.5	12	70 – 100	15
3 – 6	3.15	10	85 – 120	20
6 – 10	4.0	8	140 – 180	20
10 – 20	5.0	6	180 – 230	25
20 – 35	6.3	4	230 – 290	30

5.3.3.Types of Electric Arc Welding Processes. The common electric arc welding processes are :

1. Carbon Arc Welding
2. Shielded Metal Arc Welding
3. Flux Cored Arc Welding
4. Gas Metal Arc Welding
5. Gas Tungsten -Arc welding
6. Submerged Arc Welding
7. Atomic Hydrogen Welding
8. Plasma Arc welding, and
9. Stud welding
10. Electro Slag welding.

Since most metals are readily oxidized on heating to the temperature required by welding, the molten weld metal, the adjacent heat affected zone in the base metal, and the welding zone must be protected or shielded from the atmosphere. This shielding serves to exclude oxygen and nitrogen from the air and, in this manner, eliminates the formation of metal oxides and nitrides which lower weld metal ductility and toughness and sometimes strength.

Shielding may be accomplished by :

1. a covering applied to the electrode rod or wire.

2. a powdered or granular flux which covers the electric arc, the molten weld metal and the adjacent areas in the base metal.

3. an active gas (generally hydrogen) projected around the arc and over the heated weld-and-base metal area, and

4. an inert gas (generally helium, argon and carbon dioxide) projected around the arc over the heated weld-and-base metal area.

Sometimes a suitable flux solution, emulsion, or paste may also be painted over those parts of the base metal which will be heated by the welding operations, such as the underside of the weld joints.

1. Carbon Arc Welding. In this, Coalescence is produced by heating with an electric arc between a carbon electrode and the work. Shielding is generally not used. Pressure is not used, and filler metal may or may not be used. The electric arc can also be struck by the "twin arc method", that is, between two carbon (graphite) electrodes. Filler metal, when used, is fed into the arc and allows a fairly high rate of weld-metal deposition. Sometimes a filler rod is placed into the joint groove, and the carbon arc is passed slowly along the joint until fusion is completed.

The weld metal is not shielded from contamination of oxygen and nitrogen in the atmosphere. Moreover, very little, if any, carbon is picked up by the weld from the carbon electrode. Thus, this process is generally limited to those materials which are not sufficiently contaminated by these elements, that is, copper alloys, brass, bronze, aluminium alloys etc. It will be better if the filler metal (if used) incorporates deoxidizer (Silicon, phosphorous etc.).

2. Shielded Metal Arc Welding, (SMAW). The method is also known as manual Metal Arc welding, MMAW. This is most widely used arc welding method. It is defined as : "an arc welding process wherein coalescence is produced by heating with an arc between a covered metal electrode and the work. Shielding is obtained from decomposition of the electrode coating. Pressure is not used and filler metal is obtained from the electrode". The chemically coated electrode decomposes and vaporizes with the heat of the electric arc. The ingredients in the vaporised coating

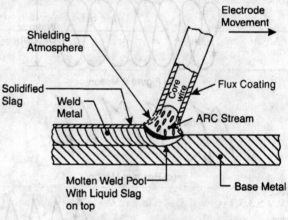

Fig. 5.16. Shielded Metal Arc Welding.

creates a protective gas atmosphere over the weld puddle and also, the melting of the coating provides a molten slag cover on the weld. This prevents the molten metal from reoxidizing. The coating performs other functions also as discussed earlier. The coating on the electrode melts at a slower rate than the metal core wire since it melts at a higher temperature than the metallic core, leaving a slight extension of the coating beyond the core wire. This produces a cup shaded end, (Fig. 5.16), which helps to direct and concentrate the heat from the arc.

The process is versatile and suitable for field application, but requires considerable skill. Welding in all positions, including overhead welding is possible if the metal and slag solidify fast enough. The method is used almost exclusively for job-shop (nonproduction and general maintenance and repair) work, and also in many high production operations, for example, in the manufacture of machinery, transportation equipment, piping systems and in various structures (on site erection) such as buildings, trusses, machine bases etc.

After welding, the slag or molten flux must be removed to avoid possible flux corrosion.

As already noted, the coated stick electrodes are suitable only for manual arc welding. The method is also known as "Stick Welding".

After the arc is established (as explained in Art. 5.3), the welder feeds the electrode uniformly to the work, maintaining a short-arc. The electrode is held at an angle of 15° to 20° from the vertical, on a flat weld, to produce a weld bead. By changing the angle of inclination of the electrode, the welder can vary the depth to which the parent metal is melted and the cooling rate of the welding pool.

During the process of welding, the electrode is given three movements. The electrode is continuously fed downward along its axis to maintain the arc length. It is progressively fed along the weld and thirdly the electrode tip is given an osillating movement across the weld. The side ways oscillating movement of the electrode tip is given to :-

(i) obtain and maintain proper bead width.

(ii) Float out slag.

(iii) Secure good pentration at the edges of the weld.

(iv) Allow gases to escape and thereby avoid porosities.

Transverse osillating movements of the electrode tip also improve the heating of the joint edges, retard cooling of the molten. pool of deposited metal, enable a more homogeneous, sound efficient and strong weld to be obtained and eliminate inadequate joint peretration.

Fig. 5.17. shows the various oscillating motions of the electrode tip.

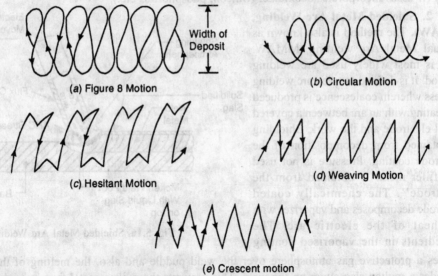

(a) Figure 8 Motion

(b) Circular Motion

(c) Hesitant Motion

(d) Weaving Motion

(e) Crescent motion

Fig. 5.17. Various Oscillating Motions of Electrode Tip.

The type of oscillating motion and the rate of oscillations depends upon : thickness of the job, the length of run and the type of electrode and level of current employed. However, these are mainly decided on the basis of experience.

In multiple-pass welding, Fig. 5.18., the brittle slag coating present on the bead after the first pass (root pass), is chipped off and cleaned by wire brush, before the second pass is started and similarly for the remaining passes.

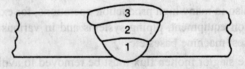

Multiple - pass (3) weld

Fig. 5.18. Multiple-pass Arc Welding.

In metal arc welding, the thermal action of the arc melts the end of the electrode and the edges of the work. It has been established that the drops of the molten metal pass along the arc at a velocity of 40 m/s and that the number of drops varies from 10 to 30 per sec.

In hand arc welding, the main factor in high-quality welding, is a proper selection of the welding conditions, which are determined by the electrode diameter, welding current and voltage.

(*a*) **Electrode diameter.** The diameter of the electrode will depend upon the thickness of the metal being welded and the type of the joint. Electrode diameter, according to the thickness of the metal to be welded, is given below :

Metal thickness, mm	:	Upto 2	2 to 4	4 to 6	6 to 8	over 8
Electrode diameter, mm	:	2	3	4	5	5-6

(*b*) **Welding current.** The magnitude of the welding current depends upon : the thickness of the welded metal, type of joint, welding speed, position of the weld, the thickness and type of the coating on the electrode and its working length.

However, for practical purposes, the welding current is determined on the basis of the selected electrode diameter, as given below :

Welding current, $I = k.\,d$, amperes; d is in mm.

where $k = a$ constant

            = 45 to 60 for ordinary steel electrodes

            = 18 to 22 for graphic = 5 to 8 for carbon electrodes

In general practice, welding is performed with currents over 50 A.

Voltage. The arc voltage depends only upon the arc length. It is given by the relation :

$$V = k_1 + k_2\,l, \text{ volts}$$

where l is the arc length in mm and k_1 and k_2 are constants,

$$k_1 = 10 \text{ to } 12; \text{ and } k_2 = 2 \text{ to } 3$$

The minimum Arc voltage is given by $V_{min} = (20 + 0.04\,I)$, V

Arc Length. As already defined, it is the distance between the end of the electrode and the surface of the molten metal on the work.

For getting good welds, a short arc length is necessary, because :

1. It permits the heat to be concentrated on the joint.

2. Is more stable due to the reduced arc blow effect.

3. The molten weld pool is protected from atmosphere due to the vapours surrounding the electrode metal and molten weld pool.

On the other hand, a long arc results in :

(*i*) Large amounts of heat loss into the atmosphere leading to poor penetration and fusion.

(*ii*) Unstable arc due to increased effect of magnetic arc below.

(*iii*) Weld pool is not protected from the atmosphere. Because of this, the weld gets contaminated due to the absorption of O_2 and N_2.

(*iv*) Weld has : low strength (due to high porosity), less ductility, poor fusion and excessive spatter.

The arc length depends upon : kind of the electrode used, its coating, its diameter, current used and position of welding. Generally, shorter arc lengths are used for vertical, horizontal and overhead welding as compared to flat welding. As already noted, the stable arc needed for high quality welding can be achieved with an arc length of 0.6 to 0.8 times the electrode diameter.

SMAW is applicable for almost all metals and alloys except, pure copper, aluminium and some low melting point and reactive metals.

3. Flux - Cored Arc Welding, (FCAW). The difference between SMAW and FCAW is that in the latter case, the consumable electrode is in the form of welding wire which can be coiled. The flux which provides shielding is supplied from the hollow core within the tubular wire electrode. Since the electrode is in the form of a coil, automatic and conti- nuous welding becomes possible with the electrode continuously fed from a spool. There are two designs of this method :

(*a*) **Self shielding.** Here, the shielding is provided as the flux burns and produces protective gas, (Fig. 5.19).

(*b*) **External shielding.** Sometimes, additional shielding is provided (for steel) with a gas (normally CO_2) from an external source.

The method is suitable for quantity production

4. Inert Gas Arc Welding. In this, coalescence is produced by heating with an electric arc between a suitable electrode and the work. Shielding is obtained from an inert gas such as carbon dioxide, helium and ar gon. Pressure is not used, and the filler metal may or may not be used. Inert gas welding is done either with nonconsumable electrode or with consumable metal electrode.

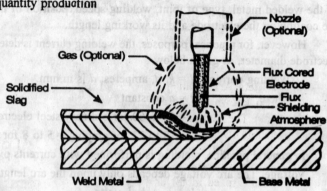

Fig. 5.19. Flux-Cored Arc Welding.

(*i*) **Gas Tungsten Arc Welding, (GTAW).** GTAW is also called as Tungsten Inert Gas Welding (TIG). The arc is maintained between the workpiece and a tungsten electrode protected by an inert gas. The electrode is non consumable since its melting point is about 3400°C. The arc tempe- rature may be in the range of 10,000 K.

The mechanism of TIG is shown in Fig. 5.20. The welding head (gun or torch) consists of a lightweight handle, with provisions for holding a stationary tungsten electrode. In the welding head, the shielding gas flows by or along the electrode through a nozzle at the end of the gun into the arc region. This is done to keep the electrode cooler and permits higher currents to be used. Most guns are also water cooled. A filler metal may or may not be used. In the tungsten electrode, 1 to 2% thorium and zirconium are added to improve electron emission, arc stability, arc striking and current carrying capacity, and to increase the melting point of tungsten. Electrode diameters of 0.8 mm to 5 mm are commonly used with welding speeds ranging from about 8 mm/s to over 50 mm/s. Both hand and automatic operations are possible. The process demands considerable skill. The method was originated in 1940 for welding magnesium which is highly oxidising and whose oxides have a much higher melting point than the parent metal. Now the method has developed as a means for welding a wide range of other materials : aluminium and its alloys, stainless steel, cast iron, silicon bronze, titanium, Nickel, copper and carbon steels and where very high quality and neat welds are required. The method is especially suitable for welding thinner metals (below 6 mm). DCRP is rarely used, because it tends to melt tungsten electrode.

DCSP is used when maximum penetration is needed or when welding metals that do not need cleaning of oxide film, like copper and Stainless steel etc. When welding metals that have an oxide film on the surfaces (Aluminium, Magnesuim). A.C. high frequency supply is used to break up the surface oxides. The angle of inclination of the torch shield is 80° to 90° with the horizontal, C.C.W., and that of the filler rod is 10° to 20° C.W.

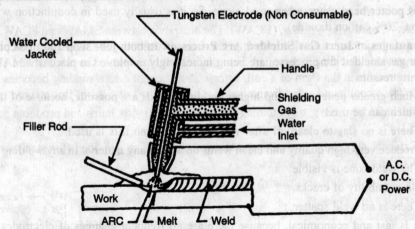

Fig. 5.20. TIG

(*ii*) **Gas Metal Arc Welding, (GMAW).** The method is also known by the acronym, MIG (metal inert gas). The method differs from TIG in that a consumable electrode in wire form is fed into the arc, (Fig. 5.21). The same shielding gases are used. The wire is automatically fed from the reel by a variable speed motor at a preset rate that is determined by the arc voltage. The wire feed increases with an increase in arc voltage caused by an increase in arc length. This process has a greater effi- ciency than TIG and is more rapid. In semi-automatic weld- ing, the welder guides the gun and adjusts process para- meters; in automatic welding all functions are taken care of by the welding machine or robot. Electrode wire diameter ranges from 0.6 to 4 mm. For welding of C steels, electrodes are coated with Cn to improve electric conductivity and corrosion resistance.

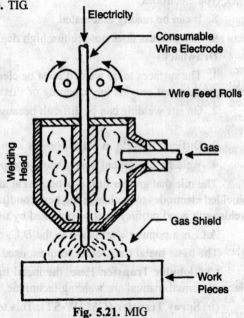

Fig. 5.21. MIG

Shielding Gases. The shielding gases commonly used are : Helium, Argon and CO_2 or their mixtures. The gases must be pure, clean and free of moisture.

Helium. It yields better penetration than argon. It has high specific heat co-efficient. So, the temperature of the weld is reduced, minimizing distortion as well as facilitating penetration. But it is costlier than argon. Also it is much lighter than argon, so more gas flow is required for a given performance as compared to argon. This method using the is most common in US due to the availability of the gas from natural gas wells and the method is known as Heliarc Welding.

Argon. It has better electrical properties than helium, for example, ionization voltage is lower which helps in producing more stable arc conditions when using a.c. It is cheaper than helium. It gives a superior oxide cleaning action with a.c. on Aluminium, Magnesium, Copper and Beryllium. It gives a softer arc and less penetration, so it is generally more suitable for thinner metals. This method is most common in U.K. and is called Argon Arc Welding.

Carbon Dioxide. It is considerably cheaper than helium or argon. But it produces more spatter and poorer bead shape when used alone. So it is usually used in conjunction with argon (80% argon, 20% carbon dioxide).

Advantages of Inert Gas Shielded Arc Processes. In both job- shop and mass production work, inert gas shielded arc processes are being increasingly employed in place of SMAW, due to the following reasons :

1. Much greater penetration and higher welding speeds are possible, because of the higher currents which can be used.

2. There is no slag to clean off after welding, because no flux is used.

3. Produce very high quality and clean welds on almost any material in any welding position.

4. The weld zone is visible.

5. No possibility of cracks.

6. There is no weld spatter.

7. It is fast and economical, because there are no frequent changes of electrodes, as with stick type electrodes.

8. It can be readily automated.

9. The process does not require high degree of operator skill.

Drawbacks

1. The surfaces to be welded must be clean and free of oil, grease, paint or rust, because the inert gas does not provide any cleaning or fluxing action.

2. On site welding can be difficult because drafts blow the shielding gas away from the weld zone.

3. Difficult to weld in small corners

4. Welding equipment costly, more complex and less portable.

The rule that greater heat is produced at anode is valid when using bare electrodes. However Shielded electrodes may change the heat conditions. As such, better results (spray transfer, smooth welds with good profile) may be obtained by using DCRP mode.

A.C. is a popular alternative to the D.C. conditions.

The basic metal transfer techniques, used in GMAW are discussed below :

(*i*) **Globular Transfer.** Here, the metal transfer is in blobs, that drop by gravity. This takes place in normal manual arc welding technique, that is, at low current and voltages.

(*ii*) **Spray Transfer (GMAW-ST).** This technique requires high current densities. The metal droplets become very small and more frequent. With this, the metal is transferred from the electrode to the weld zone in a fine spray. The method of employed on the heavier butt welds or fillets.

(*iii*) **Dip Transfer or Short-circuting Technique (GMAW-S).** This technique uses low currents. The electrode wire dips into the weld pool, causing a momentary short-circuit stoppage. The resulting current surge burns back the wire, again forming the arc. This takes place at a very high speed, about 100 dips/s. This frequency may vary with the voltage used and may be as low as 50 dips/s. Drops of liquid metal get transferred by gravity and surface tension.

The technique is very suitable for welding thin sections or sheets (down to 0.7 mm) because of lower heat. Positional welding is quite easily carried out and fit-up is not so critical, since there is greater tolerance of irregularities because of the cooler weld pool. CO_2 gas is used as the shielding gas.

Spray transfer and dip transfer are the techniques used in fine- wire MIG process.

(*iv*) **Pulsed Arc Welding (GMAW-P).** Pulsed arc welding is a new welding technique and has extremely attractive features. By the use of a special dual power unit, pulses or peaks of current are imposed on the welding current at a rate of 50 to 100 per second, which results in rapid acceleration of the droplets in transit across the arc. Both similar and dissimilar metals can be joined in a period of milli-seconds. Because of a short duration of arcing, temperatures are reduced, resulting in a number of benefits :

(*a*) Thinner sections can be welded.

(*b*) Spatter is drastically reduced, because of the smooth and quiet arc produced.

(*c*) Control is improved to alter the shape of the weld pool and vary the penetration.

(*d*) The technique is cheaper, as the energy or power needed to make a weld is considerably less than the other methods.

(*e*) Heat sensitive parts and high conductivity metals can be welded.

(*f*) Distorsion of the weldment is reduced or eliminated.

(*g*) High speed of the process is attractive for productivity.

Types of GMAW Process. In addition to the conventional MIG process (bare-wire gas shielded process), other processes have also been developed along similar lines :

(*i*) One variation uses a special magnetic flux (A flux containing magnetic material) in addition to CO_2 shielding. Magnetic powder flux enters the welding head alongwith the shielding gas (Fig. 5.19). Since a magnetic field surrounds a current carrying electrode wire, the flux adheres to it. This results in a flux-coated electrode. The flux is 30 to 50% of the weight of the wire used. The process is more tolerant of variations in base metal composition and of rust, moisture, scale and surface conditions.

(*ii*) Similar results can be obtained by using a specially prepared tabular mould-steel electrode with a flux core, still using the CO_2 gas shield.

The above variations result in higher rates of metal deposition with manual metal-arc welding. This makes these processes attractive for general welding, without the need for special preparation or cleaning of weldments.

Table 5.2. Relation between Job thickness and supply current in Inert gas arc welding:

Job thickness, mm	Current, A	
	TIG Welding	MIG Welding
1 – 1.5	50 – 60	80 – 100
1.5 – 2.0	60 – 80	100 – 120
2 – 2.5	80 – 100	120 – 130
2.5 – 3	100 – 120	130 – 140
3 – 3.5	120 – 140	140 – 150
4 – 4.5	140 – 160	150 – 160

Metal Active Gas Welding : MAG Welding : In MIG arc welding, inert gases are used as shielding gases. These gases (He, Ar) are very costly. To make the method cheaper, many companies use the MAG welding process. The gas used in this method in not inert gas. Mainly CO_2 gas is used for this purpose and it does the job effectively and efficiently.

Welding parameters at Yamaha Motors Escorts Limited (Faridabad) for MAG welding process are :

Voltage = 26 – 30 V

Current = 120 – 150 A

Pressure of gas = 25 – 35 bar

Wire (Cu coated) = 8 mm thick

The Cu coated electrode prevents its oxidation and rusting, and also increases electrical conductivity of the electrode wire. For the same reasons, the electrodes used in SAW are coated slightly with Cu mist.

DCRP is used in the MAG process. It does not require high degree of operator skill and deeper penetration is possible.

MAG process or CO_2 welding is being used at Maruti Udyog.

5. Submerged Arc Welding, (SAW). In this, coalescence is produced by heating with an arc between a bare wire electrode and the work. The weld zone is shielded by a blanket of fusible granular flux material supplied directly on the weld seam ahead of the electrode to shield the arc. Pressure is not used and molten filler metal is obtained from the electrode. The flux also acts as a deoxidizer and scavenger and may contain powder metal alloying elements.

The method can be used in fully automatic equipment where the feeds of both the electrode and granular flux are controlled, Fig. 5.22. The method is also adaptable for semiautomatic equipment where the feed of the electrode and granular flux are controlled manually.

This method is characterised by good appearing welds, high welding speeds and high welding currents upto several thousand amperes. Because of the large diameter electrodes which can be used, rather large welds can be made in one single pass in plates over 25 mm thick. Deep penetration is also obtained.

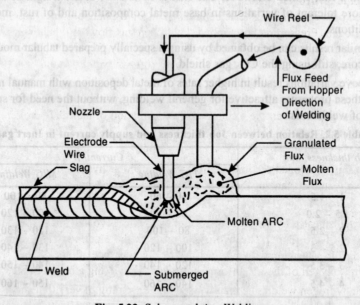

Fig. 5.22. Submerged Arc Welding.

Since the granular flux must cover the joint to be welded, this method is restricted to making straight welds in the flat position. Thus it is suitable for steel line pipes, boiler pressure vessels, railroad tank cars, structural shapes and cylinders etc. and also for circular welds if the workpiece is rotated under the welding head. Double submerged arc welding (with one weld from the inside, the other from the outside) is used in making spiral- welded pipelines. It can also be used with welding robots, with the workpiece manipulated into appropriate positions.

Submerged arc welding can be used to weld low C- steels, high strength low alloy steels, chromium steels, and austenitic chromium-nickel steels. With special methods, it is also possible to weld high-alloy air hardening steels.

Advantages

1. Joints can be prepared with a shallow V-groove, resulting in lesser electrode consumption.

2. Wire electrodes are inexpensive.

3. Weld spatters are eliminated.

4. Nearly 100% deposition efficiency is achieved.

Limitations

1. It can not be used for plates less than 5 mm thick.

2. It can not cut C.I. because of high heat input.

3. Slag has to be removed continuously after it has melted in order to avoid entrapment between passes.

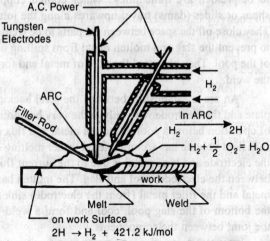

Fig. 4.23. Atomic Hydrogen Welding.

6. Atomic Hydrogen Welding. In this, the coalescence is produced by heating with an electric arc maintained between two tungsten electrodes in an atmosphere of hydrogen. Shielding is obtained from the hydrogen. Pressure is not applied. Hydrogen gas flows by the tungsten electrodes in the holder, keeping them cooler and lengthening the electrode life. Fig. 5.23. Since hydrogen is not inert, it will react chemically with its environment to form water vapours.

In this process an a.c. arc is formed between two tungsten electrodes along which streams of hydrogen are fed to the welding zone. The molecules of hydrogen are dissociated by the high heat of the arc in the gap between the electrodes. The formation of atomic hydrogen proceeds with the absorption of heat :

$$H_2 = 2H - 421.2 \text{ k J / mol}$$

This atomic hydrogen recombines to form molecular hydrogen outside the arc, particularly on the relatively cold surface of the work being welded, releasing the heat gained previously :

$$2H = H2 + 421.2 \text{ k J / mol}.$$

The metal is heated by the indirect arc and by the heat evolved above, producing a temperature of about 3700° of the flame. The hydro-gen protects the electrodes and the welding pool from oxidation and from saturation with nitrogen. At the outer surface of this gaseous shield, the hydrogen combined with oxygen of the air to form water vapour, making a bright orange flame.

Atomic hydrogen welding is mainly used in the welding of very thin sheets or small diameter wires (2 to 10 mm thick), particularly those of noble metals and refractory metals. It is so, because of its much lower thermal efficiency as compared to direct arc processes. Since the arc is struck between two electrodes, non-conducting materials such as ceramics may be arc welded. Alternating current is used usually so that both electrodes burn off at the same rate.

7. Electro-Slag Welding, (ESW). In this process, electrode wire (consumable) is fed into a molten slag pool. An arc is drawn initially, but is then snuffed out by the slag, and the heat of fusion is provided by resistance heating in the slag.

The components to be welded are set in a vertical position with a distance of 15 to 30 mm between the butted edges depending upon their thickness. The welding wire and the flux are fed automatically into the clearance, (Fig. 5.24). Several electrode wires can be fed simultaneous-ly if the parts to be welded are quite thick. Water cooled copper shoes or slides (dams) travel upwards along the joint. They close off the space between the parts to be welded to prevent the slag and molten metal from spilling out of the pool. They also cool the pool of metal and form the weld.

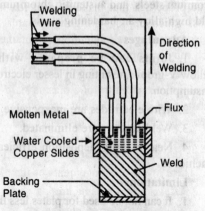

Fig. 5.24. Electro-Slag Welding.

An arc is established between the steel backing plate and the electrode wire only at the very beginning of operation before a pool of molten metal and flux of sufficient volume has accumulated. Further melting of the electrode and base metal is due to the current flow between the electrode, pool and slag. The molten base metal and the filler metal (from the electrode) sink to the bottom of the slag pool, cool and form a weld in the joint between the components.

The chief advantage of ESW is that very thick components (up to 400 mm thick) can be welded together in a single pass without bevelling the edges. This is due to the fact that several electrode wires are brought simultaneously into the welding zone. A very clean weld is obtained, without any slag inclusions.

The method is highly productive and pre-dominantly applied in heavy engineering in the manufacture of bed and frames for heavy machinery, drums, boilers etc.

8. Electro-Gas Welding (EGW). This method is a variant of electro-slag welding (ESW). The electric wire is either solid or flux-covered. Protection is provided by an inert gas (typically 80% Ar and 20% CO_2). The molten pool is again retained with copper dams. The major difference between ESW and EGW is that in EGW, an inert gas is used to protect the weld from oxidation and there is continuous arc (such as in SAW) to heat the weld pool.

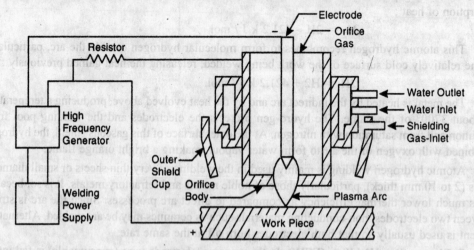

Fig. 5.25. Plasma Arc Welding.

9. Plasma Arc Welding, (PAW). The term 'plasma' refers to a gas which is sufficiently ionized (by raising it to a high temperature) to conduct current freely. A conventional welding arc is an example of a plasma. A plasma jet is created when the arc is passed through a constrictive nozzle. As a result of this constriction, the plasma jet will take on a narrow, columnar shape with unique properties that make it ideal for welding. Plasma jet welding is an electric-arc welding process which employs a high temperature constricted arc or plasma jet to obtain the melting and coalescence of metal. shielding is obtained from the hot, ionized gas issuing from the nozzle, which may be supplemented by an auxiliary source of shielding gas. Pressure is not applied and filler may or may not be supplied.

The basic circuitry of a plasma - arc - welding torch is shown in Fig.5.25. The plasma torch is constructed with an electrode (tungsten) centrally within a metal cup that guides an inert streaming gas past the electrode. The discharge end of the cup is smaller in diameter than the upper diameter so that a discharge nozzle is created. In addition, the inner wall of the nozzle is lined with a ceramic material. The torch has passages for supplying gas and water (to cool it).

There are two arrangements of the plasma arc welding :

(a) Transferred plasma arc.

(b) Non - transferred plasma arc.

In the transferred plasma arc, the arc is produced between the electrode (– ve) and the work (+ ve). In the non-transferred arc, the arc is produced between the electrode (– ve) and the nozzle (+ ve). The work is heated indirectly by radiation. The heat is carried to the workpiece by the plasma gas.

The gases used should be inert (non-oxidising) and with a higher thermal conductivity, so that they can transfer more heat, making it possible to weld bulky section more easily. Usually, the shielding gas is the same as the orifice (nozzle) gas. Argon, Helium and hydrogen or their mixtures are the gases most frequently used.

Plasma arc provides an intense source of heat (Arc temperature of about 14000 K) and ensures greater arc stability. PAW is used for quality welding and can easily weld 127 mm thick aluminium sections or stainless steel sections upto 100 mm thick. The welded joints have no porosity and display a strong resistance to high stresses and impact loading.

10. Stud Welding. In this coalescence is produced by heating with an electric arc drawn between a metal stud (electrode) or a simi-larly shaped piece, and the part with which it is to be joined, until the surfaces to be joined are properly heated, after which they are brought together under pressure but without the use of a shielding gas.

The end of the studs have a cap that encases a dry flux and a ceramic ferrule that is used to maintain a gap between the end of the stud and the work, concentrate the heat of the arc, protect against oxidation and confine the melt; making the process an electric arc rather than an electrical resistance one, (Fig. 5.26).

The equipment used for stud welding consists of a special welding gun and a timing device. The sequence of operations during stud welding is as follows :

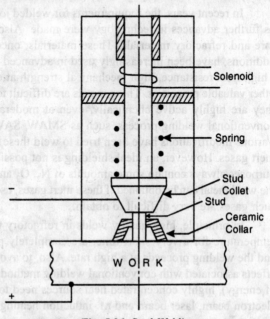

Fig. 5.26. Stud Welding.

(*i*) The stud, or other pro- jection, to be welded to the work- piece is loaded into the end of the gun, which very often is a portable hand tool. One end of the stud is projecting over which a ceramic. ferrule (collar) is placed.

(*ii*) The stud is then properly positioned on the workpiece and held in contact with it by spring pressure.

(*iii*) By operating a trigger on the gun, a timed automatic welding cycle begins. Current passes through the stud to the work.

(*iv*) Immediately this occurs, a solenoid lifts the stud against the spring pressure, a short distance away from the work to produce an arc.

(*v*) The arc melts the end of the stud and the weld area on the work.

(*vi*) The stud is then released and firmly plunged into the weld pool by the spring.

(*vii*) After a short dwell of about 1/25s, the current is switched off and the ceramic collar is removed to allow the end of the stud to freeze in place.

Applications. This process is widely used to join bolts and other projections onto workpieces without the need for drilling and tapping holes and is therefore very economical. It is also used for attachment of handles and feet to appliances and electrical panel construction. The method is extensively employed in the automotive, ship building, railroad and building construction industries.

11. Vacuum Shielded Welding of Metals. As has been discussed before, a very crucial task in fusion-welding is to protect the weld pool against exposure to the atmosphere, to avoid oxidation and contamination of the weld metal, due to the absorption of various gases. The other sources of gases can be : Surface oxides of the metals, rust, paint, grease, coatings, electrode, fluxes etc. Gases present in the weld metal inevitable degrade its physico-mechanical properties. Therefore, cleaning of the weld surfaces and protection of the weld pool are very important. The various shielding mediums in use are : heavy electrode coating, fluxes and inert gases alongwith CO_2 gas. The adoption of these measures have resulted in : increased rate of output, improved and stable quality of weld metal and making the process automated.

In recent years, the requirements for welded joints have become progressively more stringent as further advances in technology were made. Also, the problem arose regarding the welding of rare and refractory materials. These materials, once used on a limited scale, mainly as alloying additions, have been increasingly used in advanced fields of engineering. These materials possess : high treat resistance, high mechanical strength at elevated temperature, corrosion resistance and other valuable properties. These metals are difficult to weld, because apart from high melting points, they are highly active chemically, even at moderate temperatures. As a result, majority of the conventional welding process, such as SMAW, SAW and gas welding, have proved inapplicable. Various modifications have been tried to weld these metals by providing shielding with the help of inert gases. However, an ideal shielding is not possible, because the inert gases used for industrial purposes always contain some amounts of N_2, O_2 and water vapour. Improvement in the quality of the weld metal can be obtained if these inert gases, used for shielding, are chemically pure. However, such gases are very difficult to obtain.

In principle, high quality welds in refractory metals can be made if they are heated to high temperature for a very short time, are completely protected against exposure to the atmosphere, and the welding proceeds at a high rate. Also, to avoid heavy residual strains and other detrimental effects associated with conventional welding methods (where there is a relatively low concentration of energy), highly concentrated heat sources need to be used. Special mention can be made of the electron beam, laser beam and r.f. induction heating.

Welding process have been developed in which shielding has been provided by vacuum. These are : EBW, arc-vacuum welding and some others. Vacuum reliably shields the molten metal in the welding of active and refractory metals and assists in securing a high- quality weld metal. Vacuum-shielding is very essential in the welding of vacuum-melted refractory and active metals (which are high quality products), since the shielding media ordinarily used, usually degrade their quality, secured by vacuum treatment.

Vacuum-shielding offers a number of technical and economic advantages over other shielding methods :

1. It is inexpensive, easy to apply and easy to maintain.

2. It provides shielding, right at the scene of work and makes welding independent of shielding-gas suppliers, cuts down the need for cylinders and reduces the cost of transportation etc.

3. The cost of vacuum-shielding is only a fraction of that of inert-gas-shielding.

4. It secures high-quality welded joints in any metals and non- metallic materials. In welding some materials, it is the only one possible.

Note:- Welding of Sheet Metal by Electric Arc Welding

Normally, the electric arc welding is not recommended for sheet metal welding due to the intense heat generated during the operation and the risk of sheet metal getting burnt. But, sheet metal welding can be made successful by taking the following precautions when welding unequal thickness :

1. Directing the arc towards the thicker sheet.

2. Conducting away heat from the thinner sheet by copper blocks in contact with it, [Fig. 5.27]. The copper blocks are shown by hatched lines. The use of copper blocks prevents melting away of the thinner sheets.

5.3.4. Electric Arc Cutting. Both carbon and metal electrodes are employed in the arc cutting of metals. The cutting is affected by melting the metal with the heat of an electric arc at the cut. Metal arc cutting is done with a coated electrode. Coating being insulator helps the electrode to be inserted deeper into he cut and the coating helps control the arc and form fluid slag. The use of metal electrodes improves the quality of the cut, reduces the width of the kerf and produces more evenly cut edges. The application of compressed air just behind the arc, to blow out a molten metal speeds up the cutting process. For under water cutting (for salvage of sunk vessels, repair of underwater structures etc.) the electrode is with a water tight coating.

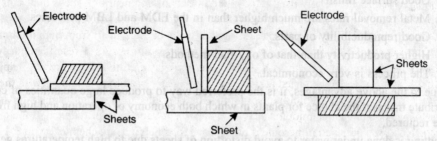

Fig. 5.27. Sheet Metal Electric Arc Welding.

O_2 - arc cutting is done with a coated steel tube electrode through which oxygen is blown. The technique is similar to that of oxy-acetylene flame cutting, except that the preheat is supplied by an arc instead of a flame.

It is in effect a combination of flame cutting and metal arc cutting. Because the heat is concentrated into such a small area, the process is very useful for piercing holes in plate upto thickness exceeding 15 cm.

Cuts of better quality are produced by Plasma arc cutting, Electron- beam machining (EBM), and Laser-beam machining (LBM). The last two methods will be discussed in a separate chapter.

Gas-Tungsten Arc Cutting (GTAC). The basic circuit and the protective gases are similar to the used in GTAW. The difference lies in the fact that in GTAC, the jet of shielding gases leaves the nozzle at high velocity to expel the molten metal.

Gas-Metal Arc Cutting (GMAC). To cut the metals by MIG technique, the electrode wire feed rate and other variables are adjusted in such a manner that electrode wire completely penetrates through the workpiece. Thus, cutting is accomplished instead of welding. The width of cut wil depend upon the potential difference in the circuit and the quality of cut will depend upon the rate of feed of the electrode wire.

Powder Oxy Fuel Cutting (POC). The method of POFC or Powder Metal Cutting method for cutting oxidation resistant materials or hard- to-cut materials, has been briefly mentioned in Art. 5.2.9. The method consists in introducing into the cutting zone a finely divided iron powder. The powder is carried from a hopper by the stream of oxygen, while the oxy-acetylene cutting torch travels along the reaction zone. The powder burns in the oxygen stream, generating additional heat, which facilitates melting of refractory oxides. The metal is removed from the cutting zone by the stream of oxygen, as usual. This process has proved useful for cutting stainless and heat resistant steels, cast iron and certain non-ferrous metals.

Chemical Flux Cutting. In Chemical Flux Cutting (FOC), fine stream of special flux is added to the cutting oxygen stream, to increase the fluidity of the high melting point oxides.

Plasma Arc Machining (PAM) or Plasma Arc Cutting (PAC) : As we know, plasma is the high temperature ionised gas. The PAC is done with a high speed jet of high temperature plasma. The plasma jet heats up the work-piece causing a quick melting. PAC can be used on all those materials which conduct electricity, including those which are resistant to oxy-fuel cutting. The process is extensively used for profile cutting of sheets (upto 40 mm thick) by using programmable logic controllers (PLC) or CNC.

Plasma is generated by subjecting the flowing gas to the electron bombardment of an arc. For this, the arc is set up between the electrode and anodic nozzle, the gas is forced through the arc. Gases used for plasma arc O_2, N_2 and H_2. The method produces highest temperatures (about 9500°C).

The process has got the following advantages:

1. The process is fast, that is, high cutting speeds.
2. Narrow kerf.
3. Good surface finish.
4. Metal removal rates are much higher than in the EDM and LBM processes.
5. Good reproducibility of parts.
6. Higher productivity than that of oxy-fuel methods.
7. The process is very economical.

Due to the above advantages, it is the preferred way to produce large quantities of cut parts. This attribute makes it the choice for plants in which both economy of operation and high frequency rates are required.

Cutting is done under water to avoid distortion of sheets due to high temperatures generated. Water also helps in:

— accurate cutting.
— cooling the metal.
— protecting eyes from plasma arc.

As noted above, PAC is highly automated process to-day due to the use of PLC and CNC.

EBM and LBM : Electron beams and Laser beams are used for very accurate cutting of a large variety of metals. As compared to other thermal cutting processes, the kerf is narrower and the surface finish is better.

5.4. RESISTANCE WELDING

Resistance Welding is "a group of welding processes wherein coalescence is produced by the heat obtained from resistance of the work to electric current in a circuit of which the work is a part, and by the application of pressure and without the use of a filler metal".

The amount of heat generated at the contacting area of the elements to be welded, is determined from Joule's law,

$$Q = I^2 Rt.k \text{ joules}$$

where I = current in amperes

R = resistance of the circuit at the contacting area of the elements in ohms.

t = time during which the current flows, in seconds.

k = a constant to account for losses due to radiation and conduction.

k is usually < 1.

The voltage can be low, typically 0.5 to 10V, but currents are very high (thousands of amperes). Metals can be joined by this process using both alternating and direct current. However, heavy currents (upto 10kA) can be easier and more efficiently applied through transformers, and therefore, in practice only alternating current is used in resistance welding.

Materials of high heat conductivity and specific heat (Al and Cu) call for very high currents to prevent dissipation of heat.

A special feature of resistance welding is the rapid heating of the surface being welded (in hundredths of a second) due to the application of currents of high amperage. The advantages of the resistance welding are : The heat is localised, action is rapid, no filler metal is needed, the operation requires little skill and can be easily mechanised and automated, suitable for large quantity production, all the common metal and dissimilar metals can be resistance welded, the parent metal is normally not harmed and none is lost, many difficult shapes and sections can be processed, and a high degree of reliability and reproductibility can be achieved.

The main disadvantage is high cost of equipment, and there are limitations to the types of joints made.

The resistance welding process finds extensive application in construction and the engineering industries.

There are six types of resistance welding processes :

(1) resistance spot welding (2) resistance seam welding (3) projection welding (4) flash welding (5) upset welding, and (6) percussion welding.

1. Resistance Spot Welding (RSW). In resistance spot welding, the overlapping metal parts are held between two bar type metal electrodes which apply pressure, while an electric current is passed through them, Fig. 5.28 When the current is switched on and applied for a predetermined number of cycles (in the automotive industry 20 - 30 cycles), the lapped pieces of metal are heated in a restricted area. The generated heat melts the surface layer of the metal in the central, more highly heated, area of contact with the electrodes, and the adjacent layers of metal are softened to a plastic state. Then the current is switched off and the electrodes are pressed and the pressure is released only after the weld stop (nugget) has solidified. The spot weld (nugget) is approximately the same size as the electrode tip, usually between 3 or 6 mm in diameter. Electrode tip diameter Thickness of plate to be welded. Distance between the nearest edge of the plate and centre of weld = 1.5 × electrode tip diameter. The sheet surface shows a slight depression and decolouration.

The welding cycle to produce one spot can be written as :

(*i*) Position the workpieces and squeeze between the electrodes.

(*ii*) Apply a low voltage current to the electrodes.

(*iii*) Hold until the proper temperature is attained.

(*iv*) Release current, continue pressure.

(*v*) Release pressure and remove work.

The electrode pressure can be in the range of upto 2 kN

The electrodes used must possess high electrical and thermal conductivity and retain the required strength at temperatures upto 400°C. Electrodes are made of cold-rolled electrolytic copper with some Cd, Cr, or Be additions, or copper - tungsten or molybdenum alloys. Electrodes are usually of hollow construction and are cooled with water during operation to prevent their overheating.

Because of the widespread application of sheet metal parts, resistance spot welding finds extensive application in the aircraft and automobile industries for manufacturing air frames and bodies (there are some 8000 to 10,000 spot welds per car), attaching handles of cookware, as well as in railway car building and the instrument industry and for making reinforcement in concrete construction etc.

Spot welding is primarily restricted to thin metals (for example 0.025 to 3.2 mm thick for steel and magnesium and 4 mm thick for aluminium), namely steels, stainless steels, aluminium, magnesium, nickel, nickel alloys, bronze and brass. Some dissimilar metals can be spot welded, but with difficulty. The method is also difficult to use for highly conducting materials like Al and Mg.

(*a*) The diameter of spot welds,

$$d = 1.4\ t + 4 \text{ mm, for } t < 3 \text{ mm} = 1.5\ t + 5 \text{ mm, for } t > 3 \text{ mm}$$

where t = Thickness of parts being welded.

(*b*) Spacing of spot welds = 3 d

Spot Welding Machines. There are three types of spot welding machines which are in use:

  I. Standard machines.

  II. Special multiple-electrode machines

  III. Portable welders

I. Standard Machines. These machines have an upper and lower horn (arm) carrying the electrodes and extending from an upright frame. The upper horn is movable (up and down) while the lower horn is fixed. There are two designs of standard machines :

(*i*) Rocker arm type   (*ii*) Press type spot or projection welders.

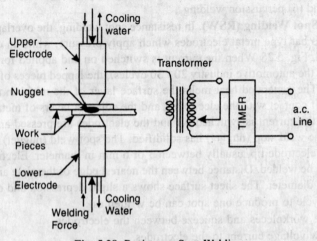

Fig. 5.28. Resistance Spot Welding.

(*i*) **Rocker Arm Type Machine.** In this machine, the movable horn is mounted on a rocker arm which is pivoted in the frame. It is tilted upward to open the gap and downward to apply the pressure, by the rocking action of the upper arm (the lower electrode arm being stationary). This design is adaptable to a wide range of work, usually for light production work with lighter gauges. The throat depth (distance from the face of the upright frame to the end of the horn) is about 1.2 m for these machines. These machines are of two types :

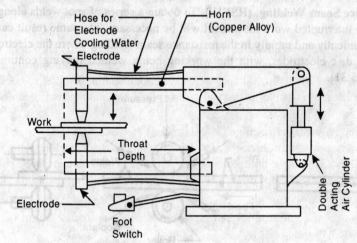

Fig. 5.29. Rocker-Arm Spot Welding Machine.

(*a*) **Foot Type.** When the foot treadle is pressed down, the two electrodes are brought together. The welding pressure is then transmitted to the work through a compression spring on the rear rod (see Fig. 5.29, where an air cylinder is shown in place of a rod, the other construction of the machine is same). After a suitable amount of compression is obtained, the welding circuit is closed by means of a mechanical switch. As the compression movement of the rear rod follows through, the switch trip opens and welding current ceases to flow. Releasing the pressure on the foot treadle opens the electrodes and resets the trip switch.

(*b*) **Air Operated Machines.** In this design, a double acting air cylinder replaces the rear rod and compression spring, (Fig. 5.29).

(*ii*) **Press Type Machine.** The name comes from straight line vertical stroke of the upper welding head. The straight line motion is provided by an air or hydraulic cylinder, (Fig. 5.30). These machines are used for mass production. The throat depth for these machines is about 1.5m.

II. Special Multiple Electrode Machines. These machines are employed for high-production jobs.

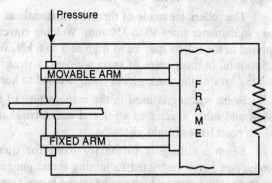

Fig. 5.30. Press Type Spot Welding Machine.

(*i*) In one system, there is one common welding transformer and a hydraulic cylinder for each electrode pair. The electrodes are brought in contact with the work one pair at a time.

(*ii*) In another system, all electrode pairs are pressed together against the work at one time, and the current from the transformer secondary is commutated to one electrode pair at a time. Some machines have a separate transfer and controls for each electrode pair.

III. Portable Spot Welding Guns. These welders are used when the work is too large to be moved to a welding machine, for example, trucks and railroad cars. The gun consists of a transformer and controls in a case, usually hung from the ceiling, with leads and an air line to a pair of jaws. This permits bringing the welding unit and the operator to work. The jaws carry the electrodes and can be moved about in the work area. The jaws are closed by an air cylinder and the electrodes bite like teeth on the work and pass current to make the weld. These guns ca make 200 spots/minute.

2. Resistance Seam Welding, (RSEW). To obtain a series of spot welds along a line by the RSW method, an interrupted work movement will be necessary. The same result can be achieved much more conveniently and rapidly in the resistance seam welding where the electrodes are in the form of rotating disc electrodes, with the working being welded moving continuously by the electrodes, (Fig. 5.31).

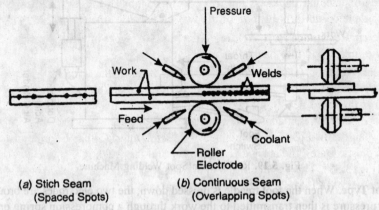

(a) Stich Seam
(Spaced Spots)

(b) Continuous Seam
(Overlapping Spots)

Fig. 5.31. Resistance Seam Welding.

Seam welding may be either intermittent (stitch seam or spaced spots) or continuous seam (over lapping seam). In the former case, a current interrupter is employed. When the a.c. is left on, a spot weld is made every time the current reaches its peak, and the welds are spaced close enough to give a gas and liquid- tight joint.

The rollers are made of the same materials as the electrodes for sport welding. Rollers may vary in diameter from 40 to 350 mm. Welding currents range from 2000 to 5000A while the force applied to the rollers may be as high as 5 to 6 kN. Welding speeds range is commonly from 0.5 to 3.5 m/min. In most cases of seam welding, a stream of water is directed over the disc electrodes and the area of the work pieces being welded to keep everything cool except the joint interface.

Seam welding is used in the manufacture of tanks, tubes and other articles of steel and non ferrous metals which must have airtight joints.

Seam welding is primarily used for quantity production but is restricted to joining metal gauges that are thinner than those which can be joined by spot welding. The normal range of thickness compatible with seam welding is 0.25 to 3.2 mm.

3. Resistance Projection Welding, (RPW). The projection welding process is similar to spot welding except that the current is concentrated at the spots to be welded, when small dimples or projections are embossed or coined on one of the sheets, (Fig. 5.32). When the current is

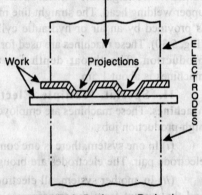

Fig. 5.32. Resistance Projection Welding.

applied, the projections soften and are pushed back in place by the electrode pressure as the weld nuggets form. Electrodes are relatively large and several welds can be made simultaneously with a single electrode, resulting in a lower cost of operation. Also, because larger diameter elec- trodes can be used with a greater heat capacity, the need for water cooling is often eliminated. The projections tend to localize the heat, permitting thicker materials to be welded resulting in a stronger weld structure than that obtained with spot welding. Unlike spot welding, the method leaves no depression on the free surface.

Projection welding is used extensively by Automobile industry for joining nuts, bolts and studs to steel plates in car bodies. Because of their higher thermal conductivity, the method is especially suitable for copper, aluminium, brass etc.

Projections at the point of contact should be approximately = 10 to 80% of the sheet thickness.

If pieces of unequal thickness are to be welded, jobs of bigger thickness should have the projections to develop uniform heating of the two pieces.

4. Electric Resistance Butt Welding. There are two types of electric resistance butt welding processes : the 'upset' and the 'flash'.

(*i*) **Upset Welding, (UW).** In this process, the ends of the two parts (having the same X-section) to be joined together are clamped in position in the electrodes. The movable head is moved towards the fixed head until the abutting surfaces of the work pieces are in light contact. Then the proper current is made to flow across the interface for a preset time, while the light pressure between the two parts is maintained. When the interface has been heated to the welding temperature (plastic state), the current is switch off and the welding pressure is increased to form an "upset", (Fig. 5.33). This results in the lateral flow of the surface oxide layers, bringing clean metal surfaces in contact. Metal is not melted when upset butt welded and there is no spatter.

In order to obtain uniform heating of the joint, the two parts to be joined should preferably have the same resistance.

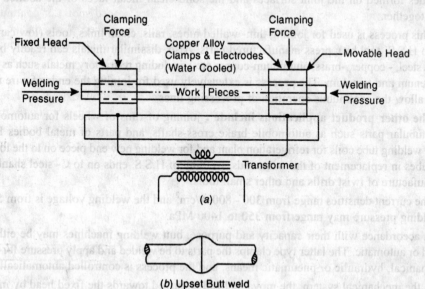

Fig. 5.33. Resistance Upset Butt Welding.

The welding voltage may vary from 5 to 15V while the current densities range from 300 to 800 A/cm^2. Because the contact resistance is inversely proportional to the pressure, therefore, the pressure is less at the start and is then increased to whatever is necessary to affect the weld. Final pressures range from 17 to 55 MPa. Upset butt welding is extensively used in the fabrication of tubular sections, pipe and heavy steel rings. It is also used for joining small ferrous and non ferrous strips. Areas upto 0.05 m^2 have been successfully welded, but generally the process is limited to smaller areas (upto 1000 mm^2) because of current limitations.

When joining dissimilar materials, the lengths projecting out of the clamps of the two parts should be in proportion to the specific resistance of the two materials. The same rule applies, if materials of two different cross-section are to be joined.

(*ii*) **Flash Butt Welding, (FW).** In this process, the parts to be welded approach towards each other and come into contact with the current switched on. The procedure of butt welding is as follows : After the parts are properly positioned and correct current, head speed and time are selected, a cycle start button is actuated. This makes the movable head to approach the fixed head. As the abutting surfaces come very near to each other, extremely rapid heating takes place when surface asperities first make contact. Molten metal is violently expelled and burns in air with considerable force and "Sparking" or "arcing", thus giving the process its name "flash butt". As this process continues for a

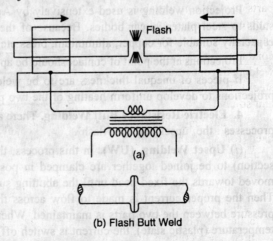

Fig. 5.34. Resistance Flash Butt Welding.

few seconds, a very thin layer at the interface is melted. The current is then shut off and the two parts are rapidly pressed together causing a small upset, (Fig. 5.34). This squeezes out liquid metal and oxides formed on the joint surfaces and the solid clean metal faces of the abutted parts are welded together.

This process is used for joining thin- walled tubes, rails, chain links, tools (low carbon steel shank to H.S.S. tool bit), press manufactured parts. Also, dissimilar metals can readily be welded (such as steel, - copper, -brass; aluminium-copper etc.), including re-fractory metals such as tungsten, molybdenum and tantalum. The process is extensively used for joining the ends of wire and sheet coils to allow the continuous operation of processing lines.

The other product applications include : joining of rims of wheels for automobiles and cycles, tubular parts such as automobile brake cross-shafts, and parts of metal bodies for motor cars, for welding tube coils for refrigeration plant and for welding new end piece on to the locomotive boiler tubes in replacement of the worn ends, welding of H.S.S. ends on to C- steel shanks during the manufacture of twist drills and other small tools.

The current densities range from 300 - 800 A/cm^2 and the welding voltage is from 5 to 15 V. The welding pressure may range from 350 to 1400 MPa.

In accordance with their capacity and purpose, butt welding machines may be either hand-operated or automatic. The latter type clamps the parts to be welded and apply pressure for upsetting by mechanical, hydraulic or pneumatic means, and the process is controlled automatically.

In the mechanical system, the movable head is moved towards the fixed head by means of a cam drive.

The upset metal is usually removed by subsequent rolling or grinding.

(*iii*) **Percussion Butt Welding, (PEW).** This process uses the heating effect of a high-intensity electric arc produced by a rapid discharge of electric energy, in combination with a percussion blow to forge weld metal pieces together. When the movable clamp is released, it moves rapidly alongwith one of the workpiece (Fig. 5.35). When the two parts are about 1.6 mm apart, there is a sudden discharge of electric energy. This causes intense arcing over the surfaces and brings them to high temperature. The arc is extinguished by the percussion blow of the two parts coming together with sufficient force to effect the weld.

Percussion welding makes it possible to weld parts having considerable difference in mass and in thermal and electrical conductivity, for example, welding of copper to steels, steel to magnesium alloys and so on.

Percussion welding is used for special joining situations, for example, joining dissimilar metals

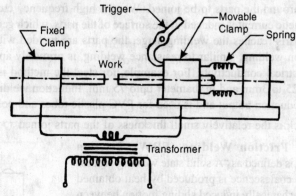

Fig. 5.35. Percussion Butt Welding.

that can not be welded economically by flash welding. The method is also used to weld pins, studs, bolts, and so on, to other components as well as to join sections of pipe, rod, or tube to each other or to flat sections. Since control of the path of an arc is difficult and also because of the impact required, the method is limited to small pieces (about 150 to 300 mm^2).

Commercial product applications include : Butt welding steel or other metals without flash or upset, joining aluminium rods, tubes or bars to copper, joining corrosion-resistant alloys to steel or non-ferrous pieces, joining of threaded steel studs to aluminium or magnesium alloys or forgings, joining of silver contact tips to copper studs and joining of stellite tips to steel or non-ferrous metals.

5.5. MISCELLANEOUS WELDING PROCESSES

The welding processes discussed below are listed under miscellaneous processes because they are not used as extensively as those previously described.

1. Forge Welding (FOW). Forge welding is defined as "A solid state welding process wherein coalescence is produced by heating and by applying pressure or blows sufficient to cause permanent deformation at the interface," (Fig. 5.36 (a)). This is the oldest industrial welding process. The parts to be welded are heated in a forge or some other furnace to within the hot-working temperature range and then forged together by hand or power hammering or pressing. During forging, oxides, slag and other contaminants are squeezed out, ensuring inter-atomic bonding. The workpieces commonly forge welded are of wrought iron and steel. The commonly used forge welding processes are : (i) Hammer welding (ii) Die welding, and (iii) Roll welding.

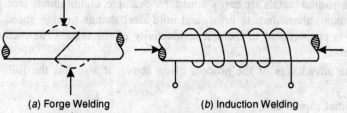

(a) Forge Welding   (b) Induction Welding

Fig. 5.36. Forge Welding, Induction Welding.

Roll welding is employed in the cladding of dissimilar materials. Die welding is used in the manufacture of seamless piping.

2. Induction Welding (IW). Induction welding is defined as "A welding process wherein coalescence is produced by the heat obtained from resistance of the work to the induced electric current with or without the application of pressure", (Fig. 5.36 (*b*)).

The heat obtained is both a function of current and frequency. A given degree of heating can be obtained by using high current at low frequency or a low current at high frequency. A coil is placed around the parts to be joined. When a high frequency current is passed through the coil, a sympathetic current is induced in the surface of the parts, which generates heat. When the temperature of the parts reaches the welding stage, the parts are welded with or without the use of pressure. Induction welding, similar to resistance welding, is primarily applicable to materials of relatively low electrical conductivity. For example, for steel the method is successful for thickness ranging from 0.25 to 3mm and in diameter upto 75 mm. Induction welding provides for quality joints and high production output and is used for PVC plastic tubes and polyethylene components. The main drawback is the relatively small thickness of the parts joined (⊁ 5 mm).

3. Friction Welding (FRW). Friction welding is defined as "A solid state welding process wherein coalescence is produced by heat obtained from mechanically induced sliding motion between rubbing surfaces. The parts are held together under pressure". One part is rotated at relatively high speeds and under pressure against the second part which is held stationary. The frictional work at the contacting surfaces is transformed into heat. The contacting surfaces are thus heated to a high temperature below the melting temperature. At this

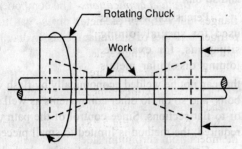

Fig. 5.37. Friction Welding.

point, the relative motion between the two is stopped. The weld is then completed (by upsetting) due to the pressure which still continues or additional pressure may be necessary, (Fig. 5.37), to produce a solid state weld. Axial pressure, when rotating, may be upto 70 MPa and at the end it may reach 140 MPa. Relative motion is stopped by :

    (*i*) a braking system to the machine spindle.

    (*ii*) an arrangement which releases the stationary part to permit the two parts to rotate together.

Weld time is relatively short (fraction of a second to a few seconds). Short weld times and confinement of the heat generated to the weld interface surface results in comparatively narrow heat-affected zones. A wide variety of metals and metal combinations can be welded with this process. Filler metals, fluxes, or shielding gases are not required, and welds can be made with a minimum of joint preparation.

The method is most suitable for circular parts, that is, butt welding of round bars or tubes. Also welding of a round part to a flat part, for example, stud welding. The heat zone being very thin, therefore, dissimilar metals are easily joined, for example, aluminium to steel, copper to steel, copper to aluminium, aluminium to brass, and mild steel shanks to high speed steel tools. The rotational speed is proportional to thermal conductivity of the metal. The method is limited to smaller components.

Besides the advantages of the process given above, it also has the following additional advantages :

    1. Low initial capital cost

    2. Low - cost power requirements.

    3. The process is clean.

    4. High quality welds.

5. Annealing of weld zone is not necessary.

6. Very little loss of material through exclusions.

7. The process welds the whole surface of contact, unlike OAW and Arc welding which weld only round the periphery.

For welding a round bar to a flat plate, the thickness of the plate should not exceed one quarter of the bar diameter. This combination of dimensions provides an equal balance of heat.

The high quality of welds obtained by FRW is due to the following factors :

(*i*) As the surfaces rub against each other, all oxide and adsorbed films and foreign particles are removed into flash, because the metal is deformed in radial directions. Also, no oxides are formed during welding due to the intimate contact between the rubbing surfaces.

(*ii*) The metal at the joint and in the heat-affected area acquires a structure having equi-axial and fine grains.

Product applications. The components successfully produced include: H.S.S. Twist drills, flanges upto 15 cm diameter pipes, gas turbine shafts, Aero-engine drive shafts and valves, refrigerator tubes of dissimilar metals, hydraulic tubes, steering columns, welding of sintered products, and sulphur - bearing steels.

Other applications are given below :

1. Manufacture of measuring tools and running centres for lathes. In the past, plug and screw-thread gauges were forged in several passes from Chromium steel. By FRW, a gauge blank is made up from two parts, (Fig.5.38). An automatic machine joins a common-steel shank to the gauging members from chromium steel. This results in saving a sizeable amount of the expensive chromium steel and greater output.

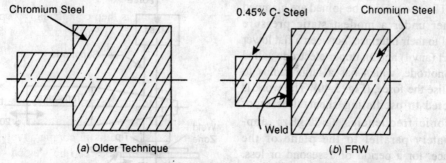

Chromium Steel   0.45% C- Steel   Chromium Steel

(*a*) Older Technique   Weld   (*b*) FRW

Fig. 5.38. Fabrication of a Gauge.

2. Before the development of FRW, valves for internal combustion engine were all-stamped. Valve manufacture by FRW involves a greater number of operations. However, this factor is offset by savings in high temperature steel, increased productivity, and by the fact that no heavy forging plant is needed any longer, (Fig. 5.39).

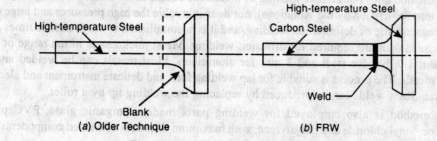

High-temperature Steel

High-temperature Steel   Carbon Steel

Weld

Blank

(*a*) Older Technique   (*b*) FRW

Fig. 5.39. Fabrication of an Engine Valve.

3. FRW has also found use in rocket building, construction, the manufacture of farm machinery, electrical engineering, power plant building; machine tool building and many other industries.

In FRW, which is also known as "Continuous-drive FRW", friction is produced by rotating one of the pieces, relative to the other (Fig. 5.34), or both, while they are clamped together by a force. Due to very short cycle time, the process is very fast and only electric resistance welding can vie with it in this respect. Power consumption in FRW is one-fifth to one-tenth of that used for electric resistance welding.

Inertia Welding. Inertia welding or "Inertia-Drive FRW", differs from the conventional FRW (continuous-drive) that the spinning part is now attached to a rotating flywheel. The flywheel is brought to a specified rotational speed and is then detached from the driving motor. After that, the rotating assembly is pressed against the stationary part. The kinetic energy of the flywheel is converted into heat energy, as the two parts rub against each other. The welding operation is completed as the flywheel comes to rest, with the two parts remaining pressed together. The kinetic energy and hence the rotational speed of the flywheel is calculated, so that the weld is completed when rotation stops.

Friction Welding :– The method of Friction Welding is very convenient, where a small bar (75 ϕ × 300 mm) is to be welded to a large blank (200 ϕ × 50 mm). The larger blank is held in the lathe chuck and rotated at high speed. The small bar is held in the lathe tool past and kept pressed against the rotating blank. Heat generated due to friction, welds the two surfaces. During the process of welding, the molten metal flies out and proper guards should be provided. Each welding cycle takes about 5 to 10 minutes and gives a very strong welded joint.

4. Ultrasonic Welding (USW). Ultrasonic welding is defined as "A solid state welding process wherein coalescence is produced by the local application of high frequency vibratory energy as the work parts are held together under pressure".

The two parts to be joined are clamped together under a modest static pressure normal to their interface, between a flat lower support (anvil) and an upper electrode called the sonotrode, which has a large radius to centralise the force, (Fig. 5.40). The work is subjected to oscillating shear stresses of ultrasonic frequencies (≥ 20 kHz) approximately parallel to the plane of the interface, for a period of 1 second or less. The vibrations and pressure cause movements of the metal molecules breaking up the surface oxide, thus lowering the surface resistance of the alloys and the two surface diffuse into each other to give a solid state weld.

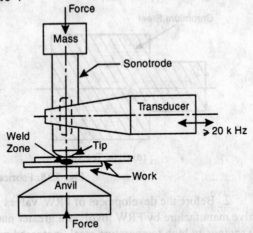

Fig. 5.40. Ultrasonic Welding.

The method does not involve melting of metals (of course there is some heating of the work due to the internal friction by the vibrations), nor does it involve the high pressures and large deformations characteristic of deformation welding, and it is accomplished in much shorter times and at lower pressures than are required for diffusion welding. Metal thickness is in the range of 0.005 mm to about 1.0 mm for steel and 3 mm for aluminium. Most metals can be welded and also dissimilar metals. The process is suitable for lap welding foils and delicate instrument and electronic components. Seam welds can be produced by replacing the welding tip by a roller.

The method is also employed for welding parts made of organic glass, PVC plastic, polyethylene, vinyl chloride and polystyrene, with maximum thickness of welded components being 10 mm. The method provides high productivity.

Other advantages of the process include :

1. Welds are strong and free from foreign inclusions.
2. Very little preparation is needed for the weld; usually, it invol-ves degreasing.
3. Post cleaning of welds is usually not necessary.
4. Thin pieces can be welded to thicker pieces.

Product applications. The range of applications of the process can meet many of the requirements of the atomic and electronic sections of industry. The process is used for :

Air-craft construction, for the building of transistors, for fine-wire assemblies, bimetal electrical contacts, light-gauge metal for the production of containers and for the welding of aluminium foil for packaging requirements.

5. Explosive Welding (EXW). Explosive welding or Explosion welding is defined as "A solid state welding process wherein coalescence is effected by high velocity movements produced by a controlled detonation". The technique eliminates the problems generally associated with fusion welding-melting, heat effects and microstructural changes. The process can join many combinations of metals not possible or extremely difficult or expensive to combine using standard methods.

A schematic description of a typical explosive-bonding set up for joining two flat plates is shown in Fig. 5.41. The two plates can be placed at angle to each other also. A single electric detonation cap can be used to ignite the explosive. When the explosive mat placed on top of the cladding sheet (flyplate) is detonated, the sheet joins to the base metal by forming tight whirls or vortexes at the interface.

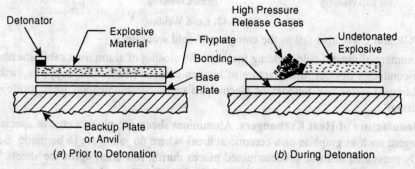

Fig. 5.41. Explosive Welding.

The most extensive use of flat clad products has been in coinage and in heat exchangers. Clad tube sheets for heat exchangers are produced by explosive cladding as an adjunct to the more expensive weld overlay process. Composite armour and metal-matrix reinforced composites are also being produced as well as clad plates and sheets for use in the fabrication of chemical processing equipment.

Explosive cladding is finding use in the die-casting industry for nozzles, die-casting biscuits, and other components. Work is underway for the cladding of components for the glass industry, and many potential applications exist for the automotive industry, such as bimetallic disk brakes, clad piston faces and motor-block repairs. The method augments other processes for the conduct of jobs difficult or impossible to accomplish by other means.

6. Flow Welding. In flow welding, coalescence is produced by heating with molten filler metal, poured over the surfaces to be welded until the welding temperature is attained and until the required filler metal has been added. This process is not used to any extent.

7. Cold Welding (CW). Cold welding is defined as "A solid state welding process wherein coalescence is produced by the external application of mechanical force alone". Since it is carried out at room temperature, the bonding of the molecules at the interface may not be of very high quality.

The process is quite similar to electric resistance welding with the exception that no heat is used to remove the oxide and gas layers but rather severe plastic deformation is relied upon to get metal to metal contact. The equipment for this process is very simple and inexpensive : light presses with simple "dimpling dies" being required for cold welding thick sections and special pliers similar to bolt cutters being sufficient for thin sections.

Fig. 5.42 (a) shows the lap welding of sheets. It relies on a 50 to 90% expansion of surfaces when indentors penetrate the sheets to be welded. Shoulders on indentors promote welding and limit distortion. Butt welding of wires is shown in Fig. 5.42 (b). Roll bonding, (Fig. 5.42 (c)) is highly effective because large extensions can be obtained.

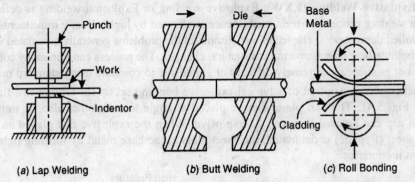

(a) Lap Welding (b) Butt Welding (c) Roll Bonding

Fig. 5.42. Cold Welding.

EXW and USW also fall in the category of cold welding.

Commercial uses of cold welding include : the closing of aluminium cable sheaths and cases for semi-conductor devices, manufacture of kitchen utensils (tea kettles, supports, racks), lap and butt welding of wires and busbars of electrolysis cells, communication lines, trolley wires and home wiring.

Manufacture of Heat Exchangers. Aluminium sheets are given a coat of special paint or a parting agent such as graphite or a ceramic at areas where no joints are to be made. Bonding will be locally prevented at these predetermined places during roll bonding of the sheets. Due to the deformation produced by rolling, the sheets form bonds except where parting agents have been applied. The bonded sheets are then annealed and the parting agent is evaporated. Pressurised air or a fluid is passed through the areas formerly coated with parting agent. These get inflated or expanded to form parts such as evaporator plates, and heat exchanger tubes for refrigerators.

8. Diffusion Welding (DFW). Generally, better bonding is obtained when the temperature is high enough to ensure diffusion, typically above 0.5 times the melting point. Diffusion welding is defined as "A solid state welding process wherein coalescence is produced at the faying surfaces by the application of pressure and elevated temperatures. The process does not involve macroscopic deformation or relative motion of parts. A solid filler metal may or may not be inserted".

The method has been used for centuries by goldsmiths. Filled gold is obtained by placing gold face sheets over a silver or copper core. When a weight is placed on top of the sandwich and it is held in a furnace for a sufficient long time, a permanent bond is established. The required pressure can also be generated by : a press or by restraining the assembly with a fixture made of a lower expansion material, for example, Molyb- denum.

Since 1970s, the method has been extended to airframe construction. Parts of complex shapes are made of titanium.

9. Electron Beam Welding (EBW). EBW can be defined as "A welding process wherein coalescence is produced by the heat obtained from a concentrated beam composed primarily of high velocity electrons impinging upon the joint to be welded. The kinetic energy of the electrons is changed into heat on impact with work, giving intense local heating".

The electron beam is produced in a high vacuum environment by an electron gun, usually consisting of a tungsten or tantalum cathode, a grid or forming electrode and an anode. A stream of electrons is given off from a tungsten filament heated to about 2200°C (Fig. 5.43). The electrons are gathered, accelerated to high velocity and shaped into a beam by the potential difference between cathode and anode. The beam is collimated and focused by passing through the field of an electromagnetic focusing coil or "magnetic lens". Beams typically are focused to about 0.25 to 1 mm diameter and have a power density of about 10 kW/ mm^2, which is sufficient to melt and vaporize any metal. The operation is carried out in a vacuum, which enables the beam source to be at a distance of upto about 1 m from the work. Deep penetration with a

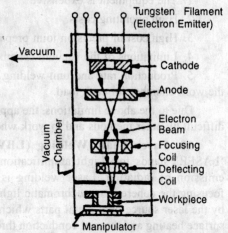

Fig. 5.43. Electron Beam Welding.

very narrow heat affected zone is achieved by this process. Aluminium can be fused upto a depth of about 40 mm and stainless steel upto about 30 mm, with a width of fusion area of about one-tenth of the penetration.

The equipment comprises :

    (*i*) an electron beam gun

    (*ii*) a vacuum chamber

    (*iii*) a means of moving the work under the beam while weldin

    (*iv*) A microscope for viewing the work.

Electron beam guns are rated at about 30 to 175 kV and a beam current of about 50 to 1000 mA.

The use of vacuum chamber is :

    (*a*) to prevent the tungsten filament of gun from oxidising.

    (*b*) it prevents the electrons from colliding with molecules of air and becoming scattered, with a loss of power.

    (*c*) enables the welding to be done in a very pure atmosphere eliminating the need for a shielding gas.

Other advantages of EBW are :

    (*i*) Ability to make welds that are deeper, narrower and less tapered than arc welds with a total heat input much lower than in arc welding.

    (*ii*) Superior control over penetration and other weld dimensions and properties.

    (*iii*) Higher welding speeds

    (*iv*) Clean and sound welds.

    (*v*) Energy conversion efficiency is high, about 65%.

All the above characteristics make possible : minimize distortion and shrinkage in welding, welding of hardened or work strengthened metals, no significant deterioration in mechanical properties at the joint, welding of parts that have already been finished to final assembly dimensions, welding of refractory and reactive metals and welding of combination of dissimilar metals not usually joined by arc welding.

Disadvantages :

1. The equipment is expensive

2. High operating costs.

3. High cost of precision joint preparation and precision tooling.

4. Limitations of the vacuum chamber. Work size is limited by the size of the chamber.

5. Production rate and unit welding cost are adversely affected by the need to pump down the work chamber for each load.

Due to the above limitations, the application of EBW is confined to the welding of materials difficult by other methods and to work where exceptionally good results are important.

10. Laser Beam Welding (LBW). The word 'LASER' stands for: Light amplification by stimulated emission of radiation. Laser welding is performed by focusing the coherent monochromatic light beam emitted by the laser source onto metal parts which are welded by surface heating and thermal conduction through the metal. There are two types of lasers in use : solid state lasers, for example, ruby (an Al_2O_3 crystal with Cr ions) and Gas lagers. Here we shall deal with solid laser.

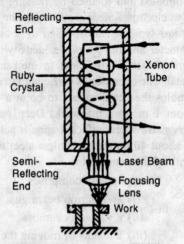

Fig. 5.44. Laser Beam Welding.

The laser crystal (Ruby) is in the form of a cylinder, (Fig. 5.44), the ends being flat and parallel to a high degree of accuracy and silvered to give mirror reflecting surfaces. There is a small aperture on the axis of the crystal, through the mirror at the output end. When the crystal is pumped with high-intensity white light from a xenon or krypton lamp, the Cr ions in the crystal get excited. The excited ions possess more energy and some of it is given as a red fluorescent light. This light is reflected backward and forward in the crystal between the two ends (mirrors), striking more Cr ions on the path. These ions affected by the collisions are each caused to emit their quota of red light. There is a cumulative effect of the increasing red light exciting more and more Cr ions, until the number of collisions is high enough to cause a burst of red light through the small aperture in the mirror at the output end of the crystal. The beam produced is extremely narrow and can be focused to a pin point area by an optical lens.

The method is finding growing application, particularly for thin gauge metals, upto about 0.5 to 1.5 mm thick. LBW provides as high quality weld as EBW ; it can be remote controlled and requires no vacuum to operate in.

11. Thermit Welding (TW). Thermit welding is "A group of welding processes wherein coalescence is produced by heating with superheated liquid metal and slag resulting from a chemical reaction between a metal oxide and aluminium with or without the application of pressure. Filler metal, when used, is obtained from liquid metal".

Thermit is a mixture of powdered aluminium (1 part) and iron oxide in the form of roll scale (3 parts). When the thermit mixture is heated or ignited with a torch or ignition powder, to the temperature of 1100°C, it burns according to the following reaction :

$$8Al + 3Fe_3O_4 \rightarrow 9Fe + 4Al_2O_3 + heat$$

The reaction is nonexplosive and requires about a minute to go to completion. A temperature of about 2760° and higher is reached in the combustion of thermit mixture. The reaction results in the formation of liquid reduced iron and slag (Al_2O_3) which are used for welding the pieces.

There are two types of thermit welding processes :

(*i*) plastic or pressure welding process.

(*ii*) fusion or non-pressure welding process.

Pressure Welding Process. The parts to be welded are butted tightly together and enclosed in a removable mould which provides a space between the inner surfaces of the mould and the parts. The products of the reaction are then poured into the mould in such a manner that slag enters the mould first. On contact with the metal parts, the slag cools rapidly and provides a layer of brittle, glasslike material so that the thermit iron which flows does not fuse with or adhere to the surface of the parts. The heavier thermit iron sinks to the lower half of the mould. This and the aluminium slag on top will both give up their heat to the pieces being welded. When the ends of the pieces to be welded reach the welding heat, they are forced together by means of clamps to make a pressure butt weld. The mould is then removed and the thermit iron and slag are knocked off from around the weld.

Non - pressure Welding Process. Here, the sections to be joined are lined up and a parallel gap or vee joint is cut at the fractured interface. A wax pattern is then formed between and around the ends which are to be joined. Then a sand mould complete with sprue, gate and riser is built around the joint area. The mould is then heated to melt the wax, causing it to flow into the sand mould and leaving a void space at the joint. The thermit powder is ignited in a crucible placed on top of the mould and the resulting iron is tapped-through a bottom hole of the crucible, directly into the mould. This highly superheated iron results in a deep penetration weld between the sections to be joined, (Fig. 5.45). After solidification, the mould is destroyed and the still hot excess iron is chiselled off.

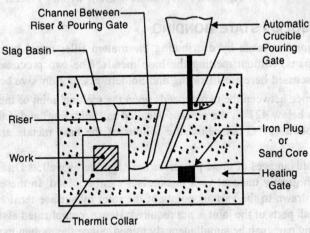

Fig. 5.45. Thermit Welding.

Thermit welding is mainly used for the repair and built up of heavy sections on crankshafts, steel rolling mills, in marine applications and in joining rails and pipes. Large electrical bus bars are similarly welded, using aluminium and The chemical reaction being :

$$3Cu_2O + 2Al \longrightarrow 6Cu + Al_2O_3 + Heat$$

It is clear that the thermal reaction (discussed above) results in temperature such higher than necessary. Again, the end product is iron and not steel, which must be the case when steel parts are to be joined by the non-pressure thermit welding process. For this, the reaction mix is added with Carbon, ferro-manganese and ferro-silicon. Carbon is added to convert iron to steel at the end of the reaction. Ferro-manganese and ferro-silicon are added as de-oxidising agents. They will help in cooling-off the reaction and getting an adequate final temperature. The reaction is started by burning a magnesium ribbon dipped in the reaction mix.

Fig. 5.46 shows a non-pressure thermit welding process for joining thick sections like rails etc. As already noted, the sand mould is in one piece. For this, wax is placed in the joint space and around. The gating system, also in wax, is attached. The complete assembly is embedded is moulding sand. The mould is inverted and heated. The wax melts and pours out leaving the cavity around the metal parts to be joined and also the pouring basin, runner and gating system.

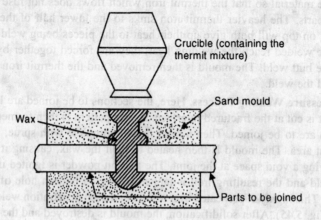

Fig. 5.46. Non-pressure Thermit Welding Process.

5.6. LIQUID - SOLID - STATE BONDING

Here, the joint is made by distributing the molten filler metal between the closely fitted surfaces of the parts, without melting the base metals. The two processes under this category, which will be discussed here are : Brazing and Soldering. For Adhesive bonds, see Chapter 12.

The difference between the two depends upon the melting point of the filler metal. When the filler metal melts below 427°C, the process is called as 'Soldering' and if the melting point of the filler metal is above 427°C but below the solidus of the base metals, the process is called as 'Brazing'.

The major advantages of these processes are : Similar as well as Dissimilar materials can be joined. Parts with greatly unequal wall thicknesses can be joined. In these processes, the molten filler material is drawn to the various points of the joint by surface tension (capillary attraction). So, the access to all parts of the joint is not required. Hence, complicated assemblies and assemblies consisting of many parts can be simultaneously joined. Since the molten metal is distributed in the closely spaced joint by capillary action, the strength of the brazed or soldered joint is markedly affected by the width of the gap between the parts being joined together. Closing the gap will improve the strength of the joint. However, two narrow a gap may spoil the capillary flow of the molten filler metal. The optimum gap width depends on the type of filler and base metals. In brazing steel parts with copper or Silver fillers, the optimum gap width ranges between 0.03 and 0.15 mm. In soldering with a binary tin-lead solder, it is from 0.05 to 0.2 mm. It should be understood that the strength of the brazed joint increases upon a certain gap between the two joining surfaces beyond which it decreases.

In these processes, no post joining heat treatment is normally necessary and joints are virtually free of internal stresses. The processes lend themselves to automation. However, these processes have the following limitations :

1. Relatively lower strength, particularly in the case of the lower melting point alloys.

2. Temperature resistance is limited by the melting point of the filler material.

3. Inspection of joint could be difficult.

4. Cost of joint could be high.

5. The process calls for narrow and uniformly spaced joints, due to which large parts/ assemblies, allthough apparently brazable or solderable, are seldom made in this way.

6. Compared to welding, these processes require more accurate surface preparation (for better spreading and wetting action of filler metal) and assembly before the job can be done.

The two processes find extensive use in : the manufacture of automobile radiators, plate and tube heat exchangers, impellers, fans, fuel and oil pumps, appliance parts and for the joining of wires.

Brazing makes stronger joints as compared to soldering. The strength of a brazed joint ranges from 3 to 4.5 N/mm^2 while that of the soldered joint ranges from 0.3 to 1.0 N/mm^2. The term 'brazing' implies the use of brass as the filler material, but now a days a number of other alloys are also in use. The filler metal is called 'spelter'.

5.6.1. Brazing. The brazing process can be defined as the process to join two metal pieces heated to suitable temperatures by using a filler metal having a liquidus above 427°C and below the solidus of the base metals. The filler metal is distributed between the closely fitted surfaces of the joint by "capillary attraction".

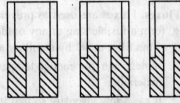

Fig. 5.47. Brazing Joints.

During brazing, the base metal of the two pieces to be joined is not melted. Some diffusion or alloying of the filler metal with the base metal takes place even though the base metal does not reach its solidus temperature. The greater the degree of adhesion and inter-diffusion between the molten filler metal and the base metals, the higher the mechanical strength of the joint will be. To achieve this and to obtain a strong joint, the basic requirement is that the filler metal must thoroughly wet the base metal surfaces. Therefore, the surfaces must be cleaned and free of contaminants that would prevent adhesion. Thus the scale is removed by mechanical (with a steel wire brush or emery cloth) or chemical (pickling in acids) means and heavy oily residues (oil, grease, paint etc.) are removed by degreasing with hot alkaline solutions or organic solvents. Again, when the assembly is heated to melt the filler metal, oxides may form which will prevent wetting of the surfaces by the molten filler metal. This can be overcome by :

1. performing brazing is vacuum or an appropriate (neutral or reducing) atmosphere.

2. Wetting of the surfaces is also ensured by the application of fluxes.

Steps in Brazing

(*i*) The surfaces to be joined are cleaned (and subsequently rinsed and dried) and fitted closely together.

(*ii*) A flux is applied to all surfaces where the filler metal is to flow.

(*iii*) After that, the joint is heated to the proper brazing temperature. Solid filler metal may be preplaced on the metal pieces and thus melted as the metal pieces are heated, or it may be applied to the metal pieces after the brazing temperature is reached. Only a small amount of filler metal is needed to fill the joint completely, (Fig. 5.47), which shows the various ways of placing the filler metal at the joint.

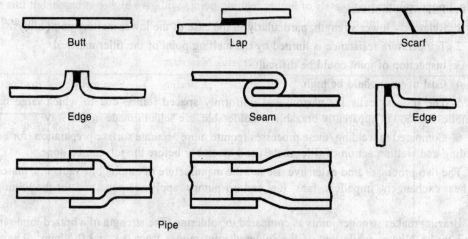

Fig. 5.48. Brazing Joints.

Some other commonly used joints in brazing are shown in Fig. 5.48.

Fluxes. Fluxes are used to prevent oxidation of the base metal and the filler metal during brazing, form a fusible slag of any oxides which may be present or formed, and promote the free flowing of the filler metal by capillary attraction. The requirements of a good flux are :

1. It melts at a low enough temperature to prevent oxidation of the base metals and the filler materials.

2. It has a low viscosity so that it is replaced by the molten filler metal.

3. It may react with surfaces to facilitate wetting.

4. It shields the joint while the filler is still liquid.

5. It is relatively easy to remove after the solidification of the filler.

6. It lowers the surface tension of the molten filler metal and thus promotes its flow into the joint.

Common fluxes are : compositions of borates, fluorides, chlorides, borax and boric acid in various proportions according to specific requirements. Fluxes are used in form of powder, paste, or slurry. Borax is used as fused borax, because water in it will cause bubbling during heating. Alcohol can be mixed with fused borax to form a paste. Most fluxes are corrosive and the residue should be removed from the work after the brazing is completed.

Filler Materials. The filler metal or the braze metal must :

1. wet the surfaces of the base metals at the joint.

2. have high fluidity to penetrate crevices. For capillary attraction to exist, the clearance between the parts being joined must be quite small (0.03 to 0.05 mm), otherwise the filler metal would run out of the joint. A wider clearance in a joint leads to its reduced strength.

3. preferably have a narrow melting range

4. not lead to galvanic corrosion during service.

The filler metal is applied in the form of wire, strip, preforms, powder or paste to the joint area as noted above in step (*iii*) under "steps in brazing". Alternatively, the filler metal is pre-applied to the surface of one of the contacting parts as a coating or cladding, often by rolling, electrolytic deposition or hot dipping.

Typical filler metals are listed in Table 5.3, for various classes of base metals. Because the base metals are not melted, the brazing metal is always different in composition from the base metals. In general, brazing metals of higher melting points will give higher strength, but this may affect the strength of the base metals. These brazing metals are based on Ag, Cu and Ni and are also called as 'Hard solders'.

Table 5.3. Brazing Materials

Braze metal	Composition %	Brazing process	Base metal	Brazing Temp.°C
Brazing Brass	Cu : 60, Zn : 40	Torch, Dip Furnace	Steel, Cu, High Cu alloys, Ni alloys, Stainless steel	900
Manganese Bronze	Cu : 58 : 5, Sn : 1, Fe : 1, Mn : 0.25, Zn : 39.5	Torch	-do-	-do-
Nickel Silver	Ni : 18, Cu : 55 to 65, Zn : 27 to 17	Torch Induction	Steel, Ni, Ni alloys	-do-
Copper	Si : 1.5, Mn : 0.25, Cu : 98.25, or Si : 1.5, Zn	Torch	Steel	-do-
Silicon	: 1, Cu : 97.5			
Silver alloys	Ag : 5 to 80, Cu = 15 to 52 balance : Zn + Sn + Cd	Torch, Furnace Induction Resistance, Dip	Steel, Cu, Cu alloys, Ni, Ni alloys, Stainless Steel	700
Silver alloys with P	Ag : 15, P : 5, Cu = 80	-do-	Cu, Cu alloys	-do-
Copper phosphorus	Cu : 93, P : 7	-do-	-do-	-do-

Brazing Methods. Depending upon the heat source used to melt the brazing metal, the various brazing methods are given below :

1. Torch Brazing. A joining process that may employ acetylene, natural gas, butane or propane in combination with air or oxygen to supply the heat required to melt the filler rod and diffuse it into the surface of the base metal. This technique is not extensively used for continuous mass production. Flux used is in the form of paste or powder.

2. Furnace Brazing. This is a high production process where the heat is supplied by gas or electric heating coils. The furnaces are of box type (batch type) or continuous type. The latter employs a wire mesh belt to transport the parts to be brazed. In this process, preformed shapes of filler metal be placed on the parts to be joined prior to entering the furnace. The process is well suited to high production. The use of flux can be avoided if an inert atmosphere is maintained in the furnace. The flux is applied in paste form.

3. Induction Brazing. Here also, the filler metal is used in the preformed shape. The parts are heated by placing within the field of high frequency induction coil. The parts are heated by eddy currents because the parts to be joined offer electric- magnetic resistance to the changing induction field. Heating is very rapid, and by properly shaping the induction coils, the heat can be applied in the local area of the joint to be brazed. The process can be mechanised. Flux is applied in the form of paste.

4. Dip Brazing. dip brazing is of two kinds :

(i) In chemical dip brazing, the parts with preformed filler metal are placed into a molten bath of flux.

(ii) In the molten metal bath process, the assembled parts are first prefluxed and then immersed into a molten bath of filler metal.

The first method is more adaptable for joining large parts, whereas the latter method is restricted to small parts.

5. Resistance Brazing. Here, the same equipment is used as for resistance welding, excepting that a filler metal is placed in the joint. Rapid heating minimizes oxidation and the heat affected zone (HAZ) is small.

6. Laser Brazing and Electron Beam Brazing. These high cost techniques are justified only for precision work of high value and relatively high-temperature materials.

Only the first four brazing methods are of industrial importance.

In the conventional Brazing and soldering methods, the use of flux can be avoided by doing the process in inert gas (say Ar) atmosphere or in vacuum (As in EB brazing).

Braze Welding. It differs from the conventional brazing in that much wider gap is filled with brazing brass with the help of torch. Here, capillary action plays no part in making the joint. The technique is also used for the repair of iron and steel castings. The grooves and fillets can also be filled by using bronze rods and then the process can be called as "Bronze welding". The method is particularly useful for repairing cast iron castings. Straight welding of the casting requires its complete preheating, which is not always desirable or feasible. The brasses and bronzes have greater strength and ductility than cast iron and form a strong and satisfactory bond with the base metal. Since the base metal is not fused or highly heated, internal stresses are kept to a minimum and cracking is not likely upon cooling.

Silver Brazing. When silver alloys are used for brazing, the method is called as "Silver brazing" which is often referred to as "Silver Soldering" or "Hard soldering". The method is more expensive than plain brazing because the filler metal is more expensive. The method is preferred where a superior joint is needed and where the quantity of filler metal required is small. It is very popular in small area repair work and is used widely in the electrical and refrigeration industries.

Advantages of Brazing

1. Lower temperatures are involved in brazing than in fusion welding. This minimizes distortion and allows joining at lower preheat temperature than required for fusion welding. Thus, medium carbon, and high-carbon steels and C.I. which harden in the heat affected zone and may be susceptible to cracking may be brazed or braze welded with little or no serious hardening.

2. Almost all the common engineering materials may be satisfactorily brazed or braze welded.

3. Inaccessible joint areas which could not be made by MIG or TIG processes, and spot or seam welding can be formed by brazing.

4. Thin-walled tubes and light-gauge sheet metal assemblies not joinable by welding can be joined by brazing.

5. Brazing can join dissimilar metals such as brass to stainless steels and carbon steels to alloy steels.

6. Multiple joints can be made at one time, as in furnace brazing.

7. Can be employed for joints which may have to be later disassembled.

8. Neat appearing joint requiring a minimum of cleaning.

9. The process can be done more quickly and more economically.

10. Many brazing operations can be mechanised.

11. Because of lower temperatures involved as compared to fusion welding, metallurgical damage to the base metal may be avoided.

Limitations

1. Limited size of parts. Very large assemblies, although brazable, can be made more economically by welding because of the cost and availability of large equipment such as brazing furnaces.

2. Machining of the joint edges for getting the desired fit is costly.

3. Degree of skill required to perform the brazing operations is high.

Uses of Brazing. Assembly of pipes to fittings, carbide tips to tools, radiators, heat exchangers, electrical parts and repair of castings. Leak-tight joints for pressurized and vacuum systems are readily joined by brazing. The copper-brazed joints in steel and the nickel-alloy-brazed joints in stainless steels are made for high-temperature service. Corrosion resistance can be provided for infood-service equipment which employs silver-brazing alloys for joining stainless steels. The chemical industry uses nickle alloy brazing for brazing stainless steels subject to corrosive service.

5.6.2. Soldering. In soldering, two parts are joined by the use of a molten filler metal whose melting point is below the solidus (melting point of the base metals) and in all cases below 427°C.

Soldered joints are weaker than brazed joints. Because of lower working temperatures, good wetting is more critical than in brazing. The soldering process comprises the same steps as the brazing process, that is,

(*i*) Surface preparation which involves fitting the surfaces to each other, cleaning them mechanically and chemically and covering the cleaned surfaces with a flux. The clearance in a joint is about 0.05 to 0.20 mm (for steel).

(*ii*) After this, soldering proper is done.

Commonly used soldering joints are : Lap, butt, seam and pipe joints.

The fluxes used in soldering are : corrosive type and non corrosive type. The common corrosive fluxes are : Zinc chloride, mixtures of zinc chloride and ammonium chloride. The flux must be washed off after soldering to prevent corrosion. Common non corrosive fluxes are rosin and rosin plus alcohol. These are essential for electrical connections where corrosion can create local high resistance and even loss of conduction.

The most widely used solders are alloys of tin and lead in various proportions. Small quantities of some other metals may be added. These filler metals used in soldering are called "Soft solders".

(*i*) 63/37 Tin-lead solder has the lowest melting point and solidifies at a constant temperature. It is most suitable for electrical connections.

(*ii*) 70/30 Tin lead : Good alloy pretinning

(*iii*) 60/40 Tin lead : Good electric - grade solder

(*iv*) 50/50 Tin lead : General purpose solder

(*v*) 32/68 Tin lead : Plumber's solder.

(*vi*) Tin-lead-silver solder : High temperature electrical solder for instruments.

(*vii*) 96.5/3.5 Tin-silver : High temperature electrical instrument solder.

(viii) A low (<5%) tin content gives higher strength and is suitable for automotive radiators and lock seam cans, and tubes made of tin plate.

(ix) 35/65 Tin Lead : Its wide freezing range makes it ideal as a wiping solder for the joining of copper tubes.

(x) Lead silver solders are used for higher temperature service. Ag : 1.5 to 3.5%. Certain other metals such as cadmium, bismuth and indium may be added for some specific purposes.

Lead being toxic has adverse effects on the environment. Due to this, lead free solders are being developed and are now in wider use. They are being used in connection with supplying drinking water and other applications. Typical examples are :

1. Tin-silver (given above) for electronics.
2. Tin-Bismuth (42%, 58%) : for electronics.
3. Tin-zinc alloys with 9 to 100%. Zinc for soldering of aluminium in conjunction with special fluxes.
4. Zinc-aluminium : for corrosion resistance, soldering of aluminium.
5. Cadmium-silver : for strength at high temperatures.

Soldering Techniques. The various techniques used for brazing can also be employed for soldering (flame, hot dip, resistance, induction). Ultrasonic soldering (similar to ultrasonic welding) is used for fluxless soldering of aluminium and some nonferrous metals such as silicon and germanium.

In 'Radiant heating (infrared heating)', special quartz-iodine incandescent tubular lamps are used which can be easily focused to concentrate the heat at the area to be soldered. Radiant heating can also be used for brazing. In "wave soldering" fresh, hot solder is lifted to the connections by one or more standing waves of molten solder. The wave is formed by continuously pumping the solder through a narrow slot, to the surface. All joints are formed as the assembly passes over the waves. The operation is continuous and limited in speed only by time and heat requirements. This method is applicable to such items as the terminals of transformers and the lips of cans. The method is of great value in assembling printed-circuit boards.

Because of the lower temperatures involved, a hand-type heated copper or iron-plated copper bit (soldering iron) is extensively used. The tip of the iron is tinned before applying it to the work. The most common iron is of electric type and is used in many fields like radio and electronic industries. To do a soldering job, the iron is heated to 250 – 300°C, the tip is dipped into the flux, tinned with the solder and then applied to the parts prepared for soldering to heat them at the joint. At the same time, solder is applied to the joint where it is melted by the iron moving along the joint and enters the clearance. Here the solder cools and forms the seam.

5.7. WELDABILITY

Weldability of metals refers to their capacity of being welded into reliable permanent joints (sound welded joints) having specified properties, for example, definite weld strength, proper structure etc. In other words, weldability relates to the ease with which a metal can be welded and to the properties of the joint compared with those of the parent metal. Ease of welding depends upon the melting temperature, thermal conductivity, thermal expansion and the surface condition of the work. The weld quality is related to the possibility of the occurrence of weld defects, the partial loss of constituent elements from the metal due to vaporization and to changes in mechanical properties due to grain growth.

Effects of Various Elements on Weldability

1. Carbon. Carbon has a strong influence on the quality of the weld. An increase in the carbon content affects the strength, hardness and toughness of the weld. When steels having carbon content more that about 0.3% are welded and then cooled suddenly, a brittle zone results along the weld. The effect produced by carbon is much less in arcwelding than in gas-welding process.

2. Manganese. Manganese increases the tendency for hardening. When its content exceeds 0.6%, it lowers the ease of welding especially if the percentage of carbon is also high and such steels are subjected to cracking. On the other hand, a very low percentage of manganese tends to promote internal porosity with cracking. Optimum percentage is 0.4 to 0.6%.

3. Silicon. A high percentage of silicon especially alongwith a high carbon content may result in excessive cracking.

4. Phosphorus. Phosphorus in steel in excess of 0.04% has an unfavourable effect on the mechanical properties of weld since brittleness is increased.

5. Sulphur. Sulphur is added to some steels to give easy machining properties but too high a content has an extremely detrimental effect on the weldability of steels since it causes redshortness and tends to cause cracking at a sulphur content over 0.04%.

Elements such as nickel, chromium and vanadium in steels will lead to the formation of hard brittle zones. To prevent this, heat treatment processes will be required.

Weldability of Various Materials

1. Low Carbon Steels or Mild Steel (C content upto 0.30%). weld easily, no tendency to harden except those having the upper limit of carbon content.

2. Medium Carbon Steels (C content 0.3 to 0.55%). Some care is necessary. Hardening effect of the higher C-content can be prevented by preheating to about 250°C and then slow cooling of the weld.

3. High Carbon Steels (C content 0.55 to 1.20%). These steels can be welded but preheating and post weld treatments are necessary. With the higher carbon contents, a brazing operation is preferred because brazing temperature has little effect on the metallurgical condition of steel.

4. Low Alloy Steels. These steels have good weldability, especially if the carbon content does not exceed about 0.18%. With carbon content greater than this amount, special electrodes are necessary and preheating with slow after cooling will generally be required.

5. Cast Iron. The presence of free graphite and the high carbon content in cast iron lead to considerable difficulties in welding. Also, since its ductility is low, cracks may form in the weldment when cast iron is heated and due to uneven expansion and contraction caused by local heating. Cast iron may be welded either hot or cold.

Hot Welding. The work is preheated to 600 – 650°C and this temperature is maintained throughout the whole welding process. A considerable volume of liquid metal is produced at the weld. This retards the cooling of the molten metal and thereby prevents the chilling. The hot welding of cast iron can be done with either an electric arc or a gas flame and with either complete or restricted preheating of work. For welding small parts of intricate shape, complete preheating is done and is accomplished in metal boxes heated by charcoal. After completing the weld, the part is covered with asbestos or coal dust or embedded in hot sand to retard cooling.

The welding flame or arc tends to burn the silicon out of the weld, allowing the carbon to assume the combined form and render the metal hard when cold. This is overcome by using cast iron welding rods rich in silicon (upto 3.6% Si) so that the loss is replaced by the rod.

Cold Welding. The more widespread method is cold welding of cast iron with an electric arc. No preheating is necessary, because the heat is much more highly concentrated and localised. The finish weld is covered with sheet asbestos or embedded in hot sand to retard cooling.

6. Stainless Steels. Stainless steels always contain chromium, which forms an extremely dense Cr_2O_3 film, which tends to reduce the corrosion resistance of these steels. So, these steels need shielding during welding.

7. Aluminium Alloys. Aluminium oxidises easily and the film of aluminium oxide that forms on its surface has a melting point higher than the parent metal and impedes the fusion of the edges. So, aluminium and its alloys need to be protected against oxidation when welding. Before welding with OAW, the material must be covered with a flux. Preferred welding methods are : TIG and MIG. Also, aluminium and its alloys possess high heat conductivity and a high latent heat of fusion, therefore, they require more heat for welding.

8. Magnesium Alloys. Magnesium alloys are highly inflammable, have low melting point and form very refractory magnesium oxide on the surface of the welding pool. They get easily oxidised and also combine with nitrogen to form magnesuim nitride which weakens the weld. Magnesium also dissolves hydrogen which leads to porosity of the weld. Due to all these factors, these alloys need perfect shielding during welding. The welding techniques are similar to those used for aluminium alloys.

9. Copper and Copper Alloys. Copper and its alloys can be welded by taking certain measures. Electrolytic copper can be welded with a gas flame or a carbon arc. The filler rod used in gas welding is of pure electrolytic copper or of copper containing upto 0.2% P and upto 0.3% Si. These two elements are intensive deoxidisers of welding pool. Because of the high heat conductivity of copper, the torch used should be from 1.5 to 2 times larger than for welding steel.

Brasses are welded by oxidising flame to prevent the fuming away of zinc. Similarly Bronzes are also welded by oxidising flame or arc and argon-arc methods.

10. Nickel Alloys. Most of these alloys are easily oxidised at the welding temperature and so shielding is necessary for good welds. Coated electrodes and shielded arcs can be used.

11. Titanium and Zirconium alloys. These alloys readily combine with N_2, O_2, C and H_2, especially when in the molten state. Therefore effective shielding by an inert gas is essential.

12. Refractory metal alloys. Tungsten, Molybdenum and Niobium can be welded, but the volatility of the oxides makes special techniques (*e.g.* EBM) mandatory.

Table 5.4 illustrates the suitability of various welding processes for various materials.

Table 5.4. Suitability of Various Welding Processes

Materials	Welding / Brazing Process							
	SMAW	SAW	TIG	MIG	Spot	OAW	Furnace Braze	Torch Braze
L-C Steels	R	R	S	S	R	R	R	S
M-C Steels	R	R	S	S	R	R	R	S
L-alloy steels	R	R	S .	S	R	S	S	NR
Austinitic Stainless Steels	R	R	R	R	R	S	S	S
Ferritic and Martensitic Stainless Steels	R	S	S	S	S	S	S	S
High temperature high strength alloys	R	S	S	S	S	S	NR	NR
C.I.	S	NR	S	NR	US	R	NR	R

Al and alloys	S	NR	R	R	R	S	R	R
Mg and alloys	US	US	R	S	S	NR	NR	NR
Ni, Zr and alloys	R	S	R	R	R	S	R	R
Ti and alloys	US	US	R	S	S	US	S	S
Cu and alloys	NR	NR	R	R	S	S	S	R

R : recommended, S: satisfactory

NR : not recommended, US : unsuitable

5.8. TESTING AND INSPECTION OF WELDED JOINTS

Testing and inspection of welded joints is done on the same lines as for castings. The tests fall under two categories : Destructive testing and Non-destructive testing.

Destructive Testing. These tests are done on a sample to improve the design of the weld, welding technique etc. and to know the mechanical properties of the weldment. These mechanical tests included : Tensile test, Bend test, impact strength test, hardness test and relative elongation test. The shape and size of the test specimen are selected to comply with state standards.

Non - Destructive Testing (NDT). The tests under this category include :

(1) **Visual Inspection.** Visual inspection of the weld and checking of its dimensions can reveal : shape of profile, uniformity of surface, undercuts, surface cavities and slag inclusions, cracks, porosity, unfilled craters etc.

(2) Hydraulic tests (pressure tests) are applied to weldments that are to operate under pressure.

(3) Air (pressure) tests are done to check the air tightness of the work.

The other NDT include :

— Radiographic inspection of the weld (x-ray and γ- ray testing) will reveal such defects as porosity, blowholes, cracks, poor fusion and slag inclusion.

— Fluorescent penetrant inspection to reveal fine surface cracks.

— Magnetic inspection reveals fine cracks and pores in the weld.

— Ammonia penetrant test : This is a leak test. The welded vessel is filled with compressed air to which 1% ammonia has been added. The welded joint is then covered with paper impregnated with a 5% solution of mercuric nitrate. Black spots appear on the paper in case of leakage.

5.8.1.Welding Defects

When a weld is completed, the parent (base) metal is hottest at the point of fusion. The temperature of the base metal progressively decreases further away from the centre of fusion zone. Due to this temperature gradient, a fusion weld and the metal adjacent to it contain various zones having distinctly different grain structures and hence different properties.

Various zones of a typical weld are shown in Fig. 5.49. These are :–

(i) *Fusion Zone* :– It is the portion of weld in which the base (parent) metal has been fused (melted).

(ii) *Heat Affectel Zone (HAZ)* :– This is the zone wherein the base metal is metallurgically affected by the heat of welding, but is not melted.

(iii) *Weld Metal Zone (WMZ)* :– This is the portion of the weld which consists of weld metal. This zone includes any base metal which is melted and resolidified, as well as any filler metal which did likewise.

(iv) *Weld Zone* :– Weld Zone = WMZ + HAZ

The welded joint should be free from any defect that would make it unsuitable for its intended purpose. The principal defects to be found in welded joints are as follows :

1. *Cracks* :– Cracks that occur in or near a weld act as stress raisers which make the service life of the weldment very unreliable. Welding cracks are of the following types :

(*a*) *Micro-cracks* :- They are very small and are revealed only under a microscope.

(*b*) *Macro-cracks* :- These cracks can be seen by the unaided eye or by the use of a low power (5 to 10 X) magnifier.

(*c*) *Fissures* :- These are wide cracks which emerge to the surface of the metal.

Cracks may occur at the following locations :-

    (*i*) In the weld (Fuse) Metal Zone

    (*ii*) In the Base metal zone

    (*iii*) Sometimes, the cracks originate in one Zoneand then spreal to theother Zone.

Cracks in the base metal usually occur at low temperatures (around 200°C) and are known as Cold cracks, On the other hand, the cracks in the weld metal zone occur while the metal is still very hot. Such cracks are called Hot cracks.

Cracks in the weld may be due to structural stresses in the metal (for example, the formation of martensite), heavy shrinkage, extra high amount of sulphur, phosphorous or carbon in the metal, excessively rigid clamping of the parts being welded or the presence of gases in the weld metal.

Cold cracking can occur due any to the following several factors :- improper welding conditions, the presence of gas and other impurities in the weld, wrong choice of filler rod and metallurgical factors such as excessive cooling rate resulting in the formation of martensite and formation of brittle phases in the weld when cold or the formation of phases which are brittle at high temperatures [Allotropic transformations].

Cracks in the base metal can occur due to the following reasons :- Corrosion, Base metal defects, Base metal composition variations, hydrogen embrittlement and internal stresses set up due to restrained shrinking after welding.

The phenomenon of cracks can be explained as below :-

With thick parts, the weld zone is normally a small spot within a large mass of cooler metal. Heat flows off rapidly into the surrounding metal. When the welding is completed, what is called a "mass quench" results. This causes hard martensite to form in hardenable steel in part or all of the zone heated above the critical temperature. The martensite is brittle and does not yield but breaks when the stresses in the weld becomes high enough. Formation of martensite must be avoided. The more hardenable the steel, the slower must be the rate of cooling. The parts should also be preheated to retard the cooling rate.

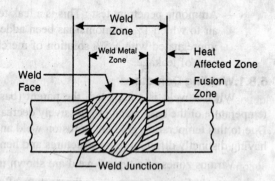

Fig. 5.49. Welding Zones.

Heating and cooling cause expansion and contraction in the weld. The metal in the joint is hotter and tends to shrink more on cooling than the bulk of the metal on either side. If the members being welded are restrained in a fixture or by a structure to which they are attached, high stresses are induced across the weld and thus cause cracking. Even if cracking does not occur, residual stresses may impair fatigue strength and cause warpage or distortion when they are unbalanced by later machining. These can be prevented by : using as thin material and as little filler metal as possible, preheating to minimize temperature difference between the weld and the base metal, and welding from the inside or confined portion of a structure to the outside or points of most freedom, a minimum number of welds and the maximum use of intermittent welds.

Gases such as O_2, N_2 and H_2 are readily absorbed by the molten weld metal. As the molten metal cools, its solubility for these gases diminishes and the gases try to escape. If they are not able to escape and remain within the weld, they will cause porosity and gas pockets in the weld. If they are able to reach just under the outer surface and are not able to escape (if the metal has cooled), they exert pressure and crack the metal. H_2 is a major cause of cracking in steel. Cracking due to gases can be avoided by preventing the evolution of these gases during welding (by thoroughly cleaning the joint from moisture, oil, grease, paint etc.) and absorbing of these gases from the atmosphere (by proper shielding). Slow cooling also eliminates cracking as the gases are able to escape.

2. Udercut. An undercut is a groove melted into the base metal adjacent to the toe of the weld, Fig. 5.50. The reasons for this can be : non-uniform feed of the filler rod, improper position of the electrode or torch tip or excessive heating. Undercutting can sometimes be corrected by adding additional metal to fill the groove.

3. Porosity or voids. Blowholes and gas pockets weaken welds appreciably and act as stress raisers from which cracks spread. The causes of these defects and the remedies have already been discussed above under cracking defect.

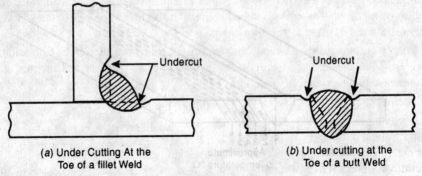

(a) Under Cutting At the Toe of a fillet Weld   (b) Under cutting at the Toe of a butt Weld

Fig. 5.50. Unercut.

4. Inclusions. Inclusions usually refer to slag but may be scale or dirt entrapped in the weld deposit during welding. The inclusions are due to the contamination of the base metal and the deposited metal by oxides, non uniform melting of the electrode coating, high melting point and high viscosity of the slag or insufficient deoxidising of the metal in the weld.

5. Lack of fusion. It is the lack of coalescence between the deposited and the base metal or incomplete penetration of the weld metal into the base metal. The usual cause is in ability to raise the temperature of the base metal to its melting point, and faulty welding conditions and/or techniques.

6. Burning. It is oxidation of the metal in the weld and adjacent base metal. It is caused by a strong oxidising medium, an arc of excessive length or excessively high welding current.

7. Internal residual stresses and distortion. Internal residual stresses and distortion or warping have already been discussed under "cracking".

WELDING MATALLURGY

It may be defined as the science dealing with the factors which affect the properties of the finished weld.

Since most welding is fusion welding, both the base metal welded and any filler rod which may be used, are melted and then resolidified during the process. Consequently, there is a close relationship between casting metallurgy and welding metalllurgy. Both are concerned with the relationship of properties to identifiable micro-structural features, such as dendrites, segregation, columnar grains, centre-line weakness, porosity and inclusions. The problems associated with the solidification of castings, such as, hot tearing, shrinkage stresses, cracking, warping and dimensional changes, also occur in weldments.

The topic of metal working, both hot and cold, is another concern of welding metallurgy. Welds may be worked hot or cold by peening to obtain the sometimes benefitial effects of these processes. The microstructural characteristics of grain size, grain shape, phenomenon of slip, strain hardening, recrystallization and growth are the business of both metal working metallurgy and welding metallurgy.

Heat treatment accompanies every thermal welding process. Both the weld metal itself and the adjacent base metal (HAZ) undergo such heat treating processes as annealing, austenizing, preheating, postheating, normalizing, overheating, quench hardening, tempering, and recrystallization, either by deliberate attempt (intent), or as unavoidable *accompanying effects* of the welding process.

Thermal Effects on Weldment, Heat Affected Zone, Grain Size and its Control : As has been mentioned above when a weld is completed, the parent (Base) metal is hottest at the point of fusion. The temperature of the base metal progressively decreases further away from the centre of fusion zone, Fig. 5.51 due to this temperature gradient, a fusion weld and the metal adjacent to it contain various zones having distinctly different grain structures and hence different properties.

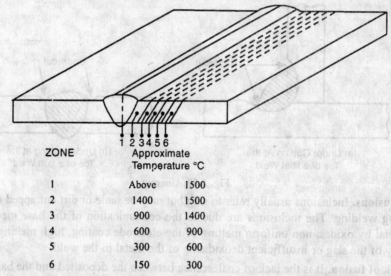

ZONE	Approximate Temperature °C	
1	Above	1500
2	1400	1500
3	900	1400
4	600	900
5	300	600
6	150	300

Fig. 5.51. Temperature Gradient in the Welding Zone (for steel).

As already noted the weld zone (WZ) comprises of weld metal zone (WMZ) and heat affected zone (HAZ), that is,

$$WZ = WMZ + HAZ$$

HAZ extends from the fusion line (which is the junction between weld dilution and the unmelted base metal) to the base metal which has not been sufficiently heated to alter the original structure.

After the completion of the welding process, the molten weld joint is allowed to cool to ambinet temperature. The solidification process is similar to that in a casting. Thus, in this zone

(WMZ or fusion zone), the grain structure has many of the characteristics of a casting. The solidification process beings with the formation of columnar-grains. These grains are relatively long (their lateral growth being restricted due to the neighbouring grains growing longitudinally) and form parallel to the direction of heat flow. Because the molten metal has cooled slowly, it generally generates coarse grains. Thus, the grain structure in the fusion zone has low strength, toughness and ductility.

The HAZ can be divided into sub-zones as shown in Fig. 5.52. The first sub-zone of HAZ, next outward from the WMZ is the grossly HAZ or overheated zone. Here, the temperature of the metal is somewhat less than its melting point. Overheating causes severe grain growth which is very pronounced throughout this zone. It results in coarse grain structure and reduced mechanical properties in comparison with base metal. However granular refinement can be carried out by post-weld heat treatment.

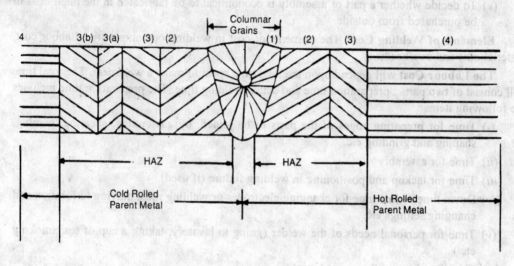

(1) WMZ
(2) Zone of extreme grain growth
(3) Zone of allotropic refinemnt
(3a) Zone of grain growth after recrystallization
(3b) Zone of recrystallized grains
(4) Unaffected zone

Fig. 5.52. Garain Structures in Various Zones of a Welded Joint.

The next sub-zone of HAZ, attains a temperature just above the critical temperature, AC_3 (See Chapter 2), and long enough for the complete allotropic transformation to austenite. It is followed by a cooling rate fast enough to prevent grain growth from taking place. This results in a fine grain structure. This zone is called "refining zone" "or" zone of allotropic refinement".

The nature of the grain structure beyond the refining zone will depend on whether the parent metal was originally in the hot rolled or cold-rolled condition. In the case of hot-rolled condition, the next zone will consist of metal with the unchanged structure of the original base metal and is called as "Unaffected Zone".

If in the cold worked condition, another metallurgical phenomenon will take place, of "recrystallization". The coarse and elongated grains resulting from cold working, will start breaking into fine, equi-axed grains. This sub-zone (of HAZ) of recrystallized fine grains will be separated from the "refining zone" by a small sub-zone containing grains of larger size than those which remained fine after re-crystallization. This is caused by the growth of recrystallized grains nearer the high temperature zone (refining zone). Beyond the recrystallized zone, will be the unaffected zone.

5.9. WELDING COST

Estimates of welding cost may be done for one or more of the following reasons :

(i) To compare the economics of welding process with other processes of fabrication or manufacturing.

(ii) To compare the economics of various methods of welding process.

(iii) To determine the selling price of a product for a quotation, so as to ensure a reasonable profit to the company.

(iv) To check the quotations supplied by vendors.

(v) To decide whether a part or assembly is economical to be fabricated in the plant or is to be purchased from outside.

Elements of Welding Cost. The elements of cost in welding operations are : Labour cost, material cost and overheads.

The Labour Cost will depend upon the total time spent to make a weldment. The total time will consist of two parts : preparation time and actual welding time. The preparation time includes the following items :

(i) Time for preparing edges of the parts to be joined, by gas cutting, shearing, planing, shaping and grinding etc.

(ii) Time for assembly

(iii) Time for tackup and positioning in welding fixture (if used).

(iv) Down time or lost time for changing electrodes or welding rods, moving to location and changing settings etc.

(v) Time for personal needs of the welder (going to lavatory, taking a cup of tea, smoking etc.)

(vi) Time for cleaning the welded joint.

(vii) Time for stress relieving (if required).

Operation factor, OF, is defined as :

$$\text{OF, \%} = \frac{\text{Actual welding time}}{\text{Total time}} \times 100$$

$$= \frac{\text{Actual welding time}}{\text{Actual welding time} + \text{Preparation time}} \times 100$$

$$\text{Actual welding time} = \frac{\text{Total length of job to be welded, m}}{\text{Welding speed, m/hr.}}$$

$$\therefore \quad \text{Labour cost} = (\text{Total welding time, hr.}) \times (\text{Labour rate/hr.}) \qquad \qquad \text{... (a)}$$

Material Cost will consist of : In case of OAW, the cost of welding rods, flux and gases (O_2 and C_2H_2) In case of arc welding, the items to be considered will be electrodes, flux or shielding gas, filler metal (if used) and power.

(i) OAW.

Cost of welding rods = welding rod consumption per m of weld ×

total length of weld, m × welding rod price

Cost of flux = Amount of flux used per kg of welding rod ×

Total kg of welding rod consumed × flux price ... (b)

Note. If flux is coated on the welding rods, then the cost of flux will be included in the welding rod price.

Cost of fuel gases = Amount of gases used, litres × gas price   ... (c)

(ii) Arc Welding

Cost of electrodes = Electrode consumption per m of weld ×

total length of weld, m × electrode price

Cost of flux or shielding gas

$$= \text{flux or shielding gas used per kg of electrode}$$

$$\times \text{ Total kg' of electrode consumed} \times \text{flux or shielding gas price} \quad ... (d)$$

Electrode consumption per metre of weld can be calculated as,

$$m_e = \frac{m}{1-f}$$

where m_e = mass of electrode required, kg

m = mass of the metal deposited, kg

= area of weld, m^2 × length of weld, m × density of weld material, kg/m^3.

f = percentage of electrode mass lost of stub ends, spatter etc.

For SMAW, the value of f can be more 30%

Note. In case of SMAW and FCAW, the cost of flux is not calculated separately, as it is included in the electrode price.

$$\text{Power cost } = \frac{V \times I}{1000} \times \frac{T}{60} \times \frac{1}{\eta} \times \text{rate per unit (k Wh)} \quad ...(e)$$

where V = volts

I = current, amps.

T = welding time in minutes

η = efficiency of the welding machine

= 0.6 for a welding tranformer (a.c.)

= 0.25 to 0.30 for a welding generator (d.c.)

Overheads. There is no direct method of calculating overheads. It is calculated indirectly as proportional to labour cost, as

Overhead cost = labour cost × overhead rate, where   ...(f)

$$\text{Overheads rate } = \frac{\text{Total overheads of the company, for a period}}{\text{Total labour charges of the company, for a period}}$$

Overheads include : equipment depreciation and maintenance, taxes, insurance, technical supervision etc.

The sum of the items (a), (b), (c) and (d) will give the total welding cost.

For various welding processes, the cost items appear in different proportions. For example, for SMAW (manual),

Labour and overheads   = 80 to 86%

Electrodes   = 8 to 15%

Power and Equipment   = 2%

On the other hand, for RW processes, the cost may be mostly for power and equipment and little for labour and non for consumable electrodes.

5.10. DESIGN ASPECTS

The following points should be kept in mind when designing a weldment :

1. Weldments should be designed to require a minimum of weld metal.

2. Thermal contraction of metal, which has been heated by welding, may cause internal residual stresses and distortion. These can be controlled or reduced by :

   (a) Preheating (b) Minimum number of welds (c) Smallest size of weld that fulfills requirements (d) Maximum use of intermittent welds (e) Slow after cooling.

3. Sharp discontinuities in metal should be kept at a minimum since these cause stress concentration.

4. An important strength weld should not be located where much of it may be removed later by machining.

5. Welds should be located so that adequate strength will be provided at the proper places on a structure or part.

6. As far as possible, a straight line force pattern should be provided.

7. Laps, straps and stiffening angles should be avoided except as required for strength.

8. Lap welds and lap strap welds are not recommended for elements over 10 mm thick.

9. Where ever possible, use butt welds.

10. The ends to be welded should be of equal thickness.

11. Welds at the vulnerable cross-sections should be avoided.

12. The use of welding fixtures should be avoided as far as possible.

13. Welds should not be subjected to bending.

14. A weld should not be located at the point of maximum deformation.

15. Ribs should be designed correctly and these should be used with care.

16. Provide for easy access to welds so that they are accessible for inspection.

17. Distribute heavy loading over long welds in the longitudinal direction.

18. Avoid large flat walls, which tend to bulge and flex.

19. The joint should have properly prepared grooves.

20. If alternating stresses are involved, avoid running a weld at right angles to the direction of maximum principal stress owing to the low fatigue resistance offered by welds.

21. Whenever possible, the design should provide for welding in the flat or horizontal position, not overhead.

22. Some design can avoid or minimise edge preparations.

23. Weld bead size should be kept to a minimum to conserve weld metal.

24. Components should fit properly before welding.

5.10.1. Heat input and Efficiency Calculations

(a) **Electric Arc Welding :–**

We know that the power input by the heat source is given as,

$P = V \times I$, watts, where

V = potential of the power source, volts

I = Current, amperes.

Heat input into the workpiece = P × efficiency of heat input/transfer

∴ $Hi = P \times \eta_t$, watts (J/s)

Now heat needed for melting of the workpiece,

H_m = Heat needed to melt a unit volume of workpiece × volume of workpiece melted per unit time.

∴ Melting efficiency, $\eta_m = \dfrac{H_m}{H_i}$

H = Heat energy input (J/mm) = P/v , where v = velocity of heat source (mm/s)

(*b*) **Electric Resistance Welding :–**

We have already noted that the amount of heat generated at the contacting area of the elements to be welded, is given by Joule's law as,

$Q = I^2 Rt$, Joules

where, I = Current in amperes

R = Resistance of the circuit at the contacting area of the elements, in ohms

t = time during which the current flows, in seconds.

Example 1 :– Calculate the melting efficiency in the case of arc welding of steel with a potential of 20 V and current of 200 A. The travel speed is 5 mm/s and the cross-sectional area of the joint is 20 mm². Heat required to melt steel may be taken as 10 J/mm³ and the heat transfer efficiency as 0.85.   (*PTU Dec. 2004*)

Solution : The power input by the heat source is,

$P = V \times I$, watts

$= 20 \times 200 = 4000$ watts

Heat input into the workpiece,

$Hi = P \times \eta$, watts

η_t = Heat transfer efficiency = 0.85

∴ $Hi = 4000 \times 0.85 = 3400$ watts

Now heat needed to melt the workpiece material,

Hm = volume of material melted per unit time × Heat needed to melt a unit volume of the material

Now heat needed to melt a unit volume of material (here steel) is given as = 10J/mm³

Again volume of material melted per unit time

$= 20 \times 5 = 100$ mm³/s

Note :– Heat needed to melt a unit volume of material is also given approximately as,

$$H_{vol.} = \frac{(T_m + 273)^2}{300,000}, \text{J/mm}^3$$

where T_m = Melting point of the material, °C

Now, $H_m = 10 \times 100 = 1000$ J/s = 1000 watts

where $\quad T_m$ = Melting point of the material, °C

Now, $\quad H_m = 10 \times 100 = 1000$ J/s = 1000 watts

$$\therefore \quad \eta_m = \frac{H_m}{H_i} = \frac{1000}{3400} = 29.41\%$$

Example 2: Two steel plates each 1 mm thick are spot welded at a current of 5000 A. The current flow time is 0.1 s. The electrodes used are 5 mm in diameter. Determine the heat generated and its distribution in the weld zone. The effective resistance in the operation is 200 $\mu\Omega$.

Solution. Heat generated,

$$Q = I^2. R.t. \text{ joules} = (5000)^2. 200 \times 10^{-6}.0.1 = 500 \text{ J}$$

In spot welding, there is a depression on the free surface of the plates, so the actual weld area can be taken as a cylinder of 5 mm diameter and height less than (1 + 1 = 2 mm), say 1.5 mm.

$$\therefore \text{ Weld nugget volume } = \frac{\pi}{4} \times 5^2 \times 1.5 \cong 30 \text{ mm}^3$$

$\therefore$ Heat required for melting = 30 × 10 (from example 1) = 300 J

$\therefore$ Heat dissipated into the metal surrounding the nugget = 500 – 300 = 200 J.

Note :– Heat required for melting can also be determined as follows :–

It has been seen that the heat needed to melt 1 gm of steel = 1400 J

Now taking the density of steel as 7800 kg/m³, the

mass of nugget = 0.0078 × 30 = 0.234 gm

$\therefore$ Heat needed for melting = 0.234 × 1400 = 327.6 J

$\therefore$ Heat dissipated = 500 – 327.6 = 172.4 J

Example 3:– How much heat would be generated in the spot welding of two sheets of 1 mm thick steel that required a current of 10000 A for 0.1 seconds ? An effective resistance of 100 $\mu\Omega$ is assumed.

Solution : – Heat generated is given as,

$$Q = I^2. R.t, \text{ Joules}$$
$$= (10,000)^2 \times 100 \times 10^{-6} \times 0.1 = 1000 \text{ J}$$

Example 4 :– Two 1.2 mm thick, flat copper sheets are being spot welded using a current of 6000 A and a current flow time of t = 0.18 s. The electrodes are 5 mm in diameter. Estimate the heat generated in the weld zone. Take effective resistance as 150 $\mu\Omega$.

Solution :-

$$Q = I^2 Rt, \text{ joules} = 6000 \times 6000 \times 150 \times 10^{-6} \times 0.18 = 972 \text{ joules}$$

Example 5:– Calculate the temperature rise in the Example 4, assuming that the heat generated is confined to the volume of material directly between the two electrodes and the temperature is distributed uniformly.

Solution :– Nugget can be taken as a cylinder of 5 mm diameter and 2 mm height.

$$\therefore \text{ Volume of material } = \frac{\pi}{4} \times 25 \times 2 \cong 40 \text{ mm}^3$$

Now density of copper $\cong 9000$ kg/m³

C = specific heat, J/gm K = 0.3936 for Cu. (For steel, it is $\cong 0.46$)

$$\therefore \quad 972 = 0.3936 \ 0.36 \times \Delta T$$

$$\therefore \quad \Delta T \cong 6860°C$$

Example 6 : What amount of heat would be required to melt 200 mm^3 of metal, whose melting temperature is 1050°C.

Solution :– Heat needed to melt a unit volume of material is

given as, $\qquad H_{vol.} = \dfrac{(T_m + 273)^2}{300,000}$, J/mm^3

Now, $\qquad\qquad T_m = 1050°C$

$$\therefore \qquad \frac{1323^2}{300,000} = 5.83 \text{ J/mm}^3$$

$\therefore$ Amount of heat needed to melt 200 mm^3 of material

$$5.83 \times 200 = \textbf{1166 J}$$

General Characteristics of Common Welding Processes are Given in Table 5.5, Below :

Table 5.5. Characteristics of Welding Processes

Welding Process	Materials to be welded		Min. Thickness mm	Costs			operator skill	Operation
	General	Preferred		Equip-ment	Labour	Finishing		
OAW	All but refractory	C.I., Steels	0.6	D-E*	A	A	A	Manual
SMAW	All but Zn	Steels	1.5 - 2.0	D	A	A-B	A	-do-
FCAW	All Steels	L - C Steels	1.5	B - D	A - D	A - C	A - D	All
SAW	All Steels	-do-	5	B - C	B - D	A - C	C - D	Automatic
MIG	All but Zn	Steels, Al, Cu	0.5	B - C	A - C	B - D	A - D	All
TIG	-do-	All but Zn	0.2	B - C	A - C	B - E	A - D	All
EBM	-do-	-do-	0.05	A	A - D	C - E	A - D	All

* A indicates the highest value and E indicates the lowest value.

5.11. HARD FACING OF METALS

Hard facing or surfacing is the technique of depositing a layer of hard material on a component to increase the hardness, strength and wear resistance of the base metal. The technique is widely used in bearings, camshafts, valves and valve seats, hot extrusion dies, closed dies especially for abrasive powders, earth handling and mining equipment of many types such as rock drills, stone crushers etc., hammer mills, shear blades, and many types of trimming and cutting dies.

The composition of the surfacing metal differs from that of the base metal. Hard facing materials include stellite and other cutting and wear-resistant alloys. Tips or rods from 5 to 10 mm thick, cast from stellite alloy, are used in the hard facing of tools by welding techniques. The cutting tool materials with very hard phases (mostly carbides) have such a high alloying-element concentration that they can not be manufactured into welding rods. The ingredients are incorporated in the flux coating or packed inside tubular rods, and the alloy is formed in the welding process itself.

Hard facing is done by means of gas, arc, or shielded arc welding techniques. Gas and shielded arc welding ensures a more uniform composition of the deposited layer. Surfacing by ordinary arc welding is faster and cheaper, but there is greater danger of dilution of the surfacing metal with the base metal. Deposition of tungsten carbide by an electric arc is called "spark hardening", useful for cutting tools. When thick layers are deposited, one speaks of 'weld overlays'. However, the thickness of the deposit should not, as a rule, exceed 2 mm, because the susceptibility to cracking increases with thicker layers.

The hard facing techniques and conditions should ensure a strong bond of the deposit with the base metal, restrict their mixing and avoid the formation of cracks and other defects in the deposited layer. Parts to be hard faced are first preheated to 3500 to 500°C, the hard faced parts are to be cooled slowly.

Hard facing increases the service life of certain parts by 3 or 4 times and enables worn parts to be repeatedly restored.

5.12. CHARACTERISTICS OF WELDING PROCESSES

The characteristics of the main welding processes are given next page in Table 5.6.

Table 5.6. Main Welding Processes and their Characteristics

S. No.	Welding process	Welded Materials	Recommended thickness or cross-section of components welded	Type of welded joint	Methods of cleaning components before welding
1.	Gas welding	Steel, Al alloys, Cu alloys, hard alloys	< 2 mm – 10 mm	Butt, Edge	By steel-wire brush
2.	PGW	Steel	< 25,000 mm^2	Butt	Machining ends with cutting
3.	SMAW	Steel, Al Alloys	> 1.5 – 2 mm	Butt, Lap, T-, and Edge	By steel-wire brush
4.	Carbon-arc Welding	Low C-Steel, Al, Cu	> 4 – 12.0 mm	Butt and Edge	-do-
5.	SAW	Steel	> 2 – 2.5 mm	Butt, Lap, T-, and Edge	-do- or gas flame
6.	Argon-shielded arc welding	Stainless steel, Al and Mg alloys	< 4 mm	Butt, T and Edge	By steel wire brush

7.	Resistance spot welding	Low-carbon, alloyed and stainless steels; Al and Cu alloys	< 12 mm, < 10 mm, < 6 mm, < 2.5 mm	Lap	Cold-drawn steel without cleaning; hot rolled steel cleaning by etching, sand blasting or machining
8.	Flash butt welding	Steel and alloys		Butt	By steel-brush
9.	Upset Butt Welding	Steel, Al Alloys and Cu alloys	upto 1000 mm^2	-do-	Ends cleaning by machining
10.	Atomic hydrogen welding	Alloyed steels	Bars < 10 mm	Butt, T- and Edge	By steel-wire brush
11.	Cold welding (Roll welding)	Low C-, alloyed, and stainless steels; Al and Cu alloys	< 8 mm, < 2 mm	Lap	Sand blasting or machining
12.	LBW	Chemically aggressive and refractory metals and alloys	< 1 mm	Lap	Careful cleaning and degreasing not essential
13.	EBW	-do-		Butt	-do-
14.	USW	Similar and dissimilar metals and alloys	< 10 mm, < 0.05 – 0.5 mm	Lap	-do-
15.	Friction Welding	Carbon and alloys steels, non-ferrous alloys	Round section components < 40 mm dia.	Butt	By steel-wire brush or sand blasting.
16.	ESW	Carbon and alloyed steels	20 – 600 mm	Butt	-do-

PROBLEMS

1. Define the "welding process".
2. Give the applications of the "welding process".
3. Write the advantages and drawbacks of the "welding process".
4. How the "welding process" may be classified ?
5. Differentiate between "autogeneous", "homogeneous", and "hetro- geneous" welding processes.
6. Sketch the various weld joints.
7. Sketch the various types of welds used in making a joint.
8. Sketch and write on the various edge preparations used for welded joints.
9. Sketch and write on the various "welding positions".
10. Why the cleaning of a joint is important before welding ?
11. What is meant by "fluxing" ? Why it is done ? What are the properties which a good flux should possess ?
12. Define : OAW and PGW processes.
13. Sketch and compare the two systems of OAW process.
14. Write on the "Gas welding equipment".
15. Sketch the three types of flames used in OAW process. Give the uses of each.
16. Write the steps in lighting up the OAW flame.
17. Write the closing down procedure of OAW flame.
18. Define power of blow pipe and nozzles.
19. Sketch and compare the two welding techniques used in OAW process.
20. Sketch and explain PGW process.
21. Write about the other gases used in OW process, in place of acetylene.
22. Write on "oxy-acetylene flame cutting". How the cutting tip differs from a welding tip ?
23. Define "electric arc welding".
24. List the principal advantages of :
(a) Arc welding over gas welding.
(b) Gas welding over arc welding.
(c) D.C. arc welding over a.c. arc welding.
25. Sketch the two polarities of d.c. supply and compare these for welding process.
26. Write on the different types of electrodes used in arc welding.
27. What is the purpose of coating on an arc welding electrode ?
28. Write the constituents of a "coating" and write the function of each.
29. Write on "coding" of electric arc electrodes.
29. (a) In a resistance welding process, the applied voltage is 5V. Determine the rate of heat generated per unit area with 25 bridges/cm^2, each brdige having a radius of 0.1mm. The resistivity of the material is given to be 2×10^5 Ohm-cm. (PTU; **Ans.** 1.136×105 $J/s/cm^2$)
30. Name the ten methods of arc welding. Of these methods, which is the most widely used ?
31. Explain the following electric arc welding processes with the help of neat sketches :

a. SMAW	b. FCAW	c. GTAW	d. GMAW
f. Atomic hydrogen welding		g. Electro-slag welding	
h. PAW	i. Stud welding	e. SAW	

32. Name the shielding gases used in "Inert gas arc welding" methods and compare them.

33. What metals can be joined by "shielded arc welding" ? What are some of the most important advantages gained by this type of welding ?

34. Write a note on "electric arc cutting".

35. Define "Resistance welding process".

36. Name six types of resistance welding methods. For what kind of production is resistance welding mainly employed ?

37. With the help of a neat sketch explain the "spot - welding method".

38. What metals may be spot - welded ? Can dissimilar metals be spot - welded ?

39. Sketch and write on the various spot welding machines.

40. How does "seam welding" differ from "spot welding" ?

41. From what materials are spot welding electrodes usually made ?

42. What are the special features of "resistance projection welding" ?

43. With the help of neat sketches explain the following welding methods:
    a. Upset butt welding   b.   Flash butt welding
    c. Percussion butt welding.

44. What is the difference between "flash" and "upset welding" ?

45. With the help of neat sketches explain the following welding methods:
    a. Forge welding   b. Induction welding
    c. Friction welding   d. Ultra-sonic welding
    e. Explosive welding.   f. Cold welding
    g. Electron-beam welding   h. Laser-beam welding
    i. Thermit welding

46. For what commercial applications can the EBW process be economical?

47. What are "flow welding" and "diffusion welding" processes ?

48. Distinguish between "welding", "brazing" and "soldering" processes.

49. Which method of resistance welding is used to join dissimilar metals ?

50. Distinguish between "brazing" and "braze welding".

51. Write the steps to be taken in brazing process.

52. Write about the various fluxes used in brazing process.

53. Write about the filler materials used in brazing process.

54. Write a note on the various brazing methods.

55. Write the advantages and limitations of brazing process.

56. Write the common uses of brazing process.

57. Distinguish between "soft solder" and "hard solder".

58. Write about the various soldering techniques used

59. Define "weldability".

60. What effect does carbon content of steel have on weldability ?

61. What are the effects of the following elements on weldability ? Mn, Si, P, and S.

62. What is the purpose of preheating a part to be welded ? How would you select a preheat temperature?

63. Write briefly on "Testing and Inspection of welded joints".

64. What causes weldments to crack ? Explain the reasons and suggest the remedies.
65. Write the various welding defects. Give their reasons and suggest the remedies.
66. Write a note on welding costs.
67. Give the design aspects of a weldment.
68. Write on "hard facing of metals".
69. List the safety measures to be taken in welding shop.
70. Explain the principle of Arc welding.
71. List the work preparation for welding operation.
72. Identify various welded joints by BIS symbols.
73. List the major advantages and limitations of OAW.
74. Write about selection of filler rod and flux for OAW.
75. List the functions performed by the electrode coatings.
76. How electrodes are selected for a job ?
77. List the common solders used in the soldering method.
78. Write the various fluxes used in the soldering method.
79. State applications of Soldering process.
80. State the advantages and limitations of soldering pocess.
81. Explain fusion as it relates to welding processes.
82. Explain the chemical reaction that takes place in an OAW torch.
83. What is the level of temperature obtained in the three types of flames of an OAW torch ?
84. Why for welding Brasses and Bronzes, an oxidizing flame is desirable ?
85. Why is SMAW a commonly used method of electric arc welding ? Why is it also called stick welding and MMAW ?
86. Why is the quality of SAW very good ?
87. Why a flux is not needed in GTAW and GMAW ?
88. Why is tungsten the preferred material for non-consumable electrodes ?
89. What is the advantage of EBW and LBW as compared to arc welding ?
90. What are : Weld Zone, Fusion Zone, Weld metal Zone and Heat affected Zone ?
91. Discuss the matalurgical effects due to thermal gradients in HAZ.
92. Why is OAW limited to rather thin sections ?
93. What is Arc stability ? How is it achieved ?
94. What is Arc blow ? How is it avoided ?
95. What are the sources of weld spatter ? How can it be controlled ?
96. List a few products that can be fabricated by resistance welding processes.
97. Explain the principle of Electric Resistance Welding/
98. Describe the features of a fusion weld. Identify the different zones.
99. Differentiate between Hot welding and Cold welding.
100. How can cracking in weldments be aboided ?
101. The voltage – arc length characteristic of a D.C. arc is given by $V = (20 + 40L)$ volts, where L is the arc length in cm. The static – volt ampere characteristic of the power source is approximated by a striaght line with no load voltage of 80V and a short circuit current of 1000 A. Determine the optimum arc length and the corresponding Arc power. (*GATE, 1991*

(**Ans.** 0.5 cm, 20 kVA)

102. The voltage – arc length of a.d.c. source is given by
$V = (20 + 4L)$ volts, where L = length of the arc in mm. The arc length is expected to vary between 4 mm and 6 mm and it is desired to limit the current in the range 450 to 550 A. Assuming a linear power source characteristic determine the open circuit voltage and the short circuit current of the power source. **(Ans. 80 V, 1000 A)**

102. (a) In a given are welding operation, the power source is at 20V and current at 300A. If the electrode travel speed is 6mm/s, calculate the cross-sectional area of the joint. The heat transfer efficiency may be taken as 0.80 and melting efficiency as 0.30. Heat required to melt the steel is 10 J/mm^3. **(PTU, Ans. 24 mm^2)**

103. Describe the formation of slag in welding.

104. Discuss the effect of atmospheric gases on welding.

105. Name a few of coating materials and their properties.

106. Which of the following gases is not present in the atmosphere :
    (a) Argon   (b) CO_2 (c) H_2 (d) He   (DU, AMIE)

107. Which of the following gases is removed by the process of reduction :   **(Ans. c)**
    (a) He   (b) H_2 (c) O_2 (d) N_2 **(Ans. c)**

108. Name a few of the inert gases and their functions in welding.   (AMIE, MU, UT)

109. What is the technical meaning of :–
    (a) Hot cracking   (b) Cold cracking   (c) Grain growth   (d) Recrystallization
                                          (L.U.)

110. Which of the following would help to reduce distortion ?
    (a) Concentration of welding to one area.
    (b) Increasing the input of welding heat.
    (c) Use of single V-preparation
    (d) Use of welding sequence.   **(Ans. d)**

111. Which one of the following statements is incorrect.
    (a) The greater the distortion, the less the residual stress.
    (b) The greater the distortion, the greater the residual stress.
    (c) The greater the restraint, the greater the residual stress.
    (d) The greater the weld concentrations, the greater the residal stress. **(Ans. b)**

112. Describe the effects of distortion on welded structure.

113. The type of crystal normally found in a single run are weld in the as welded condition is :-
    (a) Equi-axed   (b) Columnar
    (c) Polycrystalline   (d) Dendritic   **(Ans. b)**

114. When weld metal refinement takes place in a multi-run deposit, it is known by the term :
    (a) Weld annealing   (b) Weld refining
    (c) Weld Normalizing   (d) Weld recrystallization   **(Ans. c)**

115. The first sub-zone in the HAZ of the present metal nearest the weld metal deposit will consist of :
    (a) Large crystal grains   (b) Small crystal grains
    (c) Elongated crystal grains   (d) Distorted crystal grains   **(Ans. a)**

116. Which one of the following statements is correct ?
    (a) Preheating increases hardness   (b) Preheating increases cooling
    (c) Preheating increases dilution   (d) Preheating increases shrinkage stress. **(Ans. c)**

117. During welding, the parent metal in HAZ undergoes certain changes, Discuss these changes.

118. Discuss the effects of preheating.

119. Describe the welding of Cast Iron.   (DU, AMIE, UPSC)

120. What is the effect of Carbon in welding of plain carbon steels.

121. Which one of the following NDT would be used to examine a completed weld for surface defects :
    (a) Ultrasonics   (b) Dye-penetrant
    (c) Radiography   (d) Acoustics   (*I. Mech E., AMIE*) (**Ans.** *b*)

122. If a fabricated vessel is to be pressure tested using water, it will come under the heading of :
    (a) Ultrasonics   (b) Pneumatics   (c) Hydraulics   (*DU*) (**Ans.** *c*)

123. Describe the testing of weldments with penetrants
    (a) Dye   (b) Fluorescent

124. State some of the NDT used for testing weldments. Give their advantages and disadvantages.

125. The voltage- arc length characteristics of a power source is V = 20 + 40 L, where V = operating voltage, L = arc length, mm.

   Determine OCV and short circuit current for arc length ranging from 3 to 5 mm and the current from 400 to 500 A during welding operation.   (*GATE, 1993*)

   Solution : – Voltage - arc length characteristic is :—

   V (voltage drop across arc) = 20 (electrode drop) + 40 L (column drop).

   Power source characteristic is :—

   $$\frac{V}{OCV} + \frac{I}{SCC} = 1$$

   Now $V_1 = 20 + 40 \times 3 = 140$ V
                $V_2 = 20 + 40 \times 5 = 220$ V

   $$\therefore \quad \frac{140}{OCV} + \frac{500}{SCC} = 1 \quad \text{and} \quad \frac{200}{OCV} + \frac{400}{SCC} = 1$$

   From here, OCV = 540 V and SCC = 675 A

   Note :—   For welding arc
                  $V = a + bL$ .... (1)

   For Power source,

   $$V = OCV - \left(\frac{OCV}{SCC}\right) I \qquad\qquad ... (2)$$

   where I = Arc current, V = Arc voltage

   OCV = open circuit voltage, SCC = short circuit current

   For stable arc, (1) = (2)

6

Machining Process

6.1. GENERAL

Metal cutting or "Machining" is the process of producing a workpiece by removing unwanted material from a block of metal, in the form of chips. This process is most important since almost all the products get their final shape and size by metal removal, either directly or indirectly. The major drawback of the process is loss of material in the form of chips. Inspite of these drawbacks, the machining process has the following characteristics :

1. They improve the dimensional accuracy and tolerances of the components produced by other processes.

2. Internal and external surface features which are difficult or not possible to be produced by other processes, can be produced by machining processes.

3. Specified surface characteristics or texture can be achieved on a part or whole of the component.

4. It may be economical to produce a component by machining process.

In this chapter, we shall have a fundamental understanding of the basic metal cutting process.

6.2. THE MECHANICS OF CHIP FORMATION

A typical metal cutting process can be schematically represented as shown in Fig. 6.1. A wedge-shaped tool is made to move relative to the workpiece. As the tool makes contact with the metal, it exerts a pressure on it resulting in the compression of the metal near the tool tip. This induces shear-type deformation within the metal and it starts moving upward along the top face of the tool. As the tool advances, the material ahead of it is sheared continuously along a plane called the "Shear plane". This shear plane is actually a narrow zone (of the order of about 0.025 mm) and extends from the cutting edge of the tool to the surface of the workpiece. The cutting edge of the tool is formed by two intersecting surfaces. The surface along which the chip moves upwards is called "Rake surface" and the other surface which is relieved to avoid rubbing with the machined surface, is called "Flank". The angle between the rake surface and the normal is known as "Rake angle", α (which may be positive or negative), and the angle between the flank and the horizontal machined surface is known as the "relief or clearance angle", γ. Most cutting processes have the same basic features as shown in Fig. 6.1, where a single point cutting tool is used (a milling cutter, a drill, and a broach can be regarded as several single-point tools joined together and are known as multi-point tools).

6.3. SINGLE POINT CUTTING TOOL

A single point cutting tool consists of a sharpened cutting part called its point and the shank, (Fig. 6.2). The point of the tool is bounded by the face (along which the chips slide as they are cut

405

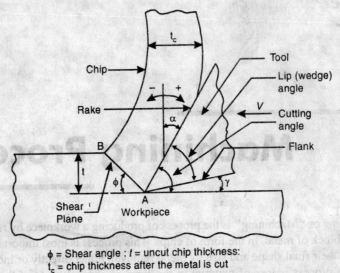

ϕ = Shear angle : t = uncut chip thickness:
t_c = chip thickness after the metal is cut

Fig. 6.1. Schematic Representation of Machining Process.

by the tool), the side flank or major flank the end flank, or minor flank and the base. The side cutting edge, *a-b*, is formed by the intersection of the face and side flank. The end cutting edge *a-c* is formed by the intersection of the face and the end flank. The chips are cut from the work piece by the side-cutting edge. The point '*a*' where the end and side-cutting edges meet is called the "nose" of the tool. Fig 6.2 is for a right hand tool. Below, we give the definitions of the various tool elements and tool angles :–

Shank. It is the main body of the tool.

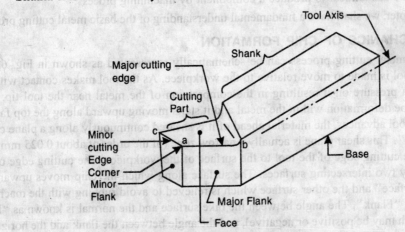

Fig. 6.2. A Single Point Cutting Tool.

Flank. The surface or surfaces below and adjacent to the cutting edge is called flank of the tool.

Face. The surface on which the chip slides is called the face of the tool.

Heel. It is the intersection of the flank and the base of the tool.

Nose. It is the point where the side cutting edge and end cutting edge intersect.

Cutting edge. It is the edge on the face of the tool which removes the material from the workpiece. The total cutting edge consists of side cutting edge (major cutting edge), end cutting edge (minor cutting edge and the nose).

A single point cutting tool may be either right or left hand cut tool depending on the direction of feed. In a right cut tool, the side cutting edge is on the side of the thumb when the right hand is placed on the tool with the palm downward and the fingers pointed towards the tool nose (Fig. 6.3 *b*). Such a tool will cut when fed from right to left as in a lathe in which the tool moves from tailstock to headstock. A left-cut tool is one in which the side cutting edge is on the thumb side when the left hand is applied (Fig. 6.3 *a*). Such a tool will cut when fed from left to right.

The various types of surfaces and planes in metal cutting are explained below with the help of Fig. 6.4, in which the basic turning process is shown. The three types of surfaces are :—

(1) the work surface, from which the material is cut.

(2) the machined surface which is formed or generated after removing the chip.

(3) the cutting surface which is formed by the side cutting edge of the tool.

The references from which the tool angles are specified are the 'cutting plane' and the 'basic plane' or the 'principal plane'. The cutting plane is the plane tangent to the cutting surface and passing through and containing the side cutting edge. The basic plane is the plane parallel to the longitudinal and cross feeds, that is, this plane lies along and normal to the longitudinal axis of the workpiece. In a lathe tool, the basic plane concides with the base of the tool.

6.3.1. Designation of Cutting Tools. By designation or nomenclature of a cutting tool is meant the designation of the shape of the cutting part of the tool., The two systems to designate the tool shape, which are widely used, are :—

1. American Standards Association System (ASA) or American National Standards Institute (ANSI).

2. Orthogonal Rake System (ORS).

ASA System. In the ASA system, the angles of tool face, that, is its slope, are defined in two orthogonal planes, one parallel

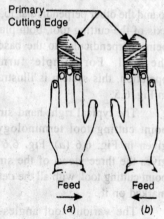

Fig. 6.3. Left and Right Cut Tools.

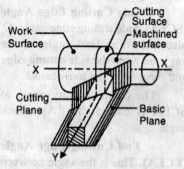

Fig. 6.4. Principal Surfaces and Planes in Metal Cutting.

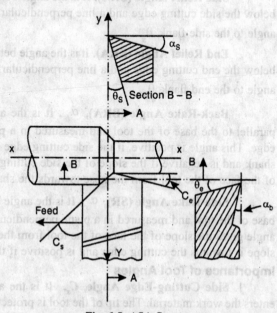

Fig. 6.5. ASA System.

to and the other perpendicular to, the axis of the cutting tool, both planes being perpendicular to the base of the tool. For simple turning operation, this system is illustrated in Fig. 6.5.

The typical right hand single point cutting tool terminology is given in Fig. 6.6 (a). Fig. 6.6 (b) gives the three views of the single point cutting tool, with all the details marked on it.

The various tool angles are defined and explained below :

Side Cutting Edge Angle (SCEA). Side cutting edge angle, C_s also known as lead angle, is the angle between the side cutting edge and the side of the tool shank.

The complimentary angle of SCEA is called the "Approach angle"

End Cutting-Edge Angle (ECEA). This is the angle between the end cutting edge and a line normal to the tool shank C_e.

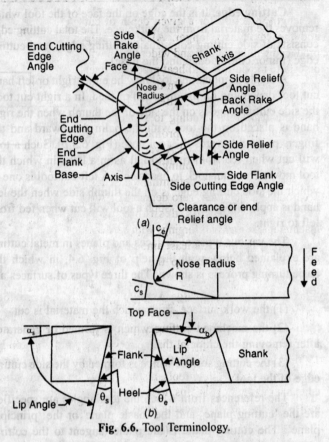

Fig. 6.6. Tool Terminology.

Side Relief Angle (SRA). It is the angle between the portion of the side flank immediately below the side cutting edge and a line perpendicular to the base of the tool, and measured at right angle to the side flank θ_s.

End Relief Angle (ERA). It is the angle between the portion of the end flank immediately below the end cutting edge and a line perpendicular to the base of the tool, and measured at right angle to the end flank θ_e.

Back-Rake Angle (BRA), α_b. It is the angle between the face of the tool and a line parallel to the base of the tool and measured in a plane (perpendicular) through the side cutting edge. This angle is positive, if the side cutting edge slopes downwards from the point towards the shank and is negative if the slope of the side cutting edge is reverse. So this angle gives the slope of the face of the tool from the nose towards the shank.

Side-Rake Angle (SR), α_s. It is the angle between the tool face and a line parallel to the base of the tool and measured in a plane perpendicular to the base and the side cutting edge. This angle gives the slope of the face of the tool from the cutting edge. The side rake is negative if the slope is towards the cutting edge and is positive if the slope is away from the cutting edge.

Importance of Tool Angles :

1. **Side Cutting-Edge Angle,** C_s. It is the angle which prevents interference as the tool enters the work material. The tip of the tool is protected at the start of the cut, Fig. 6.7, as it enables the tool to contact the work first behind the tip. This angle affects tool life and surface finish. This angle can vary from 0° to 90°. The side cutting edge at increased value of SCEA will have more of

its length in action for a given depth of cut and the edge lasts longer. Also, the chip produced will be thinner and wider which will distribute the cutting and heat produced over more of the cutting edge. On the other hand, the larger this angle, the greater the component of force tending to separate the work and the tool. This promotes chatter. Satisfactory values of SCEA vary from 15° to 30°, for general machining. The shape of the workpiece will also determine the SCEA. To produce a shoulder, zero degree SCEA is needed. No SCEA is desirable when machining castings and forgings with hard and scaly skins, because the least amount of tool edge should be exposed to the destructive action of the skin.

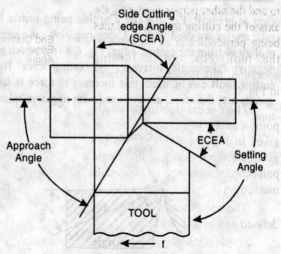

Fig. 6.7. SCEA and ECEA.

2. **End Cutting-Edge Angle, C_e.** The ECEA provides a clearance or relief to the trailing end of the cutting edge to prevent rubbing or drag between the machined surface and the trailing (non-cutting) part of the cutting edge. Only a small angle is sufficient for this purpose. Too large an ECEA takes away material that supports the point and conducts away the heat. An angle of 8° to 15° has been found satisfactory in most cases on side cutting tools, like boring and turning tools. Sometimes, on finishing tools, a small flat (1.6 to 8 mm long) is ground on the front portion of the edge next to the nose radius, to level the irregular surface produced by a roughing tool. End cutting tools, like cut off and necking tools often have no end cutting-edge angle.

3. **Side Relief Angel, (SRA) and End Relief Angle (ERA).** These angles (denoted as θ_s and θ_e in the figure) are provided so that the flank of the tool clears the workpiece surface and there is no rubbing action between the two. Relief angles range from 5° to 15° for general turning. Small relief angles are necessary to give strength to the cutting edge when machining hard and strong materials. Tools with increased values of relief angles penetrate and cut the workpiece material more efficiently and this reduces the cutting forces. Too large relief angles weaken the cutting edge and there is less mass to absorb and conduct the heat away from the cutting edge.

4. **Back and Side Rake Angle (α_b, α_s).** The top face of the tool over which the chip flows is known as the rake face. The angle which this face makes with the normal to the machined surface at the cutting edge is known as "Back-rake angle, α_b", and the angle between the face and a plane parallel to the tool base and measured in a plane perpendicular to both the base of the tool holder and the side cutting edge, is known as "Side-rake angle, α_s" The rake angles may be positive, zero, or negative. Cutting angle and the angle of shear are affected by the values for rake angles. Larger the rake angle, smaller the cutting angle (and larger the shear angle) and the lower the cutting force and power. However, since, increasing the rake angle decreases the cutting angle, this leaves less metal at the point of the tool to support the cutting edge and conduct away the heat. A practical rake angle represents a compromise between a large angle for easier cutting and a small angle for tool strength. In general, the rake angle is small for cutting hard materials and large for cutting soft ductile materials. An exception is brass which is machined with a small or negative rake angle to prevent the tool form digging into the work.

The use of negative rake angles started with the employment of carbide cutting tools. When we use positive rake angle, the force on the tool is directed towards the cutting edge, tending to chip or break it, Fig. 6.8 (*a*). Carbide being brittle lacks shock resistance and will fail if positive rake angles are used with it. Using negative rake angles, directs the force back into the body of the tool away from the cutting edge, Fig. 6.8 (*b*), which gives protection to the cutting edge. The use of negative rake angle, increases the cutting force. But at higher cutting speeds, at which carbide cutting tools can be used, this increase in force is less than at normal cutting speeds. High cutting speeds are, therefore, always used with negative rakes, which requires ample power of the machine tool.

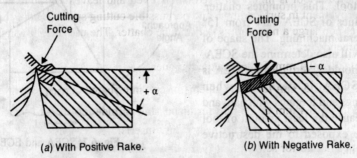

(*a*) With Positive Rake.   (*b*) With Negative Rake.

Fig. 6.8. Cutting with Positive and Negative Rake Tools.

The use of indexable inserts has also promoted the use of negative rake angles. An insert with a negative rake angle has twice as many cutting edges as an equivalent positive rake angle insert (as will be discussed ahead). So, to machine a given number of components, smaller number of negative rake inserts are needed as compared to positive rake inserts.

The use of positive rake angles is recommended under the following conditions :

1. When machining low strength ferrous and non-ferrous materials and work-hardening materials.

2. When using low power machines.

3. When machining long shafts of small diameters.

4. When the set up lacks strength and rigidity.

5. When cutting at low cutting speeds.

The use of negative rake angles is recommended under the following conditions :

1. When machining high strength alloys.

2. When there are heavy impact loads such as in interrupted machining.

3. For rigid set ups and when cutting at high speeds.

Recommended rake angles are given in Table 6.1.

Table 6.1. Recommended Rake Angles

Work Material	Tool Material					
	H.S.S. and Cast Alloys		Cemented Carbide			+
			Brazed		Throw away	
	Back	Side	Back	Side	Back	Side
Free Machining Steels	10	12	0	6	− 5	− 5
Mild Steel	8	10	0	6	− 5	− 5
Med. Carbon Steels	0	10	0	6	− 5	− 5
Alloy tool Steels	0	10	− 5	− 5	− 5	− 5
Stainless Steels	0	10	0	6	− 5	− 5
Cast Iron	5	5 to 10	0	6	− 5	− 5

Aluminium Alloys	20	15	3	15	0	5
Copper Alloys	5	10	0	8	0	5
Magnesium Alloys	20	15	3	15	0	5
Titanium Alloys	0	5	0	6	– 5	– 5

5. Nose Radius. Nose radius is favourable to long tool life and good surface finish. A sharp point on the end of a tool is highly stressed, short lived and leaves a groove in the path of cut. There is an improvement in surface finish and permissible cutting speed as nose radius is increased from zero value. Too large a nose radius will induce chatter. The use of following values for nose radius is recommended :

$R = 0.4$ mm, for delicate components.

≥ 1.5 mm for heavy dpeths of cut, interrupted cuts and heavy feeds.

$= 0.4$ mm to 1.2 mm for disposable carbide inserts for common use.

$= 1.2$ to 1.6 mm for heavy duty inserts.

The rules of thumb for selection of Nose radius are :-

(*i*) For a strong cutting edge, select the largest prossible Nose radius.

(*ii*) A large nose radius permits higher feeds.

(*iii*) Select a smaller nose radius if there is a tendency to vibrate.

For rough machining, the most commonly used nose radii are 1.2 to 1.6 mm

Tool Designation. The tool designation or tool signature, under ASA system is given in the order given next :

Back rake, Side rake, End relief, Side relief, End cutting edge angle, Side cutting edge angle, and nose radius that is,

$$\alpha_b - \alpha_s - \theta_e - \theta_s - C_e - C_s - R$$

If tool designation is :

$$8 - 14 - 6 - 6 - 6 - 15 - \frac{1}{8}, \text{ it means that,}$$

$$\alpha_b = 8°, \qquad \alpha_s = 14°$$

$$\theta_e = 6°, \qquad \theta_s = 6°$$

$$C_e = 6°, \qquad C_s = 15°$$

and $$R = \frac{1"}{8}.$$

In ASA system of tool angles, the angles are specified independently of the position of the cutting edge. It, therefore, does not give any indication of the behaviour of the tool in practice. Therefore, in actual cutting operation, we should include the side cutting edge (principal cutting edge) in the scheme of reference planes. Such a system is known as Orthogonal Rake System (ORS).

Orthogonal Rake System (ORS). As mentioned above, in this system the planes for designating tools are the plane containing the principal or side cutting edge and the plane normal to it. In the plane NN which is normal to the principal cutting edge and is known as Orthogonal plane or the chief plane, we have the following angles : side relief angle the side rake angle (known as Orthogonal rake angle) wedge (lip angle) and the cutting angle (see Fig. 6.9).

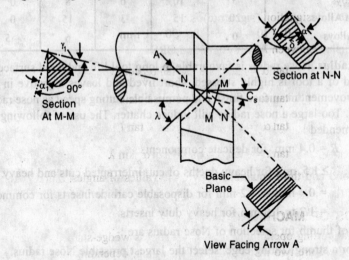

Section at N-N

Section At M-M

Basic Plane

View Facing Arrow A

Fig. 6.9. ORS of Tool Angles.

The side relief angle is the angle between the side (main) flank and the cutting plane. The side rake angle, α, is the angle between the toolface and a plane normal to the cutting plane and passing through the main cutting edge. This angle is positive when the face slopes downward from the plane perpendicular to the cutting plane (as shown in Fig. 6.9), equal to zero when the face is perpendicular to the cutting plane and negative when the face slopes upwards. The "wedge angle, β" is the angle between the tool face and the main flank. The "cutting angle, δ" is the angle between the tool face and the cutting plane. When α is positive, we have,

$$\alpha + \gamma + \text{ wedge angle} = 90°$$

$$\gamma + \beta = \delta$$

The usual values of α and γ are :

$$\alpha = -10° \text{ to } + 15°, \ \gamma = 6° \text{ to } 12°$$

In the ORS, the back rake angle is the inclination angle (i) between the principal cutting edge and a line passing through the point of the tool parallel to the principal plane. This angle is measured in a plane passing through the main cutting edge and perpendicular to the basic plane. In Fig. 6.9, the angle i is negative with tool nose being the highest point of the cutting edge. It will be zero when the cutting edge is parallel to the basic plane and positive if the cutting edge is towards the right (Fig. 6.9) of the line passing through the point of the tool and parallel to the principal (basic) plane, that is, the tool nose is the lowest point of the cutting edge.

In addition to the angles discussed above, angles are also measured in the plane MM (known as Auxiliary reference plane) which is normal to the projection of the end cutting edge on the basic plane. These angles are the end relief angle γ_1, and the back rake angle α_1 (also called auxiliary rake angle). The plan angles are the Approach angle or entering angle λ which is equal to (90° – C_s) and the end cutting edge angle, C_e.

$$\gamma_1 = 8° \text{ to } 10°, \ \lambda = 30° \text{ to } 70°, \ C_e = 10° \text{ to } 15°$$

The tool designation under ORS is :

$$i - \alpha - \gamma - \gamma_1 - C_e - \lambda - R$$

A typical tool designation (signature) is :

$$0 - 10 - 6 - 6 - 8 - 90 - 1 \text{ mm}$$

Interconversion between ASA system and ORS

$$\tan \alpha = \tan \alpha_s \sin \lambda + \tan \alpha_b \cos \lambda$$

$$\tan \alpha_b = \cos \lambda \tan \alpha + \sin \lambda \tan i$$

$$\tan \alpha_s = \sin \lambda \tan \alpha - \cos \lambda \tan i$$

$$\tan i = -\tan \alpha_s \cos \lambda + \tan \alpha_b \sin \lambda$$

In the second and third equations above, the values of angles α and i are taken with their signs.

6.4. METHODS OF MACHINING

In the metal cutting operation, Fig. 6.1, the tool is wedge-shaped and has a straight cutting edge. Basically, there are two methods of metal cutting, depending upon the arrangement of the cutting edge with respect to the direction of relative work-tool motion :

1. Orthogonal cutting or two dimensional cutting.

2. Oblique cutting or three dimensioning cutting.

In orthogonal cutting, Fig. 6.10, the cutting edge of the tool is arranged perpendicular to the cutting velocity vector, V, whereas in oblique cutting, it is set at some angle other than to the cutting velocity vector, which gives an "inclination angle i". The analysis of oblique cutting being very complex, the relatively simple arrangement of orthogonal cutting is, therefore, widely used in theoretical and experimental work.

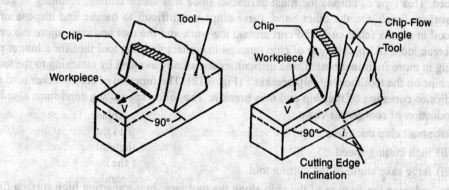

Fig. 6.10. Methods of Machining.

In pure orthogonal cutting, $i = 0°$, $C_e = 0°$, and $\lambda = 90°$. This is also known as orthogonal system of second kind. When $i = 0$, and $0 < \lambda < 90°.0$, it is called as orthogonal system of first kind. A common example of pure orthogonal cutting process is the turning of a thin pipe with a straight edged tool set normal to the longitudinal axes.

6.5. TYPES OF CHIPS

Whatever the cutting conditions can be, the chips produced may belong to one of the following three types, (Fig. 6.11) :

1. Discontinuous Chips.

2. Continuous Chips

3. Continuous Chips with build-up-edge (BUE).

Discontinuous Chips. These types of chips are usually produced when cutting more brittle materials like grey cast iron, bronze and hard brass. These materials lack the ductility necessary for appreciable plastic chips formation. The material ahead of the tool edge fails in a brittle fracture manner along the shear zone. This produces small fragments of discontinuous chips. Since the chips break up into small segments, the friction between the tool and the chips reduces, resulting in better surface finish. These chips are convenient to collect, handle and dispose of. Discontinuous chips are also produced when cutting more ductile materials under the following conditions :

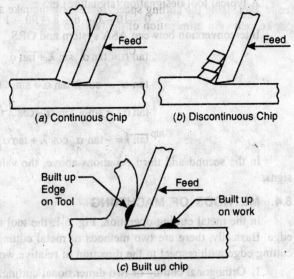

(a) Continuous Chip   (b) Discontinuous Chip

(c) Built up chip

   (i) large chip thickness.

  (ii) low cutting speed.

 (iii) small rake angle of the tool.

 (iv) cutting with the use of a cutting fluid.

Fig. 6.11. Types of Chips

Continuous Chips. These types of chips are produced when, machining more ductile materials. Due to large plastic deformations possible with ductile materials, longer continuous chips are produced. This type of chip is the most desirable, since it is stable cutting, resulting in generally good surface finish. On the other hand, these chips are difficult to handle and dispose off. The chips coil in a helix (chip curl) and curl around the work and the tool and may injure the operator when break loose. Also, this type of chip remains in contact with the tool face for a longer period, resulting in more frictional heat. These difficulties are usually avoided by attaching to the tool face or machine on the tool face, a 'chip breaker', (Fig. 6.12). The function of chip breaker is to reduce the radius of curvature of the chip and thus break it. The following cutting conditions also help in the production of continuous chips :

   (i) small chip thickness.

  (ii) high cutting speed.

 (iii) large rake angle of the cutting tool.

 (iv) reducing the friction of the chip along the tool face, by : imparting high surface finish to the tool face, use of tool material with low co-efficient of friction, and use of a good cutting fluid.

Continuous Chips with Built-up-edge (BUE). When machining ductile materials, conditions of high local temperature and extreme pressure in the cutting zone and also high friction in the tool-chip interface, may cause the work material to adhere or weld to the cutting edge of the tool forming the built-up edge. Successive layers of work material are then added to the built-up edge. When this edge becomes larger and unstable, it breaks up and part of it is carried up the face of the tool alongwith tne chip while the remaining is left over the surface being machined, which contributes to the roughness of the surface. The built-up edge changes its size during the cutting operation. It first increases, then decreases, then again increases etc. This cycle is a source of vibration and poor surface finish. Although, the built-up edge protects the cutting edge of the tool, it changes the geometry of the cutting tool. Low cutting speed also contributes to the formation of the built-up edge. Increasing the cutting speed, increasing the rake angle and using a cutting fluid contribute to the reduction or elimination of the built-up edge.

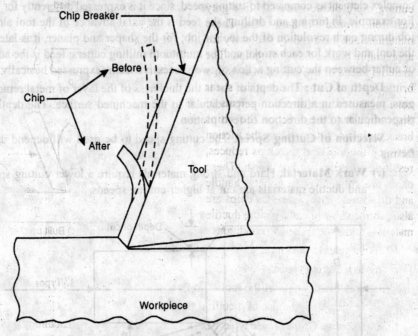

Fig. 6.12. Chip Breaker.

From the above discussion, we can summarize the factors that are likely to influence the formation of various types of chips.

Factors	Types of Chips		
	Continuous	*Continuous with B.U.E.*	*Discontinuous*
Material	Ductile	Ductile	Brittle
Tool :-			
Rake angle	Large	Small	Small
Cutting edge	Sharp	Dull	–
Cutting conditions :			
Speed	High	Low	Low
Feed	Low	High	High
Friction	Low	High	–
Cutting Fluid	Efficient	Poor	–

6.6. PRINCIPAL ELEMENTS OF METAL MACHINING

The principal elements of metal machining are :

(*a*) Cutting Speed   (*b*) Feed   (*c*) Depth of Cut

Cutting Speed. The cutting speed can be defined as the relative surface speed between the tool and the job. It is a relative term, since either the tool or the job or both may be moving during cutting. It is expressed in metres per minute (mpm). It is thus the amount of length that will pass the cutting edge of the tool per unit of time.

Feed. It may be defined as the relatively small movement per cycle of the cutting tool, relative to the work piece in a direction which is usually perpendicular to the cutting speed direction. It is expressed in millimetres per revolution (mm/rev) or millimetres per stroke (mm/str). It is more complex element as compared to cutting speed, since it is expressed differently for various operations. For example, in turning and drilling, the feed is the axial advance of the tool along or through the job during each revolution of the tool or job; for the shaper and planer, it is lateral offset between the tool and work for each stroke and for multitooth milling cutters, feed is the advance of the work or cutter between the cutting action of two successive teeth (expressed basically as mm/per tooth).

Depth of Cut : The depth of cut is the thickness of the layer of metal removed in one cut, or pass, measured in a direction perpendicular to the machined surface. The depth of cut is always perpendicular to the direction of feed motion.

Selection of Cutting Speed. The cutting speed to be used will depend upon the following factors :

(*i*) **Work Material.** Hard and strong materials require a lower cutting speed; whereas soft and ductile materials are cut at higher cutting speeds.

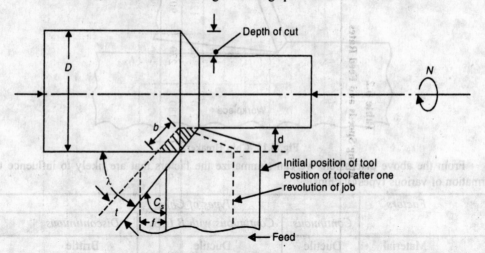

Fig. 6.13. Elements of Machining Process.

(*ii*) **Cutting Tool Material.** Special cutting tool materials, for example, cemented carbides, ceramics, Stellite and H.S.S. will cut at much higher cutting speeds than alloy or carbon steel tools.

(*iii*) **The Depth of Cut and Feed.** A light finishing cut with a fine feed may be run at a higher speed than a heavy roughing cut.

(*iv*) **Desired cutting tool life.** The tool life is a direct function of cutting temperature which increases with increase in cutting speed. Thus as the cutting speed is increased, cutting tool life is decreased.

(*v*) **Rigidity and conditions of the machine and tool and the rigidity of the work.** An old, loose machine working with a poorly supported tool on a thin bar, will not cut at such a high speed, as a good machine with rigid tool operating on a well supported bar of reasonable dimensions.

Table 6.2
Cutting Speeds and Feed Rates

Work material	Cutting Speed V in mpm									Feed rate f in mm/rev.	
	H.S.S. tool				Carbide tool		Stellite tool				
	Turn		Ream and Thread	Drill	Turn		Turn				
	Rough	Finish			Rough	Finish	Rough	Finish		Rough	Finish
Mild Steel	40	60	7.5 to 15	30	90	180	50	75		0.625 to 2.0	0.125 to 0.75
Cast Steel	15	24	3.5	12	45	100	24	33		0.5 to 1.25	0.125 to 0.175
Grey C.I.	18	27	3.5	13	60	100	33	45		0.4 to 2.5	0.2 to 1.0
Aluminium	90	150	15	72	240	360	120	180		0.1 to 0.5	0.075 to 0.25
Brass	75	100	18	60	180	270	90	150		0.375 to 2.0	0.2 to 1.25
Phosphor Bronze	18	36	4.5	13	120	180	30	50		0.375 to 0.75	0.125 to 0.5

Selection of Feed. Feeds, to be used, will depend upon the following factors :

(*i*) **Smoothness of the finish required.** A coarse feed will give wider and deeper machining marks and an inferior finish to a fine feed. A blunt nosed tool will give a better finish than a sharp tool for the same feed.

(*ii*) **Power available, condition of the machine and its drive.** The product of the speed, feed and depth of cut gives the amount of metal being removed and hence the power necessary. A coarse feed on a poor or badly driven machine will be harmful both for the machine and the tool. This will also result in slipping of the drive or belt.

(*iii*) **Type of Cut.** As a general rule, give coarsest feed possible for a roughing cut because finishing is unimportant. For a finishing cut, the feed should be fine enough to give the class of finish required.

(*iv*) **Tool Life.** The cutting temperature increases with increase of feed, resulting in decreased tool life.

A simple rule of thumb connecting feed and nose radius is, for rough turning, :

f (mm/rev.) = 0.5 × Nose Radius

The maximum recommended feed rate is of the order of $\dfrac{2}{3}$ of the nose radius.

The higher feeds apply for inserts :-

(*i*) having a strong cutting edge with at least a 60° cutting edge angle

(*ii*) that are single sided.

(*iii*) that are used with a smaller entering angle than 90°.

(*iv*) that are used in materials with good machinability and moderate cutting speeds.

Selection of Depth of Cut. The depth of cut to be used will depend upon the following factors :-

(*i*) **Type of Cut.** Use large depths of cut for roughing operations than for finishing operations.

(*ii*) **Tool Life.** The cutting temperature increases with increase of depth of cut, resulting in decreased tool life.

(*iii*) **Power Required.** As discussed above, the cutting speed multiplied by area of cut (feed x depth of cut) gives the metal removal rate, which gives the power requirements. For a given area of cut, a large ratio of depth of cut to feed usually gives the most efficient performance as well as a better surface finish.

The three elements of machining process are shown in Fig. 6.13, for a simple turning operation on a centre lathe.

The cutting speed is given as :

$$V = \frac{\pi D N}{1000}, \text{m / min}.$$

where D = Diameter in mm of work or cutter

N = rev. / min. of work or cutter.

V = cutting speed of work or cutter

The common values of cutting speed and feed are given in Table 6.2. The depth of cut can be taken as equal to 4 to 5 mm in rough turning. 0.5 to 2 mm for semi finish turning and 0.1 to 0.4 mm for finish turning.

Depth of cut is usually takew 3 to 5 times the feed for rough opeatious. The values for finishing operations are usually small.

6.7. THERMAL ASPECTS OF CHIP FORMATION

Work is done during the process of chip formation, which results in the generation of heat. The work also is done in the plastic deformation of the layer being cut and the layers adjoining machined surface and the surface of the cut and in overcoming friction on the tool - face and flank.

The heat balance in chip formation can be written as :

Total amount of heat generated

$$= \begin{cases} \text{Amount of heat carried away in chips +} \\ \text{Amount of heat remaining in the cutting tool +} \\ \text{Amount of heat passing into the workpiece +} \\ \text{Amount of heat radiated into the surrounding air.} \end{cases}$$

On an average, for a lathe operation, the above heat dissipation percentages are : 50 to 86%, 10 to 40%, 3 to 9% and 1% respectively of the total amount of heat generated. In finish operations, more heat (in per cent) passes into the work than in rough operations. Heat passing into tool reduces its hardness and makes it less wear - resistant. Heat evolved in the chip formation zone and at the interface between the tool and the chip and at the tool-work interface strongly affects the condition of the rubbing surfaces (by changing their co-efficient of

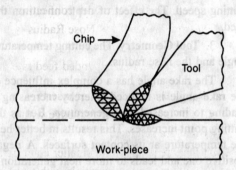

Fig. 6.14. Regions of Heat Generation.

friction), machining accuracy and the whole cutting process, and the related phenomenon, that is, deformation, tool wear, Built - up edge formation and work hardening etc. Fig. 6.14 shows the regions where the heat is mainly generated.

The distribution of heat, both in the chip and the tool, is non- uniform. Hence, they are heated to non-uniform temperatures. The temperature in layers of the chip nearer to the tool-face will be higher than in those farther away.

The highest temperature in the work-piece is observed at the point of contact of the tool with the work. It then decreases farther away from the machined surface.

The highest temperature in the tool is observed in the boundary layers of the areas of contact with the chip and the job. The temperature farther away will depend upon the heat conduction.

The tool-face is heated to a higher temperature than the flank. The tool-face receives heat both from the highly heated chip and from the considerable work done in overcoming the friction of the chip on the face. On the other hand, the flank is in contact with the surface of the cut and the machined surface, which undergo less plastic deformation than the chip. Also, the work done in overcoming friction is less on the tool flank than on the tool - face.

The temperature on the tool-face is higher than the average temperature of the chip ; the thicker the chip, the greater the difference in temperature will be.

6.7.1.Factors Affecting Cutting Temperature. Factors affecting cutting temperature are: Work material, Tool material, Cutting variables cutting speed, feed and depth of cut, Tool geometry and the cutting fluid used.

1. **Work Material.** The cutting temperature is strongly affected by the mechanical properties of the work material, more resistance it will offer in chip formation. So, more work will have to be

done for metal cutting. This will result in more heat generation and consequently higher cutting temperature. The higher the thermal conductivity of the work material, the lower is the developed temperature. Similarly, tool materials with higher thermal conductivity will result in lower cutting temperatures than the tool materials with lower thermal conductivity.

2. **Cutting Variables.** Even though, the cutting forces decrease with an increase in cutting speed, but it is substantially smaller than the increase in speed. Therefore, more heat will be generated with an increase in cutting speed, since

Heat generated = cutting force × cutting speed

hus, the cutting temperature (maximum temperature on the tool surface) increases with the cutting speed.

The cutting forces increase with the increase in the rate of feed, resulting in increased heat generation. But the amount of heat generated and hence the rise in cutting temperature, will be slower than the increase in feed. So, the effect of feed on cutting temperature is lesser than of the cutting speed. The effect of depth of cut on the cutting temperature is even less than that of the feed.

3. **Tool Geometry.** The cutting temperature is affected mainly by the rake angle, plan approach angle and the nose radius.

The rake angle has a complex influence on the cutting temperature. As discussed earlier, as the rake angle is reduced (thereby increasing the cutting angle), the work done gets increased, leading to increased heat generation. But as the cutting angle increases, the material behind the cutting point increases. This results in better heat conduction into the tool shank, thereby, lowering the temperature at its contact surfaces. A negative rake angle causes greater deformation than a positive one and leads to more heat generation during metal cutting.

The larger the plan approach angle, the higher the cutting temperature will be and more the tool is heated by cutting.

The larger the nose radius, the greater the deformation and the cutting force, and more heat will be generated in chip formation. However, the increased nose radius results in increased length of the active part of the cutting edge and the mass of the tool point. This promotes better heat removal both into the tool shank and into the workpiece. This heat removal intensity is more predominant, leading to reduction in the cutting temperature. So, the cutting temperature decreases with an increase in nose radius of the tool.

The larger the cross-sectional area of the tool shank will help in increased removal of heat by conduction resulting in lower cutting temperature.

4. **Cutting Fluids.** The cutting fluids help in reducing the cutting temperature by : reducing friction, facilitating chip formation, absorbing and carrying away a part of the generated heat. The cooling effect of the cutting fluids gets increased with their higher specific heat and thermal conductivity.

6.7.2. Measurement of Temperature in the Cutting Zone

The various techniques used for the measurement of temprature in the cutting zone (work-tool interface) are :-

1. Tool-work thermo-conple
2. Thermo-couples embedded in the tool and/or the workprice.
3. Radiation Pyrometers
4. Temperature sensitive paints
5. Indirect calorimetric techniques, etc.

1. Tool-work Thermo-couple :- This is the most common and simpler technique for measuring temperature in the cutting zone.

Here, the e.m.f. generated between the tool-work interface (hot junction) and their cold ends (cold junction) is taken as the mesure of average temperature in the cutting zone. The e.m.f. generated is measured with a millivoltmeter. Fig. 6.15. shows schematically a typical layout of tool-work thermocouple. Both the work and the tool should be insulated from the machine tool. There should be a good contact between the two junctions and the measuring instrument. For this, a copper disk is mounted at the free end of the lathe spindle. The edge of the disk dips in a cup of mercury. The circuit is completed with mercury and the tailend of the tool through a millivoltmeter. The magnitude of e.m.f. generated will depend upon the temperature difference between hot and cold junctions, and the nature of tool and workpire. The measured e.m.f. is converted into temperature with the help of a calibration curve.

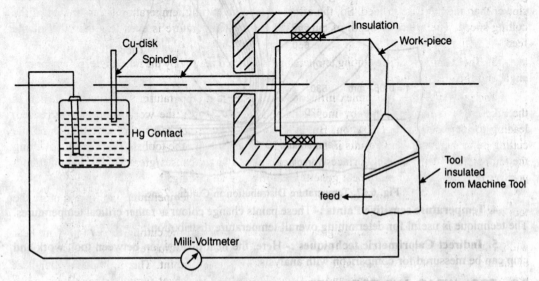

Fig. 6.15. Tool-Work Thermo-couple.

The calibration is done with the help of a standerd thermo-couple, Fig. 6.16. A chip and a piece of tool material are heated in an oven or lead bath at known temperatures. The resulting thermal e.m.f. E_1 is measured. A standard thermo-comple (chromel-alumel) E_2 records the bath temperature at which the e.m.f. E_1, is measured. If the plot of E_1 versus θ is the same while θ increases at it is while θ decreases (that is, there is no hysteresis), the calibration is satisfactory.

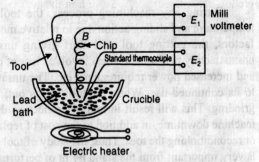

Fig. 6.16. Tool-Work Thermo-couple Calibration.

2. Embedded Thermo-couples :- This technique has been successfully used for determining the temperature distribution on the rake face of a cutting tool. But, the method involves considerable effort.

3. Radiation Pyrometers :- Here, the infrared radiation from the cutting zone is monitored with a radiation pyrometer and interpreted in terms of temperature. The method involves taking photographs of the side face of the cutting zone and also of strips of known temperatures. The intensities of radiation at different points in the cutting zone (tool, chip, workpice) are compared with strips of known temperatures. This will give temperature distubution on the tool, chip and workpice, Fig. 6.17. The technique has been exetensively used by Boothryod. The drawback is that it indicates only the surface temperatures. Also, the accaracy of the results depends upon the emissivity of the surfaces, which is very difficult to determine accurately.

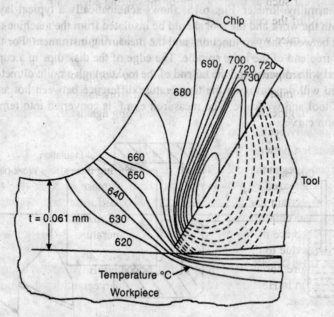

Fig. 6.17. Temperature Distrubution in Cutting Zone.

4. Temperature sensitive Paints :- These paints change colour at rather critical temperatures. The technique is useful for determining overall temperature distribution.

5. Indirect Calorimetric techniques :- Here, the heat distubution between tool, work and chip can be messured for comparison with analysis.

6.8. TOOL WEAR AND TOOL LIFE

During any machining process, the tool is subjected to three distinct factors : forces, temperature and sliding action due to relative motion between tool and the workpiece. Due to these factors, the cutting tool will start giving unsatisfactory performance after some time. The unsatisfactory performance may involve : loss of dimensional accuracy, increased surface roughness, and increased power requirements etc. The unsatisfactory performance results from tool wear due to its continued use. When the tool wears out, it is either replaced or reconditioned, usually by grinding. This will result in loss of production due to machine downtime, in addition to the cost of replacing or reconditioning the tool. Thus, the study of tool wear is very important from the stand point of performance and economics. Due to a large number of factors over which the tool wear depends (hardness and type of tool material, type and condition of workpiece, dimensions of cut, *i.e.*, feed and depth of cut, tool geometry, tool temperature, which, in turn, is a function of cutting speed, surface finish of tool temperature and cutting fluid), the majority of studies in tool wear are based on experimental observations, since the analytical study will be very difficult.

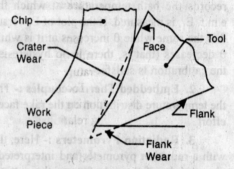

Fig. 6.18. Tool Wear.

Tool wear or tool failure may be classified as follows:

(a) Flank wear.

(b) Crater wear on tool face

(c) Localized wear such as the rounding of the cutting edge, and

(d) Chipping off of the cutting edge.

Flank wear and crater wear are shown in Fig. 6.18. Flank wear is attributed usually to the following reasons :

1. Abrasion by hard particles and inclusions in the workpiece.

2. Shearing of the micro welds between tool and work-material.

3. Abrasion by fragments of built-up edge blow- ing against the clearance face of the tool.

Crater wear usually occurs due to :

1. Severe abrasion between the chip and tool face.

2. High temperatures in the tool-chip interface reach- ing the softening or melting temperature of tool resulting in increased rate of wear. The sharp increase in wear rate after the interface temperature reaches a certain temperature is attributed to 'diffusion'. diffusion is the movement of atoms between tool and chip materials resulting in loss of material from the face of the tool. It depends upon the workpiece materials, in addition to temperature. So, unless these conditions are favourable, crater wear due to diffusion may be absent.

Crater wear is more common in cutting ductile materials, which produce continuous chips. Also, it is more common in HSS (high speed steel) tools than ceramic or carbide tools, which have much higher hot hardness.

The reasons for 'Nose wear' may be one or more of the reasons discussed above. Chipping of the tool may occur due to the following factors :

1. Tool material is too brittle.

2. As a result of crack that is already in the tool.

3. Excessive static or shock loading of the tool.

4. Weak design of the tool, such as a high positive rake angle.

6.8.1. Tool Life. The total cutting time accumulated before tool failure occurs, is termed as 'tool life'. There is no exact or simple definition of tool life. However, in general, the tool life can be defined as tool's useful life which has been expended when it can no longer produce satisfactory parts. The two most commonly used criteria for measuring the tool life are :

1. Total destruction of the tool when it ceases to cut.

2. A fixed size of wear land on tool flank. On carbide and ceramic tools, where crater wear is almost absent, tool life is taken as corresponding to 0.038 or 0.076 mm of wear land on the flank for finishing respectively.

As discussed above, tool wear and hence tool life depends on many factors. The greatest variation of tool life is with the cutting speed and tool temperature which is closely related to cutting speed. Tool temperature is seldom measured and much study has been done on the effect of cutting speed on tool life. Tool life decreases with increased V, the decrease being parabolic. To draw these curves, the cutting tools are operated to failure at different cutting speeds. In 1907, Taylor gave the following relationship between cutting speed and tool life,

$$VT^n = C \qquad \qquad ... (6.1)$$

where V is the cutting speed), T is the time (min) for the flank wear to reach a certain dimension, i.e., tool life, C is constant and n is an exponent which depends upon the cutting conditions. If cutting speed-tool life curves are plotted on a log-log graph, straight lines are obtained, (Fig. 6.19), n is the negative inverse slope of the curve and C is the intercept velocity at $T = 1$. The results are valid only for the particular test conditions employed. Thus 'C' is the cutting speed for tool life of 1 min.

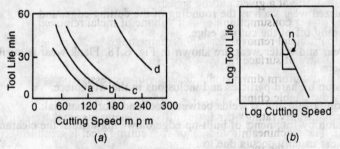

Fig. 6.19. Cutting Speed—Tool Life Curves.

The following values may be taken for 'n' :

$n = 0.1$ to 0.15 for *HSS* tools

$= 0.2$ to 0.4 for carbide tools

$= 0.4$ to 0.6 for ceramic tools

The tool life also depends to a great extent on the depth of cut d and feed rate per revolution, f. Assuming a logarithmic variation of C with d, the equation (6.1) can be written as,

$$VT^n . d^m = C \qquad \qquad ... (6.2)$$

It has been seen that decrease of life with increased speed is twice as great (exponentially) as the decrease of life with increased feed.

Considering feed rate also, the general equation can be :

$$VT^n . d^m . f^x = C \qquad \qquad ... (6.3)$$

6.8.2. Variables Affecting Tool Life. Tool life is primarily affected by a high temperature in thin surface layers subject to wear. The variables affecting cutting temperature will also affect tool life. These variables are: workpiece material, tool material, cutting variables, tool geometry and cutting fluids. The effects of these variables on cutting temperature has already been discussed under Art. 6.7.1.

6.9. MACHINEABILITY

In spite of efforts by a number of investigators, so far there has been no exact quantitative definition of machineability. This is because of a large number of variables involved and their complexity. However, the major factors involved in metal cutting are : forces and power absorbed, tool wear and tool life, surface finish, dimensional accuracy and machining cost. These factors depend upon a large number of variables, such as properties of work materials, tool geometry, cutting conditions, machine tool rigidity etc. Due to this, it is impossible to combine these factors, so as to give a suitable definition for machineability. Many authors give a qualitative measure of machineability of a material as :

(1) the ease with which it could be machined,

(2) the life of tool before tool failure or resharpening,

(3) the quality of the machined surface, and

(4) the power consumption per unit volume of material removed.

However, in production, tool life is generally considered the most important factor and, so, most of the investigators have related machineability with tool life. Higher the tool life, the better is the machineability of a work material. The various materials have been given machineability ratings, which are relative. Supposing a material is given the rating of 100. Those materials which have a better machineability will have higher ratings and those materials with lower machineability have a lower one.

According to one investigator, the machineability may be evaluated as given below :

1. Long tool life at a given cutting speed.
2. Lower power consumption per unit volume of metal removed.
3. Maximum metal removal per tool resharpening.
4. High quality of surface finish.
5. Good and uniform dimensional accuracy of successive parts.
6. Easily disposable chips.

The machineability rating or index of different materials is taken relative to the index which is standardised. The machineability index of free cutting steel is arbitrarily fixed at 100 per cent. For the other materials, the index is found as below :

$$\text{Machineability index, \%} = \frac{\text{Cutting speed of material for 20 min. tool life}}{\text{Cutting speed of free cutting steel for 20 min. tool life}} \times 100$$

The machineability indexes for some common materials are given below :

C - 20 steel   = 65
C - 45 steel   = 60
Stainless steel = 25

Table 6.3

Problems	Remedies and Satuters									
	Reduce the cutting speed	Increase the cutting speed	Reduce the feed	Increase the feed	Reduce the depth of cut	Increase the depth of cut	Select a more wear resistant Grade	Select a tougher grade	Select a smaller nose radius	Select a positive geometry
Flank Wear	✓						✓			
Notch wear	✓						✓			
Cratering	✓		✓				✓			✓
Plastic Deformation	✓		✓				✓			
Built-up edge (BUE)		✓								✓
Small cracks normal to the cutting edge								✓		
Small cutting edge fracture (frittering)		✓						✓		✓
Insert Breakage			✓		✓			✓		
Curling of Long Chips				✓		✓			✓	
Vibrations	✓			✓					✓	✓

Copper	= 70
Brass (red)	= 180
Aluminium alloys	= 300 – 1500
Magnesium alloys	= 600 – 2000

Table 6.3. gives the various problems encountered during a machining process and the possible remedies and solution.

PROBLEMS

1. Define machining process
2. With the help of a sketch, explain the machining process.
3. Explain the various elements of a single point cutting tool, with the help of a neat sketch.
4. What is meant by 'hand' of a single point cutting tool ?
5. With the help of a sketch, discuss the principal surfaces and planes in metal cutting.
6. Name the two systems of designating the cutting tool.
7. Sketch a single point cutting tool under ASA system. Define various tool angles and discuss their importance.
8. Why negative rake angle is normally employed for cutting hard and strong materials ?
9. What is meant by 'tool designation' or 'tool signature' ?
10. What is Orthogonal Rake System ?
11. Show the ORS of tool angles with the help of a sketch.
12. Write the relations between ASA and ORS of tool angles.
13. Sketch and explain the two methods of metal machining.
14. Discuss the various types of chips produced during metal machining.
15. Why are discontinuous type chips preferred over continuous type ?
16. Explain, how built up edge on a cutting tool is undesirable ?
17. What is the use of a 'Chip breaker' ?
18. Name and discuss the principal elements of metal machining.
19. Define Tool life.
20. Discuss the variables affecting tool life.
21. What is meant by orthogonal cutting and oblique cutting ?
22. Explain the term "Machinability".
23. Explain why large amounts of frictional heat are produced when machining very ductile materials ?
24. How does the rake angle affect the life of the cutting tool ?
25. What two pressure areas of the cutting tools are subjected to wear ?
26. With the help of a sketch, show crater wear and flank wear on a cutting tool.
27. Name the factors that contribute to flank wear.
28. Name the factors that contribute to crater wear.
29. Name the factors that contribute to the formation of discontinuous chips.
30. Name the factors that contribute to the formation of built-up edge.
31. Differentiate between positive and negative rake angles.
32. Discuss the various methods of meassuring temperature at the cutting zone.
33. How is the nose radius of a cutting tool selected ?
34. What is machining time ? Find the time required for one complete cut on a piece of work 350 mm long and 50 mm in diameter. Cutting speed is 35 m/min and feed is 0.5 mm/rev.

(PTU **Ans.** π minutes)

Chapter

7

Cutting Tool Materials and Cutting Fluids

7.1. GENERAL

We have seen in the last chapter, that the cutting tool is subjected to: static and dynamic forces, high temperatures, wear and abrasion. To get a reasonable tool life, the tool material should meet the following requirements:

1. Hot hardness, so that the tool does not loose its hardness and strength at the high temperatures developed during machining. It ha been shown that the tool material must be at least 35% to 50% harder than the work material.

2. Wear and abrasion resistance, so that the tool retains its shape and cutting efficiency for a reasonably long time before it is reconditioned or replaced.

3. Impact toughness, so that the fine cutting edge of the tool does not break or chip, when the tool is suddenly loaded.

In addition to the above basic requirements, the tool material should possess the following properties: increased thermal conductivity, lower co-efficient of thermal expansion, lower chemical and mechanical affinity for the work-material and it should be easy to form, grind and sharpen to the desired tool geometry, high specific heat and low co-efficient of friction between work and the tool. It should also be easy to cveld/braze or fix to the tool holder.

The selection of a proper tool-material depends upon a number of factors such as: type of cutting operation, material of the work piece, machine tool to be used and surface finish required. Usually, a compromise has to be made in the selection of tool-material, since the requirements to be met by tool-material are often contradictory in nature. Over the years, a wide variety of cutting tool materials have been developed to meet the ever increasing demand of machining harder and harder materials. The various cutting tool-materials can be grouped as follows:

1. Plain Carbon Steels.
2. Medium Alloy Steels.
3. High Speed Steels (H.S.S.).
4. Non-ferrous Cast Slloys
5. Cemented Carbides.
6. Ceramics or Oxides.
7. Cermets.
8. Diamond.

9. Cubic Boron Nitride (CBN).

10. UCON.

11. Sialon.

12. Coronite

Plain carbon steels, Medium alloy steels and High speed steels are known as "Tool Steels". Medium alloy steels and high speed steels contain one or more alloying elements to impart the desired properties to the cutting tools. The function of each alloying element is given below.

(*i*) **Carbon.** Carbon combines with iron to form carbide which makes it respond to hardening, thus increasing the hardness, strength and wear resistance. The percentage of carbon varies from 0.6 to 1.4%.

(*ii*) **Manganese.** It is added to steels as a deoxidizing and desulphurizing agent. It lowers the critical range of temperature. It increases the time required for transformation, so that, oil quenching, becomes practicable. Its content is about 0.5 to 2%.

(*iii*) **Chromium.** The addition of chromium results in the formation of various carbides of chromium which are very hard, yet the resulting steel is more ductile than a steel of the same hardness produced by a simple increase in carbon content. Chromium also refines the grain structure so that, these two combined effects result in both increased toughness and hardness. The addition of chromium increases the critical range of temperature and raises the strength at high temperatures. Alloy of chromium resists abrasion and wear. Its content ranges from 0.25 to 4.5%.

(*iv*) **Molybdenum.** Molybdenum is a strong carbide forming element and its action is very much like chromium but is more powerful. It increases strength, wear resistance, hardness penetration and hot hardness. It is always used in conjunction with other alloying elements. Its content ranges upto about 10%.

(*v*) **Cobalt.** Cobalt is commonly used in high speed steels to increase the hot hardness so that the cutting tools can be used at higher cutting speeds and temperatures and still they retain their hardness and a sharp cutting edge. Its content ranges from 5 to 12%.

(*vi*) **Vanadium.** It increases hot hardness and abrasion resistance. As vanadium has a very strong tendency to form carbides, hence, it is used only in small amounts (0.2 to 0.5% in alloy carbon tool steels and 1 to 5% in H.S.S).

(*vii*) **Tungsten.** It is widely used in tool steels because the tool maintains its hardness even at red heat. Tungsten produces a fine dense structure and adds both toughness and hardness. Its effect is similar to molybdenum except that it must be added in greater quantity(1.5 to 20%).

Note : Most of the tool-steels contain two or three alloying elements, as the combined action of several elements is more effective than that of one element even when its content in steel is considerable.

7.2 CUTTING TOOL MATERIALS

7.2.1. Plain Carbon Tool Steels. These are the oldest type of tool steels. The material is inexpensive, can be easily formed and ground. The properties of the material will depend upon the percentage of carbon content. Low carbon steels are tough and shock resistant, whereas, high carbon steels are abrasion resistant. They are basically water hardening materials (Type W tool steels), that is, they are hardened by heating followed by quenching in water to obtain hardness of H_{RC} 60 – 67. Their hardness decreases rapidly above 200°C and so they are useful for low speed operations — drilling, tapping, reaming, broaching etc. They are also used to manufacture; woodworking tools, cold chisels, hammers, knives and punches. These materials are prone to deformation and cracking when hardened.

7.2.2. Alloy Tool Steels. The various alloying elements (discussed above) are added to plain carbon steel to impart the desired properties to the tool steel. These alloying elements slow down the transformation rates. Due to this, the materials can be hardened in oil or air, and the alloy steels become less susceptible to cracks while quenching. These steels have greater wear resistance and hot hardness than the plain carbon steels. These are widely used for drills, taps, reamers etc., but do not have sufficient hot hardness to be used in high speed turning or milling. Depending upon the method of quenching, these steels are of two types.

(*a*) **Type – O Tool Steels.** These steels are hardened by quenching in oil. Type O – 1 is most commonly used which has the following composition :

C: 0.90%, Mn = 1.00%, W = 0.5%, Cr = 0.5%

These steels find use in cold-working applications, such as punching and blanking, shearing, forming and drawing dies.

(*b*) **Type – A Tool Steel.** These steels are hardened by cooling in air. In these steels, the content of alloying elements is higher as compared to type O steels. Usually, C is 1.0% and Cr is 5%. Chiefly used for cold working applications, for example thread rolling dies, coining dies and gauges.

The alloy tool steels can operate upto cutting temperature of about 300°C.

7.2.3 High Speed Steel (H.S.S.). This tool material is basically high carbon steel, to which the various alloying elements (Tungsten W, Molybdenum Mo, Chromium Cr, Vanadium V and Cobalt Co) have been added in larger amounts as compared to alloy tool steels, to improve hardness, toughness and wear resistance properties. These materials are deep hardening and can be quenched in oil, air, or salt. They are capable of retaining their hardness upto 600°C and so can be operated at much higher cutting speeds as compared to alloy tool steels, hence the name "high speed steel". This tool material was developed in 1905.

There are two basic types of high speed steels:

1. Tungsten type steels (T series) which has tungsten as the major alloying element (12 – 20%).

2. Molybdenum type steels (M Series) in which tungsten is partially or completely replaced by molybdenum.

The molybdenum type of H.S.S. is cheaper than the tungsten based material and is more readily sharpened. Also, it generally has a slightly greater toughness at the same level of hardness.

The popular 18-4-1 H.S.S. contains 18% tungsten, 4% chromium and 1% vanadium. Cobalt (5 to 8%) may also be added to increase red hardness. Carbon is about 0.75%. This material is designated as T-4. The ISI designation of this steel is (T 75 W 18 Co 5 Cr 4 V 1 Mo 70). The most commonly used types of H.S.S. steels are listed in Table 7.1, with their designations and compositions.

The most commonly used grades of high speed steels are: $M - 1$, $M - 2$, $M - 7$, $M - 10$, $T - 1$ and $T - 2$. $M - 2$ tool steel has the applications of: turning carbon and alloy steels of hardness up to 375 *BHN*, turning nitriding steels of hardness upto 350 *BHN*, turning ultra high-strength steels of hardness upto 300 *BHN*, turning tool steels, cast steels of hardness upto 300 *BHN*, turning armour plate of hardness upto 325 *BHN*, and turning non-ferrous materials such as copper, brass, aluminum, magnesium and plastics. Broaches to cut ferrous materials of hardness upto 260 *BHN* are made of $M - 2$ grade.

Milling cutters for cutting ferrous materials of hardness upto 350 *BHN* are made of M – 2 and M – 7 grades. Gear hobbing, shaping and shaving tools are also made of M – 2 and M – 7

Table 7.1 High Speed Steels

Designation	Percentage of Constituents						Relative properties from 1 (low) to 10 (high)			
	C	M_0	W	Cr	V	Co	Wear Resistance	Toughness	Hardness	Cost
M – 1	0.80	8.50	1.75	3.75	1.15	–	4	10	5	3
M – 2	0.85	5.00	6.00	4.00	2.00	–	5	10	5	3
M – 3	1.05	5.00	6.00	4.00	2.40	–	6	7	6	4
M – 4	1.30	4.50	6.00	4.00	4.00	–	6	5	6	4
M – 7	1.00	8.75	1.75	4.00	2.00	–	6	8	5	3
M – 10	0.90	8.00	–	4.00	2.00	–	5	8	5	3
M – 33	0.88	9.50	1.75	3.75	1.15	8.25	5	5	8	5
M – 36	0.85	5.00	6.00	4.00	2.00	8.25	5	5	8	5
M – 41	1.10	3.75	6.75	4.25	2.00	5.00	6	4	8	5
M – 42	1.10	9.50	1.50	3.75	1.15	8.25	6	4	9	5
M – 43	1.20	8.00	2.75	3.75	1.60	8.25	6	4	9	5
M – 44	1.15	6.50	5.25	4.25	2.00	12.00	6	3	10	6
M – 45	1.25	5.00	8.25	4.25	1.60	5.50	6	3	8	5
M – 46	1.25	8.25	2.00	4.00	3.20	8.25	8	3	9	5
T – 1	0.75	–	18.00	4.00	1.00	–	4	8	5	5
T – 2	0.85	–	18.00	4.00	2.00	–	5	6	5	5
T – 4	0.75	–	18.00	4.00	1.00	5.00	5	4	7	6
T – 5	0.80	–	18.00	4.25	2.00	8.00	–	4	8	6
T – 6	0.80	–	20.00	4.50	1.75	12.00	5	2	9	8
T – 15	1.50	–	12.00	4.50	5.00	5.00	10	3	9	6

grades. Drills and reamers for steels of hardness upto 325 *BHN* are made of M – 1, M – 2, M – 7 and M – 10 grades. Taps are mostly made from M – 1 grade. Form tools are usually made from M – 2 or T – 2 grade of H.S.S.

High speed steels with cobalt (for example grades: M – 33, M – 36, T – 4, T – 5 and T – 6) have high hot hardness and wear resistance but lower toughness as compared to M – 2 H.S.S. Tool bits for planing and heavy duty turning are made from T – 4, T – 5 and T – 6 grades. Grades M – 33 and M – 36 are used for: drilling and milling hard alloy steels, stainless steel, titanium and heat resistant materials. T – 6 grades are also called "Super H.S.S". They have a high W (18 to 22%) and high Co (10 to 12%) content. They are less tough than other types and need to be well supported on a very rigid machine. This type is the most expensive H.S.S.

H.S.S. with high percentage of vanadium (For example M – 3, M – 4, and T – 15 grades) possess increased red hardness and wear resistance but their toughness and grind ability is reduced. Due to increased red hardness and wear resistance, these steels have greater tool life as compared to conventional H.S.S. They are used for machining conventional alloys, super alloys and refractory materials. Single point lathe tools, flat and form cutters, broaches and drills are made of these steels.

H.S.S. with cobalt (grades *M* – 41, *M* – 42, *M* – 43, *M* – 44, *M* – 45 and *M* – 46) have high hot hardness and wear resistance. Their grind ability is better as compared to H.S.S. with vanadium. These steels are used for machining: heat treated steels, titanium alloys and aerospace materials of high hardness (cobalt and nickel base alloys). Drills, milling cutters, form tools, broaches, hobs, shavers, taps and tool bits are made of these steels.

In the conventional H.S.S., there is every possibility of large dispersion and segregation of carbides. Due to this, there will be local variations in the chemical composition and structure of the material, resulting in difficulty in producing the tool and also poor performance of the tool. These drawbacks are overcome by using powder metallurgy (*P/M*) for the manufacture of tool steel. The powder of the steel alloy is made by atomizing the molten metal. The powder is then compacted under pressure in dies, to produce billets. These billets are then transformed to the desired shape and size by conventional hot forging. In this tool steel, there is better and more uniform distribution of carbides and the alloying elements. H.S.S. produced by *P/M* prossesses higher wear resistance greater toughness, greater impact strength, better hot workability, improved grindability, higher material removal rates and good dimensional stability.

7.2.4 Non - Ferrous Cast Alloys (Stellite). This material which was introduced in 1915 is an alloy of Cobalt, Chromium and Tungsten with composition: Cobalt, 38 to 53 per cent, Chromium, 30 to 33 per cent, Tungsten, 10 to 20 per cent and Carbon, 1 to 3 per cent. 1 per cent Carbon content gives a relatively soft and strong tool and 3 per cent Carbon content gives a hard and more wear resistant grade. Cast alloy tools are cast and ground to any desired shape. Cast alloys bridge the gap between H.S.S. and Carbides (the next tool material). They have properties intermediate between H.S.S. and cemented Carbides. This material maintains great hardness at high temperatures and has good wear resistance but is not as tough as H.S.S. and is sensitive to shock loading. The tool material is available in the form of tool bits for use in holders and in the form of tips brazed to a medium carbon steel shank. The material is recommended for deep roughing operations at relatively high speed and feed rates and it can machine more difficult materials such as high tensile steels, stainless steels and heat resistant steels, and C.I. This material is used at surface speeds above those of H.S.S. and below those of Carbides, and can withstand a cutting temperature in the range of 900°C.

The introduction of Cast alloys as cutting tool materials somewhat overlapped that of the Tungsten carbide and since these carbides were, in general, superior cutting tools, the cast non-ferrous alloys never caught on to the extent anticipated.

7.2.5 Sintered or Cemented Carbides. The first sintered carbide cutting tool (tungsten carbide) was marketed in 1926. Since then lot of research has been done and many types of sintered carbide materials have been produced to improve their performance. This has been achieved by improving the methods of their manufacture and their composition. For example, carbides of titanium, tantalum, niobium and columbium etc. can be added to straight tungsten carbide to extend the range of their application. Sintered carbides are produced by P/M technique and have the following properties. Very high red hardness (of about 1000°C), very high wear resistance, high modulus of elasticity, low thermal expansion and high thermal conductivity.

There are three general groups of cemented carbides in use :

1. Straight tungsten carbide with cobalt as a binder.

2. Tungsten carbide with cobalt as a binder and having large percentages of carbides of Ti, Ta and Nb, which along with WC form a solid solution of WC – TiC – TaC – NbC.

3. Titanium carbide with nickel or molybdenum as the binding material.

Manufacture. The cemented carbides are manufacture by *P/M* technique involving the following steps:

1. Firstly, we should get the ingredients. Tungsten oxide is reduced in hydrogen to get tungsten metal powder. Similarly, to obtain titanium and tantalum, titanium oxide, and tantanlum oxide are reduced in hydrogen atmosphere, respectively.

2. Tungsten powder is then mixed with lamp black and the mixture is heated at about 1600°C to form carbide of tungsten, and so on.

3. The lump of the carbide so produced is crushed to a powder. Then, powdered cobalt metal which acts as a binder to hold together the particles of carbide powder, is thoroughly mixed with the latter.

4. To increase the mouldability of WC – Co mixture, it is mixed with a lubricant such as paraffin, ethylene glycol or camphor. Sometimes, only water is used.

5. After drying and refining, the mixture is compacted in a press to get the desired blocks.

6. The strength of the green compacts so obtained is quite low. To give the necessary strength to the compact, it is heated at 1300°C to 1865°C (sintered process) depending upon the composition and the cobalt content. As a rule, the sintering temperature is 90°C to 100°C below the melting point of pure cobalt. The sintering process is done for about 1.5 to 2 hours and it should be done preferably in an inert atmosphere to avoid oxidation or decarburization.

During sintering, there is about 15 to 25% shrinkage and this factor must be taken into account while designing the product shape.

7. The product is finally ground or lapped depending on the requirements.

Properties and Uses. The properties of the carbide tool material depend upon:

   (*i*) Chemical composition

   (*ii*) Method of manufacture

   (*iii*) Micro-structure of the tool material.

The finer the grain size, the higher is the hardness. Out of these, the major effect is of the chemical composition (the method of manufacture and the grain size can be properly taken case of).

Straight tungsten carbide contains cobalt from 3 to 20%. With increase in the percentage of cobalt, the hardness, the brittleness and compressive strength of the material decreases. However, with increase in cobalt content, the transverse rupture strength of the tool material increases. This material has high abrasive wear resistance and high strength in respect of a given hardness. The main drawback of straight tungsten carbide is its affinity for steel. Due to this, the steel chips tend to weld to the tool surface resulting in crater wear. Hence, this tool material is not suitable for cutting steel, but gives superior performance with non-ferrous, non-metallic material and cast iron. This material is called as 'C' grade cemented carbide material.

To reduce the tendency of the metal chips to weld to the tool and to decrease the diffusion of the tool material to the chips, TiC is added to WC – Co system. However, with increase in the percentages of TiC, compressive, transverse and impact strengths and also the thermal conductivity and the modulus of elasticity of tool material decrease. These drawbacks of TiC are overcome by adding TaC, which increases the transverse strength and the hot hardness of the tool material. The effect of adding NbC is similar to that of TaC. These mixed carbides are used for machining steel. This cemented carbide material is known by 'S' grade. It contains: about 16% TiC, O to 10% TaC. Cabalt content varies from 3 to 16%.

With TiC tool material nickel and molytdenum are used as binding materials. Molybdenum is added to check the very high grain growth with TiC-Ni system. This material has low wettability. This improves its crater wear resistance and hence it is used when cutting temperatures are high, because of high cutting speeds or hard workpiece material.

According to ISO (International Standards Organization), the various grades of carbide tool material have been grouped in three series:

1. Carbide tools used for cutting cast iron and non-ferrous metals are designated from: K_{01} to K_{40}.

2. Grades of carbide tools used for machining steel are designated as: P_{01} to P_{60}.

3. Grades of carbide tools used for general purpose applications are designated as: M_{10} to M_{30}.

In all the above three series, the harder and brittle materials have the lowest number and the less hard and most tough materials have the higher numbers.For example in K-series, K_{01} is the hardest and most brittle and K_{40} is the least hard and the most tough material. The K-grades of carbides are essentially straight tungsten carbides with cobalt as the binder, and are used for machining cast iron, non-ferrous metals, plastics and similar materials. P-grade carbides are combined carbide tool materials (carbides of W, Ti, Ta and Nb) with cobalt as the binder. These materials are similar in composition to the K-grade, but have different properties due to different manufacturing methods. These are used to cut heat resistant steels and stainless steels.

All carbides, when finished, are extremely brittle and weak in their resistance to impact and shock loading. Due to this, vibrations are very harmful for carbide tools. The machine tools should be rigid, faster and more powerful. Light feeds, low speeds and chatter are harmful. Due to the high cost of carbide tool materials and other factors, cemented carbides are used in the form of inserts or tips which are brazed or clamped to a steel shank, Fig. 7.1.

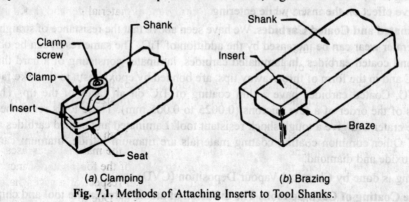

(a) Clamping   (b) Brazing

Fig. 7.1. Methods of Attaching Inserts to Tool Shanks.

In the case of a brazed tip, when it is worn out, it is resharpened with the help of special grinding wheels on a Tool and Cutter grinder. The main drawbacks of a brazed tip are : For resharpening purposes, the tool will have to be removed from the machine involving a resetting operation. Also, because of the difference in co-efficients of expansion of tip material and tool shank material, the brazing has to be done very carefully.

Mechanically clamped tips are known as "Indexable tips or inserts", because these have more than one cutting edge which are used one by one by indexing the tip. These tips are also known as "Throw-away" or "disposable", because once all the edges of the tip have been used, the tip or insert is removed from the tool shank seat and thrown away or disposed-off. In this way, a rectangular tool bit (tip or insert) can be used upto eight times before disposal and requires no resharpening cost. The inserts are available in a variety of shapes, such as square, triangle, diamond and round, as shown in Fig. 7.2

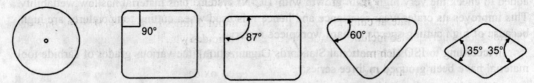

Fig. 7.2. Different Shapes of Inserts.

The various parameters depend upon the shape of the insert. For example,

   (*a*) Higher the cutting edge angle, higher is the cutting edge strength. That is, cutting edge strength increases from right to left in Fig. 7.2

   (*b*) Power reguirement decreases as the cutting edge angle decreases. (Left to Right)

   (*c*) Tendency to vibration increases with increase in cutting edge angle. (Right to Left).

   (*d*) Versatility and accessibility increases as thecutting edge angle decreases. (Left to Right)

There are certain rules of thumb to be followed when selecting an insert for a particular Job:-

   (*i*) For strength and economy, the largest possible cutting edge angle should be selected.

   (*ii*) When there is a tendency to vibration during operation, strength versus versatility and assessibility through the use of smaller cutting edge angles should always be considered.

To inprove the cutting edge strength, the insert edges are usually honed and chamfered or produced with a negative land. The radius of honing may be about 0.025 mm. When using ceramics, re-chamfering is recommended to minimize the risk of burrs when the insert exits the cut. It also has a positive effect on the insert while entering.

Laminated and Coated Carbides. We have seen above that the resistance of straight tungsten carbide to crater wear can be increased by the addition of TiC. The same result can be obtained by laminated and coated carbides. In laminated carbides, laminates consisting of a hard thin surface layer of TiC and in the form of throw-away tips, are bonded by epoxy resin to the rake face of a tip body of WC. Coated carbides have a thin coating of TiC on all faces of the tip. The coating thickness is of the order of a few microns (0.0025 to 0.005 mm). These tools resist the diffusion wear on the crater and give a tough shock resistant tool. Laminated and coated carbides are shown in Fig. 7.3. Other common coating coating materials are titanium nitride, titanium carbonitride, aluminium oxide and diamond.

Coating is done by Chemical Vapour Deposition (CVD).

Oxide Coating of Carbide tools. The diffusion of atoms between the tool and chip material (which is the major cause of carbide tools) can be retarded by coating the tool surface of the carbide tools with oxides of aluminium and zirconium. This considerably increases the tool life. Coated Carbides are used for machining super alloys.

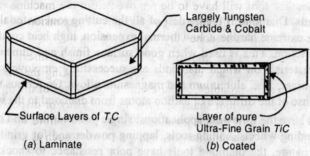

(a) Laminate   (b) Coated

Fig. 7.3. Laminated and Coated Carbides.

These tools operate at cutting speeds which are about 5 times of that for H.S.S. Cemented carbide tool materials also include: nitrides, borides and silicides which are compounds of nitrogen, boron and silicon with such metals as Tungsten, Titanium, Tantalum, Niobium and Molybdenum.

7.2.6 Ceramics and Oxides. Ceramics or sintered oxides were developed as cutting tool materials during 1950 – 1960. These materials are basically aluminium oxide (Al_2O_3) containing additions like MgO, NiO, Cr_2O_3, TiO and TiC etc. to improve the grain structure, cutting properties and sintering.

These materials are produced in the same manner as sintered carbides, that is, by P/M technique. Th aluminium powder is ball milled to a suitable grain size. Water is added and the ingredients are thoroughly mixed to make a stiff paste. This is then pressed into pallets of required form in punch and die. The pallets are dried and then sintered at temperature of 1500°C to 1700°C. The grain particles then get bonded to one another by the process of diffusion. The pallets are then cut and ground to the required shape, size and surface finish, with the help of resinoid bonded grinding wheels. Ceramics are always used in the form of indexable inserts of standard shapes and sizes. At present there is no satisfactory method of brazing the tool tips to steel shank. So, the ceramic tool tips are clamped mechanically to the steel tool shank.

Ceramic tool materials have a very high abrasion resistance, are harder than cemented carbides and H.S.S. and have less tendency to weld to metals during machining. However, they lack impact toughness, so, vibration and chatter are fatal to these tools. Due to this, the tool mountings should be rigid and the machine tools should be rigid. These materials are especially effective at very high cutting speeds (2 to 5 m/s) and for uninterrupted cutting operations. These materials are particularly successful for machining cast iron, and high tensile materials, at cutting speeds which are 2 to 3 times of that of comented carbides. These tools can retain cutting edge hardness upto about 1400°C and exhibit uniform strength upto 1200°C.

Another ceramic tool material is Silicon nitride (Code named S-8), which is particularly used for cast iron machining applications. These ceramic tools have a tool life that was effective over 1500 C.I. pieces, where coated tungsten carbide tools lasted only 250 pieces before dulling. Ceramics are less expensive than carbides and the trend now is to replace the latter with the former whenever possible and reasonable. Ceramics are mainly used for finishing and super-finishing. Poor results are obtained if Al_2O_3 tool material is used to machine Al or Ti alloys, because strong bonds tend to form between the chip and the tool.

7.2.7 Cermets: The cermets are combinations of ceramics and metals, bonded together in the same manner in which *P/M* parts are produced. They combine some of the high refractoriness of ceramics and toughness and thermal shock resistance of metals. For cutting tool materials, the usual combination is Al_2O_3 plus metal additions (W, Mo, Boron, Ti etc.) in an amount upto 10%. These additions reduce the brittleness to some extent, but they reduce the wear resistance of the material as well.

7.2.8. Diamonds. Diamond is the hardest of all the cutting tool materials. Diamond has the following properties: extreme hardness, low thermal expansion, high heat conductivity, and a very low co-efficient of friction. This is used when good surface finish and dimensional accuracy are desired. The work-materials on which diamonds are successfully employed are the non-ferrous one, such as copper, brass, zinc, aluminium and magnesium alloys. On ferrous materials, diamonds are not suitable because of the diffusion of carbon atoms from diamond to the work-piece material.

Diamond tools have the following applications: single point turning and boring tools, milling cutters, reamers, grinding wheels, honing tools, lapping powder and for grinding wheel dressing. Due to their brittle nature, the diamond tools have poor resistance to shock and so, should be loaded lightly. For fine turning, the following values are recommended: cutting speed 200 to 500 m/min, feed 0.01 to 0.05 mm/rev. and depth of cut 0.10 to 0.15 mm.

Diamonds are available either as naturally or as man made (synthetic). The natural diamonds are, however, of low grade. For metal cutting applications, polycrystalline diamond instead of single crystal diamond, has been recently introduced. This tool material known as "Compacts" has increased strength and shock resistance. This material is made of diamond powder by sintering into moulded shapes by high pressure and temperature technology.

Polycrystalline diamond has been successfully used for machining tough, abrasive non-ferrous materials, plastics, ceramics and glass. The material can be moulded into standard shaped inserts and used as conventional indexable inserts. Indexable inserts can also be made by brazing compacts of polycrystalline diamond to each cover of a carbide insert. This material can also be used by bonding its thin layer (about 0.5 mm thick) to a WC substrate. These blanks are brazed on to a steel shank in position, ground and then used. WC being tougher than diamond will increase the shock resistance of the tool. such tools are called as "Compax" tools. Diamond tools can with stand heat upto 2000°C with highest tool life (50 to 100 times more than that of WC).

7.2.9 Cubic Boron Nitride (CBN): Next to diamond, CBN is the hardest material currently available. This material, which consists of atoms of nitrogen and boron, was produced in the early 1970's by high pressure, high temperature processing. As a cutting tool material, CBN is used in the polycrystalline form. CBN has high hardness and high thermal conductivity. It has much higher tensile strength ($1000 N/mm^2$) as compared to diamond ($300N/mm^2$). CBN being chemically inert, is used as a substitute for diamond for machining steel. Other applications are: as a grinding wheel on H.S.S. tools, for machining high temperature alloys, Titanium, Nimonic, Stainless steel, Stellites and Chilled C.I.

In dealing with iron-based alloys and hardened steels, the life of a CBN tool is 4 to 5 times higher than that of a diamond tool.

CBN, as a cutting tool material, can be used in different ways: In "Compax" tools, a 0.5 mm thick layer is bonded to a cemented carbide substrate at high temperature and pressure. These tools combine the high hardness and wear resistance of CBN with the high shock resistance and toughness of WC. CBN can also be made in the form of indexable inserts and blanks of standard shape and size. The blanks can be brazed on to steel shanks, form ground and then used. This material is known by the trade name "Borazon", in U.S.A. and 'Elbor' in Russia.

7.2.10 UCON. This is also new cutting material developed by Union Carbide, U.S.A. Its constituents are: Columbium 50%, Titanium 30%, and Tungsten 20%. This tool material is manufactured according to the following steps:

1. The powders of columbium, Titanium and Tungsten are thoroughly mixed and blended.

2. The mixture is compacted in a punch and a die.

3. The compact is then melted in an electric arc furnace and the alloy is cast into ingots.

4. The ingot is rolled into sheets which are then cut into strips.

5. The strips are then cut into blank of desired shape and size.

6. The blanks are then can ground and honed subsequently by tumbling to produce a radius of 0.05 to 0.075 mm at cutting points.

7. Lastly, the blanks are nitrided in a nitrogen atmosphere at a very high temperature.

UCON has the following properties : High hardness, High toughness, excellent shock resistance and excellent resistance to diffusion and adhesion wear. This is a basically steel cutting material and is not preferred for cutting cast iron, stainless steel and super alloys containing Ni, Co and Ti as base materials. Cutting operations recommended for UCON are: roughing, semi-roughing and finishing, turning, facing and boring operations. It permits 60% increase in cutting speed when compared with WC.

7.2.11 Sialon (SiAlON): The research on this tool material has been going on for the last about 14 years. The material is produced by milling together Si_3N_4, Aluminum oxide, Al_2O_3 and yttria. The powder is dried, pressed to shape and sintered at a temperature of about 1800°C. This material has been found to be considerably tougher than ceramics, and thus can be successfully used for machining with interrupted cuts. Cutting speed can be 2 to 3 times, those with carbides. At present, the field of application of this tool material (in the form of tips) is for machining aerospace alloys, Ni-based gas turbine blades etc. at cutting speed in the range of 3.3 to 5 m/s.

7.2.12. Coronite : It is a new cutting tool material whose properties lie in between those of H.S.S. and cemented carbides.

It combines the toughness of H.S.S. with hardness and wear resistance of cemented carbides. This improves tool life, reliability and surface finish. Cutting tools made from this material are mainly endmills used for machining grooves, pockets and for profiling in majority of the workpiece materials.

The material consists of fine grains of Ti N evenly dispersed in a material of heat treatable steel. The hard grains of Ti N form about 35 to 60% of material's volume. The properties of the material are attributed to : very small size of hard grains of Ti N (about 0.1 micron) as compared to 1 to 10 microns in H.S.S. and Cemented carbides and the proportion of hard grains in the material (which is higher than in H.S.S. but less than in cemented carbides). The material is producced by particle metal technology.

Majority of the tools are not produced from solid coronite but by compound and coating technology as follows :-

1. A core of H.S.S or spring steel.

2. A layer of about 15% of diameter of core is created over the core by extrusion process at about 540°C. The bar thus produced is the raw material for coronite cutting tools.

3. A thin coating (about 2 microns) of TiCN or TiN is created on the material by PVD method.

7.3. CUTTING FLUIDS

In any metal cutting operation lot of heat is generated due to: plastic deformation of metal, friction at the rake face of the tool between the tool and the chip and also the friction between the workpiece and the flank of the tool. This increases the temperature both of the workpiece and the tool point, resulting in decrease in hardness and hence life of the tool. The machined surface will also be rough and the possibility of built up edge increases. So, the use of a cutting fluid during a machining operation is very essential. Its application at the workpiece-tool interface produces the following effects:

1. Friction at the workpiece -tool interface is reduced, due to lubricating action.
2. Heat is reduced due to cooling action at the interface.
3. Chips are washed off.

So, the cutting fluid performs the following functions:

1. Reduces heat generation.
2. Provides lubricating action.
3. Carries away the heat generated and so provides cooling action, thus, reducing workpiece temperature and distortion.
4. Provides flushing action in washing off the chips and swarf.
5. Reduces friction and wear, which improve tool life and surface finish.
6. Reduces force and energy consumption.
7. Protects the newly machined surface from environmental corrosion.
8. **Prevents surface welding of points at high presssure, thus, controlling formation of B.U.E.**
9. Facilitates chip breaking in certain materials.

Due to reduction in friction because of lubricating action: shear angle increases, chips produced are thin, cutting force is decreased, less heat is produced and there is low built up edge. Due to reduction in heat produced and cooling effect of the cutting fluid, the tool and the workpiece remain cooler. This results in: maintenance of tool hardness, less tool wear and longer tool life, less distortion and easy handling of the job. Washing off the chips helps in better surface finish and use of higher feed rate.

7.3.1. Lubrication and Cooling Action of Cutting Fluids. During metal cutting, the area of contact between tool and job is very large and also the ratio of real to apparent area of contact is very nearly equal to unity. Again, the contact pressure at the tool-workpiece interface is very high. Due to the above two factors, the type of lubrication in metal cutting can never be full fluid film lubrication. It can only be boundary lubrication. Because of this, the chemical properties of a cutting fluid are more important than its physical properties. Additives like chlorine, phosphorous, sulphur and fatty acids in the cutting fluid react with workpiece material and form a layer of solid lubricant. This lubricant has a low shear strength, and can withstand high temperature. Due to this lubrication action, the amount of heat generated is considerably reduced, the formation of weld between the tool and the chip is prevented and the chips shear easily in sliding. However, at cutting speeds of more than 60m/min, the lubricating effect of chemically active cutting fluids is only marginal and for such high speed cutting operations, the cooling action of the cutting fluid is more predominant than its lubricating action.

7.3.2. Requirements of A Cutting Fluid. A cutting fluid should have the following properties:

1. It should wet the surfaces of cutting tool and workpiece for better cooling and lubricating effects.
2. Good lubricating property.
3. High heat absorbing capacity.
4. High flash point.
5. It should not damages or react with the materials of machine tool parts.
6. It should not stain or leave residues on the workpiece surface.
7. It should not emit toxic vapours.
8. It should be stable, that is, it should not get oxidised or decomposed when left in air.

7.3.3 Types of Cutting Fluids. There are basically two main types of cutting fluids:

1. Those which are mixed with water, such as, soluble oils and soaps. These are emulsions of oil and water or soap and water.

2. Those which are not mixed with water, called cutting oils, which can be pure oils or a mixture of two or more oils.

Soluble Oils. Water increases the cooling effect and oil provides the best lubricating properties. By mixing various proportions of water with soluble oils or soaps, cutting fluids with a wide range of cooling and lubricating properties, can be obtained. The ratio of oil to water depends upon the application of the cutting fluid and ranges from about 1: 5 to 1: 50. The usual ratios for the various machining operations can be:

Turning : 1 : 25;   Milling : 1 : 10

Drilling and reaming : 1 : 25;   Grinding : 1 : 50

Cutting Oils. These are fixed oils and mineral oils. Fixed oils consist of animal, fish and vegetable oils. Chiefly used fixed oils are: lard oil, sperm or whale oil, and olive, cotton seed and linseed oil. Turpentine oil distilled from vegetable oils is also used. Fixed oils have greater oiliness than mineral oils but are not so stable as mineral oils and tend to become gummy and decompose when heated. Mineral oils come from crude petroleum oils, for example, paraffin.

To combine stability of the mineral oils with good lubricating properties of fixed oils, they are often mixed. Sometimes chlorine and sulphur is added to give the property of "Wetting" the metal with a highly adhesive oil film. This imparts the antiwelding properties which help to prevent the formation of built up edge on the cutting tool. Such cutting oils are known as "sulphonated oils". To prevent the growth of bacteria and fungi which makes the cutting fluid to become injurious to the human skin, a phenol disinfectant is added.

During machining of heat resistant and stainless steels, nimonic alloys etc. the pressure and temperature at the cutting edge can be very heavy. The normal cutting oil may not be able to support this heavy presure at the cutting edge, resulting in welding of metal chips of the tool face. To prevent this, extreme pressure (EP) additives are added to the cutting oils. The most commonly used EP additive is sulphur and next is chlorine. These additives form solid films of iron chloride and iron sulphide between the tool face and the chips. These films are easily sheared and have high melting points. Thus, they help in preventing the chips from welding to the nose of the tool where the pressure is maximum. Chlorine will form a film between surfaces at points of high pressure, preventing their contact, but at the same time allowing them to slide over one another.

So, depending upon the working conditions, four types of cutting oils can be had:

(*i*) Straight mineral oils. These are suitable for light duty and high speed work.

(*ii*) Mixture of mineral oils and fixed oils. These are suitable for light and medium duty.

(*iii*) Mineral oils with EP additives suitable for heavy duty.

(*iv*) Mixture of mineral oils and fixed oils with EP additives suitable for the heaviest duty.

7.3.4. Application of Cutting Fluids. The cutting fluid may be applied to the cutting tool in the following ways:

1. By hand, using a brush.

2. By means of a drip tank attached to the machine body.

3. By means of a pump.

For the effective use of cutting fluid and for heavy and continuous cutting, the fluid should penetrate into the cutting zone. For this, the third method (using a pump) of supplying the cutting fluid is the most common. This is known as "Flood application". Here, a continuous stream of cutting fluid is directed at the cutting zone with the help of a nozzle or jet, (Fig. 7.4). This is also known as "Hi-jet Method". The used cutting fluid drops into a tank at the bottom. Before it, is recirculated by the pump, it passes through many filters to remove chips and dirt. To avoid excessive splashing and vapourization of the fluid, it is supplied to the cutting zone from the top also, (Fig. 7.5).

For some applications, the cutting fluid is supplied through the tool itself and directed along the flank face of the tool.

Under suitable circumstances, the 'high-jet' method gives a significant increase in tool life. However, the apparatus for applying the cutting fluid is expensive and also the high-presure just may be of some danger to the operator. Thus, it may be an economical procedure of coolant application, it is not universally adopted.

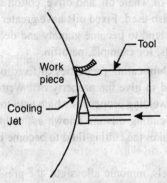

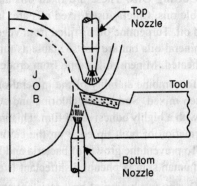

Fig. 7.4. Flood Application of Cutting Fluid.   Fig. 7.5. Use of Two Nozzles.

Mist method of coolant application. The application of the cutting fluid as a fine atomized mist (combination of the carrier air and very fine drops of fluid) has received considerable attention in the last 25 years. The size of the fluid drops is of the order of 10 to 25 μ m. The mist is sprayed onto the cutting zone at high velocities of about 300 mps and more and under pressures of the order of 0.28 to 0.42 N/mm^2. The beneficial cooling effects of mist cooling result from the following facts:

1. Due to the high velocity of fluid application the dispersal of heat by convection currents, is intensified. This maintains the desirable high temperature gradient near the tool surface.

2. The surface area of the coolant is much greater in the form of mist than in flood applications. This increases the cooling capacity of the coolant.

3. Due to the expansion of the mist in the issuing nozzle, its temperature falls down considerably.

Mist cooling can be applied to almost all cutting operations, but it is generally more useful with high-hardness work materials.

It has been proved by research workers that mist cooling is less effective than flood cooling at significantly higher and lower temperatures (480° and 150°C). At low temperatures, the cooling is by heat conduction into the coolant and in this case, the stream of coolant is more effective than the mist. At very high temperatures, the mist produces a substantial blanket of vapours around the cutting zone. Its heat-transfer co-efficient becomes poor and its cooling efficiency descreases. Thus, mist cooling is more effective than flood cooling within a limited temperature range where the flood cooling loses its effectiveness due to the formation of a vapour layer under it.

The process of producing mist of the cutting fluid is based on the venturi principle, (Fig. 7.6). The high pressure air flowing by a siphon tube, draws the fluid into the nozzle. The shape and the density of the mist is then controlled by the nozzle. The basic components of a mist producing system are: air pump with an air storage, the cutting fluid container, piping and the spray nozzle.

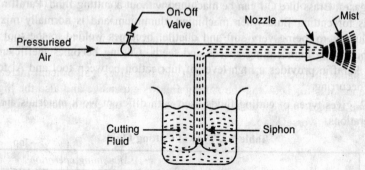

Fig. 7.6. Production of Mist.

7.3.5. Selection of a Cutting Fluid. The type of cutting fluid to be employed depends upon the work material and the characteristics of the machining process. For some machining process, a cutting fluid which is predominantly a lubricant is desirable, while with other machining processes, a cutting fluid which is predominantly a coolant should be used. For machining free cutting steels and "yellow" metals, soluble oils are used as cutting fluids. For expensive cutting tools, such as, form tools, gear cutters, broaches and milling cutters, a carefully selected cutting oil which does not effect the material of the cutting tool is selected. For machining difficult materials and for severe cutting conditions, a cutting oil is preferred to a soluble oil. Cast iron is usually machined dry, because, the usual cutting fluid forms a sort of slurry or mud with the powdery chips and this can enter the grooves and recesses in the machine tools. The graphite flakes within gray cast iron provide excellent lubrication. Brass, bronze and aluminum may be machined dry or wet with water soluble oils. Steel should always be machined with a lubricant. Magnesium and zincalloy die castings are generally machined dry when light cuts are taken or when cutting is done at low speeds. For heavy stock removal and for cutting at high speeds, cutting oils are used for magnesium and for zinc, kerosene lard oil mixture (50: 50) is most efficient.

By far, the most common of all cutting fluids is the use of soluble oils which are emulsions of mineral oil with an emulsifier such as soap in water. These are combination of fatty oils, fatty acids, wetting agents, softening agents, emulsifiers, sulphur, chlorine, rust and foam inhibitors, germicides and water.

Water as a cutting fluid is the best cooling medium and is most effective fluid for high speed cutting, but it has little lubricating value, it does not spread well over a surface to wet it because of high surface tension, it causes rust and corrosion. To improve it as a cutting fluid, small proportions of inorganic additives are mixed with it. These additives include amines and nitrites to prevent rust, nitrates for nitrite stabilization, phosphates and borates to act as water softeners, wetting agents, and in some cases phosphorous, chlorine, or sulphur to prevent extreme pressure lubrication.

The general working rules for cutting-fluid selection are:

1. Select oil with extreme pressure properties for low cutting speeds (less than 30 to 60 mpm). At low cutting speeds, lubrication is the important factor in order to reduce the tendency to produce B.U.E.

2. At higher cutting speeds, temperatures increases substantially and cooling is the important consideration. So, select coolants (oil-in-water emulsions or water with rust inhibitor) for medium to high speed cutting.

Recently, pure compounds like carbon tetrachloride (CCl_4), chloroform ($CHCl_3$), trichloroethane and certain other chlorinated hydrocarbons have been found to be efficient lubricants when cutting many metals at low speeds (few cms. per min). However, their main drawback is their toxicity and their use involving high temperatures is out of question, since, when heated they give off poisonous gases. Brass like C-I can be machined without a cutting fluid. Paraffin is sometimes used as a basis for cutting fluid when machining aluminium and is normally mixed with 50% mineral oil. Aluminium, being very soft and ductile, becomes welded to the tool cutting edge, particularly when using high cutting speeds and feeds. Cutting becomes inefficient resulting in rough surface. Paraffin provides a high level of lubrication between tool and Al to prevent this situation from occurring.

Table 7.2. gives types of cutting fluids used with different work materials and for different machining operations.

Table 7.2. Type of Cutting Fluids

Material being machined	Machining operation			
	Turning	Drilling	Tapping	Milling
Cast Iron	Dry	Dry	Dry or 25% Lard oil + 75% Mineral oil	Dry
Alloy Steels	25% sulphur base oil + 75% mineral oil	Soluble oil	30% Lard oil + 70% mineral oil	10% Lard oil + 90% mineral oil
Low carbon and Tool steels	25% Lard oil + 75% Mineral oil	Soluble oil	25–40% Lard oil with mineral oil	Soluble oil
Malleable Iron	Soluble oil	Soluble oil	Soluble oil	Soluble oil
Bronze	Soluble oil	soluble oil	30% Lard oil with mineral oil	Soluble oil
Copper	Soluble oil	Soluble oil	Soluble oil	Soluble oil

Effect of Coolants on Cutting Variables, i.e., cutting speed, feed and depth of cut :–

Tool life is a direct function of cutting temperature (temperature at the work – tool interface). Excessive temperature is the most serious limitation to tool life, because cutting tool materials markedly soften at sufficiently high temperature, thus adversely affecting the tool life. The cutting temperature increases with increase in three process variables. Increased speed and feed and depth of cut magnify the thermal problems of the tools and the surface finish of the job. However, the work-tool interface temperature can be sufficiently reduced and hence the tool life can be enhanced by the effective use of a cutting fluid. Reduced average temperature at the tool-work interface permits a sufficiently high cutting speed and feed. This inhibits the formation of build-up edge, increases the metal removal rate and shortens the cycle time. Also, higher cutting speed leads to a higher shear-plane angle and a reduced co-efficient of friction, both advantageous with respect to optimum cutting conditions.

PROBLEMS

1. Enumerate the essential requirements of a tool-material.
2. Name the various cutting tool materials.
3. Discuss the role of carbon, manganese, chromium, molybdenum, cobalt, vanadium and tungsten in tool steels.

4. Give the field of application of type 'O' tool steels and type 'A' tool steels.

5. What are the significant characteristics of high-speed steels ?

6. Discuss the T- series and M- series high-speed steels.

7. Enumerate the advantages of high-speed steel produced by powder metallurgy.

8. How are carbide tools made? Describe the process.

9. Which sintered carbides are employed for machining steels and for machining non-ferrous metals ?

10. Name the various binding materials used in the manufacture of sintered carbides.

11. What do you understand by "laminated" and "coated carbides" ?

12. Give the advantages of coating the face of tungsten carbide tools with a thin coating of titanium carbide.

13. Enumerate the advantages of ceramic cutting tools over tungsten carbide tools.

14. Give the constituents of stellite tool material. How this is manufactured?

15. How 'UCON' is produced ?

16. List the various tool materials used in industry. State the advantages and disadvantages of each material.

17. State the optimum operating temperature of each of the tool materials used in industry.

18. What are the main functions of a cutting fluid ?

19. List the essential characteristics of a cutting fluid.

20. Discuss the various types of cutting fluids.

21. Discuss the various methods of applying the cutting fluid at the cutting zone.

22. Give the constituents of ceramics. How these materials are produced ?

23. What are cermets ? Give their composition and properties.

24. Give the advantages of C.B.N. as a cutting tool material.

25. What are EP additives ? Why are these added to a cutting fluid ?

26. Write the note on "selection of a cutting fluid".

27. Why were cutting tool inserts developed ?

28. What are "Indexable Inserts" and "Throw away inserts" ?

29. Discuss the two methods of attaching inserts to tool shanks.

30. What is the composition of Sialon ?

31. Explain the application and limitation of ceramic tools ?

32. Why are tools coated ?

33. What is 18-4-1 type of cutting tool material ?

34. What are "Compax tools" ?

35. Write on "Oxide Coating" of carbide tools.

36. What is "Compact" diamond tool material ?

37. Why C.I. is usually machined dry ?

38. Why gray C.I. does not need any lubrication during machining ?

39. List the additives added to water to improve its properties as a cutting fluid.

40. What is "Coronite" cutting tool material ?

41. List the major elements in cast-cobalt tools.

42. List the advantages of Cermets.

43. Which is the hardest known material, next to diamond ?

44. Write about the use of H.S.S. in the form of inserts and also about coated H.S.S. tools.

Note :– Till recently, H.S.S. tools have been used as solid tools. However, of late, there has been an increasing tendency to use H.S.S. in the form of inserts just like inserts of WC, Al_2O_3, Sialon etc. This has resulted due to the high cost of H.S.S. tool material . These inserts are attached to the tool shank (Carbon or low alloy steel) by clamping or by brazing (See Fig. 7.1), or welded to it. For example, H.S.S. cutting ends of drills are welded to the steel shank by "Friction Welding" (see Chapter 5 Art. 5.5 (3)). Similarly, in band saws, narrow H.S.S. strips are welded to the steel bands by Electron Beam Welding (EBW).

Coated H.S.S. tools :– Just like coated carbides, coated H.S.S. tools have recently been introduced in the market. The cutting tool (in the form of insert) is given a thin coating (2 to 6 μm thick) of a refractory carbide or nitride, for exaple TiC, TiN, Hafnium nitride and Alumina (Al_2O_3).

Cost of coated tool = 2 to 5 times the cost of uncoated tool.

However, life of coated tool = 5 to 10 times the life of uncoated tool.

Coated tools perform much better while cutting general material as well as hard to machine alloys such as $Cr - Mo$ steels.

45. Write about whisker reinforced tool materials.

Whisker reinforced tool materials, Kyon :

The preformance of cutting tool materials has been further enhanced by the development of whisker reinforced cutting tool materials (composite Materials). Whiskers have been used as reinforcing fibres in composite cutting tool materials. For example, SiC whiskers are used as reinforcement in Al_2O_3 matrix (See Chapter 12). The resultant material is wear resistant and very tough. The material is used in the form of inserts. This cutting tool material is superior to coated carbides, because, it is resistant to chipping.

Cutting speed = 2 to 3 times that for plain carbide tools. Such cutting tool materials are suitable for intermittent cutting and machining of Ni-based alloys.

46. Why most of the tool-steels contain 2 or three elements ?
47. Write the benefits of "Coronite" cutting tool material.
48. How is the "Coronite" cutting tool material produced ?
49. What is a "Substrate"?
50. How is the "Compact" diamond cutting tool material produced?
51. What are "Borazon" and "Elbor" cutting tool materials?
52. Sketch the various shapes of inserts used in metal cutting tool industry.
53. What are "Sulphonated Oils"?
54. Write the benefit of adding chlorine to a cutting fluid.
55. Can Brass be machined without a cutting fluid?
56. How Paraffin helps in the machining of Aluminium?
57. Discuss the four types of cutting oils used in a machine shop.
58. What is the main drawback of using carbon tetrachloride and chloroform as cutting fluid?
59. Write the drawbacks of "Mist method" of applying coolants.
60. Discuss the effect of coolants on Cutting Variables.

Chapter

8

Machine Tools

8.0. GENERAL

The readers should understand the difference between a machine and a machine tool. A machine is or device which converts some form of input into output, e.g., Air coolers, Air conditioners and refrigerators etc., where the input is electric energy and the output is the cooling effect. On the other hand, machine tools are machines that produce the various articles. Thus, whereas, all the machine tools are machines, but all the machines are not machine tools.

All the machine tools used in manufacturing can be categorized into two groups :-

1. Metal Forming Machine tools.

2. Metal Cutting Machine tools.

Metal forming machine tools produce the various articles by displacing material from one place of workprice to another place by its plastic deformation (See Chapter 4 on "Mechanical Working of Metals").

A machine tool is a power driven machine for making articles of a given shape, size and accuracy (according to the blueprints) by removing metal from workpieces in the form of chips. Machine tools are factory equipment for producing machines, instruments and tools of all kinds. So, it can be said that the machine tool is the mother of all machines. Hence, the size of a country's stock of machine tools and their technical quality and condition largely characterizes its industrial potential.

Most machine tools perform the following four functions:

1. Hold the job.

2. Hold the cutting tools.

3. Move one or both of these (rotary motion or reciprocating motion).

4. Provide a feeding motion for one of these.

Classification of Machine Tools. Machine tools can be classified in various ways. From the point of view of their field of application, machine tools are classified as:

1. General Purpose Machine Tools : General purpose or universal machine tools are used for performing a great variety of machining operations on a wide range of workpieces. These are employed chiefly in piece and small-lot production and for repair work. Machine tools used for a particularly wide range of work are known as multipurpose machine tools. Especially versatile machine tools are also called "Omniversal". General purpose machine tools include : plain turning lathes, turret lathes, milling machines, drilling machines, grinding machine etc.

2. Single Purpose Machine Tools : These machine tools are designed to perform a single definite machining operation, *e.g.,* broaching, thread cutting, gear shaping and hobbing machines, machines for machining pistons, crank shafts, camshafts and for turning the cam contours on camshafts etc.

3. Limited Purpose Machine Tools : These machine tools are capable of a narrow range of operations on a wide variety of workpieces, *e.g.,* automatic cutting off machines.

4. Production Machine Tools : These are mainly used in batch and mass production and feature high power and rigidity. These machine tools include : multi-tool lathes, single-and multi-spindle automatics, and semi- automatic lathes, plunge-cut cylindrical grinders, centreless, planer-type milling machines, thread rolling machines for tap production, numerically controlled machine tools etc.

5. Specialized Machine tools : These are used for machining articles similar in shape but different in size. This group includes unit built machine tools. These machine tools allow the machining of several surfaces in different planes. Their advantage is that they are readily changed over from one job to another. This is done by mounting additional unit heads, positioning them at an angle to a horizontal or vertical plane or other-wise. These machines are used mainly in large-lot production.

6. Special Machine Tools : These machine tools are designed and manufactured individually and are intended for performing a certain definite operation in machining a certain definite workpiece. These machine tools include : machines for sharpening round threading dies, for grinding relief surfaces at the chamfer of round threading dies, for marking round threading dies and shank-type tools, for threading by die taps, for grinding flutes on taps and reamers, tap chamfers, flutes on twist drills etc. These machines find applications in large-lot and mass production.

The general purpose machine tools have the following characteristics:

(*i*) Usually less initial investment in equipment.

(*ii*) Greater machine flexibility.

(*iii*) Fewer machines may be required.

(*iv*) Less maintenance cost.

(*v*) Less set up and debugging time.

(*vi*) Less danger of obsolescence.

The special purpose machines have the following characteristics:

(*i*) Uniform product flow.

(*ii*) Reduced in-process inventory.

(*iii*) Reduced manpower requirements.

(*iv*) Reduced factory floor space.

(*v*) Higher output.

(*vi*) Higher product quality.

(*vii*) Reduced inspection cost.

(*viii*) Reduced operator skill requirements.

According to Accuracy the Machine Tools are Divided into Five Classes :

(*a*) **Normal Accuracy :** Machine tools of normal or standard accuracy include the majority of the general purpose machine tools.

(*b*) **Higher Accuracy :** Machine tools of higher accuracy are manufactured to the same drawings as the normal accuracy models, except that higher requirements are made to the accuracy with which the critical parts are manufactured, as well as to the quality of assembly and adjustments.

(*c*) **Precision :** Machine tools have certain parts that have been specially designed with the aim of maintaining the high accuracy standards. In addition, narrow tolerances are stipulated for the machining of all the parts, as well as for their assembly and adjustment as a whole.

(d) **High Precision :** Machine tools are manufactured according to even more rigorous accuracy requirements than "Precision" class machine tools.

(e) **Super-high Precision :** Master machine tools are intended for machining the parts which determine the accuracy of machine tools belonging to "precision" and "high precision" class.

To ensure the required accuracy of their operation, the machine tools of the last three classes are to be installed in special constant-temperature rooms, with automatically controlled (Constant) temperature and humidity.

According to Weight, machine tools can be classified as :- Light weight (upto 1 tonne), medium-weight (upto 10 tonnes), and heavy-weight (over 10 tonnes). The last group can be further divided into subgroups as: Large size (10 to 30 tonnes), Heavy (30 to 100 tonnes) and Extra-heavy (over 100 tonnes).

According to the type of processing operations they perform or the tools they employ, all machines can be divided into nine groups, as under:–

1. Lathes : Engine and facing lathes, cutting-off lathes, multiple-tool lathes, Turret lathes, Automatics and Semi-automatics (Single spindle, multiple-spindle). Vertical turning and boring mills, and specialized machine tools.

Vertical turning and boring mills are used to machine blanks of large diameter and relatively small height. Most of the larger machines (some can accommodate work 25 m in diameter) are called vertical boring mills and the smaller models are usually known as vertical turret lathes.

2. Drilling and Boring Machines : Upright drill presses, Semi-automatic single-spindle drilling machines, Semi-automatic multiple-spindle drilling machines, Jig borers, Radial drills, Boring machines, Precision boring machines, and horizontal drilling machines.

3. Planers, Shapers, Slotters and Broaching Machines : Open side Planers, Double-housing Planers, Shapers, Slotters, Horizontal broaching machines, Vertical broaching machines.

4. Milling Machines : Horizontal knee-type milling machines, Vertical knee-type milling machines, Tracer controlled milling and engraving machines, Continuous milling machines, Vertical-spindle compound-table milling machine, Fixed-bed and planer-type milling machines, and Ram-head milling machines.

5. Grinding and Micro-finishing Machines : Cylindrical grinders, Internal grinders, Snagging grinders, Specialized grinders, Tool and cutter grinders, Surface grinders, and Micro-finishing machines.

6. Gear and Thread Cutting Machines : Shapers and Planers for Spur and Helical gears, Bevel gear generators, Hobbers for Spur and helical gears and splined shafts, Worm Wheel and Worm cutting machines, Gear tooth Chamfering machines, Thread-milling machines, Gear finishing machines, Gear and thread grinders.

7. Combination Machine Tools : General purpose machines, Semi-automatic machines and Automatic machines.

8. Cutting-off Machines : Cutting off lathes, Abrasive cutting machines, Circular-saw friction cutting machines, Straightening and cutting off machines, Bond saw cutting-off machines, Circular Cold sawing machines, and Power hacksawing machines.

9. Miscellaneous Machine Tools : Coupling and pipe thread cutting machines, Saw-cutting machines, Centreless bar turning and straightening machine, Tool Testing machines, Dividing machines, and Balancing machines.

Motions in Machine Tools : To obtain a finished workpiece on a machine tool, certain co-ordinated motions must be imparted to the work and the cutting tool. These motions are of two types : Primary or working motions and auxiliary motions. Primary motions consist of principal or cutting motions and feed motions. They serve the purpose of removing metal from the workpiece. The speed of the principal motion depends on the optimum cutting speed, while the speed of the feed motion depends on the required degree of surface finish.

Auxiliary motions help in the completion of the machining process and include such motions as : handling and clamping the work in the machine, advance and withdrawl of the cutting tool, engagement and disengagement of working motions, and changing their speeds etc. Working motions are power driven. However, certain small machines have hand feeds. Auxiliary motions may be either hand or power operated. On automatic machine tools, practically all auxiliary motions are automated.

Principal motions are of three types : rotary, reciprocating or a combination of these. This motion can be imparted either to the workpiece or to the tool.

Rotary motion to work : Lathes

Rotary motion to tool : Milling, grinding and drilling machines.

Both simultaneously : In drilling small diameter holes.

Reciprocating motion of tool : Shapers, slotters, broaching machines etc.

Reciprocating motion of work : Planers

Feed motions may be : Continuous, intermittent or compound.

Continuous feed : lathes, milling, drilling machines etc. Intermittent feed : Shapers, planers etc.

Compound feed : Gear cutter for cutting helical geacs.

Combined feed : Cylindrical grinders.

Methods of Machining a Shape

1. Forming. Here the shape of the tool is the finished shape of the workpiece and the tool is called "Form tool" to finish the job, all that is necessary, in addition to the relative movement required to produce the chip (primary motion) is to feed (plunge) the tool in depth, e.g., turning as shown in Fig. 8.1(a). Other examples are : drilling, plunge cut method of cylindrical grinding and plunge cut method of thread grinding.

2. Generating. Here, the required shape of the workpiece is obtained by combining several motions that not only accomplish the chip forming process (primary action) but also move the point of engagement (of the job and the tool) along the surface (called as feed motion), e.g., in cylindrical turning on a centre lathe, Fig. 8.1(b), the tool is set to cut a certain depth of cut and then traverses along the job to produce the chips. Other examples are : shaping and planning a flat, surface grinding, peripheral milling and so on.

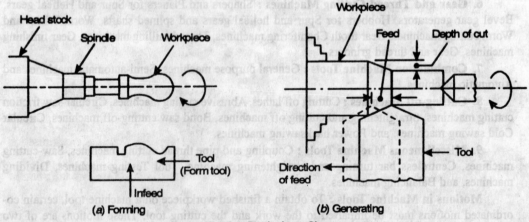

Fig. 8.1. Producing a Shape.

3. Combined forming and generating: Thread cutting with a single point tool and hobbing etc.

When discussing the various machine tools, the various motions of the tools, the various motions of the tool/workpiece will be represented as given below:

(*i*) **ReciprocatingMotion :**

Right :		→ ;	Left :	→
Combined Right-Left			:	↔
Up :		↑ ;	Down :	↓
Combined Up-Down			:	↕
In		⊕ ;	Out :	⊙

(*ii*) **Rotary Motion : About,**

Horizontal Axis : ⊖——— ;   Vertical Axis :

8.1. LATHE MACHINES

A lathe is one of the oldest and perhaps most important machine tools ever developed. The job to be machined is rotated (turned) and the cutting tool is moved relative to the job. That is why, the lathes are also called as "Turning machines". If the tool moves parallel to the axis of rotation of the workpiece, cylindrical surface is produced, while, if it moves perpendicular to this axis, it produces a flat surface.

A lathe was basically developed to machine cylindrical surfaces. But many other operations can also be performed on lathes, for example, facing, parting, necking, knurling, taper turning, thread cutting and forming etc., (Fig. 8.2). We also can perform operations of other machine tools on a lathe, for example, drilling, reaming, milling and grinding operations etc. No wonder, a lathe is called "the father of the entire machine tool family". About one half of machine tools operating in engineering plants are of the lathe group.

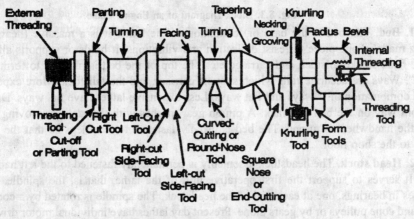

Fig. 8.2. Common Lathe Operations.

On the basis of their purpose, design, number of tools accommodated, degree of mechanisation and other factors, lathe-type machine tools may be classified as :

1. Limited or low-production Machines. The lathes included in this category are : engine lathe (centre lathe), bench lathe, tool room lathe and speed lathe.

2. Medium-production Machines. Turret lathes and duplicating (or tracer controlled) lathes.

3. High-production Machines. Semi automatic and automatic lathes.

The construction and principle of lathe-type machine tools will be illustrated by the example of the most common representative of this class-the engine lathe.

8.1.1. Engine Lathe. It is so called because the first of this type of lathe was driven by a steam engine. It is also called "Centre lathe", because, it has two centres between which the job can be held and rotated. A very high percentage of all lathe work is turned between centres.

The main parts of a centre lathe are : Bed, Head stock, Tail stock, Carriage and the Electric drive, (Fig. 8.3).

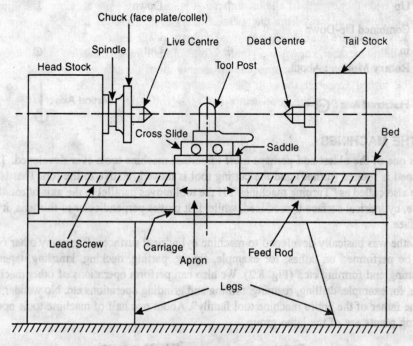

Fig. 8.3. Block Diagram of an Engine Lathe.

1. Bed. The bed is the base or foundation of the lathe. It is a massive (heavy) and rigid casting made in one piece to resist deflection and vibrations. It holds or supports all other parts, that is, head stock, tailstock and carriage etc. The top of the bed is planned to form "guides" or "ways". Ways are accurate rails which support carriage and the tailstock. More expensive lathes have a combination of V ways and flat ways. Less expensive lathes have flat ways. Directly under the front way on the bed is a rack. A pinion gear meshes with the rack for moving the carriage when the handwheel is turned. The bed is usually fastened to steel legs so that the lathe can be bolted to the shop floor.

2. Head stock. The headstock assemebly is permanently fastened to the left hand end of the lathe. It serves to support the first operative unit of the lathe, that is, the spindle. The spindle revolves in bearings, one at each end of the headstock. The spindle is rotated by a combination of gears and cone pulleys or by gears alone. Present day lathes have individual motor drives and most of them have geared headstocks. The steel spindle is hollow to take long bar stock. The spindle has a definite taper at the front end for holding centres and other tools having a tapered shank. The hole through the spindle makes it possible to use a knockout bar to remove such tools. Work-holding attachments such as driving plate, face plate or various types of chucks may be mounted on the threaded spindle nose. Some type of work may also be held in a collet which is inserted into the hollow headstock spindle. A taper sleeve fits into the taper spindle hole. The headstock or live centre fits into the sleeve. This centre is called live centre because it turns with the work. The centre is a tapered metal part with a pointed end. This supports the end of the workpiece as it turns between the centres. All centre points have a 60-degree included angle.

3. Tail stock. Tail stock is on the other end of the bed from the head stock. Its chief function is to hold the dead centre so that long workpieces (L/D > 4) can be supported between centres. It can be moved along the bed and clamped to the bed at the various desired locations to suit the length of the workpiece.

Tailstock consists of two main parts. The lower part rests directly on the bed ways, and the upper part rests on the lower part. Adjusting screws hold the two parts together. The upper casting can be moved toward or away from the operator to offset the tailstock for taper turning and to re-align the tailstock centre for straight turning. The body of the tailstock has a bore for the hollow cylindrical sliding member, known as a "quill". This quill is sometimes called as "tailstock spindle" even though it can not rotate. The quill moves in and out of the tailstock bore when the tailstock handwheel is turned. Once set, the quill may be clamped to remain in a desired position. The quill has a taper hole into which the dead centre is fitted. Drills, reamers, taps and other end cutting tools are held and fed to the work piece by the quill, the shanks of the tools being held in the tapered hole of the quill.

4. Carriage. In between the headstock and the tailstock is the carriage. It is movable on the bed ways and its purpose is to hold the cutting tool and to impart to it either longitudinal or cross feed. It has five major parts :

(a) **Saddle.** The base of the carriage is the saddle which slides along the ways of the lathe bed.

(b) **Cross-Slide.** The cross-slide is mounted on the saddle. It provides cutting tool motion which is perpendicular to the centre line of the lathe itself. The cross-feed movement may be controlled by manual (with cross slide handle) or by power feed.

(c) **Compound Rest.** It is mounted on top of the cross-slide. The compound rest has a graduated base and can be swivelled around a vertical axis. In this way, its slide can be set at any angle with the axis of the workpiece. It can be clamped to remain at any angular setting. The range of compound rest is only limited and is used for obtaining angular cuts and short tapers, as well as convenient positioning of the tool to the work. Both the cross slide and the compound rest screws are equipped with micrometer collars. These are used in making accurate adjustments when turning workpieces to close measurements, and when cutting screw threads. There is no power feed for the compound rest.

(d) **Tool post.** The tool post is mounted on the compound rest and slides in a T-slot. Cutting tool/tool holder is firmly held in it. The tool can be swivelled as well as tilted by means of a rocker and a concave ring collar, (Fig. 8.4).

(e) **Apron.** The apron is secured underneath the saddle and hangs over the front of the bed. It contains the gears, clutches, and levers for operating the carriage by hand and power feeds. The apron hand wheel can be turned to move the carriage longitudinally by hand. This hand wheel is attached to a pinion that meshes with the rack under the front of the bed. The apron also contains friction clutches for automatic feeds and a splitnut or halfnut. The split nut can be closed over the lead screw threads and is used only when cutting screw threads.

8.1.2.Drive. The centre lathe has primarily two motions : the primary cutting motion and the feed motion. These motions are accomplished by means of corresponding drives, which are systems of mechanisms for transmitting power from its source (the electric motor) to the operative units of the lathe, that is, to the spindle for primary cutting motion (main drive) and to the carriage for feed motion (feed drive).

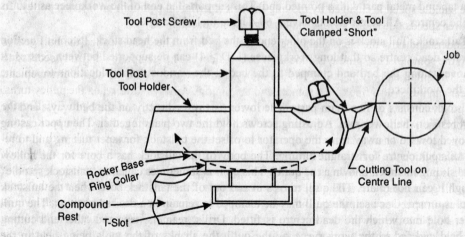

Fig. 8.4. Tool Post.

1. Main Drive. The function of main drive is to drive the spindle and to change its speed so as to obtain the most expedient cutting speeds. Power for driving the spindle is provided by an electric motor.

Two general types of main drives are used on lathes : Stepped drive and Step -less drive.

In the first case, the maximum, minimum and a series of intermediate spindle speeds in definite steps are available. In the step-less system, or the infinitely variable spindle speed system, any spindle speed from the minimum to the maximum can be obtained. This feature allows the most suitable cutting speeds for each workpiece diameter to be set up, thereby maintaining the specified surface finish without decreasing the rate of production.

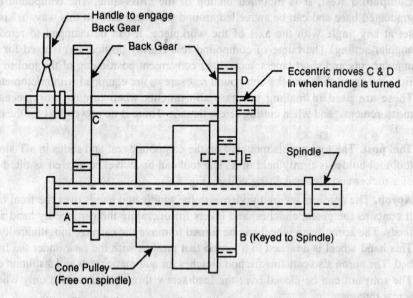

Fig. 8.5. Step-cone Pulley with Back Gear Arrangement.

Stepped spindle speed variation can be achieved in two ways :

(*a*) **Cone Pulley System.** In the smaller lathes, we have the cone or step pulley arrangement. The power flows from the motor in the base to the cone pulley attached to the spindle, by means of a belt. The spindle speed is changed by moving the belt to different positions on the step pulley. To obtain slower speeds and more power, the back gears are used.

To understand how the back gears operate, (see Fig. 8.5). The gear B called the bull gear is fastened to the spindle. The spindle is a loose fit over a sleeve. The step pulley is firmly secured to the sleeve. The small end of the pulley has a pinion A attached to it. With the above arrangement, the bull gear can never turn free of the spindle and the pinion A always turns when the pulley turns. The step pulley and the pinion A are connected with the bull gear by a sliding pin E called the bullgear lockpin. At the back of the headstock are two gears C and D, called the back gears, mounted on the same shaft (an eccentric one). They are spaced to line up or mesh with the bull gear B and the pinion A. To make the back gears mesh with bull gear B and the pinion A, the back gear handle is pulled forward. When the back gears are not in mesh and the bull gear lock-pin is in place, we will get a direct drive. The speed of the spindle will then be the same as that of the cone. If a reduction in speed is desired, the bull gear lock-pin is disengaged and the back gear lever is pulled forward. Now the power from the step pulley is delivered to the bull gear through the pinion A and the back gears, which turns the spindle. So, there will be a direct as well as a back-gear speed for every step on the cone pulley.

The cone pulley drive is very simple, and cheap in design, but it occupies lot of space and the number of speed steps are limited. The flat belt drive is not positive and shifting of belt from one step to the other takes time affecting the rate of production.

(*b*) **All Geared Drive.** In this arrangement, we have a completely geared headstock with a combination of shifting levers. The power from the motor is delivered to the spindle through a belt drive and speed gear box. A geared headstock has got the following advantages :

(*i*) It is more efficient and compact than the cone pulley drive.

(*ii*) Possibility of transmitting high power.

(*iii*) The available power on the spindle remains almost constant for the different speeds

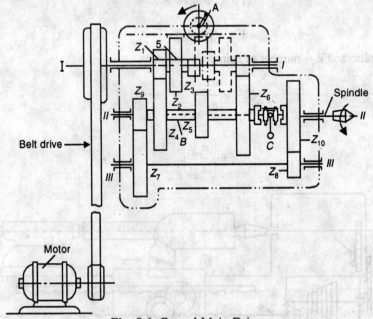

Fig. 8.6. Geared Main Drive.

Fig. 8.6 shows a simple geared headstock. Power is transmitted from the motor through a belt drive to shaft I-I. This shaft carries three cluster gears Z_1, Z_2 and Z_3. The cluster gear can be shifted with help of lever A, on key 5 along the shaft I-I, so that its three rims mesh in turn with the gears Z_4, Z_5 and Z_6 which are rigidly mounted on sleeve B. This sleeve is freely mounted on the lathe spindle II-II. The gears Z_9 and Z_{10}, mounted directly on the spindle are constantly in mesh with gears Z_7 and Z_8 of the countershaft III-III. When the clutch C is shifted into engagement to the left, countershaft III-III is disengaged. The spindle will obtain one of the three speeds- n_1, n_2 and n_3 – depending upon the position of the cluster gear.

If n_1 = Speed of the shaft I – I, then

$$n_1 = n_0 \times \frac{Z_1}{Z_4}, \ n_2 = n_0 \times \frac{Z_2}{Z_5}, \text{ and } n_3 = n_0 \times \frac{Z_3}{Z_6}.$$

When the clutch C is shifted to the right, the counter shaft is also included in the gear train. Its gearing ratio will be,

$$\frac{Z_{10}}{Z_8} \times \frac{Z_7}{Z_9}$$

With this, the spindle obtains three more speeds. Therefore, the countershaft enables additional speeds to be obtained, in the present case 6 spindle speeds can be obtained. Geared headstocks are commonly designed for 3, 4, 6, 8, 12, 16 and 24 spindle speeds. In properly designed, geared head stock, the values of the spindle speeds in the available range vary in a geometrical progression. The constant ratio has one of the following values : 1.06, 1.12, 1.26, 1.41, 1.58 and 2. The less the constant ratio, the less the difference will be between successive speeds and the more exactly the required speed can be approximated. In geometrical progression, the various spindle speeds will be given as :

$$n_1, \ \varphi \, n_1, \ \varphi^2 n_1, \ \varphi^3 n_1, \ \ldots \varphi^{z-1} . n_1$$

where

$$n_1 = n_{min} .; \ \phi^{Z-1} . \, n_1 = n_{max}$$

and φ = step ratio and Z = number of spindle speed steps

$$\therefore \qquad \qquad \phi^{Z-1} = \frac{n_{max}}{n_{min}}$$

$$\therefore \qquad \qquad \phi = \left(\frac{n_{max}}{n_{min}} \right)^{\frac{1}{Z-1}}$$

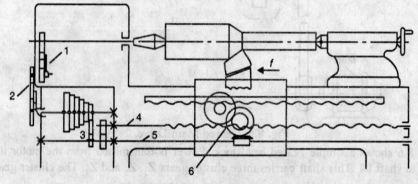

Fig. 8.7. Feed Drive of Engine Lathe.

The "Step-less drive" is discussed in volume II (A Textbook of Production Engineering).

2. Feed Drive. The feed drive serves to transmit power from the spindle to the second operative unit of the lathe, that is, the carriage. It, thereby, converts the rotary motion of the spindle into linear motion of the carriage. It also enables the specific rate of feed as well as its direction to be selected. The feed drive not only provides the different feeds required in machining but also provides a wide range of pitches for thread cutting operations.

The feed drive of an engine lathe consists of : the reversing mechanism (1), change gear quadrant (2), quick-change gear box (3), leadscrew (4), and feed rod (5), and apron (6), (Fig. 8.7).

(*i*) **Reversing mechanism.** Its function is to reverse the direction or movement of the lead screw/feed rod. The most frequently used reversing mechanism for engine lathe comprises : four spur gears with consecutive engagement of the bracket holding the reverse gears, (Fig. 8.8).

The gear Z_1 is mounted on the spindle I and the gear Z_4 - on shaft II which is usually a shaft of the change gear quadrant. Gears Z_2 and Z_3 are freely mounted on studs III and IV of the bracket. P is the feed reverse lever. The bracket is mounted on shaft II and the feed reverse lever can be moved to three positions 1, 0, or 2. Gears Z_2, Z_3 and Z_4 are constantly in mesh with each other. If the lever is shifted to position 1, gears Z_1, Z_2, Z_3 and Z_4 are put into consecutive mesh and with the automatic feed engaged, the shaft II begins to rotate in a direction opposite to that of the spindle. With lever in position 2, only gears Z_1, Z_3 and Z_4 will be in mesh and shaft II will rotate in the same direction as the spindle. With lever in the centre position O, both gears Z_2 and Z_3 are pulled out of mesh with gear Z_1 and no motion is transmitted from the spindle to shaft II. The reversing bracket is thus disengaged.

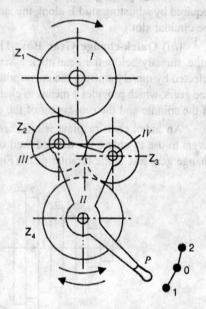

Fig. 8.8. Feed Reversing Mechanism.

(*ii*) **The change gear quadrant.** The change gear quadrant of an engine lathe consists of a set of change gears and the device known as the quadrant proper. It serves to set up the feed drive to different speeds of the lead screw and feed rod. The quadrant also transmits motion to the quick-change gear box or to leadscrew.

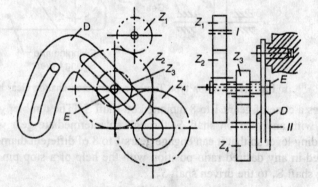

Fig. 8.9. Change Gear Quadrant.

A frequently used change-gear quadrant for an engine lathe is shown in Fig. 8.9. It is a two-pair arrangement. There can also be single-pair or three-pair arrangement. The two pair arrangement has four gears Z_1, Z_2, Z_3 and Z_4. Gear Z_1 is mounted on shaft I of the reversing mechanism and the gear Z_4 - on shaft II of the quick- change gear box. The intermediate gears Z_2 and Z_3 are keyed on a sleeve which, in turn, is mounted freely on stud E. The stud E can be adjusted and clamped as required along a straight slot in quadrant D. The latter is mounted on shaft II and can turn freely in reference to this shaft. The gearing ratio of the change gear quadrant is

$$\frac{Z_1}{Z_2} \times \frac{Z_3}{Z_4}$$

For new gearing ratios with new sets of change gears, the centre distances are changed as required by adjusting stud E along the straight slot and swivelling the quadrant about shaft II along the circular slot.

(*iii*) **Quick-change Gear Box.** The quick-change gear box is located on the front of the lathe, directly below the headstock assembly. It allows a variety of feeds to be easily the rapidly selected by merely shifting the corresponding levers. This gear box contains a number of different-size gears, which provides a means to change (1) the rate of feed and (2) the ratio between revolutions of the spindle and the movement of the carriage for thread cutting.

An index chart or plate is attached to the front of the gear box. It tells the position of the levers to use to obtain the desired feed or threads per cm. The most widely used design of quick-change gear box is the tumbler gear, (Fig. 8.10).

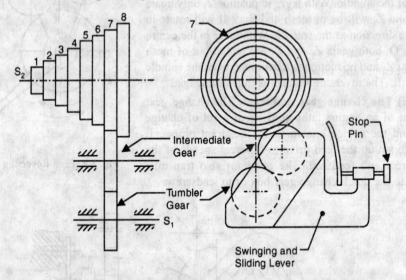

Fig. 8.10. Norton type Tumbler-gear quick-change Gear box.

It comprises a cone of gears 1 to 8 mounted on shaft S_2. The tumbler gear can slide on shaft S_1. It can mesh with any gear on shaft S_2 through an intermediate gear which is located on a swinging and sliding lever so that it can engage gears 1 to 8 of different diameters, on shaft S_2. The lever can be fixed in any desired ratio position with the help of a stop pin. The drive is usually from the driving shaft S_1 to the driven shaft S_2.

(*iv*) **Apron.** The function of the apron has already been explained. Power comes to the apron for feeding the carriage (from lathe spindle) through feed reversing mechanism, change- gear quadrant or quick-change gear box and the lead screw/feed rod. The apron encloses clutches, systems of spur and worm gearing, Fig. 8.11. Its feed mechanisms convert rotary motion of the lead screw or feed rod into linear motion (feed) of the carriage.

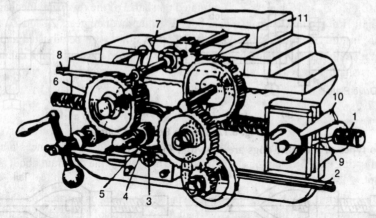

Fig. 8.11. Lathe Apron Mechanism.

The lead screw 1 is only used to move the carriage for cutting threads. For other lathe operations, feed rod 2 is used so as to save the lead-screw. Worm 3 with its key slides along the feed rod which has a key way along its whole length. When the feed rod rotates, the worm turns. The worm meshes with a worm wheel 4 and the motion is transmitted to spur gear 5 mounted on the same shaft. When the automatic feed knob is turned to the right, the clutch engages another gear (gear 5 meshes with gear 6) which transmits rotation to pinion 7 since the gear 6 and pinion 7 are mounted on the same shaft. Pinion 7 runs along the stationary rack 8, fastened to the bed, thus feeding the carriage 11, rigidly secured to the apron, along the bed. Thus, the rotary motion of the feed rod is converted into linear motion of the carriage.

Other gearing arrangements in the apron convert the rotary motion into cross feed of the cutting tool by rotation of the cross-feed screw in the cross slide. For this, the feed-change lever on the apron is moved to the "down" position and the automatic feed knob is turned to the right.

For thread cutting, the feed rod is disengaged from the apron gearing by placing the feed-change lever on the apron in the centre or neutral position. The lead screw feeds the carriage lengthwise through two half nuts 9 mounted on the rear wall of the apron. Upon engaging lever 10, the half nuts are closed and they engage the rotating lead screw. Then the half nuts and, with them, the carriage are fed along the bed. Disengagement of lever 10 spreads the half nuts to release the lead screw and the carriage stops.

8.1.3. Work-holding devices. The common work holding devices used for a centre lathe are discussed below :

1. Centres. A very high percentage of all lathe work is turned between centres. Long work pieces (shafts and axles) with L/D ratio >4, are turned length wise between centres. The work-piece, in whose ends centre holes have been previously drilled, and on which a driving dog has been clamped on one end, is mounted between the headstock (live) and tailstock (dead) centres. The workpiece is rotated by driving the lathe dog. The lathe dog is driven with the help of a drive plate. The drive plate is mounted on the threaded nose of the spindle. It has one open slot and three closed slots. A pin is inserted in the open slot which engages with the tail of the lathe dog, (Fig. 8.12 *a*). When the spindle rotates, the workpiece will rotate through this pin and the dog. If the dog has a bent tail, it will fit into one of the slots, (Fig. 8.12 *b*).

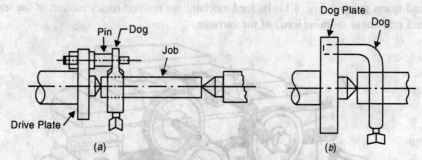

Fig. 8.12. Turning Between Centres.

The two types of the lathe dogs are shown in Fig. 8.13.

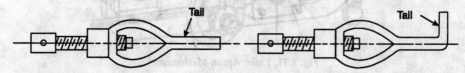

Fig. 8.13. Lathe Dogs.

Since the tailstock centre does not rotate, it acts as a bearing. It, therefore, must be lubricated and excessive pressure should be avoided. To avoid this process of lubrication in production work, a revolving centre is used.

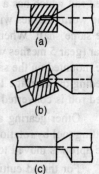

Fig. 8.14. Types of Lathe Centres.

Three designs of lathe centres are illustrated in Fig. 8.14. An ordinary centre lathe is shown in Fig. 8.14 a. A ball- ended centre (Fig. 8.14 b) is used when the tail stock is set over to turn a taper. A half centre (Fig. 8.14 c) enables external straight turning to be combined with facing the end of the workpiece. The wear resistance of the centres can be substantially increased by tipping the point with cemented carbide or metallizing it with a hard-facing alloy.

2. Chucks. Work piece with a length L < 4D may be clamped in a chuck without the need of additional support of the free end. Three- and four-jaw chucks, screwed on the spindle nose, are employed for this purpose. The chuck may be adapted to the screwed nose spindle by using a back plate, whilst on the flanged spindle, it is bolted direct.

Among the chucks used in a lathe, the most widespread are three- jaw universal self-centring chucks. These are used for holding symmetrical work as a rule. Here, the three jaws move together towards or away from the centre of the chuck.

In the 4 -jaw chuck, each of the four jaws is moved by its own screw independent of the other jaws along radial slots of the chuck body. These chucks are used for holding complex and non-symmetrical work pieces.

Pneumatically and hydraulically operated chucks are used to speed up and facilitate handling operations of certain parts in mass and large-lot production.

3. Collets. They are the most accurate of the chuck family. They are like three jaw chucks and are used primarily for bar stock or other sections upto about 63 mm, for example round, square, hexagonal etc.

4. Face Plate. A face plate is larger than a drive (dog) plate and is screwed on the spindle nose. It usually has four T-slots and a number of plain radial slots, (Fig. 8.15). It is highly efficient in machining asymmetrical work or work of complex and irregular shape which is inconvenient or even impossible to clamp in jaw-type chucks. The workpiece is clamped to the face plate with bolts and straps. Sometimes, it is more convenient to mount an angle plate on the face plate and to clamp the work on the angle plate.

5. Mandrels. A mandrel is used to locate and held a work-piece with a central hole, such as, gear blanks, pulleys etc. A mandrel is a solid hardened bar, with centres and flats on each end. The mandrel is usually tapered so that the work can be forced on it with a press fit and then removed after working. A mandrel is held between centres and rotated with a lathe dog clamped on its flat, Fig. 8.16. The taper is about 0.005 mm per cm. length.

6. Steady Rests. When very long workpieces (L/D >10 or 12) or long slender workpieces of low rigidity are machined between centres, steady rests are used to additionally support the workpiece and prevent it from bending due to the pressure of cut. There are two types of steady rests used on a lathe :

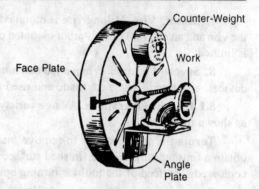

Fig. 8.15. A face Plate.

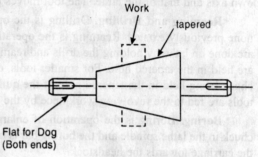

Fig. 8.16. A Mandrel.

(*a*) **Fixed Steady Rest.** This type of steady is fixed on both bed ways of the lathe, between the headstock and tailstock. The workpiece is supported by three adjustable jaws, (Fig. 8.17 *a*). Steady rests for high-velocity turning have ball or roller bearings contacting the rotating workpiece, the bearings being built into the jaws. This type of steady rest has the drawback that since the carriage can not pass it, the job will be turned in two stages by being reversed end for end after half its length has been machined.

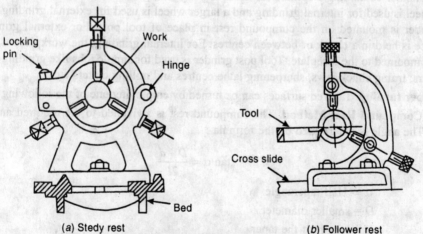

(*a*) Stedy rest   (*b*) Follower rest
Fig. 8.17. Steady Rests.

(*b*) **Follower or travelling Steady Rest.** This steady is mounted on the saddle and moves together with the tool. It has two jaws which support the work opposite the tool, (Fig. 8.17*b*) This design does not have the drawback of fixed steady rest.

7. **Milling Vise.** Milling vise is mounted in place of the compound rest. The work is held in the vise and an end mill or stub-arbor mounted cutter is inserted in the lathe spindle. Work movement is limited.

8. **Special Fixtures.** When a job can not be held in one of the above discussed work holding devices, a fixture is designed, made and used for that job.

8.1.4. Lathe Operations. A large variety of operations can be performed on an engine lathe, as shown in Fig. 8.2.

Turning is the operation to remove material from the outside diameter of a workpiece to obtain a finished surface. The finished surface may be of continuous diameter, stepped, tapered or contoured. The feed of the tool for turning operation is along the axis of the lathe,

Facing is the operation of machining the end of a workpiece to make the end square with its own axis and that of the lathe. The tool moves perpendicular to the axis of the lathe.

Reaming and Drilling. Drilling is the operation of making a hole in a work piece where none previously existed. Reaming is the operation of finishing the drilled hole. These operations are done on lathe by holding the drills and reamers in the tailstock quill. The shanks of these tools are held in the tapered hole. For smaller tools, drill chucks can be used to hold the tools, the drill chuck being held in the tapered hole of the quill by its shank. The job is held in a chuck and the tools are fed to the revolving workpiece by the quill by rotating the tailstock handle.

Boring. Boring is the operation of enlarging the drilled hole. The workpiece is held in a chuck in the lathe spindle and the boring bar is mounted in the tool post. Boring is done by moving the carriage towards the headstock.

Knurling. It is the operation of plastically displacing metal into a particular pattern for the purpose of creating a hand grip or roughened surface on a workpiece. The knurling tool is held in the tool post and is pressed against the surface of the workpiece by cross feed.

Milling. For the milling operation, small milling cutters are held in the headstock and revolved while the work is clamped in a vise mounted over the top of the compound rest, instead of the tool post. The operation is used only for small work.

Grinding. Cylindrical and internal grinding can be done on a lathe, with a tool-post grinder. This is a holder containing a spindle for mounting a grinding wheel and a motor for driving it. A small wheel is used for internal grinding and a larger wheel is used for external grinding. The tool post grinder is mounted on the compound rest in place of tool post. For external grinding, the workpiece is held in a chuck or between centres. For internal grinding, the workpiece is held in a chuck or mounted to the faceplate. Tool post grinder is used for simple jobs like grinding mandrels or reamers, truing chuck jaws, sharpening lathe centres and milling cutters etc.

Taper turning. Tapered surfaces can be turned by employing one of the following methods:

1. **Compound Rest Method.** The compound rest is swivelled to the required angle, (Fig. 8.18 *a*). The angle is determined by the formula :

$$\tan \alpha = \frac{D-d}{2l}$$

where α = Half taperangle.

D = smaller diameter

l = length of the taper

After swivelling the compound rest to this angle about the vertical axis, it is clamped in position. The taper is turned by hand wheel by rotating the handle. The method can be employed for turning short internal and external tapers with a large angle of taper. The workpiece is commonly held in a chuck.

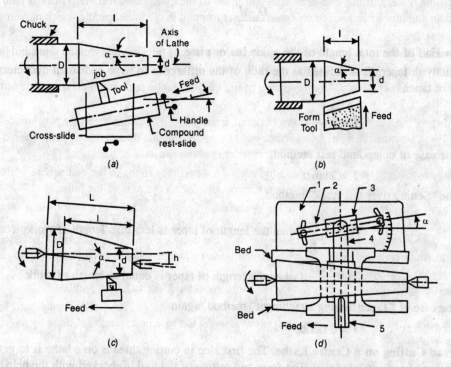

Fig. 8.18. Taper Turning Methods.

2. With a Form tool. Short external tapers with various angles of taper can be turned with a form tool, Fig. 8.18 b, using cross feed. The width of the form tool slightly exceeds that of the taper being turned. The work is held in a chuck or clamped on a faceplate.

3. Setting over the Tail-stock. Long workpieces with a small angle of taper (not exceeding 8°) are usually turned by setting over the tailstock centre, (Fig. 8.18 c). Tailstock setting over or offset can be determined from the formula,

$$h = \frac{L(D-d)}{2l} \text{ mm}$$

where, L = full length of the workpiece

l = length to be taper turned

4. Taper turning attachment. Long tapered work is frequently turned with a taper turning attachment, Fig. 8.18 d. Bracket 1 is attached to the lathe bed. It carries guide bar 2 which can be turned to the required angle and clamped in place. Guide block or slide 3, linked to the lathe cross slide 5 by tie member 4, is free to slide along the guide bar. The cross slide is disengaged from the cross feed screw. Upon travel of the saddle along the bed ways, the guide block slides along the guide bar, and through the tie member, forces the cross slide with the cutting tool to travel parallel to the guide bar at the given angle and the work is turned to the specified taper. The angle of taper can be found out by the relation :

$$\tan \alpha = \frac{D-d}{2l}$$

In some taper turning attachments, the bracket carries divisions in mm, instead of in degrees. In such cases, the guide bar has to be swivelled through mm divisions, which can be found out as :

$$S = \frac{D-d}{2l} \times lg$$

where lg = Half of the total length of the guide bar or plate.

Conicity or taper, T, is defined as the ratio of the difference in large and small diameters to the length of taper.

$$\therefore \qquad T = \frac{D-d}{l}$$

In the case of compound rest method,

$$T = 2 \tan \alpha$$

In the "Setting over tail stock" method,

$$h = \frac{L \times T}{2}, \text{ when the length of taper is less than length of workpiece}$$

and

$$h = \frac{T \times l}{2}, \text{ when the length of taper is equal to length of work.}$$

In the case of "Taper turning attachment" method, again

$$T = 2 \tan \alpha.$$

Thread Cutting on a Centre Lathe. The first step in cutting threads on a lathe is to get an accurately shaped and mounted tool. The form and setting of the tool is checked with the help of a thread template or centre gauge, (Fig. 8.19). The job is either mounted between centres or held in

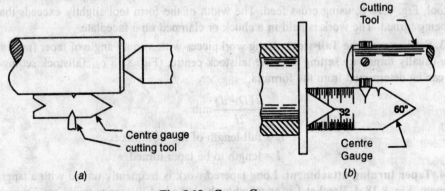

Fig. 8.19. Centre Gauge.

a chuck (for external threads) and held in a chuck for internal threads. When mounting the tool in the tool post, it must be ensured that the top of the tool is horizontal and is in line with the axis of rotation of the job, Fig. 8.20. After this, the second step is to establish a specific relationship between the longitudinal movement of the tool parallel to the axis of rotation, and the rotation, of the job. This will determine the pitch or lead of

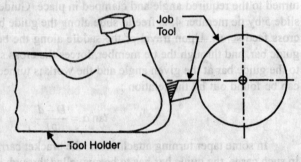

Fig. 8.20. Setting of Cutting Tool.

the thread. This is achieved with the help
of lead screw and a split nut. The two halves of the split nut are fastened to the carriage. When the
nut is closed on to the lead screw, it acts as complete nut, and the carriage starts moving as the lead
screw rotates. The lead screw is geared to the spindle and the proper speed ratio between the two
is set by means of a gear-change box. Therefore, as the lead screw rotates, the carriage will move
a pre- determined distance (depending upon the pitch or lead of the thread) per revolution of the
job. The third requirement is that the split nut must be engaged at an exact predetermined time, for
taking successive cuts, so that the tool enters the helical groove of the cut previously produced,
otherwise the tool may remove some of the desired thread. This is
achieved with the help of a 'thread dial', which is mounted on the carriage
and is driven by the lead screw through a worm gear. The face of the
thread dial is graduated into an even number of full and half divisions,
(Fig. 8.21). Whenever the lead screw rotates and the split nut is not
engaged, the thread dial rotates. The split nut must be engaged when a
particular line on the dial face coincides with the zero line For cutting
even number of threads, the split nut should be engaged when any line
on the dial coincides with zero line, and, for cutting odd-number threads,
when any numbered line coincides with zero line.

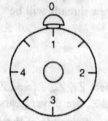

Fig. 8.21. Thread Dial.

To start cutting a thread, the tool is fed inward until it first scratches the surface of the job.
The graduated dial on the cross-slide is noted or set to zero. The split nut is then engaged and the
tool moves over the desired job length. At the end of tool travel, it is quickly withdrawn by means
of cross slide. The split nut is disengaged and the carriage is returned to the starting portion, for the
next cut. These successive cuts are continued until the thread reaches its desired depth (checked on
the dial of cross-slide). The depth of first cut is usually
0.25 to 0.40 mm. This is gradually decreased for the
successive cuts until for the final finishing cut, it is
usually 0.027 to 0.075 mm. The tool can be fed inward
either radially or at an angle of 29° by swiveling the
compound rest, (Fig. 8.22). The drawback of the first
method is that the absence of side and back rake will
not produce proper cutting except on brass and cast
iron. In the second method, the cutting mainly takes
place on one face of the tool and some side rake can
be provided. Also, the chip will curl more easily. For
cutting square, cane and worm threads, the first method
is used. For cutting L.H. threads, the tool is moved
from left to right and for cutting right hand threads, it
is moved from right to left. Thread cutting on a lathe
is a slow process, but it is the only process of producing
square threads, as other methods develop interference
on the helix.

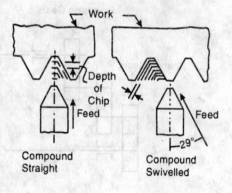

Fig. 8.22. Feeding the Tool into the
Job.

Cutting Screw Threads on a Lathe Without a Quick-Change Gear Box. When an engine
lathe does not have a quick-change gear box or when the thread pitch is non-standard and not
covered by the given gear box or when precise threads are required, the screw threads can be cut
by selecting the change gears and setting up these on the change-gear quadrant.

As a rule, the gearing ratios of the pair of gears linking the spindle to the reversing mechanism
and that of the mechanism itself are equal to unity. Now in one revolution of the spindle, carriage

must travel the pitch of the screw thread to be cut. Thus, the equation of the spindle-to-carriage gear train is :

$$P = L \cdot i_{cg}$$

where
P = pitch of the screw thread to be cut

L = pitch of the lead screw

i_{cg} = gearing ratio of the change-gear quadrant

For quadrants with two pairs of gears the set up formula for change gear selection in cutting screw threads will be

$$i_{cg} = \frac{Z_1}{Z_2} \times \frac{Z_3}{Z_4} = \frac{P}{L}$$

where Z_1, Z_2, Z_3 and Z_4 are number of teeth of the change gears, (Fig. 8.23). Gears with teeth Z_1 and Z_3 are driver gears and those with number of teeth Z_2 and Z_4 are driven gears.

Principle of thread cutting in a Lathe (Fig. 8.23). In thread cutting practice a thread pitch is said to be even if the lead screw pitch is an exact multiple of this pitch and odd if it is not. An even screw thread can be cut by disengaging the half nuts at the end of each pass, retracting the tool and returning the carriage back to the beginning of the thread manually and without stopping or reversing the lathe. When the half nuts are engaged for the next pass and the tool is advanced again it will exactly follow the previously cut thread groove. In cutting an odd thread, the half nuts are not disengaged after each pass. The lathe is stopped at the end of the pass, the tool is withdrawn and the carriage is returned to the beginning of the thread by reversing the lathe, otherwise the tool will not fallow the previously cut thread groove in the subsequent pass.

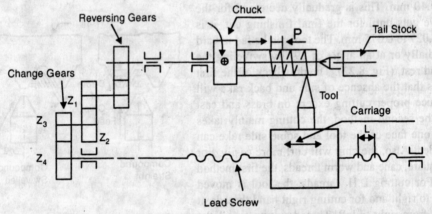

Fig. 8.23. Principle of Thread Cutting in a Lathe.

In thread cutting, the job is mounted between centres or clamped in a chuck, depending upon its length. The form of the thread cutting tool must coincide with the profile of the thread being cut.

Cutting external threads with Button Dies and a Die Holder. For smaller diameter threads, a fast method of cutting threads is to use adjustable round split (button dies) in a die holder. Select a button die of the correct size. Select a lathe die holder to match . Insert the die in the die holder. Place the die holder in the tailstock spindle. The workpiece is held in a chuck or a collect and rotated at a very slow speed. Turn in the tailstock hand wheel as the die cut the threads. Use plenty of cutting fluid. Be careful to stop the machine as soon as the correct length of the thread is machined. The external threads can also be cut by screwing the button die (held in a die stock) on the workpiece held and rotated between centres.

Cutting Internal Threads. Internal threads are cut in the same general way as the external threads. However, the cutting is more difficult because one can't see the cutting operation. Also, it is not possible to hold the tool so rigidly.

A forged boring tool can be used with the end ground the same way as for external thread cutting. The cutting edge may need a little more end relief to keep the bottom of the tool from rubbing on the work. A standard tool bit ground as a threading tool can be used with a boring bar if the hole is large enough. A centre gauge is used for grinding the tool and setting it.

Setting up the Lathe

(i) The size of the hole to be threaded must be no smaller than the minor diameter of the thread. This would give a full depth of thread.

(ii) If the thread is cut only part way through the hole, it is good idea to cut a recess at the end of the thread. This recess should equal the depth of the thread. This will permit you to release the split nut without turning in the cross feed.

(iii) Set the compound rest to 30 degrees to the left (clockwise) of the cross-feed. This is just the opposite of the setting for external threading.

(iv) Fasten the threading tool in a holder or boring bar.

(v) Hold the centre gauge against the face surface of the workpiece as shown in Fig. 8.19. This can also be done by holding the centre gauge against the side of the workpiece. Adjust the tool on centre and at right angles to the workpiece. To set the tool at centre height, use a surface gauge. Set the scriber point to the point of dead centre. Then set the tool bit to the surface- gauge scriber point.

(vi) If the thread is cut only partially through the hole, move the carriage by hand to the point where the thread will end. Mark a line on the lathe bed with a piece of chalk or a pencil. During thread cutting, this reference line will indicate that the tool bit has reached the end of the thread length so that the operator can open splitnut lever and stop carriage.

Cutting the Threads. While cutting the internal threads, the following procedure is adopted:

1. Set the micrometer collar of the cross-feed a zero.

2. Turn the compound-rest feed out until the point of the tool just touches the workpiece. Set the micrometer collar at zero.

3. Then the same general procedure is followed as explained for cutting external threads. The following two points must be remembered :

(a) The cross-feed must be turned in rather than out when opening the split nut at the end of the threading.

(b) If a recess was already machined at the end of the threaded area, the split nut can be opened without turning in the cross slide to stop the carriage. However, the cross-feed must be turned in before moving the carriage back for the next cut.

Cutting Internal Threads on a Lathe with a Tap. The best and simplest way to cut internal threads is with a tap. The hand tap is held in the tail stock after removing the dead centre. The tap is fed into the workpiece by moving the tailstock spindle with the help of hand wheel. The workpiece is held and rotated by means of a collet or chuck fastened to the headstock spindle. The hand tap can also be held in a tapstock which is supported on the dead centre. The tap engages the workpiece and is fed in the same manner as above.

Change Gear Ratio. There are several change gear sets available. A typical set contains the following change gears with number of teeth : 20, 25, 30, 35, 40, 45, 50, 55, 60, 65, 70, 75, 80, 85,

90, 95, 100, 110, 120, 125 and 127. The change gear ratio, must be transformed by multiplying numerator and denominator by a suitable number, to obtain gears available in the change gear set.

The change gear ratio may result either in a "Simple gearing" or "Compound gearing".

8.1.5. Size of a Centre Lathe. The size of a centre lathe is given by the "Swing" and the length of the bed. The swing is twice the distance from the live centre point of the spindle to the top of the bed, that is,

Swing = 2 × Height of centres from the top of the bed

In other words, it gives the largest diameter that can be turned over the ways of a lathe, but not over the carriage cross-slide. The length of the bed includes the part the headstock rests on. It indirectly gives the maximum length of the job that can be accommodated between lathe centres.

These machines are available with about 22.5 cm to 125 cm swing and with bed lengths of about 1 m to 5 m. Other factors to be considered while selecting an appropriate lathe are : Hole diameter in the headstock spindle, Power ratings, change gear equipment and type of attachments and accessories. Designating the size of the centre lathe by "Swing" is the American system. In the continental system, it is given by the height of centres from the top of the bed.

Accessories. Accessories of a centre lathe are common work and tool holding devices and supports, for example, chucks, collets, centres, drivers, dogs, face plate, dog plate, rests, fixtures and mandrels etc.

Attachments. These are special devices used to perform specific operations, for example, thread chasing dials, taper turning attachments, stops and devices that enable milling, grinding, boring, gear cutting and cutter relieving to be done on the lathe.

8.1.6. Other Low-Production Type Lathes

1. Bench Lathe. Small lathes with beds upto about 1.8 m long and swing upto about 30 cm are commonly set on benches. In most cases, they are as complete as larger lathes, but are smaller and lighter.

2. Toolroom Lathe. This lathe looks like a conventional engine lathe, but is built more accurately, has more speeds and feeds and will be equipped with all the accessories and attachments. It costs more and is mainly used for the manufacture of small tools, dies, gauges, fixture and precision parts of all kinds. It may either be a pedestal or a bench type.

3. Speed Lathe. A speed lathe is a lathe in its simplest form. It consists simply of a headstock, tailstock and a tool post, mounted on a light frame bed. Headstock may have a step-cone pulley arrangement or may be equipped with a variable speed motor. The lathe has no gear box, leadscrew, or carriage. The speeds of these lathes are much higher as compared to conventional lathes. Such lathes are used for making centre holes in workpieces prior to holding them between centres, for metal spinning, polishing and wood working.

8.1.7. Medium Production Lathes. The operation of an engine lathe (by hand) requires considerable skill. The skill of an operator is poorly utilized in repetitive production. Therefore, various efforts at automation have long been made. For medium production, we have the following types of lathes :

1. Turret Lathes. A turret lathe is a medium production, semi- automatic lathe to make parts in greater quantities, to close tolerances and faster. It is an adaptation of engine lathe where the tail stock is replaced by a turret slide (cylindrical or hexagonal). At least six tools can be held on the six faces of the turret. Tool post of the engine lathe is replaced by a square cross-slide (front cross slide) which can hold four tools. Two more tools can be mounted on the rear cross-slide, (Fig. 8.24).

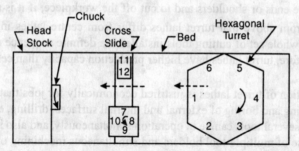

Fig. 8.24. Block Diagram of a Turret Lathe.

The movement of the tools on the turret slide is axial while that of the tools on the cross-slides is perpendicular to the lathe axis. The feed movement of the tools is terminated when a preset stop is reached. The work is held in collet or chuck. The turret lathe can be "set up" to perform many different operations: drilling, boring, reaming, threading, turning and cutting off etc. These operations can be done in any order. Once the machine is "Set up", it requires relatively little skill to operate.

There are two types of Turret Lathes :

(a) **Ram Type Turret Lathe.** Here, the turret is carried on a ram (intermediate slide) which moves longitudinally on a saddle positioned and clamped on the ways of the bed, at any desired position. This lathe which is also called as "Capstan lathe" is used for small and medium sized work (mainly bar stock).

(b) **Saddle Type Turret Lathe.** Here the turret is carried directly on a saddle which moves on the bed ways. This design is used for heavier work (castings, forgings etc.). This design has no rear cross-slide.

The size of a turret lathe is given by two numbers. The first number gives the "swing" and the second number gives the diameter of the bar that can be passed through the hole in the spindle.

Another difference is the two features in the headstock : rapid shifting between at least two spindle speeds with a brake to stopthe spindle very rapidly and automatic feeding out and clamping the bar stock which passes through the spindle. Yet another constructional difference is that in place of the tool- past, there is square turret and there can be a rear tool slide also (in Ram type turret lathe).

The hexagonal turret can be indexed about its vertical axis, to bring each of its faces into working position. The turret, alongwith its saddle, can be moved longitudinally, either by a manual feed or a power feed. At the end of its working travel towards the spindle, when the turret is moved back with the help of the star wheel, it automatically indexes (or is manually indexed, in the case of heavy machines) at end of the movement, thus bringing each of the six faces into working position.

The square turret on the cross-slide can be indexed manually about a vertical axis, to bring each of the four tools into working position. This square turret can be moved longitudinally through power or manual operation of carriage and tranversally, either by power or manually by means of the cross slide. The tools held in the rear slide can be traversed only crosswire. As shown in Fig. 8.23, at least 12 tools can be held in the tool holders. By using special tool holders on the hexagonal turret, this number can be increased.

A turret lathe can perform all lathe operations on either piece blanks or bar stock. The tools on the front square turret can do the same operations as in an engine lathe, except for chasing thread. In a turret lathe, threads are usually cut from the hexagonal turret, using round dies or a die head for external threads and taps for internal threads. The tools in the rear cross slide are used to cut gooves, to face ends or shoulders and to cut off the workpiece, if it is made of bar stock.

It is clear from above that turret lathes differ from centre lathes in that they can perform operations with a whole set of cutting tools installed ina definite sequence on the turret and on the cross-slide. Therefore, turret lathes have higher production capacity than centre lathes and are used in lot production.

The application of turret lathes is justified economically for jobs that require consecutive or simultaneous turning and boring of external and internal surfaces, drilling, enlarging holes, tapping etc.; that is, when several tools can be in operation simultaneously, and also in machining workpiece in batches. The use of multiple-tool holders and simultaneous machining of workpiece with tools, both of the turret and the cross slide, help to reduce machining time, while the presetting of the machine for working with several tools helps to reduce non-cutting time. However, because of the lack of sufficient rigidity of the machine-fixture-tool workpiece, cutting speeds, feeds and the depths of cut are much lower in turret lathe. Setting up of the turret lathes is quite time-consuming, so these set ups are economical only when large batches are to be machined. This has led to the wide application of group set ups for turret lathes can be used with very slight readjustments to machine a whole "family" of selected similar parts.

2. Tracer Lathes. A tracer or a duplicating lathe or a copying lathe is one with an attachment that enables the machine to perform various operations from templates (or models of the workpiece). The cutting tool is made to follow a path that duplicates the path of a stylus or tracer finger moving along the template. These machines produce parts by semi-automatic means. Except for tape controlled (NC) lathes, the operator is required to load and unload the workpiece and to start the automatic operation for each cutting cycle.

The movement of the cutting tool is coordinated with that of the traced finger either by a mechanical, hydraulic, or pneumatic derive.

3. Vertical Turret Lathes. These turret lathes, with vertical orientation, (Fig. 8.25), are used for machining large and/or heavy parts, such as motor bodies, pinions, ring gears and couplings etc. Such components can be mounted more conveniently on the rotary table of the vertical turret lathe than to be held in chucks or face plates in the case of horizontal turret lathes. Also, the turret of a vertical turret lathe has movement in the two axes as compared to a horizontal turret lathe, where the turret moves only in the longitudinal direction.

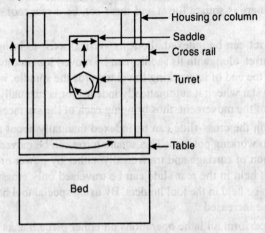

Fig. 8.25. Vertical Turret Lathe.

Vertical Turret Lathe, Turning and Boring Mill

Vertical turret lathes and vertical turning and boring mills are employed to machine workpieces that are difficult to set up and machine in centre lathes and horizontal turret lathes, that is, heavy piece of large diameter and relatively small length. They are used for turning and boring cylindrical and tapered surfaces, facing, cutting annular gooves, drilling, countersinking, counterboring and reaming, etc.

In design arrangement, smaller vertical boring and turning machines have a single upright column or housing, and are called as vertical turret lathes. They can machine workpieces from 300 to 2000 mm in diameter. Larger machines, which can machine workpiece from 1.5 to 2 metres and above, have double-upright column or housing and are called as "Vertical turning and boring mills". These machines have 18 or more table speeds. Special (unique vertical turning and boring mills) can machine huge workpiece of a diameter upto 20 metres. These machine tools can perform all lathe operations with the exception of thread chasing, and have as many as 4 or 5 tools in simultaneous operation.

A vertical turret lathes is shown in Fig. 8.25. The workpiece is placed on the revolving table, which performs the rotating principal movement. The main tool head is mounted on the cross rail, along which it travels horizontally and with which it travels vertically. The five sides turret or tool holder is mounted on a ram, which travels vertically in the cross-rail tool head. The turret can be easily and quickly indexed from hole to hole and clamped with a lever. Tools are clamped in the tool holes of the turret by the same types of holders as those used in horizontal turret lathes. A side tool head is mounted on the upright and carries a square turret or tool holder. The side tool head accomodates one or two single-point tools. They can travel either horizontally or vertically. All the cross-rail tool heads and the side tool head have power feeds in the forward and reverse directions, as well as rapid traverse motions for tool approach and return motions.

Double-upright vertical turning and boring mills have some special features. Medium and heavy-weight models are characterized by portal-type frame formed by bed with revolving table, uprights secured to the bed, and top brace linking uprights at the top. Unique models are provided with two revolving tables (annular), that is, inner and external, which are driven separately or together. The inner table is rotated at a higher speed than the external one, which makes it possible to machine workpieces varying in diameter at optimum cutting speeds. The portal frame of these models is adjustable and is set up, depending on the diameter of the job to be machined. These machines are provided with two rail heads, placed on the cross rail and a movable side head, mounted on the guide ways of the right-hand upright. Some heavy models have a third rail head, travelling along the guideways of an additional overhanging cross rail fastened to the main one.

The main trends in vertical boring and turning machine development are : higher productive output through faster speeds and greater power, reduction of non-cutting, time through simplification and automation of handling, widening of capability and improvements in the design of machine units.

8.1.8. High Production Lathes. The high production lathes come in the category of "Automatic lathes". An automatic lathe is a kind of engine or turret lathe that operates automatically. It requires very little attention after the set up has been made and the machine loaded.

8.1.9.Special Purpose Lathes. The lathes included in this category are:

1. Gap Lathe. This is a special lathe used for machining extra large diameter pieces. To accommodate large swing of the workpiece, the bed ways are stopped short of the headstock, to provide a sufficient gap. To restrict the gap, the workpiece must be relatively short in thickness. The work is mounted primarily for the facing or some internal operations.

The size of the gap lathe is given by the maximum diameter and length of the job that the gap will accomodate.

2. Special-purpose Engine Lathes. These engine lathes are designed for machining special types of workpieces. Examples are : Wheel turning lathes for turning the tread on railroad-car and locomotive and so on.

3. Instrument Lathes. These lathes come in the category of all purpose, low-production lathes. These lathes are of smaller size than "Bench lathes" and are used by instrument makers.

4. Facing Lathes. These lathes are used to machine workpieces of large diameter, but short in length in single piece production and in repair shops. These lathes are similar to engine lathes, but the bed is shorter in length and the faceplate in much larger in diameter [upto 4 m]. The workpiece is clamped on the faceplate by means of jaws or clamps and hold-down bolts. When required, the workpiece is supported by tail-stock centre. However, many facing lathes do not have tail-stocks. The feed mechanism is powered by a separate motor.

Facing lathes are now rarely used, because of : inadequate accuracy, labour-consuming set-up of workpiece and low productivity. They have been replaced by more advanced boring and turning machines.

5. Flow Turning Lathes. A flow turning lathe is used for roll flowing, as a method of cold-flowing metal. A heavy pressure is applied spirally with two hardened rollers against a metal block (See Fig. 4.101). The lathe and the flow turn process may be used with flat plates and forgings and castings and for extruded and other shapes.

6. Heavy Duty Lathe. If the swing of centre lathes ranges from 250 to 1200 mm, these models are known as larger-sized lathes. As noted above, the smaller lathes are called Bench lathes and Instrument Lathes. A lathe, that has a swing of 500 mm or more and is used for roughing and finishing cuts, is often referred to as a Heavy-duty lathe.

SOLVED PROBLEMS

Example 1. *Find the angle at which the compound rest should be set up to turn taper on the workpiece having a length of 200 mm, larger diameter 45 mm and the smaller diameter 30 mm.*

Solution. Now half the taper angle is given as,

$$\tan \alpha = \frac{D - d}{2l}$$

where $\qquad D = 45$ mm, $d = 30$ mm and $l = 200$ mm

$$\therefore \qquad \tan \alpha = \frac{45 - 30}{2 \times 200} = \frac{3}{80} = 0.0375$$

$$\therefore \qquad \alpha = \tan^{-1} 0.0375 = 2°, 9'$$

∴ Angle at which the compound rest should be set up is,

$$\alpha = 2°, 9'$$

Example 2. *A taper pin of length 80 mm has a taper length of 48mm. The larger diameter of taper is 83 mm and the smaller diameter is 73 mm. Determine (i) taper in mm/metre and in degrees (ii) the angle to which the compound rest should be set up (iii) the tail stock setting over.*

Solution. $\qquad L = 80$ mm, $l = 48$ mm

$$D = 83 \text{ mm}, d = 73 \text{ mm}$$

(i) Taper, $T = \dfrac{D - d}{l} = \dfrac{83 - 73}{48} = \dfrac{10}{48}$

i.e. for a length of 48 mm, the taper is 10 mm

$\therefore$ Taper in mm/metre $= \dfrac{10}{48} \times 1000$

$$= 208.33 \text{ mm/metre length}$$

Now $\tan \alpha = \dfrac{D-d}{2l} = \dfrac{10}{96} = 0.1042$

$\therefore$ $\alpha = 5°, 57'$

(*ii*) The angle to which the compound rest should be set up is,

$$\alpha = 5°, 57'$$

(*iii*) Tail stock set over, $h = \dfrac{D-d}{2l} \times L$

$$= \dfrac{10}{96} \times 80 = \mathbf{8.33 \ mm}$$

Example 3. *Find the intermediate speeds of a head stock spindle for a lathe given the following data :*

         Minimum speed   = 45 rev/min

         Maximum speed   = 2000 rev/min

         Number of speeds = 18

Solution. Now $n_{\min} = 45$ rev/min

           $n_{\max} = 2000$ rev/min

            $Z = 18$

$\therefore$ Step ratio, $\phi = \left(\dfrac{n_{\max}}{n_{\min}} \right)^{\frac{1}{Z-1}} = \left(\dfrac{2000}{45} \right)^{\frac{1}{17}} = \left(\dfrac{400}{9} \right)^{0.0588}$

$$= (44.44)^{0.0588} = \mathbf{1.25}$$

$\therefore$ Speeds are $45, \varphi \times 45, \varphi^2 \times 45 \ldots \ldots \mathbf{2000}$

Example 4. *Calculate the change gears to cut a single start thread of 3 mm pitch on a centre lathe, having a lead screw of 6 mm pitch.*

Solution. $P = 3$ mm, $L = 6$ mm

$\therefore$ Change gear ratio, $i_{cg} = \dfrac{P}{L} = \dfrac{3}{6} = \dfrac{1}{2}$

Now from the available change gear set, this gear ratio can be obtained by selecting gears

            $Z_1 = 20$ and $Z_2 = 40$

or $Z_1 = 25$ and $Z_2 = 50$

$\therefore$ It will be a simple gearing.

Example 5. *Calculate the change gears to cut a single start thread of 0.5 mm pitch on a centre lathe having a lead screw of 12 mm pitch.*

Solution. $P = 0.5$ mm, $L = 12$ mm

$\therefore$ Change gear ratio, $i_{cg} = \dfrac{P}{L} = \dfrac{0.5}{12} = \dfrac{1}{24}$

     Since no convenient change gears can be found in the change gear set, this ratio must be split into two factors.

So,
$$i_{cg} = \frac{1}{24} = \frac{1}{4} \times \frac{1}{6} = \frac{25}{100} \times \frac{20}{120} = \frac{Z_1}{Z_2} \times \frac{Z_3}{Z_4}$$

∴   Driver gears Z_1 and Z_3 = 25 and 20 teeth

        Driven gears Z_2 and Z_4 = 100 and 120 teeth

∴   It will be a compound gearing.

Example 6. *Calculate the change gears to cut a single start thread, four threads per inch, on a centre lathe with lead screw of 3 mm pitch.*

Solution. $P = \dfrac{1}{4}$ inch $= \dfrac{25.4}{4}$ mm, L = 3 mm

∴
$$i_{cg} = \frac{P}{L} = \frac{25.4}{4} \times \frac{1}{3} = \frac{12.7}{6} = \frac{127}{60} = \frac{Z_1}{Z_2}$$

Z_1 = 127 teeth

Z_2 = 60 teeth

Note. For a single start thread,

$$i_{cg} = \frac{P}{L}$$

For a multi-start thread,

$$i_{cg} = \frac{P \times \text{No. of start}}{L}$$

PROBLEMS

1. List some of the operations that can be done on the Engine Lathe.
2. How will you classify the Engine Lathes ?
3. Name the four main parts of a Lathe.
4. Sketch a Tool Post.
5. What are the four major parts of a Carriage ?
6. Describe how the back gears operate
7. Sketch and describe the geared main drive of the Engine Lathe.
8. Sketch and explain the feed drive of the engine lathe.
9. Sketch and explain "feed reversing mechanism".
10. Sketch and explain "change gear quadrant".
11. What is the purpose of the quick-change gear box ? Sketch and explain a tumbler type gear box.
12. What is the difference between the 'live' and 'dead centre' ?
13. How do you obtain power cross-feed ?
14. How can the movement of the carriage be reversed ?
15. When is the split nut or half nut used ?
16. Sketch and describe the three types of Centres used in the Engine Lathe.

17. Sketch the two types of Lathe Dogs.

18. Sketch and explain the use of a Face Plate.

19. What is the difference between a 'face plate' and a 'drive plate' ?

20. Sketch and explain the working of a Mandrel.

21. What are the advantages of using a Collet Chuck ?.

22. What is the use of Steady Rests ? What is the difference between a steady rest and a follower rest ?

23. Sketch and explain the various methods of turning a Taper.\

24. Name some of the advantages of using a 'taper turning attachment'.

25. What is a centre gauge used for in threading ?

26. Why is the compound rest set at an angle of for most threading ?

27. What is the use of a thread dial ?

28. When cutting odd number of threads per cm, when is the split nut or half nut closed ?

29. How is the size of the Engine Lathe given ?

30. What are : Bench lathe, Toolroom lathe, Speed lathe ?

31. Sketch a block diagram of a Turret Lathe. Name its major parts.

32. Sketch and describe a Vertical Turret Lathe.

33. What are : Tracer lathes and Gap lathes ?

. 34. What are : Special purpose engine lathes, Instrument lathes, Facing Lathes, Flow turning lathes and Heavy duty Lathes.

8.2. SHAPERS, PLANERS AND SLOTTERS

Introduction. The main function of shapers, planers and slotters is the machining of flat surfaces by means of straight line reciprocating single point cutting tools similar to those used in lathe operations. The flat surfaces produced may be horizontal, vertical or inclined at an angle. These machine tools can also be arranged for machining contoured surfaces, slots, grooves and other recesses.

The processes of planing, shaping and slotting are similar to one another, but in the first case the main cutting motion is transmitted to the workpiece on the worktable which travels past the cutting tool (except in pit and edge planers where the work is stationary and the cutting tools reciprocate), while in the second and third cases, the workpiece is stationary and the cutting motion is transmitted to the tool. The cutting tool/ workpiece travels horizontally in shaping and planing and vertically in slotting. In all cases, the feed motion is accomplished in a plane perpendicular to the cutting motion (of the workpiece or tool). Feed may be either parallel or perpendicular to the cutting edge, or in a circle.

Shaping is limited to small and moderate size workpieces, whereas planers are designed for machining large workpieces. They can take heavy cuts. Cutting is intermittent in all the three processes, since cutting is done in one direction only. The return stroke is idle stroke, and is faster than the cutting stroke.

8.2.1.Shapers. The shaping process can be defined as a process for removing metal from surfaces in horizontal, vertical and angular planes by the use of a single point cutting tool held in a ram that reciprocates the tool in a linear direction across the workpiece held on the table of the machine. The work is fed at right angles to the direction of the ram in small increments, at the end of the return stroke.

Types of Shapers. There are mainly two types of shapers : Horizontal shapers and vertical shapers depending upon whether the ram and the cutting tool reciprocates in the horizontal plane or in the vertical plane.

Construction details of a Horizontal Shaper. Fig. 8.26 shows the block diagram of the horizontal shaper.

1. Base. The base is the necessary bed or support required for all machine tools. All other parts are mounted on and above the base. The shaper is installed by rigidly bolting the bed to the shop floor. The bed takes up the total dead weight of the machine as well as the dynamic load during machining operations. Its material is usually gray cast iron.

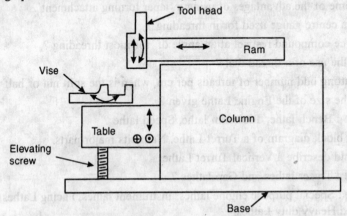

Fig. 8.26. Horizontal Shaper.

2. Column. The column of the shaper is a hollow casting and is mounted on the base. It houses the drive mechanisms for the ram and the table. At the top of the column, the bearing surfaces known as "guide ways" are provided on which the ram reciprocates.

3. Table. The worktable of a shaper is fastened to the front of the column. The table moves across the column on crossrails to give the feed motion to the job. The cross rails are a part of the slide which can be moved up and down on the column ways (with the help of elevating screw) to accommodate various sizes of the workpiece.

Shaper tables are provided with T-slots so that most jobs are directly held on the table by means of bolts, blocks and clamp plates. Jobs can also be held in vises which are secured to the table. Sometimes special work holding devices (fixtures) may be needed to hold the jobs. Heavy duty shapers are provided with a table support bolted to the outer end of the table and supported by resting upon the bed. This makes the table rigid and prevents work deflection under heavy cuts.

4. Ram. The ram carries the tool head at its front end and travels in "guideways" to give straight line reciprocating motion to the tool. The ram is either mechanically driven or hydraulically operated. A single point tool is fastened in the tool post. As the ram moves forward, it completes the cutting stroke. As it returns and completes its idle stroke, the table feeds cross-wise a preset incremental distance equal to the feed desired. The ram travels upto two times faster on the return stroke than on the forward stroke.

5. Tool Head. The tool head, (Fig. 8.27), holds the cutting tool and is fastened to the front of the ram. The tool is held in a tool holder/tool post similar to the lathe tool post. The tool post and the tool block fit snugly in the clapper box and is hinged at the upper edge. During the forward cutting stroke, the tool block is solidly supported against the clapper box due to the cutting force. On the return stroke, the tool block is free to swing forward from its pivot, (Fig. 8.27 (b)). This lifts the tool block out of the clapper box a sufficient amount to prevent the tool from rubbing the work surface. The tool head has a tool slide and feed screw rotated by a bellcrank handle for raising and lowering the tool to adjust the depth of cut. The down feed of the tool is usually manual, but power feed can also be provided. The slide is mounted on a swivel plate, which enables the tool head to be rotated or swiveled enabling it to take angular cuts to machine inclined surfaces. Then the tool slide will be parallel with the desired surface. When machining inclined surfaces, the clapper box must be swiveled to enable the cutting tool to swing along an arc away from the work surface on its return stroke. A rule of thumb is that the top of the clapper box should be swiveled away from the surface to be machined.

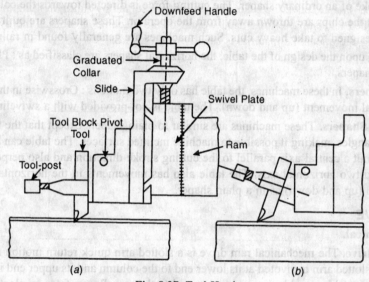

Fig. 8.27. Tool Head.

The details of the tool head are illustrated in Fig. 8.28.

In the front of the slide, an apron is provided which carries the clapper box at its lower end. The clapper block or tool block fits snugly in the clapper box and is hinged about a pin passing through the clapper box and clapper block near its top ends as shown. The apron is secured to the slide with the help of a bolt with its back abutting against the slide. The bolt-passes through a slot (in the shape of a sector) in the upper end of the apron. By unscrewing the nut on the bolt, the apron and hence the tool can be swivelled as shown in the Fig. 8.28. After swivelling to the desired position, the nut is tightened.

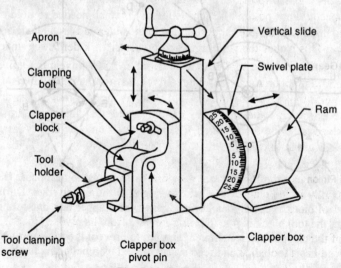

Fig. 8.28. Tool Head.

The slide is mounted on a swivel plate at its back. The swivel plate is bolted to the front of the ram. The bolt can be loosened and the slide and hence the tool head can be swivelled as shown, for machining inclined surfaces. The angle of inclination with the vertical can be read from the graduations on the swivel plate.

The above shaper in which the cutting takes place in the forward stroke is called the "Push cut Shaper", and is the most widely used. "Pull or draw cut" shapers cut in the direction corresponding to the return stroke of an ordinary shaper. The cutting force is directed towards the column and its advantage is that the chips are thrown away from the operator. These shapers are built with a long stroke and are designed to take heavy cuts. Such machines are generally found in railroad shops.

Depending upon the design of the table, the horizontal shapers are classified as : Plain Shapers and Universal Shapers.

Plain Shapers. In these machines, the table has only two motions : Crosswise in the horizontal plane and vertical movement (up and down). The table is not-provided with a swiveling motion.

Universal Shapers. These machines are similar to plain shapers except that the table can be tilted to various angles, making it possible to machine inclined surfaces. The table can be swiveled through 360° about a central axis parallel to the cutting stroke direction and also perpendicular to it, that is, around two horizontal axis. The table also has movements in the horizontal plane and vertical direction (up and down) as in a plain shaper.

SHAPER DRIVE

1. Mechanical.

(*a*) **Ram drive.** The mechanical ram drive is a slotted arm quick return motion mechanism, (Fig. 8.29). The slotted arm is pivoted at its lower end to the column and its upper end is connected by a link to an adjustable ram block which is secured to the ram. Power from an electric motor is transmitted to the bull gear through gears and bullgear pinion. A pin fits freely into a hole in the bullgear block which can slide in the slot of the rocker arm. As the bull gear rotates, it carries the pin in a circular path with the help of the crank. This makes the rocker arm to swing back and forth about its stationary pivot C. Thus the rotary motion of the bull gear is converted into the reciprocating

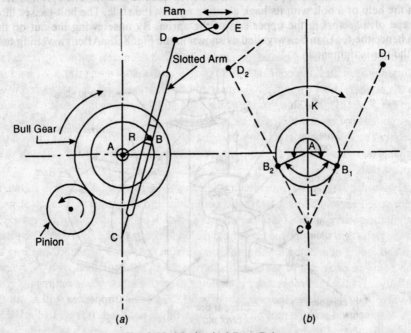

Fig. 8.29. Machanical Ram Drive.

motion of the ram with the cutting tool. The length of the ram stroke depends upon the radius of the crankpin on the bull gear, that is, AB which can be adjusted. The larger the crank radius, the longer the ram stroke will be and vice versa.

$$\frac{\text{Cutting Stroke time}}{\text{Return Stroke time}} = \frac{\angle B_2 \times B_1}{\angle B_1 \; \angle B_2}$$

It is clear that the return stroke is quick so as to minimise the return idle stroke time. The bull gear is massive in size so that it also performs the function of a flywheel. This makes the reciprocating movement of the ram smooth and without any jerks.

(b) **Feed Mechanism.** We know that the table feed is intermittent and is accomplished on the return (non cutting) stroke when the tool has cleared the workpiece. The cross feed is given to the table with the help of a cross feed screw, (Fig. 8.30), which is actuated by a pawl which engages a notched wheel (ratchet) keyed to the screw [Fig. 8.30(b)]. The spring loaded reversible pawl gets its motion from a slotted disc through a connecting rod and pawl arm or rocker arm. The slotted disc is driven from the bull gear through a spur gear drive and rotates at the same speed as the bull gear.

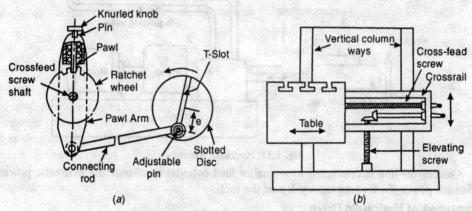

Fig. 8.30. Feed Mechanism.

Because the pawl is straight on one side and slanted on the other, it moves the ratchet wheel in one direction only. A spring pushes against the pawl to keep it in contact with the ratchet wheel. As the slotted disc rotates, the connecting rod oscillates the pawl about the cross feed screw, so that it moves the ratchet wheel by engaging with it and hence rotates the cross feed screw which moves the table, (Fig. 8.30 (a)). The straight side of the pawl pulls or pushes the gear for positive movement, while the slanted side merely slides over the teeth preparatory to taking another bite. A knob at the top of the pawl enables the operator to rotate it 180° to reverse the direction of feed or 90° to stop it altogether. The rate of feed is controlled by adjusting the eccentricity or offset of the driving pin in the slotted disc.

2. Hydraulic Drive. A typical hydraulic drive for a horizontal shaper is shown in Fig. 8.31. A constant speed motor drives a hydraulic pump which delivers oil at a constant pressure to the line. A regulating valve admits oil under pressure to each end on the piston alternately, at the same time allowing oil from the opposite end of the piston to return to the reservoir. The piston is pushed by the oil and, being connected to the ram by the piston rod, pushes the ram carrying the tool. The admission of oil to each end of the piston, alternately, is accomplished with the help of trip dogs and pilot valve. As the ram moves and completes its stroke (forward or return) a trip dog will trip the pilot valve which operates the regulating valve. The regulating valve will admit the oil to the other side of the piston and the motion of the ram will get reversed. It is clear that the length of the ram stroke will depend upon the position of the trip dogs. The length of the ram stroke can be changed by unclamping and moving the trip dogs to the desired positions.

The above system is a constant pressure system. Hence, the ram will travel to slightly different speeds under varying load conditions. The velocity of the ram travel will be directly proportional to the oil pressure and the piston area to which it is applied. The return stroke is quicker, since the piston area on which the oil pressure acts is greater as compared to the other end for which it gets reduced because of the piston rod.

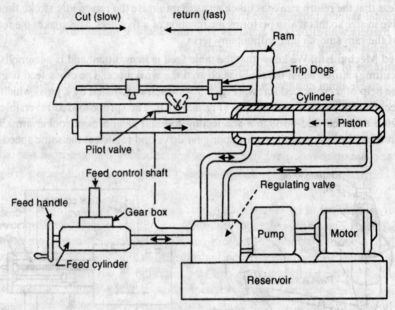

Fig. 8.31. Hydraulic Drive.

Another oil line is connected to a smaller feed cylinder to change the hydraulic power to mechanical power for feeding the work past the tool.

Advantages of Hydraulic Drive

1. Offers greater flexibility of speed.

2. Smoother operation.

3. Ability to slip when the tool is over loaded.

4. Ability to stall against an obstruction without damage to the tool or the machine.

5. Ability to change length and position of stroke or speed while the machine is running.

6. The hydraulic drive shows a very nearly constant velocity as compared with a mechanical drive, which has a constantly changing velocity because the horizontal component of the crankpin moving about its circle is constantly changing, Fig. 8.32.

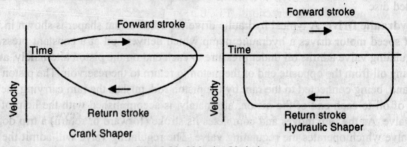

Fig. 8.32. Velocity Variation.

On the other hand, a mechanical shaper has the following plus points: lower first cost and simpler in operation. The cutting stroke has a definite stopping point.

Shaper Size. Shaper size is designated by its longest nominal cutting stroke. Thus a 600 mm shaper has ram travel enough to drive a tool across a 600 mm surface. On most horizontal shapers, the table can be fed cross-wise a distance at least as large as the stroke. That means, a 600 mm × 600 mm square.

Horizontal shapers range in size from small bench models with stroke of 175 or 200 mm to heavy duty models with strokes as much as 900 mm. Shaping machines are commonly provided with power feeds ranging from 0.2 to 0.5 mm/stroke.

Advantages of Shapers. The shapers have got the following advantages :

1. The single point cutting tools used in shapers are inexpensive. these tools can be easily grounded to any desired shape.

2. The simplicity and ease of holding work, its easy adjustment, and the simple tool give the shaper its great flexibility.

3. Shaper set up is very quick and easy and can be readily changed from one job to another.

4. Thin or fragile jobs can be conveniently machined on shapers because of lower cutting forces.

However, a shaper is by nature a slow machine, because of its straight line, forward and return (idle) stroke. The single point tool requires many strokes to complete a work. Also, cutting speeds in these types of machining operations (shaping, planing and slotting) are not usually very high since difficulties are encountered in designing machine tools with high speeds of reciprocating motion due to high inertia forces developed in the motion of the units and components of the machine. For all these reasons, the shaper does not find ready adaptability for assembly and production line. But because of its advantages discussed above, the shaper finds best use in toolroom, jobbing shops and die or jig making shops (for small or medium-sized work), where its flexibility is important and the relative slowness unimportant because so few identical pieces are made.

8.2.2. Vertical Shapers / Slotters. Vertical shapers and slotters are similar to the horizontal shaper except that the ram reciprocates in a vertical direction, cutting on the downward stroke, the upward stroke (return stroke) being idle. The terms vertical shaper and slotter are often used interchangeably by shopmen, although there is a slight difference between them. Whereas the vertical shaper has the facility of allowing the adjustment of ram nearly upto 10° from the vertical position, the slotting machine has only the vertical straight line movement of the ram. Therefore, on vertical shapers, inclined surfaces can also be cut. A slotter is, however, a more robust machine than a vertical shaper.

Most of these machines are provided with a rotary table. The rotary table can be indexed accurately for various operations or rotated continuously about the vertical axis by hand or power, to produce an arc. The table moves on a saddle that slides on the bed and has horizontal adjustments and feeds in two perpendicular directions, (Fig. 8.33). The rotary plus the two straight line motions of the table permit easy machining of circular, convex, concave and other curved surfaces. Slots and grooves can be accurately spaced around a workpiece. On the vertical shaper and slotter, the work is almost always clamped to the table.

Uses of Vertical Shaper / Slotter

1. Internal machining of blind holes.

2. Work requiring machining on internal sections such as splines, keyways, various slots and grooves, and teeth.

3. Cutting of teeth on ratchet or gear rings which require primarily rotary feed.

4. Machining of die, punches, straight and curved slots.

Types of Slotters

1. Puncher Slotter. This type is used for machining heavier jobs produced by forging or stamping.

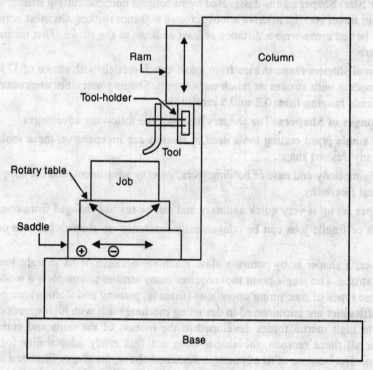

Fig. 8.33. Block Diagram of a Slotter.

2. Production Slotter. Here, the upper portion of the machine frame and hence the ram, can be tilted for machining tapered jobs. This machine is of very heavy construction.

3. Tool Room Slotter. This machine is a refined and more accurate form of production slotter. It is fitted with various sophisticated arrangements for accurate machining.

4. Keyseater. It is a special purpose slotter which is designed for cutting keyways in gears, pulleys, cams and similar parts.

Size of Vertical Shaper/Slotter. The size of these machines is given as : Maximum length of stroke (mm) × Diameter of work table (mm). The stroke of these machines ranges from 300 to 1800 mm. Feed ranges from 0.05 to 2.5 mm/stroke and the ram speed usually ranges from 2 to 40 m/min.

Ram Drive Mechanism. The common drives for vertical shapers and slotters are :

1. Hydraulic Drive. This drive is similar to the one explained for horizontal shapers.

2. Variable Speed Reversible Motor Drive. This machine incor- porates a reversible motor with a multi-speed gear box to give a range of speeds to the ram.

3. Slotted Disc Mechanism. A slotted disc mechanism is shown in Fig. 8.34. The slotted disc is rotated with the help of a pinion and gear drive, from an electric motor. The rotary motion of the slotted disc is converted into the reciprocating motion of the ram with the help of connecting rod. The length of stroke of the ram can be changed by varying the eccentricity of the pin (its distance from the centre of the slotted disc).

Fig. 8.35 shows some typical surfaces machined on shapers and Slotters.

8.2.3. Planers. In conventional planers, the work held on the table reciprocates past the tool/tools. However, in unconventional planers (pit planer and edge planer), the table is stationary and the tool head reciprocates. The planer is the largest of the reciprocating machines (shapers and millers). It has got the following advantages :

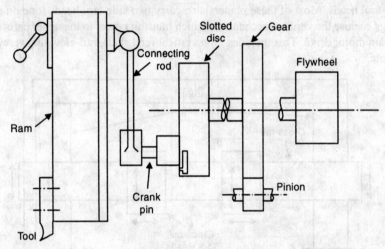

Fig. 8.34. Slotted Disc Mechanism.

1. Larger work can be handled as compared to shapers and millers.

2. Capable of taking much heavier cuts as compared to shapers and millers.

3. There are no overhanging parts such as a ram. So, there is no work or tool deflection or distortion.

4. The work is mounted on a table which is supported throughout its entire movement. So, a maximum support is obtained.

Principal parts of a Planer. Fig. 8.36 is the block diagram of a double housing (column) planer. Its principal parts are discussed below :

1. Bed. The bed is a large, heavy casting strengthened with cross ribs to provide a stiff, heavy support for this heavy machine. Very large beds consist of two or more castings, carefully machined and bolted together. The length of the bed is about twice the length of the table. The bed provides the ways for the table to run on. It also houses the drive mechanism for the table.

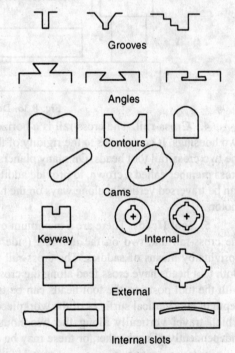

Fig. 8.35. Typical Surfaces Machined on Shapers and Slotters.

2. Table. The table on which the work is clamped, reciprocates along the ways of the bed and has T-slots in its upper surface for clamping the workpiece. The table is a single casting except in the case of two tables bolted together end to end. The table is powered from a variable speed motor through a reducing gear and a rack and pinion arrangement. The other drives can be : hydraulic drive and fast and loose pulley drive.

3. Housings. At the sides of the bed, two vertical housings, columns or uprights are arranged. The front face of each column is machined as a set of ways on which travel the cross rail which carries two tool heads. Most of these planers also carry two side tool heads (one on each housing). The housings enclose the various mechanisms which transmit power to the upper parts of the machine from the main motor drive. This includes : the vertical feed shaft, rail-elevating screw, feed bar for cross feed etc.

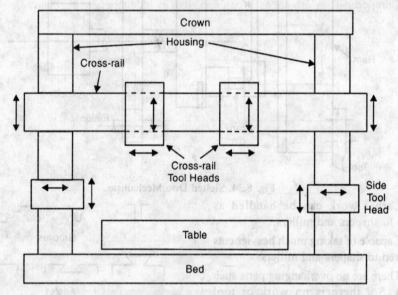

Fig. 8.36. Double House Planer.

4. Cross-rail. The cross-rail is a horizontal member of heavy cross-section connecting the two housings. It contributes to the rigidity of the machine. Its face is machined to provide ways for the two cross-rail tool heads. On many planers, the housings are connected together at the top by a cross member called a crown, to provide additional strength and rigidity to the structure. Cross-rail can be traversed vertically along ways on the housings by means of a drive powered from a separate motor.

5. Tool Heads. There are a maximum of four tool heads on a double housing planer, two on the cross-rail and two on the uprights (side tool heads). They are mounted on the rail and the uprights by means of saddles. The cross-rail tool heads are used for planing horizontal surfaces. Both tool heads have cross feed along the cross rail ways powered by their motors. The tool-slides with the tool posts on the tool heads can be traversed vertically to feed the tools down for a new depth of cut. Vertical surfaces of the workpiece are planed by tools mounted on the side tool heads which travel vertically along the two housings. The four tool heads of the planer operate independently of each other, or these may be controlled together.

A planer tool head can be normally swiveled on its base (saddle), upto about of each side of its neutral position. The plate that swivels carries a slide that has a clapper box on the end for mounting the tool. The clapper allows the tool to swing upward from the workpiece on the re turn stroke as on a shaper. Many planers have air or hydraulic tool lifters (due to heavy tool head block of planers) that automatically swing the clapper box to raise the tool on the return stroke. The clapper box can usually be swivelled about 20° in each direction to place the tool in advantageous position as needed.

Types of Planers

1. Double Housing Planer. The double housing planer discussed above is the most commonly used planer. This design has one drawback. Because of the two housings, one on each side of the bed, it limits the width of the work that can be machined.

2. Open Side Planer. This design has only one column, (Fig. 8.37), which supports a cross-rail, with the cross rail cantilevered from it. Thus the maximum number of tool heads on this planer is 3. Its advantage is that it can accommodate jobs which are too wide to fit between columns of an equivalent double housing planer. The portion of the hob extending beyond the table side must be supported properly. They are not as strong and rigid as a double housing planer.

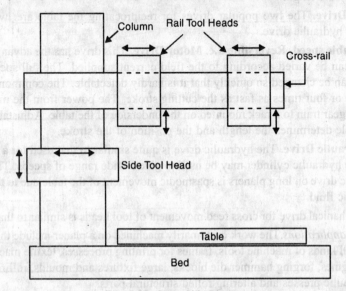

Fig. 8.37. Open Side Planer.

3. Planer Miller or Grinder. It is essentially the same as a double housing planer except that it has a milling cutter or a grinding head in place of one or more of the conventional tool heads on the cross rail.

4. Pit Type Planer. When the work becomes extremely large and heavy, its reciprocation becomes very difficult. In such cases, the table is kept stationary and the tool reciprocates. Massive rails are mounted on both sides of the table. Tool heads (usually two) are mounted on the cross rails for two way planning. This design (Pit planer) is used to plane the largest kind of work (bases and slabs) which no other machine could handle. A pit planer is one of the largest machine tools. Because of the size of the parts machined on these planers, it is convenient and economical to move the machine than the work.

5. Plate Planer. In plate planer, the job/table is stationary while the tool and operator more bark and forth along the work for feed and cut. It is a special purpose (single purpose) machine tool, designed specifically for squaring or levelling the edges of the heavy steel plates (armour plate for squaring or levelling the edges of the heavy steel plates (armour plate, plate for ships and for vessels upto about 20 cm thick and preparing plates for pipe lines). The plate is clamped to a bed and the side mounted carriage supporting the cutting tool is moved back and forth along the edge.

6. Divided or Latching Table Planer. In planers, lot of time is consumed in setting up the work. To reduce it and particularly when many identical pieces are machined at the same time, any type of planer may be provided with a divided table. The work on one table is set up while that on the other is machined. The two sections of the table may be coupled together for long work.

Planer Size. For a double housing planer, the size is given as : width, height and length of the largest workpiece which can be accommodated between the columns, under the cross rail in its highest position and on the length of the table, that is, distance between vertical housings, the height from the top of the table to the rail in its upper most position and the maximum length of the table travel.

Double housing planers have been built upto Size : 4.8 m square by 18 m.

The largest size of a pit planer is about : 12.5 m × 5.4 m × 22.8 m.

The size of an openside planer is given by the distance between table and maximum rail height and by table length.

Planer Drive. The two popular drives for reciprocating the table are: with d.c. reversible motor and the hydraulic drive.

1. Variable speed, Reversible d.c. Motor Drive. This drive has the advantage that the speed of the motor can be varied according to the field current supplied. The full speed forward to full speed return can be changed so quickly that it is hardly detectable. The common return spoke of a planer is three or four times as fast as the cutting stroke. The power from the motor goes through a clutch and a gear train to a rack mounted on the underside of the table. Adjustable trip dogs at the side of the table determines the length and the position of the stroke.

2. Hydraulic Drive. The hydraulic drive is quite similar to that used for a horizontal shaper. More than one hydraulic cylinder may be used to give a wide range of speeds. The chief drawback of the hydraulic drive on long planers is spasmodic movement of the table due to the compressibility of the hydraulic fluid.

The mechanical drive for cross feed movement of tool heads is similar to that used on shapers.

*Product applications.*The work customarily machined on a planer include the following: bases and tables of all kinds of machine tools, frames for printing processes, textile machines, locomotive frames and engines, forging hammer die blocks, large fixtures and moulds, rolling mill parts, parts for large hydraulic presses and altering rolled structural parts.

8.2.4. Cutting Speed, Feed and Depth of Cut. The cutting speed, V, in planing, shaping and slotting operations is the speed of the tool (or the work) in the direction of the primary cutting motion during the working stroke when the metal is being cut. The cutting speed may be either cons-tant or variable depending upon the design of the machine tool.

Shapers with crank and slotted arm mechanisms have a variable cutting speed and a variable return speed (Fig. 8.30) of the tool. The speed is minimum at the beginning and end of the stroke and maximum in the middle of the stroke. The cutting speed can be determined by the formula:

$$V = \frac{L\,N(1+K)}{1000}\,\text{m / min}.$$

where L = Length of ram stroke, mm

N = number of full strokes/min,

that is, a full stroke comprises working and return strokes.

K = Ratio of return time to cuttingtime.

Planers with a rack and pinion drive for the table have a constant cutting speed, which can be determined from the formula :

$$V = \frac{2N\,L}{1000},\,\text{m / min}.$$

The feed, f, in planing, shaping or slotting (Fig. 8.38) is the relative movement of the tool or work in a direction perpendicular to the primary cutting motion per full stroke and is expressed in mm/stroke.

The depth of cut, d, is the thickness of layer of metal removed in one cut or pass. It is measured in a direction perpendicular to the machined surface.

The cross-sectional area of the undeformed chip is the product of the thickness, t, and the width, b, of the undeformed chip :

Area of undeformed chip = $t \times b = f \times d$ mm^2.

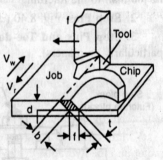

Cutting speeds in these kinds of machining operations are not usually very high, since difficulties are encountered in designing machine tools with high speed of reciprocating motion due to high inertia forces developed in the motion of the units and components of machine. Thus in planing cast iron, the recommended cutting speed is 15 to 20 for roughing and 4 to 12 for finishing. The corresponding depths of cut are 0.5 to 0.8 mm, and 0.08 mm respectively, with feed ranging from 1.50 to 2.00 mm/stroke.

Fig. 8.38. Cutting Action in a Planer.

8.2.5. Planing and Shaping Tools

The tools used in planing and shaping are similar to single-point lathe tools, consisting of the shank and the point. Planing and shaping tools are made of H.S.S. or tipped with cemented carbides. In the latter case, the shanks are made of carbon tool steel. It is a good practice to use planing and shaping tools with an offset, or gooseneck shank to reduce jamming of the tool during operation. When a straight shank tool is used, backward spring of the tool about point O, owing to the cutting forces acting on the tool, leads to gouging of the tool nose into the work, [Fig. 8.39 (a)]. The tendency for the tool to dig into the work will be less for a gooseneck shank, and will be completely eliminated if the tool nose is lined up with the base of the tool shank [Fig. 8.39 (b)] since the radius R along with the tool nose springs is equal to the overhang L.

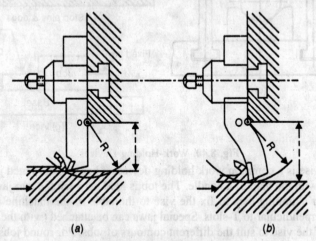

(a)   (b)

Fig. 8.39. Shanks of Planing Tools.

8.2.6. Work-holding Devices for Shapers, Slotters and Planers

The commonly used work holding devices on these machine tools are given below :

1. T-Bolts and Clamps. The tables of machine tools such as shapers, slotters, planers, drilling machines and milling machines are provided with T-slots. Most jobs can be held on the machine table by means of T-bolts, blocks and clamp plates, Fig. 8.40 (a, b, c). A simple block or a step block (to accommodate jobs of different heights) can be used as the fulcrum block. For round jobs,

V-blocks are used for the proper location of the jobs, Fig. 8.40 (*b*, *c*). T-bolt should be nearer to the job than to the fulcrum.

2. Stop Pins. Fig. 8.40 (*d*, *e*).

3. Stop Pins and Toe-dogs. Fig 8.40 (*f*). This arrangement is used for holding thin jobs (particularly on planers).

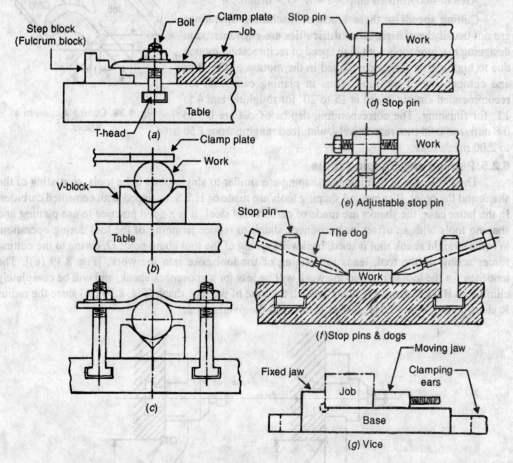

Fig. 8.40. Work-Holding Devices.

4. Vises. A vise is a common work holding device. It has two hardened jaws, one fixed and the other movable with the help of a handle. The job is held between the two jaws. The base of the vise carries slots or clamping ears to fix the vise to the table of the machine tool, with the jaws either parallel or perpendicular to T-slots. Special jaws can be attached (with the help of set screws) to the plain jaws of the vise to suit the different contours of jobs. For round jobs, Vees may also be fitted instead of standard plain jaws.

The 'Swivel vise' is made in two parts. It consists of a round swivel base over which the vise body is mounted. The base is graduated into The body is clamped to the base by means of clamping bolts. The body can be adjusted at any angle relative to the base and so the jaws can be set at any angle. If the vise, apart being swivelled in the horizontal plane, can also be tilted in the vertical plane, it is called 'Universal Vise'.

5. Fixtures. If a job cannot be held in the general purpose work holding devices mentioned above, then a special purpose work holding device, known as fixture, will have to be designed and fabricated.

PROBLEMS

1. What is a Shaper used for ?
2. Draw the block diagram of a horizontal Shaper and write about its important parts.
3. How the jobs are held on the table of a horizontal Shaper ?
4. Sketch the Tool Head of a Shaper and write how it functions.
5. What is the difference between a Push cut Shaper and a Pull cut Shaper?
6. What is the difference between Plain Shapers and Universal Shapers ?
7. What is the value of having a universal table on a Shaper ?
8. Sketch and explain the mechanical drive for the ram of a horizontal Shaper.
9. Sketch and explain the mechanical feed drive of a horizontal Shaper.
10. Sketch and explain the hydraulic drive of a horizontal Shaper.
11. Write the advantage of hydraulic drive over mechanical drive.
12. How will you give the size of a horizontal Shaper ?
13. Write the applications of shapers.
14. What is the difference between a vertical shaper and a slotter ?
15. Write the uses of a slotter.
16. Sketch and explain the working of a slotter.
17. Write about the various types of slotters.
18. Write about the various ram drive mechanisms of a slotter.
19. How will you give the size of a vertical shaper or a slotting machine.
20. Describe the difference in operation between a planer and a shaper.
21. Write the advantages of planers.
22. Sketch and write about the principal parts of a double housing planer.
23. Write about the various types of planers.
24. How will you give the size of a planer ?
25. Write about the various drives for planers.
26. Write the product applications of planers.
27. List the advantages of Shapers.
28. List the Limitations of Shapers, Planers and Slotters.
29. Why the shanks of cutting tools used on Shapers, and Planers have gooseneck ?
30. Discuss the common work-holding deviCes used on shapers, slotters and planers.

8.3. DRILLING MACHINES

8.3.1.General. Hole machining, constituting a considerable percentage of all machining operations, is accomplished as a rule, be rotary and axial feed motions of the cutting tool or work. Round holes are machined in drilling machines, boring machines, engine lathes, vertical boring mills, turret lathes, semi- automatic and automatic lathes, broaching machines and grinders. Whereas, drilling machines and machine tools of lathe type are used to originate or cut a hole where none previously existed, the boring machines, broaching machines and grinders are mainly used to enlarge and finish the existing holes (produced by machining, casting, forging or punching). Of course, holes can also be enlarged and finished on drilling machines and lathe type machine tools.

Holes upto 80 mm in diameter can be machined from the solid on drilling machines and machine tools of lathe type, holes over 80 mm in diameter are usually cut by special drilling heads and, as a rule, this operation is performed in boring machines.

Depending upon their purposes, holes should meet the following requirements :

1. The diameter size must be held within given limits.

2. The straightness of hole axis or its cylindrical surface must be as specified.

3. The hole must be of true cylindrical shape, that is, absence of taper, ovality and lobed-form.

4. The hole must be square to the faces of the part.

The machining of accurate holes always requires more machine time and more expenditure on cutting tools than the machining of an external surface of revolution of the same size and to the same grade of accuracy. The reason is that the hole making tools do not possess the same rigidity, especially as to the design of their mounting elements and clamping facilities, as turning tools. To attain the required accuracy in hole making, an increased number of passes is resorted to. This enables the error of the initial machining operation to be gradually reduced to the permissible limits.

8.3.2. Drilling Process. The drilling process is an extensively used machining operation by which through or blind holes are cut or originated in a workpiece. The drilling tool is called a "drill" which is a multi-point cutting tool. The hole is produced by axially feeding the rotating drill into the workpiece which is held on the table of the drilling machine.

8.3.3. Drilling Tools. The most widely employed drilling tool is the twist drill with two cutting edges or lips, (Fig. 8.41). A twist drill consists of the following main parts : the point, the body, the neck, and the shank. The point comprises the cutting elements while the body guides the drill in operation. The body of the twist drill has two helical grooves called "flutes" cut into its surface. The flutes form the cutting surface and also assists in removing the chips out of the drilled hole and making the coolant to get to the cutting edges. The drill is held and rotated by its shank. The cutting edges are straight and are separated by web thickness of the drill. To help provide adequate strength and rigidity to the drill, the web becomes progressively thicker towards the shank.

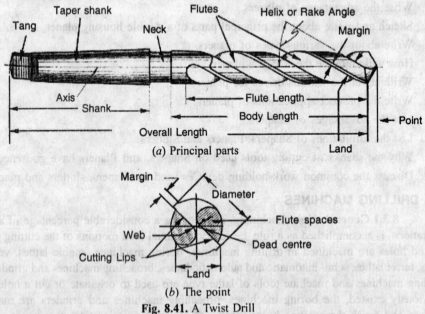

(a) Principal parts

(b) The point

Fig. 8.41. A Twist Drill

The body of the drill is made slightly less in diameter leaving a narrow "margin" at full nominal diameter along the edge of each flute. This reduces the rubbing action between the drill and the hole wall and allows the cutting fluid to reach the point of the drill. The two margins facilitate the removal of heat generated in drilling and properly guide and locate the drill. To help further in reducing the rubbing action, drill bodies are given a slight back taper (about 0.0075 mm per cm of length).

Lip relief (Clearance) angle. The heel of the drill point is backed off when ground to give relief behind the cutting lips. This will allow the cutting edges to cut without interference. This is equivalent to end relief angle of a single point cutting tool. It is kept 12° to 15°.

Point angle. The point angle is selected to suit the hardness and brittleness of the material being drilled. It is 116° to 118° for medium hard steel and cast iron, 125° for hardened steel and 130° to 140° for brass and bronze. It is only 60° for wood and fibre. This angle (half) refers to side cutting edge angle of a single point tool.

Helix angle. This angle is equivalent to back rake angle of a single point cutting tool. It is 24° to 30° for most drills.

Dead centre. The intersection of the two ground surfaces of the point with the web at the centre of the drill, produces a sharp raised line, known as the "dead centre" or "chisel edge".

The angle which the raised line at the dead centre makes with the cutting edges is called the "chisel-edge angle". This angle is an indication of the clearance on the cutting edge near the chisel edge. This angle generally varies from 120° to 135°.

The chisel edge does not do any cutting action. It only plastically displaces the material to be subsequently removed by the cutting edges. The 'chisel edge tends to wander or walk over the surface when starting a hole. The drill must be kept in place by creating an indentation on the job where the hole is to start, with a centre punch or a centre drill. The drill can also be kept in place by using drill bushings to guide it.

Materials. Carbon tool steels drills have a low first cost, but these should be used occasionally and at slow speeds. High speed steel drills are the most popular and have good strength. Drills tipped with cemented carbide are economical for high production but are expensive and must be handled carefully to avoid breakage. These are used mainly for drilling of malleable iron castings and nonferrous metals and alloys such as copper, brass, aluminium, Magnesium, zinc and also plastics, hard rubber etc. These are not used for steel components as there is likelihood of their breakage due to high tip pressure.

Drill Sizes. Standard drills are available in four size series, the size indicating the diameter of the drill body :-

(*i*) **Fractional Size.** Size range is $\dfrac{1}{64''}$ and $\dfrac{1}{4''}$ with increments of $\dfrac{1}{64''}$.

(*ii*) **Millimeter Size.** Size range is 0.5 to 10 mm with increments 0.1 mm.

(*iii*) **Numbered Size** (80 to 10). Size range is 0.0135″ to 0.228″ with very slight increments.

(*iv*) **Lettered Size (A to Z).** Size range is 0.234″ to 0.413″ with very slight increments.

How Drills are held. As written above, a drill is held and rotated by its shank. The drill shank can be tapered or straight. The straight or cylindrical shank is provided for smaller sized drills (upto 12.7 mm diameter). Taper shank drills are inserted directly into the taper hole of the drilling spindle (the taper is standard Morse taper, 1 : 20). To ensure against any possible slippage, the tang at the end of the taper shank engages a slot at the end of the tapered hole, Fig. 8.42. When the sizes of the tool shank and spindle hole tapers do not coincide, adapting devices such as tapered sockets or sleeves are employed. To remove the drill from the spindle hole, a wedge shaped drift which fits the hole through the spindle is used. Straight shank drills are held in drill chucks and clamped either by hand or by means of a chuck key, depending upon the design of the chuck. These chucks have taper shanks that enable them to be held in the tapered hole of the drilling machine spindle.

Advantages of Two Cutting Edges Twist Drill

1. Two cutting edges are more efficient.
2. Cutting forces are balanced.
3. Helical flutes allow access of cutting fluid and help to dispose off the chips.
4. The small margins left on the cylindrical surface provide guidance.

Core Drills. The body of a core drill has three or four helical flutes. These drills can not start holes but are used to enlarge holes previously drilled or for enlarging punched, cast or forged holes. The helix angle varies from 10° to 30°. These drills have got the following advantages over a standard twist drill :

1. The three or four margins (locating and guiding elements of the drill) ensure higher machining accuracy by preventing deviation of the tool to one side in operation.

2. More cutting edges allow greater feed per revolution resulting in greater productivity.

These drills are sometimes called spiral reamers or core reamers.

Straight Fluted Drills. These drills are commonly used for drilling soft metals like brass or copper. The standard twist drill shows a tendency to grate or dig in the soft metal. A straight or flat drill consists of the head, the neck and shank, (Fig. 8.43). The head may have either parallel sides or sides with a certain amount of back taper. A back taper of 2° to 3° may be provided to reduce the friction in drilling. The drills with parallel sides are more accurate in operation and have a higher tool life. The point angle of a flat drill ranges from 90° to 120°.

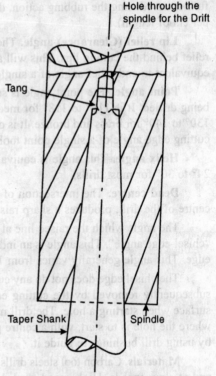

Fig. 8.42. Holding of a Taper Shank Drill.

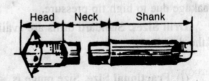

Fig. 8.43. Straight Fluted Drill.

8.3.4. Allied Operations. Holes drilled from the solid with one drill are further machined to : enlarge and finish the holes, produce seats for bolt head, nut, head of a screw or rivet and for a washer. These allied operations are shown in Fig. 8.44 and defined below :

1. Core drilling. Core drilling of holes is done with a core drill to enlarge and improve the geometric shape of the previously drilled hole.

2. Step drilling. It is the operation of cutting a hole of two or more diameters by one drill called the "Step drill" or "combination drill".

3. Boring. Boring is the operation of enlarging and finishing the complete hole with a single point cutting tool. This operation is normally done on boring machines but can also be accomplished on lathe group of machine tools. Boring corrects the position of the hole and makes it concentric with the axis of rotation of the spindle.

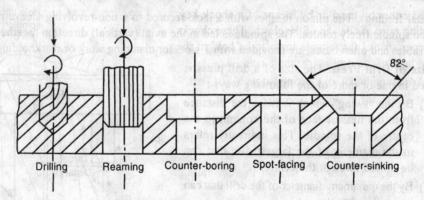

Fig. 8.44. Drilling and Allied Operations.

4. Reaming. Reaming usually follows drilling or core drilling and its purpose is to remove all coarse traces of previous machining operations with the help of a multipoint cutting tool called "reamer". A reamed hole is of accurate size and good surface finish. Reaming can not correct the position of the hole since reamer merely follows the previously drilled hole.

5. Counter boring. Consists in enlarging a portion of an existing hole to a larger diameter and making the surface at the bottom of the larger diameter flat and square. This is done to accommodate a screw head, bolt head or nut below the upper surface of the hole. The operation is accomplished by a special tool called a "Counterbore" or with a regular boring tool.

6. Counter sinking. is done after drilling a hole to chamfer the entrance to a hole or to make a conical recess or a seat for a flat headed screw or rivet so that the heads are flush or below the main surface. Standard countersinks are 60, 82, or 90° included angle. The tool, a countersink, is a short tool similar to a reamer.

7. Spot facing. It is the machining of a boss or pad at the face of a hole. It is normally done to produce a square bearing surface for a washer and nut or the head of a bolt. Both spot facers and counterborers are pilot guided.

8.3.5. Drilling Machines. Drilling machines are classified into : general-purpose, single-purpose and specialised drilling machines.

General Purpose Machines. Any hole making operation can be performed in the general purpose machines. This class includes : bench type drill press, Single- and multiple-spindle upright drill presses, radial drilling machines and others.

Single Purpose Machines. This class includes : Centre-drilling and deep hole drilling machines (horizontal and vertical types) ; semi- automatic and automatic drilling machines.

Specialised Machines. Special unit-built multiple-spindle drilling machines, intended for performing a single definite operation, are used in mass production.

1. General purpose Drilling Machines. The block diagram of a single-spindle general purpose machine (drill press) is shown in Fig. 8.45. Its main parts are : the base, column, table and head. The upright column is supported by a heavy base. The table is suspended from the column and may be moved up and down and clamped at the desired height. The drill head is mounted on the top of the column and consists of the main operating parts. The cutting tools (held in spindle) are power driven from the motor by a pair of cone pulleys-V belt drive or through a speed gear box to obtain various speeds. The axial feed of the tool is controlled by hand (on small machines) but larger machines provide power feed for the drill spindle. The spindle has a keyway or spline, so that it may be moved up and down along its axis for feeding, but, still retains its drive at any point, (Fig. 8.46). The rack pinion is rotated through a worm gearing (in power feeding) and hand feed lever (in manual feeding). The pinion meshes with a rack secured to a non-revolving sleeve or quill in which the spindle freely rotates. The spindle is fed in the axial (vertical) direction together with the sleeve. Tables and often bases, are provided with T slots for clamping work or workholding devices.

Size of Drill Press. The size of a drill press is expressed in one or more of the following ways :

(*i*) By the "swing" which is twice the distance from the nearest face of the column to the centre of the spindle. This indirectly refers to the diameter of the largest disc that can be drilled through the centre.

(*ii*) By the maximum diameter of the drill that can be used on steel.

(*iii*) By the maximum distance between the spindle and the table, that is, the maximum height of the job that can be accommo-dated with the table in its lowest position.

(*iv*) By the distance the spindle moves up and down, that is, by the length of the spindle feed.

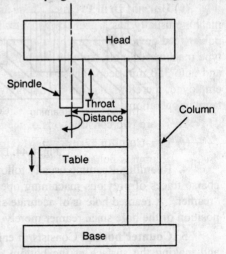

Fig. 8.45. Block Diagram of a Drill Press.

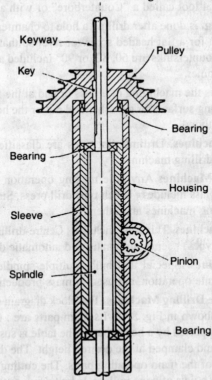

Fig. 8.46. Feeding Arrangement.

Types of Drill Presses

(*a*) **Bench type.** This is the simplest type used in industry. They are also called "sensitive" drill presses because the feed lever is operated by hand. This allows the operator to "feel" how the drill is cutting. If the drill gets into trouble, the pressure on it can be released. This design is used for light work using small drills (upto about 9.5 mm to 12.5 mm diameter drills). The controls are light and delicate speeds from 800 to 9000 rev/min are a typical range.

(b) **Upright Drill Presses.** These are medium heavy duty machines and stand on floor. This machine usually has a gear- driven mechanism for different spindle speeds and an automatic or power feed device. This machine will take larger drills and cutting tools than the standard bench type machines. Single- spindle upright drilling machines can drill holes upto 75 mm in diameter and upto 350 mm deep. These machines have a wide range of spindle speeds and feeds and are employed, therefore, not only for drilling from the solid, but also for core drilling, reaming and tapping operations.

There are two constructions of the column :

(i) **Box-Column arrangement (Upright Machine).** The column is of box section. The box column is bolted to the base. The work table is incorporated with a bracket which slides on ways at the front of the machine. Support and elevating movement of the table is provided by a telescopic screw underneath its centre. The table on these machines can be swung.

(ii) **Round-Column type (Pillar Machine).** Here, the table instead of being carried on vertical slides is carried on the round pillar. This helps in swinging the table to one side so that tall work pieces can be mounted on the base. Here, the table support is less rigid than the upright machine and places a restriction on its width. A box-column machine being more rigid than a round column machine, is adopted for heavier work.

(c) **Multiple-spindle Drilling Press.** These machines also called as "cluster drilling machines" are mass production machines with the several spindles (from 4 to 48 or more) driven by a single power head and fed simultaneously into the work. These machines are very useful when a number of parallel holes must be drilled in a part. These machines are subdivided into two group (according to the design of their spindles) : those with nonadjustable (fixed position) spindles and those with adjustable spindles.

(i) **Non-adjustable Spindle Machine.** (Fig. 8.47). The main drive spindle is rotated by an electric motor through a change-speed gearbox. From the main drive spindle, the motion is transmitted to the drilling spindles, through appropriate gearing. The multiple-spindle head is moved up and down by the

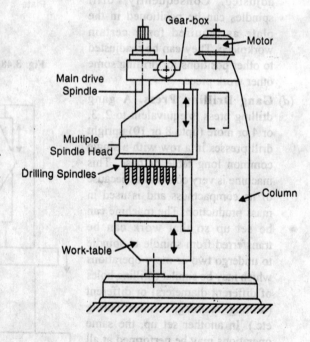

Fig. 8.47. Non-Adjustable Multi-Spindle Machine.

feed drive which has facilities for rapid traverse and feed motions. The worktable can be raised or lowered along the ways on the column. The drilling spindles have a fixed position in the head designed for drilling the holes in a definite work piece. Their arrangement may be either symmetrical or asymmetrical, as the case may be. The spindle head can be replaced by another head designed for some other workpiece or to perform some other operations. Different spindles in such a head may run at different speeds but they all have the same feed.

(*ii*) **Adjustable Spindle Machine.** The drilling head of a multiple- spindle machine with adjustable spindles is shown in Fig. 8.48. Here, the main drive spindle travels up and down the column ways with the drilling head, being actuated by the feed drive. The drill spindles are driven from the main drive spindle through gears and through the universal joints and telescopic shaft. This arrangement enables the offset spindles to be driven. The drill spindles are mounted in a plate which has slots in various directions along which the spindles can be adjusted. Consequently, drill spindles can be positioned in the plate as required for a certain workpiece. They can be readjusted to other positions for drilling some other work piece.

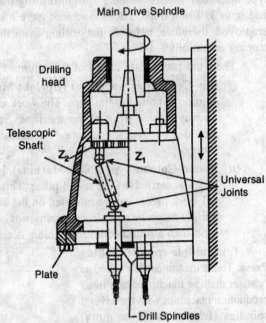

Fig. 8.48. Adjustable Multi-Spindle Machine.

(*d*) **Gang Drilling Press.** A gang drilling press is equivalent to 2, 3, or 4 or more (upto 8 or 10) upright drill presses in a row with a single common long table or base. This machine is very convenient because of its compactness and is used in mass production. The machine can be set up so that work can be transferred from spindle to spindle to undergo two or more operations which may be similar (drilling holes of different diameters) or different (drilling, reaming, counter- boring etc.). In another set up, the same operations may be performed at all spindles. With automatic feed control, two or more operations may be going on simultaneously attended only by one operator.

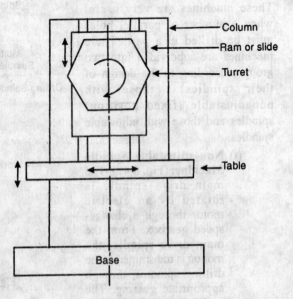

Fig. 8.49. Turret Drilling Press.

(*e*) **Turret Drilling Press.** A turret drilling press, (Fig. 8.49), over- comes the floor space restriction caused by a gang drill press. Numerical control is also available. Two fixtures can be located on the worktable. This enables loading and unloading of one part while the other part is being machined. This reduces the cycle time.

(*f*) **Radial Drilling Machine.** These machines, (Fig. 8.50), are used for drilling holes at different locations on heavy and bulky workpieces which are either inconvenient or impossible to mount on the table of an upright drilling machine and can not be moved easily. A large arm extends out from the column. It can be raised or lowered along the column with the help of an elevating screw and it also swings in a complete circle around the column. The drilling head moves back and forth on this arm. On most radial drilling machines, the movements of the arm, the drill head, and the spindle are controlled by power feeds. Due to the back and forth movement of the drilling head along the arm and the swinging motion of the arm around the column, holes can be drilled in many different locations without moving the workpiece.

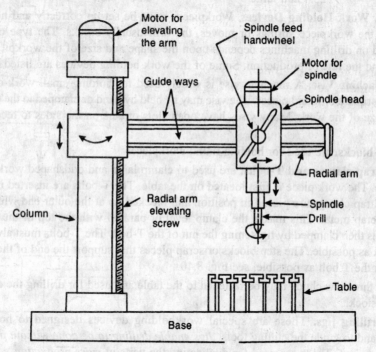

Fig. 8.50. Radial Drilling Machine.

A radial drilling machine is available in three designs :

(*i*) **Plain.** This design has only vertical spindle motion.

(*ii*) **Semi-universàl.** In this machine, the spindle head can be swung about a horizontal axis normal to the arm to permit the drilling of holes at an angle in a vertical plane.

(*iii*) **Universal.** Radial arm can also be rotated about a horizontal axis. This enables holes to be drilled at any desired angle.

Size of a Radial Drilling Machine. The size of a radial drilling machine is given as :

1. Diameter of column in cm;

2. In metres which is the radius of the largest disk in which a centre hole can be drilled with the drilling head at its outermost position on the arm.

8.3.6. Cutting Speeds and Feeds. As already discussed, the cutting speed depends upon: the type of material being drilled, cutting tool material, the quality of hole desired, the efficient use of cutting fluid, the way in which the work is set up or held and the size and type of drilling machines. The suggested cutting speeds for drilling process on drill presses are given in Table 6.1.

Feed of the drill is the axial distance the drill advances into the work piece for each complete revolution of the drill and is given in mm/rev. The correct feeds for different sizes of drill are given below :

Drill size, mm	feed, mm/rev
3.2 and less	0.025 - 0.050
3.2 to 6.4	0.050 - 0.10
6.4 to 12.7	0.10 - 0.18
12.7 to 25.4	0.18 - 0.38
25.4 and large	0.38 - 0.64

8.3.7. Work Holding Devices. Workpieces must be set up correctly and held securely for drilling. If the workpiece springs or moves, the drill usually breaks. The type of work holding device used on drilling machines depends upon the shape and size of the workpiece, the required accuracy and the rate of production. Some of the work holding devices are listed below :

1. Machine Vise. A machine vise is widely used for holding small work of regular shape such as flat, square or round pieces. The vise may be held by hand or clamped to the table, depending upon the size of the work. Many vises have open slots or ears on the sides to receive T-bolts see Fig. 8.40.

2. V-blocks. are used for holding round workpieces.

3. Strap clamps and T-bolts. are used to clamp large and oddshaped work pieces directly to the table. The work piece is first located on the table. The T-bolts are inserted in the T- slots of the table. Strap clamps are placed in position and blocked up at the outer end with step blocks or pieces of scrap metal. This makes the clamp level or parallel with the top of the workpiece. The workpiece is then clamped by tightening the nut of the T-bolt. The T-bolts must always be as close to the work as possible. The step blocks or scrap pieces that support the end of the clamp must be as far from the T bolt as possible, see Fig. 8.40.

4. A three jaw chuck may be fastened to the table and used for drilling the ends of round or hexagonal stock.

5. Drilling jigs. These are special workholding devices designed to hold *a particular workpiece* and to guide the cutting tools. *Jigs enable drilling to be done without previously laying out the workpiece.* These are used for duplicating the parts in mass production.

8.3.8. Deep Hole Drilling. Holes with a length to diameter ratio over 5 are called deep holes, for example, holes through machine tool spindles, hollow shafts etc. In drilling deep holes with the use of twist drills in ordinary drill presses, it is impossible to obtain accurately straight holes. The straightness of the hole depends upon the rigidity of the twist drill and the guiding action of the margins, adjacent to the flutes, which slide on the surface of the drilled portion of the hole. If the drill lips are of unequal length after sharpening, or if they become dull unequally, the drill will begin to run off the centre of the hole. The amount of drill run off also depends upon drill operation at the initial stage of drilling when only the chisel edge, square to the drill axis, cuts the metal. Other factors, such as large elastic deformation of the drill in operation (buckling), excess play in the spindle bearings, and nonuniform adhering of chips on the lips of the drill may lead to run off. Other difficulties encountered with deep hole drilling are the supply of coolant to the cutting edge and removal of chips.

To avoid drill run off and enable straight holes to be obtained in deep-hole drilling, the following measures are taken :

(1) Holes are drilled with low rates of feed ; the drill is carefully sharpened so that both lips are inclined at the same angle ; excess wear of the drill or adherence of chips to the lips is avoided ; and proper and ample cutting fluid is provided.

(2) The hole is first spotted with a short starting twist drill of large diameter and with a point angle of 90° This is especially bene-ficial in drilling holes with small- diameter drills in turret lathes and automatics.

(3) Twist drills should be guided by a jig bushing in drilling holes with a comparatively low length-to-diameter ratio.

(4) It is better to drill deep holes with workpiece, instead of drill, rotation. In this case, the drill seems to centre itself, and the tendency to run off centre is substantially reduced.

If the workpiece rotates in the deep-hole drilling, the drill may be either stationary or rotate in the opposite direction to the workpiece. Drill rotation, in this case, is a means for increasing the cutting speed. Hole drilling with rotation of the workpiece is used in engine and turret lathes as well as in deep-hole-drilling machines (for drilling the bores of gun barrels, machine tool spindles, hollow shafts, etc.) which are most frequently of the horizontal type.

Special Deep Hole Drills. Where length-to-diameter ratio of the hole is 10 or more, the following special types of drills are used :

Half round drills, gun drills and trepanning drills. These special drills require the provision of a sufficiently reliable guidance for axial motion of the drill along the surface of the portion of the hole that has already been drilled. Such drills may have a single or several cutting edges (lips):

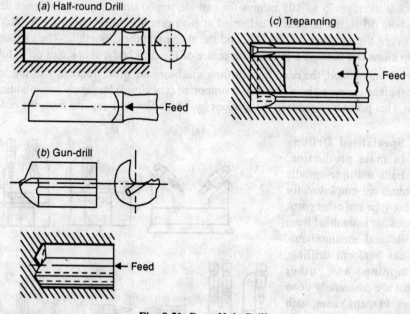

Fig. 8.51. Deep Hole Drills.

1. Half-round Drills. This is the simplest type of deep-hole drill, (Fig. 8.51 (a)). These drills have a single lip and a long bearing surface of the hole over an arc of an angle slightly larger than 180°. To reduce friction between the bearing surface and the hole walls and possible jamming of the drill, the head of the drill has a back taper (0.03 to 0.05 mm per 100 mm of length), the diameter being smaller towards the shank.

To start the drill with proper guidance at the beginning of the operation, it is necessary first to accurately bore the end of the hole to the diameter of the drill over a depth at least one half of the diameter. Half round and similar drills can be used either to drill holes from the solid or to enlarge holes previously drilled by twist drills of smaller diameters.

2. Gun Drill. A more efficient type of deep-hole drill is the gun drill, (Fig. 8.51 (b)). The bearing surface of these drills provides better guidance for the cutting element because it extends over an arc of the hole circumference of an angle from 250° to 260°. The bodies of these drills, like the half round design, have a back taper, the largest diameter being at the point. Flats are provided on the guiding member to reduce friction in the hole and improve cooling. The lip (cutting edge) of these drills is often designed in the form of a zig zag line to break up the chip.

Gun drilling was originally used to produced long, straight holes in gun barrels ; but the technique is now widely used for producing all sorts of true, straight holes. A hydraulically operated head withdraws the drill each time it drills a depth about equal to its diameter ; this clears chips and assures penetration of coolant. Gun drills can drill holes from the solid in addition to enlarging previously drilled holes.

3. Trepanning Drill. The most efficient design of special drill for large-diameter deep hole drilling is the "trepanning drill", Fig. 8.51 (c). This drill cuts an annular recess through the hole, leaving a core that is removed at the end of the operation in the form of a cylindrical rod. These drills consist of a head, in which cutting blades or bits are secured to cut the annular recess from the solid, and a hollow drive tube, joined to the head by thread. Such drills are used in deep-hole-drilling machines for making large hollow shafts, long machine tool spindles, etc.

The rates of feed used in deep-hole drilling range from 0.02 to 0.5 mm per revolution, depending upon the hole diameter, workpiece material, required finish and specified accuracy of the hole. Speeds average 75 to 105 m/min for carbide-tipped drills in steel. In most designs of special deep-hole drills, the coolant is delivered at high pressure to the cutting edge through the clearance between the periphery of the hole and the shank and the drive tube. The coolant flushes the broken-up chips out through a hole in the centre of the drill body, shank and drive tube.

As already mentioned, the deep hole drilling machines are most frequently of the horizontal type. The workpiece is rotated by a chuck a~d supported (stabilised) by steady rests, while the drill is fed axially. This procedure reduces the amount by which the drill departs from the hole axis in drilling.

8.3.9. Specialised Drilling Machines. In mass production, special unit-built multiple-spindle drilling machines are employed for drilling housing-type and other parts. These machines are assembled from standard units and mechanisms. Such machines perform drilling, reaming, tapping and other operations that are commonly done in drill presses. In many cases, such multiple-spindle machines are built into an automatic transfer line. As a rule, the only special units of these machines are the spindle head and the jig or fixture for holding the workpiece. To changeover to the

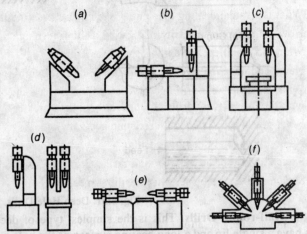

Fig. 8.52. Specialised Unit Built Drilling Machines.

production of a new part, it is usually necessary to design, manufacture and install these two special units only. Various arrangements of the standard units to obtain different designs of unit-built machines are illustrated in Fig. 8.52.

PROBLEMS

1. Define drilling operation.
2. Write the requirements which must be met by a drilled hole.
3. Sketch a Twist Drill. Write its main parts and their functions.
4. Why the body of a Drill is made slightly less in diameter than the full nominal diameter ?
5. Why the Drill bodies are given a slight back taper ?
6. Write about the materials for Drills.
7. What are the four systems of drill sizes ?
8. How drills are held in a drilling machine ?
9. What is a core drill ? When it is used ? Write its advantages over a 'standard twist drill'.
10. What is a 'flat drill' ? Sketch it.
11. What is a "Step drill" or "Combination drill" ?
12. Sketch and explain the following allied operations : reaming, counterboring, countersinking and spot facing.
13. How the different drilling machines are classified ?
14. Draw the block diagram of a drill press. Name its four major parts.
15. How is the size or capacity of a drill press determined ?
16. How is the feed controlled on most bench and small floor-type drill presses ?
17. What is the difference between Box-Column type and Round-Column type upright drill presses?
18. What is a 'multispindle drilling press' ?
19. Sketch and describe the two types of multiple-spindle drill presses.
20. What is the difference between a gang type and a multiple-spindle- type drilling machine ?
21. Sketch and describe a Turret Drilling Press.
22. What is a radial drilling machine ? Sketch and describe it.
23. How is the size or capacity of a radial drilling machine is specified ?
24. What factors affect the cutting speed for drilling ?
25. Name and describe five devices or methods for holding work to be drilled.
26. What is 'deep hole drilling' ? What difficulties are encountered while drilling deep holes with the use of twist drills on conventional drill presses ?
27. What precautions are taken to obtain accurate deep holes ?
28. Name the special deep hole drills.
29. Sketch and describe : Half-round drills, Gun drill and Trepanning drill.
30. Sketch and describe specialised drilling machines.

8.3.10. REAMING

Reaming is the operation of finishing a hole very smoothly and accurately in size. A drill will not produce a hole having sufficiently good qualities of finish and accuracy for many purposes. Therefore, when a very accurate, smooth hole is required, the hole is first drilled a little undersize. Then it is reamed to the correct size.

Reamer. A reamer is a multipoint rotary cutting tool, generally of cylindrical shape, which removes relatively small amounts of material as it is rotated and fed into a previously drilled or bored cylindrical hole. It imparts to the hole the necessary smoothness, parallelism, roundness and accuracy in size. It will not correct any error in the hole, because it follows merely the previously drilled hole.

A reamer consists of three main parts : fluted section, neck and shank, (Fig. 8.53). The fluted part consists of chamfer l_1, starting taper l_2, sizing section l_3 and the back taper l_4. Chamfer length or bevel lead length l_4 ensures proper and easy entry of the reamer into the hole. The main cutting action of reamer is done by starting taper l_2. The sizing section serves to guide the reamer and also smooths or sizes the hole. The back taper l_4 (with a difference of from 0.01 to 0.08 mm between the maximum and minimum diameters) reduces friction between the reamer and the hole surface.

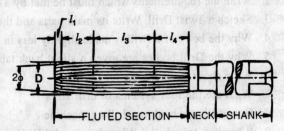

Fig. 8.53. A Reamer

Types of Reamers. Reamers can be classified in various ways :

(*a*) **According to shape.** In shape, reamers are made cylindrical, for machining cylindrical holes and taper, for tapered holes. Collars, pulleys etc. are often secured to the shaft by a taper pin. Taper holes for this are drilled and then finished by taper reamers to suit the taper pins.

(*b*) **According to the method of application.** By the method of application, they may be hand-type and machine-type.

1. Hand Reamers. These reamers are operated by hand with a tap wrench fitted on the square end of the reamer, the work being held in the vise or vice versa. These are solid straight reamers and have straight shanks with square tang for a wrench. The reamers cut on the flutes which may be straight or helical. They may be made of carbon steel or H.S.S. The depths of cut for these reamers are about 0.13 mm. These reamers produce the most accurate diameters and are used only for sizing holes.

2. Machine Reamers. A machine reamer is similar to a hand reamer except that it has a taper shank, and reaming can be done in a drill press, in a lathe or in a milling machine. There are two designs of machine reamers :

(*i*) **Rose Reamers.** A rose reamer does not cut on the circum-ference of its flutes, but is bevelled off or chamfered at usually 45° to cut on its ends. The chamfered ends form the cutting edges. Rose reamers are used for greater depths of cut (upto about 1.6 mm) and as roughing reamers particularly for clearing out cored holes. These reamers are also called as "Rose chucking reamers".

(*ii*) **Chucking Reamers.** Chucking reamers or "Fluted chucking reamers" have the ends of their teeth ground on a slight chamfer for end cutting like a rose reamer. In addition, cutting is also done from the side edges of the teeth along the circumference of the reamer just like a fluted reamer. These reamers are considered precision machine reamers and can produce more accurate holes than rose reamers.

(*c*) **By Construction.** By construction, the reamers can be classified as :

Solid type reamers and shell type reamers of one diameter and adjustable with inserted blades. Reamers are also classified as "floating reamers", and "expansion reamers".

1. Solid Reamers. Solid-type reamers are made from one piece of material, such as H.S.S.

2. Shell Type Reamers. Solid-type reamers in large diameters become very costly. To reduce the cost of such reamers, the cutting portions are made as separate shells made of H.S.S. These shells are mounted on standard shanks made of a lower-cost steel and which can be used interchangeably with other reamer shells. Shell type reamers are made with diameters greater than 19 mm. Large diameter shell type reamers are quite cheap as compared to equivalent solid type reamers. However, they are not very rigid and accurate and may not ream tougher materials with sufficient accuracy.

3. Adjustable Reamers. For very large diameter reamers, the reamer cost can be further reduced by using inserted teeth or blades in the shells. Only the blades are made of H.S.S. For large quantity production, the teeth or blades with tungsten carbide tips can be used. The blades can be moved up or down to increase or decrease the diameter. Also, the blades can be adjusted for wear when regrinding. The blades may be replaced individually. The drawbacks of such reamers are that the blades are difficult to adjust and they do not have the rigidity of solid reamers.

4. Expansion Reamers. The body of an expansion reamer is bored taper and is slitted to permit a slight expansion. A taper plug which runs through the hole is the expander, which is operated by a screw. This permits adjustment of the reamer diameter within a relatively small range as compared to adjustable-blade reamer. As the reamer wears or is resharpened, it can be adjusted back to its original size. Also, if a slightly larger hole than standard size is required, this reamer can be slightly enlarged to meet the need.

5. Floating Reamers. Here, the holders are not rigid but are floating. This permits the reamer to follow the previously made hole naturally and without restraint resulting in a better hole.

(*d*) **Left hand and Right Hand Reamers.** Reamers are classified as left-hand or right hand depending upon whether they are rotated to the left or to the right while looking from the shank toward the cutting end of the reamer.

(*e*) **According to the Type of Flute.** The reamers can be made either with straight flutes or with helical flutes. Helical flutes have got the following advantages :

1. Smoother surfaces are produced because the cutting action is more of a shearing action in this case.

2. Reamers with helical flutes should be used when the surfaces to be reamed have interruptions, such as a keyway parallel to the axis of the hole.

The helical flute can be "right-hand" or "left-hand". If the helical flute of a reamer rotates as it advances to the right toward the cutting end, it is known as "right-hand helical flute". If the opposite is true, it is known as "left-hand helical flute". Generally, for best results, a right-hand reamer with right-hand helical flutes is used for roughing cuts, and a right-hand reamer with left-hand helical flutes is used for finishing cuts.

Hints on Reaming Operation

1. Holes to be reamed must always be drilled undersize. Common practice is to drill the hole about 0.4 mm undersize. Depending upon the material and hole size, the following is usually allowed on diameters for machine reaming :

0.25 mm on a 6.35 mm hole

0.375 mm on a 12.7 mm hole

upto 0.625 mm on a 38 mm hole

For hand reaming, not more than 0.125 mm to 0.25 mm of stock should be left in the hole, owing to pressure required to force the tool through.

2. Never turn a reamer backward. It will ruin the delicate cutting edges.

3. Reamers are made with an even number of flutes.

4. Apply plenty of cutting oil or coolant to the reamer when reaming all metals except cast iron which contains free graphite.

5. Reamers are operated at cutting speeds slower than for drilling, to avoid early resharpening. A speed that is about half to two-thirds that for a drill of equal size is correct. Feeds may be large compared with those for drilling (upto about five times large), because depths of cut are small.

PROBLEMS

1. Define the reaming operation.
2. Define a Reamer.
3. Sketch a Reamer and explain the functions of its different parts.
4. Discuss the various types of Reamers.
5. What is the difference between Rose Reamers and Chucking Reamers?
6. Write a brief note on reaming operation.
7. Write briefly on :- Solid Reamers, Shell type Reamers, Adjustable Reamers, Expansion reamers and Floating reamers.
8. What are Left handed and Right handed reamers ?
9. What are left-hand flute and Right-hand flute reamers ?

8.4. BORING

When the internal surface of a hollow part is turned, that is, a single point tool is used for enlarging a hole, the operation is called as "boring", (Fig. 8.54). The single point cutting tool for this purpose is mounted on a bar called "boring bar". Even though a boring bar may on occasion use more than one tool bit, at is still spoken of as "Single point boring".

Boring tools usually operate with a large overhang from the tool holder. This factor does not allow shank type boring tools to cut a heavy chip. For this reason, deep holes are commonly bored by bar-type tools (often called bits) held is a holder or a bar (see Fig. 8.54).

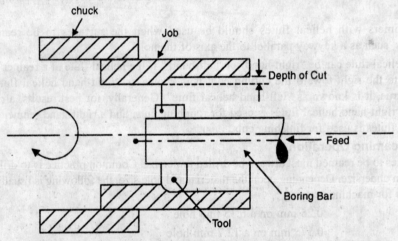

Fig. 8.54. Boring Operation.

While remaining is widely used to size holes more accurately than is possible with drills, boring as a rule must be resorted to in order to obtain the maximum in precision sizing, location and surface finish accuracy. Boring operation is chiefly used for machining holes with precise centre to centre distance in housing type parts (engine blocks, gear boxes etc.). Boring is also used for machining large diameter holes, since drills in larger sizes are relatively expensive.

Boring Vs. Reaming

1. Boring can correct hole location, size, or alignment and can produce a good finish if a fine feed and a correct tool are used. The reamer follows the hole already in the workpiece and so can not correct location.

2. Reaming is faster than boring but boring operation is often preferred because of location correction advantage.

3. Reaming involves the use of a tool of fixed size, which is different for each size of hole and a large hole would require an expensive reamer, while a boring tool can make a hole of any size.

8.4.1. Boring Machines. Boring can be done on most machine tools that do turning (workpiece rotating with tool stationary), for example, lathes. However, boring also can be done using a rotating tool with the workpiece remaining stationary (drill presses, milling machine). Also, specialized machine tools (boring machines) have been developed that will do boring operation.

General purpose boring machines can be subdivided into machines for ordinary and precise boring operations. The latter include jig-borers, used to produce holes with especially high precision centre-to-centre distances. Boring machines can be of either horizontal or vertical design.

Horizontal Boring Machines. Horizontal boring machines can be used to drill, bore and ream holes and to mill flat surfaces. Such machines are widely used in piece and small-lot production for machining housing type parts (gear boxes, machine tool headstocks etc.). In mass production, holes of larger diameter are bored in multiple-spindle boring machines, using boring cutter heads as tools.

In horizontal boring machines, the tool revolves and the work is stationary.

The workpiece is mounted on the table and is clamped with ordinary strap clamps, T-slot bolts and nuts, or it is held in a special boring fixture if so required.

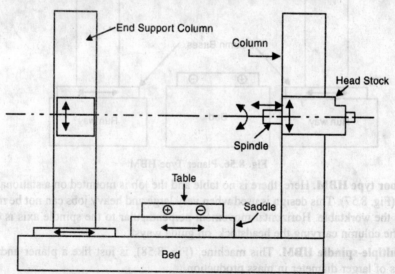

Fig. 8.55. Table Type HBM.

Various types of rotary and universal swivelling attachments can be installed on the boring machine table to bore holes at various angles in horizontal and vertical planes.

In piece and small-lot production, holes are bored to layout lines ; in medium-and large-lot, as well as mass production, devices for coordinate positioning are used, as well as jigs for guiding the cutting tools.

Types of Horizontal Boring Machines. Horizontal boring machines are of four principal types : Table, planer, floor and multispindle head type.

1. Table type HBM. (Fig. 8.55). The work is held stationary on a coordinate work table having in-and-out as well as back-and-forth movements, that is, perpendicular and parallel to the spindle axis. The head stock carrying the spindle can be moved vertically along a column for adjustment to varying heights of work. At the opposite end of the bed is a support column which carries a bearing for supporting the end of the boring bar. The spindle carrying the tool can be fed axially. Alternatively, the table travels parallel to the spindle axis (longitudinal feed). This method of boring with longitudinal feed of the table is employed when the holes are of considerable length and bending of the boring bar is possible. Machines of this type built for high spindle running accuracy and high positioning accuracy along the two axes of traverse which are at right angle to the spindle axis, are known as horizontal jig boring machines.

2. Planer type HBM. This machine, (Fig. 8.56), is similar to the table type HBM except that the work table has only in-and-out movements, that is, perpendicular to the spindle axis. Other features and applications of this machine are similar to the table type HBM.

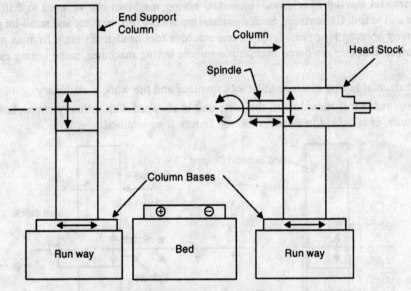

Fig. 8.56. Planer Type HBM.

3. Floor type HBM. Here, there is no table and the job is mounted on a stationary T-slotted floor plate, (Fig. 8.57). This design is used when very large and heavy jobs can not be mounted and adjusted on the worktable. Horizontal movement perpendicular to the spindle axis is obtained by traversing the column carrying the headstock, on guide ways.

4. Multiple-spindle HBM. This machine, (Fig. 8.58), is just like a planer and is used for boring holes of larger diameter in mass production.

Vertical Boring Machines. For convenience, parts whose length or height is less than the diameter are machined on vertical boring machines. On a VBM, the work is fastened on a horizontal revolving table, and the cutting tool or tools, which are stationary, advance vertically into it as the table revolves.

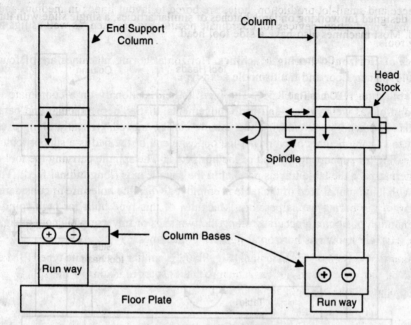

Fig. 8.57. Floor Type HBM.

There are two designs of a VBM : Single column VBM and double column VBM. The single column VBM looks like a drill press or a knee-type vertical milling machine. Guide ways are employed on the column to support the spindle head in the vertical direction. A double column VBM is shown in Fig. 8.59. The work is accommodated on the horizontal revolving table at the

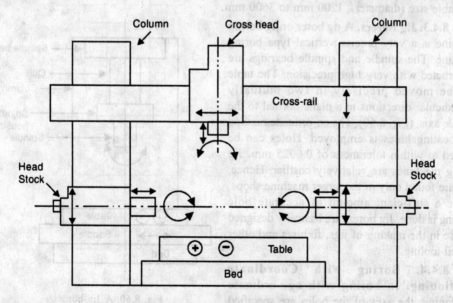

Fig. 8.58. Multi-spindle HBM.

front of the machine. The circular work can be clamped on to the table with the help of jaw chucks whereas the T-slots can be used with bolts and clamps for setting up and holding irregular work. A horizontal cross rail is carried on vertical slide ways and carries the tool holder slide or slides. On machines designed for working on large batches of similar articles, a single slide with turret may be employed. Most machines also have a side tool head.

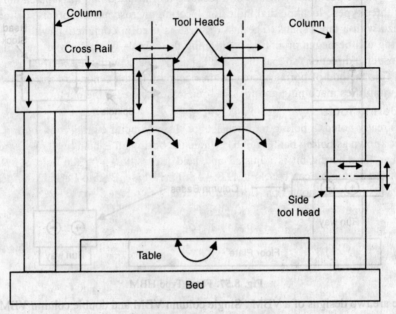

Fig. 8.59. Double Column VBM.

8.4.2. Size of Boring Machines. The size of boring machines is given by the diameter of the spindle (75 to 350 mm). In the case of VBM, one also has to give : dimensions of column height and table size (diameter), 1200 mm to 3600 mm.

8.4.3. Jig Borers. A jig borer or jig boring machine is a very precise vertical type boring machine. The spindle and spindle bearings are constructed with very high precision. The table can be moved precisely in two mutually perpedicular directions in a plane normal to the spindle axis, (Fig. 8.60). The co-ordinate method for locating holes is employed. Holes can be located to within tolerances of 0.0025 mm. Jig boring machines are relatively costlier. Hence, they are found only in the larger machine shops, where a sufficient amount of accurate hole locating is done. Jig borers are basically designed for use in the making of jigs, fixtures and other special tooling.

8.4.4. Boring with Coordinate Positioning. In boring with co- ordinate positioning, the axes of the holes are specified by two co-ordinate dimensions from the basic

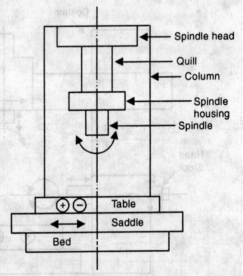

Fig. 8.60. A Jig-borer.

datum surfaces of the part. The axis of the boring machine spindle is set to the co-ordinate position, that is to the co-ordinate dimensions, by means of scales and vernier reading devices, installed on the machine, or by means of inserting the required end measures in accordance with the co-ordinate dimensions of each hole axis. Before beginning to bore the holes, the work is properly set up on the machine table to a dial indicator mounted in the boring spindle. Then the spindle is set to the "Zero" co-ordinate position by means of a locating tool inserted into the tapered hole. These tools may be of three types : locating dial indicator, locating microscope or a precise cylindrical bar of a definite size with a taper shank. The last of these is used in conjunction with clearance gauges. Then, boring can be begun after first positioning the spindle vertically and the table horizontally (in the transverse direction) so that the spindle axis coincides with the specified axis of the hole to be bored. This method of boring increases the accuracy of the centre-to-centre distances between the holes, simplifies machining and may in some cases, increase the output.

8.4.5. Boring Tools

As already noted, a boring tool consists of a single point cutting tool (boring bit) held in a tool holder known as boring bar, Fig. 8.61, where the boring bit is held in a cross-hole at the end of a boring bar. The boring bit is adjusted and held in position with the help of set screws. The material of the boring bit can be: Solid H.S.S., Solid carbide, Brazed Carbide, Disposable carbide tips, Ceramic tips or diamond tips. Boring tools are of two types:

  1. Fixed type   2. Rotating type

Fixed type boring tools are used on work rotating machines, such as lathes, whereas rotating type boring tools are used on tool rotating machines such as drill presses, milling machines and Boring machines. Lathes, drill presses and milling machines can be used only for small jobs. However, for large jobs boring machines or mills are used. The boring bar or the boring head in the case of rotating type tools, is held in the main spindle of the machine.

In the case of centre lathe, fixed type tools are mounted in the tools post and the longitudinal feed to it is given with the help of compound rest slide or carriage. In such tools, there is no in built arrangement for tool adjustment for bore sizes. However, for fixed type tool holders held in turret of turret lathes and rotating type tools used in boring machines, there is in-built size adjusting facility. Such adjustable boring bars can be preset away from the machine, on a presetting device. Boring bars are also built with cartridges which hold throw away type inserts. Built in adjustment facility (set serews) is provided both for radial and axial adjustment. For precision boring or on jig boring machines, micrometer adjustment facility is built in, to ensure the true boring of the hole. For multi-point boring, the boring bars are built with more number of cartridges.

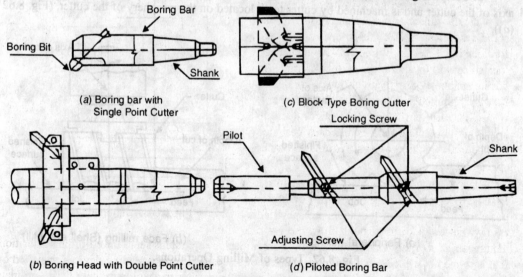

(a) Boring bar with Single Point Cutter

(b) Boring Head with Double Point Cutter

(c) Block Type Boring Cutter

(d) Piloted Boring Bar

Fig. 8.61. Boring Tools.

Since the boring bar is to reach the whole length of the job and it is overhanging, the problem of its deflection, chatter and vibration, is there. Due to this, maintaining dimensional accuracy can be a significant problem. The boring bar, therefore, must be sufficiently stiff, that is, made of a material with high modulus of elasticity, for example, WC, to minimise deflections and avoid vibration and chatter. However, boring bars have been designed with capabilities for damping vibrations.

PROBLEMS

1. Define boring operation.
2. Compare 'boring' and 'reaming' operations.
3. Name the various types of HBM. Discuss them with the help of neat sketches.
4. Sketch a double column VBM and explain its working.
5. How the size of boring machines is specified ?
6. What is the difference between a VBM and a Jig borer ?
7. Sketch a Jig borer and explain its working.
8. Discuss : Boring with co-ordinate positioning.
9. Write a short note on "Boring Tools".

8.5. MILLING

Milling may be defined as a machining process for removing excess material from a work piece with a rotating cutting tool. The rotating cutting tool called the "Milling cutter" is a multiple-point tool having the shape of a solid of revolution with cutting teeth arranged (equally spaced) either on the periphery or on end face or on both. The work may be held in a vise, a 3-jaw chuck, an index head, a rotary table, between centres, in a special fixture or bolted to the machine table. Milling process involves simultaneous rotary cutter and usually linear (sometimes rotary) motion of the work, with the work fed against the cutter. Milling process is used for producing flat, contoured or helical surfaces, for cutting threads and toothed gears and for making helical grooves.

In general, all milling operations can be grouped into the following two types :

1. Peripheral Milling or **Horizontal Milling.** Here, the finished surface is parallel to the axis of the cutter and is machined by cutter teeth located on the periphery of the cutter, (Fig. 8.62 (*a*)).

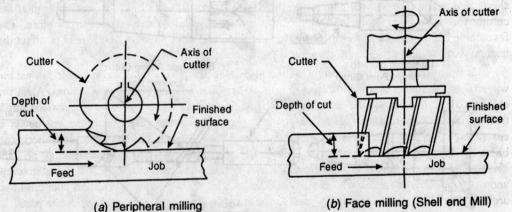

(*a*) Peripheral milling   (*b*) Face milling (Shell end Mill)

Fig. 8.62. Types of Milling Operations.

2. Face Milling or **Vertical Milling.** In face milling, the finished surface is at right angle to the cutter axis and it is obtained by the teeth on the periphery and the flat end of the cutter, (Fig. 8.62 (b)).

Surface Generation Methods. There are two methods of milling flat surfaces with plain milling cutters (these cutters have teeth only on the periphery of the cutter) depending upon the relative direction of feed of the worktable and the rotation of the cutter:

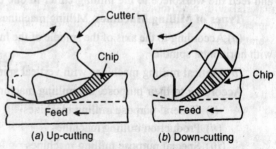

(a) Up-cutting   (b) Down-cutting

Fig. 8.63. Up and Down Milling.

1. Conventional (Up) Milling. Here, the direction of feed of the worktable is opposite to the direction of rotation of the cutter, Fig. 8.63 (a).

2. Climb (Down) Milling. Here, the direction of the worktable feed and the rotation of the cutter is the same, Fig. 8.63 (b).

In either case, the individual chips cut in the milling process are of variable thickness, having a cross section resembling a comma. In conventional milling, the thickness gradually increases during the cut; in climb milling the cutter tooth takes a chip of maximum thickness at the beginning of cut and of zero thickness at the end.

. The advantages of conventional milling are that the load on each cutter tooth is gradually increased and the teeth start cutting under the metal skin of the workpiece. The initial tooth contact usually occurs in clean metal and ends by lifting or peeling off the rough surface scale. Due to this reason, this method of milling is preferred for machining sand castings, forgings and metals that have a rough or hard abrasive surface scale. The disadvantages are that the cutter tends to lift the workpiece from the worktable and as the teeth tend to dull, each tooth slides across the workpiece surface a minute distance before it begins to cut, producing a characteristic wavy surface. There is tendency of lifting the work table also, alongwith lifting the job from the table or fixture (since the cutting forces are directed upwards). This increases the clearance between the table and bed or saddle ways. In making heavy cuts, such clearances lead to vibrations which impair the surface finish produced on the job. Again, chips accumulate ahead of the cutting zone where they can be picked up by the teeth and carried around to impair the finish. Also, it is difficult to machine thin sheets and workpieces where clamping is inadequate. Since, the table is to be fed against the cutting force, the feed motor and main motor powers consumed are comparitively more. The favourable conditions for conventional milling are that the work must be rigidly held to offset the tendency of the cutting forces to lift or pull the work out of the vise or fixture.

The advantages of climb milling are : job is forced against the table and the table against the ways. This eliminates excess clearance in jointing surfaces and the resulting vibrations. Also, the chips are deposited behind the cutter and out of its way. These factors give a better surface finish than in conventional milling. Again, less power is required in climb milling, because, less power is consumed in the feed motion. Increased cutting speeds and feeds are possible. Also, thin sheets can be easily machined. The favourable conditions for climb milling are : the workpiece has no hard skin, the milling machine is in good condition and there is no excessive backlash in the table screw and nut, since any looseness will allow the cutter to draw the workpiece ahead and take bites that are too large. The method is usually used for milling operations on slender and intricate parts.

8.5.1. Milling Machines. Milling machines were basically develop-ed to machine flat surfaces. But, the present milling machines can machine flat, contoured and helical surfaces, cut gears and do various other jobs. Due to all this, a milling machine is one of the most useful and necessary machine tools found in the shop and it ranks next to the lathe in importance.

Milling machines are designed to hold and rotate milling cutter or cutters, hold the workpiece and feed the workpiece to the milling cutter in one of several directions.

Types of Milling Machines. Milling machines can be classified in different ways :

(a) According to the axis of the spindle of the machine, we have : Horizontal milling machines with horizontal spindle

(b) Vertical milling machines with vertical spindle.

According to their purpose, the milling machines may be classified as:

    (i) General purpose milling machines

    (ii) Production milling machines

    (iii) Special purpose milling machines

1. General purpose Milling Machines. The most common kinds of milling machines in this category are the column and knee type models which are all single spindle machines. The various models under this category are :

    (a) Plain (Horizontal spindle)

    (b) Universal (Horizontal spindle with swivel table)

    (c) Omniversal (Horizontal spindle with swivel table and swivel knee).

    (d) Vertical spindle.

(a) Plain Column and Knee Type Milling Machines. This machine is called by this name because the spindle (the part that rotates) is fixed in the column. A block diagram of the machine is shown in Fig. 8.64 (a). The structure of the machine is mounted on the base or bed of the machine.

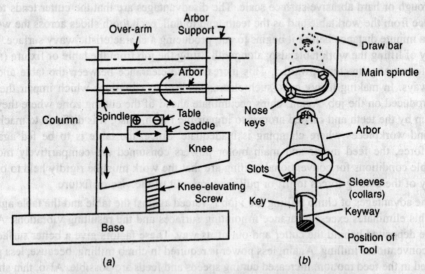

Fig. 8.64. Plain Column and Knee Type Milling Machine.

It provides rigidity and strength to the machine. It may also serve as a reservoir for cutting fluid. The column is the main supporting frame. It is a heavy box like structure. Inside this is space for motor and much of the driving mechanism. The face of the column is a very accurate slide. The "knee" slides vertically (up and down) on the column face. A feed, or elevating screw extends from the base to the knee. On top of the knee is a "saddle". The saddle can move transversely (cross movement toward and away from the column). On top of the saddle is the "table". The table moves longitudinally (back and forth) in front of the column. The surface of the table is cut with T slots to which work holding devices such as the vise can be clamped. The machine provides for three movements of the workpiece :

        (*i*) Vertical (up and down) movement of the knee.

        (*ii*) Transverse or cross (in-and-out) movement of the saddle.

        (*iii*) Longitudinal movement (back-and-forth) movement of the table.

    Along any one of these coordinate directions, feeding may be accomplished. Movements along the other two coordinate directions are then used for locating the cut, which includes obtaining the depth of cut.

    The driving power for all the cutting tools comes from the rotation of the spindle. This is a hollow shaft that rotates in bearings. The front (end near the table) has a tapered hole. The arbor is an accurately machined shaft for holding and driving the arbor-type cutter (Fig. 8.64 (*b*)). It is tapered at one end to fit the spindle nose and also has two slots to fit the nose keys for locating and driving it. When it is in place, a draw in- bar goes through the spindle and is threaded on one end to screw into the threaded taper end of the arbor, holding the arbor tightly in place. The outer end of the arbor is supported by an overarm support in a proper bearing. The overarm extends out from the top of the column above the spindle. It can be moved in or out and clamped at different distances from the column.

(*b*) Universal Milling Machine.

    . The universal horizontal milling machine differs from the plain horizontal type in that its table can be swivelled through an angle of $\pm 45°$ in the horizontal plane to enable helical grooves to be milled (*e.g.* the helical flutes of twist drills or the teeth of helical gears). The saddle is in two parts so that the table can be horizontally rotated.

(*c*) Omniversal Milling Machine.

    An omniversal milling machine has an additional movement as compared to universal milling machine. The knee can be rotated about the column face on an axis perpendicular to it. This enables to machine tapered spiral grooves in reamers, teeth on bevel gears and angular holes etc.

(*d*) Vertical Milling Machines.

    The vertical milling machine is very similar to the plain horizontal milling machine except that the spindle is held in a vertical position instead of horizontal. Vertical milling machines are of two types :

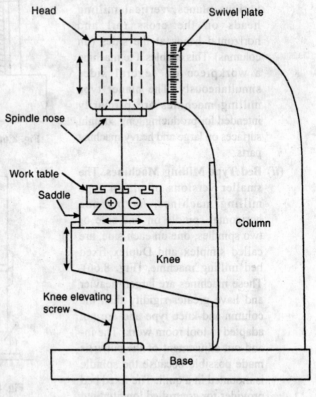

Fig. 8.65. Vertical Milling Machine.

    Fixed bed type, and column - and - knee type, (Fig. 8.65)

The column-and-knee type vertical machine has a vertical head and spindle, but the same feeds and adjustments as the plain horizontal machine. The overarm provides a strong support to the spindle. On some models, the head can be moved up and down to perform operations like grooving, slotting, die forming, facing, drilling and boring of accurate holes, with their exact locations. The machine can be with a fixed head and of swivelling head type with the head swivelling around a horizontal axis.

Size of Milling Machines. The sizes of column-and-knee milling machines are given in terms of the following parameters :

(a) *Table Travel*. This indicates the distance the table will move longitudinally. It can be upto the range of 1.5 m.

(b) In terms of the power of the machine.

(c) In terms of the type of the machine : plain, universal, omni-versal, vertical etc.

2. Production Milling Machines. Production or Manufacturing milling machines are designed to remove metal rapidly and to require a minimum amount of attention from the operator. The various models in this category are discussed below :

(i) **Planer Type Milling Machines.** A planer type milling machine will look like a double column planer, but has milling heads mounted in various planes, vertical milling heads on the cross rail and horizontal heads at the sides (on columns). This enables it to machine a workpiece on several sides simultaneously. The planer type milling machines are primarily intended for producing long straight surfaces on large and heavy machine parts.

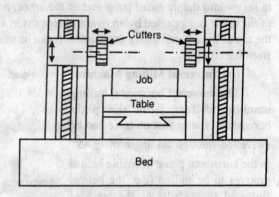

Fig. 8.66. Duplex Bed Type Milling Machine.

(ii) **Bed Type Milling Machines.** The smaller versions of planer type milling machines, having one horizontal spindle on one side or two spindles, one on each side, are called simplex and Duplex fixed bed milling machine, (Fig. 8.66). These machines are larger, heavier and have greater rigidity than the column-and-knee type and are not adapted to tool room work. The in-and-out adjustment of the cutter is made possible because the spindle is mounted in a quill. The fixed bed provides for controlled longitudinal travel only.

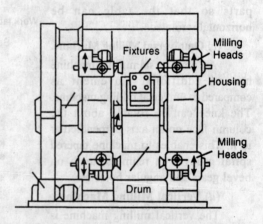

Fig. 8.67. Drum type Milling Machine.

(iii) **Drum Type Milling Machines.** These machines are of the continuous-operation type. They are mostly found in large-lot and mass production shops for production of large parts such as motor blocks, gear cases, and clutch housings. Two flat surfaces of the workpiece can be milled simultaneously. A drum type milling machine is shown in Fig. 8.67. A square drum (sometimes it may be a regular pentagon or hexagon), is mounted on a shaft passing through the frame. Parts are carried in fixtures mounted on the drum faces. The drum rotates continuously, carrying the parts between face mills. The milling heads can be adjusted along the housing and clamped as required for the set up. In addition to rotation, the milling spindles also have axial adjustment to set the cutters to the depth of cut. The output of such machines depends upon the number of simultaneously machined parts and the speed of rotation of the drum (rate of feed).

(*iv*) **Hand Operated Millers.** These machines are usually of the column-and-knee type and are common among the smaller production machines. Table movements are hand controlled through a handwheel or lever (which rotates a pinion that engages a rack on the underside of the table), providing high sensitivity and making them ideal for delicate operations (light cuts) on small parts, e.g., slotting the heads of screws. The cutter is driven by a motor.

(*v*) **Continuous or Rotary Millers.** These machines are usually of the vertical spindle type and have a rotary table for feeding jobs under the cutter continuously and are normally used for facing operations. It is used for facing automobile cylinder heads and crank pins etc. An unusual departure from the conventional rotary machines is the rotary-head machine. Suited primarily for tool, die, and small- quantity production, this miller adds a bit to the versatility of the rotary-table machine but is designed for much smaller work. Intricate radial cam work can be produced readily from drawings without the use of templates or patterns.

(*vi*) **Tracer Controlled Production Milling Machines.** The vertical spindle rotary-head machine discussed above eliminates the need for templates or patterns in the production of small quantities of complicated forms, cams etc. However, when mass production is required an automatic tracer controlled miller is indicated. A variety of vertical and horizontal tracers are available and represent the ideal machine for the production milling of odd shaped parts such as connecting rods, complicated gear housings, and extremely large or small cam tracks of intricate shape. Intricate machine parts can be profiled in stacks or groups where high accuracy for interchangeability is necessary but quantity does not warrant expensive tooling.

A roller on a tracer control valve rides on a template bolted to the rear of the table and causes the cutter to cut in a path corresponding to that of the template.

3. Special purpose Milling Machines. The number and design of special purpose millers is probably unlimited as the design of machine parts themselves. Where quantity is sufficiently large, a special machine can offset its cost by virtue of increased output and automaticity. Thus we have : die sinking machines, cam millers, thread millers and keyway millers etc. Die-sinking machines are duplicating machines used to make forging dies, moulds, forming dies etc. "Profilers" are capable of reproducing external and internal profiles from templates in two dimensions, "Duplicators" do the job in three dimensions. Some machines are hand operated, others are power fed.

"Cam millers" produce disk cams. The profile of the cam is cut on a slowly revolving workpiece by an end mill positioned by a master cam revolving in unison with the workpiece.

8.5.2. Milling Cutters. A milling cutter is a multiple-edged rotary cutting tool having the shape of a solid of revolution with cutting teeth arranged either on the periphery or on end face or on both. Usually, the cutter is held in a fixed (but rotating) position and the workpiece moves past the cutter during the machining operation.

Types of Milling Cutters. There are very many different kinds of milling cutters :

According to the design, milling cutters may be of the solid or inserted blade type. The latter have replaceable blades that are mechanically retained and are usually adjustable. Cutters over

75 mm in diameter are usually of inserted blade design to save tool steel. According to how the teeth are sharpened, milling cutters may be either "profile sharpened" or "form relieved". Most cutters (former) are sharpened by grinding a narrow land back of the cutting edges ; On form-relieved cutters, only the face of each tooth is ground to sharpen it without changing the shape. Hence, the profile of the form-relieved cutters is maintained after resharpening throughout the life of the cutter. This is of importance for form cutters which are very difficult to sharpen if they are of profile-sharpened design.

Some of the more common kinds of cutters are discussed below :

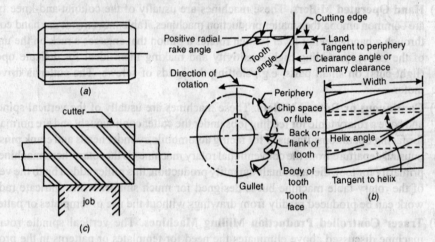

Fig. 8.68. Plain Milling Cutters.

1. Plain Milling Cutters. These cutters are cylindrical in shape and have cutting teeth on the periphery (around the outside) only. They are used for milling plain or flat surfaces. A plain milling cutter may have either straight (Fig. 8.68 (a)) or helical teeth (Fig. 8.68 (b)). In the operation of a cutter with straight teeth each tooth enters the cut simultaneously along its full length. This leads to intermittent loads acting on the machine and impairs the quality of the surface machined. Cutters with helical teeth operate more smoothly since the teeth enter the cut gradually and the load on the machine is more uniform. When the width of the cutter is more than the width of the workpiece, it is called "Slab cutter", (Fig. 8.68 (c)). If a set of two plain cutters operate side-by-side to mill a wide surface, one has right hand helix and the other has left-hand helical flutes so that the axial forces are counterbalanced.

2. Face Milling Cutters. Face milling cutters, with teeth on the end face are used for machining large, flat surfaces, (Fig. 8.69 (a)). The cutter may be mounted on an arbor or rigidly clamped on the nose of the machine spindle. Face milling cutters are similar to end mills but they are considerably larger in diameter. They are designed to machine flat surface which are perpendicular to the rotational axis of the spindle. These cutters are used on vertical milling, planer type milling and bed type milling machines. Facing milling is more of a production operation done with cutters from about 140 mm to 380 mm in diameter.

3. Profile Milling Cutters. Cutters with a curved tooth outline of the same shape as the profile of the workpiece, (Fig. 8.69 (b)), are called "profile or form milling cutters". some of the common shapes are concave, convex and corner rounding cutters[a]. Gear milling cutters are a kind of form milling cutters to machine any standard gear tooth.

4. End Mills. End mills have cutting teeth on the end as well as on the periphery. End mills may be made as solid cutters in which the cutter body is part of the shank, (Fig. 8.69 (c)). They may also be made as "Shell end mills" in which the cutters have a centre hole for mounting them on a short arbor. End mills are used in tracer-controlled profile milling operations. They are employed for making deep grooves in base parts, profile recesses, steps, perpendicular planes etc.

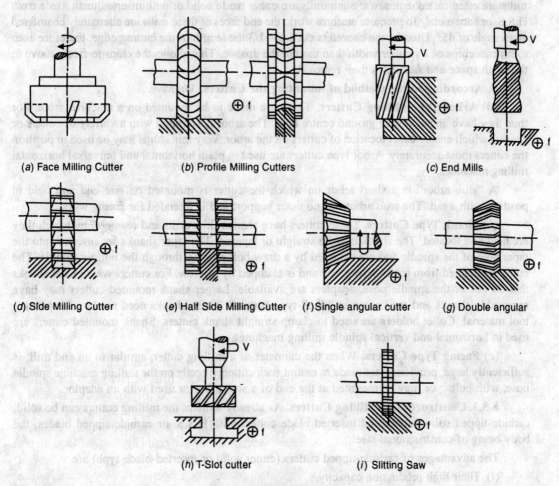

| (a) Face Milling Cutter | (b) Profile Milling Cutters | (c) End Mills |

| (d) Side Milling Cutter | (e) Half Side Milling Cutter | (f) Single angular cutter | (g) Double angular |

| (h) T-Slot cutter | (i) Slitting Saw |

Fig. 8.69. Milling Cutters.

End mills can be used on a horizontal milling machine, but it is better to use them on a vertical milling machine. Their diameter varies from about 3 mm to 50 mm. Shell end mill vary from about 30 mm to 150 mm in diameter.

5. Side Milling Cutters. These cutters have teeth around the periphery and also on one or both sides. Plain side milling cutters have straight teeth around the outside and side teeth on both sides [Fig. 8.69 (d)]. These cutters are made in width from about 5 mm to 25 mm and in diameters from 50 to 200 mm. "Half-side milling cutters" have teeth on only one side and around the circumference. They are made as right-and left-hand cutters, [Fig. 8.69 (e)].

6. Angular Milling Cutters. These are made as single-(Fig. 8.69 f) or double-angle (Fig. 8.69 g) cutters and are used to machine angles other than 90°. Some of the common cutters are the 45° and 60° single angle cutter and the 45°, 60° and 90° double-angle cutters. They find the most wide application in tool production for milling chip flutes on various cutting tools.

7. According to the purpose or use, we have T-slot milling cutters, (Fig. 8.69 h), Woodruff keyslot milling cutters and dove tail cutters for milling dovetail guides.

8. Metal - slitting Saws. For cutting splines and narrow grooves on workpieces and also for cutting materials, metal slitting saws are used, (Fig. 8.69 *i*). Large diameter (over 120 mm) slitting mills are often called disk saws. Such mills are either made solid or with inserted teeth made from H.S.S. or hard metal. To promote uniform work, the end faces of these mills are alternately chamfered at an angle of 45°. Usually, the chamfers cut 1/5 – 1/3 the length of the cutting edge, therefore each tooth cuts chips of a smaller width than than of the groove. This allows the chips to freely move in the tooth space and facilitates their removal.

9. According to the method of mounting the Cutters. We have

(*a*) **Arbor Type Milling Cutters.** These are made to be mounted on a machine arbor. For this, they have an accurately ground centre hole. The arbor is supplied with a variety of collars or spacers which enable exact location of cutters on the arbor. Very thin shims may be used to position the cutters most accurately. Arbor type cutters are used in plain horizontal and universal horizontal milling machines.

A "stub arbor" is a short arbor on which the cutter is mounted on one end and held in position with a nut. The stub arbor has no outer support and is intended for facing work.

(*b*) **Shank Type Cutters.** These cutters have shanks (like drills and reamers) by which they are held and located. The shank may be straight or tapered. The taper shanks are inserted into the taper hole of the spindle and are clamped by a draw bolt passing through the hollow spindle. The cutter is retained from rotation by a key and is clamped by a screw. For cutters which have shanks that do not fit the spindle nose, adapters are available. Larger shank mounted cutters may have removable shanks and are known as "Shell-type cutters". These shanks need not be of expensive tool material. Collet holders are used to clamp straight shank cutters. Shank mounted cutters are used in horizontal and vertical spindle milling machines.

(*c*) **Facing Type Cutters.** When the diameter of a milling cutter, similar to an end mill, is sufficiently large, provisions are made to mount such cutters directly on the milling machine spindle nose, with bolts ; or may be mounted at the end of a stub arbor or used with an adaptor.

8.5.3. Construction of Milling Cutters. As already written, the milling cutters can be solid, carbide-tipped solid cutters and inserted blade cutters with H.S.S. or carbide tipped blades, the body being of constructional steel.

The advantages of carbide-tipped cutters (either solid or inserted-blade type) are :

(*i*) Their high production capacity.

(*ii*) The high quality of the surfaces they produce.

(*iii*) Elimination of grinding operation in some cases, the possibility of machining hardened steels and the reduction in machining costs that their use leads to.

Due to these advantages, they have been successfully applied in metal cutting industry where they have replaced many solid cutters of tool steels. Alongwith the especially popular carbide-tipped face milling cutters, carbide-tipped side and form milling cutters and various end mills are used in industry.

8.5.4. Cutter Materials. General purpose solid milling cutters are commonly made of H.S.S. Some cutters are tungsten-carbide teeth which may be brazed on the tips of the teeth or individually inserted and held in the body of the cutter by some mechanical means. Carbide-tipped cutters are especially adapted to heavy cuts and increased cutting speeds.

8.5.5. Hand of Milling Cutters. The hand of any cutter may be determined by looking at the cutter end of the spindle (that is viewing from the front end as mounted on the spindle). If the cutter rotates counter clockwise, it is right handed ; if it rotates clockwise, it is left handed. Among all the types of milling cutters, only face mills and end mills can be classified as to direction of rotation. Other cutters are changed from one hand to the other by reversing their mounting on the arbor.

8.5.6. Cutting Speeds, Feeds and Depths of Cut. Since the milling cutter is a multi-point cutter, the feed may be given as :

Feed per rev., mm/rev, f, = Feed per tooth, mm × number of cutter teeth

Feed per min. (table feed), F = Feed per rev × cutter speed (r.p.m)

or $\qquad F \text{ (mm/min)} = f_1 \times n \times N$

where $\qquad f_t$ = Feed rate per tooth, mm

$\qquad\qquad n$ = number of cutterteeth

For H.S.S. plain milling cutters,

$\qquad f_t$ = 0.05 to 0.6 mm/tooth for milling steel = 0.1 to 0.8 mm/tooth for milling C.I.

The r.p.m. of the cutter is obtained as,

$$N = \frac{1000 \times V}{\pi D}, \text{D is cutter diamteter in mm. V is the cutting speed in m/min.}$$

The average cutting speed is given in Table 8.1

Table 8.1 Cutting Speed (H.S.S. Cutter)

Material being cut	Brass	C.I.	Bronze	Mild Steel	Hard C-steel	Hard alloy Steel	Al
V, mpm	45 - 60	21 - 30	24 - 45	21 - 30	15 - 18	9 - 18	150 - 300

The cutting speed with carbide tools can be as high as five times the cutting speeds for H.S.S. Tools.

Depth of cut = 3 to 8 mm for roughing = 0.5 to 1.5 mm for finishing.

Example. A slot is to be milled by a side and face milling cutter with 10 teeth and of diameter 150 mm. The cutting speed is 50 m/min. and feed is 0.25 mm/tooth. Determine the table feed in mm/min.

Solution. Given. n = 10, V = 50 m/min

Diameter of cutter = 150 mm

Feed, $\qquad\qquad f_t$ = 0.25 mm/tooth

Now Table feed, F, mm/min $= f_t \times n \times N$; N = RPM of the cutter

$$= \frac{1000 \times V}{\pi \times D} = \frac{1000 \times 50}{\pi \times 150} = 106 \text{ r.p.m}$$

∴ $\qquad\qquad F = 0.25 \times 10 \times 106 = 265 \text{ mm/min.}$

Example. A steel workpiece is to be milled. Metal removal rate is 30 cm³/min. Depth of cut is 5 mm and width of cut is 100 mm. Find the Table feed.

Solution. Now, Metal removal rate, MRR is given as,

$\qquad\qquad$ MRR = Depth of cut × width of cut × rate of feed

∴ $\qquad\qquad 30 \times 10^3 = 5 \times 100 \times F$

∴ $\qquad\qquad$ Rate of feed (Table feed), F = **60 mm/min.**

8.5.7. Work-holding Devices. There are many different devices for holding the workpiece to be machined :

(*i*) The work may be clamped on the table by means of T-bolts, strap clamps and pads.

(*ii*) **Plain Vise.** This is the most common work holding device used on a milling machine. It can be fastened to the table by means of T- bolts with the jaws either parallel or at right angles to the T- slots.

(*iii*) **Swivel Vise.** The vise is made in two parts. The top part can be turned in a complete circle. The base is divided into 360°. The jaws can be set to any angle.

(*iv*) **Universal Vise.** If the vise, apart from being swivelled in the horizontal plane, can also be tilted in the vertical plane, it is called as "Universal Vise". It is used for milling compound angles.

(*v*) **Universal Chuck.** It is used to hold round workpieces and is used mostly on the dividing head (discussed ahead).

(*vi*) **Rotary Table.** The rotary table is made in two parts and is fastened to the machine table by means of T-bolts. The base is divided into allowing the workpiece to be rotated in a complete circle. It is used to hold workpieces for accurate spacing, dividing and radius milling operations.

(*vii*) **Dividing Head.** The dividing head is a device for holding and turning the workpiece so that a number of equally spaced divisions or cuts can be taken around it. It consists of a headstock and a tailstock. The job may be held between centres or it may be held in a chuck mounted on the headstock spindle.

(*viii*) Work may also be held in various types of milling fixtures.

8.5.8. Principal Types of Milling Operations. Milling machines can be employed to produce a large variety of surfaces :

1. Milling flat Surfaces. Horizontal Flat surfaces may be milled on:

(*i*) Plain horizontal and Universal horizontal machines with plain milling cutters as shown in Fig. 8.68 (*c*).

(*ii*) Vertical-spindle milling machines with face milling cutters, as shown in Fig. 8.62 (*b*).

Vertical flat surface are milled on :

(*i*) Plain horizontal and Universal horizontal machines by using side milling cutters.

(*ii*) Vertical-spindle milling machines using end mills.

(*iii*) Vertical flat surfaces may also be milled on planer-type machines with face milling cutters, (Fig. 8.70 (*a*))

Inclined flat surfaces are milled on :

(*i*) Plain milling machines with single angle cutters (See Fig. 8.69 (*f*)).

(*ii*) On vertical spindle machines with the spindle swivelled to the required angle, (Fig. 8.70 (*b*)) This arrangement is possible only on swivel-head vertical spindle milling machine in which the head can be swivelled in a vertical plane parallel to the column face.

"Recesses" are milled on vertical spindle machines with end mills (See Fig. 8.69 (*c*)). In this case, the two perpendicular surfaces are machined simultaneously.

Milling Slots, Grooves and Splines. Rectangular, T-and dovetail slots are milled, as a rule, on vertical-spindle machines by means of suitable shank-type milling cutters, (see Fig. 8.69 (*h*)). Rectangular slots can also be machined on plain horizontal spindle milling machines with side milling cutters.

Keyways of rectangular cross section are milled on vertical- spindle machines or on keyway milling machines by using end mills and special cutters. Keyways can also be milled on horizontal spindle machines by using side milling cutters.

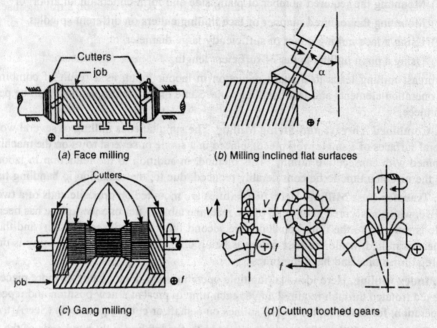

(a) Face milling (b) Milling inclined flat surfaces

(c) Gang milling (d) Cutting toothed gears

Fig. 8.70. (Milling Operations)

Splines may be milled on horizontal spindle machines by using single-and double-angle cutters.

Milling contoured surfaces. Contoured surfaces of relatively small width are milled on plain milling machines, using formed milling cutters. The profile of the cutter coincides with that of the workpiece. Surfaces of more complex shape are milled by a gang of simple cutters, (Fig. 8.70 (c)). The operation is called as "Gang milling". Complex shaped surfaces can also be milled using a template on a tracer-controlled machine. Three dimensional contoured surfaces (for example on dies etc.) are milled on tracer-controlled contouring machines.

Cutting Toothed Gears and Helical Grooves. Spur and helical gears are cut by form milling cutters on plain milling machines or by end-mill type cutters on vertical-spindle machines, (Fig. 8.70 (d)). The cutter profile must exactly coincide with the tooth space of the gear. Dividing head is used to index the gear blank through the required angle from one tooth space to the next.

Helical groves are milled on a universal milling machine. Here, the table is swivelled to the helix and the work is rotated by the dividing head which is linked by gearing to the lead screw of the table.

Gang milling, Straddle Milling, String Milling. When two or more milling cutters are mounted on an arbor so that each cutter will produce its own distinctive surface as the workpiece is fed to it, the operation is called "Gang milling", (Fig. 8.70 (c)).

"Straddle milling" is a special form of gang milling in which side milling cutters are used to machine both sides of a workpiece simultaneously (see Fig. 8.69 (e)).

In "String milling", two or more workpieces are mounted on the milling machine table in a line, so that they are successively fed to one or more milling cutters.

String milling results in a substantial reduction in handling time, as it is overlapped by the machining time

Depending upon the job set-up and tool set-up, the other milling methods are given below:

1. Abreast Milling. This is the simultaneous milling of several workpieces, placed in a row, parallel to cutter axis or of several surfaces of the same workpiece. It can be accomplished by :

(*i*) Mounting the required number of plain, side and form cutters on an arbor, or

(*ii*) Mounting the required number of face milling cutters on different spindles

(*iii*) Using a face milling cutter of sufficiently large diameter, or

(*iv*) Using a plain milling cutter of sufficient length.

Abreast milling leads to a sharp reduction in labour input, as a result of combination of several operation elements and less handling time. Same or different operations can be performed on each piece.

2. Combined Abreast-and-String Milling. The simultaneous milling of several workpieces (or several surfaces of a single workpiece), placed in a single or several rows on the machine table, is combined with consecutive milling. This method, in addition to the reduction in labour input, enables the machine time to be considerably reduced, due to, the reduction in handling time.

3. Transfer-Base Milling. Here, two fixtures are mounted on opposite ends of a two-station index base, which is secured at one end of the machine table. After one workpiece has been milled, the table is returned to the initial position, the second fixture is indexed through and the second work-piece is milled, while the first fixture is being unloaded and loaded. Economy is due to the combining of machine and handling times.

4. Index Milling. Here identical multiple operations are done on one or more pieces, which are indexed (rotated through required angle) each time to present a new position and repeating the same operation, for example, milling of splines on a shaft or cutting gear teeth (See Art. 8.5.10).

5. Reciprocal Milling. Fixtures are mounted on the left and right-hand ends of the machine table. While milling the workpiece in one fixture, the other fixture is being unloaded and loaded. Thus, the machine is performing the productive work during the handling time.

6. Progressive Milling. Here, two or more similar or different operations are performed either simultaneously or successively, on separate workpieces on the same machine. Workpieces are progressively moved from one fixture station to the next, until all the desired operations are performed [Fig. 8.71].

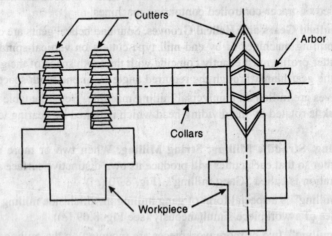

Fig. 8.71. Progressive Milling.

8.5.9. Cutter Angles. Refer to Fig. 8.68.

1. Radial rake angle = 10° to 20°.

Larger values are used for milling soft materials and smaller values for harder materials.

Carbide tipped cutters have negative rake angles = 10° to 15°.

2. Clearance of relief angle = 12° to 25°.

3. Helix angle : = 20′ to 30′ for plain milling cutters.

                   = 20′ to 15′ for side cutters and end mills.

8.5.10. Dividing Heads. The general construction and function of a dividing head has already been given under work holding devices.

An important function and use of milling machines is for cutting slots, grooves etc. which are to be equally spaced around the circumference of a blank, for example, gear cutting, ratchet wheels, milling cutter blanks, reamers etc. This necessitates holding of the blank (workpiece) and rotating it the exact amount for each groove or slot to be cut. This process is known as "Indexing". The dividing head is the device used for this purpose. It is lined and bolted to the machine table so that the axis passing through the headstock centre and tailstock centre is at right angle to the spindle axis of the machine. The headstock of the dividing head consists essentially of a spindle to which is keyed a 40-tooth wormwheel. A single threaded worm meshes with this wheel. The worm spindle projects from the front of the head and has a crank and handle attached. The head spindle is bored with a taper hole and is also screwed on its end. The workpiece is mounted between centres, one inserted into the dividing head spindle and the other into the tailstock of the head. The workpiece may also be mounted on a mandrel between these centres. A chuck may be mounted on the spindle nose for holding short work pieces having no centre holes.

The workpiece is rotated by turning the index crank by means of handle. Since the gear ratio of worm and worm wheel is 40 : 1, it takes 40 turns of the crank to rotate the spindle and hence the workpiece through one complete revolution. Thus one turn of the crank rotates the work $\frac{1}{40}$ th of a turn. If divisions other than factors of 40 are required "Index plates" are used. An index plate has several circles of holes (each circle containing a different number of holes) and is mounted on the worm shaft, (Fig. 8.72). A pin on the crank can be adjusted to a radius such that it will fit in any desired circle of holes. By using different circles of holes and index plates, any fractional part of a turn of the index crank can be obtained. The two sector arms shown on the front of the index plate, determine the angle through which the index crank is turned for indexing.

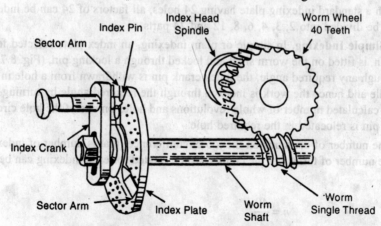

Fig. 8.72. Indexing Mechanism of a Dividing Head.

Types of Dividing heads. The various dividing heads used with milling machines are :

1. Plain. A plain dividing head has a fixed spindle axis and the spindle rotates only about a horizontal axis.

2. Universal. In these models, the spindle can be rotated at different angles in the vertical plane from horizontal to vertical. A universal dividing head performs the following functions : indexes the workpiece, imparts a continuous rotary motion to the workpiece for milling helical grooves (flutes of drills, reamers, milling cutters etc.) and setting the workpiece in a given inclined position in reference to the table.

3. Optical. These models are used for high precision angular setting of the work piece with respect to the cutter. For reading the angles, an optical system is built into the dividing head.

Methods of Indexing. The various methods of indexing are discussed below :

1. Direct Indexing. In direct indexing, the index plate is directly mounted on the dividing head spindle. The intermediate use of worm and worm wheel is avoided, (Fig. 8.73). For indexing, the index pin is pulled out on a hole, the work and the index plate are rotated the desired number of holes and the pin is engaged. Both plain and universal heads can be used in this manner. Direct indexing is the most rapid method of indexing, but fractions of a complete turn of the spindle are limited to those available with the index plate.

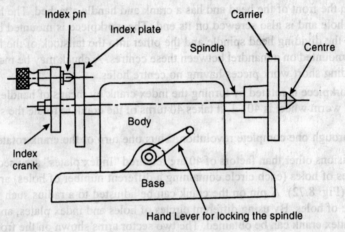

Fig. 8.73. Direct Indexing.

With a standard indexing plate having 24 holes, all factors of 24 can be indexed, that is, the work can be divided into 2, 3, 4, 6, 8, 12 and 24 parts.

2. Simple Indexing. In simple or plain indexing, an index plate selected for the particular application, is fitted on the worm shaft and locked through a locking pin, (Fig. 8.72). To index the work through any required angle, the index crank pin is withdrawn from a hole in the index plate. The spindle and hence the work is indexed through the required angle by turning the index crank through a calculated number of whole revolutions and holes on one of the hole circles, after which the index pin is relocated in the required hole.

If the number of divisions on the job circumference (that is number of indexings) needed is z, then the number of turns that the crank must be rotated for each indexing can be found from the formula,

$$n = \frac{40}{z}$$

Dividing heads are usually furnished with a set of three index plates having six concentric hole circles with different numbers of equally spaced holes on each hole circle. A typical set has the following number of holes:

I	15, 16, 17, 18, 19, 20
II	21, 23, 27, 29, 31, 33
III	37, 39, 41, 43, 47, 49

Example. Let $\quad z = 16$

$$\therefore \quad n = \frac{40}{16} = 2\frac{8}{16}$$

That is, for each indexing we need two complete rotations of the crank plus 8 more holes on the 16 hole circle of plate I.

Example. Let $\quad z = 45$

$$\therefore \quad n = \frac{40}{45} = \frac{8}{9} = \frac{8}{9} \times \frac{2}{2} = \frac{16}{18}$$

We will employ index plate I and use hole circle with 18 holes. For each indexing, the crank will rotate through 16 holes.

3. Compound Indexing. When none of the index plates has a hole circle which would enable the work to be divided by simple indexing method, more involved methods are employed. One method is "compound indexing". The compound indexing is achieved in two stages, by using two different hole circles of one index plate :

(*i*) By a movement of the crank in the usual way as in simple indexing, say, n_1 holes in hole circle N_1, with the lockpin engaged in circle N_2 of the index plate.

(*ii*) By adding or subtracting a further movement by rotating the crank and the index plate together forward or back ward, through n_2 spaces in the N_2 circle. (by disengaging the locking pin of the index plate so that it is free to turn).

The procedure is explained below :

Let z = number of divisions needed on the work.

$\therefore$ Crank rotations for each indexing = $40/z$

Since this can not be obtained by simple indexing, it is achieved by compound indexing. Therefore, addition or subtraction of the two movements given above should be equal to $40/z$. This is done as explained below :

(*i*) Write z above and 40 below a straight line and factorise them.

(*ii*) Select two numbers representing two hole circles in the same plate. Write these numbers below 40 and factorise them. Write their difference above z and factorise it. These hole numbers are to be chosen in such a manner that all the factors above the line get cancelled out with factors below the line.

Let these hole numbers be N_1 and N_2.

(*iii*) Let n_1 be the number of holes to be indexed in N_1 hole circle and n_2 the number of holes to be indexed in N_2 hole circle.

Then,

$$\frac{n_1}{N_1} \pm \frac{n_2}{N_2} = \frac{40}{z}$$

From here, n_1 and n_2 are found out by trial and error. Then the total indexing will be :

n_1 holes in N_1 hole circle by rotation of the crank $\pm n_2$ holes in N_2 hole circle by rotating the crank and index plate together.

Example. Let $z = 87$

Steps.

(i) $$\frac{87 = 29 \times 3}{40 = 2 \times 2 \times 2 \times 5}$$

(ii) Let $N_1 = 29$ and $N_2 = 33$

$$\therefore \qquad 4 = 2 \times 2$$

$$87 = 29 \times 3$$

$$40 = 2 \times 2 \times 2 \times 5$$

$$29 = 29 \times 1$$

$$33 = 11 \times 3$$

Since all the factors above the line get cancelled out, therefore, selection of N_1 and N_2 is correct.

(iii) Now, indexing equation is :

$$\frac{n_1}{29} \pm \frac{n_2}{33} = \frac{40}{87} \qquad \text{or} \qquad 33n_1 \pm 29n_2 = 440$$

By trial and error $n_1 = 23$ and $n_2 = 11$ with minus sign.

that is, $33 \times 23 - 29 \times 11 = 440$

$\therefore$ Indexing equation will be :

$$\frac{23}{29} - \frac{11}{33} = \frac{40}{87}$$

that is, Movement of crank by 23 holes in 29 hole circle forwards and movement of crank and index plate both by 11 holes in 33 hole circle backwards.

Note. The method of compound indexing is little used to-day, as it has been replaced by differential indexing.

4. Differential Indexing. Differential indexing in reality is an automatic method of doing compound indexing. It is achieved in a single step as compared to two stages needed in compound indexing.

In differential indexing, the index plate is connected to the headstock spindle by means of a gear train. Fig. 8.74 shows one such design where z_1, z_2, z_3 and z_4 are interchangeable gears. During indexing, the index plate rotates in relation to the crankmovement. For this, the locking pin which kept the index plate locked while doing simple indexing, is disengaged. As the index crank is turned for indexing, rotating the spindle through worm and worm gear, the index plate will receive power through the change gears, equal bevel gear and the sleeve, and will rotate slowly. The index plate can be made to rotate either in the same direction or in the opposite direction to the index crank (by gear train design).

Indexing is performed in the same manner as that for simple indexing except that the location of the hole from which the index pin is turned will move slightly during indexing. The required movement of the index plate is calculated and taken care of by the gear train.

Differential indexing is thus more straight forward and so has wider applications as compared to compound indexing.

Procedure

Let z = number of divisions required to be indexed for one complete revolution of the spindle and hence the work-piece.

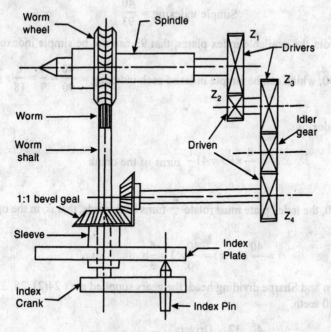

Fig. 8.74. Differential Indexing.

k = A number very nearly equal to z and which can be used in simple indexing method.

∴ number of crank turns for each simple indexing,

$$n = 40 / k$$

∴ Number of crank turns needed for z indexings,

$$N = \frac{40}{k} \times z$$

But, we know that the crank must make only 40 turns for the spindle (and hence the work) to turn through one complete circle. So,

(i) If $N > 40$, then $(N - 40)$ turns have to be subtracted. This is achieved through the change gears so that while the spindle makes one turn, the index plate makes (N – 40) turns in the opposite direction to that of the crank.

(ii) If $N < 40$, then the index plate should rotate $(40 - N)$ turns in the same direction as that of the crank.

The gear ratio will be :

$$i = \frac{40}{k}(k - z)$$

Thus, the movement of the index handle (crank) operates according to the principle of simple indexing and the gear ratio makes it possible to find gears which take care of residual divisions.

Example. Do differential indexing for 93 divisions.

Solution. $z = 93$

$$\therefore \qquad \text{Simple indexing} = \frac{40}{93}$$

It is clear from the available index plates, that 93 can not be simple indexed.

So, let $k = 90$, which can be simple indexed each indexing $= \dfrac{40}{90} = \dfrac{4}{9} = \dfrac{8}{18}$, that is, 8 holes in an 18 hole circle.

$\therefore$ for 93 indexings,

$$N = \frac{8}{18} \times 93 = 41\frac{1}{3} \text{ turns of the crank}$$

Since $N > 40$, the index plate must rotate $\dfrac{4}{3}$ turns backwards, that is, in the opposite direction.

$$i = \frac{40}{k}(k - z) = \frac{40}{90} \times 3 = \frac{4}{3}$$

In the Brown and Sharpe dividing head, the gears supplied are : 24(2), 28, 32, 40, 44, 48, 56, 64, 72, 86 and 100 teeth.

$$\therefore \qquad i = \frac{4}{3} = \frac{32}{24} = \frac{\text{Drivers}}{\text{Driven}}$$

It is a simple gear train.

Example. $z = 127$

Let $k = 128$

$$\text{Simple indexing} = \frac{40}{128} = \frac{5}{16}$$

$$\therefore \qquad N = \frac{5}{16} \times 127 = 39\frac{11}{16} \text{ turns of the crank.}$$

since N is < 40, therefore, the index plate must rotate $\left(40 - 36\dfrac{11}{16}\right)$, that is, 5/16 turns in the same direction as the crank, as the spindle completes one turn.

$$i = \frac{40}{k}(k - z) = \frac{40}{128} \times 1 = \frac{5}{16} = \frac{5 \times 1}{8 \times 2} = \frac{40}{64} \times \frac{24}{48} = \frac{\text{Drivers}}{\text{Driven}}$$

It is a compound gear train.

In Fig. 8.74, gears Z_1 and Z_3 drivers and gears Z_2 and Z_4 are driven gears.

$\therefore$ With this gear train and an indexing of 5 holes in a 16 hole circle, the 127 divisions would be obtained.

Rule of Thumb.

(*i*) If $(k - z)$ is positive, the index plate must rotate in the same direction as that of the crank.

(*ii*) If $(k - z)$ is negative, the rotation of the index plate is in opposite direction to that of the crank.

Example. Let $z = 153$

(*i*) Let $k = 155$

$$\therefore \text{ Simple indexing } = \frac{40}{155} = \frac{80}{155}, \text{ that is, 8 holes in 31 hole circle.}$$

$$\text{Change gears } = \frac{40}{k}(k - z) = \frac{40}{155} \times 2 = \frac{80}{155} = \frac{16}{31}$$

It is clear that this gear ratio can not be accommodated with the gears available. Therefore, choice of $k = 155$ is not correct.

(*ii*) Let $k = 150$

$$\therefore \text{ For simple indexing } = \frac{40}{150} = \frac{4}{15}, \text{ that is, four holes in 15 hole circle.}$$

$$\text{Change gears } = \frac{40}{k}(k - z)$$

$$= \frac{40}{150} \times 3 = \frac{12}{15} = \frac{2 \times 6}{3 \times 5} = \frac{32}{48} \times \frac{48}{40} = \frac{\text{Drivers}}{\text{Driven}}$$

$$\therefore \text{ Change gears : } Z_1 = 32, Z_2 = 48, Z_4 = 40$$

(*ii*) We can obtain another solution also.

Now indexing of 153 divisions by

simple indexing $= \dfrac{40}{153} = \dfrac{1}{3.825}$ which is approximately equal to $\dfrac{7}{27}$, that is, 7 holes in a

hole circle 27 for each indexing.

Now number of crank turns for 153 indexings

$$= \frac{7}{27} \times 153 = 39\frac{18}{27}$$

which is less than 40 by $\dfrac{9}{27}$ turns. Therefore, the gear train must rotate the index plate in

the same direction as the crank.

$$\text{Changes gears } = \frac{\text{Drivers}}{\text{Driven}} = \frac{9}{27} = \frac{1}{3} = \frac{24}{72}, \text{ that is, a simple train.}$$

∴ For 153 divisions the indexing is : 7 holes in a 27 hole circle ; gear ratio 24/72 and the crank and the index plate rotating in the same direction.

Note. It is clear from above that for a given problem, many solutions are possible. Solution (*iii*) is better than (*ii*) as a simple gear train is needed. To avoid wastage of time if the gear ratio does not fit the available gears as in solution (*i*) above, the hole circle selected for approximate simple indexing should be a number whose factors are accommodated in the available gears, for example, use hole circles of 18, 20, 21, 27 etc.

Rules of Thumb for Gear Trains

(a) If $k > z$ and the gear train is simple, then only one idler gear is to be used.

(b) If $k > z$ and the gear train is compound, no idler gear is to be used.

(c) If $k < z$ and the gear train is simple, then two idler gears are to be used.

(d) If $k < z$ and the gear train is compound, then no idler gear is to be used.

5. Angular indexing. Angular indexing is used when it is necessary to cut grooves or slots subtending a given angle at the centre of the circle upon which they are spaced.

We know that 40 turns of the index crank will rotate the head spindle and hence the workpiece through one revolution, that is, 360°.

$\therefore$ 1 turn of the crank = 9° of the spindle

$$\therefore \text{ Turns of crank to give any angle } = \frac{\text{Angle required}}{9}$$

Example. Do angular indexing for 38°.

$$\text{Indexing} = \frac{38}{9} = 4\frac{2}{9} = 4\frac{4}{18}$$

that is, four complete turns of the crank and 4 holes in a 18 hole circle.

Example. Do angular indexing for 51° 37′

$$\text{Indexing} = \frac{51° 37′}{9} = 5 + \frac{6° 37′}{9°} = 5 + \frac{397′}{540′}$$

Now no index plate is available with 540 hole circle. So, the exact indexing is not possible. For approximate indexing, let us convert the residual turn to a continued fraction :

```
397 ) 540 ( 1
      397
      ―――――――――
      143 ) 397 ( 2
            286
            ―――――――――
            111 ) 143 ( 1
                  111
                  ―――――――――
                  32 ) 111 ( 3
                       96
                       ―――――――――
                       15 ) 32 ( 2
                            30
                            ―――――――――
                            2 ) 15 ( 7
                                14
                                ―――――――――
                                1 ) 2 ( 2
                                    2
                                    ―――――――
                                    0
```

∴ We can write the residual fraction as :

$$\frac{397}{540} = \cfrac{1}{1 + \cfrac{1}{2 + \cfrac{1}{1 + \cfrac{1}{3 + \cfrac{1}{2 + \cfrac{1}{7 + \frac{1}{2}}}}}}}$$

First fraction $= \dfrac{1}{1}$

Second fraction $= \dfrac{1}{1 + \frac{1}{2}} = \dfrac{1}{\frac{3}{2}} = \dfrac{2}{3}$

Third fraction $= \cfrac{1}{1 + \cfrac{1}{2 + \frac{1}{1}}} = \cfrac{1}{1 + \frac{1}{3}} = \dfrac{1}{\frac{4}{3}} = \dfrac{3}{4}$

Fourth fraction $= \cfrac{1}{1 + \cfrac{1}{2 + \cfrac{1}{1 + \frac{1}{3}}}} = \cfrac{1}{1 + \cfrac{1}{2 + \frac{3}{4}}} = \cfrac{1}{1 + \cfrac{1}{\frac{11}{4}}} = \cfrac{1}{1 + \frac{4}{11}}$

$$= \dfrac{1}{\frac{15}{11}} = \dfrac{11}{15} \text{ and so on}$$

All the fractions will be :

$$\frac{1}{1}, \frac{2}{3}, \frac{3}{4}, \frac{11}{15}, \frac{25}{34}, \frac{186}{253}, \frac{397}{540}$$

Now with the available index plates, the nearest indexing for the residual turn is $\dfrac{11}{15}$, that is, 11 holes in a 15- hole circle.

∴ Angle will be $= 5\dfrac{11}{15} \times 9 = 51°, 36'$, that is, an error of $1'$.

Now Cincinnati and Parkinson Index Plates have the following hole circles :

First   : 24, 25, 28, 30, 34, 37, 38, 39, 41, 42, 43

Second : 46, 47, 49, 51, 53, 54, 57, 58, 59, 62, 66

Using the cincinnati plate, the closest fraction to the residual fraction is 25/34

$$\therefore \quad \text{Angle will be} = 5\frac{25}{34} \times 9 = 51°, 37', 3\frac{9''}{17}$$

That is an error of only $3\frac{9''}{17}$ in the angle. This is well within the accuracy of the ordinary dividing heads.

PROBLEMS

1. Define the "milling" process.
2. Define a "milling cutter".
3. What type of surfaces can be produced by a milling process ?
4. Sketch and explain the two basic types of milling operations.
5. Sketch and contrast the two milling methods of machining flat surfaces.
6. What is the basic type of milling machine ?
7. Sketch and explain the working of a plain column and knee type milling machine.
8. What are the three motions on a plain milling machine ?
9. What are universal and omniversal horizontal milling machines ?
10. Sketch and describe a vertical milling machine.
11. What is the difference between a fixed head and a swivelling head vertical milling machine ?
12. Describe the difference between a horizontal milling machine and a vertical milling machine.
13. What is feed on a milling machine ?
14. How is the size of a column and knee type milling machine given ?
15. Sketch and describe a Bed type milling machine.
16. Sketch and describe a Drum type milling machine.
17. Write on the following milling machines :
    (a) Planer type milling machine.
    (b) Hand operated millers.
    (c) Continuous or rotary millers.
    (d) Tracer controlled production milling machines.
    (e) Special purpose milling machines.
18. How the milling cutters are classified according to :
    (i) design.   (ii) the way the teeth are sharpened.
19. What is a plain milling cutter ?
20. What is a "slab cutter" ?
21. What is face milling ?
22. Name four types of side-milling cutters.
23. What is the difference between face milling and end milling ?
24. What is a "shell end mill" ?

25. Why is end milling done best on a vertical milling machine ?

26. How can sawing be done on a milling machine ?

27. Describe the three types of milling cutters according to the method of mounting the cutters.

28. Describe the construction of milling cutters.

29. Write the advantages of carbide-tipped milling cutters.

30. Write on the materials for milling cutters.

31. What is meant by hand of milling cutters.

32. Describe the various work holding devices used on milling machines.

33. How will you cut the following types of surfaces on milling machines:

    (a) flat surfaces.   (b) Slots, grooves and splines.

    (c) Recesses.   (d) Contoured surfaces.

    (e) Toothed gears and helical grooves.

34. Write on the following milling operations :

    (i) Straddle milling   (ii) Gang milling   (iii) String milling.

35. Describe a dividing head.

36. What are : plain, universal and optical dividing heads ?

37. Sketch and explain the direct method of indexing.

38. Describe Simple indexing method.

39. Describe compound indexing method.

40. Sketch and describe Differential indexing method.

41. What is angular indexing ?

42. Do the indexing for the following number of divisions :

    (i) 16   (ii) 45   (iii) 53   (iv) 18

43. What is the advantage of a helical-tooth cutter over a straight- tooth cutter for slab milling ?

44. How does a duplicator differ from a profiler ?

45. Write briefly on :- Abreast milling, combined Abreast and String milling, Transfer-base milling, Index milling, Reciprocal milling and Progressive milling.

8.6. GRINDING OPERATION

Grinding Operation is a method of machining workpieces by the use of a rotary abrasive tool, called "grinding wheel". Such wheels are made of fine grains of abrasive materials held together by a bonding material, called a 'bond'. Each individual and irregularly shaped grain acts as a cutting element (a single point cutting tool). The grinding operation can be : rough grinding or finishing (precision grinding). Rough grinding is a commonly used method for removing excess material from castings, forgings and weldments or as a method for removing or snagging thin fins, sharp corners, burrs or other unwanted projections from various shapes of workpieces. Precision grinding is the principal production method of cutting materials that are too hard to be machined by other conventional tools or for producing surfaces on parts to higher dimensional accuracy and a finer surface finish as compared to other manufacturing methods. Since cutting edges of the grits are extremely thin it is possible to remove much smaller chips and refine surfaces to a much greater accuracy of finish and dimension than with other machining methods.

    8.6.1. Abrasives. Abrasives include fine crushed substances in the form of grains and powders obtained by crushing natural or synthetic materials. The main characteristics of abrasive materials are : grain size and shape, hardness, toughness, resistance to attrition and friability. After attrition takes place, a grain must be friable to break apart in chunks to form new sharp edges.

There are two types of abrasives used in metal machining : Natural and Artificial or Synthetic.

(a) **Natural abrasives.** The natural abrasive materials are : Sandstone or Solid quartz, emery (50 to 60% crystalline Al_2O_3 + Iron oxide), corundum (75 to 90% crystalline Al_2O_3 + Iron oxide) and natural diamond. In the case of natural diamonds, the abrasive grains called "borts" are produced by crushing unsuitable gem stones to the required particle size. Their use is limited because of the tendency of dulling and glazing of the cutting faces. Natural abrasives lack uniformity of properties and reliability and have been largely replaced by manufactured abrasives.

(b) **Artificial abrasives.** These abrasives include : Aluminium oxide, Silicon carbide, Diamond (a form of pure carbon), boron Carbide and Cubic Boron nitride. The manufactured abrasives have well defined and controlled properties of hardness, toughness and type of structure.

1. Aluminium Oxide. Aluminium oxide, Al_2O_3, is known by such trade names as "Alundum" and "Aloxite". Aluminium oxide abrasive is composed chiefly of crystalline aluminium oxide. It is obtained by melting materials rich with this oxide (bauxite ore which is mainly aluminium hydroxide) in an electric furnace. Iron chips and coke are added to combine with and remove impurities. The refined aluminium oxide comes out of the furnace in a large lump called a "pig". It is crushed and rolled into small grains, treated magnetically to remove ferrous impurities and washed. Aluminium oxide is softer than silicon carbide. So it is tough and is not easily fractured. Hence it is extensively used for grinding materials of high tensile strength, such as, most steels, H.S.S., ferrous alloys, non-ferrous cast alloys and annealed malleable and ductile iron.

White Aluminium Oxide :- It is the most refined form of Al_2O_3 and contains a very high percentage of it. This cutting tool material is recommended for cool and precision grinding, where heat is required to be kept at a minimum temperature. It is especially recommended for tool room jobs. This material is particularly suitable for surface grinding and tool and cutter grinding.

2. Silicon Carbide. Silicon carbide is a chemical compound of silicon and carbon. It is produced by fusing quartz sand and powdered coke in an electric furnace. Sawdust and salt are also added to the mix. At temperature around 2300°C, the silicon of sand combines with carbon of coke to form silicon carbide. The sawdust burns and leaves pores to let the gases escape. The salt helps remove impurities. After the process has run its course, the furnace is cooled. The core of loosely knit silicon carbide crystals is broken into individual grains. Two types of silicon carbide are available : Pure silicon carbide of green variety and black or grey. Green silicon Carbide is harder and so is more brittle and friable and is in general a better abrasive than black silicon carbide. Both the types of silicon carbide have a higher hardness than artificial Al_2O_3. Being extremely brittle, SiC is not recommended for grinding hard materials. Silicon carbide wheels are used for grinding non-ferrous metals, non-metallic elements and cast irons.

Green Silcon Carbide :- This variety of SiC catting tool material is used for grinding Tungsten Carbide tools. This abrasive material is especially prepared for this class of work and has long been recognised as the only efficient abrasive for carbide tipped tools.

3. Diamond. Synthetic diamonds (a form of pure carbon) are mainly used for truing and dressing other grinding wheels, for sharpening carbide tools, and for processing glass, ceramics and stone.

4. Boron Carbide. Boron carbide is a combination of boron and carbon (B_4C). It is manufactured as a powder of grayish-black colour with the grain size not over 120μm. The grains are characterized by sharp faces and a higher abrasive ability. Boron Carbide is mainly used for grinding and lapping very hard metals, hard alloys, glass and jewels (ruby, topaz).

5. Cubic Boron Nitride. Cubic boron nitride is a combination of boron and nitrogen. Its manufacture and properties have already been discussed under chapter 7. It is used for grinding workpieces of tool and die steels as well as many types of hard high-alloy steels

Grain Size. For manufacturing abrasive tools and for application of abrasives in finishing and polishing operations, abrasive materials are crushed to obtain particles of desired size. These particles are known as "grains" or "grits". For some applications, the crushing is continued until the abrasive becomes a fine powder, often called a "flour". The metal removal rate and the quality of a ground workpiece depends largely on the grain size of the abrasive material of which the grinding wheel is made. Grain size is denoted by a number indicating the number of meshes per linear inch of the screen through which the grains pass when they are graded after crushing. A grain size of 60 means that the abrasive will pass through a screen having 60 openings per linear inch. The screen or sieve number and the mean diameter of the abrasive grain are related approximately

as, Mean diameter of abrasive grain $\cong \dfrac{15}{\text{grit size}}$ mm.

The grain size may be broadly classified as given below : Generally, coarse-sized grains (upto 24) are normally used for roughing which involves heavy material removal. Finer grits (70 to 180) are used for finishing operations where material to be removed is less. For producing very high surface finish, the grain sizes ranging from 220 to 600 and finer (upto 1000) are used, for example, grinding threads etc. Medium size grains (30 to 60) are used in operations which require both stock removal and finish, that is, for ordinary grinding and tool grinding.

The standard grain sizes are :

1. Coarse : 10, 12, 14, 16, 20, 24   2. Medium : 30, 36, 46, 54, 60
3. Fine : 70, 80, 90, 100, 120, 150, 180
4. Very fine : 220, 240, 280, 320, 400, 500, 600, 700, 800, 900, 1000

8.6.2. Bonding Materials. A grinding wheel consists of abrasive grains that are supported or held together by a bond. All bonds must be sufficiently strong to with stand the stresses of the high speed rotating grinding wheel. They must be capable of holding the abrasive grains firmly, yet must not be so dense as to impede the cutting action. The choice of bond depends on operating conditions of the abrasive tool : grinding speed, pressure on the tool, heat formation in the grinding zone and conditions of cooling.

Bonds are classified as non-organic and organic. Metallic, Vitrified and silicate bonds are non-organic. Resinoid, Rubber, Shellac and Oxychloride bonds are organic. These bonds are discussed below :

1. Vitrified bond. The most widespread is the vitrified bond. It is made of refractory clay, feldspar and quartz. It hardens to a glass like structure on heating, (The literal meaning of "Vitrified" is : to convert into glass by the action of heat). The advantages of vitrified bond are : it is strong, highly porous, resistant to heat, highly chemically stable (not affected by water, oils and acids), has a high cutting capacity and properly removes heat. Vitrified-bonded wheels can be used with a peripheral speed upto 35 m/s. The disadvantage of vitrified-bonded wheels is their brittleness. Vitrified bonds are strongest and hardest.

2. Silicate bond. This bond consists of water glass ($NaSiO_3$) mixed with zinc oxide, lime and other fillers. It hardens on heating at about 260°C. It is not as strong as vitrified bond, because self-dressing (crum-bling-out of dull grains) occurs more intensively. The wheels become soft when exposed to moisture. Silicate bonded wheel is the softest. Silicate bond is used for face grinding with large area of wheel in contact and for grinding of items sensitive to heat, such as cutters and precision tools.

3. Resinoid bond. A resinoid bond is a synthetic resin or plastic. Grinding wheels with a resinoid bond are very strong and elastic, highly stable under variable loads, but their porosity is lower than that of vitrified-bonded wheels. Resinoid has a polishing effect on the surface, thus diminishing its roughness. Resinoid-bonded wheels work at the surface speed of 35 - 40m/s and is used for high speed operations such as cutting off or fettling. It gives a very rapid stock removal rate. The disadvantages of these wheels are : loss of hardness when heated to a temperature of 200 – 250°C and insufficient resistance to alkaline coolants (it becomes soaked). These wheels can be readily reinforced with steel rings, or fibreglass or other fibres to increase their flexural strength.

4. Rubber bond. It basically consists of synthetic rubber with vulcanizing additions and fillers. In manufacturing the wheels, the abrasive material is mixed with rubber, then sulphur and other components are added. This mixture is pressed in heated moulds ; rubber becomes hard and retains elasticity when heated to 150°C. The resulting grinding wheels are stronger and may be rotated at higher rotational speeds. These wheels being slightly elastic are used in slitting and cutting-off operations (Elastic wheels less than 8 mm thick) and also in finish grinding. They are not softened by alkaline cooling liquids and are water resistant. However at temperatures above 150° the wheel becomes soft (dull) and requires cooling and dres- sing. These wheels are also used for centreless grinding control wheels.

5. Shellac bond. This is also a organic bond like resin and rubber. The abrasive material is mixed with shellac in a heated solution. It is then pressed and rolled into the desired shapes. Baking is done for several hours at about 150°C. This bond is primarily used for making strong, thin wheels having some elasticity. These wheels produce high surface finish and are used for grinding parts like camshafts and mill rolls. Occasionally, these wheels are used for slitting wheels (> 0.80 mm thick).

6. Oxy-Chloride bond. This organic bond is used particularly for disc grinding wheels. These wheels are less brittle and less sensitive to side loads as compared to vitrified-bond wheels. Also, the temperature during grinding is lower than with other bonds except the silicate bond. The drawbacks of these wheels are : affected by acidic solutions, dampness and sudden changes in temperature. Also, the strength of these wheels is lowered with long storage.

7. Metallic bond. Metallic bond is used for holding together the grains of diamond and cubic boron nitride. Copper, tin, aluminium and their alloys are used as bonding materials.

8.6.3.   Grinding Wheels

(*i*) **Manufacture.** The manufacture of the organic-bond grinding wheels have been explained in the previous article. To make vitrified grinding wheels, there are three methods : puddling, tamping and pressing. Firstly, the clay and abrasive material are thoroughly machine mixed. In the puddling method, water is added and the mixture is poured into moulds. For pressed wheels, the dry or semidry mixture is moulded and squeezed in hydraulic presses. In the tamping process, the squeezing pressure is less than in pressed wheels. Then the wheels are baked and dried. The puddled wheels must be trimmed to size.

Grinding wheels are vitrified by being fired for several days at high temperatures, like pottery. When hard, the wheels are trued, their arbor holes are bushed with babbit metal or lead and large wheels are balanced.

(*ii*) **Shape.** The shape and size of grinding wheels depend on the design of the machine whereon it will be used, the power of the machine, the operation to be performed, the shape and size of the workpiece and the grinding conditions. According to their shape, the wheels are classified as:

1. Straight wheels. , (Fig. 8.75 (*a*)), for cylindrical, internal, centreless and surface grinding.

2. Bevelled-face straight. , (Fig. 8.75 (*b, c*)), for grinding thread, gear teeth etc.

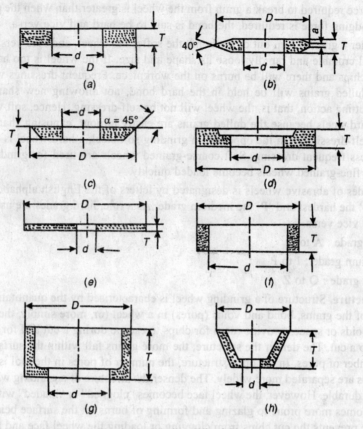

Fig. 8.75. Grinding Wheel Shapes.

3. Straight recessed. , (Fig. 8.75 (*d*)), for cylindrical grinding and facing.

4. Abrasive-cutting types. , (Fig. 8.75 (*e*)), are from 0.5 to 5 mm thick are used for abrasive-cutting off and slotting operations.

5. Cylinder, Straight Cup and Flaring Cup. , (Fig. 8.75 (*f, g, h*)), for surface grinding with the end of the wheel.

(*iii*) **Size.** The principal dimensions of a grinding wheel are the outside diameter, *D*, bore *d* and the width *T*. Straight wheels are available with an outside diameter from 3 to 1100 mm and with width from 6 to 200 mm.

(*iv*) **Properties of Grinding Wheels.** The properties of a grinding wheel that determine how it acts are : kind and size of abrasive, how closely the grains are held and the kind and amount of bonding material.

(*a*) **Grade.** The grade or hardness of a grinding wheel is a measure of the resistance offered by the combined strength of the bond and the abrasive grains to the external forces striving to tear the grains from the wheel. The bonding material surrounds the individual grains and links them together by connectors called "Posts" (Fig. 8.76). The sizes and strengths of the posts depend upon the kind and amount of bonding material in a wheel. If these posts are large in cross-

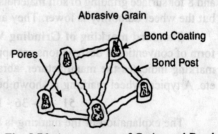

Fig. 8.76. Arrangement of Grains and Bond.

section, the force required to break a grain from the wheel is greater than when the posts are small. If a high dislodging force is required, the bond is said to be hard and vice versa.

The easier a grain is torn out of the bond, the softer the wheel, and vice versa. A wheel that is too soft will crumble and rapidly loose its shape and size. If the wheel is too hard, it will load quickly with chips and there will be burns on the workpiece. Frequent dressings will be required because the dulled grains will be held in the hard bond, not allowing new sharp grains to be exposed for cutting action, that is, the wheel will not be self-dressing. Hence, soft wheels are used in grinding hard steels because the dulled grains are easily tornout, exposing sharp-edged grains underneath (self-dressing). On the opposite, in grinding soft steel, a hard wheel is used because it will require less frequent dressing. Soft coarse-grained wheels are used for grinding copper and brass because fine-grained wheels become loaded quickly.

The grades of abrasive wheels is designated by letters of the English alphabet, 'A' denoting the softest, 'Z' the hardest and 'P' the medium grade. As a rule, hard grades are used to grind soft materials, and vice versa.

1. Soft grade : A to H
2. Medium grade : I to P
3. Hard grade : Q to Z

(b) **Structure.** Structure of a grinding wheel is characterised by the quantitative relation and arrangement of the grains, bond and voids (pores) in a wheel (or, more simply, the spacing of the grains). The voids or spaces provide room for chips to escape during a cut and for cutting fluid to be carried into a cut. The denser the structure, the more grains fall within the surface unit and the lower the number of pores. In the open structure, the number of pores in the tool is higher and the abrasive grains are separated more widely. The denser the structure of a grinding wheel, the harder it is and more durable. However, the wheel face becomes "clogged" or "loaded" with cut chips and the wheel becomes more prone to glazing and forming of burns on the surface being ground. The open structure prevents the cut chips from clogging or loading the wheel face and hence increases the efficiency of cutting. The proportion of bond to total wheel volume can vary from 10% to 30% giving either a very close abrasive spacing or open abrasive spacing respectively.

The grinding wheels are made with a specified structure. The structures are denoted by numbers from 0 to 12 inversely proportional to the content of abrasive grains in the wheel.

1. Dense structure : 0, 1, 2, 3
2. Medium structure : 4, 5, 6, 7, 8
3. Open structure : 9, 10, 11, 12

The dense structures containing much grain and small-size pores are mainly used for lapping, finish grinding and polishing.

Medium structures 4 and 5 are applied in grinding hard and brittle materials, when a high quality of surface finish is specified. Structure 6 is used for cylindrical grinding and structures 7 and 8 for surface grinding of soft materials. The open structures allow for more productive operations but the wheel durability is lower. They are used for high-velocity grinding.

Standard marking of Grinding Wheel. All grinding wheels are marked. Markings in the form of conventional designations are applied with an indelible paint to the wheel flat surface. The marking indicates the manufacturer, abrasive material, its grain size, grade, structure, bond type etc. A typical wheel marking is shown below :

$$51 - A - 36 - L - 5 - V - 23$$

The explanation of the marking is :

51   →   Manufacturer's symbol indicating exact kind of abrasive, (use optional).

A	→	Abrasive type : A for Al_2O_3, C for Si C and D for diamond.
36	→	grain size
L	→	grade
5	→	structure
V	→	Bond type
V	:	Vitrified
S	:	Silicate
R	:	Rubber
B	:	Resinoid
E	:	Shellac
O	:	Oxychloride
BF	:	Reinforced resinoid
RF	:	Rubber reinforced
23	→	Private marking to identify wheel (use optional).

8.6.4. Selection of a Grinding Wheel. The selection of a grinding wheel is based on the following factors :

1. Size and shape of wheel
2. Kind of abrasive
3. Grain size of abrasive particles
4. Grade of bond
5. Structure
6. Kind of bond material
7. Function of grinding wheel
8. Other factors : wheel speed, work speed, materials to be ground and general condition of the machine.

The factors 1 to 6 have already been discussed in the previous articles. The surface speed of the grinding wheels is given in Table 8.2 :

Table 8.2. Surface speeds of grinding wheels

Type of bond	Surface Speed m/s
1. **Vitrified or Silicate**	
Soft	23 – 28
Medium	25 – 30
Hard	28 – 33
2. **Organic**	
Soft	23 – 33
Medium	35 – 40
Hard	38 – 50

In a summary, the general guide lines for selection of grinding wheel, are given below :

1. Aluminium oxide abrasive is best for grinding steel (both hardened and unhardened), malleable iron and soft bronzes. Black silicon carbide abrasive is most efficient in grinding cast iron, bronze and aluminium castings, and cemented carbides. Green silicon carbide is used in sharpening carbide-tipped cutting tools.

2. The harder the metal being ground, the softer the wheel should be, and vice versa, since in grinding a hard metal the grains will wear more intensively and be broken out of the wheel more readily to expose new sharp grains. So, choose a hard-grade wheel for soft materials and a soft grade wheel for hard materials.

3. Coarser wheels (a large grit abrasive) are used in grinding ductile and soft metals to avoid rapid loading of the wheel ; fine-grained wheels are used for brittle and hard metals.

4. The larger the area of contact with the work, the coarser the grain of the wheel should be. That is, choose a large grit for the maximum metal removal rate and a small grit for a good finish.

5. To avoid breaking down, harder wheels should be more coarse- grained, since, other conditions being equal, the grain of a coarse-grained wheel is subject to a higher load than that of a fine-grained wheel.

6. The longer the arc of contact with the work, the less the grain depth of cut, and the greater the tendency to load the wheel and overheat the surface being ground. Therefore, the longer the arc of contact, the softer the wheel should be.

7. Regarding the structure of the wheel :

Choose wheels of dense structure for finish and form grinding, since they retain their shape well. Choose wheels of medium-dense structure for grinding hardened steel parts, for sharpening cutting tools, for cylindrical, centreless and internal grinding and for surface grinding with the periphery of the wheel. Wheels of open structure are used in grinding soft and ductile metals and in surface grinding with the face of a cup, cylinder or segmental wheel.

8. Choose a resinoid, rubber or shellac bond for good finish and a vitrified bond for a maximum metal removal rate.

Diamond Grinding Wheels. In contrast to grinding wheels of other abrasive materials, diamond wheels are not solid throughout, but consist of a diamond layer (0.5 to 3 mm thick) secured on a body of duralumin, steel or plastic. The diamond concentration of the wheel, that is, concentration of diamond grains per unit volume of the layer [consisting of diamond grains, bond and a filler (solid minerals)] may be 50, 100 or 150 per cent. Vitrified, resinoid and metal (most frequently bronze) bonds are employed.

8.6.5. Dressing and Truing of Grinding Wheels. Grinding wheels are dressed to restore their cutting capacity which is lost when the voids between grains are loaded with the waste material of the grinding process (sintered metal dust, abrasive grit and particles of binding material) and the grains are dull from wear. The former defect is called "loading" and the grains affected as "loaded" and the latter defect is known as "Glazing" and the affected wheel face as "Glazed". Truing, an allied operation done with the same tools, restores the correct geometric shape of the wheel, that is, it makes the face of the wheel concentric to its axis of rotation and its sides flat and parallel and normal to its axis of rotation. It also makes the face and sides of the wheel concentric to its axis of rotation when a new wheel is mounted on the grinder.

Dressing and truing involve the removal of a layer of worn abrasive grains from the surface of the wheel. Wheels are dressed and trued by cutting by means of industrial diamonds in the form of multiple-stone diamond tool bits or by pressing against diamond crystals fixed in some type of setting (mechanically, by hand setting or soldering) in a steel holder. Diamond substitutes are also applied : cemented carbide or special abrasive disks (called wheel dressing rollers), steel rollers and star-type dressers. The method of crush dressing a grinding wheel by pressing a high strength roller against its surface, is very fast and particularly economical for dressing forming tools. The dressing of the grinding wheel is usually done in the grinder itself so that alignment and wheel balance are not lost.

8.6.6. Grinding Ratio. Grinding ratio is defined as the volume of material removed from the work per unit volume of wheel wear. It is a very useful term to describe "grindability" of a given material. This ratio is determined experimentally by using a set of specific boundary conditions. Thus, the ratio for a given material, will vary according to the type of operation, nature of grinding wheel, type of grinding fluid, speeds and feeds and so on.

8.6.7. Abrasive Machining. The term "abrasive machining" refers to the processes in which metal is removed by a multitude of hard, angular abrasive grains or grits which may or may not be bonded to form a tool of some definite geometric form. Grinding is a form of abrasive machining in which the abrasive tool is in the shape of a wheel, called grinding wheel.

8.6.8. Grinding Machines. Grinding machines are classified as : cylindrical, internal, centreless, surface and special grinding machines.

1. Cylindrical Grinding Machines. The term "cylindrical" is applied to the large group of grinding machines which employ centres for mounting the workpiece to be ground. Most common of the external cylindrical grinding machines is the plain grinder, which is a general purpose production machine for the grinding of axles, shafts, splines etc. A plain grinding machine is illustrated in Fig. 8.77. All the units of the machine are arranged on the base which also houses the drive mechanisms and the hydraulic drive. Sliding or traversing table (lower table) is reciprocated by the hydraulic drive to obtain the longitudinal feed at a speed from 0.08 to 10 m/min or it is traversed manually by a handwheel through a system of gearing. The worktable or the swivel table (upper table) with T slots for securing the head stock and tailstock is mounted on the sliding table.

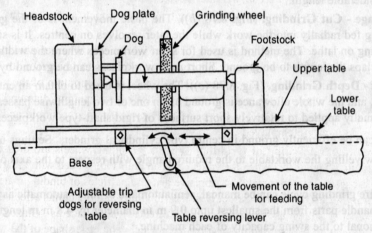

Fig. 8.77. External Cylindrical Grinding Machine.

The headstock serves to mount and drive the workpiece which is held either between centres or in a chuck. The work spindle in the headstock is powered by a motor located in the upper part of the headstock. The workpiece held between centres is rotated in the same manner as is done in a centre lathe. The tailstock supports the rear end of the work mounted between centres. Its spindle can be advanced and retracted. The tailstock spindle with the centre is commonly advanced and clamped by a spring device. The tailstock can be adjusted along the slots of the worktable to suit the length of the workpiece and can be clamped in the required position by bolts or an eccentric clamp.

The grinding wheel is mounted and clamped on the spindle of the wheel head which travels along cross ways at the rear of the base. The wheel is driven at speeds upto 1500 rev/min from a motor in the upper part of the head.

Adjustable trip dogs clamped in longitudinal slots provided at the side of the sliding table are set up to reverse the table at the end of the stroke. Cross feed of the wheel after each stroke of the table is obtained by manually or hydraulically operated crosswise movement of the wheel head.

Chucking type cylindrical grinders are production type machines for use in rapid grinding of relatively short parts, such as ball-bearing races.

Various methods of cylindrical grinding are employed. The most extensively used are : traverse grinding, plunge-cut grinding and full-depth grinding.

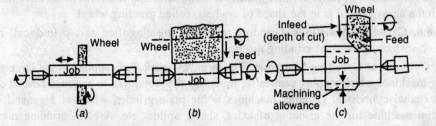

Fig. 8.78. Methods of Cylindrical Grinding.

(*i*) **Traverse Grinding.** (Fig. 8.78 (*a*)). In traverse grinding or infeed grinding, the grinding wheel is moved into the work. The desired surface is then produced by traversing the workpiece across the wheel on vice-versa. This method is used to grind workpieces of considerable length.

(*ii*) **Plunge - Cut Grinding.** (Fig. 8.78 (*b*)). The basic movement is of the grinding wheel being fed radially into the work while the later revolves on centres. It is similar to form cutting on lathe. The method is used for short workpieces where the width of the wheel overlaps the length to be ground. Short rigid workpieces can be ground by this method.

(*iii*) **Full - Depth Grinding.** (Fig. 8.78 (*c*)). The wheel is trued to obtain an entering taper or step, and the whole allowance is ground off in one or two lengthwise passes. The method is usually applied to relatively short surfaces of rigid shaft-type workpieces.

Tapers can be efficiently ground in centre type cylindrical grinders. Settings upto $\pm 10°$ can be made by swivelling the worktable to the required angle with respect to the axis of the grinding wheel.

The entire grinding cycle can be manual, semiautomatic or fully- automatic as desired. Plain grinders can handle parts from the smallest upto 0.9 m in diameter by 4.8 m in length, the lengths being proportional to the swing capacity of each machine.

Note. In very large grinders, the wheel is reciprocated across the workpiece held and rotated between centres, because of the massiveness of the work.

Universal Cylindrical Grinders. These grinders, in addition to the features offered by plain grinders, are provided with a swivelling headstock and a swivelling wheel head. This permits the grinding of taper of any angle, much greater than is possible in plain grinders. Universal machines are available to handle parts requiring swings upto 450 mm and centre distance of 1800 mm.

2. Internal Cylindrical Grinding Machines. Internal grinding is employed chiefly for finishing accurate holes in hardened parts, and also when it is impossible to apply other more productive methods of finishing accurate holes, for example, precision boring, honing etc.

There are two general methods of internal grinding : (1) with a rotating workpiece (2) with the workpiece held stationary. The first method is used in grinding holes in relatively small workpieces, mostly bodies of revolution, for example, the bores of gears and the inner surfaces of ball bearing rings. The workpiece is held in a chuck or special fixture and rotated in the same manner as in a lathe, (Fig. 8.79 (a)). A straight type grinding wheel is rotated and has two feeds - longitudinal feed along the wheel axis and is thus reciprocated back and forth through the length of the hole, and intermittent cross feed (radial feed) at the end of each pass, which determines the depth of cut. The grinding wheel is carried in a grinding head. In another design of the machine, the grinding wheel is rotated in a fixed position while the workpiece is slowly rotated and traversed back and forth.

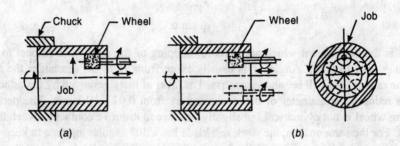

Fig. 8.79. Internal Grinding.

The peripheral speed of the wheel in grinding small holes does not exceed 10 m/s. The speed increases with the diameter of the hole to be ground, reaching 30 m/s for diameters over 30 mm. The depth of cut (infeed per stroke) is limited by the relatively low rigidity of the wheel spindle. Infeeds range from 0.005 to 0.02 mm in rough grinding steel and cast iron, and from 0.002 to 0.01 mm per stroke in finish grinding. Lower rates of infeed are used for holes less than 40 mm in diameter and for holes with a large length-to- diameter ratio. An over-travel equal to $\frac{1}{3}$ of the wheel width is required at each end of the stroke in internal grinding.

The second method of internal grinding is used for grinding holes in large bulky workpieces (housing-type parts) that are inconvenient or even impossible to clamp in a chuck of the grinder. They are mounted on the table of a planetary grinding machine, (Fig. 8.79 (b)). In addition to rotation about its axis, the wheel spindle of this type of machine also rotates with a planetary motion about the axis of the hole being ground. Axial motion of the wheel provides the longitudinal feed.

The essential difference between internal and cylindrical (external) grinding is that the former is performed with a wheel of much smaller diameter, usually from 0.7 to 0.9 of the hole diameter. Owing to their small diameters, the life of the internal grinding wheels in naturally shorter than for other kinds of grinding. Wheels of a lower grade (softer wheels) should be selected for internal grinding than for similar conditions in cylindrical (external) grinding, since the angle of contact with the surface being ground is much larger and the workpiece may be heated to a high temperature in grinding.

3. Centreless Grinding. Centre less grinding is performed on workpieces which do not or can not have centres, such as, pistons, valves, rings, tubes, balls, wrist pins, drills, bushings, drill rods, shafts and balls and rollers for bearings etc. Centreless grinding can be done both for external and internal surfaces.

(a) **External Centreless Grinding.** External centreless grinding can be carried out by three methods : Through feed, infeed and end feed methods.

(i) **Through Feed Grinding.** The principle of through feed centreless grinding is illustrated in Fig. 8.78 a. The workpiece rests on the workpiece rest blade and passes between two abrasive wheels : the grinding wheel and the regulating wheel. The grinding process is extended over the full length of the workpiece by its axial movement past the grinding wheel. This traverse motion is imparted to the workpiece by the regulating wheel. The regulating wheel is of rubber-bonded abrasive, having the frictional characteristics to rotate the work at its own rotational speed. The speed of this wheel, which may be controlled, varies from 0.6 to 1.0 m/s. The axial movement of the work past the grinding wheel is obtained by tilting the regulating wheel downward at the feeding end, at a slight angle from horizontal. Due to this inclination, the peripheral speed of the regulating wheel is resolved into two components – work rotation speed, $V_{wk} = V_{rw} \cdot \cos \alpha$ and the rate of longitudinal feed,

$$f_{lg} = V_{rw} . \mu \sin \alpha$$

where μ is the co-efficient which accounts for slipping of the work with respect to the grinding wheel ($\mu = 0.94$ to 0.98). Angle α is usually taken from $1°$ to $5°$; the larger the angle α, the higher the rate of feed will be, and vice versa. The layer of metal removed by the grinding wheel in one pass reduces the diameter of the workpiece by from 0.02 to 0.3 mm. The periphery of the regulating wheel is not cylindrical but slightly concave to improve contact between the wheel and the work. For the same reason, the work rest blade has a $30°$ angular top face to keep work against the regulating wheel face. This method is used for parallel work of any length which has no obstructions. The grinder can be automated by installing a magazine feeding device.

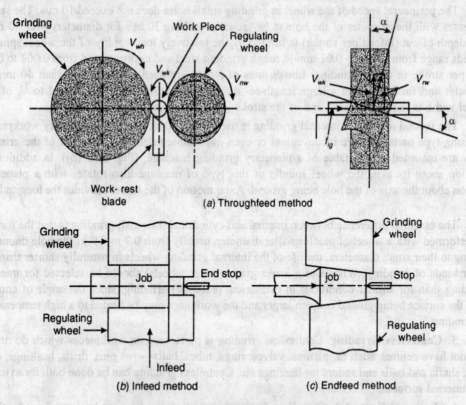

Fig. 8.80. External Centre-Less Grinding.

The centre of the workpiece is normally kept above the line connecting the centres of the grinding and regulating wheels [Fig. 8.80 (a)]. This is to ensure that a true cylindrical surface is ground on the work. This distance is about 0.125 to 0.25 times the workpiece diameter. If it is too small, the ground surface may not be round but may resemble an equilateral triangle with arcs as sides. If it is too large, chatter and vibrations will occur. It should not be more than 10 to 12 mm.

(*ii*) **Infeed Grinding.** (Fig. 8.80 (*b*)). If the workpiece is of stepped or irregular profile and therefore can not be traversed between the wheels, infeed centreless grinding is resorted to. Here the workpiece is placed on the workrest blade after the regulating wheel is retracted. Then the regulating wheel is advanced towards the workpiece so that it is fed towards the grinding wheel. When the grinding is completed, the regulating wheel is retracted again and the finished workpiece is ejected. Since no longitudinal feed of the workpiece is required in this method, the axes of both grinding and regulating wheels are strictly horizontal, that is, $\alpha = 0$.

(*iii*) **End Feed Grinding.** (Fig. 8.80 (*c*)). In this method, both the grinding and the regulating wheels are tapered and thus produce tapered workpieces. The workpiece is fed from one side until it reaches the stop. This method results in exact taper and size.

Advantages of Centre Less Grinding

1. The main advantage is its high productivity, which is several times higher than cylindrical grinding between centres.

2. The operator need be less skilled.

3. The work is rigidly supported and there is no chatter or deflection of the work.

4. Size of the work is easily controlled.

5. As a true floating condition exists during the grinding process, less grinding stock is required.

Disadvantage

1. Work with flats and keyways can not be ground.

2. Work having several diameters is not easily handled.

3. In hollow work, there is no assurance that the outside diameter will be concentric with the inside diameter.

4. Changeover of a centreless grinder to grind other sizes requires considerable time. Hence, it can be more expediently used in large lot production.

(*b*) **Internal Centreless Grinding.** Holes in ring type parts can be ground on internal centreless grinding machines, (Fig. 8.81). The work- piece 1 is loaded into the grinding zone where it is held between three steel rolls - support 2, pressure 3 and regulating 4 - mounted in housing 5. The lever mounted pressure roll 3 exerts a preset force on the workpiece holding it against the support and regulating rolls. The regulating roll, linked to the workdrive, rotates the work piece at a peripheral speed of from about 0.7 to 1.0 m/s. An axial force acting on the workpiece, due to the fact that the regulating wheel axis is inclined to about 1/2°, holds the workpiece axially with one end face against a roller stop. The hole is ground with a wheel mounted on spindle 6. The rotation of the work on grinding is the result of the friction force between the work and the regulating roll. The workpiece is loaded and unloaded by moving the pressure roll outward. Very high accuracy can be maintained in centreless grinding. Internal tapered surfaces are ground on centreless machines by swivelling

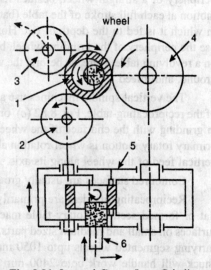

Fig. 8.81. Internal Centre Less Grinding.

housing 5 and the workpiece to the taper angle.

4. Surface Grinding. Flat surfaces are ground on surface grinding machines. Heavy workpieces are clamped on the table by means of pads, strap clamps and other devices or they are held in fixtures. Small work is usually held by a magnetic chuck. The surface grinders are available with horizontal spindle and vertical spindle and with either reciprocating table or rotary table.

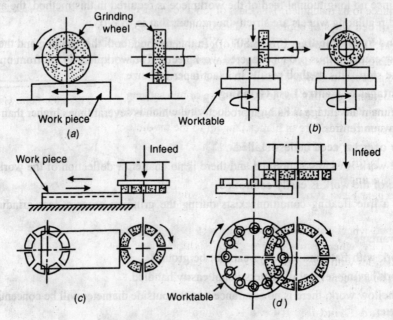

Fig. 8.82. Surface Grinding Methods.

In horizontal-spindle reciprocating table grinders, (Fig. 8.82 (*a*)), grinding is done with the periphery of a straight wheel, besides its rotary motion, the grinding wheel also has a crossfeed motion at each full stroke of the table (back and forth). The other motion is the infeed of the wheel in which it is fed to the depth of cut. Horizontal-spindle rotary-table grinders (Fig. 8.82 (*b*)) also use the periphery of the grinding wheel, but the workpieces are held, usually by a magnetic chuck, on a revolving table. Here, as before, the wheel has rotation, cross feed parallel to the surface being ground, and infeed.

The vertical-spindle machines use a cup-, cylinder-, or segmental wheel. They may be either of the reciprocating-table, Fig. 8.82 (*c*), or rotary-table, (Fig. 8.82 (*d*)). The movements of the work in grinding with the end face of the wheel are the same as when the wheel periphery is used. The primary rotary motion is wheel rotation about the vertical axis and the depth of cut is provided by vertical feed of the wheel along its axis.

Contoured surfaces are usually ground with specially trued form wheels.

Reciprocating grinders are primarily designed for producing long, straight surfaces of either flat or formed section. Rotary-table machines are adapted primarily to rapid production of flat surfaces on small and medium sized parts, singly or continuously. Vertical machines are capable of carrying segmented wheels upto 1050 mm diameters and with a 1500 mm magnetic rotary table chuck will handle work upto 2400 mm in diameter. Vertical-spindle rotary table machines are available also in multiple- spindle models for rough, semifinish, and finish grinding at one pass with automatic sizing and wheel advance as well as gauging.

5. Special Grinding Machines. Grinders of the cylindrical type also include form grinders, tool and cutter grinders for sharpening tools, cam grinding machines, gear grinding machines, Thread grinding machines, Grinding machines for grinding rolls for rolling mills, tool post grinder and so on.

(a) **Form Grinders.** Formed surfaces are finished on cylindrical or surface grinding machines depending upon the type of workpiece to be machined. This class of job also includes the grinding of bed ways of complex cross-section, Fig. 8.83.

(b) **Gear Teeth Grinding.** The teeth of gears are ground on gear grinding machines either by the generating process or by a forming process in which formed wheels are used.

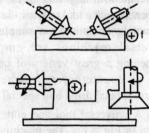

Fig. 8.83. Form Grinding.

The generating grinding method makes use of two saucer-shaped grinding wheels, Fig.8.84 (a), set so that their active faces (on the spindle side) are in planes tangent to the involute curvatures of two teeth on the gear. This is accomplished by truing the wheels to an angle equal to the pressure angle of the gear being ground. In grinding, the gear has a complex rolling (generating) motion.

In formed-wheel grinding of gears, Fig. 8.84 (b), the contour of the wheel is trued by a special fixture so that it coincides with the profile of the tooth spaces on the gear. The adjacent flanks of two teeth are ground simultaneously.

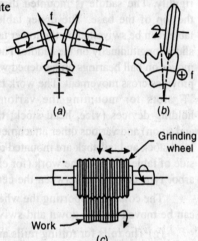

(a)   (b)

(c)

Fig. 8.84. Grinding of Gear Teeth.

(c) **Thread Grind-ing.** Thread is ground on thread grinding machines. These machines differ from conventional cylindrical grinding machines only in that the grinding wheel is either single-or multiple-rib wheel. The work is mounted between centres and is rotated at a definite speed. The ribbed grinding wheel is mounted on the wheel head spindle and is rotated by a separate drive. The wheel also has a longitudinal (axial) movement which amounts to one pitch of the thread per revolution of the work, (Fig. 8.84 c).

(d) **Cam Grinders.** An arrangement for grinding the cams of a camshaft is shown in Fig. 8.85. The grinding wheel is arranged so that it can be moved radially toward or away from the workpiece in coordination with the rotation of the workpiece. A master cam imparts the desired radial movement to the workpiece relative to the grinding wheel. The grinding wheel is continuously in contact with the cam surface during operation. The camshaft has simultaneous rotary and oscillating motion, as well as an axial motion, to obtain a fine surface finish.

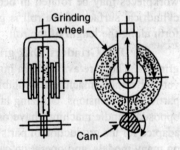

Fig. 8.85. Cam Grinding.

(e) **Tool Post Grinder.** Tool post grinder is used for miscellaneous and small grinding work on a lathe. The grinding wheel is held on the tool post and fed across the work, the regular longitudinal or compound rest feed being used. A common application of tool post grinder is the truing of lathe centres.

(f) **Tool and Cutter Grinders.** Grinding of tools and cutters is performed in special tool-grinding fixtures fitted with abrasive and diamond wheels of appropriate shapes and dimensions.

Tool grinding machines are classified as :

    1. ordinary   2. universal, and 3. special machines (for instance, drill sharpeners).

The ordinary machines, like emery sharpeners with a tool rest, are used for simple sharpening operations on simple tools. The universal machines are employed for sharpening a great variety of cutting tools, such as counterborers, reamers, milling cutters, special drills and special cutters.

A universal tool and cutter grinder is shown in Fig. 8.86. The machine has heavy box type base which provides it stability and rigidity. The saddle is mounted directly on the top of the base. The upper table (work table) can be swivelled on the lower table that slides longitudinally on the saddle. The saddle moves on ball bearings on hardened ways and provides cross movement. The work table has 'T' slots for mounting the various work holding devices (vice, head stock, tailstock and so on) and various other attachments. The head stock and tailstock are mounted on either side of table and hold the work (for example, arbor type cutters) in between the centres.

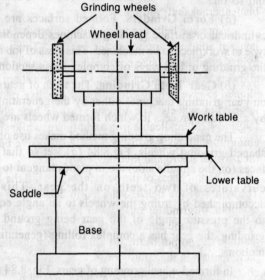

Fig. 8.86. Universal Tool and Cutter Grinder.

The column supporting the wheel head is mounted on the base on the back of the machine. It can be moved up and down and swivelled to either side of the column for varied set ups.

(*g*) The rolls for rolling mills are heavy, large diameter workpieces. The cylindrical grinding machines are specially designed for grinding them. Such workpieces can be rotated with more rigidity when mounted on a solid base. Instead of being supported between centres, these large workpieces may be rotated in bearings, which fit previously machined cylindrical surfaces. The cylindrical surface of the roll is ground by traversing the grinding wheel and its stand back and forth along the length of the roll.

(*h*) **Disk Grinders.** Disk grinders are the important machines among the production surface grinders. They are available in horizontal-spindle models with single or opposed spindles. Single vertical spindle machines available are used mainly for surfacing flat areas without maintaining particular dimensions. Utilizing large, solid abrasive disks or cylinder wheels, horizontal single or opposed spindle machines have oscillating, reciprocating, rotary, or through feeds and are ideally adapted for the production of parts requiring parallel, flat faces. Automatic work sizers are provided on many models, and operation can often be fully automatic. Work upto 350 mm in length can be ground in opposed wheel grinders with wheels upto 750 mm.

8.6.9. Coated Abrasives. Traditionally, the coated abrasives consist of abrasive grains attached to a flexible backing such as paper or cloth. They have been used for low-speed finishing of surfaces. However, with the development of stronger adhesives and backings, "Coated belts" have become important production tools. They operate at high speeds (upto 60 m/s) and have high metal removal rates, typically 200 cm³/min.cm width. Abrasive belt grinding is replacing turning, planing or milling in mass production (for example, in machining the gasket surfaces of engine blocks and cylinder heads).

Abrasive belt grinding is used for finishing metal and non-metal parts and not only for surfaces of revolution, but for flat and curved complex shaped surfaces as well, for example, turbine blades, crankshaft journals etc.

Abrasive belts are made with a cloth backing (for example, twill) by depositing grains on a layer of adhesive applied to the backing. This is called "make coat". The grains are held in place by a second layer (size coat). Bond strength is balanced to prevent stripping of new grains while allowing release of worn grains. Grains with sharp edges and of elongated shapes are electrostatically aligned to give cutting edges of low negative rake angles, spaced some 10 times farther apart than in grinding wheels. The adhesive may be hide glue etc. Aluminium oxide abrasive grains are used to grind steel, malleable iron and bronze, while silicon carbide is used for grey cast iron, brass and aluminium alloys. Multi-layer coated abrasive belts are seldom employed owing to difficulties of their manufacture and their high cost.

The thickness of the belt (together with the layer of abrasives) does not usually exceed 2 mm. The width of the belt is selected in accordance with the length of the surface to be ground. For example, in grinding surfaces of revolution (shafts) the belt width equals the length of the shaft. The length of the abrasive belt also depends upon the size of the workpiece and the requirements made to the output of the grinding operation. The longer the belt, the greater the number of grains participating in the cutting process during one revolution of the belt (for the given belt width). The coated abrasive belts used in practice have a width from 10 to 3000 mm and are from 500 to 7000 mm long.

The methods of abrasive belt grinding differ in the way the belt is pressed against the surface to be ground. Various methods are illustrated in Fig. 8.87. Depending upon its shape, the surface can be ground with the unsupported section of the belt, with a part supported by the driving contact wheel or by an intermediate contact roller whose shape is followed by the belt.

Grinding with the unsupported section of the abrasive belt has the highest production capacity as the belt has an increased area of contact, covering the largest part of the workpiece surface. This enables all kinds of surfaces, with the exception of cylindrical and curvilinear surfaces with a small radius of curvature, to be ground.

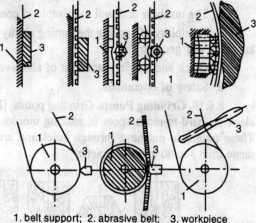

1. belt support;   2. abrasive belt;   3. workpiece

Fig. 8.87. Abrasive Belt Grinding.

Grinding with a part of the belt supported by a contact wheel requires a much higher pressure to attain the same output. The output in this case is inversely proportional to the diameter of the contact wheel. It is not advisable, however, to use wheels less than 150 mm in diameter.

Sometimes two supports, arranged at the two sides of the workpiece, are more efficient than a contact wheel. They increase the angle of contact with the workpiece and, consequently, the area of contact. The tension of an abrasive belt is adjusted by idlers.

The contact pressure between the abrasive belt and the surface being ground should preferably be :

$$0.05 \text{ to } 0.2 \text{ N/mm}^2 \text{ for steel and cast iron}$$

and $\not> 0.04$ for non- ferrous alloys and aluminium

Cutting speeds depend upon the workpiece material, type of operation being performed (roughing or finishing) and other factors. In rough abrasive belt grinding of external surfaces of revolution on work-pieces of steel with a tensile strength of less than or equal to 800 N/mm^2 the recommended cutting speed is 25 to 30 m/s and steels with tensile strength greater than 800 N/mm^2 and for cast iron and bronze workpieces, it is 15 to 20 m/s, and for grinding aluminium, it is 45 to 50 m/s.

Mineral oils, kerosene, emulsions and fatty oil pastes are used as cutting fluids in abrasive belt grinding operations.

Advantages

1. The working surface of the abrasive belt is much greater than that of the grinding wheel which promotes dissipation of the heat generated during grinding. This lengthens belt life and almost completely excludes distortion of the workpiece.

2. More uniform surface of the belt in comparison with a grinding wheel, as a result of uniform application of the abrasive grains by the electrostatic field method so that they are oriented vertically and embedded in the glue covered backing.

3. Increased number of abrasive grains per unit area compared to that of the grinding wheel, thereby increasing the grinding capacity and output.

4. Absence of vibration and impact loads, ensuring a higher class of surface finish.

5. The machine and tool are simple in construction and are inexpensive.

6. Possibility of varying the cutting ability of the belt by selecting a contact roller of proper hardness and geometry.

7. Quick and easy replacement of abrasive belts.

8. Safety of operations.

8.6.10. Grinding Points. Grinding points, [Fig. 8.88] are employed for internal grinding and to clean up hard-to-reach spots in making moulds and dies, when grinding wheels are unsuitable. These points do not have through holes and are cemented onto a special stem. Grinding points range from 3 to 40 mm in diameter.

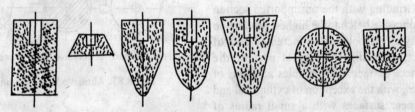

Fig. 8.88. Grinding Points.

8.6.11. Grinding Segments. A segmental grinding wheel consists of several abrasive segments, clamped in some manner in chuck. The segments have a length from 125 to 300 mm. Some of the shapes of the grinding segments are shown in Fig. 8.89. Segmental wheels are used in surface grinding. An essential advantage of a segmental wheel is that a damaged segment can be readily replaced, without discarding the whole wheel. The spaces between the segments facilitate the delivery of cutting fluid to the grinding zone and the disposal of chips and worn-out particles of the wheel. Owing to the smaller area of contact with the wheel, the workpiece is heated less in grinding with a segmental wheel.

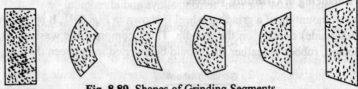

Fig. 8.89. Shapes of Grinding Segments.

8.6.12. Abrasive Sticks. Abrasive sticks are used for hand fitting operations and for honing and super-finishing operations performed in special machines for micro-finishing. The various shapes of the abrasive sticks are shown in Fig. 8.90. Honing and super-finishing are done with sticks of square (first), flat (second) and special flat (last one) honing shapes, which are mounted in special heads.

Fig. 8.90. Abrasive Sticks.

8.6.13. Grinding Process Variables

Wheel Speeds. Proper grinding-wheel speeds have been fairly well established, and most machines can be adjusted to attain the desired cutting efficiency. Major problem in the past has been with the internal grinding where proper peripheral wheel speeds were difficult to obtain. Today, however, high-cycle, direction-driven wheel heads are rapidly supplanting previous types. Efficient peripheral wheel speeds, observing manufacturers' maximum limits for specific wheels, are generally as follows :

Types of Grinding	speed, m/s
Cylindrical grinding	
Resinoid	27.5 – 60.0
Vitrified	27.5 – 32.5
Surface grinding	20.0 – 25.0
Internal grinding	10.0 – 30.0
Diamond wheels	25.0 – 32.5

Work Speeds. For obtaining the desired finish as well as maximum stock removal commensurate with good wheel life, proper work speeds are necessary. At the line of cutting, the work and the abrasive wheel pass in opposite directions except in internal centreless grinding. Work speed at this point should be set according to the material being ground. The low end of this range is used for roughing cuts and the high end for finishing.

Material	speed,, m/s
Soft steel	0.15 – 0.25
Hard steel	0.35 – 0.50
Cast iron	1.00 – 2.00
Aluminum	0.50

Stock Removal. Most efficient stock removal is obtained with coarse-grit wheels, and while surface finish is distinctly rougher, commercially acceptable dimensional accuracy can be maintained. Maximum economy in manufacture thus depends to a large extent upon judicious selection of surface finish. The following stock removal per single pass indicates the comparative rates, though these will vary somewhat for different materials :

Rough grinding	0.05 – 0.50 mm
Semifinish grinding	0.025 – 0.25 mm
Finish grinding	0.0125 – 0.125 mm

8.6.14. Balancing of Grinding Wheels:

One way of mounting of a grinding wheel is shown in Fig. 8.91. It is clamped by flanges (one each on its either side) directly on the spindle. Thick compressible washers (0.5 to 3 mm thick) made of cardboard, rubber or leather etc. should be inserted in between the flanges and the wheel.

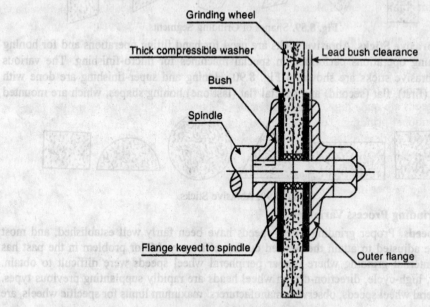

Fig. 8.91. Mounting of Grinding Wheel.

The grinding wheels rotate at very high speeds. Therefore, any out of true and out of balance wheel will produce large unbalanced forces which will lead to excessive vibrations. This will result in poor surface finish of workpiece and reduced wheel life. Thus, before mounting on the grinding wheel spindle, each wheel with its sleeve should be balanced. The test should be carried out after truing up the wheel face. The wheel is mounted at the centre of a perfectly straight and round arbor. The assembly is then rested on straight knife edged ways or roller rests of the balanced machine, Fig. 8.92. Out of balanced wheel will not remain stationary. It will come to rest with its heavy side undernearth. The wheel is balanced by cutting some of the lead from the heavy side of the bush.

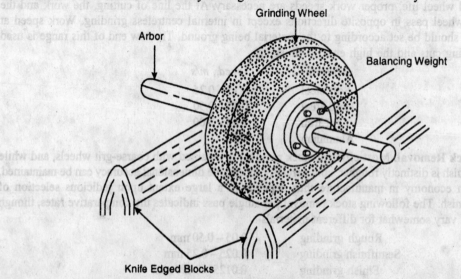

Fig. 8.92. Static Balancing Device.

Another method of balancing the wheel is shifting three balanced weights in an annular groove of the wheel sleeve (or mounting flange). These adjustable segments can be fixed around a circle at any position by tightening the screws.

8.6.15. High Speed Grinding : Conventional grinding is basically a finishing process. It is employed to obtain high dimensional and geometric accuracies so as to obtain a good surface finish. Due to this, the metal removal rate (MRR) in conventional grinding process is quite low as compared to turning and milling operations. In high speed grinding, it is possible to achieve increased MRR comparable to turning and milling operations and at the same time obtain accuracy and surface finish equivalent to that for conventional grinding.

High speed grinding (High-efficiency grinding) differs from conventional grinding in that the grinding wheel speeds are quite high (usually 60 m/s and above upto 80 m/s) as compared to about 30 m/s for conventional grinding. The work speeds and indeed rates are also comparably higher since the force on the work is reduced (from the power, force, velocity relationship).

High speed grinding is not a simple matter of increasing the wheel speed on conventional grinding machines. The process variables (wheel speed, work speed and infeed rate) must be compatible with the operating variables, such as machine condition, wheel structure, coolant application, surface quality required and the hardness of the work-material.

The grinding machines used for high speed grinding must be rigid (that is, with vibration free structures) and must have higher machine and spindle stiffness, powerful wheel and work drives and proper and strong safety guards.

The abrasive used for fabricating high speed grinding wheel is Al_2O_3 and the bond used is either a special high strength vitrified bond or polyurathene bond.

Because of the increased metal removal rate, the wheel structure has to be quite open. The problem of wheel loading is less with open structure. The feeding of the coolent is also more efficient with open structure. To ensure proper cooling of the interface, a high pressure coolant systems with special nozzle is used. Also, an oil coolant in place of an emulsion will greatly increase the metal removal rate.

To increase the metal-removal rate, the infeed rate must be increased proportionately with the wheel speed to present a full layer of material for each revolution.

From above, it is clear that high speed grinding results in:

1. Reduced thickness of chip removed by individual abrasive grain leading to reduced grinding forces.

2. Increased MRR.

3. Increased grinding ratio.

4. Improved surface finish.

8.6.16. Abrasive Machining: The conventional grinding process being a finishing process, its metal removal rate is very less. When the metal removal rate is the main consideration and surface finish and accuracy are secondary, such grinding operations are included under the term "Abrasive machining". It includes all the operations where cost is a major factor in deciding between grinding and other machining methods. Increased metal Removal Rate can be obtained by increasing process parameters (feed and/or depth of cut). The process compares favourably with other machining processes such as milling, turning and broaching etc. The geometric tolerances and surface quality obtained are of the same order as those obtained by these machining operations. However, the power consumption per unit MRR is about 3 times in Abrasive machining as compared to milling. But it is much less as compared to conventional grinding process.

However, Abrasive machining has become competitive with other machining operations due to the following factors :

1. Any material, such as metals, ceramics, refractory alloys and super-alloys can be machined by this process.

2. Work surface conditions do not have the adverse effects on the process.

3. Rough and finishing cuts can be done in one operation.

4. Handling cost is greatly reduced, because the machine set up is not changed for rough and finish cuts.

5. Work-holding devices/fixtures can be eliminated or made simpler as compared to other machining processes such as milling.

6. Less machining allowance needs to be allowed for abrasive machining than for other machining processes. There is thus initial saving (in material).

The machines used for abrasive machining are grinding machines of high power and rigidity.

Product Applications : Valve manifolds, cylinder heads, steam turbine casings, Aluminium piston skirts, Steering knuckles.

PROBLEMS

1. Define grinding operation.
2. What is the difference between 'rough' grinding and 'precision' grinding?
3. Why is grinding so important in modern production ?
4. Why the natural abrasives are not suitable for making grinding wheels?
5. How is aluminium oxide abrasive produced ? Write its field of application.
6. How is silicon carbide abrasive produced ? Write its field of application.
7. Under what conditions are diamond, boron carbide and cubic boron nitride used as abrasive materials for making grinding wheels ?
8. What is meant by 'grain size' of an abrasive material ?
9. Discuss the various types of bonding materials used for making grinding wheels ?
10. Define a grinding wheel.
11. Discuss the various methods of making grinding wheels.
12. Sketch the various shapes of grinding wheels and write their fields of application.
13. What is meant by "grade" and "structure" of a grinding wheel ?
14. What is meant by standard marking of grinding wheels ?
15. How the grinding wheel is selected for a particular job ?
16. What is meant by dressing and truing of grinding wheels ?
17. Define "grinding ratio".
18. Sketch and explain the working of an external cylindrical grinding machine.
19. Sketch and explain the three methods of cylindrical grinding.
20. What is the difference between plain and universal cylindrical grinders?
21. Describe in detail how an internal grinder operates.
22. What are the advantages and disadvantages of centreless grinding ?
23. Sketch and explain the three methods of external cylindrical centreless grinding.
24. Sketch and explain internal centre less grinding process.

25. Sketch and explain the various methods of surface grinding.

26. How the jobs are held during surface grinding operation ?

27. Sketch and explain the following grinding processes : Form grinding, Gear tooth grinding, Thread grinding and cam grinding.

28. What is a tool post grinder ?

29. What kind of grinding can be done on the lathe ?

30. Sketch and discuss a tool and cutter grinder.

31. What are disk grinders ?

32. What are coated abrasives ?

33. Explain abrasive belt grinding .

34. Write the drawbacks of abrasive belt grinding.

35. Discuss the various grinding process variables.

36. Write a short note on : High speed grinding.

37. Write a brief note on :- Abrasive machining.

8.7. BROACHING MACHINES

Broaching is a process of machining a surface with a special multipoint tool called a "broach", whose teeth remove the whole machining allowance in a single stroke. The process differs from other machining processes in that the only motion is the primary cutting motion of the tool. The feed is obtained by placing the teeth progressively deeper within the tool, thus, each tool edge takes off a successive layer of the material. The primary cutting motion is translational along the broach axis.

Broaching is used for machining through holes of any cross sectional shape, straight and helical slots, external surfaces of various shape, external and internal toothed gears, splines, keyways and rifling. Broaching of inside surfaces is called "internal or hole broaching" and that of the outside surface as "Surface broaching". Typical internal broaching operations are : the sizing of holes, cutting of serrations, straight or helical splines, keyways and gun rifling.

Although the cutting speeds used in broaching are relatively low (2 to 15 m per min), the production capacity is very high since the total length of the cutting edges that are simultaneously in operation is very great. The output in broaching can be raised still higher if broaching machines with a continuous working motion are used, in conjunction with automatic workpiece loading and unloading.

Owing to the high output and machining accuracy, as well as fine surface finish produced, broaching is finding wider and wider application in the engineering and metal-working industries. Broaches are expensive tools, however, and their use is justified, in the main, only in large lot and mass production.

8.7.1. Details of an Internal Broach (Hole Broach). A typical internal broach is shown in Fig. 8.93. To machine an internal hole, the broach is gripped by a puller at the shank end. The front pilot centres the broach in the hole before the teeth begin to cut. The front taper (5 to 20 mm) facilitates the insertion of the front pilot in the hole. The first set of teeth behind the front pilot, removes most of the material and are called "roughing teeth". Theses are followed by a few teeth called "semi-finishing teeth" where the depth of cut of individual tooth is quite small. Finally, there are finishing or sizing teeth which are all of the same size and have the shape of the finished hole. Sometimes, a few burnishing teeth may be provided after the finishing teeth. These have no cutting edges but are button shaped and from 0.025 to 0.075 mm larger than the size of the hole. The resulting rubbing action smooths and sizes the hole. They are used primarily on cast iron and non-ferrous metals. The "rear pilot" supports the broach after the last tooth leaves the hole.

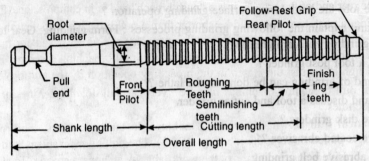

Fig. 8.93. A typical Internal Broach.

(a) **Tooth Elements.** The tooth shape of a typical broach is shown in Fig. 8.94. The front rake angle (face angle or hook angle) refers to rake angle of a single point cutting tool and the back -off angle (relief angle) is provided to prevent rubbing of tool with workpiece.

Hook angle: 15° to 20° for steel

6° to 8° for C.I.

Back-off angle: 1° to 3°

(b) **Material.** High speed steel (H.S.S.) is by far the most widely used material for the broaches. Brazed carbides or disposable inserts are sometimes used for the cutting edges when machining cast iron parts which require close tolerances and production rates. Carbide tools are also used to an advantage on steel casting to offset the damaging effect of local hard spots.

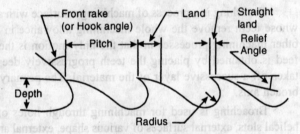

Fig. 8.94. Tooth Shape of a Broach.

(c) **Construction.** A broach may be either solid or assembled or built up from shells, replaceable sections or inserted teeth. Replaceable sections, teeth or shells make a broach easier to repair.

8.7.2. Types of Broaching Machines. A broaching machine consists of a work-holding device (fixture), a broaching tool, a drive mechanism and a suitable frame. The broach is usually secured in the main slide of the broaching machine and travels with the slide.

A broaching machine may be a horizontal or a vertical one depending upon whether the slide travels in the horizontal plane or in the vertical plane. A horizontal machine has the following characteristics :

(i) Any part of it, especially, the work station can be reached readily from the floor.

(ii) A long slide can be supported at many points and levelled to keep it straight.

A vertical machine has the following characteristics :

(a) It occupies less floor area.

(b) For a machine with a long stroke, a pit should be sunk or there should be a platform for the operator to reach the workstation.

1. Internal Broaching Machines. We have pull broaching machines and push broaching machines and these machines may be horizontal or vertical. In pull broaching machines, the force is applied to the shank and the body of the broach is in tension, (Fig. 8.95 (*a*,*b*)). If the force is applied to the rear end of the broach, it is a "push broach" and is in compression, (Fig. 8.95 (*c*)). To avoid buckling, a push broach should be shorter than a pull broach and its length usually does not increase 15 diameters. A vertical push broaching machine is mostly used for internal broaching such as hole sizing, and key way cutting. In horizontal pull broaching machine, Fig. 8.95 (*a*), the work is held tightly against the platen in the broaching operation by the cutting force.

Vertical pull broaching machines may be : vertical pull-down machines or vertical pull up broaching machines.

(*a*) **Vertical Pull Down Broaching Machines.** In these machines, the broach, instead of being pushed, is pulled through the job (Fig. 8.95 *b*). The pulling mechanism is in the base of the machine. The broach is suspended above the work-table by an upper carriage. To start the broaching process, the broach is lowered through the workpiece held in a fixture on the worktable. The broach is automatically engaged by the pulling mechanism and is pulled down through the job. After the operation is completed, the broach returns to its starting position.

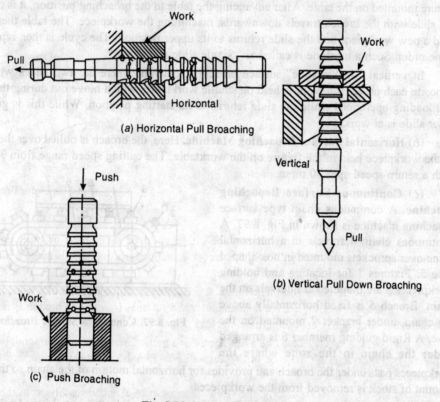

(*a*) Horizontal Pull Broaching

(*b*) Vertical Pull Down Broaching

(*c*) Push Broaching

Fig. 8.95. Internal Broaching.

(*b*) **Vertical Pull Up Broaching Machine.** Here, the pulling mechanism is above the worktable and the broach is in the base of the machine. The broach enters the job held against the underside of the table and is pulled upward. At the end of the operation, the work is free and falls down into a container.

2. Surface Broaching Machines. External surface broaches are classified in respect to the surface they machine into : flat (slab), peripheral and contour broaches. The common surface broaching machines are discussed below :

(*a*) **Vertical Broaching Machine.** A vertical broaching machine, (Fig. 8.96) has a box shape column 5 which houses electric drive 6 with the units of hydraulic drive. Broaching tools 4 are mounted on slide 3 which is hydraulically driven and accurately guided on the column ways. Slide with the broaches travels at various speeds controlled by the hydraulic drive. Its stroke is adjusted to suit the broaching operation to be per-formed. The slide has a rapid return stroke.

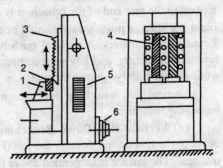

Fig. 8.96. Vertical Surface Broaching Machine.

The worktable 1 is mounted on the base in front of the column. It can be retracted to unload and load the broaching fixture and advanced to a preset broaching position. Workpiece 2 is held in a broaching fixture mounted on the table. After advancing the table to the broaching position, it is clamped and the slide with the broach travels downwards, machining the workpiece. The table then recedes to load a new workpiece and the slide returns to its upper position. The cycle is then repeated in the same order. Such a machine is called as "Single slide machine".

In vertical "double slide" surface broaching machine, there are two slides which operate opposite each other. The work is held on shuttle worktables which move out during the unloading and loading operations while the slide returns to its starting position. While this is going on, the other slide is at work.

(*b*) **Horizontal Surface Broaching Machine.** Here, the broach is pulled over the top surface of the workpiece held in the fixture on the worktable. The cutting speed range from 3 to 12 mpm with a return speed upto 30 mpm.

(*c*) **Continuous Surface Broaching Machine.** A continuous chain type surface broaching machine is shown in Fig. 8.97. A continuous chain 4 travels in a horizontal plane over sprockets mounted in box-shaped base 2. Fixtures 1 for locating and holding workpieces 3 are mounted at intervals on the chain. Broach 5 is fixed horizontally above the chain, under bracket 7 mounted on the base. A Rigid guiding member 6 is arranged under the chain in the zone where the

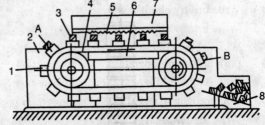

Fig. 8.97. Continuous Surface Broaching Machine.

workpieces pass under the broach and provides for horizontal motion of the chain so that a definite amount of stock is removed from the workpieces.

The workpieces are loaded into the fixtures at station A where they are clamped either manually or automatically. The workpieces, located and clamped on the travailing chain, passes between the broach and the guiding plate and then are automatically unclamped and ejected at station B where they drop into hopper 8 of the machine. Continuous surface broaching machine increases the productivity.

8.7.3. Broaching Drives. The drives used to reciprocate the broaching tools are : Hydraulic and Electro-mechanical. Hydraulic drives cost less, give smoother action and are more popular. An electro- mechanical drive employs a screw engaged with a recirculating ball nut. This type of drive is preferred for longer strokes and high speed machines.

Most H.S.S. broaches cut at less than 0.15 m/s and the carbide broaches around 0.50 to 1.50 m/s.

8.7.4. Size of Broaching Machines. The size of a broaching machine is given by two numbers : $a \times b$ where

a = Force the machine can apply in tonnes

b = stroke of the slide, mm.

8.7.5. Advantages of Broaching

1. Rapid operation since the whole machining allowance is removed in a single stroke of the broach.

2. Very high production capacity.

3. High degree of surface quality.

4. The process can be used both for internal as well as external machining.

Limitations

1. Cost of tool is very high.

2. A separate broach has to be made for each shape and size, therefore, broaching is primarily a method for mass production.

3. The workpiece must be rigidly held and the broach firmly guided.

4. Large amounts of metals can not be removed.

PROBLEMS

1. Define a broaching operation.
2. Sketch and discuss a typical Internal Broach.
3. Sketch a typical tooth shape of a Broach.
4. Write briefly about the materials of broaching tools.
5. Write briefly about the construction of broaching tools.
6. With the help of neat sketches, explain the horizontal pull broaching operation and the vertical push broaching operation.
7. With the help of a neat sketch, discuss the working of a surface broaching machine.
8. With the help of a neat sketch, discuss the working of a continuous surface broaching machine.
9. Write the advantages and limitations of broaching process.

8.8. SAWING MACHINES

The various construction materials (stock) available in shop stores are of standard forms and sizes. The stock is cut to correct length to make a product. The operation of cutting stock to correct length is called "sawing". The process can be accomplished either by hand (hand hacksaw) or by power operated machines. Sawing by hand is very slow and laborious. These troubles are overcome by using power operated sawing machines.

All the sawing machines use saw blades to cut the stock. Although different in overall form, they all contain a series of cutting teeth that operate in the same basic way. When the teeth are laid out into a straight line, one obtains a hacksaw, or, if the sawblade is flexible and made into an endless loop, a band saw. All these tools are form tools and the cut progresses by positive infeed or by the pressure exerted on the tool.

8.8.1. Saw Blade. The important features of a saw blade are : Material, Tooth form, Tooth set, Tooth spacing and Size.

1. Material. Blades are made of carbon steel, Tungsten alloy steel, High Speed tungsten steel, Molybdenum steel, High speed molybdenum steel and Cemented carbide. Most saws are solid, some have teeth of a hard material backed by flexible steel, and many have tipped or inserted teeth.

2. Tooth Form. Two commonly used tooth forms for saw blades are shown in Fig. 8.98. The straight tooth form, (Fig. 8.98 (*a*)) is suitable for finer pitches whereas the tooth form shown in (Fig. 8.98 (*b*)) is used with coarser pitches. This tooth form is theoretically better because the cutting edges are backed up by more metal. However, it is more difficult to obtain this tooth form on smaller teeth.

3. Tooth Set. Tooth set refers to how the teeth are bent or offset to one side or the other, and the amount of the offset. The set makes the cut or "kerf" (width of cut) wider than the blade thickness so that the blade will not stick or bind. This makes cutting much easier. We have three types of tooth sets, Fig. 8.99, which are used as per tooth spacing or pitch.

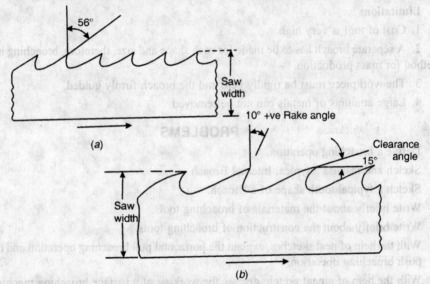

Fig. 8.98. Tooth Forms.

(*a*) **Straight Set.** When the teeth are offset alternately to the right and left, (Fig. 8.99 (*a*)), it is called straight set or alternate set. This set is most suitable for non-ferrous metals and non-metals, and hacksaw blades with p = 1.6 mm

(*b*) **Wavy Set.** When several teeth are offset (mainly, every two consecutive teeth) in one direction, and then several are offset in the opposite direction, it is called a wavy set, (Fig. 8.99 (*c*)). This set is employed with small teeth for sawing thin sheets and sections.

(*c*) **Raker Set.** One tooth is offset to the left, the next tooth is offset to the right and the third tooth is unbent. This form is repeated and we get a raker set, Fig. 8.99(*b*). This set is used for cutting ferrous metals unless the metal thickness is too thin.

4. Tooth Spacing. Tooth spacing or pitch has an important influence upon saw performance. Selection of pitch for a sawing job will depend upon the length of saw in contact with the job and the work material. Longer saw cuts require coarser pitched teeth because these cuts will produce longer chips needing more space for chips between the teeth. Softer materials will also produce longer chips and so will need coarser pitched saws. Finer pitched teeth are used for sawing harder materials. For cutting thin workpiece or thin sections, at least 2 or 3 teeth should always be in contact with the workpiece to avoid snagging of the teeth.

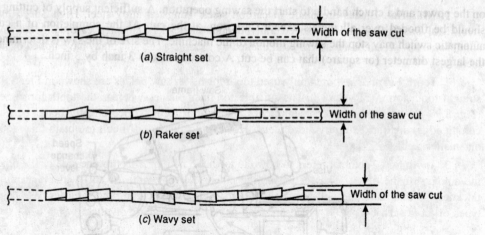

Fig. 8.99. Tooth Sets.

The commonly used hand hacksaw blades are furnished with 14, 18, 24 and 32 teeth per inch. Power hacksaw blades are coarser (from 4 to 14 teeth per inch). Band saws are also with coarser pitches and may have as few as 2 teeth per inch. The pitch may run from 0.20 inch on small circular saws to 2 inches on large diameter saws for soft materials.

5. Size. The size of hand hacksaw blades is :

thickness = 0.64 mm, width = 12.7 mm

Length = 254 and 304.8 mm.

The size of power hacksaw blades is

thickness = 1.27 to 2.54 mm, width = 25.4 to 50.8 mm

Length = 304.8 to 609.6 mm.

The heavier the cut, the longer should be the blade. Most band saws are welded in continuous

loops and commonly are from 0.020 to 0.060 inch thick and $\frac{1}{16}$ to 1 inch (a few upto 2 inch) wide.

The narrower blades are required to cut around small radii. Circular cold saws are tooth disks from 1/32 to 1/12 inch thick and 8 to 80 inch in diameter.

6. Cutting Speed. Cutting speed for tungsten H.S.S. blades :

Mild steel	= 0.75 m/s
Cast iron	= 0.50 m/s
Brass and	= 1.5 m/s Aluminium
Bronze	= 1.25 m/s
Thin sections,	= 1.5 m/s. pipes and tubes

8.8.2. Types of Sawing Machines. The common sawing machines are discussed below :

1. Power Hacksaw (Reciprocating Sawing Machine). The power hack saw is a power driven tool for cutting off stock, (Fig. 8.100). The machine consists of a base with a worktable and vise on it. The vise is adjustable for cutting at right angles and at several other angles. A saw frame holds the blade. In operation, the stock is held in a vise. The sawing takes place only on the forward, or draw, stroke. The frame lifts up slightly on the return stroke. There are switches to turn on the power and a clutch handle to start the sawing operation. A sufficient supply of cutting fluid should be flooded over all metals except Cast iron, at the cut. At the completion of a cut, an automatic switch may stop the sawing motion of the machine. The size of the saw is determined by the largest diameter (or square) that can be cut. A common size is 3 inch by 3 inch.

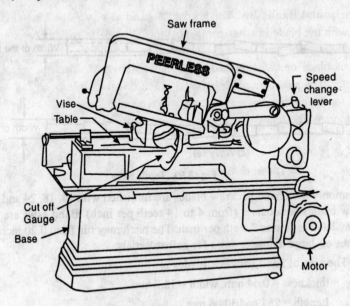

Fig. 8.100. Power Hacksaw.

2. Circular Sawing (Cold Sawing Machine). A saw for cold sawing of a metal is a profile sharpened cutter for milling a narrow slit. Saws of small diameter may be made in the form of a solid disk with teeth located on the periphery. At present, circular saws upto 250 mm in diameter are usually made solid with integral teeth. Circular saws over 250 mm in diameter are of either segmental or inserted-blade construction. The working of a circular sawing machine is illustrated in Fig. 8.101.

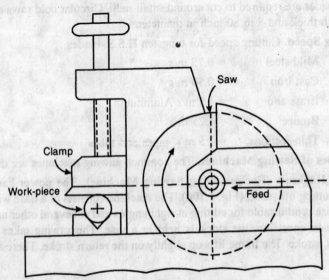

Fig. 8.101. Circular Sawing Machine.

3. Band Saws. Band saws with an endless saw blade are being used to a greater and greater extent for cut off and straight sawing operations for metals since they enable the width of the kerf to be substantially reduced. They are used in special power bandsawing machines. A continuous saw blade runs over the rims of two wheels on the machine.

(*a*) **Horizontal Band Saw.** The horizontal band saw is a small metal cutting band saw that can be used with the blade in a horizontal position, (Fig. 8.102). The saw consists of a base with a worktable and vise. The saw frame is hinged at one end. On the frame are two wheels over which the continuous blade operates. Most of the blade is covered. Machine size is determined by the wheel diameter. The saw carried on a frame is fed downward through the workpiece held in the vise. Except for the continuous cutting action of the endless band saw blade, horizontal band saws incorporate most of the features of the power hacksaw.

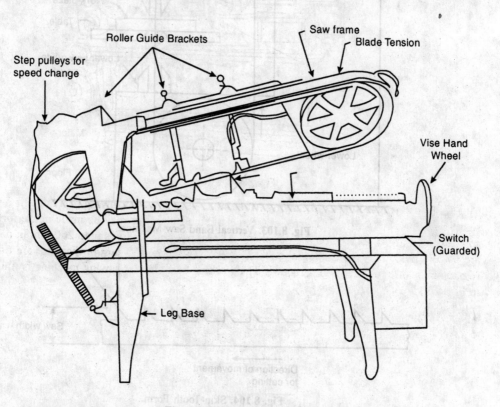

Fig. 8.102. Horizontal band Saw.

(*b*) **Vertical Band Saw.** In this machine, (Fig. 8.103), the endless band saw blade runs over two wheels in a vertical position. Saw guides help support the sides of the saw band near the sawing. Cutting speeds may range from 0.25 m/s to 7.5 m/s depending upon the metal to be cut. The blade tooth form, (Fig. 8.98 (*a*)), is commonly used for band saws. However, for sawing softer metals such as aluminium and lead alloys, the tooth form shown in Fig. 8.104 (buttress or skip-tooth form) is employed. This provides more space for chips and, therefore, the saw will not become overloaded. In the Fig. 8.103, the power is given to the power wheel from a variable speed motor.

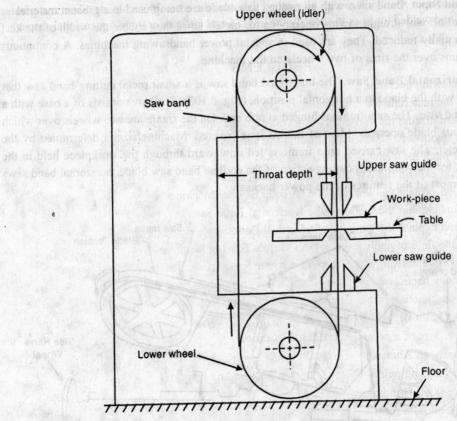

Fig. 8.103. Vertical Band Saw Machine.

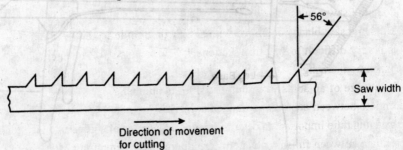

Fig. 8.104. Skin-Tooth Form.

8.8.3. Field of Application of Sawing Machines. Hacksaw machines are relatively slow and find usage in low-output production and toolroom and maintenance work.

Cold Saw. Where production is in the medium or high ranges, cutoff and similar sawing operations are normally done on the cold saw. Manually operated cold saws are used for low production work and automatic-cycle and special units are used in the higher production ranges. Much larger sizes and cuts are possible than with hack saws. Standard machines commonly available employ blades with diameters ranging from 1016 to 1143 mm. Some machines use blades as much as 3.05 m in diameter. A typical machine with a 1143 mm blade will cut a full 406.4 mm square or a rectangle 330 × 644 mm.

Band Saw. Capable of cuts other than straight, the band saw is useful for production operations other than cut off. With conventional plain contour band sawing, it is practicable to produce blank parts in quantities upto about 500 pieces, eliminated the usual die costs for such parts. Sheet material is compressed and welded together to simplify the sawing, and intricate or three-dimensional shapes are practical.

PROBLEMS

1. Define "sawing operation".
2. Discuss the materials for saw blades.
3. Sketch and discuss the various tooth-forms used for saw blades.
4. What is "tooth-set" ? Sketch and discuss the various tooth-sets used for saw blades.
5. How the pitch for a saw blade is selected ?
6. Sketch and explain the working of a Power Hacksaw.
7. Sketch and explain the working of a Circular Sawing Machine.
8. Sketch and explain the working of a Horizontal Band Saw.
9. Sketch and explain the working of a Vertical Band Saw.
10. Discuss the field of applications of the Various Sawing Machines.
11. Explain why broaching is a commonly used process ? Give some typical applications.
12. Explain why hacksaws are not as productive as horizontal band saws ?
13. What is the function of burnishing teeth on broaches ?
14. Write briefly on Broaching drives.
15. How is the size of a broaching machine specified ?
16. Write briefly on Abrasive sticks.
17. What are grinding points ? Sketch the various grinding points.
18. Write briefly on Grinding segments.
19. What is skip-tooth form ? For which materials it is preferred ?
20. Explain why hacksaws are not as productive as band saws ?
21. Why do some saw blades have staggered teeth ?
22. Why are some saw blades equipped with H.S.S. or carbide teeth ?
23. Why is it very difficult to saw thin sections ?
24. What is friction sawing ?
25. How is the size of an abrasive grain related to its number ?
26. Differentiate between coated and bonded abrasives ?
27. Is the grinding ratio important in determining the economics of a grinding operations ? Explain.
28. Differentiate between finishing by form grinding and by generating.
29. Why are speeds so much higher in grinding than in cutting ?
30. What are the advantages and disadvantages of puss and push broaches ?
31. Under what conditions broaching would be the preferred method of machining ?
32. Explain why the cutting tool many easily chip or break during climb milling ?
33. Differentiate between form milling and straddle milling.
34. How are T-solts machined ?
35. What is the difference between a feed rod and the lead screw in the case of a lathe ?
36. How is the boring mill different from a lathe.
37. Explain the functions of Saddle on a lathe.
38. What are the ways in a lathe ?

39. Differentiate between a blind hole and a through hole.
40. What are the advantages of having a hollow spindle in the headstock of a lathe ?
41. Give the Main Specifications of Grinding Machines.

Grinding Machine	**Main Specifications**
External Cylindrical Grinder	Swing ϕ, Centre Distance
Internal Cylindrical Grinder	Max. Grinding Bore ϕ
Centreless Grinder, External	Job ϕ
Centreless Grinder, Internal	Bore ϕ
Surface Grinder, Reciprocating Table	Table Size (Length × Width)
Surface Grinder Rotary Table	Table ϕ

42. Give the Main Specifications of Sawing Machines.

Machine	**Main Specifications**
Power Hacksaw Machines	Job ϕ
Circular Sawing Machine	Blade ϕ
Band Saw (Hor., Vert)	Job ϕ (Throat Depth)
Friction Sawing Machines	Job Size
Abrasive wheel cut-off Machines	Wheel ϕ
Pipe and Tube Cutting Machines	Job ϕ
Jig sawing and Filing Machines (Reciprocating)	Table ϕ

43. **What is Trepanning ?**

It is an operation used for drilling deep holes of 50 mm in ϕ and above, without twist drill, Fig. 8.51 (*c*). The tool comprises an annular body with single point cutters arranged uniformly on its periphery, which can number 6 to 12 for tools with 30 to 150 mm ϕ. Also, See Art 8.3.8.

44. **What are Flat Drills ?**

Flat drills or spade drills (the point of these drills being in the shape of a spade, Fig. 8.105), are used to drill holes upto 25 mm ϕ in non-critical applications, mainly hard forgings and castings. The point angle is 118° to 120° and the clearance angle is 10° to 20°. These drills come in two designs : Two ways, Fig. 105(*a*) and one way, Fig. 105(*b*). The cutting angle for one way drill is 75° to 90° for steel and 45° to 60° for non-ferrous materials. For two way drill, this angle is 120° to 135°. These drills (made of alloy steel and H.S.S.) do not stand high cutting speed (drilling is affected by Ratchet drills and plain hand drills) and can not be used to drill deep holes as chips do not come out of the hole, but keep rotating with the tool and spoil the hole surface. Also, they wear out rapidly and loose cutting ability and tend to wander.

(a) Two-way

Point   Shank

(b) A one-way

Fig. 8.105. Flat drills

Chapter
9

Unconventional Manufacturing Methods

9.1. GENERAL

Unconventional manufacturing methods fall under two categories : Unconventional machining methods and Unconventional forming methods.

(*a*) **Unconventional Machining Methods.** The unconventional machining methods are also called "Non-traditional Machining Methods, (NTMM)", also known as "New Technology".

The basic principle of metal removal in the conventional methods of machining involves the use of some sort of tool which is harder than the workpiece and is subject to wear. The metal removal is by mechanical energy through the use of physical force (the tool and the workpiece being in direct contact with each other), which shears the chips. That is, the conventional machining methods involve removal of metal by compression shear chip formation. The conventional machining methods have the following inherent drawbacks :

(*i*) Metal removal by chip formation is an expensive and difficult process.

(*ii*) Chips produced during the process are an unwanted by-product.

(*iii*) Removal of these chips and their disposal and recycling is a very cumbersome procedure, involving energy and money.

(*iv*) Proper holding of the workpiece and to avoid its distortion are very important, due to the very large cutting forces involved.

(*v*) Due to the large cutting forces and large amount of heat gene- rated at the tool-workpiece interface, undesirable deformation and residual stresses are set up in the workpiece. These undesirable effects have to be removed afterwards.

(*vi*) Delicate components, for example, semi-conductor 'chip' can not be produced by conventional machining methods.

On the other hand, the NTMM are generally non-mechanical, don't produce chips or a lay pattern on the work surface and often involve new energy modes. There is no direct physical contact between the tool and the workpiece and so, the tool need not be harder than the job.

The impetus for developing most of these new methods was the search for better ways of machining complex shapes (dies, moulds etc.) in hard, high strength temperature resistant alloys, such as nimonics, carbides, titanium alloys, hastalloy, nitralloy, waspalloy, stainless steels and heat resisting steels etc. The use of these difficult to machine materials has lead to rapid developments in the aerospace and nuclear engineering industries. Many of these materials also find applications in other industries, owing to their high strength-to-weight ratio, hardness and heat-resisting qualities.

The conventional machining processes, inspite of recent technical advancements, are inadequate to machine these materials economically. Besides, machining of these materials into complex shapes is difficult, time consuming and sometimes impossible. The NTMM have been developed to overcome all these difficulties. They also meet better dimensional and accuracy requirements.

Classification of NTMM. The Non-traditional Machining Methods are classified according to the major energy sources employed in machining.

1. Thermal Energy Methods. In these methods, the thermal energy is employed to melt and vaporize tiny particles of work-material by concentrating the heat energy on a small area of the workpiece. The required shape is obtained by the continued repetition of this process. These methods include : Electrical discharge machining (EDM), Laser beam Machining (LBM), Plasma Arc Machining (PAM), Electron Beam Machining (EBM), and Ion Beam Machining (IBM).

2. Electro - Chemical Energy Methods. These methods involve electrolytic (anodic) dissolution of the workpiece material in contact with a chemical solution. These methods include: Electro-Chemical Machining (ECM), Electrochemical grinding (ECG), Electro-Chemical Honing (ECH) and Electro-chemical Deburring (ECD).

3. Chemical Energy Methods. These methods involve controlled etching of the workpiece material in contact with a chemical solution, for example, Chemical Machining Method (CHM).

4. Mechanical Energy Methods. In these methods, the material is principally removed by mechanical erosion of the workpiece material. These methods include : Ultra Sonic Machining (USM), Abrasive Jet Machining (AJM), and Water Jet Machining (WJM).

Process Selection. The following aspects must be considered for the correct selection of the non-traditional machining method :

1. Physical parameters of the process.
2. Shapes to be machined.
3. Process capability.
4. Economics

1. Physical Parameters of Unconventional Methods. The physical parameters of different unconventional machining methods are given in Table 9.1.

Table 9.1. Physical Parameters of NTMM

Parameters	NTMM							
	USM	AJM	CHM	ECM	EDM	EBM	LBM	PAM
Potential, V	220	220	-	10 - 30	100 - 300	150×10^3	4.5×10^3	100
Current, A	12	1.0	-	10,000	50	0.001	2	500
Power, kW	2.4	0.22	-	100	2.70	0.15	-	50
Gap, mm	0.25	0.75	-	0.20	0.025	100	150	7.5
Medium	Abrasive in water, Paraffin	Abrasive in Gas	Liquid Chemicals	Electrolyte	Di-electric fluid	Vacuum	Air	Argon or Hydrogen

2. Shapes Cutting Capability. The various NTMM have some special shape cutting capability as given below :

(a) Micro-machining and Drilling : LBM and EBM
(b) Cavity sinking and standard Hole Drilling : EDM and USM
(c) Fine hole drilling and Contour Machining : ECM
(d) Clean, rapid Cuts and Profiles : PAM
(e) Shallow Pocketing : AJM

3. Process Capability. Table 9.2. gives the typical values of the various process capabilities.

Table. 9.2. Process Capability of NTMM

Process	Process Capability				
	Metal Removal Rate, (mm³/s)	Surface Finish (µm, CLA)	Accuracy (µm)	Specific power (kW/cm³/min)	Penetration rate, (mm/min)
ECM	2700	0.1 - 2.5	50	7.5	12.0
EDM	14	0.4 - 12.5	10	1.8	12.0
EBM	0.15	0.4 - 6.0	25	450	160.0
LBM	0.10	0.4 - 6.0	25	2700	100.0
PAM	2700	Rough	250	0.90	250
USM	14	0.2 - 0.5	7.5	9.0	0.50
AJM	0.014	0.5 - 1.2	50	312.5	-
CHM	0.8	0.4 - 2.5	50	-	0.02

By going through the Table 9.2, it can be observed that : EDM has the lowest specific power requirement and can achieve sufficient accuracy. ECM has the highest metal removal rate, MRR. USM and AJM have low MRR and combined with high tool wear, are used for non-metal cutting. LBM and EBM have high penetration rates with low MRR and, therefore, are commonly used for microdrilling, sheet cutting, and welding. CHM is used for manufacturing PCB and other shallow components. PAM can be used for clean, rapid cuts and profiles in almost all plates upto 20 cm thick with 5° to 10° taper.

4. Process Economy. The process economy of NTMM is given in Table 9.3.

Table 9.3. Process Economy

Process	Capital Cost	Tooling and fixtures	Power require-ment	Efficiency	Total consu-mption
USM	Low	Low	Low	High	Medium
AJM	V. Low	Low	Low	High	Low
ECM	V. High	Medium	Medium	Low	V. Low
CHM	Medium	Low	High	/Medium	V. Low
EDM	Medium	High	Low	High	High
EBM	Medium	High	Low	High	High
EBM	High	Low	Low	V. High	V. Low
LBM	Medium	Low	V. Low	V. High	V. Low
PAM	V. Low	Low	V. Low	V. Low	V. Low
Conventional mechining	Low	Low	Low	V. Low	Low

Limitations of NTMM. These methods are generally more expensive to set up, have a slower rate of metal removal and require considerable technical know how. Out of the above machining methods, the electrical machining methods have the following advantages :

1. The tool material does not have to be harder than the work material.

2. Tool forces do not increase as the work material gets harder.

3. Economic metal removal rate does not decrease as the work material gets harder.

However, the limitation of electrical machining methods is that the work material must be an electrical conductor. Also, consumption of electrical energy is very large.

The NTMM which have not been proved commercially economical are : USM, AJM, CHM, EBM and PAM.

(b) **Unconventional Forming Methods.** In these methods, the metals are formed through the release and application of large amounts of energy in a very short time interval. This makes it possible to form large parts and difficult to form metals with less expensive equipment and tooling than would otherwise be required.

Unconventional forming methods can be broadly grouped under two categories : High Energy Rate Forming methods (HERF) and High Velocity Forming methods (HVF). In HERF, the released energy is used directly to form the metals, whereas, in HVF it is converted into mechanical energy which imparts high velocities to ram/die. The important processes under the first category are explosive forming, electro-hydraulic forming, electromagnetic forming etc. The important processes in the second category are : pneumatic mechanical forming, petro-forge hammer, high velocity forming machines from dynapack, clearing hammer, trans-energy and linear induction motors.

HERF methods have one more plus point. The "Spring back" is minimal. This is due to the following fact : High energy pressure waves generated due to the release of energy produce high compressive stresses in the metal when it is forced against the die surface. Due to this, some elastic deformation of the die occurs, which results in over forming of the workpiece. Due to all this, the spring back will be almost nil or minimal when the forming is completed and the forming load is taken off.

In this chapter, we shall discuss some of the above mentioned non-conventional manufacturing methods.

9.2. ELECTRICAL DISCHARGE MACHINING (EDM)

It has long been recognized that a powerful spark, such as at the terminals of an automobile battery, will cause pitting or erosion of the metal at both the anode and cathode. This principle is utilized in Electric Discharge Machining (EDM), also called spark erosion. If anode and cathode are of the same material, it has been found that greater erosion takes place at anode (positive electrode). Therefore, in EDM process, work is made the anode and the tool is the cathode (negative electrode).

9.2.1. Description of Process. The mechanical set up and the electrical set up are shown in Fig. 9.1. Power for generating the spark is fed from an A.C. source to a rectifier. The D.C. output is then fed to the spark generating circuit. The tool and work and also the tool slide servo-mechanism, are connected into the circuit. The tool and work are submerged in a fluid having poor electrical conductivity (dielectric fluid). The function of the servo-mechanism is to maintain a very small gap (approximately 0.025 to 0.075 mm) between the tool and the work. The spark is a transient electric discharge across the gap between work and tool. When the potential difference (voltage) across the gap becomes sufficiently large, the dielectric fluid becomes ionized and breaks down to produce an electrically conductive spark channel and the condensers discharge current across the channel in the form of a spark. When the voltage drops to about 12 volts, the spark discharge extinguishes and the di-electric fluid once again becomes deionized. The condensers start to recharge and the process repeats itself. The spark occurs in an interval of from 10 to 30 microseconds and with a current density of approximately 15 - 500 A per mm^2. Thus, thousands of spark-discharge occur per second across the gap between tool and work, which result in a local temperature of approximately 12000°C. At each discharge, heat transfer from high temperature spark (plasma) to both tool and work, melts, partially vaporizes and partially ionizes the metal in a thin surface layer. The resulting work surface is composed of extremely small craters. The time interval between the sparks is so short that the heat is unable to conduct into the tool and work.

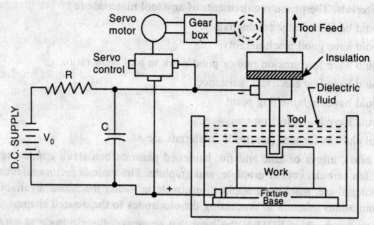

Fig. 9.1. Schematic Arrangement of EDM Method.

Power Supplies. Many types of electric circuits are available to provide pulsating D.C., across the workpiece-tool gap. The earliest models of ED Machines were fitted with Resistance-Capacitance (R-C) relaxation circuit (Fig. 9.1). In this system, a current flowing through a resistor R charges a capacitor C to a voltage (50 to 200 V), at which spark-breakdown occurs. The value of C, which may be as high as 400 μf (on heavy machines) is generally kept variable on most EDM machines, so that the machining conditions (rough, medium and finish) can be varied, to get the desired accuracy and surface finish. This value of R is kept sufficiently high, to prevent continuous arcing after the spark. The ratio of the discharge or breakdown voltage and the applied D.C. source voltage lies between 0.7 and 0.9. In this circuit, tool becomes alternately positive and negative terminal. At each reversal of polarity, there is more wear on tool than on work. So, tool wear is greater in this arrangement. Another disadvantage is that the metal removal rate is not high.

Rotary Impulse Generator. In this system, the capacitor is charged through a diode, during the first half cycle. During the second half of the cycle, the sum of the voltage generated by the generator (which is rotated by a motor) and the charged capacitor, is applied to the workpiece-tool gap. The metal removal rate is higher, but the surface finish is not good.

Transistorized Pulse Generator Circuit. In the above two systems, there is no provision to stop the current flow in the event of a short circuit. To overcome this problem, a transistor is used as the switching device for an automatic control in Transistorized pulse generator circuit. Circuits are also available in which reverse pulse can be eliminated, resulting in lesser tool wear.

Potential volts = 100 to 380, current amperes = 50.

Dielectric Fluid. A dielectric fluid is a medium that does not conduct electricity. In EDM process, the functions of dielectric fluid are :

1. It acts as an insulating medium.

2. It cools the spark region and helps in keeping the tool and workpiece cool

3. It maintains a constant resistance across the gap.

4. It carries away the eroded metal particles.

The dielectric fluid is circulated through the tool at a pressure of 0.35 N/mm^2 or less. To free it from eroded metal particles, it is circulated through a filter. Dielectric fluids must not be hazardous to operators or corrosive to equipment. The various mediums which are used as dielectric fluids are : petroleum based hydrocarbon fluids, paraffin, white spirit, transformer oil, kerosene, mineral oil or mixture of these. Occasionally, ethylene glycol and water miscible compounds are also used as dielectric fluids.

Tool Materials. The prime requirements of any tool material are :

1. It should be electrically conductive.
2. It should have good machinability.
3. It should have low erosion rate or good work to tool wear ratio.
4. It should have low electrical resistance.
5. It should have high melting point.
6. It should have high electron emission.

The usual choices for tool (electrode) materials are :

Copper, brass, alloys of zinc and tin, hardened plain carbon steel, copper tungsten, silver tungsten, tungsten carbide, copper graphite, and graphite. The various factors affecting the choice of electrode material are: machining applications, material being machined, availability, cost and the practical limitations inherent in processing the electrodes to the desired shape.

One major drawback of EDM is the wear that occurs on the electrode at each spark. Tool wear is given in terms of wear ratio which is defined as,

$$\text{Wear ratio} = \frac{\text{Volume of metal removed work}}{\text{Volume of metal removed tool}}$$

Wear ratio for brass electrode is 1 : 1. For most other metallic electrodes, it is about 3 : 1 or 4 : 1.

With graphite (with the highest melting point, 3500°C), the wear ratio may range from 5 : 1 upto 50 : 1.

Servo-Mechanism. As already mentioned, the gap between the tool and work has a critical importance. As the workpiece is machined, this gap tends to increase. For optimum machining efficiency, this gap should be maintained constant. This is done by servo- mechanism which controls the movement of the electrode. The servo-mechanisms can either be electro-mechanical (Fig. 9.1) or hydraulic. In the electro-mechanical system, the electrode is moved by a rack and pinion arrangement which is driven through reduction gearing from a D.C. servo motor. As the gap between the tool and workpiece increases because of their wear, the voltage across the gap drops. This voltage drop is automatically measured and a feedback is given to the servo control which sends a signal to the servo-motor, which operates the electrode downward until the gap reaches its critical value again.

Metal Removal Rate and Surface Finish. Metal removal rate (volume of metal removed from the work per unit time) depends upon current density and it increases with current. But high removal rates produce poor finish. Therefore, the usual practice in EDM is (as in conventional methods) : a roughing cut with a heavy current followed by a finishing cut with less current. Metal removal rates are usually low, approximately 80 mm^3/s, but this can be increased on machines having more efficient pulse generators. Tolerances of the order of $\pm\,0.05$ to 0.13 mm are commonly obtainable and with extra care, tolerances of $\pm\,0.003$ to 0.013 mm are possible. Surface finish of the order of 0.2 μm Ra is possible.

In addition to current density or the electric eneregy expended per spark, the MRR per spark also depends upon the period over which it is expended. To minimize the structure-damaging heat transfer into the bulk of the workpiece, a spark duration of 10 to 20 micro-seconds appears to be optimum.

The MRR :

(*i*) increases with discharge time until an optimum value, after which it suddenly drops.

(*ii*) increases with forced circulation of dielectric fluid.

(*iii*) is maximum when the pressure is below atmospheric, that is, cavitation helps in increasing MRR.

(*iv*) increases with capacitance.

(*v*) increases upto optimum work-tool gap, after which it drops suddenly.

Advantages

1. EDM can be used for machining any material that is electrically conductive, thus including metals, alloys and most carbides.

2. The melting point, hardness, toughness or brittleness of the material poses no problems. Due to this EDM can be used for machining materials that are too hard or brittle to be machined by conventional methods.

3. The method does not leave any chips or burrs on the work piece.

4. Cutting forces are virtually zero, so very delicate and fine work can be done.

5. The process dimension repeatability and surface finish obtained in finishing are extremely good.

6. The characteristic surface obtained, which is made up of craters, helps in better oil retention. This improves die life.

7. The process once set up does not need constant operator's attention.

Disadvantages

1. Only electrically conductive materials can be machined by EDM. Thus non - metallics, such as plastics, ceramics or glass, cannot be machined by EDM.

2. Electrode wear and overcut are serious problems.

3. A rehardened, highly stressed zone is produced on the work surface by the heat generated during machining. This brittle layer can cause serious problems when the part is put into service.

4. Perfectly square corners cannot be made by EDM.

Product Applications. EDM is widely used for machining burr free intricate shapes, narrow slots and blind cavities etc., for example, sinking of dies for moulding, die casting, plastic moulding, wire drawing, compacting, cold heading, forging, extrusion and press tools. Almost any geometry (negative of tool geometry) can be generated on a workpiece if a suitable tool can be fabricated (the use of punch as a tool to machine its own mating die is commonly employed in EDM method). The method is also employed for blanking parts from sheets, cutting off rods of materials, flat or form grinding and sharpening of tools, cutters and broaches. In EDM method, small holes, about 0.13 mm, in diameter and as deep as 20 diameters can be drilled with virtually no bending or drifting of hole. Due to this, EDM is particularly useful for machining of small holes, orifices or slots in diesel-fuel injection nozzles, or in aircraft engines, air brake valves and so on.

9.2.2. Wire Cut Electro-Discharge Machining (WCEDM, Fig.9.2). The basic mechanism of metal removal in WCEDM (also known as Travelling wire EDM) is identical to that in die-sinking type EDM. However, there are some important differences :-

1. Instead of a moving electrode (as in EDM), the electrode in this process is a moving wire of Cu or brass. A vertically oriented wire is fed into the workpiece continuously travelling from a supply spool to a take up spool, so that it is continuously renewed, since it will get worn out during the process. For this purpose, a hole is predrilled in the work- piece, through which the wire electrode will pass.

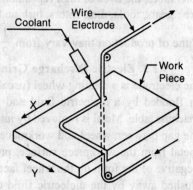

Fig. 9.2. Schematic of WCEDM.

2. The whole workpiece is not submerged in dielectric medium (as in EDM). Instead, the working zone alone is supplied with a co-axial jet of dielectric medium, which in this process is deionized water instead of hydrocarbon oils in EDM. This system removes the eroded particles efficiently and keep the working zone cool.

3. One of the most important aspects in WCEDM is its ability to cut complex two dimensional profiles. For this, the machine table on which the workpiece is held, has movements along X-axis and y- axis. The drive unit for the machine table (close loop DC motor drive system or a DC stepper motor drive) are controlled by the numerical control units based on CNC system. This system is easily programmable for linear and circular path interpolation and they provide high resolution data for accurate control of the slides of the worktable. This makes this method capable of machining any complicated through hole dies of electrically conductive materials.

Advantages

In addition to the above advantages, the process has got the following advantages also :

1. Saving of stages in sequential tools, due to absence of split lines in the die, hence permitting more punch opening per stage.

2. Moulded parts will not have flashes, as the moulds with draught can be made without vertical divisions.

3. Tool manufacturing and storage is not required.

4. Heat treatment distortions are totally avoided, as the workpieces are hardened before cutting.

5. Cycle time for die manufacture is shorter, as the whole work is done on one machine.

6. Inspection time is reduced, due to single piece construction of dies with high positioning accuracy.

7. The time utilization of WCEDM is high, as it can cut right through the day (24 hours a day).

8. Economical, even for small batch production, including prototypes, as most of the programming can be easily done.

9. High surface finish, with low thermal affected zone depths are obtained. This reduces the manual finishing operation time.

10. Avoids rejections, due to initial planning and checking the programme.

11. Improvement in design technique allows for easier layout in the compound dies.

The method is best suited for parts having extra-ordinary workpiece configurations, close tolerances, the need of high repeatability and of hard to work materials. Common examples of jobs are : gears, tools, dies, rotors, turbine blades and cams, for small to medium size batch production.

Time of production may vary from $\frac{1}{2}$ hour to 20 hours.

9.2.3. Electric Discharge Grinding (EDG). EDG (Fig. 9.3) is similar to EDM except that the electrode is a rotating wheel (usually graphite). Positively charged workpieces are immersed in or flooded by a dielectric fluid and fed past the negatively charged wheel by servo-controlled machine table. Metal is removed by intermittent high frequency electrical discharges passing through the gap between wheel and workpiece. Each spark discharge melts or vaporizes a small amount of metal from the workpiece surface, producing a small crate at the discharge sit, as in EDM. The negative of the form on the wheel face is transferred to the workpiece surface. The metal chips are flushed away by the dielectric fluid carried through the cutting area by the wheel rotation. The spark gap is normally held at 0.013 to 0.076 mm by a servomechanism that controls the motion of the worktable. The graphite wheel is rotated at 0.5 to 3 m/s.

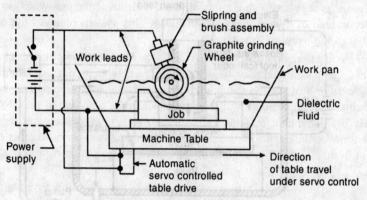

Fig. 9.3. Schematic of EDG.

The power supply and the dielectric fluid are similar to those used in EDM, but lower amperage is used in most EDG applications, because the cutting area is usually small and the method is used primarily to achieve accuracy and smooth finish. The method can be used for : external cylindrical grinding, internal grinding and surface grinding.

EDG is generally used for operations such as,

1. Grinding carbide and steel at the same time without wheel loading.

2. Grinding thin sections where abrasive wheel pressures might cause distortion.

3. Grinding brittle materials or fragile parts where abrasive materials might cause fracturing.

4. Grinding through forms, where diamond wheel costs would be excessive.

5. Grinding circular forms, in direct competition with abrasive wheel methods.

9.3. ELECTRO-CHEMICAL MACHINING (ECM)

In ECM, the principle of electrolysis is used to remove metal from the workpiece. The principle of electrolysis is based on Faraday's laws of electrolysis which may be stated as : "The weight of substance produced during electrolysis is directly proportional to the current which passes, the length of time of the electrolysis process and the equivalent weight of the material, which is deposited". ECM is just the reverse of electroplating (which also uses the principle of electrolysis). In electroplating, two dissimilar metals are in contact with an electrolyte (an electrically conductive fluid) and anode loses metal to the cathode. In ECM, work is made the anode and the tool is the cathode. Therefore, work loses metal, but before it can be plated on to the tool, the dissolved metal is carried away in the flowing electrolyte.

Description of Process. Schematic view of ECM method is shown in Fig. 9.4. In the D.C. supply circuit, the workpiece is made the anode and the tool is made the cathode. The tool is of hollow tabular type, to provide passages for circulating electrolyte between the tool face and the work. As the power supply is switched on and the current starts flowing through the circuit, electrons are removed from the surface atoms of the workpiece. These ions tend to migrate to the hollow cutting tool. But before these can get deposited on the cutting tool face, these are swept away by rapidly flowing electrolyte, out of the gap between the tool and the workpiece. The tool is fed towards the workpiece automatically at constant velocity to control the gap between the electrodes. Tool face has the reverse shape of the desired workpiece. The sides of the tool are insulated to concentrate the metal removal action at the bottom face of the tool.

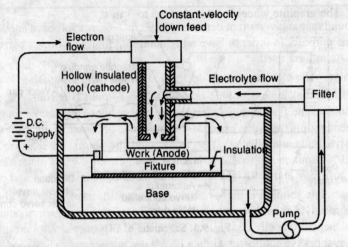

Fig. 9.4. Schematic Arrangement of ECM.

Advantages

Like EDM, the ECM method has also been developed for machining new hard, and tough materials (for rocket and aircraft industry) and also hard refractory materials. ECM has the following outstanding advantages :

1. ECM is simple, fast and versatile method.

2. The metal removal is entirely by metallic ion exchange and so there are no cutting forces and the workpiece is left in an undisturbed, stress free state. It is never subjected to high temperatures or stresses. Also, due to the absence of cutting forces, very thin sections can be machined. Again, there will be no residual stresses in the workpiece as a result of the operation.

3. If proper electrolytes are used, there is no tool wear at all.

4. The process character does not depend at all upon the physical properties of the metal (hardness, toughness etc.).

5. Surface finish can be extremely good.

6. No burrs are produced.

7. Fairly good tolerances can be obtained.

8. The process can be easily automated.

Limitations of ECM

1. Large power consumption, and the related problems.

2. Sharp internal corners cannot be achieved.

3. Post machining cleaning is a must, to reduce the corrosion of the workpieces.

4. Tool design is complicated and needs cut and try method to achieve the final shape.

5. Maintenance of higher tolerances requires complicated controls.

Power Supply. The electrical supply circuit in ECM is simpler as compared to EDM. ECM power supplies are currently available in sizes upto 10,000 amperes (a few machines are rated upto 40,000 amperes). The range of voltage on most machines is from 5 to 30 volts d.c. In ECM method, a constant voltage has to be maintained. For this, voltage regulation circuits are available. Cut-off circuits are also available in the power-supply units to stop the supply of power to the machining gap. In ECM, the current density is usually high. At low current densities, the metal removal rate is low. In order to have a metal removal of the anode, a sufficient amount of current has to be given.

It has been found that at low current densities ($5A / cm^2$), O_2 is evolved at anode and all the energy is used for this purpose. In order to have a high current efficiency, higher current densities, of the order of 200 A/cm^2, are used.

Electrolyte. The electrolyte in ECM method serves two purposes.

(1) It is essential for electrolytic process to work, and (2) It cools the cutting zone which becomes hot due to the flow of high current. The electrolytes vary from strong salt to strong acid solution, depending on the work material. Neutral salts are used as electrolytes in preference to highly corrosive acids and alkalies. The sodium and the potassium salts are probably the most common. A 20% common salt (NaCl) solution is appropriate for many materials. Some electrolytes are naturally corrosive and so ECM equipment is made of stainless steel and plastics.

The electrolyte solution is pumped between the tool/workpiece gap at about 2.5 N/mm^2 and 30 m/s. The electrolyte should never be allowed to boil. For this, the temperature of the electrolyte in the tank is thermostatically controlled (35° to 65°C), by electric heaters together with a heat exchanger or evaporative condenser. Unlike EDM, it is not necessary for the work to be submerged in liquid solution.

Tool. As mentioned above, there is virtually no tool wear, so, any material that is good conductor of electricity can be used as tool material. Other requirements of good tool material are:

1. It should have good thermal conductivity.

2. It should be strong enough to withstand the high hydrostatic pressures caused by electrolyte flow.

3. It should be easily machined.

4. As the surface finish of the workpiece mainly depends upon the condition of the bottom face of the tool, this portion of the tool should be polished.

The tool may be made from titanium, copper, brass, or stainless steel. The outer surface of tool is insulated by Vinyl, Teflon, epoxy, enamels or high temperature varnish. A constant gap of about 0.01 mm is maintained between the tool face and work. For this, the tool is fed towards the work at constant velocity with feed rate of about 0.5 mm to 25 mm per minute. The movement of the tool slide is controlled by a hydraulic cylinder.

Machined Surface. The machining rate and surface finish are directly proportional to current density. Surface finish values as low as 0.1 μm Ra are possible with a tolerance of the order of 0.005 mm. The metal removal rates are high, upto 550 mm^3/s.

Metal Removal Rate. Even though, the metal removal rate depends on the current density, there is a limit upto which it can be done. Forcing more and more current per unit area through the electrolyte-surface combination, will saturate the system due to one of a number of effects given below :

1. Too much heating of the electrolyte (due to 12.R effect) may cause its boiling. This will appreciably reduce the electrolytic action.

2. The metallic ions react with an electrolyte component, to form a reaction product, which will greatly impede the action, unless it is removed from the surface.

3. Polarized ionic layers may build up at either electrode, causing large voltage drops near the surfaces.

4. Gas evolution (H_2) at the cathode surface may reduce the current flow.

The limiting effect of the above factors can be reduced by increasing the flow of clean electrolyte in the anode-cathode gap. Because this gap is small (0.025 to 0.125 mm) the high rate of electrolyte flow will require high fluid pressures. This will result in large hydrostatic separating forces between the tool and the work. For most operations, the maximum flow rate is determined by the practical considerations imposed by the phenomenon of cavitation. During cavitation, vapour bubbles are hydro-dynamically formed in the fluid and produce uneven metal removal.

Product Application. ECM methods find wide application in rocket, aircraft and gas turbine industries. ECM is a standard method for machining gas turbine blades. ECM is increasingly being used in airframe component fabrication, die sinking and the manufacture of general machine parts. The different operations like turning, drilling, milling, shaping and planing etc. can be combined and done quickly by ECM method. Product applications of ECM include producing simple to complex cavities (die sinking), embossed surfaces, blind holes, through holes, irregular holes and complex external shapes; cutting test blocks and sawing ingots to various desired lengths in

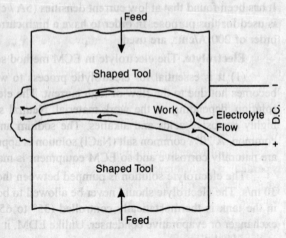

Fig. 9.5.

steel mills; rough machining of massive forgings; honey-combing aircraft panels ; jet engine blade airfoils (Fig. 9.5) and cooling holes ; operations on rock boring bits, transformer cores, pump impellers, gears ; operations on rock boring bits, transformer cores, pump impellers, gears ; extremely rapid deburring operations and salvage operations on worn machine parts or on dies.

One very important advantage of ECM is that by merely changing electrolyte and current density, we can shift from roughing to polishing. At very high current densities and high electrolyte velocities, a very high polish can be obtained.

9.4. ELECTROLYTIC GRINDING OR ELECTRO-CHEMICAL GRINDING (ECG)

In ECG method, the work is machined by the combined action of electro-chemical effect and conventional grinding operation. The majority of the metal removal results from the electrolytic action. A schematic view of electrolytic grinding is shown in Fig. 9.6. Here, the tool electrode is a rotating, metal bonded diamond or aluminium oxide wheel and it acts as cathode. The work acts as anode and hence current flows between the work and wheel. A constant gap of about 0.25 mm is maintained between work and wheel and through this gap, an essentially neutral electrolyte is circulated. The electrolyte is carried past the work surface at high speed by the rotary action of the grinding wheel. The grinding wheel runs at speeds of 900 to 1800 m/min. The important functions of abrasive particles are : (1) they act as insulators to maintain a small gap between the wheel and the workpiece (2) they remove electrolysis products from the working area (3) to cut chips if the

wheel should contact the workpiece particularly in the event of power failure. When the process is started, about 90% of metal is removed by electrolytic action and only about 10% by abrasive grinding. The abrasive particles rub against the workpiece, scrubbing off the electrolysis products, thus allowing good dimensional control. For best dimensional control and efficiency, the non-cutting areas of the tool (wheel and its spindle) should be insulated from the rest of the machine. Surface finish, precision and metal removal rate are influenced by the composition of the electrolyte. The metal

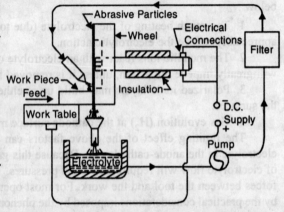

Fig. 9.6. Schematic set up of Electrolytic Grinding.

removal rate also depends upon the pressure between the wheel and workpiece and is directly proportional to it. The following values can be commonly obtained : accuracy of 0.01 mm, surface finish of 0.1 μm Ra and metal removal rate 15 m m³/s. The commonly used electrolytes are : Aqueous solutions of sodium silicate, borax, sodium nitrate and sodium nitrite. The power supply is : D.C. voltage of 5 to 20 V, current density of 100 to 200 A/cm². The ECG method is used for workpieces sensitive to the heat of the usual grinding methods. It is used almost exclusively for shaping and sharpening carbide cutting tools. It has been also successfully applied to refractory metals, high-strength steels, nickel and cobalt base alloys. The method has the following advantages over conventional grinding :

1. Tool wear is negligible which greatly increases the life of the grinding wheel. This factor is particularly valuable in the grinding of hard metals such as tungsten carbide where, costly diamond wheels are ordinarily used. In ordinary grinding there are high wear rates on these expensive diamond wheels.

2. It produces a smoother surface and does not produce surface stresses and distortion as in conventional grinding.

3. ECG is much more rapid than ordinary grinding. Like EDM and ECM, power consumption is high in ECG.

4. Requires very light grinding pressures and eliminates thermal problems.

5. Delicate parts can be machined without distortion.

6. Can machine burr-free parts.

7. Improved surface finish upto 0.μ m Ra, with no grinding marks.

8. In ECG, the ECM action is particularly efficient because,

  (a) the grinding grits remove all reaction products and polarized layers, presenting very clean metal to the electrolyte.

  (b) the grinding wheel continuously pumps fresh electrolyte into the active zone.

Disadvantages of ECG :

1. Higher cost of grinding wheel.

2. Higher cost of maintenance.

3. Tolerances achieved are rather low, (of the order of 0.025 mm). Due to this, the workpieces need final abrasive machining.

4. Difficult optimization, due to the complexity of the process.

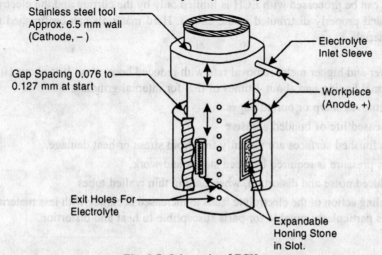

Stainless steel tool
Approx. 6.5 mm wall
(Cathode, –)

Gap Spacing 0.076 to
0.127 mm at start

Electrolyte
Inlet Sleeve

Workpiece
(Anode, +)

Exit Holes For
Electrolyte

Expandable
Honing Stone
in Slot.

Fig. 9.7. Schematic of ECH.

9.4.1.Electro-Chemical Honing (ECH), (Fig. 9.7). Electro-chemical honing is similar to ECG in that it combines the anodic dissolution of material with abrasive cutting action. ECH, however, uses rotating and reciprocating, non-conducting bonded honing stones instead of a conducting grinding wheel. ECH is a modification of conventional honing and it combines the metal removal capabilities of ECM with the accuracy capabilities of honing. Electrolyte is introduced into the gap between the cathodic honing tool and the anodic workpiece, while D.C. is passed across the gap and the rotating tool is reciprocated through the work bore. The gap between the tool and the workpiece is usually about 0.075 to 0.125 mm at the start of the cycle and increases by the amount of stock removal per cycle. The gap can increase upto 0.50 mm or more. Most of the metal removal is by electro-chemical action.

Because the honing stones keep the workpiece surface clean, the electrolyte does not have to be as corrosive as is necessary for ECM. On many metals, sodium nitrate can be used instead of more corrosive sodium chloride or acidic electrolytes. Several rows of small holes in the tool body enable electrolyte to be introduced directly between the tool and the work surface. Supply of the electrolyte can be upto 112.5 lit/min under a pressure of upto 1.05 N / mm^2. depending upon the workpiece size.

Bonded - abrasive honing stones are inserted in slots in the tool (which is normally of stainless steel). These stones are forced out radially by the wedging action of the cone in the tool. The expansion is controlled by an adjusting heat in the spindle of the machine. The stones, which must be non-conducting, assist in the metal removal action and generate a round, straight cylinder. They are fed out with equal pressure in all directions so that their cutting faces are in constant contact with the cylinder's surface. They abrade the residue left by the electro-chemical action so that a clean surface is always presented for continuing electrolysis. If the cylinder is tapered, out of round or wavy, the stones cut most aggressively on the high or tight areas and remove the geometric error. Automatic gauging devices designed into the system initiates a signal when the cylinder is of the desired diameter size and the cycle is automatically terminated. If the surface finish must be held to a special roughness, the stones are allowed to cut for a few seconds after electricity has been cut off.

The direct current power source is a 3000 A, 24 V rectifier. Current density is of the order of 15 to 40 A/cm^2 as compared to 100 to 240 A/cm^2 for ECG.

Commercial ECH equipment is available only for internal cylindrical grinding, with a size tolerance of 0.013 mm on diameter and 0.005 mm on roundness and straightness. The size of the cylinder that can be processed with ECH is limited only by the current and the electrolyte that can be supplied and properly distributed in the circuit. Hard materials can be finished more quickly than soft materials.

Advantage

1. Faster and higher metal removal rate with reduced hone wear. It is about 10 times of that for conventional honing and about 4 times of that for internal grinding.

2. It removes sharp or burred edges.

3. Increased life of bonded abrasive.

4. The finished surfaces are virtually free from stress or heat damage.

5. Less pressure is required between stones and work.

6. Reduced noise and distortion, when honing thin walled tubes.

7. Cooling action of the electrolyte leads to increased accuracy with less material damage, so the process is particularly suitable for parts susceptible to heat and distortion.

9.4.2. Electro-Chemical Deburring

(ECD). The process of ECM deburring (ECD) is identical to that of ECM countersinking except that there is no relative movement of the tool with respect to the workpiece. The tool and the workpiece are placed in a fixed relative position with a gap of 0.1 to 1.0 mm, (Fig. 9.8). The tool which is positioned near the base of the burr, is designed so that only that portion of the workpiece containing burrs is exposed to tool material. The remaining portion of the tool is insulated.

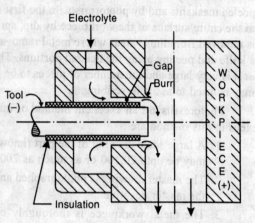

Fig. 9.9. Schematic of ECD.

The current levels in ECD are of the order of 6A/cm of linear edge length at 7 to 25 V DC supply. The electrolyte which is generally sodium nitrate is circulated at a pressure of 0.1 to 0.4 N/mm^2 to give flow rate of 5 to 20 lit/min for a 100 A electrolyzing current.

Advantages

1. Both external and internal burrs, which may be inaccessible, can be removed.

2. The equipment is simple to operate and easy to maintain.

3. The system is very fast (5 to 40 times faster than hand deburring) and the operating costs are low.

4. Burrs may be removed even after heat treatment.

5. No stresses or embrittlement caused by ECD.

6. No tool wear, and tool designs are fairly simple.

7. Electrolytic system is small and simple to maintain.

8. A simple power supply system, without an extensive rapid shut off system, can be used.

9. ECD can be included in transfer lines.

Applications. Automobile connecting rods, gear teeth, blanking dies, valve ports, nozzle interesting holes etc.

9.5. CHEMICAL MILLING

In chemical milling, also known as chemical machining (CHM), photochemical machining, photo fabrication or photo etching, material is removed from selected areas of a workpiece by controlled chemical dissolution with chemical reagents, which may be either acidic or basic, depending on the material of the workpiece. The areas of the workpiece which are not to be machined are masked, (Fig. 9.9). The workpiece is then either immersed in or exposed to a spray of chemical reagent. The time of immersion or exposure depends upon the amount of material to be removed by chemical action. The component to be machined is first cleaned in trichloroethylene vapour or in a solution of alkali at 80 to 85°C. This remove dust and oil. This ensures a good adhesion of the coating or mask which is applied to protect the portions which are not to be machined. The component is then dried.

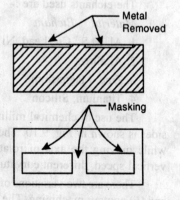

Fig. 9.9. Chemical Milling.

The simplest method of masking is with masking tape. The usual methods are : scribed-and-peeled maskants and by photoresists. In the first method, a maskant (paint like material) is applied to the entire surface of the workpiece by dip, spray, brush or stencil. After the maskant hardens, it is removed from those areas where metal removal is desired, by scribing through the maskant with a knife and peeling away the desired portions. This method is used when the workpiece is not flat, or it is very large and the number of pieces to be produced are small. Where economical, templates may be used to assist in scribing.

Photoresists are an excellent method of masking, especially for complex work. The various steps in this method are :

1. A large scale drawing of the part (know as 'artwork') is pre- pared. The scale of drawing may be upto 20,100 or as much as 200 to 1.

2. The master drawing is photographed and reduced to final size on a process camera, to get the master negative.

3. The metal workpiece is thoroughly cleaned and is then coated with an emulsion of photosensitive resist. The coating may be applied by dipping, spraying, brushing, roller coating or flow coating.

4. The coating is then dried and hardened by baking in an oven upto about 120°C.

5. The master photographic negative is placed over the dried photoresist coating and exposed to ultraviolet radiation from a mercury lamp. The clear areas of the master allow radiation to harden the resist. The black areas of the master protect the resist from the radiation and keep it unhardened in these areas. Each side of the workpiece can be printed individually or the two sides can be exposed simultaneously by using special mirror image master equipment.

6. The workpiece is then de- veloped by immersing it into a tank containing an organic solvent bath solution. The unexposed areas on the work- piece are dissolved away in the developer, while the exposed remain on the workpiece.

7. The final step is to spray the workpiece with or immerse it in the chemical reagent. The material is etched away from the surface of the workpiece except that portion on which the protected image is printed.

Maskants and Etchants used in CHM :

Maskant materials are   :   Plastics and Elastomers

Plastics commonly used are   :   PVC, polystyrence, polyethylene

The commonly used elastomers are   :   acrylonitrile rubber and butryl rubber

The etchants used are :-

Material   Etchant

1. Al, M.S., Cu, Lead, Ni and Stainless steel   Ferric chloride
2. Al alloys   NaOH at 50°C
3. Zinc, Magnesium HNO_3
4. Titanium, Silicon   Hydrogen fluoride

The use of chemical milling in the making of a disk with tapered sides is shown in Fig. 9.10. The disk is rotated in the chemical reagent while moving the axis of rotation gradually upward. By varying the vertical speed, different curvatures can be obtained.

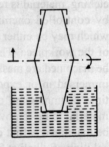

Fig. 9.10. Chemical Milling.

There are two variations of chemical milling : (*i*) Chemical blanking and (*ii*) contour machining. The difference between the two is that while in chemical blanking, the material is etched entirely through a work piece, in contour machining the material is selectively etched from certain areas on the workpiece. Chemical blanking is a method of cutting or stamping out parts from flat thin metal or foil sheets.

In practice, the following results are achieved by chemical milling :

(*i*) Metal thickness of blanked parts : About 1.50 mm.

(*ii*) Depth of etch in contour machining : Approximately from 3.8 mm to 12.7 mm. Of course, heavy cuts have been made successfully (upto about 50 mm). However, lighter cuts are more characteristic of this process.

(*iii*) Tolerance : About ± 0.05 mm per 2.54 mm of depth.

(*iv*) Surface finish : Depending upon the material, characteristics of the chemical and the depth of cut, surface finishes can vary form 0.25 to 6.25 $\mu m R_a$ values.

(*v*) Metal removal : Approximately 0.015 to 0.030 cm^3 per minute.

Advantages

1. The process is comparatively simple and there is no need of highly skilled labour, excepting for artwork and photography.

2. The process does not induce any stresses in the metal.

3. The process can be applied to any metal.

4. Parts of any shape and minimum thickness can be machined.

5. Parts of large sizes can be machined.

Limitations

1. The metal removal rate is slow.

2. The material has to be fine grained, sound and homogeneous for best results. Any imperfections on the surface in the form of tool marks, scratches etc. must be removed before chemical milling, because the chemical reagent has the tendency to etch surface imperfections at a faster rate. Also, the parts should be heat treated and stress relieved before chemical milling. If there are any residual stresses in the part, these will get relieved during chemical milling resulting in warping of the part.

3. Weldments are usually not suitable for chemical milling because of non-uniform grain structure near welds.

Product Applications. The chemically milled parts find main application in aerospace, aviation, automotive, electronic and instrument making industry. chemically blanked parts are used in the following products : tape recorders, computers, cameras, television sets, electric motors, timers, telephone systems, electric shavers and medical instruments etc. In aviation industry, chemical milling (contour machining) is used to produce special surface configurations on aircraft wing and fuselage sections. In aerospace industry, contour machining is used to produce contoured pockets on surfaces of bulkheads, skin panels etc. Chemical contour machining is also used to produce special geometries on the surfaces of parabolic radar reflectors, gyrohousings and heat exchangers etc. Other uses of contour machining are : to produce decorative surfaces on various flat or contoured parts, for example, elevator doors, ashtrays, plaques, signs, panels, instrument dials, metal tags or nameplates. The process is used for hard to reach spots, narrow recesses, form and helical grooves etc

9.6. ULTRASONIC MACHINING (USM) ; (FIG. 9.11)

Ultrasonic machining is a kind of grinding method. An abrasive slurry is pumped between tool and work, and the tool is given a high frequency, low amplitude oscillation, which, in turn, trans- mits a high velocity to fine abrasive particles which are driven against the workpiece. At each stroke, minute chips of material are removed by fracture or erosion. The general arrangement of ultrasonic machining is shown in Fig. 9.11. The equip-ment consists of a transducer, a tool holder and the tool. The linear oscillatory motion of the tool is obtained by magnetostrictive transducer which converts electric energy into mechanical energy. The transducer consists of a stack of nickel laminations that are wound with a coil. When a high frequency current is passed through the coil, changes in the electromagnetic field produce longitudinal strains in the laminations. These longitudinal strains are transmitted to the tool through a tool holder. The tool oscillates linearly with an amplitude of about 0.05 mm at ultrasonic frequencies of from 15 to 25 kHz. Power supply is : Potential volts = 220, current = 12A.

The tool, whose shape is essentially re-produced in the workpiece is also subjected to the impact-fracture action and should be made of a soft ductile material that is easily machined, for example, unhardened steel, copper or brass. The tool is ordinarily 0.075 to 0.10 mm smaller than the cavity it produces. The tool is brazed, soldered or fastened mechanically to the transducer through a tool holder. For selecting tool holder material, factors to be considered are : Conductivity, how well the material can be brazed and fatigue properties. The material for tool holder can be : titanium alloys, Monel, Aluminium, stainless steel etc. Important factor in tool fastening is that no relative motion and hence energy loss occurs. So, soldering and brazing have proved more satisfactory than mechanical clamping. The tool feed rate is about 0.1 mm/s, maximum.

The abrasive used in USM can be aluminium oxide, boron carbide or silicon carbide grains in a slurry which also carries away debris. The slurry can be made in water which also acts as a coolant. The usual combinations are : boron carbide in water and silicon carbide in paraffin. Grain size of abrasive particles ranges from 200 to 1000.

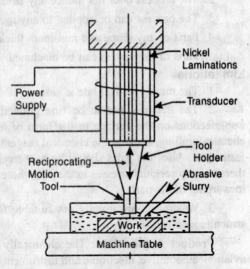

Fig. 9.11. Ultrasonic Machining.

The other commonly used abrasives are :- diamond dust and Boron Silicon Carbide and the liquid carriers are :- kerosene, benzene, glycerol or thin oil. Ratio of abrasive and liquid carrier ranges from 1 : 4 to 1 : 1 by weight. Slurry can be fed externally or internally. In external feeding, the slurry is pump fed by several jets covering the circumference of the tool or by a single jet. In internal feeding, hollow tools carry the slurry centrally to the workpiece. The slurry is to be fed continuously to avoid any drying up at the tool face.

This method involves brittle fracture and obviously works only on relatively brittle materials. So, USM has been applied very successfully to hard, refractory, difficult to machine materials which are quite brittle, for example, ceramics, borides, ferrites, carbides, glass, precious stones, hardened steel, cermets and some super alloys etc. It is used chiefly for drilling holes, engraving, cavity sinking (carbide wire drawing dies), slicing and broaching etc. Hole diameter as small as 0.01 mm can be produced.

Tolerance and surface finish depend upon grit size. More practical values for tolerance are ± 0.001 mm/mm. Of course, tolerance of ± 0.0005 mm/mm can be obtained. Usual values for surface finish are 0.25 to 0.50 μm*Ra*. Metal removal is about 3 mm³/s.

The ratio of workpiece wear to tool wear ranges from 1 : 1 to 100 : 1.

· The difference between conventional grinding and ultrasonic machining also known as grinding is that whereas in the former, the motion of the grinding grit is tangential to the surface of workpiece, in USM (USG), the motion of grinding grits is normal to the work surface. Advantages of the process are : no thermal stresses, low tooling costs and the use of semiskilled workers for precision work.

The limitations of the process are :- Its sonotrode vibration uniformity may limit the process to objects less than 100 mm in diameter and it has a low MRR.

9.7. USE OF HIGH ENERGY DENSITIES FOR MACHINING

If a sufficiently high energy density can be produced and concentrated on a small zone of the workpiece, small-scale material removal can be accomplished. The material will get removed either mechanically or thermally. These processes include : Electron beam machining, Laser beam machining and Plasma arc machining, which will be discussed below :

9.7.1. Electron Beam Machining. In electron beam machining (EBM), electrons emitted by a hot surface and accelerated by a voltage of 10 to 50 kV are focused to a very small areas on the workpiece. This stream of high energy electrons posses a very high energy density (of the order of 10^4 kW / mm^2)and when this narrow stream strikes the workpiece (by impact), the kinetic energy of the electrons is converted to powerful heat energy which is quite sufficient to melt and vapourize any material. Even though, the electrons can penetrate metals to a depth of only a few atomic layers the electron beam can melt metal to a depth of 25 mm or more. The electron beam which travels at about half to three-fourth the velocity of sound is focused on the workpiece by electrostatic or electro-magnetic lenses. EBM is done in a high vacuum chamber to eliminate the scattering of the electron beam as it contacts the gas molecules on the workpiece. Fig. 9.12 shows schematic view of EBM.

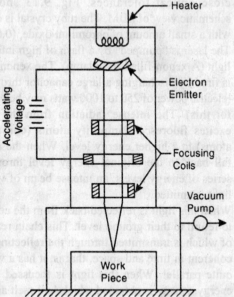

Since a continuous beam loses considerable heat by conduction through the workpiece, a pulsed beam at a frequency of less than 100 cps is used in electron beam machining. This consists of repeatedly striking the electron beam on the workpiece for a few milli-seconds and then turning it off for a certain period of time.

Recent developments have made it possible to machine outside the vacuum chamber. In this arrangement, the necessary vacuum is maintained within the electron gun proper by removing gases as soon as they enter. The fully vacuum system is more costly, but it has the advantage that no contaminating gases are present and the electron gun can be located at a considerable distance from the workpiece. The most commonly used electron-beam power are 1 to 25 kW, current = 0.001 A.

Product Applications. Electron beam machining is mainly used for micromachining operations on thin materials. These operations include : drilling, perforating, slotting, scribing the

Fig. 9.12. Schematic View of EBM.

engraving. A micromachining technique called "Electron-beam lithography" is being used in the manufacture of : field emission cathodes, integrated circuits and computer memories.

Holes as small as 0.03 mm (with surface finish of 0.4 to 0.6 μ m) can be drilled with ease. EBM is being used to drill holes for the following products : Thousands of holes in turbine blades for transpiration cooling, holes in mixer plates, combustion chamber rings, metering or flow orifices. EBM is particularly useful for materials with high melting points and low thermal conductivity.

Limitations

1. Holes produced in materials of thickness greater than about 0.13 mm, are tapered, with a side wall taper of about 1 to 2°, the minimum diameter being at the exit of the hole.

2. The method is quite cumbersome and the equipment is very costly.

3. The metal removal rate is very low.

4. At the spot where the electron beam strikes the material, a small amount of recasting and metal spatter can occur. This has to be removed afterwards by abrasive cleaning.

9.7.2. Laser Beam Machining (LBM). A Laser (Light Amplification by Stimulated Emission of Radiation) is a device which produces a beam of light. Laser light can be a very powerful source of power. In LBM, exceedingly high electromagnetic energy densities (of the order of 10^5 kW/mm^2) are focused on the surface of the workpiece (in air or vacuum) to remove metal by melting and evaporation.

There are many types of lasers used for different purposes, e.g., solid state, gas, liquid and semi-conductor. For machining and welding, high power lasers are required and, in general, only the solid state lasers can provide the required power levels.

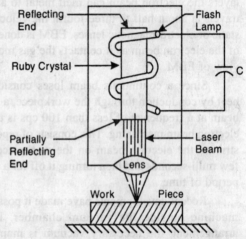

The most commonly used solid-state laser is the ruby laser (crystalline aluminium oxide or sapphire). These lasers are fabricated into rods about 150 mm long and their ends are finished to close optical tolerances. Fig. 9.13 shows a schematic view of LBM. The ruby crystal is doped with a small amount of chromium oxide, (0.05%). The laser is "pumped" by a flash of high intensity light (A xenon-filled flash lamp). The xenon lamp is fired by discharging a large capacitor through it (electric power of 250 to 1000 watts may be needed for this). The intense radiation from the lamp excites fluorescent impurity atoms (chromium atoms) to a higher energy level. When the atoms fall back to the original energy level through a series of energy levels, an intense beam of visible light is emitted.

Fig. 9.13. Schematic View of LBM.

When this light is reflected back from the coated rod ends, more atoms are excited and stimulated to return to their ground level. This chain reaction results in a stimulated avalanche of light, some of which is transmitted through the reflecting coatings (about 80% reflective). This light is highly coherent in time and space, that is, it has a very narrow frequency band, is highly in phase, and is quite parallel. When this light is focussed with ordinary lenses at spot on the workpiece, high energy density is obtained which will melt and vaporize the metal. It is clear that LBM is a pulsed operation. After discharge, the capacitor must be recharged. Power supply is : Potential = 4.5 kV, current = 2A.

The ruby laser works with maximum efficiency when kept at a very low temperature. For this, liquid nitrogen at –196°C is employed. On the other hand, the light flash works best when warm. For this, hot air is circulated over it. The vacuum chamber between the ruby crystal and the flash lamp acts as an insulator and enables the two temperatures (discussed above) to be maintained. The flash lamp operates from 1 flash every 3 min to 12 flashes per minute. The laser beam energy is applied to the workpiece in less than 0.002 s.

Advantages of LBM :

1. Non-contact process with no workpiece distortion.
2. Minimum heat affected zone.
3. Precise operation.
4. High production rates.
5. Process can be easily automated.
6. Inaccessible areas for conventional methods can be processed.
7. Hardness of the material does not affect the process.
8. Multiple holes or welds possible in one exposure.
9. Dissimilar materials can be welded.

For welding, high power lasers with longer pulses are used, so that the surface of the material can be heated to the melting point without any significant vaporization taking place. Spot welding with continuous or repetitively pulsed CO_2 lasers are commonly used.

Product Applications. LBM is again a "micromachining" method which can be used for drilling, scribing, cutting and shaping. Holes as small as 0.005 mm in diameter have been produced. It has got the following drilling applications :- holes in rubber baby bottle nipples ; relief holes in pressure plugs ; holes in nylon buttons, in aerosol spray nozzles, in surgical and hypodermic needles ; flow holes in oil or gas orifices etc. LBM is finding increasing use in industrial and non-industrial fields.

As compared to EBM, LBM has higher energy density levels and it does not need vacuum for its operation.

9.7.3. Plasma Arc Machining or Plasma Jet Machining (PAM or PJM).

We know that all gases burning at high temperatures are ionized gases. In plasma arc machining, the gases are ionised by placing an arc across the path of gas flow. The gas molecules get dissociated causing large amounts of thermal energy to be liberated. This generates temperatures of the order of 16500°C, which are than utilized in removing metal by melting and vaporization. Fig. 9.14 shows a schematic view of PAM.

An arc is struck between tungsten (or tungsten alloy) cathode and the water cooled copper (or copper alloy) anode. An inert gas such as argon is passed through a small chamber in which the arc is maintained. As the gas flows out the nozzle, it is heated and gets ionized by the arc and forms the moving plasma flame. The cathode is eroded by the high spark temperature and must be adjustable.

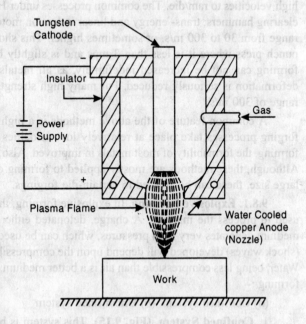

Fig. 9.14. Schematic view of PAM.

Plasma torches have been used for cutting and gouging in hard materials such as stainless steel. As compared to ordinary flame cutting torches, these can cut plain carbon steel four times faster.

Power supply: 100 — 200V; 100 — 300A.

9.8. HIGH ENERGY RATE FORMING (HERF, HVF)

These methods have been developed to form parts made of, new temperature-resistant, high strength metals, that require processing in short production runs and that, often, could not be formed by conventional methods. These methods can be grouped under two categories :

1. **High Energy Rate Forming Processes (HERF).** These methods are so called because the energy (mainly chemical energy in explosive materials and electric/magnetic energy) needed for processing the material is released in a very short time, usually in milli- seconds or micro-seconds. The important processes in this category are : Explosive forming (using chemical energy in explosive materials), Electric spark forming or Electro-hydraulic forming, and electro-magnetic forming (using electric energy)

2. **High Velocity Forming Processes (HVF).** In these processes, the metal is deformed by using very high velocities (movement of ram/die). Since kinetic energy is proportional to velocity square, high energy (mechanical) can be delivered to the metal in these methods with relatively small weights (of ram or die). This reduces the cost and size of the machine. Also, due to very high accelerations, high velocities can be obtained by using short strokes of the ram, which makes it possible to increase production rate. In these methods, the energy stored in air/gas (at high pressure) or the stored chemical energy of a hydrocarbon (petrol or diesel) is used to move the ram/die. So, the difference between HERF and HVF is that whereas in former, the energy stored in some medium is used directly to deform the metal, in HVF, it is converted into mechanical energy which imparts high velocities to ram/die. The common processes under HVF are :- petro-forge hammers, Dynapac, clearing hammers, trans- energy and linear induction motor. In HVF, the forming velocities usually range from 30 to 300 m/s, or sometimes higher. This should be compared with velocity of ram in punch press where it is less than 3 mps and is slightly higher in drop hammers. The velocity of forming can not be increased indefinitely, as all metals have a critical strain rate above which deformation is seriously reduced. For many high strength materials, the critical velocity is in the range of 300 m/s.

A common feature of the above methods is a high rate of strain (conventional forming and forging processes take place at relatively low velocities and strain rates). With increased rate of forming, the formability of most metals in improved. Also, spring-back is minimal in these methods. Although, these methods are mostly applied to forming of sheet and plate products, often of very large size, these can be applied to certain-die forgings.

9.8.1. Explosive Forming. In explosive forming, the chemical energy stored in explosives is used to process the material. A charge, detonated either above or within a pressure transmitting medium generates very high pressures, which can be used to form parts of large size. The pressure (shock waves) developed will depend upon the compressibility of the energy- transmitting medium. Water, being less compressible than air is a better medium. There are two basic systems of explosive forming :-

(a) Confined system, (b) Unconfined system

1. **Confined System, (Fig. 9.15).** This system is basically used for small and tubular parts for flaring and bulging operations. This system is not used much due to the following reasons :

    (i) Being a closed-die opera- tion, there is a greater hazard of die failure due to high pressure genera- ted.

    (ii) Die erosion is a big pro- blem.

In this system, a die in two or more pieces is used which comple- tely encloses the workpiece. When the explosive is detonated, a shock wave is produced in the energy transmitting medium (in this case, air) which forces the workpiece into the die. Vacuum should be created in between the die and the workpiece, otherwise, the trapped air will be subjected to virtually adiabatic compression, resulting in very high temperatures which can burn or melt the workpiece or the die. The trapped air will also prevent the complete forming of the part.

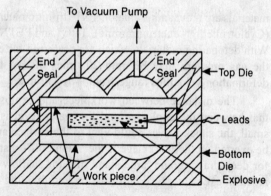

Fig. 9.15. Explosive Forming (confined system).

2. **Unconfined System, (Fig. 9.16).** This system is used for forming large parts from very thin sheet metal upto large ship plates about 25 mm thick. This method has been used for many years in ship building. The workpiece or blank is clamped to the die and the entire die-work assembly is lowered into a swimming pool. An explosive is denoted above or within the water. The shock waves are produced in the body of water (energy trans- mitting medium) which in turn forces the workpiece into the die. Again, vacuum should be drawn in between the workpiece and the die.

The important process varia- bles are : type and amount of explosive, the distance between the explosive and workpiece, the type of energy transmitting medium, and the workpiece.

Use of water as the trans- mitting medium has the following advantages :

1. Since air is very much more compressible than water, the shock pre- ssures produced are very much lower.

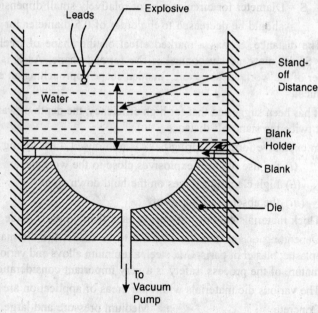

Fig. 9.16. Explosive Forming (Unconfined system).

2. With water, the noise level of explosion is reduced.

3. Possibility of damage to the workpiece from particles of explosive and detonator is greatly reduced.

Basically two types of explosives are used :

(a) Low pressure explosives or firing explosives, such as smokeless powder and black powder. With low pressure explosives, known as cartridge system, the expanding gas is confined (confined system) and the pressure may built upto 700 MPa.

(b) High pressure explosives or detonating explosives. The most widely used detonating materials are :- dynamite, amatol, TNT (tri-nitrotoluene), RDX, Research and Developement Explosive (Cyclotrimethyl- enetrinitramine), Tetryl and PETN (Pentaerythriol tetranitrate) and their mixtures. With detonating materials which are preferred for explosive forming process (unconfined system), the gas pressure may be upto 20 times of that for low pressure explosives. The approximate deformation velocities range from 9 to 230 m/s.

The distance between workpiece and explosive charge (called as "Stand off" distance) or that between the explosive and the water level is also important, since, if the latter distance is small, the shock waves could vent to the surface and lose much of their energy. Greater force can be exerted on the workpiece if the "stand off" distance is smaller. Thus, small stand offs are used for deep drawing and large stand offs for shallow drawing. A too small a stand-off distance will result in excessive local deformation and thinning of the workpiece.

The evaluation of the effects of stand-off distance are usually (normally) based on the criterion that the optimum distance is that at which a central charge will produce the maximum deformation in free forming. Since the optimum distance depends on several factors such as the type of explosives used and the geometry of the tank-workpiece system, it is not possible to define a universal optimum distance. However, as a general guide, where a single point charge is used, the stand-off distance is given as,

S = Diameter for circular jobs of relatively small dimensions, say less than 60 cm.

= should be decreased to the order of 0.5 diameter for larger jobs.

The distance 'S' has a marked effect on the shape of freely formed parts. Generally, the greater S, the more nearly conical is the formed shape. As S is decreased to the order of 0.2 diameter of the workpiece, a more rounded shape approaching an ellipsoid or segment of a sphere is produced.

It has been suggested that for high efficiency, the depth of water over the explosive should be at least twice the stand-off distance.

In explosive forming, spring back is minimised. Less spring back occurs with :

(i) the use of sheet explosives close to the workpiece.

(ii) high clamping forces on the hold down areas.

(iii) the absence of lubricant.

Thick materials exhibit less spring back than do parts made from thin blanks.

Depending on the number of parts to be made, the die-material can be : concrete, wood, epoxy, plastic, plaster of paris, C.I., steel, aluminium alloys and various composite materials. Because of the nature of the process, safety is a very important consideration.

The various die materials with their areas of application are given below :

Concrete	:	Medium pressure and large parts.
Cast Iron (ductile)	:	High pressure and many parts.
Concrete and epoxy resin	:	Low pressure and large parts.
Concrete and fibre glass	:	Low pressure and large parts.
Kirksite	:	Low pressure and few parts.
Kirksite and fibreglass	:	Low pressure and few parts.

Explosive forming has got the following fields of application :

1. For the production of components having a wide-range of sizes and shapes, like radar dishes, and rocket motor cases etc.

2. The capital cost being low and the rate of output limited, the method is economically suitable only for low volume production and for the production of prototype parts.

3. For the production of very large parts with re-entrant sections, which are not possible by conventional methods.

9.8.2. Electro-Hydraulic Forming. The effect produced in explo- sive forming (generation of high intensity shock waves), can also be obtained by discharging stored-electrical energy in a bank of condensers, across electrodes submerged in an electrolyte (usually water). This is the principle of operation of "electro- hydraulic forming" which is also known as "electric spark forming", "electric discharge forming" or "underwater spark forming".

The stored electric energy can be discharged either through a wire or across a gap. A potential difference of 50 kV can jump a gap of about 25 mm. When this discharge takes place under water, the arc (spark) produced converts water into steam. This generates high pressures which are utilized for forming the workpiece. Again, if a potential difference of 30 kV is discharged through a wire of 1 mm diameter, in water, the centre of the wire will instantaneously be raised to about 5100°C. The wire melts and vaporizes resulting in very high pressures and formation of water bubbles. The flow of current is temporarily disrupted due to formation of vapour. As the water bubbles expand, vapour pressure drops and an arc is struck between the electrodes. Due to this, high pressure shock waves are generated, which are used to form a workpiece. The second method is more efficient than the first, and also low voltage is needed. Typical set ups of "electro-hydraulic forming", are shown in Fig. 9.17. In Fig. 9.17(*a*) and (*b*) the parts are formed freely in air. However, a female die can be used, Fig. c, to produce a specific shape. In this case, arrangements must be made to remove air from in between the workpiece and die. This process can be used for : forming, bulging, beading and drawing. The main advantage of this process is that large amounts of energy can be directed to isolated areas of the workpiece. The main limitation of the process is the critical impact velocity of the material to be formed. Materials with critical impact velocities less than 30 m/s are not suitable for this method.

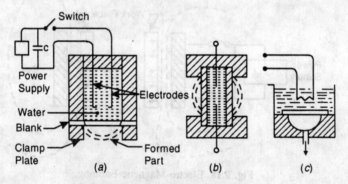

Fig. 9.17. Electro-Hydraulic Forming.

The die material can be as given below :

For small quantity production (upto about 12) : Kirksite, epoxy resin, plaster of Paris, provided the die is well supported to prevent cracking or deformation,

For large. quantity output : Steel.

Electro-hydraulic forming has got the following fields of application

1. It is a versatile process and can be used for the forming of tubular and dished shapes. Shapes impractical by conventional methods can be made by this method.

2. Since only female die is needed, tooling costs are substantially reduced. The die materials being also of low cost, the method is economically more attractive for short run and prototype production.

3. Production rate is higher as compared to explosive forming.

4. Only relatively small components can be made.

9.8.3. Electro-Magnetic Forming. Electro-magnetic forming, also called magnetic pulse forming, is based on the fundamental principles of electrical technology viz., when a current flows in a conductor, a magnetic field is set up around it. If the current and hence the magnetic field changes, a current is induced in any other conductor placed in the magnetic field. The direction of this induced current is such that the induced magnetic field opposes the magnetic field producing it. The two conductors get repelled due to the interaction of the two magnetic fields. In electro-magnetic forming, one conductor is a coil, through which current is suddenly discharged, giving rise to a rapidly changing magnetic field. The work-piece is the second conductor, in which the eddy current are set up. The repelling forces between the coil and the work-piece are high (of the order of 350 N/mm^2 for several micro/seconds), and since the coil is held rigidly in place, the work-piece is repelled and forced against a die. Fig.9.18 shows the basic circuit for electro-magnetic forming. The energy source is a bank of capacitors, charged to a predetermined voltage. The electric energy is discharged through a forming coil. By suitably designing the coil, the process can be used for compression, expansion or for forming contours from sheet metal and tubes. For example, for compressing a tube, the coil is wound around the tube which is contracted onto a mandrel and for expanding, it is inserted inside of a tube surrounded by die. The product applications of this process are : it works effectively on relatively thin materials and is particularly suitable for ; bulging of tubes, shrinking of tubes, flaring and swaging tubes over rods etc. The work-piece must be an electrical conductor, but it need not be magnetic. In this process, since the pulse duration is very short, sufficient pressures are not generated for forming thick material; so, its use is only limited to sheet metal working.

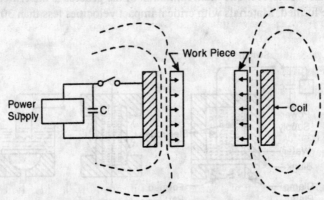

Fig. 9.18. Electro-Magnetic Forming.

To minimise the magnetic cushion effect, the die materials should be of low electrical conductivity. Due to this, the dies are made usually of steel or epoxy resin. To ensure good reproduction of detail and prevent distortion, air is evacuated from the die. Steel dies have longer life than resin dies but with these, the cushion effect is not entirely prevented.

Electro-magnetic forming has got the following characteristics :

1. The process is simple, clean and safe to operate. The operating costs are low. A high cycle rate can be attained and the process is suitable for automation.

2. Deep drawing is not possible, because of the very short duration of the pressure pulse.

3. Asymmetrical parts are not suitable for this method.

4. Irregularities such as slots, holes and slits present problems, because the magnetic field is disrupted.

9.8.4. High Velocity Forming. The HERF methods discussed above are used for the deformation of metals in the form of flat sheet or thin walled tubes. So, these methods are sheet metal forming methods. when the metal is in the form of solid billets, HVF methods (Calied Billet forming methods) are used. The conventional sheet metal forming machines are mainly : Crank and hydraulic presses. In high speed sheet metal forming (HERF) machines, there are no moving parts at all. The energy for metal formation is derived solely from the shock wave from the source. The conventional billet forming machines are usually :- Hydraulic presses, crank and eccentric presses, screw presses, drop hammers and power hammers. Their comparison with high speed billet forming machines is :

(*i*) **Crank or Hydraulic Press.** Large force, low kinetic energy and large mass of the ram.

(*ii*) **Drop Hammer.** Zero force, large kinetic energy and fairly large mass of ram.

(*iii*) **High Speed Machine.** Small force, large kinetic energy and small mass of ram.

The speeds of movement of the deforming material in conventional and high speed machines is compared below :

(1) Conventional Machines

    (*a*) Hydraulic press   :   Upto 0.3 m/s

    (*b*) Crank press   :   Upto 1.5 m/s

    (*c*) Drop hammer   :   Upto 4.5 m/s.

(2) **High Speed Machines**

    (*a*) Billet forming machines :   6 to 24 m/s

    (*b*) Sheet forming machines :   30 to 300 m/s.

Comparison of Conventional and High Speed Billet Forming Machines

(1) **Impact Speed.** The speed of impact of the ram or punch with the work-piece is the most obvious difference between conventional and high speed machines. However, this difference is only significant in the early stages of forming, since, the ram speed is always zero at the end of the forming operation, regardless of the type of the machine used. Below is given the impact speeds of the various metal forming machines :

    (*i*)   Hydraulic press   :   0.03 to 0.3 m/s

    (*ii*)   Crank press   :   0.3 to 1.5 m/s

    (*iii*) Screw press   :   0.3 to 1.5 m/s

    (*iv*) Drop hammer   :   3 to 4.5 m/s

    (*v*)   Power hammer   :   4.5 to 9 m/s

    (*vi*) High speed machine   :   6 to 24 m/s

Fig. 9.19. shows the variation of ram speed with ram stroke for the various machines. Full lines denote the speeds set by machines and dotted lines denote the speeds set up by the resistance of the work-piece. In a hydraulic press, the ram speed is virtually independent of the resistance of the work-piece, provided the press capacity is big enough. At the end of the stroke, the ram speed falls to zero, usually as a result of opening of the relief valve.

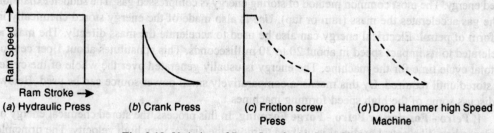

(*a*) Hydraulic Press   (*b*) Crank Press   (*c*) Friction screw Press   (*d*) Drop Hammer high Speed Machine

Fig. 9.19. Variation of Ram Speed with Ram Stroke.

In a crank or eccentric press, the ram speed depends upon the geometry of the crank and connecting rod. It decreases gradually as the ram advances towards the end of its downward stroke. Thus the ram speed is not much influenced by the resistance of the work-piece. For screw press, the design of the driving mechanism and the resistance of the work-piece both affect the ram speed. In drop hammer, power hammer and high speed machines, the ram speed before impact depends upon the design of the drive mechanism, but after impact, it will be determined by the resistance of the work-piece.

While setting up the hydraulic and crank presses, the stroke is adjusted to suit the particular work-piece. These machines are essentially constant stroke devices, their capacities being determined by the resistance of the work-piece. For hammers and high speed machines, the energy level is pre-set by the operator and the length of the stroke is largely determined by the resistance to deformation of the work-piece.

(2) **Energy Available for Forming.** The energy supplied by the machine may either be pressure energy or kinetic energy. Pressure energy can only be supplied when the ram experiences resistance, that is, during the forming operation, whereas, the kinetic energy is supplied before the forming operation begins. The pressure energy is supplied directly from the power source, whereas, the kinetic energy is invested into the whole moving ram or platen and is absorbed by the work-piece. The proportion of pressure energy and kinetic energy in various forming machines is given in Table 9.1.

Table 9.1

Machine	Percentage of total energy available	
	Pressure energy	Kinetic energy
Hydraulic Press	100	0
Crank Press	90	10
Screw Press	60	40
Power Hammer	5	95
Drop Hammer	0	100
High Speed machine	5	95

It is clear from this table that the high speed machine is more closely allied to the power hammer and so is a logical development of the hammer. As has already been discussed (chapter 4), the hydraulic, crank and screw presses are rated in terms of the maximum force which can be exerted on the work- piece. High speed machines and hammers are rated in terms of the maximum energy which can be transferred to the work-piece. The practice of rating a hammer by the weight of the moving ram or tup is only a very approximate guide about the capacity of the hammer to do work and, therefore, is not recommended.

High Speed Forming Machines. High speed billet forming machines were first introduced in the midÄ1950's, in U.S.A. All these machines operate on the principle of the sudden release of stored energy. The most common method of storing energy is compressed gas. The sudden expansion of the gas accelerates the mass (ram or tup). Use is also made of the energy stored chemically in the form of petrol. Electrical energy can also be used to accelerate the mass directly. The mass is accelerated to its impact speed in about 20 to 30 milliseconds. This constitutes about 1 per cent of the total cycle time for the machine. The energy is usually generated over the whole of the cycle, and stored until required. By this means, a comparatively small power source can be used. Below, we discuss some of the high speed forming machines :

1. **Petro - Forging or Petro - Forge Forming.** In this process, the stored chemical energy of a hydrocarbon, like petrol or diesel is utilized to move the dies at very high velocity. The principle of working of a Petro-forge hammer is just similar to I.C. engine. Fig. 9.20 illustrates the working

of a petro-forge hammer. It is a piston-cylinder arrangement and a piston drives a ram (piston rod) and a die. At the beginning of a cycle, the piston is raised upward by admitting a low pressure air at the bottom of the cylinder. A projection is provided at the centre of the piston and when it enters a hole in the cover of the cylinder (during the upward stroke of the piston), it seals the combustion chamber. The seal area is 1/6 to 1/10 of area of the bottom of piston. Due to this the back pressure can support 6 to 10 times the pressure in the combustion chamber. The air-fuel mixture is now ignited in the combustion chamber. The pressure increases by 5 to 7 times which breaks the seal and the high pressure gases act on the top face of the piston. The piston, ram and die are accelerated at a very rapid rate. This is the working stroke. At the end of the working stroke, the piston is again raised upwards. The exhaust valve is opened simultaneously for the escape of exhaust gases from the combustion chamber.

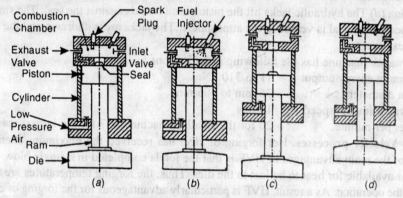

Fig. 9.20. Petro-forge Hammer.

2. Dynapak. In this process, the required energy for driving the piston, ram and die is obtained by releasing instantly high pressure gas from storage and expanding it above the piston. The return of the piston to the top of the cylinder is achieved by hydraulic jacks. This process is commonly used for : forging, powder compacting and sheet metal working etc.

The working of a Dynapak machine (manufactured by General Dynamics Corporation U.S.A.) is illustrated in Fig. 9.21. The main parts of the machine are : (1) The integral piston and ram which is an alloy steel forging (2) Cylinder (3) Face seal (4) Vent (5) Frame (Single alloy steel forging) (6) Pneumatic bellows which support the frame (7) Hydraulic jacks (8) Supporting structure (welded steel), which guides the small movement of the frame. The working medium is air or gas (preferred).

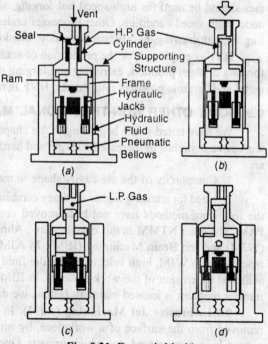

Fig. 9.21. Dynapak Machine.

Position (a) it is the ready-to-fire position. The piston is held against the seal and it is in static balance. The upward force due to gas pressure acting on the shoulder of the piston will be equal to the down-ward force due to gas acting on the very small area outside the seal.

Position (*b*) a small surge of gas is admitted through the vent into the volume inside the seal. This disturbs the static equilibrium of piston which then moves away from the seal. Now, the gas in the main cylinder acts over the full top face of the piston. This downward force will be much greater than the upward force acting on the piston shoulder. The piston and ram are then accelerated rapidly downward, the pressure energy of gas being converted to the kinetic energy of the ram.

Position (*c*) The ram strikes the work-piece by impact. Since the same is supported on bellows, it moves upwards as the ram moves downwards. Since action and reaction are equal and the frame is very heavy, its upwards movement will be very small as compared to the piston stroke. In due course, the frame returns to its original position under gravity. Since the frame is supported on bellows, very little thrust is transmitted to the ground. So, the foundations are needed only to support the structure.

Position (*d*) The hydraulic jacks lift the piston until it seats against the seal. The small amount of gas trapped by the seal is vented to the atmosphere. The jacks are withdrawn and the machine is ready for next cycle.

A Dynapak machine has the following specifications :

Maximum energy output : 11 to 310 kNm
Piston diameter : 76 mm to 305 mm.
Maximum impact speed : 18 m/s
Cycles per minute : 20 for the smallest machine to 7 for the largest machine.

High Velocity processes. Hot forging of steel has received the maximum attention under HVF. One of the main advantages of HVF is that the job is completed in a single blow. Also, very short time is available for heat to be lost to the dies. Thus, the forging temperatures are maintained throughout the operation. As a result, HVF is particularly advantageous for the forging of components having thin webs and intricate contours and made of high strength materials. If possible, closed dies should be used for high speed hot forging, since the effectiveness of a flash land is reduced under high speed condition. Other processes under HVF are : extrusion, powder compaction, cold forging, bar drawing, hydrostatic extrusion, blanking and bar cropping.

HVF is employed for the production of such items as expanded tubes, ducts, drawing tubes, forming of sheet products, extruding and forging of steel, piercing of holes and the compression of metal and ceramic powders into shapes. HVF is not a mass production process.

9.9. SOME OTHER NON-TRADITIONAL MACHINING METHODS (NTMM)

We have noted in the beginning of the chapter that NTMM have been developed to machine workpiece materials of increased strength and hardness. The other factors behind their development are :

1. Complexity of the die-cavity shape to meet the higher productivity demands, and

2. Need for attaining higher accuracy combined with automation. Out of the NTMM discussed, the following methods have not been proved economic, commercially : USM, CHM, EBM and PAM. The other NTMM in this category are : Abrasive Jet Machining (AJM), Water Jet Machining (WJM) and Ion Beam Machining (IBM). In AJM, high velocity abrasive particles are used to do machining. In WJM, high velocity hydraulic fluid is used. In both these methods, the machining is achieved by erosion of the work material. In IBM, the source of energy is electric voltage and the transfer medium is ionised material. Below, we discuss in short, AJM, IBM, and WJM.

9.9.1.Abrasive Jet Machining (AJM). In abrasive jet machining method, the material is removed from the surface of a workpiece, by impinging a focussed jet of fine abrasive particles carried by a compressed gas which imparts kinetic energy to the stream of fine abrasives. The stream leaves through a nozzle at a velocity of the order of 300 m/s and strikes the surface of the workpiece, producing impact loading on it. Severe plastic deformation or micro-cracks occur in the vicinity of the impact. Due to repeated impacts, small chips of material get loosened and a fresh surface gets exposed to the jet.

The carrier gas can be air, nitrogen or carbon dioxide, but never oxygen. The air must be filtered to remove water, oil and other contaminants. Nozzle pressure can range between 0.20 N/mm^2 and 0.85 N/mm^2 but is usually about 0.5 N/mm^2 Higher pressure results in rapid nozzle wear, low pressure gives slow metal removal rates.

To resist abrasion and wear of nozzles, these are made of hard materials such as tungsten carbide and synthetic sapphire. The useful life of sapphire nozzles is about 10 times that of tungsten carbide nozzles. The sizes of the nozzles are usually :

Tungsten Carbide

Round	: 0.0125 to 0.80 mm diameter
Rectangular	: 0.075 mm × 0.50 mm to
	0.175 mm × 3.75 mm
Square	: 0.65 mm square
Sapphire nozzle are made only round	: 0.20 to 0.65 mm diameter

The various abrasive materials used in AJM include : aluminium oxide, silicon carbide, glass powder or beads, dolomite (calcium magnesium carbonate) and specially prepared sodium bicarbonate. When sodium bicarbonate is used, it must be kept dry. The cutting performance will depend upon : hardness, strength, particle size and particle shape of the abrasive. Al_2O_3 is a general purpose abrasive and is used in sizes of 10, 25 and 50 microns. SiC is used for faster cutting on extremely hard materials. It is used in 25 and 50 microns sizes. Dolomite is used in 200 mesh size for light cleaning and etching. Sodium bicarbonate is used for extra fine cleaning and glass beads (0.635 to 1.27 mm diameter) are used for light polishing and fine deburring.

In general, larger sizes are used for rapid removal rate while smaller sizes are used for good surface finish and precision.

The metal removal rate will depend upon : the diameter of nozzle, composition of abrasive gas mixture, hardness of abrasive particles and that of the work-material, particle size, velocity of jet and distance of workpiece from the jet. The typical metal removal rates vary from 0.016 to 0.02 cm^3/min.

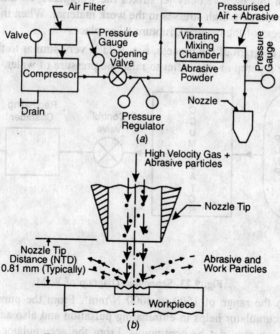

Fig. 9.22. Schematic Diagram of AJM.

Masks defining the machining area are sometimes used to prevent stray cutting. Copper is a good all purpose masking material. Glass gives excellent definition but has short life. Rubber has long life but gives poor definition.

Applications of AJM include : abrasive, cutting, or cleaning (for example electrical contacts) and for machining semi-conductors such as silicon, gallium or germanium, for making holes and slots in glass, quartz, sapphire, mica and ceramics. Other applications are : cleaning hard surfaces, deburring, scribing, grooving, polishing and radiusing. A dimensional tolerance of ± 0.05 mm can be obtained. Surface finish obtained is in the range of 0.5 to 1.2 μ m CLA.

Typical power input is 0.25 kW. The method is used chiefly to cut materials that are sensitive to heat damage and thin section of hard materials that chip easily and to cut indicate holes that would be more difficult to produce by other methods. The other advantage is its low capital cost.

The disadvantages of the method are : low metal removal rate, possibility of stray cutting, embedding of abrasive particles in soft workpiece and dust control requirements.

A schematic diagram of AJM is shown in Fig. 9.22. Dry and filtered gas (in this case air) is raised to a high pressure in the compressor. The pressurised air flows to the vibrating mixing chamber containing abrasive powder. The mixture of pressurised air and abrasive powder than flows to the nozzle. It then impinges on the workpiece after shooting out of the nozzle exit. The pressure regulator regulates the gas flow and its pressure. The feed rate of abrasive powder is controlled by amplitude or vibrations of the mixing chamber. The movement of the nozzle towards the workpiece or vice versa is controlled by a cam mechanism or a pantograph mechanism.

9.9.2. Water Jet Machining (WJM). Water jets alone (without abrasive) can be used for cutting. Thin jets of high pressure and high velocity have been used to cut materials such as wood, coal, textiles, rubber, rocks, concrete, asbestos and leather. The method has also now been used for hydraulic mining of coal, tunneling and cleaning and descaling operation. Also, automated deburring machines are being used by the automotive industry. As mentioned above, the mechanism of material removal is by erosion. When high pressure water jet emerges out of a nozzle, it attains a large kinetic energy. When this high velocity jet strikes the workpiece, its kinetic energy is converted into pressure energy inducing high stresses in the work material. When the induced stress exceeds the ultimate shear stress of the material, rupture takes place.

The schematic diagram of the process, Fig. 9.23 is very similar to that for AJM. In place of compressor, we have a pump or intensifier to raise the pressure of water. Pressures normally used

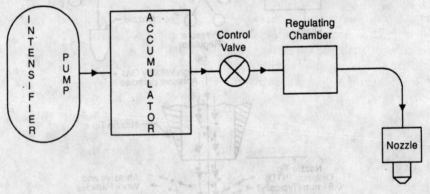

Fig. 9.23. Schematic Diagram of WJM.

in the system are in the range of 1500 to 4000 N/mm^2. From the pump, the water goes to an accumulator. The accumulator helps in eliminating pulsation and also acts as an energy reservoir since the cutting action may not be continuous. From the accumulator the water is lead to the nozzle through a high pressure thick tube which may be carbon steel jacketed stainless steel tube. The material of the nozzle may be sintered diamond, sapphire or Tungsten Carbide. The exit diameter of the nozzle is in the range of 0.05 to 0.35 mm. WJM has got the following advantages:

1. The energy transfer media (water) is cheap, non-toxic and easy to dispose off.

2. The work area remains clean and dust free.

3. The system has no moving parts, therefore, its operating and maintenance costs are low and the process is very safe.

4. Intricate contours can be cut.

5. There is no thermal damage to the work surface as little heat is generated during cutting operation.

6. The process is very convenient for cutting soft and rubber like materials for which the teeth of the conventional saw get clogged.

The limitations of the above method are : the initial cost is high and hard materials can not be cut.

Recently, a model of the WJM machine which uses high velocity water jets (with abrasives) has been developed at the University of Rhode island in U.S.A., for cutting hard materials. The principle of working is as follows : The process filters tap water to remove particles larger than 0.45microns. The water is then compressed to about 420 MPa, after which it moves through reinforced hoses to the cutting head. There, the abrasive is added and the needle thin stream of water shoots out at 600 m/s. It has been claimed that in such a machine, water jets zip through 25 mm thick pieces of Aluminium at a rate of 100 mm/minute. While lasers don't cut transparent materials, water jets dissect an approximately 32 cm thick glass in a minute. Again, it took just a minute to make a 35.5 mm long slice in a 25 mm thick Zinc-nickel steel composite. In comparison, an EDM machine goes through approximately only 2.5 mm. Also, the water jet (high tech knife) carves up hard ceramics on which even diamond tipped saws bounce off without making a scratch.

9.9.3. Ion Beam Machining (IBM).

In IBM, method, the metal is removed by bombarding the work with accelerated ions. These ions collide with the surface atoms of the workpiece and knock them out of the surface. thus the metal removal occurs on atomic scale and hence the process is also called : ion etching, ion milling or ion polishing. Unlike other thermo- electric processes (EBM, LBM, PAM and EDM), no large scale heating of the workpiece surface takes place during the process.

The schematic arrangement of IBM is basically simple and is similar to EBM. At the top end of the vacuum chamber is the ion beam generating apparatus, which consists of an electron gun which discharges free electrons into the vacuum chamber filled with argon gas. The gas gets ionized by the electrons. A stream of ions is thus generated and is directed on to the target material, which is clamped to a table at the other end of the vacuum chamber. The work table can be oscillated and rotated. This makes it possible to subject different points on the work surface to the ion beam. It is not necessary to work in an absolute vacuum. About 10^{-4} torr is suitable.

Depending upon the type of power used, there are two systems of IBM. One system uses a d.c. source. It is simple and less expensive but can be used only for conductive materials. The more universal system uses radio frequency equipment. It is more expensive but can be used for any material.

The method is similar to chemical etching in the need for masking. However, no undercutting takes place in this method. Also, powerful etchants that can propagate along cracks and degrade the masking material, are not needed in this technique. Metal removal rates will depend upon the workpiece material (for example for aluminium it is twice that for tungsten). The MRR vary upto

2×10^{-4} mm^3/min. The accuracy of etching is very high. Tolerances in the range of $\pm 5 \times 10^{-6}$ mm are possible.

Regarding the applications of IBM, the method is mainly used in micromachining of electronic components, like computer memories, figuring optical surfaces and for the precision fabrication of fine wire dies in refractory materials. Typical materials which can be etched by IBM include glass, aluminium, quartz, crystals, silica, agates, porcelains, cermets, mixtures of quartz and asbestos, and numerous metals and oxides including rare earth metals. The method holds greatest promise in the field of electronics. It can be used to etch multilayered structures (for example to form a terminal) without the risk of incompatibility. This is an important advantage since multilayered I.C. circuits are becoming increasingly common. The method has proved extremely valuable in etching surfaces of specimens prior to studying their microstructure. The material microstructure is clearly revealed, since the method does not alter the work surface. Also, the etched surface is equally well suited to both optical and electron microscope. The method is also used for the deposition of thin film of material, particularly in electronic industries. Typically, the material to be deposited is made the anode in a low-pressure argon or other rare gas atmosphere. Gaseous ions bombard the cathode, sputtering its material on the substrate. Deposition of thin coatings on such products like razor blades is also common.

The Advantages of IBM Are :

MRR are easily controlled, no residue, no undercutting as with CHM, no etchants are required, in figure etching resolution is limited only by the resolution of the mask and the method is almost universal.

The main drawbacks of the method are :

MRR are very slow, it is relatively expensive and thermal or radiation damage may occur in some materials.

PROBLEMS

1. What prompted the development of unconventional machining and forming processes ?
2. What are the advantages of electrical machining methods ?
3. What are the limitations of electrical machining methods ?
4. What is the principle of EDM ?
5. Explain the function of the dielectric fluid in EDM ?
6. Name the common dielectric fluids used in EDM.
7. Explain the function of servo - mechanism in EDM.
8. What are the requirements of tool material for EDM ? Name the common tool materials.
9. Give the advantages and disadvantages of EDM.
10. Give the product applications of EDM.
11. Explain the principle of ECM.
12. List the advantages of ECM.
13. What is the function of electrolyte in ECM ? List the common electrolytes used in ECM.
14. List the requirements of tool material for ECM. Write the commonly used tool materials.
15. List the product applications of ECM.
16. Compare the similarities and differences of ECM and EDM.
17. Explain the principle of ECG.
18. What is the difference between ECG and conventional grinding ?

19. List the product applications of ECG.
20. List the advantages of ECG over conventional grinding.
21. Explain the principle of chemical milling.
22. Explain the purpose of a chemical milling.
23. What is the purpose of a photosensitive resist ?
24. Explain the steps in chemical milling using photosensitive resists.
25. Differentiate between the chemical blanking and contour machining.
26. List the advantages of chemical milling.
27. List the limitation of chemical milling.
28. List the product applications of chemical milling.
29. Explain the principle of USM.
30. List the common materials used for tool in USM.
31. List some abrasive powders commonly used in USM.
32. Compare the methods of attaching tool faces to tool holders.
33. What is the difference between USM and conventional grinding ?
34. Give the leading advantages of USM.
35. Define an electron beam.
36. Explain why EBM process is performed usually in a vacuum chamber.
37. List the product applications of EBM.
38. List the limitations of EBM.
39. What is laser ?
40. Explain the principle of LBM.
41. Contrast LBM and EBM.
42. List the product applications of LBM.
43. Explain the principle of PAM.
44. What is the difference between HERF and HVF.
45. Compare confined system and non-confined systems of explosive forming.
46. Explain the principle of explosive forming.
47. Compare confined system and non-confined systems of explosive forming.
48. List the common explosives used in explosive forming.
49. What is "Stand-off" distance. Explain its importance in explosive forming.
50. Explain the principle of electro-hydraulic forming.
51. What are the main advantages and limitations of electro-hydraulic forming ?
52. Explain the principle of electro-magnetic forming.
53. List the product applications of electro-magnetic forming.
54. With the help of neat diagrams, explain the working of a petro- forge hammer.
55. What is the principle of pneumatic forming ?
56. What is high velocity forming ? Is drop hammer forging a high velocity process ? Describe the basic principles of high velocity forming methods and discuss the advantages and limitations of the high velocity forming methods in comparison with their low velocity counterparts.
57. Explain the method of AJM with the help of a schematic diagram.

58. Name the abrasives and carrier gases used in AJM.
59. Write the applications of AJM.
60. Explain the method of WJM with the help of a schematic diagram.
61. Write the applications of WJM.
62. Explain the method of IBM.
63. Write in detail about the applications of IBM.
64. With help of neat sketches, describe the following processes : WCEDM, EDG, ECH, ECD.
65. Explain why the mechanical properties of workpiece materials are not significant in most of the NTMM ?
66. What should be the properties of maskants used in CHM ?
67. Differentiate between ECM and CHM.
68. List the advantages of WJM.
69. What is the purpose of abrasives in ECG ?
70. What type of work is most suitable for LBM ?
71. List the main specifications of NTMM Machines.

Machine	Main Specifications
EDM	Tank Size
USM	Hole ϕ, kW
EBM	kW
LBM	kW
ECM	Amp. kVA
CHM	Tank Size
Jet Machining	Jet Pressure

72. Write a short note on Powder Mixed Electric Discharge Machining (PMEDM).

    PMEDM :- It has been noted under Art. 9.2 that the surface finish obtained by conventional EDM is of the order of 0.2 μm. To get high surface quality and mirror like characteristics, parts are subjected to mechanical polishing after EDM, which is a wastage of time and energy.

    A new variant of EDM has been developed to improve the efficiency and the surface finish of the workpiece. It consists in mixing a suitable material in the powder form, in the dielectric fluid, as a suspension at the tool-workpiece interface, and is termed as Powder mixed EDM (PMEDM). The mixed powder facilitates the bridging action and minimizes the insulation strength of the dielectric fluid. The machining becomes more stable and efficient. Graphite powder is mixed in the dielectric fluid and the performance is measured in terms of MRR, Surface roughness (SR), and Tool Wear Rate (TWR). The results show that MRR increases, whereas, SR and TWR are reduced.

73. What for CHM is used?
74. What are the limitations of USM?
75. Where is USM employed?
76. How much power density a LASER can produce?
77. What are the different types of Lasers used in machining operations.
78. What are the limitations of LBM?
79. What is the effect of ECM on mechanical properties of work materials?
80. What is the effect of EDM on mechanical properties of work materials?

10

Powder Metallurgy

10.1. INTRODUCTION

Powder Metallurgy, P/M, is a manufacturing process in which components are directly produced by bringing a powder of the starting material into the desired final shape by compressing the powder in dies. Strength and other properties are imparted to the components by subsequent sintering operations. It is one of the cheapest mass production process for manufacturing high quality, high strength, complex parts with a high degree of accuracy. Porous parts as well as parts with high density structures may be produced. The process is commercially and economically adaptable only to mass production, due to expensive dies and machines.

Basic steps of the process:— The production of a component by P/M involves the following basic steps:—

1. *Preparation* of powder/powders of the desired composition.

2. Mixing and Blending: In this step, more than one powders are mixed thoroughly and blended to ensure their even distribution, or a powder is mixed with lubricants, additives or binders that might be used.

3. *Compacting*: In this step, the blended mixture is compacted to bring the finely divided particles or powder into close proximity while imparting the desired part configuration and providing green strength to the part.

4. *Sintering*: In this step, the compacts obtained after step 3 are heated at elevated temperature to establish permanent strong bonds between adjacent particles and thereby to impart strength to the compacts.

10.2. ADVANTAGES AND LIMITATIONS OF P/M

Advantages:

1. One major advantage is its cost effectiveness in producing certain parts as compared to other manufacturing processes. This is due to the fact that parts can be made with close tolerance and surface finish which eleminates the necessity of any further processing. So, scrap is eliminated. Also labour cost is low since no skilled workers are required as the process can be fully automated.

2. The second major advantage is that certain types of parts can be made only by P/M by mixing different metals, metals and non-metals, metals and ceramics etc., to achieve the desired properties of the component. Some examples are:

    (a) Electrical contact points must be both wear resistant and refractory and have good electrical conductivity. For this, many combinations of metals have been developed: W-Cu, W-Co, W-Ag, Mo-Ag, Ni-W-Cu, and Ni-Ag. As is evident, the combinations include metals that are wear resistant and refractory (W, Mo, Ni etc) and metals which are electrical conductors (Cu and Ag). Some compositions are: W or Mo with 25 to 50% Ag or Cu and WC with 35 to 55% Ag. There is no other way of combining them except P/M. If melted, these metals will not mix but will separate like oil and water.

(b) Combining metallic and non-metallic materials: Electrical brushes for motor are made by blending Cu or Ag (20 to 97%) with graphite. Tin, lead, iron and silica may also be added in small quantities to enhance wear resistance (iron and lead can not mix in a liquid state). Another example is of producing heavy duty metallic frictional materials for brakes and clutches, such as Cu-Sn or Cu-Zn alloys with embedded SiO_2, Al_2O_3 etc.

(c) Metals with melting point temperatures too high for castings can be processed by P/M. For example, particles of WC and Co are mixed together (Co acts as the binder for WC particles) to produce cemented carbides which act as tool materials. Similarly W filaments for incandescent light bulbs are manufactured by P/M. The filaments should have ductility, high melting point and proper electrical conductivity. For this W is the most suitable material. The process consists of forming billets of W from its powder by P/M method. Then the wires are made by first forging and then wire drawing these billets.

(d) Production of 'Cermets' (ceramics + metals). A typical composition is:
Al_2O_3 + upto 10% of (W, Mo, Boron, Ti etc.).The material is being increasingly used as tool material.

(e) Diamond bonded with metal (typically Cu and 15 to 20% tin).

(f) Mechanically alloyed super alloys.

(g) Nuclear fuel elements with UO_2 dispersed in alumina or stainless steel.

(h) Silver infiltrated tungsten is used in nozzles for rockets and missiles.

(i) Production of heavy metal: an alloy of W containing 6% Ni and 4% Cu. It can be used for radium containers, balancing weights and similar applications where high density is desirable.

(j) Production of electric resistance welding electrodes from mixtures of copper and tungsten. Here, it is possible to retain much of the relative high electric conductivity of copper while realizing high strength and ability to withstand high temperatures of tungsten.

(k) Dispersion strengthened alloys in which a high hot strength is secured by the presence of finely divided and distributed stable oxides, for example,

    (i) Jet engine components of thoriated dispersed nickle with 2% ThO_2

    (ii) Copper welding electrodes with dispersed alumina (Al_2O_3).

(l) Porosity of the part can be controlled over wide limits to fabricate products with special features. Special screens and filters (from bronze, Ni and stainless steel powders) used in controlling the flow of gases and liquids are made with porosity as high as 80%. Less porous structures are created for self lubricating bearings, slide strips, expan- sion plates, gears, gear pumps, cams etc. Parts of this kind are sintered with a porosity of 40% of the total volume followed by impregnation with a suitable lubricant. Parts with unusual damping properties resulting in quieter operation of mating parts can be produced.

(m) Magnetic applications: These include magnetically soft materials such as Fe, Fe-3Si, Fe-50Ni. These, because of their mechanical softness are difficult to machine, but are easily formed into final shape by P/M. Alnico permanent magnets (Fe-Al-Ni-Co) can be sintered, being superior to those cast.

Other advantages of P/M are:

(3) Powders available in pure state produce items of extreme purity.

(4) High production rates; can be 500 to 1000 pieces per hour

(5) Complex shapes can be produced

(6) Bimetallic and laminated special purpose parts can be made from mould layers of different metal powders, securely and permanently inter locked.

Limitations

1. Dies and equipment costs are high. So, the process is economically feasible only for mass production. Minimum production run of 10,000 parts is needed to offset the tooling costs. Dies are made for long production runs, of the order of 1,50,000 to 200,000 parts.

2. The material cost in powder form is high. However, high powder material costs are usually offset by an almost total absence of scrap. Part costs are also reduced by eliminating machining. Labour costs are also comparitively low.

3. Metal powders are sometimes difficult to store without some deterioration.

4. There is little flow of metal during compaction, so intricate designs in the products are difficult to attain.

5. A completely dense product is not possible by this process. Also, a uniformly high-density product is very difficult to produce.

6. Part size and weight are restricted. These are regulated by the capacity of available press and compressibility characteristics of the various powder combinations. P/M is principally restricted to the manufacture of comparatively small parts. Part weight can be under 5 newtons. However, parts weighing upto 900 newtons have been successfully mass produced by P/M. Typical part sizes:

100 mm $\phi \times 150$ mm long on 900 kN capacity press

250 mm $\phi \times 200$ mm long on 900 to 2700 kN capacity press.

7. Some metal powders in a finely divided state, for example, of Al, Mg, Zr and Ti, present explosion and fire hazards.

8. Product Design limitations, which will be discussed ahead.

9. The residual porosity, makes sintered compacts rougher than the compacting die.

10. Low mechanical properties compared to other methods for similar parts. Low impact and fatigue properties

11. Some thermal difficulties are experienced during sintering operation. This is particularly true for low melting point metals such as Sn, Pb, Zn and Cd. During the sintering operations, the atmosphere in the furnace should be reducing to avoid the formation of oxides which will have adverse effects on sintering process and result in an inferior product. The oxides of the above mentioned metals can not be reduced at temperatures below the melting point of the metal, whereas the sintering temperature is always less than the melting point of the metal.

10.3. MANUFACTURE OF METAL POWDERS

There are many methods available for the production of powders, depending upon the type and nature of the metal. We discuss below, some of the common methods :—

1. **Atomization.** In this method, Fig 10.1a, molten metal is broken up into small droplets by spraying it against an oncoming stream of compressed air, inert gas or water jets. With air and water atomization, the powder always gets oxidised. The particle shape and size can

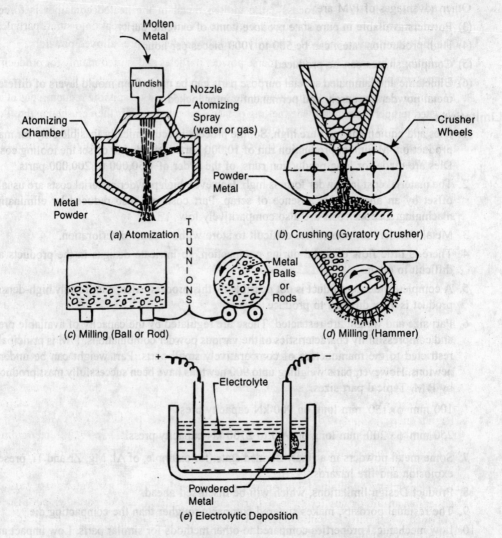

Fig. 10.1. (*a* to *e*). Methods of Producing Metal Powders.

be readily varied by controlling the process parameters, that is, metal flow rate or the pressure and temperature of the stream of air or gas. The powder particles will generally be spherical or pear shaped. A standard dust collector system may be used to collect the powder. The method is mainly used for low melting point metals/alloys such as brass, bronze, zinc, tin, lead and aluminium powders, because of the corrosion action of the metal on the orifice or nozzle (through which the molten metal emerges) at high temperature.

With suitable design, the method can be employed for producing powders of other materials also, such as : stainless steel, nickle-based super alloys, titanium alloys and cobalt-base alloys etc. The other variations of the melt atomization method are :

(*a*) An electric arc is struck between non-rotating, non-consumable tungsten electrode and rotating consumable electrode. It is carried out in a chamber filled with an inert gas (Argon gas). The metal droplets from the rotating consumable electrode are thrown off, are collected and are finally crushed to the required powder size.

(b) In the "Soluble gas process'", the molten metal in the heated container is forced under pressure to flow through a pipe into a vacuum and break into small particles.

The melt atomization method is mainly used for producing pre- alloyed powders.

2. *Machining.* This method produces coarse powder particles and is used mainly for producing magnesium powder.

3. *Reduction.* Pure metal is obtained by reducing its oxide with a suitable reducing gas at an elevated temperature (below the melting point). This pure metal is then crushed and milled to a powder. The resulting particles are of irregular shape and are quite porous. The process is cheap and a large amount of powder is made by this method. For iron, the reaction is:

$$Fe_3O_4 + + 4\,CO \xrightarrow{\text{heat}} 3\,Fe + 4\,CO_2 \uparrow$$

Hydrogen reduction:

$$Cu_2O + H_2 \xrightarrow{\text{heat}} 2\,Cu + H_2O$$

Powders of W, Mo, Ni and Co are also made by this method by hydrogen reduction.

4. *Crushing and Milling.* These methods are mainly used for brittle metals and utilize various types of crushers, rotary mills and stamping mills to break down the metals by crushing and impact.

In earlier stages of powder preparation, gyratory, cone or roll crushers (Fig 10.1b) are used to crush brittle metals. For finer powder, the metal particles are fractured by impact. In ball mill (Fig 10.1c) which is a horizontal barrel shaped container holding a quantity of balls (made of a metal or ceramic), which being free to tumble about as the container rotates, crush and abrade any powder particles that are introduced into the container. Higher energy is imparted to the balls and milling is accelerated by using a vibratory mill in which the drum rotates about the horizontal as well as vertical axes. A similar action is achieved by rotating blades in hammer mill (Fig. 10.1d) or by rods placed in a horizontal axis rotating drum (rod mill).

Finer particles are obtained when particles are hurled against a hard, stationary surface, either by an air or gas jet or in a slurry (impact milling). Finer particles can also be obtained when particles entrained in two opposing fluid streams impact on one another (fluid energy milling).

5. *Electrolytic deposition.* The process is similar to electroplating. For producing iron, impure steel plates act as anodes in tanks containing an electrolyte. Sheets of stainless steel are also placed in the tank and act as cathodes. When D.C. current is passed through the electrolyte, pure iron gets deposited on cathode. The cathode plates are then removed and the electrolytic iron is stripped from them. The deposited material usually exists as a soft spongy dendritic structure. Additional crushing and milling is necessary. The method is used for copper, iron, silver and tantalum powders, (Fig. 10.1e).

6. *Shotting.* In this method, the molten metal is poured through a sieve or orifice and is cooled by droping into water. Most metals can be shotted. The droplets are transformed into small particles as they are agitated and cooled in water.

7. *Granulation.* In this method, the molten metal is converted into small particles by rapidly stirring the metal while it is cooling.

8. *Condensation of Metal Powders.* The powders of some metals like magnesium, zinc and cadmium can be produced by boiling them and then condensing the vapours.

9. Some powders of ductile titanium alloys are made from castings. Hydrogen gas is introduced to form brittle hydrides which can be milled into a powder. Ductility is then restored by driving off the hydrogen by heating to about 350°C when the powder will dissociate into pure metal and hydrogen.

10. *Thermal Decomposition.* In this method, metals are made to combine with carbon monoxide to from volatile carbonyls. At suitable temperature and pressure, these carbonyls decompose to get pure metal. The method is used for Iron, Nickel, Molybdenum and Tungsten. The reactions are :

$$Ni + 4CO \rightleftharpoons Ni(CO)_4$$

$$Fe + 5CO \rightleftharpoons Fe(CO)_5$$

$$Mo + 6CO \rightleftharpoons Mo(CO)_6$$

$$W + 6CO \rightleftharpoons W(CO)_6$$

The powder particles obtained are almost spherical in shape.

10.3.1. Metal Powder Characteristics :— Both the consolidation and the properties of the final product depend upon certain characteristics of metal powders which are discussed below :—

1. **Surface Area.** This is the area per unit mass of the powder. It indicates the area available for bonding and also the area on which adsorbed films or contaminants may be present.

2. **Density :—** The degree of porosity in a sintered or unsintered powder metallurgy component is determined indirectly by making density measurements. The density of a metal in three different conditions is commonly dealt with in the science of powder metallurgy. These are given below :

(*i*) **Theoretical density :—** Theoretical density or True density is the mass per unit volume of the solid material. It is the density of a non-porous metal in the solid state, that is, when it has been manufactured by non-powder metallurgy methods such as casting followed by hot and cold working. Any and all the pores get completely closed and the material becomes fully homogeneous. The theoretical density of a material is the highest possible density (100%) it can have. This density is used as a standard basis of comparison with other types of density. For iron, its value is 7.87 gm/cm³.

(*ii*) **Apparent density :—** The 'Apparent density' in gm/cm³ defines the actual volume filled out by the loose powder. It is a very important property of the powder and depends upon the particle shape, size and size distribution. The apparent density of irregularly shaped particles will be lower than that of the spherical particles and so also of the coarser particles as compared to finer particles of the same shape. It is often expressed as a percentage of the fully dense material, that is, as a percentage of true density.

It is measured by subtracting the weight of an empty container from the weight of that container and the powder filling it, and then dividing by the inside volume of the container. For iron powder, its value ranges from 2.5 to 3.5 gm/cm³.

(*iii*) **Tap density :—** This density is obtained by tapping or vibrating the container and signifies the conpaction achievable without the application of pressure.

(*iv*) **Green density :—** It is the mass of compacted powder in an unsintered pressed briquette per unit volume of the briquette. The green density of iron powder usually ranges from 6.7 to 7.5 gm/cm³.

3. **Compressibility and Compression Ratio.** The term compres- sibility denotes the change in green density with increasing compacting pressure. It is usually given as the density at some specified pressure (450 to 500 MPa). Compression ratio is defined as the ratio of the unpressed volume and pressed volume of the powder for a given mass. Both these properties depend upon the shape, size and size distribution of the powder particles. The compression ratio usually varies between 1.5 and 3. Of course, for very fine powders it may be as high as 10. However a lower, compression ratio is preferred to reduce the depth of die and the plunger movement in the die and thereby the wear and tear of the tools. 'Compacting ratio' is defined as the ratio of the green density of the part to the apparent density and it means the same thing as the compression ratio.

Other related terms used in powder Metallurgy practice are :–

(*a*) **A compact** :- It is the briguette made by compacting powder. This compact is called "Green compact". After this compact is sintered, it is called "Sintered compact"

(*b*) **Fill or Powder fill** :– It is the amount of powder needed to completely fill the die or container cavity, prior to the compacting operation. The cavity should be filled in the shortest possible time to avoid delay of production. The amount of powder representing this fill is usually expressed as the height of the powder in the die-cavity needed to result in a compact of the desired dimensions and density. Thus,

Fill = Median height of compact desired × Compresion Ratio

4. **Flow Rate.** It is defined as the time required for a measured quantity of powder to flow out of a standard orifice. It is an important property of the powder because the time needed to fill the die should be small to obtain higher production rates and economy. Flow rate or flowability depends upon the shape, size and size distribution of the powder particles. Smaller and spherically shaped particles have the maximum flow rate. Very fine particles (of the order of 1 to 10 microns) will flow just like a liquid. When such a powder is pressed in die, it will flow into complex die cavities. Flowability can also be increased by the addition of stearate to the mix.

5. **Particle Shape, Size and Size Distribution.** As discussed above, these three properties greatly influence the apparent density, conpressibility and flow rate of the powder.

The particle shape depends largely on the method of powder manufacture. It may be spheroidal, nodular, irregular, angular, lamellar, acicular and dendritic. Spheroidal particles have excellent sintering properties. However, irregularly shaped particles are superior for practical moulding and achieving good green strength of the part because they will interlock on compacting.

Particle size or fineness is expressed by the diameter of the spheriodal particles and by the average diameter of the other particles. It is determined by passing the powder through standard sieves or by microscopic measurement. Particle size should neither be too large nor too small. Too large particles may not display the required structure for the P/M route and may not result in high densities. On the other hand, it is difficult to handle fine particles and they may tend to agglomerate. Also, their large surface area-to-volume ratio may introduce large quantities of undesirable adsorbed substances and on metals, also oxides. However, finer powders have excellent sintering qualities and are particularly important for 'Slip Casting'. The usual size of powders used in P/M varies from 4 to 200 microns, with 100 microns being the most used size.

Particle size distribution refers to the quantity of each standard particle size in the mix (powder). It influences apparent density, compressibility, flowability, final porosity and the strength of the part. For a given material, the strength of the part will be proportional to its final density after pressing. Theoretically, a powder containing varying particle sizes will result in greater density, because smaller particles will fill up the interspaces between the large particles. However, when mixing, the finer particles have the tendency to separate and segregate. Due to this reason, many users prefer uniform size particles and rely on the compacting pressure to get the final density required.

The ISO has defined the following qualitative particle shape classification as per ISO-3252:

1. Spherical   :   Nominally spherical, three dimensional.

           Produced by : atomization, carbonyl (Fe), precipitation from a liquid.

2. Rounded or :   Rounded, irregular shape (3D).

    Nodular   *Produced by* : atomization, chemical decomposition.

3. Angular   :   Roughly polyhedral with sharp edges (3D).

           Produced by : Mechanical disintegration, Carbonyl (Ni)

4. Acicular   :   Needle shaped (1D)

           Produced by : Chemical decomposition.

5. Dendritic   :   Branched, crystalline shape (2D). Produced by Electrolytic Process.

6. Irregular   :   Lacking any symmetry (3D). *Produced by* : Chemical

           decomposition, Mechanical comminution.

7. Granular   :   Irregular but approximately equidimensional, (3D).

           Produced by : reduction of oxides.

8. Flaky   :   Plate like (2D),

           Produced by : Mechanical Comminution

9. Fibrous   :   Regularly or irregularly thread like (1D).

           Produced by chemical decomposition, mechanical comminution

These shapes have been illustrated in Fig. 10.2.

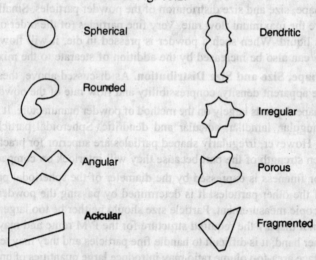

Fig. 10.2. Particle Shapes.

10.3.2. Pre-Alloyed and Precoated Powders. Conventionally an alloyed powder product is made from thoroughly mixed and blended powders of alloying metals. However, superior properties are attained if pre-alloyed powders are used, each powder particle being an alloy.

Pre-alloyed powders are alloyed in the melting process. Pre-alloyed powders of : Stainless steels. Ni base alloys such as Monel, Titanium alloys, Cobalt base alloys and some low-alloy steels are available. Pre-alloyed powder products have high strength and are corrosion and high temperature resistant. However, mixed and blended powder products are cheaper to produce and require lower pressures to compact.

In pre - coated powders, each particle is coated with another element. The product will have different properties from those of the base material, for example, superior corrosion resistance is obtained by the use of stainless steel-clad plate. Precoated powder products are more homogeneous than those made by blending. Pre - coated powders are obtained by passing the powder through a carrier gas, resulting in uniformly coated individual particle.

10.4. MIXING AND BLENDING

The aim of this step is to obtain uniform distribution of particle sizes. This step is necessary in the following situations :

1. Making of alloyed powders by combining a homogeneous mixture of carefully weighed and blended mixtures.

2. Combining metallic and non-metallic powders.

3. To ensure filling up of the interstices between large particles, coarser fraction is blended with a fine fraction. This will result in high tap density.

4. Binders are added to powder that would other wise fail to develop adequate green strength, for example, for the production of sintered carbide tool material, cobalt powder is added as a binder to the WC powder.

5. Sintering aids are added to accelerate densification on heating.

6. Lubricants are added to the powders to reduce die wall friction and friction of the individual particles relative to one another. This will result in the attainment of high green compact densities. They also increase the flowability of powders and aid in the ejection of the compacted part. Although the lubricants add to the porosity, they increase the production rate. The principal lubricants are: stearic acid, lithium stearate or powdered graphite.

Mixing and blending must be thorough. It is done mechanically often in 'ball mill'. It may be done either dry or wet. For wet, water or a solvent is added to the dry powder to reduce the possible hazards of dust and explosion.

There is a difference in these two operations. Mixing means the thorough intermixing (intermingling) of powders of two or more materials, intermixing of a powder and binder, and intermixing of a powder and lubricants etc. On the other hand, blending means the thorough intermixing of powders (of different grain sizes) of the same nominal composition.

10.5. COMPACTING (BRIQUETTING)

The purpose of this step has already been explained under Art. 10.1. The powders are compacted in moulds by the application of pressure to form a so called green compact (a compact without permanent bonding). The compacting pressure may range from 80 to 1600 MPa with more commonly used pressures being 320 to 800 MPa. The density, hardness and also the strength increases with pressure. However, for every metal powder, there is an optimum compacting pressure beyond which there is little improvement in properties. The die cost and press capacity and hence the production cost will increase with increased compacting pressure.

(a) For soft powders such as brass, bronze and aluminium, the compacting pressure may range from 100 to 350 MPa.

(b) For iron, steel and Ni alloys, the range in 400 to 700 MPa.

(c) The pressure range is still higher for harder materials such as WC.

During compacting, the green strength of a compact is achieved due to the following factors :—

1. Sliding combined with pressure promotes adhesion and even cold welding with some powders.

2. Mechanical interlocking of particles, especially with particles of irregular shape. So, green strength is lower for more spherical powders even though they pack more closely.

3. By the addition of bonding agents which evaporate during sintering, Of course, the green strength is lower when lubricants are added to the powders.

Most compacts are made by pressing in dies which have been set up in a sufficiently powerful mechanical or hydraulic presses. The compacting equipment consists of: Die or container, Upper (top) punch and Lower (bottom) punch (Fig. 10.3). The upper punch forms the top shape of the compact and applies pressure during the compacting operation. The lower punch conforms to the lower end of the die cavity. It may or may not apply pressure for compacting depending upon the design, but it acts as ejector for forcing the compact out of the die cavity at the end of the compacting stroke. The die cavity is automatically filled with the required amount of blended powder.

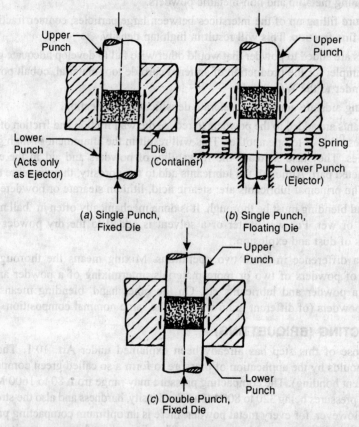

Upper Punch

Upper Punch

Lower Punch (Acts only as Ejector)

Die (Container)

Spring

Lower Punch (Ejector)

(a) Single Punch, Fixed Die

(b) Single Punch, Floating Die

Upper Punch

Lower Punch

(c) Double Punch, Fixed Die

Fig. 10.3. Compacting Equipment (Punch and Die).

1. In the '*single punch design*' (Fig. 10.3a), the bottom punch acts as a support at the start of the operation and then as ejector at the end of the compacting stroke. The upper punch enters the die cavity to compress the powder. At the end of its downward stroke when it just starts rising upward, the lower punch also starts moving upward to eject the compact out of the die cavity. The drawback of this design is that, since powder does not transmit pressure as a continuous solid would and wall friction also opposes compaction, the compacting pressure tapers off rapidly, giving compacts of higher density close to the upper punch and of diminishing density far away. This limits the depth-to-diameter ratio of the part. This design is suitable only for parts upto about 5 mm thick. The design is also satisfactory under high speed conditions for high density components where it has been found that upto 98% of the force was transmitted.

2. The improved design is to have the die or container as floating (supported on springs) and not fixed, Fig. 10.3 (*b*). It will also move downward by the friction force between the powder and container, when the upper punch enters the die cavity and starts compressing the powder. There will be more uniform density in the compact as compared to the first design. The container should have as low a mass as possible consistent with strength requirements, because it has to be accelerated downward by friction between the powder and the container walls during pressing. The design is suitable for high speed compaction also.

3. *In the double punch or counteracting punch, fixed container design*, Fig. 10.3*c*, both the punches enter the die simultaneously to compress the powder. At the end of the downward stroke of the upper punch when it starts moving upwards, the lower punch continues its upward journey to force the compact out of the die cavity. In this design, the minimum density is in the middle section. The variation in density is appreciably less than the single punch design. This design is not suitable for high speed compaction due to the difficulty of closely synchronising the two punches.

Multiple-punch Design. With irregular shaped parts and when the thickness of the part changes considerably from point to point, even with the double punch design, powder compacting creates a serious problem of pressure gradients on the part. To equalize these pressure gradients and hence the green density, dies with multiple punches guided within each-other, are used so that the same degree of compaction can be applied everywhere by applying varying pressure on the powder, (Fig. 10.4).

Rotary Table Design. In this design, 6 to 30 or more die sets, each complete with top and bottom punches,are arranged in a circle concentric with the axis of the rotating table. The dies are rotated to the stations, where the required operations (filling the die cavity, compacting etc.) are performed automatically. At the last station, the compacts are ejected and the individual dies start another cycle. These machines have high rate of production since work can be done on all of the parts at the same time. Production rate on such a machine may reach even 1000 compacts per minute.

Dies. There are two types of dies used in P/M process : non-collapsible and Collapsible. Non - collapsible dies are used when the compact can be conveniently forced out of the die cavity, without damaging the compact. When the compact design is such that it can't be forced out of the die cavity, collapsible dies (dies with removable panels) must be used. More complicated designs can be produced on these dies as compared to non-collapsible dies. However, such dies are more expensive and the production rate gets reduced.

Dies are usually made of high strength tool steels. For larger production runs and severe abrasive conditions, sintered tungsten carbide can be used. Die cavities and punch faces should be lapped and polished to a very high surface finish, preferably below 0.254 μ m. Clearances between die walls and punches should not exceed 0.127 mm and should be held between 0.005 mm and 0.0075 mm for precision parts. To

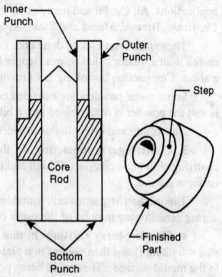

Fig. 10.4. Multiple Punch Design.

facilitate ejection of the compact and thereby avoid excessive wear, a slight taper or draft (usually less than 1°) is machined in the die. Dies of WC do not need taper in compacting dies.

Dies should include an allowance for shrinkage during sintering and also another allowance if sizing is to be done. The die design should also take into account the elastic recovery of the compact when ejected from the die, which can be of the order of 0.5 to 1.5%.

Presses. Mechanical presses being faster than hydraulic presses, are adaptable to high production rate, even upto 100 compacts per hour. The maximum production rate for a large hydraulic press may be only 100 compacts per hour. Hydraulic presses are more powerful then mechanical presses. The press capacity can reach a maximum of about 27.5 MN. Mechanical presses are used when less than about 1.5 MN compacting pressure is needed. Hydraulic presses are used for those compacts that require from 1.5 to 20 MN compacting pressure.

$$\text{Maximum area of the compact} = \frac{\text{Press capacity}}{\text{Required compacting pressure}}$$

From the press capacities and compacting pressures discussed above, most P/M products have cross-sectional area of 1935 mm^2. However, sizes upto 6452 mm^2 are quite common and even larger ones are being produced.

10.5.1 Other Methods of Compacting

1. Impact Compaction :– Impact compacting of powders on fast hammers or with the aid of explosive charges results in compacts of high density. This reduces the sintering time and limits shrinkage of the compact. The method is particularly advantageous for compact resistant powders. High speed compaction of powders using petro-forge machines has already been explained in chapter 9. In explosive compacting, one or more plungers, placed next to the powder in a closed system, are actuated by buffer plates against which the powerful explosives act.

2. Rolling and Extrusion. Improved consolidation is achieved when individual powder particles are moved relative to each other, as in extrusion or rolling of powders. The products are with uniform and excellent mechanical properties. Rolling of powders is usually used to manufacture sheets and for cladding a solid base metal. The main applications of extrusion of powders are the production of long solid bars, hollow tubes and multihole filters, which can be cut up as required. The typical applications are: nuclear solid fuel elements and other materials for high temperature applications. Al, Cu, Ni and many other metals can also be extruded. Metals that can be rolled are: Cu, Brass, Bronze, Monel and Stainless Steel.

These processes can be done both cold as well as hot. In cold rolling of powders, the powder mixed with a binder is fed from a hopper between two rolls and interlock the powder particles into a sheet. Compaction by rolling is following by sintering and perhaps re-rolling.

Some metal powders are extruded cold with a binder. However, the more common procedure is that the powder is first pressed into a billet which is then extruded in the conventional procedure.

Hot rolling and extrusion of powders will be discussed after 'Sintering'.

3. Centrifugal Compacting. In this method, the mould after it is filled with powder, is centrifuged to get a compact of high and uniform density and for this the parts should be of nearly uniform section.

The method is particularly suitable for heavy metals such as WC. The pressure generated during centrifuging may be of the order of 3 MPa.

4. Slip or Slurry Casting. In this method, the powder is converted into a slurry (particle size < 0.02 mm) and then poured in a plaster of paris mould, after mould release agents are applied to the mould surface . The mould being porous, the liquid in the slurry gradually drains off into the plaster leaving a solid compact within the mould. Vacuum aids mould filling and speeds up the process of liquid extraction. Centrifuging also helps filling. An invariant of slip casting is 'drain casting' for producing hollow compacts. The mould is filled up with slip or slurry and after sufficient time has elapsed to form a dewatered particulate shell, the mould is inverted to pour out the excess slip, leaving behind a hollow product. The compacts are dried and sintered in the usual manner. The main advantage is that expensive dies are not needed and large and complex parts can be made, with improved properties. The main drawback is the time lag in producing parts."

An important variant of slurry casting involves the forming of thin (< 1.5 mm thick) tapes, usually of cera- mic powders in an organic carrier. Rolling is one of the many techniques used for this purpose. The green tape obtained is flexible enough to be rolled up. It can be blank- ed, mechanically scored or marked with a laser beam prior to firing so that it can be made into small components such as substrates for integrat- ed circuits.

5. Cold Isostatic Pressing :— In this method a uniform density throughout the compact can be achieved. An elastic deformable mould (reusable rubber or single use metal) contains the metal powder while omni directional pressure is applied by means of a pressure medium inside a pressure vessel, (Fig. 10.5). If the medium is a gas, the method is called iso-static pressing and when the medium is a liquid (usually water) it is called hydrostatic pressing. Pressures of 300 MPa to 550 MPa can be achieved. Other advantages of the method are: uniform strength in all directions, low equipment costs and a higher green compact strength as compared to most other methods. Metal powders which can be compacted by this method are: Al, Mg, W, Beryllium, Iron and Stainless Steel. An internal cavity of the moulding is made by a metal core or mandrel properly positioned in the container. Upon completion of the compacting operation, the compact is taken out of the container and the mandrel withdrawn.

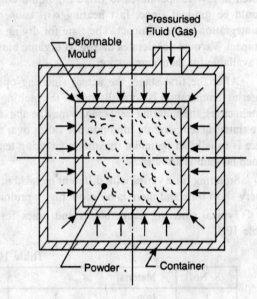

Fig. 10.5. Cold Iso-Static Pressing.

In the above method, the pressurizing medium acts directly on the powder-filled mould. This is known as "Wet-bag tooling". In "Dry-bag tooling" the pressurizing medium acts on a membrane, which is in contact with the powder-filled mould.

Advantages

1. Uniform density distribution, even in shapes with large aspect ratios and those containing undercuts.

2. No powder lubrication is necessary. Thus, no burn-off cycle is necessary during sintering.

3. Larger parts can be compacted economically.

Limitations

1. Dimensional control is not very precise.

2. Production rates are lower, compared to punch-die method.

3. Lesser surface smoothness, compared to punch-die method.

10.6. SINTERING

Green compact as obtained after compacting operation is not very strong and is very brittle and can't be used as it is. In order that it becomes a usable powder metal product, it must undergo the sintering operation. The green compact is placed in a furnace and is soaked in heat until the individual powder particles are no longer discernible. So, sintering can be defined as the bonding of adjacent surfaces of particles in a mass of metal powder, by heating. The time of exposure, the temperature and the rate of cooling are closely controlled.

The first stage in the sintering operation is the purging or drying stage. The compact is heated at low temperatures to drive off liquid constituents (lubricants, water etc.). The heating should be gradual since, fast heating will cause sudden vaporization and could result in the disintegration of the compact. The time for drying increases with increasing wall thickness of the compact. Vacuum accelerates drying. If organic binders are to be burnt off, sufficient oxygen must be available for their combustion.

After the first stage, the actual sintering operation starts at an elevated temperature. The sintering temperature is normally below the melting points of all powder constituents. However, in certain cases, the sintering temperature may be above the melting point of one of the metal powders. The sintering temperature for a powder varies over a range (0.7 to 0.9 times the melting point), but there is usually an optimum maximum sintering temperature for a given set of conditions beyond which no gain is affected.

Sintering time varies with different metals but in most cases, the effect of heat is complete in a very short time and there is no economy in prolonging the operation.

Typical sintering temperatures and times for some important metal powders are given in Table 10.1.

Table 10.1

S. No.	Material	Temp °C	Time, min.
1.	Iron	1010 — 1150	8 — 45
2.	Copper	840 — 900	12 — 45
3.	Brass	840 — 900	10 — 45
4.	Bronze	760 — 870	10 — 20
5.	Nickle	1010 — 1150	30 — 45
6.	Stainless steel	1095 — 1285	30 — 60
7.	Tungsten and Tantalum	2345	480
8.	Alnico magnets	1200 — 1300	120

At high temperatures, there is a tendency of surface oxide films to form due to the reaction between the compact and the furnace atmosphere. This is avoided by sintering in inert atmosphere (neutral or reducing). N_2 is neutral and is extensively used. H_2 is a very effective reducing agent but must be handled with care to avoid explosion. $N_2 + 10\%$ H_2+ methane, dissolved NH_3 and partially combusted hydrocarbon gases are frequently used. These gases will react with the scale on the metals and clean away the contaminations. In the sintering of steel, the carbon content is also controlled and in some cases, steels are carburized in a CO-containing atmosphere. Vacuum sintering also provides a neutral atmosphere, but is a more costly process. It improves ductility and strength.

The major type of furnace used for sintering is the electric resistance furnace. It can be batch type or continuous type. Continuous type furnace has a wire mesh belt to carry the compacts through the furnace. A typical sintering furnace has three main parts, (Fig. 10.6) :

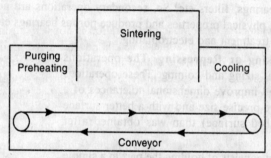

Fig. 10.6. Sintering Furnace.

1. Loading, purging and preheating portion (drying or burn-off section).
2. Sintering portion (high heat zone).
3. Cooling portion.

The strength during sintering is imparted by diffusion bonding of the atoms of the particles. Most metals remain solid during sintering. The solid-state diffusion bonding originates at the old weld zones (created during compacting) and continues until all of the powder particles are welded into a coherent mass. However, sintering process is accelerated (density increase) when one of the constituents melts and envelops the higher melting constituent (Liquid-phase sintering) or Vitreous sintering. A liquid that wets the solid particles exerts capillary pressure which physically moves and presses particles together for better densification. Best bonding is achieved, if there is mutual solubility. In the case of cemented carbides, for example, sintering increases the density of the part due to the action of cobalt (which is added as a binder), which dissolves small fragments of the carbide and promotes fusion and bonding. Particles of iron, copper base or iron base parts do not fuse, however, and are strengthened solely by the action of the atoms as they diffuse and bind to one another.Generally, the sintered part contains from 4 to 10% porosity. The other characteristics accomplished by sintering are :

1. Residual stresses within the particles, caused by the compacting operation, are relaxed, allowing the particles to deform plastically.
2. Voids tend to become closed and this causes some shrinkage during sintering. Therefore, the green compact should be oversized.
3. Individual crystals may be recrystallised within the compact if the sintering temperature is high enough to have an effect on the crystalline structure.
4. The impurities (if any) that are a part of the metal particles are forced out of each individual interstice into small impurity voids within the sintered compact.

10.6.1. Pre - Sintering. If a part made by P/M needs some machining (say drilling), it will be rather very difficult if the material is very hard and strong. These machining operations are made easier by the pre-sintering operation which is done before sintering operation. The compact is heated to a temperature well below the final sintering temperature. The compact will gain enough strength to be handled and machined without any difficulty. After this, the part undergoes the final sintering operation.

10.7. SECONDARY OPERATIONS

The relative density of a fully sintered part (that is relative to the fully dense material) is in the range of 65 to 85% depending upon powder characteristics, compacting pressure, and sintering temperature and time. Factors limiting cold densification of P/M compacts include press capacity and compressibility of powder blends. Often a higher porosity is intentionally kept to subsequently manufacture porous bearings, filters etc. So, secondary operations are needed to obtain desired dimensional tolerances, physical properties and produce porous bearings etc. Secondary operations may also include: heat treatment and electroplating.

1. Cold Restriking or Repressing. The operations included under this are: sizing and coining. These operations increase the density and improve dimensional tolerances of a part so as to get a more precise size and with a better surface finish (often a burnished surface) than was obtained after sintering.

'Sizing' operation consists of holding the part in a simple fixture so that an accurate mandrel or tool can be forced through a hole, slot or some hollow feature of the part. Another method is to 'extrude' or force the part through die openings in a special die, resembling that used originally for compacting the part. The part can also be squeezed between two flat surfaces. Fig. 10.7 shows the sizing operation for the outer and inner surfaces of a bush.

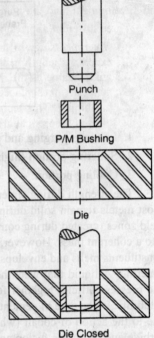

Fig. 10.7. Sizing Operation.

'Coining' is a variant of closed-die forging in which there is no flash. It consists of repressing P/M parts by use of high pressures in dies especially for this purpose. Increased densities of the order of 95% may be obtained by mechanically reducing the voids that remain between adjoining particles. Densification also improves the surface quality and precision of the part.

Further densification and strength improvement can be obtained by resintering the repressed compact obtained by sizing and coining."

Coining is not practical on carbide materials due to their low compressibility.

2. Hot Densification. Instead of the traditional pressing, sintering, repressing and resintering sequence, a preform (green compact) that closely resembles the finished part is made by P/M. It is then heated to an elevated temperature and compacted in a finishing die with a single stroke of press. The relative density attained can be as high as 99.5% or even more. The method is also called Powder Forging or P/M forging and has been discussed in chapter 4. Such hot-forged powder preform parts as well as hot-rolled bars possess the wrought properties and complex parts can be made otherwise very difficult to obtain by conventional forging.

As discussed, powder metallurgy forged parts have mechanical properties, close to wrought metals, unlike conventional pressed and sintered powder metallurgy parts, that have limited dynamic properties of impact and fatigue. These limitations can be overcome by eliminating residual density with the forging process.

In addition to the advantages of the powder forged parts, mentioned on Page 262, other advantages of the process are given below:

1. High production rates.
2. Reduction or elimination of flash.
3. Lower forging load.
4. Less die wear.
5. Lower forging temperature.
6. Ability to form quite complex components in one forging operation.
7. Lesser forging blows, than in conventional forging.
8. Forging costs are lower than in conventional forging.

9. Reduction of lead time and inventory.

However, the cost of the powder metallurgy forging process exceeds conventional powder metallurgy products, due to extra processing steps, reduced tool life of forging dies, perform design and development, and the process controls, necessary to achieve full density.

Three different approaches have been developed for powder metal forging :

(*i*) *Hot repressing.* In this method, the perform is very similar in shape to the final part, except its length in the forging direction. That is, the lateral dimensions of the perform are the same as the inner dimensions of the repressing die. Therefore, no lateral flow of material takes place during the repressing stroke. The final product needs minimum machining. This technique is generally used in applications where densities from 95 to 98% of theoretical are satisfactory. Recent modifications to this technique indicate that it may be possible to produce densities approaching 100% theoretical, with properties equivalent to wrought products.

(*ii*) *Precision forging process without flash.* In this variation, the shape of the perform is simpler than the final part shape. The final shape is produced to close dimensional control during the forging step. In this case, the perform is upset or extruded during the hot forging step, that is, there is lateral flow also of the material. This results in a more rapid densification and greater shear stresses at the pore surfaces, than in hot repressing. This method can produce densities approaching 100% theoretical and develops properties nearly equal to the equivalent wrought metal of the same composition. The method combines the advantages of P/M and conventional forging. The product may need slight machining.

(*iii*) *Powder metal forging with formation of flash.* In this method, the P/M performs are substituted for bar stock, as the raw material in conventional die forging. That is, the method is an extension of the present forging practice. The product needs trimming and finishing. It appears doubtful, however, whether the method can offer economic advanteges over conventional die forging from bar stock.

3. Infiltration :— In this operation, molten metal is used to fill the porosity in the sintered compact. It is carried out by immersing the part in the molten metal or by placing the infiltrant metal in the form of a sheet or slug either above or below the compact in a furnace. Capillary action fills the pores. Vacuum aids the process. The melting point of liquid metal used should be as low as possible and below that of any of the powders in the compact. Best results are obtained if both wetting and solubility exists between the molten metal and the powders. The operation is principally used for iron-base compacts which increases the density, strength and hardness of a part. Low melting point metals such as copper, copper alloys and brass are used as liquid metal. The operation seals the surface porosity, so that operations like electroplating can be carried out if required. Silver infiltrating tungsten is another typical application.

4. Impregnation :— If the pores in a sintered compact are filled with an oil, the operation is called as impregnation. The lubricants are added to the porous bearings, gears, and pump rotors etc. The parts are immersed in a tank of heated oil for a period of time to fill the pores. Application of vacuum aids the process. Porous components impregnated with lubricants in this manner don't need external lubrication during operation. As the part heats, because of friction during operation, the contained oil will expand and emerge on the bearing surface providing a film of lubricant. Subsequent cooling (after operation) results in re-absorption of oil into the pores of the part. Such bearings are called as "Self Lubricated bearings". Porosities for such parts range from 25% to 35%. Higher values will reduce the strength of the component.

For the production of self lubricated bearings, the iron or bronze compositions are used. Typically, the powders used include: copper, tin, graphite and a small amount of stearing acid. Graphite is added to improve the lubricating qualities of the finished bearing and stearic acid is an effective pore-generating agent. During sintering, the stearic acid, which is volatile, aids in producing interconnecting channels or pores, throughout the material. After the powder composition is compacted and sintered, the lubricating oil is impregnated in an impregnation chamber. In this chamber, vacuum is first applied to remove air from the pores. Then, lubricating oil is admitted into the chamber, where it readily penetrates and fills the empty pores due to capillary action.

A typical P/M mix can be :

Copper = 2%,   Graphite = 1%,   Zinc stearate = 0.5 to 1.0%.

Balance Iron.

Impregnation may be done for other reasons also : For example, parts may be impregnated with wax for lubrication or moisture resistance (particularly for electrical parts) ; resin impregnation for strength, bonding or corrosion resistance and plastic impregnation to improve the outer surface for plating.

P/M parts can be plated to provide a decorative, corrosion- resistant, or wear-resistant surface. Parts can also be steam treated to increase corrosion-resistance and seal-porosity. Features, that cannot be formed by compaction, can be achieved by machining. During heat treatment, protective atmospheres must be maintained.

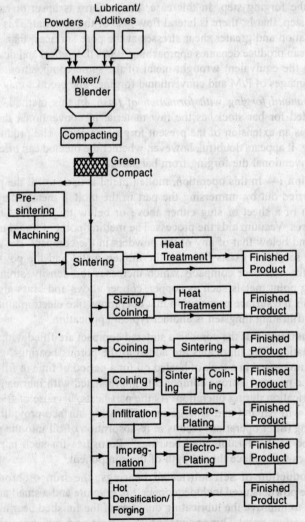

Fig. 10.8. Flow Chart of P/M Process.

Fig. 10.8 shows the flow chart of producing a part by P/M technique, by combining basic and secondary operations.

10.8. RECENT TRENDS IN POWDER METALLURGY

1. Hot Pressing. The chief trend in P/M is to produce full density, high strength parts with fewer processing steps. In the conventional P/M discussed so far, sintering is done after compacting the product. Then secondary operations, such as cold restriking, resintering etc. and hot densification are carried out to increase the density of the product. However, if both compacting and sintering are carried out simultaneously, an improved product is obtained. This is what is done in the process known as 'Hot Pressing'. Sufficient pressure is applied at the sintering temperature to bring the powder particles together and thus accelerate sintering. Under such conditions porosity can be completely eliminated. However, the chief problem in hot pressing is to find a suitable die material which can withstand the high pressures at the elevated temperatures. Hot pressing in heated graphite or ceramic dies is feasible. However, it is difficult to transmit pressure uniformly to all parts of the compact. This difficulty is overcome in `Hot Isostatic Pressing (HIP)'.

In this process the powder is encased in a deformable metal or ceramic ćan or container that has the shape of the desired part. The can is evacuated and then placed inside a furnace, which in turn is enclosed in a high pressure chamber. The chamber is pressurized with an inert gas (argon) upto 300 MPa or more. Furnace temperatures may range from 480°C to 2000°C. It is clear that the pressure applied is omnidirectional (hydrostatic). Therefore the compact will be uniformly pressed throughout its mass. The powder is compacted, densified and sintered in one step. When the container is removed, a finished product close to the final shape is obtained. This process is particularly suited to producing parts from more exotic metals (high-temperature alloys) that are difficult to forge and machine, for example, Uranium, Zirconium and high strength titanium alloys where high purity is needed.

Advantages of HIP

1. The process has the potential for the fabrication of highly refractory ceramics which are difficult to densify using more conventional processing routes such as sintering.

2. Low temperatures can be used, thus allowing a better control of microstructure (fine grain size, for instance).

3. Use of proper cans and inserts also allows the fabrication of complex geometries to "near net shape" which are especially interesting in the case of hard to machine materials.

Limitations

The HIP process is not very attractive for high volume production due to the following factors :

1. High cost of canning.

2. Relatively longer HIP process cycle.

3. Difficulty in producing and maintaining uniform temperature throughout the chamber.

Hot rolling, extrusion and forging of metal powders is also feasible. However, provisions must be made to prevent undesirable reactions with the surrounding atmosphere. For this, the metal powder is placed in a thin steel can, that then is welded, evacuated and sealed. After the operation, the can is removed. Or the process can be carried out in a protective atmosphere or carbon is added to produce a reducing environment.

2. Spark Discharge Sintering. This process is a variant of HIP, in which a high energy electric discharge spark is produced during compaction. Due to the high energy of the spark, the diffusion bonding is instantaneous. It thus combines compacting and sintering (as in HIP) the metal powders to a dense metal part in 12 to 15s. Its greatest advantage is its ability to maintain dimensional accuracy of the parts. Also, no separate sintering furnace is needed for this process.

3. Gravity Sintering. This method is used to produce thin compacts of low density and little strength. A mould (ceramic trays) may be filled under gravity upto a uniform thickness, perhaps assisted by vibration. The trays are sintered upto about 48 hours in proper furnace environment as discussed earlier. Careful handling is needed to produce a porous sintered product. The process is particularly suited to producing corrosion resistant Stainless-steel porous sheets. These sheets can then be fabricated into suitable shapes and their application is as filters for oil, petrol and chemicals.

4. Induction Sintering. Induction sintering provides extremely rapid heating rates and temperature equilibrium. Also, the process lends itself to short soaking time at temperature. At the higher sintering temperatures short-soaking times at temperatures are sufficient to reduce the oxygen content of the perform to the level achieved during conventional furnace sintering. However at more short times, the diffusion of carbon is incomplete and a post forming heat treatment is necessary to obtain a uniform distribution of carbon.

5. Some newly developed techniques for obtaining full density products are discussed below :

(*i*) **The Sinter-HIP Process.** This technique is an improvement on the conventional HIP process, in that the expenses on canning and de-canning of the powder are eliminated. The technique consists of the following steps :

1. The components are conventionally compacted.
2. The compacted parts are sintered in a HIP chamber under vacuum. The sintering time should be sufficient, so that all the remaining porosities are closed and isolated.
3. The vacuum is next broken and high pressure is applied to complete the process. The sealed surfaces produced during step.
4. Act as isolating can, during the present step.

(*ii*) **Ceracon Process.** This technique was developed to achieve full density in the conventionally compacted and sintered parts. However, the process can also be used for porous performs. The process consists of the following steps :

1. The hot perform is completely surrounded by a granular material capable of transmitting pressure in the pseudo uniform manner.
2. The complete assembly is then pressed and compacted in a conventional hydraulic press.

The technique has the following advantages :

(*a*) No need of canning and de-canning the parts.
(*b*) The compacted part and the pressurizing medium (granular material) can be separated conveniently.
(*c*) The granular material can be reheated and reused.

(*iii*) **Osprey Process.** The process is also known as "In situ consolidation". The process consists of the following steps :

1. The molten metal is atomized into powder.
2. The powder is sprayed by streams of inert gas into a shaped collector mould.
3. Cooling of the droplets is controlled is such a way that they strike the surface of the mould in a semi-solid state and quickly cool.

This process can produce 98 to 99% dense parts. The perform, so obtained, is then immediately hot-forged or otherwise hot-worked, to get the final shape. The process has the following advantages :

(*a*) No sintering step is required.
(*b*) The performs have better workability, compared to conventional P/M performs.
(*c*) The collector mould costs are low.

(*d*) The product has uniform fine grain size and uniform chemistry.

This process has been used in England and other countries, to produce parts weighing about 0.9 to 1.8 kg from medium-alloy steel, tool steel and super-alloys.

6. Metal Injection Moulding. Metal Injection Moulding (MIM) which is also known as Powder Injection Moulding (PIM) is the newest of the powder metallurgy processes. The metal powder is mixed with a suitable plasticizer. This allows the material to be forced into a closed mould, at relatively low pressure and temperature, using a conventional plastic injection moulding machine. The typical temperatures and pressures are : 120 to 250°C and 70 to 140 kPa respectively. After moulding, the organic binder is removed from the part and this is the critical step of the process. After that, the part is sintered in atmospheric or vacuum furnaces. Powders used in this process are much finer than those used for conventional P/M. Due to this, the shrinkage during sintering is very high, reaching as high as 30%. However, the shrinkage is isotropic due to uniform density of the as-moulded part. Common materials used are : pure iron, low alloy steels, stainless steels and certain speciality alloys.

The advantages of the process are :

1. Highly complex components, with densities of 96% of the theoretical and above, can be produced.

2. Close tolerance can be maintained, typically ± 0.003 per mm.

3. Ductility of as-sintered parts is usually high, with common elongation of 25% to 30%.

However, the process has the following limitations :

(*i*) Parts are usually limited in overall size and less than about 75 gms. However, larger parts are under development.

(*ii*) Due to the process to remove binder, the cross- sectional thickness of the part is limited, which is usually 6.35 mm or less.

10.9. PROPERTIES OF POWDER METALLURGY PARTS

The mechanical properties of powder metallurgy products depend on many variables, for example, shape and size of powder particles used, type of metals used, pressing pressure, sintering temperature and time and finishing treatments and so on. Due to this, it is rather difficult to give generalised information regarding them. However, in general, the sintered products have relatively low mechanical properties compared to similar parts produced by other processes. Mechanical properties are closely related to relative density because pores in the sintered compact act as internal notches resulting in stress concentration. The ductility is markedly less because of lower density. In general, strength properties of parts made from pure metals (unalloyed) are better than the sintered parts made from powders containing alloying elements.

Increasing the density of a compact invariably increase the tensile strength, hardness and usually the elongation. Tensile strengths of 275 to 345 MPa are common and strengths above about 690 MPa can be attained. As larger presses and coining and forging combined with P/M preforms are used, to provide greater density, the strength properties of P/M products more nearly equal to those of the wrought products. HIP and spark sintering are also the steps in this direction.

10.10. APPLICATIONS OF P/M PARTS

The major product applications of P/M have already been listed while discussing the advantages of the process. Almost all metals lend themselves to P/M. However, largest quantities of products are made from iron powders often alloyed with 4% to 6% copper and 1% graphite for greater strength, of porous iron infiltrated with copper and increasingly of atomized steel. Smaller but increasing quantities are being made of copper and especially aluminium alloys which are preferred in business machines because of their light weight.

P/M processing has found greatest acceptance for small parts (< 0.5 kg) in automotive and appliance applications where the ability to produce a nearly final shape requiring a minimum of machining, provides a strong economic advantage. Similarly, the near-net-shape or net-shape components for air craft, and rocket motor applications are of great importance. Such components include: superalloy turbine disks, Ti-alloy bulk heads and fuselage components and rocket nozzles made of W and Mo infiltrated with Cu. In super alloys, the P/M approach avoids the problems of alloy segregation, carbide clustering and residual cost structures.

Surgical implants is a small but important application of P/M. Filling of teeth with dental amalgams is a long established application. The amalgams represent room-temperature transient liquid-phase sintering in which an Ag-Cu alloy is amalgamated with Hg, the mercury is used up in the reaction.

Beryllium like Tungsten can be processed only by the P/M route. It is hot vacuum pressed.

Production of incandescent-lamp filaments :— As already discussed, these lamp filaments are made from Tungsten powder which is doped with small quantities of alloying elements (for example 0.5% Ni) to accelerate sintering. The Tungsten powder is first compacted and then sintered into a bar shaped body. The bar is swaged at one end to a small diameter. While hot, at a temperature of about 930°C, the entire bar is pulled through WC dies to a diameter measuring only 0.25 mm. The finished diameter of the filament is obtained by a final drawing of the material through diamond dies. Tungsten wires drawn in this manner have tensile strengths of the order of 5950 MPa.

10.11. DESIGNING THE P/M PARTS FOR PRODUCTION

1. The design of the component must be such that it can be ejected from the die. Parts with holes whose axes are perpendicular to the direction of pressing cannot be made. Similarly, multistepped diameters, reentrant holes, grooves and undercuts should be eliminated. However, no such constraints are there in the case of isostatic pressing.

2. The main quality attribute of a P/M product is uniform density of the material. Non-uniform density causes stress in the material and consequently, warping and cracking of parts. For this :—

   (a) an almost uniform thickness of walls must exist throughout the length of the component. Also parts with straight walls are preferred.

   (b) Since pressure is not transmitted uniformly through a deep bed of powder, the ratio of the unpressed length to pressed length should be kept below 2, if possible, and never exceed 3.

   (c) The part should be relatively short in length in comparison to its diameters. The length of a die-pressed component should not exceed about 2.5 times its diameter.

   (d) The height of step (Fig. 10.4) should not be more than $\frac{1}{4} \times$ height of part, in a single punch design. However, much larger steps are allowable in a multiple punch design.

3. Even under pressure, the powder can not fill very thin sections. Therefore, do not design for thin walls, narrow splines and sharp corners. Minimum wall thickness for cylindrical parts is 1 mm and for parts of other types 1.5 mm. Sharp corners on the components and hence on the punch and die reduce the strength of the tooling. The rounding radii for internal and external corners should not be less than 0.3 mm and 2.5 mm respectively.

4. Avoid abrupt changes in section thickness. Provide ample fillets.

5. Narrow deep flutes should be avoided

6. Straight serrations (lengthwise) can be readily moulded, but threads and cross knurling and similar impressions can not be pressed on vertical sides.

7. Holes should have a draft of 0.08 mm per cm and minimum hole diameter for lengths upto 12.7 mm is3.2 mm.

8. The meeting plane between moulding punches should be on a flat or cylinderical surface and never on a spherical surface.

9. Draft should be provided on the part walls perpendicular to the mould parting plane for easy ejection of the compact from the die. The draft angle should range from 5° to 10°. However, no draft is needed for ejection from a lubricated die.

10.12. COMPARISON OF POWDER METALLURGY WITH OTHER PROCESSES

Powder metallurgy process can be compared with other processes on the basis of : Tooling cost, production cost, dimensional accuracy and surface quality needed, quantity of production and other features, as discussed below :

1. Die-Casting. Both P/M and die-casting are very competitive as far as dimensional accuracy and surface finish of the components are concerned. However, tooling costs and machine costs usually favour P/M. But, die-casting can be made in sizes beyond P/M capabilities. Again, die-casting is mainly used for non-ferrous metals. Hence, P/M is the choice, when requirements for strength, wear resistance or high operating temperatures exceed the capabilities of die-casting alloys, or if the corrosion resistance of copper alloys or stainless steel is required.

2. Stamping. When a component can be made as one stamping from one die, stamping is usually more feasible and economical than P/M. However, if components need the use of multiple dies or progressive dies, the tooling costs and machine costs are significantly increased and P/M becomes competitive.

3. Fine Blanking. P/M is highly competitive with fine blanking, which runs at slower cycle than conventional stamping and has higher equipment costs. However, fine blanking has less latitude to produce shapes that can be easily designed with P/M.

4. Foundary Castings. P/M offers greater precision, eliminating most or all of the finish machining operations required for castings. P/M avoids casting defects, such as blow holes, slag and shrinkage etc. But foundary castings can be made in sizes which exceed the capabilities of conventional P/M. Where both the processes are viable, foundary castings usually incur lower tooling and material costs, but higher production costs. P/M is usually the choice when production quantities are high.

5. Investment Casting. Both investment casting and P/M are competitive, as far as precision and component materials are concerned. However, shapes which cannot be made by P/M or which require extensive machining, can often be investment cast. Tooling cost is substantially lower, and production costs are higher. Investment casting cannot compete with P/M for very large production volumes.

6. Automatic Screw Machines. Even though automatic screw machines incur the lowest tooling cost of any production methods, are highly automated, not labour intensive, but the material utilization (from bar stock) is very poor. As the production volumes increase, P/M scores over automatic screw machines. Also, P/M can produce irregular shapes, whereas screw machining operations are more advantageous, when the component shape is symmetric with a central axis.

PROBLEMS

1. Define "Powder metallurgy" process.
2. Write in brief the basic steps of P/M process
3. Define the following terms: mixing and blending, compacting or briquetting, sintering, Green compact.

4. Name the two major advantages in favour of P/M process.

5. List the limitations of P/M process.

6. Discuss the various methods of powder manufacture.

7. Define the following terms related to metal powders :—

Surface area, density, Apparent density, Tap density, compressibility, flow rate, Particle shape, Particle size, Particle size distribution. How these powder characteristics influence the properties of a P/M product? Discuss.

8. What are Pre-alloyed and Pre-coated powders? How they are beneficial ?

9. For what types of products the following are added to the powders and why: Graphite, Slearic acid, Cobalt ?

10. What are the sources of the strength of a green compact ?

11. What are the limitations of a single punch design ?

12. What is a 'multiple punch design' and 'rotary table design' of a P/M press ?

13. Compare the collapsible and non-collapsible dies.

14. Write shortly on :—

(a) Impact compacting

(b) Rolling and extrusion methods of powder compacting.

(c) Centrifugal compacting.

(d) Slip Casting.

(e) Cold Isostatic Pressing

15. How the final strength is imparted to the green compact during the sintering operation ?

16. Why special precautions are needed about the furnace atmosphere during sintering ?

17. What type of furnace atmosphere is needed during the sintering operation and how it is achieved ?

18. Name the three zones of a sintering furnace and explain the function of each zone.

19. List the properties accomplished by sintering operation.

20. What is pre-sintering ?

21. What are the functions of the following secondary operations done on a sintered product :—

Sizing, Coining, Hot densification, Infiltration, Impregnation. How these operations are carried out.

22. How the self lubricated bearings are made ?

23. How the incandescent lamp filaments are made ?

24. What is the advantage of irregular-shaped particles in powders ?

25. What are the principal advantages of fine powders over coarse powders?

26. What is 'Hot pressing' ?

27. What is HIP ? Explain the operation and its advantages.

28. Write on: Spark sintering and Gravity sintering.

29. Write on: Properties of P/M products.

30. List the major product application of P/M process.

31. Discuss the design factors of a P/M part.

32. How would the following P/M parts be made :—

Cemented carbides, Porous sheet metal, long uniformly shaped parts and Alnico magnets.

33. What is Viterous sintering ?
34. Write briefly on the following processes ?
    (a) Induction Sintering   (b) The Sinter-HIP process
    (c) Ceracon process   (d) Osprey process.
35. Write briefly on Metal injection moulding. What are the advantages and limitations of the process.
36. Compare the Powder metallurgy process with the following manufacturing proceses :
    (a) Die casting   (b) Stamping
    (c) Fine blanking   (d) Foundry castings
    (e) Investment casting   (f) Automatis screw machines
37. What is the difference between mixing and blending of powders ?
38. Explain why metal powders are blended ?
39. Explain the difference between infiltration and impregnation. Give some examples for each.
40. Why are protective atmospheres necessary in sintering ? What would be the effects on the properties of powder metallurgy parts if such atmospheres are not used?
41. What are the thermal difficulties experienced during sintering process for some metals. Name those metals.
42. Write a typical P/M mix for producing self lubricated bearings.
43. What are the limitations of HIP process ?
44. What is green strength ?
45. Under what conditions, powder metallurgy technique is superior to conventional manufacturing processes ?
46. Name the important variables in the sintering operation.
47. What is the particle size normally used in P/M method ?
48. Name the common powders employed in P/M process.
49. Explain the important of powder metallurgy.
50. List the advantages of powder metallurgy
51. List the prrducts of Powder metallurgy.
52. Explain why making alloys by melting is unsintable ?
53. Define green density.
54. What are some of the factors which affect the magnitude of the apparent density of powders of the same composition ?
55. Define Compression ratio.
56. What is the effect of the green density of a compact on the hardness it has after sintering ?
57. What is the relationship between % theoretical density and % porosity ?
58. What is meant by "Green" ? Is green strength important ? Explain.
59. Why MIM of metal powders is becoming an important process ? Explain.
60. Describe what happens during sintering operation.
61. Write a short note on sintering furnaces.
62. Discuss the effects of different shapes and sizes of powder particles in PM processing.
63. List the advantages and limitations of MIM as compared to other methods of compaction.

Chapter

11

Processing of Plastics

11.1. GENERAL

Plastics belong to the family of organic materials. Organic materials are those materials which are derived directly from carbon. They consist of carbon chemically combined with hydrogen, oxygen and other non- metallic substances, and their structures, in most cases, are fairly complex. The large and diverse organic group includes the natural materials : wood, coal, petroleum, natural rubber, animal fibers and food, which have biological origins. Synthetics include the large group of solvents, adhesives, synthetic fibers, rubbers, plastics, explosives, lubricants, dyes, soaps and cutting oils etc. which have no biological origins. Of them, plastics and synthetic rubbers are termed as "polymers".

11.2. POLYMERS

The term "polymer" is derived from the two Greek words : poly, meaning "many", and meros meaning "parts" or "units". Thus polymers are composed of a large number of repeating units (small molecules) called monomers. The monomers are joined together end-to-end in a polymerization reaction. A polymer is, therefore, made up of thousands of monomers joined together to form a large molecule of colloidal dimension, called macromolecule. The unique characteristic of a polymer is that each molecule is either a long chain or a network of repeating units all covalently bonded together. Polymers are molecular materials and are generally noncrystalline solids at ordinary temperature, but pass through a viscous stage in course of their formation when, shaping is readily carried out.

The most common polymers are those made from compounds of carbon, but polymers can also be made form inorganic chemicals such as silicates and silicones. The naturally occuring polymers include : protein, cellulose, resins, starch, shellac and lignin. They are commonly found in leather, fur, wool, cotton, silk, rubber, rope, wood and many others. There are also synthetic polymers such as polyethylene, polystyrene, nylon, terylene, dacron etc., termed under plastics, fibers and elastomers. Their properties are superior to those of the naturally occuring counterparts. Our concern, here, is therefore, with synthetic polymers, also called plastics (again from Greek *plastikos*, derived from *plassein* : to form, to mould) or resins.

11.3. POLYMERIZATION

The process of linking together of monomers, that is, of obtaining macromolecules is called "polymerization". It can be achieved by one of the two processing techniques :

(*a*) **Addition Polymerization.** In addition or chain polymerization under suitable conditions of temperature and pressure and in the presence of a catalyst called an initiator, the polymer is produced by adding a second monomer to the first, then a third monomer to this dimer, and a fourth to the trimer, and so on until the long polymer chain is terminated. Polyethylene is produced by the addition polymerization of ethylene monomers. This linear polymer can also be converted to a branched polymer by removing a side group and replacing it with a chain. If many such branches are formed, a network structure results.

"Co-polymerization" is the addition polymerization of two or more different monomers. Many monomers will not polymerize with themselves, but will copolymerize with other compounds.

(b) **Condensation Polymerization.** In this process, two or more reacting compounds may be involved and there is a repetitive elimination of smaller molecules, to form a by-product. For example, in the case of phenol formaldehyde (bakelite), the compounds are : formaldehyde and phenol. Metacresol acts as a catalyst and the by-product is water. The structure of the 'mer' is more complex. Also, there is the growth perpendicular to the direction of chain. This is called 'cross-linking'.

Size of a Polymer. The polymer chemist can control the average length of the molecules by terminating the reaction. Thus, the molecular weight (the average weight, in grams, of 6.02×10^{23} molecules) or degree of polymerization, D.P., (the number of mers in the average molecule) can be controlled. For example, the length of molecules may range from some 700 repeat units in low-density polyethylene to 1,70,000 repeat units in ultrahigh-molecular-weight polyethylene.

11.4. ADDITIONS TO POLYMERS

The properties of polymers can be further modified by the addition of agents which are basically of two types. Those that enter the molecular structure are usually called "additives", whereas those that form a clearly defined second phase are called "fillers".

1. Plasticizers. Plasticizers are liquids of high boiling point and low molecular weight, which are added to improve the plastic behaviour of the polymer. The broad role of a plasticizer is to separate the macro- molecules, thus decreasing the inter-molecular forces and facilitating relative movement between molecules of the polymer, that is, making deformation easier. They are essentially oily in nature. Organic solvents, resins and even water are used as plasticizers.

2. Fillers. A filler is used to economize on the quantity of polymer required and/or to vary the properties to some extent, for example, mechanical strength, electrical resistance etc. A filler, whose function is to increase mechanical strength, is termed a "reinforcing filler". A filler is commonly fibrous in nature and is chemically inert with respect to the polymer with which it is to be used. Common fillers are wood flour, cellulose, cotton flock, and paper (for improving mechanical strength); mica and asbestos (for heat resistance); talc (for acid resistance).Other filler materials are : fabric, chipped-wood moulding compound, wood veneer, textile or glass fibres.

Wood flour is a general purpose filler. It improves mouldability, lowers the cost with fairly improved strength of the plastics. Mica also imparts excellent electrical properties to plastics and results in low moisture absorption. The commonly used "reinforcing filler agents" with plastics are : fibres/filaments of glass, aramid, graphite or boron. Reinforcing by metal and glass fibres make plastics strong, flexible and light materials such as used in bullet proof vests. Cotton fibres improve toughness. Carbon fibres are used for high performance installations such as aircrafts etc. requiring high strength and stiffness.

3. Catalysts. These are usually added to promote faster and more complete polymerization and as such they are also called 'accelerators' and 'hardeners' e.g., ester is used as a catalyst for Urea Formaldehyde.

4. Initiators. As the name indicates, the initiators are used to initiate the reaction, that is, to allow polymerization to begin. They stabilize the ends of the reaction sites of the molecular chains. H_2O_2 is a common initiator.

5. Dyes and Pigments. These are added, in many cases, to impart a desired colour to the material.

For example, titanium dioxide is an excellent white pigment ; iron oxides give yellow, brown or red colour ; carbon black is not only a pigment but also a UV light absorbent. Finely divided calcium carbonate dilutes (extends) the colour and is used in large quantities as low-cost filler.

6. Lubricants. Lubricants are added to the polymers for the following purposes : to reduce friction during processing, to prevent parts from sticking to mould walls, to prevent polymer films from sticking to each other and to impart an elegant finish to the final product. Commonly used lubricants include : oils, soaps and waxes.

7. Flame retardants. Most plastics will ignite at sufficiently high temperatures. The non-inflammability of the plastics can be enhanced either by producing them from less inflammable raw materials or by adding "flame retardants". The common flame retardants are : compounds of chlorine, bromine and phosphorous.

8. Solvents. Solvents are useful for dissolving certain fillers or plasticizers and help in manufacturing by allowing processing in the fluid state. For example, alcohol is added in cellulose nitrate plastics to dissolve Camphor. However, subsequently, the solvents must be removed by evaporation.

9. Stabilisers and anti-oxidants are added to retard the degradation of polymers due to heat, light and oxidation.

10. Elastomers are added to plastics to enhance their elastic properties.

Note. Above, excepting fillers, all other materials used, fall under the category of "Additives".

11.5. PLASTICS

Polymers can be divided into three broad divisions : plastics, fibers and elastomers (polymers of high elasticity, for example, rubber). Synthetic resins are usually referred to as plastics. Plastics derive their name from the fact that in a certain phase of their manufacture, they are present in a plastic stage (that is, acquire plasticity), which makes it possible to impart any desired shape to the product. Plastics fall into a category known chemically as high polymers.

Thus, "Plastics" is a term applied to compositions consisting of a mixture of high-molecular compounds (synthetic polymers) and fillers, plasticizers, stains and pigments, lubricating and other substances. Some of the plastics can contain nothing but resin (for instance, polyethylene, polystyrene).

11.5.1. Types of Plastics. Plastics are classified on the broad basis of whether heat causes them to set (thermosetting) or causes them to soften and melt (thermoplastic).

1. Thermosetting Plastics. These plastics undergo a number of chemical changes on heating and cure to infusible and practically insoluble articles. The chemical change is not reversible Thermosetting plastics do not soften on reheating and can not be reworked. They rather become harder due to completion of any left-over polymerization reaction. Eventually, at high temperatures, the useful properties of the plastics get destroyed. This is called degradation. The commonest thermosetting plastics are : alkyds, epoxides, melamines, polyesters, phenolics and ureas.

2. Thermoplastic Plastics. These plastics soften under heat, harden on cooling, and can be resoftened under heat. Thus, they retain their fusibility, solubility and capability of being repeatedly shaped. The mechanical properties of these plastics are rather sensitive to temperature and to sunlight and exposure to temperature may cause thermal degradation. Common thermoplastic plastics are : acrylics, poly tetra fluoro ethylene (PTFE), polyvinyl chlorides (PVC), nylons, polyethylene, polypropylene, polystryrene, etc.

Thermosetting plastics are cross-linked polymers and the thermo- plastics are linear and branched- linear polymers. The method of process- ing a plastic is determined largely by whether a plastic is thermosetting or thermoplastic.

Thermosetting plastics are usually harder, stronger, and more brittle than thermoplastics. Since they do not soften when heated and roasted or charged at high temperatures, thermosetting plastics have applications only in moderate service temperatures, for example, saucepan handles. Thermoplastics are reclaimable while thermosetting plastics are not. They have less load carrying capacity than thermosetting plastics. Moreover, reinforcement fibres can be used to increase the load carrying capacity of the later.

11.5.2. Properties of Plastics. Their great variety of physico- chemical and mechanical properties, and the ease with which they can be made into various articles have found plastics their wide application in the engineering and other industries.

1. Their comparatively low density (1 to 2 g/cm^3), substantial mechanical strength, higher strength – to – weight ratio and high anti friction properties have enabled plastics to be efficiently used as substitute for metals, for example, non-ferrous metals and alloys-bronze. lead, tin, babbit etc., for making bearings.

2. With certain special properties (silent operation, corrosion resistance etc.), plastics can sometimes replace ferrous metals.

3. From the production point of view, their main advantage is their relatively low melting points and their ability to flow into a mould.

4. Simple processing to obtain machine parts. Generally there is only one production operation required to convert the chemically manufactured plastic into a finished article.

5. In mass production, plastics substituted for ferrous metals allow the production costs to be reduced by a factor of 1.5 to 3.5 and for non-ferrous metals by a factor of 5 to 20.

6. Good damping capacity and good surface finish of the product.

7. The high heat and electric insulation of plastics permits them to be applied in the radio and electrical engineering industries as dielectrics and as substitutes for porcelain, ebonite, shellac, mica, natural rubber, etc.

8. Their good chemical stability, when subjected to the action of solvents and certain oxidizing agents, water resistance, gas - and steam- proof properties, enable plastics to be used as valuable engineering materials in the automobile and tractor, ship building and other industries.

With the development of high - performance engineering plastics, they are successfully competing with other engineering materials. They are replacing sheet metal parts, zinc and Al alloy castings and C.I. They are being increasingly used in automobile industry, where weight reduction is one of the means of fuel economy. The initial use of plastics in this direction was for fascia panels, interior fittings, and other non-load bearing components. Now structural parts such as bumpers, brake fluid tanks and some body parts are also being made of plastics. Products from thermoplastic plastics cannot be used at high temperature. Typical examples are : refill and body of Pen, carry bags etc. Switch boards and Chairs are made from thermosetting plastics. Smaller sizes of dust bins and water tanks are made from thermoplastic plastics, while the bigger sizes from thermosetting plastics.

Disadvantages

1. Comparatively higher costs of materials.

2. Inability of most plastics to withstand even moderately high temperatures.

The properties and uses of common thermoplastics and thermosetting plastics have been given in Chapter 2 (Tables 2.16 and 2.17).

The factors which have determined the rapid growth of polymer materials in the recent past, are :

1. Ready availability of the basic raw chemical materials in large quantities and, in general, at a low cost.

2. The large number of available starting materials for their production provide us with an almost continuous spectrum of composition and structure, and hence of mechanical, optical, electrical and thermal properties of the resulting polymers.

3. The engineer now has at his disposal many well developed processes and machines to convert these materials (as they come from the factory and that he can choose according to the specification of the ultimate product) into useful goods.

11.6. PROCESSING OF THERMOPLASTIC PLASTICS

The common forms of raw materials for processing plastics into products are :– pellets, granules, powders, sheet, plate, rod and tubing. Liquid plastics are used especially in the fabrication of reinforced – plastic parts.

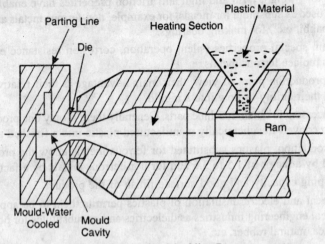

Fig. 11.1. Injection Moulding Process.

Thermoplastics can be processed to their final shape by moulding and extrusion processes. However, extruding is often used as an intermediate process to be followed by other processes, for example, vacuum forming or machining.

11.6.1. Injection Moulding. An important industrial method of producing articles of thermoplastics is injection moulding, (Fig. 11.1). The process is essentially as follows :

The moulding material is loaded into a hopper from which it is transferred to a heating section by a feeding device, where the temperature is raised to 150°C –370°C and pressure is built up. The material melts and is forced by an injection ram at high pressure through a nozzle and sprue into a closed mould which forms the part.

The mould is in at least two sections, so that it may be split in order to eject the finished component. For the process to be competitive, the mould must be fairly cool (between ambient temperature and the softening point of the plastic) and consequently the mould must be cooled by circulating water.

The improvement to the ram type injection moulding machine lies in the separation of the plasticizing and filling actions. The single-screw pre-plasticizer is probably the most successful design for injection moulding machines, (Fig. 11.2). The rotation of the screw provides the plasticizing action by shearing and frictional effects and the axial motion of the screw provides the filling action.

Injection moulding machines have a high production capacity : some can produce from 12 to 16 thousand parts per shift. This method is suitable for making parts with complex threads and intricate shapes, thin-walled parts etc. Typical parts include : Cups, containers, housings, tool handles, toys, knobs, plumbing fittings, electrical and communication components such as telephone receivers etc.

The limitations of the process are :- Equipment of cylinder and die should be non-corrosive. Also, reliable temperature controls are essential.

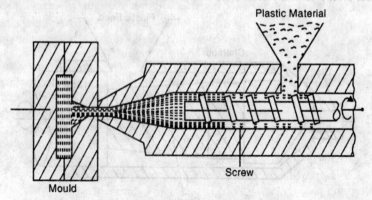

Fig. 11.2. Screw Injection Moulding Machine.

Injection moulding machines range in size from an injection capacity of 12,000 mm^3 to 2.2 × 10^6 mm^3. The locking forces are applied to the mould usually by hydraulic means, and may vary from 0.1 MN to 8.0 MN or even more. The injection pressure may range from 100 MPa to 150 MPa.

11.6.2. Extrusion Process. The extrusion process, in many cases, produces material in an intermediate form for subsequent reprocessing to its final component form. The process is the same as for metals, that is, the expulsion of material through a die of the required cross-section. The earliest extrusion machines were of the ram type. The cylinder of the machine (container) is filled with prepared plastic and extruded through a die under the pressure of the ram. The advantages of this machine are : simplicity in operation and a controlled pressure which can be virtually as high as required. If the polymer can be plasticized by pressure, then the ram extruder is advantageous in view of its simplicity. But for plastics which require heat, the separate pre-processing may be regarded as a draw back. Another major drawback of this type of machine is the reciprocating action of the ram which is time wasting since the ram must be withdrawn after its power stroke and a new dolly of material inserted in the container. Also, with many materials, the die orifice must be cleaned between each working stroke.

Nowadays, the ram machine is mainly used for "wet extrusion" that is for extruding plastics which have been softened by the addition of solvents. Although useful in homogenizing materials which contain hard inclusions, wet extrusion has the disadvantage of producing a component from which the solvent has to be removed.

For the extrusion of plastics, single-screw machine has completely replaced the ram type machine. There are two basic types of screw extruders : the melt extruder and the plasticizing extruder. In the former, the material is delivered to the extruder already melted and thus the function of the extruder is merely to push the material to the die and through the orifice. In the plasticizing extruder the material is in the form of granules or particles and so the extrude has to compress and work it until it melts before delivering it, under pressure, to the die orifice.

Fig. 11.3. illustrates a screw type extrusion machine. It consists of : a water cooled screw having a special thread form to suit the material being extruded ; a barrel in which the screw rotates (including a form of heating in the case of a plasticizing extruder) ; and an extrusion die.

The material is fed from a hopper through a port in the cylinder where the rotation of the screw imparts both axial and rotary motion to the particles. The restricting effect of the die at the far end builds up a pressure in the particulate mass which is then worked by shearing and heated by frictional effects until it is in a plastic state and can be extruded.

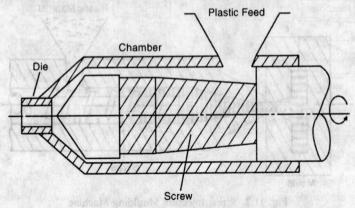

Fig. 11.3. Screw - Extrusion Machine.

Complex shapes with constant cross-sections can be extruded with relatively inexpensive tooling. The extruded product can be coiled or cut into desired lengths.

11.6.3. Sheet-forming Process. Many plastic articles are formed from sheet. The processes resemble those for metals, but require very low forces. Even atmospheric pressure may be sufficient. In "Drape forming", the sheet is heated to a moderate temperature. It is then clamped at the edges and stretch-formed over a die (See Fig. 4.99). One of the problems encountered is that the portions of the sheet first touching the die will be chilled and remain thicker than the rest. This is overcome or minimised by blowing hot air between the sheet and the die. Vacuum forming is a process, in which a heated plastic sheet is changed to a desired shape by causing it to flow against the mould surface by reducing the air pressure between one side of the sheet and the mould surface. The process consists of clamping the heated plastic sheet over a mould in such a way that the air between the sheet and mould can be evacuated, (Fig. 11.4). This vacuum, of increasing intensity, draws the sheet against the surface of the mould, where it cools and solidifies. The solidification will take place earliest in those regions which touch the mould first, (Fig. 11.5 *a*). This will cause differential cooling and, as a result of non uniform temperature distribution, there will be a marked change in thickness along any given section of the component.

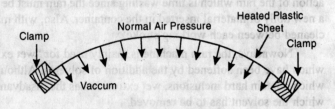

Fig. 11.4. Principle of Vacuum Forming.

Thinning is clearly worst where the sheet contacts the mould first (high spots on the mould) and near the peripheral clamping ring. This effect is reduced in drapeforming by replacing the clamping ring by a movable ring or drape, so that part of the profile is achieved before evacuation occurs, (Fig. 11.5 *b*). There is still a definite depth limitation, however, and additional steps must be taken to eliminate thinning in very deep components. Where one of the difficulties is the restriction of movement at a right-angle corner, (Fig. 11.5 *c*), the same circuit which is used to extract air can be used earlier in the cycle, to blow hot air between the sheet and the mould. The air pressure acts as a cushion and the air temperature delays cooling of the sheet.

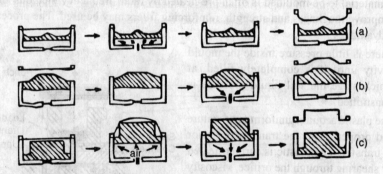

Fig. 11.5. Vacuum Forming Processes.

This method is also known as "Thermo-forming". Since high strength of the moulds is not a prerequisite, these are usually made of aluminium. So, tooling cost is quite less. Product applications are : Refrigerator liners, Packaging, Appliance housings, Panels for shower stalls and advertising signs.

11.7. PROCESSING OF THERMOSETTING PLASTICS

Compression moulding and Transfer moulding are the most common methods of processing thermosetting plastics. Although, suitable for thermoplastics also, the main application of these methods is to thermosets.

11.7.1. Compression Moulding. Compression moulding, (Fig. 11.6), is the equivalent of closed-die forging. In this process, a premeasured quantity of plastic in the form of particles or briquettes, is placed in a heated mould and compressed at suitable pressure and temperature. Hydraulic presses are usually employed to provide the pressure (which may range from 20 to 30 MPa or even higher upto 80 MPa in some cases) for compressing

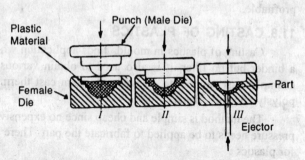

Fig. 11.6. Compression Moulding.

the plastic compound. Other equipment, such as friction and screw presses, can also be used. The object of compression moulding is to bring the plastic to virtually molten state. Thus the process is, effectively, forming from the liquid state, the material being held in the mould until the curing stage is over when polymerization is complete. The process is rather slow with the phenolics and urea resins, but some of the newer resins have shorter curing times and this has improved the production rates appreciably.

When the plastic is completely trapped between the male and female die, it is called as "positive mould". Closer tolerances can be held if a small flash is allowed to extrude, usually along the male die perimeter in "Semipositive moulds". More plastic is lost in "flash moulds", similar to those used in impression-die forging.

Typical product applications are : Disches, handles, container caps, fittings, electrical and electronic components, washing machine agitators and housings etc.

11.7.2. Transfer Moulding. Transfer moulding, (Fig. 11.7), is a modification of compression moulding in which the material is first placed in a separate chamber (transfer pot), from which it is pushed through an orifice (sprue) into the mould cavity (by the action of a punch) as the mould closes. The material to be moulded is often pre-heated by radio-frequency methods and, where it is desired to improve toughness and strength, reinforcing fillers may be used. The process has got the following advantages :

1. There is little pressure inside the mould cavity until it is completely filled, at which stage the full liquid pressure is transmitted.

2. The plastic acquires uniform temperature and properties in the transfer pot prior to transfer. The plastic is further heated by shearing through the orifice, viscosity is reduced, and the plastic fills the intricate mould cavities.

3. It scores over normal compression moulding in that cold presses can be used, since, heating of the plastic is affected, not by press itself, but by a simple heating jacket round the transfer chamber.

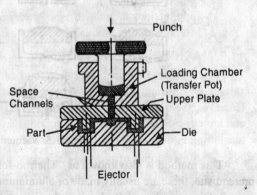

Fig. 11.7. Transfer Moulding.

Field of Application :- It is used less for mass production. Its chief application is in short runs where the shape of the moulding would make readjustment of the injection moulding machine profitable.

11.8. CASTING OF PLASTICS

Casting of plastics in moulds finds application when making parts of a plastic material with a binder but no filler. It is also used to obtain various kinds of cast thermosetting plastics, for example, cast car- bolite, as well as certain cast thermoplastic materials, such as organic glass, polystyrene and others.

The method is simple and cheap since no expensive tooling or equipment is required, and no pressure needs to be applied to fabricate the part. There are many variations of the casting method for plastics :

1. By using flexible moulds, very intricate shapes can be fabricated. The mould is peeled off afterwards.

2. Thick plastic sheets are produced by using plate glass moulds.

3. Thinner plastic sheets are produced by using moving stainless steel belts which contain and cool the resin.

4. Hollow shapes can be obtained by centrifugal casting of the molten plastic material.

5. **Potting.** In this method, the plastic material is cast around an electrical component which gets embedded in the plastic material. This is achieved by pouring the molten plastic material in a housing or case which is an integral part of the component and in which the component is prepositioned before pouring the plastic.

6. **Encapsulation.** Here, the component is covered with a layer of cooled and solidified plastic.

   Both potting and encapsulation are very important to the electrical and electronics industry. The plastic material serves as a dielectric.

7. **Foam moulding/casting.** In this method a foaming agent is mixed with the plastic resin. The mixture is placed in a mould and heated. The foaming agent makes the material to

expand (even upto 50 times the original size) to take up the shape of the mould. The amount of expansion can be controlled through temperature and time. Both rigid and flexible foamed plastics can be obtained from thermo-plastics and thermo-setting plastics. Rigid construction is used for structural purposes and flexible for cushioning. Product applications include : Shaped packaging materials for cameras, appliances and electronics etc., insulating blocks, food containers and styrofoam cups.

11.9. MACHINING OF PLASTICS

Plastics can be machined, but in most cases, machining of plastics is not required. Acceptable surface quality and dimensional accuracy can be obtained by moulding and forming methods. However, there are certain plastics like PTFE (Polytetra fluoroethylene) which are sintered products and are not mouldable by usual techniques, as they do not melt. For such "thermo stable plastics" machining is a viable alternative to moulding.

The machining of plastics (by operations such as turning, drilling and milling) has special features due primarily to the structure of the material. It also depends upon the binder and the filler and the method of moulding the component. For example, the machining of thermosetting plastics allows optimum cutting variables and tool geometry to be employed because these do not soften on heating, whereas thermoplastic resins soften under heat. The permissible maximum temperature in the cutting zone is 160°C for thermo-setting resins and only 60°C to 100°C for thermoplastics.

Special features of the machining of plastics are :

1. The tendency of certain plastics to splitting.
2. High elasticity (40 times as much as that of steels). Therefore, they must be carefully supported, to avoid their deflection during machining.
3. Non-homogeneous structure of the material, with components of different hardness. This results in poor surface finish after machining.
4. Plastics have a strong abrading action on cutting tools.
5. Their low thermal conductivity results in poor heat dissipation from the cutting zone and in over-heating of the cutting edges.
6. The intense dust formation, especially for thermosetting plastics, makes it necessary to use special dust-removing devices.
7. The hygroscopicity of plastics excludes the use of liquid cutting fluids. Compressed air is commonly used for cooling.
8. Reinforced plastics are very difficult to machine.

Plastics can be machined with H.S.S. and cemented-carbide tools. In machining a plastic material with a filler of glass, quartz or mica type, a satisfactory tool life can be obtained only with carbide-tipped tools. Only diamond tools are suitable for turning high-strength plastics of this type. The strength of cast parts of laminate plastics is 40 to 50 per cent less than that of the parts made by compression moulding. Therefore, higher cutting speeds and feeds can be used in their machining than for strong thermo-setting plastics. The main trouble in turning laminated plastics is the peeling of the surface layer.

The cutting variables are also influenced by the life of the cutting tool which is subject to abrasive wear in machining most engineering plastics. Dulling of the cutting tool leads to a poor surface finish and to breaking out of the material at the points the cutting tool enters and leaves the cut. This makes it necessary to use more keenly sharpened cutting tools for plastics. The need for sharp cutting edges also follows from the high elasticity of plastics.

The selection of cutting variables is also influenced by the low heat conductivity of the plastics, since, in machining the tool may be within a closed volume (as in drilling) with no cooling facilities. This may lead to charring of the machined surface.

The cutting tool angles for machining plastics are made somewhat different than those of tools for ferrous and non-ferrous metals. The rake angles are positive and relatively larger. Because of the viscoelastic behaviour of thermoplastics, some of the local elastic deformation is regained when the load is off. Therefore tools must be made with large relief angles (20° to 30°).

Abrasive machining of plastics has many advantages over machining with metal cutting tools. These include the absence of splitting and crack formation, and the better surface finish that can be obtained.

In grinding, the contact between the wheel and the surface being ground, should be as short as possible, to avoid burns. Organic glass is commonly ground with coated abrasive, applying an ample amount of water as a coolant. If possible, however, grinding should be replaced by polishing with a felt, broadcloth or flannel wheel charged with lapping paste, the process is known as "Buffing". The buffing wheels are of diameter 250 mm, 40 to 60 mm wide and of speed 2000 rev/min. Meduim and fine lapping pastes are used as the buffing compound for plastics. Laminate fabric base, asbestos-fibre and glass-fibre laminate can be cut with abrasive wheels (SiC) of grain size 24 to 46 and with a 5% emulsion as the cooling fluid.

11.10. OTHER PROCESSING METHODS FOR PLASTICS

1. Calendering. It is an intermediate process where the extruded plastic sections are reduced to sheet which may or may not, then be formed to final shape by vacuum forming. It is clear that the calendering process can be used only for thermoplastics and not for thermosetting plastics.

Calendering is in some ways similar to rolling process in that the material is compressed between rolls and emerges as sheet, (Fig. 11.8 a). However, there are differences. There is appreciable thickening after the material has reached minimum thickness at the roll gap and the pre-calendered material is not in sheet form, but of indefinite shape. The method of producing wide sheet and foil is illustrated in Fig. 11.8 b. The thermoplastic melt is fed to a multiroll calendar. The first roll gap serves as a feeder, the second as a metering device, and the third roll gap sets the gauge of the gradually cooling plastic which is then wound, with about 25% stretching onto a drum.

Calendering is a high-production rate (typically 100 m/min) process, mostly for flexible PVC, for example, upholstery, rainwear, shower curtains, tapes, etc. and rigid PVC, for example, trays, credit cards, laminations. PVC is also calendered into the well known transparent film widely used for packaging.

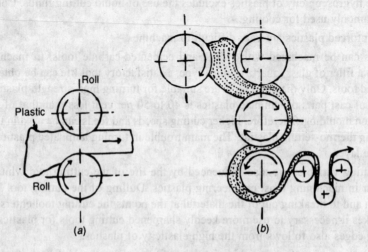

Fig. 11.8. Calendering Process.

2. Rotational Moulding. In this process, also called "roto- moulding", large relatively thin-walled hollow (open or closed) parts are made. A measured quantity of polymer powder is placed in a thin-walled metal mould. The mould is closed and is rotated about two mutually perpendicular axes as it is heated. This causes the powder to sinter against the mould walls, building up the wall thickness of the component. At the end of the heating and sintering operations, the mould is cooled while it is still rotating. Cooling is done by applying cold water and air to the outside of the rotating mould. The rotation is then stopped and the component is removed. To increase production rates, three moulds at the end of three arms joined together to the central spindle (just like centrifuge casting) are used, with one mould for each stage of the process, that is, load-unload, heat and cool positions.

The process is simple as no pressure is employed and the part is free of moulded in stresses. The technique is extensively used for the production of toys in P.V.C. such as boats, horses etc. Large containers of polyethylene (or upto 20,000 litre capacity) and large components like laminated petrol tanks for motor cars are made from polythene (outer shell) and nylon (inner shell). Other products include : Trash cans, boat hulls, buckets, housings, and carrying cases etc.

3. Blow Moulding. In this process, a hot extruded tube of plastic, called a parison, is placed between the two part open mould, (Fig. 11.9 *a*). The two halves of the mould move towards each other so that the mould closes over the tube. The tube gets pinched off and welded at the bottom by the closing moulds, (Fig. 11.9 *b*). The tube is then expended by internal pressure, usually by hot air, which forces the tube against the walls of the mould, (Fig. 11.9 *c*). The component is cooled and the mould opens to release the component, (Fig. 11.9 *d*). Typical product applications are : Plastic beverage bottles and hollow containers.

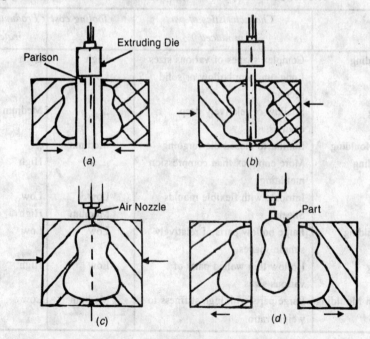

Fig. 11.9. Blow Moulding.

4. Reaction Injection Moulding (RIM). This method differs from the conventional injection moulding process in the sense that it is not the molten polymer which is injected into a mould, but a mixture of two or more monomers (reactants) are forced into a mould cavity. Chemical reaction takes place between the constituents of the mixture giving off heat to form a plastic polymer, which solidifies producing a thermoset component. The major product applications include : Automotive bumpers, and fenders, thermal insulation for refrigerators and freezers and stiffners for structural components.

5. Solid State Forming. The term is a misnomer because the temperature of the polymer is just (10° to 20°C) below the melting point of the polymer. The main operations involved are : Sheet metal techniques such as stretching, bending and deep drawing. Many food-packaging tubs and containers are fabricated from Polypropylene. Forging is also used mainly for producing gears.

6. Cold Forming. All the cold working methods used for metals can be used for polymers. Filaments and fibres are produced by "Cold drawing", that is, continuous stretch drawing. Conventional rolling can also be used for producing fibres. In "Cold pressing" or "Cold moulding", the raw thermosetting material (or mixed plastic compounds) are put in the mould and pressed to shape at room temperature. The formed part is then removed from the mould and cured in an oven. Pressures applied by the press range from 14 MPa to 84 MPa. The moulds are made of abrasion resistant tool steel. The process is quite economical and the process cycle is relatively short. However, the surface quality and dimensional accuracy of the part is not very good.

7. Thermoplastic Stamping. Thermoplastic stamping or matched-die forming is a method in which filled thermoplastic polymer sheet at melt temperature is worked between mating dies. The cycle time is greatly reduced and the springback is minimum.

8. Spinning. The extrusion process can be modified to produce filaments, fibres and yarns. The molten thermoplastic polymer is extruded through a die containing many holes. For obtaining strands, the dies can be rotated to produce twists and wraps.

11.10.1. Comparison of Various Methods for Plastic Processing

Process	Characteristics of parts produced	Tooling cost	Production rates	Surface Quality
Injection Moulding	Complex shapes of various sizes	High	High	Good
Extrusion	Long, uniform hollow or solid sections	Low	,,	tolerances
Thermoforming	Shallow or relatively deep cavities	,,	Medium	Good
Compression Moulding	Similar to closed-die forgoing	Medium	,,	Good
Transfer Moulding	More complex than compression moulding	,,	High	Good
Casting	Intricate with flexible moulds	Low	Low	Good
Calendering	Sheets	Medium	High	Good
Rotational Moulding	Large hollow parts of relatively simple shapes	Low	Low	Good
Blow Moulding	Hollow thin walled parts of various sizes.	Low	High	Good
Structural Foam Moulding	Large parts with high stiffness to weight ratio.	Medium	Low	Good

11.11. WELDING OF PLASTICS

Most plastics are available in the form of mould powders or granules, which are then fabricated into finished articles. The principal processes for the manufacture of articles from plastic materials have been discussed earlier. Plastics differ drastically from metals in their behaviour, when deformed at room and elevated temperatures. Even at their flow temperature, they behave like a highly viscous liquid. Therefore, some sort of pressure has to be applied to make a welded joint for plastic articles.

As we know that heating has no softening effect on thermo-setting plastics, therefore, they can not be welded by conventional processes. Thermo-setting plastics are available as semi-finished products, which can be either joined mechanically or cemented. On the other hand, when heated, thermo-plastics can repeatedly pass into a highly elastic and then into a plastic state, without losing their original properties on cooling again. These plastic materials are worked by the application of heat and pressure and so can readily be welded.

For making permanent connections between plastic parts and components, welding is superior to cementing and riveting, in many respects, as it offers : high speed, low labour requirements, economy, improved working conditions, stronger and tighter joints.

The various welding processes for plastics can be grouped into two broad groups, depending upon the source of heat used :

(a) Welding processes, utilizing heat from an external source, such as, a stream of hot gas, a hot extruded filler metal, or a hot tool. In all these processes, heat is transferred to the surfaces being welded by convection, conduction and partly by radiation.

(b) Process in which heat is generated within the workpiece through conversion of some other form of energy, such as, r.f. current, ultrasound, friction, infrared light, chemical reactions, or nuclear welding.

The common welding processes for plastics are discussed below. The application of heat and pressure during welding, causes the plastic workpieces to undergo autohesion.

1. Hot-Gas Welding. In this process, the edges to be joined are heated by a stream of hot gas from a torch, [Fig. 11.10 (a)]. The hot gas can be : air, nitrogen, products of combustion of some fuel gas, such as acetylene or hydrogen. The hot gas heats the edges and the filler rod to viscous fluid state. As the filler rod is forced down by hand, it welds to the softened edges and forms a weld. This technique is like manual gas welding of metals. The drawbacks of the process are : Low joint strength, reduced plasticity in the weld and near-weld area, low welding rate, especially in thick sheets, danger of overheating, and dependence on the operators skills.

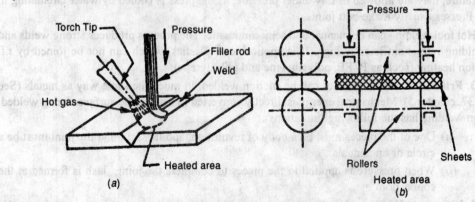

Fig. 11.10. Hot Gas Welding.

Hot gas welding, without filler rods, [Fig. 11.10 (b)] speeds up the process and enhances the mechanical properties of the point. The edges are scarfed and sheets are fitted up for welding, and the edges are uniformly heated by hot gas. The hot gas jet is followed by cold rollers, which complete the weld by pressure. The process is most often applied to make lap joints in films.

2. Hot Tool Welding. In this process, a hot tool transfers heat to the plastic workpiece by direct contact. There are many variations of this process.

In Fig. 11.11 (*a*), a hot blade is placed between the surfaces to be joined. After the hot blade has softened the surfaces, it is rapidly withdrawn. The joint is then completed by applying pressure. Lap and but joints over the entire surface of contact can be obtained at the same time.

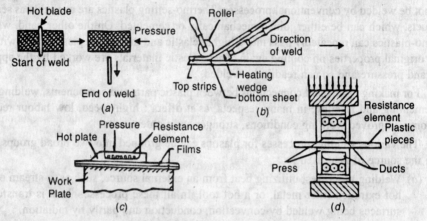

Fig. 11.11. Hot Tool Welding.

In Fig. 11.11 (*b*), a heating wedge is placed between the surfaces to be joined and is moved along the line of welding as the edges are softened. A roller applies pressure to the top strip which is then welded to the bottom sheet. This technique is applicable to elastic materials. The technique is used to weld thin rigid sheets or attach straps upto 5 mm to a thicker sheet.

In Fig. 11.11 (*c*), a hot plate heated by a resistance element is moved over the films to be lap joined, raises them to welding temperature, and applied pressure to complete the joint. In a variant of this technique, a strip heater is advanced over the strips with the help of rollers.

In hot press welding, [Fig. 11.11 (*d*)] heat is transferred to the area of welding by the hot platen of a welding press. The plastic pieces with their edges scarfed are champed in press having platens heated by resistance element. After the workpieces have been raised to the welding temperature, they are allowed to stay under pressure, as the press is cooled by water circulating in ducts. Presses usually make butt joints.

Hot tool welding can be manual and semi-automatic. The process produces strong welds and the welding rate is sufficiently high. It is applicable to plastics, which can not be joined by r.f. induction heating (such as PTFE, polyethylene and polystyrene).

3. **Friction Welding.** Plastics can be friction welded, in much the same way as metals (See Fig. 5.37, chapter 5). Mechanical energy is directly converted to heat on the surfaces being welded. Friction welding has the following limitations :

(*i*) One of the pieces must be a body of revolution, and its section at the joint must be a circle or an annuals :

(*ii*) When pressure is applied to the pieces to complete the joint, flash is formed at the connection.

4. **Ultrasonic Welding.** An ultrasonic plastic welder has the same elements as one for metals (See Fig. 5.40 chapter 5). Ultrasonic welding is applicable to acrylics, PVC, polystyrene and synthetic textile. Lap and tee spot joints are made best of all. Satisfactory joints are also made in the case of lap welds in static jigs. In all cases, neither edge preparation nor filler material is needed. Ultrasonic welds can also be made in dissimilar plastics.

5. **High Frequency Induction Welding.** The high-frequency induction welding of plastics is a widely used process. The principle is the same as of the process of induction welding of metals (See Fig. 5.36 *b*, Chapter 5). The process consists in that the workpiece is placed in a high-frequency electric field, set up between two metal electrodes. The arrangement is similar to Fig. 5.28 (Chapter 5). The electrodes can be in the form of rollers, (see Fig. 5.31.) for seam welding. After the plastics have been heated in the r.f. field, the electrodes apply pressure to complete the joint.

6. **Extruded-filler Welding.** In this method, the filler fed into the joint is in a viscous fluidic state. The hot filler material melts the edges of the plastic being joined, and a strong bond is formed between the filler and parent material. The process makes satisfactory welds in both films and heavy-gauge sheets.

7. **Nuclear Welding.** In this method, the workpieces to be joined are irradiated with a steam of neutrons. The surfaces to be welded are bombard these elements, nuclear reactions take place, resulting in the generation of heat. Due to this, the surfaces to be joined turn into a polyethylene, polystyrene, quartz, aluminium and some other metals. The method can not be applied to materials which become strongly radioactive, when irradiated with neutrons.

8. **Infra-red Welding.** In this process, welding heat is supplied by a source of infra-red light, such as, a sylite glower, a chrome-steel is carried out on a black backing plate of a formed plastic, sponge rubber or thick rubberized fabric. The resistence of the back up plate held firmly against the workpiece supplies the necessary welding pressure. The process is satisfactory for joining polyethylene films.

As noted above since the thermoplastics soften and melt as the temperature is increased, the methods discussed above, welding (fusion methods), and other methods are used to join thermoplastics.

Thermoplastics can also be joined by adhesive bonding.

Joining of Thermosets

Thermosets do not soften on heating. So, the above methods can not be used to join thermosets. Thermosets are usually joined by using :–

    (*i*) thereaded or other moulded in inserts.

    (*ii*) Mechanical fasteners.

    (*iii*) Solvent bonding. This method involves the following steps :–

        (*a*) The surfaces to be joined are roughened with an abrasive.

        (*b*) Wiping the surfaces with a solvent.

        (*c*) Pressing the surfaces together and holding the pressure until sufficient bond strength is obtained.

Solvent bonding is also applicable for certain types of thermo-plastics resins (acrylics, polystyrenes, cellulosics and some vinyls).

11.12. DESIGN OF PLASTIC PARTS

In addition to providing necessary functional requirements, the optimum moulded part design should give consideration to factors involving mould convity making (economy of manufacturing and strength of mould members) and simplification of processing problems.

While designing the moulded plastic parts, the following design rules should be followed :

1. Allow for shrinkage after moulding. All moulded parts are subject to some after shrinkage upon ageing.

2. Allow atleast a minimum draft of $\frac{1}{2}$ to 1 degree for easy withdrawal of the parts from the mould.

3. Avoid undercuts whenever possible. They prevent removal unless special mould sections are provided that move at right angles to the opening motion of the main mould halves. Such moulds are costly to construct and to maintain. Alternatively, the undercuts will need cores or split cavity moulds.

4. If possible, the parting line should be located in one plane.

5. Design corners with ample radii or fillets. Provide adequate fillets between adjacent sections also. This will assure smooth flow of the molten material into all sections of the mould and will also eliminate stress concentration at sharp corners. Such a mould will be less expensive to build and also less prone to breakage where thin, delicate mould sections are encountered.

6. The curing time of the product is determined by its thickest section. Thus, thick sections should be preferably kept as nearly uniform in thickness as possible. The minimum wall-thickness depends upon the size of the product and the type of plastic used. It is also limited by the difficulty of removing very thin parts from the mould and also by the high pressures needed to fill at a high width-to-thickness ratio. The minimum recommended wall-thickness is 0.65 mm and it can be 3.2 mm for large parts. Variation in wall thickness of the moulding should not be over 30%. The large variations is cross-section sizes and abrupt changes in geometry should be avoided for better product quality and increasedd mould life.

7. Ribs should be provided to increase strength and rigidity and to reduce distortion. When extra strength is needed at corners, it is better to provide ribs there, than to have thick corners. which are likely to lead to gas pockets, under curing or creaking. Rib height should not be more than twice its thickness, which should be 0.6 to 0.8 that of the adjoining wall. The ribs should be arranged in the direction of the material flow on the mould.

8. Plastics have low modulii of elasticity. Therefore, large flat surfaces will not be rigid and should be avoided, whenever practicable. However, their strength can be increased by ribbing or doming.

9. Through holes are limited only by the strength of the core pin and are usually held below a length-to-diameter ratio of 8. Blind holes are also made with the help of core pins and these are limited to a depth-to-diameter ratio of 4 for diameter greater or equal to 1.5 mm and to a ratio of 1 for smaller holes. Threaded holes of diameter equal to and greater than 5 mm can be moulded directly. It is better to drill smaller holes. Smaller threads of reasonable strength are best provided by metal inserts. Binding posts, electrical terminals anchor plates, nuts and many other metallic components are conveniently obtained by moulded-in inserts. Metal inserts (usually made of steel or brass), are held in the plastic only by a mechanical bond, since there is no adhesion between metals and plastics. Therefore, the metal inserts are suitably knurled or grooved so that they are gripped firmly and do not become loose in service. Plastics have much greater thermal expansion as compared to metals. This helps to shrink the plastic onto the insert, but could also cause cracking of a brittle plastic. The wall-thickness around the insert, therefore, must be made large enough to sustain the secondary tensile stresses.

10. Mouldings should be simple in shape for easy removal from moulds.

11. Back tapered features in parts should be avoided since they require complicated moulds and improper moulding conditions.

12. It is advisable to reinforce the moulding end faces with shoulders, which prevent the part from cracking. The shoulders are arranged along the end face periphery without interruption.

13. If plastic parts have holes, then the minimum thickness of the wall between the holes should not be less than 0.5 mm for holes 2.5 mm in diameter and not less than 2.5 mm for holes 16 mm in diameter. Minimum distance from the part side edge of a hole = 1 mm for holes 2.5 mm in

diameter = 4.5 mm for holes 16 mm in diameter.

14. The l/d ratio for reinforcement elements in plastic parts (bushing cores, inserts) should not be less than 2 for their reliable fit.

15. **Tolerances of Moulded Plastic Parts** : - (Courtesy Kents Hand book)

Tolerances are necessary in moulded parts because fo unintentional veriations in tools, materials or processing techniques.

The average meulded part has three types of tolerance, Fig 11.12.

(*i*) *Dimensions like A* : may be considered as fixed mould dimensions since they are independent of the two mould halves.

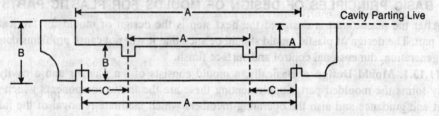

Fig. 11.12. Tolerances on Moulded Parts

(*ii*) *Dimensions like B* : are known as built-up dimensions. They are influenced by the degree of mould closure.

(*iii*) *Dimensions like C* : - exist where points being measured are on different halves of the mould. Any misalignment between the upper and lower mould halves is reflected in such dimensions.

Rule of Thumb : The amount of telerances provided should be just essential. Tighter tolerances result in high tool cost, increased product cost, annoying production delays and higher percentage of rejects.

Tolerances on Fixed dimension like A:-

Normal dimensions mm	Tolerances, mm, ±	
	Preferred	*Close*
12.7	0.125	0.050
25.4	0.200	0.075
50.8	0.30	0.125
101.6	0.400	0.250
152.4	0.500	0.375

Tolerances on Build-up Dimension Like B:-

(*i*) Small parts, transfer moulded : ± 0.125 mm

(*ii*) Compression moulded, wood flour filled, small parts : ± 0.250 mm

(*iii*) Compression moulded, learger parts, wood flour filled : ± 0.375 mm

(*iv*) Compression moulded, small rag filled : ± 0.375 mm

(*v*) Multiple cavity, wood flour filled : ± 0.675 mm

Note :- It depth of moulded part exceeds 25 mm, it may be necessary to allow fixed mould tolerances in addition to above.

Tolerances for Mould Mialignment (Dimension C) : - For average mouldes an additional tolerance of ± 0.150 mm should be allowed. more allowance shonld be made on very large moulded parts.

Warpage Allowance :- A good average value is ± 0.075 mm per mm, measured from an average plane through the warped surface.

The above tolerances are for phenolic parts.

Note :-

(*a*) Tolerances on Cold moulded parts are about double the values mentioned above.

(*b*) Tolerances on Injection moulded parts usually should be somewhat larger than those for phenolic parts.

(*c*) Grinling or machining allowance should be provided if extremely close dimensional accnracy is to be obtained.

11.13 BASIC PRINCIPLES OF DESIGN OF MOULDS FOR PLASTIC PARTS :-

After the plastic part is designed the next step is the design of mould for fabricating the plastic part. The design of plastic mould should be such that it will not cause problems concerning shape generation, dimensional control and surface finish.

11.13.1. Mould Design :- Basically, a mould consists of : a plunger and a cavity which actually forms the moulded part, Supplementing these are the frame components which provide support and guidance and also the operating members which facilitate removal of the fabricated parts from moulds.

Fig. 11.13 shows a schematic view of a compression mould and Fig. 11.14 shows a schematic view of an Injection mould which is a two plate mould. It is a mould with a single parting line. Note that the temperature control channels are in both the cavity and core. Note also the support

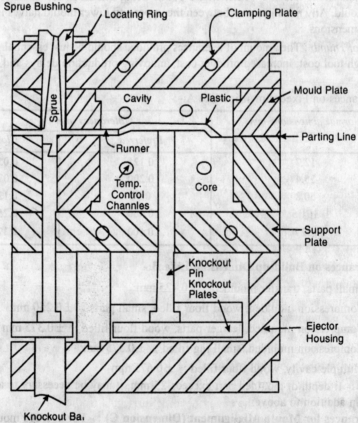

Fig. 11.13. A Schematic View of a Compression Mould.

pillars that prevent the support plate from buckling under the pressure of the injection material (fig. 11.14). The knorkout bar is atached to the machine and is the actuator for the knockout plates. A sprue puller of the "Z" type is used (Fig. 11.14)

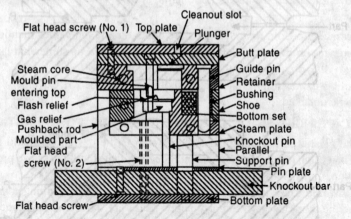

Fig. 11.14. A Schematic View of an Injection Mould.

11.13.2. Mould Materials :- The main factors influencing the selection of material for a mould are :

(*i*) Type of plastic to be moulded.

(*ii*) Method of moulding

(*iii*) Design of part to be moulded, *i.e.*, size and complexity.

(*iv*) Quantity of parts to be fabricated.

(*v*) Cost

The common materials used for moulds are :-

(*a*) *Steels :* Alloy steels (Cr, Mo; Cr, V; Cr, Ni; Cr, W, Mn; Cr, W, V)

   Stainless steels

   Prehardened steels

   Hardened steels

   Chrome plated steels

A typical composition of steel used for moulds is :-

   C : 0.42%; Cr : 1.45%; V : 0.25%; Mn : 0.30%; Si : 1.45%

(*b*) Berrylium copper (*c*) Aluminium (*d*) Soft zinc-Aluminium alloy (Kirksite) (*e*) Cobalt-Nickle alloy (*f*) Copper (*g*) Iron

Where possible, the mould pins are commonly made from commercial drill rods or music wire. Drill rod (hardened to Rockwell 48-50 C) is usually preferred.

Plate steel is usually utilized for many of the miscellaneous frame components, as it is both adequate and economical for this purpose, since such components normally do nto require hardening. If needed, about 1.6 mm depth of case can be obtained by carbusisation, although, considerable correction of distortion may then be required. Examples of such components are : Retainer shoes, steam plates, parallels and knock-out bars.

11.13.3. Cavity Design :- The following types of cavity design are available for cavity design :-

1. Flash Type : Here, the cavity depth is just equal to the part size. The excess moulding compound overflows in a hosizontal plane, forming a thin flash edge, fig. 11.15 (*a*),

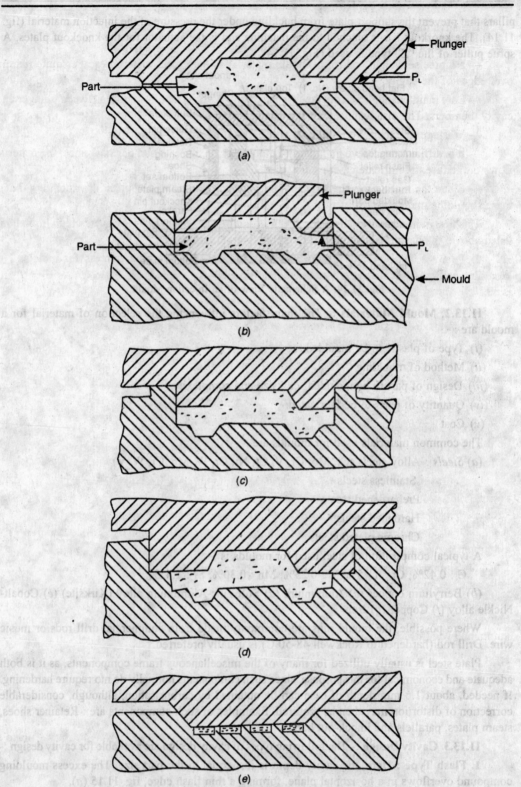

Fig. 11.15. Cavity Designs.

The advantages of this design are :-

— Simplest plunger and cavity relationship and so most economical.

— No precise weight control of mould material as the excess material escapes quite readily over edges of the cavity

— Low maintenance costs due to absence of any vertical rubbing action between plunger and cavity members. The disadvantages of the design are :-

— Wastage of expensive moulding material in the form of flash

— It is difficult to achieve high density mouldings on intricate part designs, since, the material flows out before the intricate cavities are filled.

— Since the mating members depend entirely on mould pins or builtin interlocking guides, these should be maintained diligently.

This design is exclusively used for injection and transfer moulding. However, within limitations listed above, the design is also used for compression moulding.

2. Positive Type :- This design is similar to closed-die forging porcess for metals. The moulding compound is completely trapped and forced into the cavity, fig. 11.15 (b) As such, there is no flash surrounding the mould cavity.

Advantages

— Uniformaly good resultant density of the moulded part, since the full moulding pressure is exerted against the plastic compound.

— The only flash that escapes the cavity is the vertical burr between the fit of the plunger and cavity walls, which is uniform.

Limitations

— the plastic compound should be very accurately measured, otherwise it will not be possible to maintain close tolerances on vertical dimensions.

— Mould wear due to the rubbing action that usually develops between plunger and the walls of the cavity.

3. Semi Positive Type :- This design. Fig. 11.15. (c) is a variation of the basic truly positive design. This type behaves somewhat as a flash type mould until the last fraction of the closing stroke, when the short positive portion of the plunger enters the cavity depression.

— This design permits overflow of slight excess of compound charge while retaining good alignment between plunger and cavity.

— The uniform vertical burr is especially benefitial for finishing operations, particularly if belt sanding can be utilized.

4. Landed Plunger Type :- Fig. 11.15 (d). Due to the design of the plunger as shown, wear between the plunger and the cavity walls does not affect the moulded part. Reasonable control of compound weight is required, although the situation is not so critical as in the truly positive design.

The design is somewhat expensive, but gives excellent performance. This design is extensively used for compression moulds.

5. Sub-Cavity Type : - Fig. 11.15 (e) This design is used for high production, multiple cavity moulds for simple and small parts. A thin flash will be there between the various individual cavities. However, the extremities of the common cavity area are of landed plunger type. There is operating economy in the form of ease of loading compound into such a common cavity. Instead of loading each cavity individually, the entire lot may be loaded with one large preform. To get thin flash, high moulding pressures are envisaged.

11.13.4. Manufacture of Cavity :- The various methods for getting the desired carity in the mould material are :-

(*a*) machining

(*b*) **Hubbing or Hobbing :-** This is the process of pressing a hardened and polished punch (hob/master of tool steel) into a softer metal block (See Art 4.9). This method is used for softer steels, Berrylium-copper, Aluminium and kirksite etc.

(*c*) **Casting :-** for Be-Cu alloy, Phosphor bronze, C.I., Al, Zn-Al alloy

(*d*) **Electro-forming :-** for Co-Ni alloy, Cu, Iron

(*e*) E.D.M. (Spark Erosion) : complex cavities can be machined in electrically conducting materials.

References : 1. Kent's Handbook

2. Plastics Engineering Handbook

PROBLEMS

1. Define the term "Polymer".

2. What is "polymerization" ? Discuss the various methods of polymerization.

3. What is degree of polymerization (D.P.) ?

4. What are the various agents added to polymers to modify their properties ? Discuss their functions.

5. What are plastic materials ?

6. What are thermoplastics and thermosetting materials ?

7. Discuss the properties of plastic materials and give their limitations.

8. Sketch and explain injection moulding process.

9. Why is screw injection moulding machine better than a ram type injection moulding machine ?

10. Sketch and explain extrusion process for plastics.

11. Sketch and explain the principle of vacuum forming process for plastics.

12. Sketch and explain the "Compression moulding" and "Transfer moulding" processes.

13. What special cares are taken when machining plastics ?

14. Sketch and explain calendering process for plastics.

15. What is "rotational moulding" of plastics ?

16. Sketch and explain "Blow moulding" process for plastics.

17. Discuss the various design factors for plastic parts.

18. Write short notes on : (*i*) RIM (*ii*) Cold forming (*iii*) Solid state forming (*iv*) Spinning (*v*) Thermo-plastic stamping.

19. What are "Potting" and "Encapsulation" ?

20. What is foam moulding ?

21. Discuss the various methods of welding of plastics.

22. Discuss the factors which have led to the rapid growth of polymers.

23. Write the product applications of engineering plastics.

24. List the typical product applications of compression moulding process.

25. Write the advantages of Transfer moulding process.

26. What is the difference between "Fillers" and "Additives" as used with polymers ?

27. List the advantages of cold forming of plastics.

28. What is the difference between potting and encapsulation ?

29. List several products that can be produced by Injection moulding process.
30. Give the advantages of thermo-plastic forming process. Where do the thermoformed parts find their largest market ?
31. How are the injection moulding machines rated ?
32. What is "Parison" ?
33. How is thin plastic film produced ?
34. What are the differences among three types of compression moulding methods ?
35. List the advantages of "Transfer Moulding" process.
36. What is "Wet extrusion" of plastics ?
37. What is the drawback of ram type extrusion machine ?
38. What are the forms of raw materials for processing plastics into products ?
39. List the product applications of "RIM".
40. List the product applications of Calendering process.
41. List several products that can be made by Rotational moulding process.
42. List the product applications of Blow moulding process.
43. Disuss : Design of Plastic parts.
44. Sketch and label a schematic of mould for compression moulding.
45. Sketch and label a schematic of mould for injection moulding.
46. Discuss the various cavity designs for plastic parts.
47. Write a note on "Materials for Moulds" for plastic parts.
48. How the moulds for plastic parts are manufactured ?
49. What additives are used in plastics and why ?
50. What are the differencs between thermoplastic and thermo-setting plastics ?
51. List the effects a plasticizing agent have on a polymer.
52. What is an elastomer ?
53. How can you tell whether a component is made of a thermo-plastic ?
54. Explain why thermoplastics are easy to recycle than thermo-setting plastics?
55. The various plastic components in an auto-mobile are made of thermo-plastics or thermo-setting plastics?
56. List the limitations of injection moulding process.
57. List the products made by thermo-forming process.
58. List the similarities between compression moulding and closed-die forging.
59. Write the advantages of thermo-forming process.
60. List the product applications of foam moulding process.
61. List the advantages of casting process for plastics.
62. Compare the various methods for processing plastics.
63. Give the specifications of Plastic Processing Machines :-

Machine		Main Specifications
(i) Plastic Injection Moulding Machine	:	Tonnage
(ii) Plastic Compression Moulding Machine	:	Tonnage
(iii) Plastic Blow Moulding Machines	:	Tonnage
(iv) Plastic Extruders	:	Screw Size

Chapter

12

Special Processing Methods

12.1. HOT MACHINING

A considerable percentage of the parts of up-to-date machinery are made of heat-resisting stainless steels, heat-resisting super-alloys and similar materials. This is due to the increased production of machines operating at high loads, pressures, speeds and temperatures, as well as in chemically active media.

The machining of workpieces of such materials, by conventional methods, is extremely difficult and, in many cases, impossible. Very low cutting speeds and feeds will have to be employed, resulting in heavier loads on machine bearing and slides. Also, it will be quite a problem to correctly select cutting tool materials, tool life or tool geometry. Heat- resistant materials contain considerable amount of alloying elements, have a tendency to weld onto the cutting tool, lose very little of their strength, even when heated to temperatures as high as 800°C, have a very high shear strength, combine high tensile strength with high toughness, are susceptible to considerable work-hardening and have low thermal conductivity. All these features lead to the development of high cutting forces, and temperatures, and to intensive cutting tool wear. In addition, the surface finish obtained in machining is poor. Consequently, tools for machining heat-resistant materials should be very carefully sharpened and lapped. Tool geometry should be properly selected.

To overcome these problems, entirely new machining methods have been developed. Some of these : ECM, EDM and USM have already been discussed in chapter 9. The method of "Hot machining" basically consists of applying localised heat, ahead of cutting tool, to reduce the shear strength of the workpiece metal (thus improving its machinability), and to permit the easy formation of the cutting chip. The chip is usually produced in the form of a long smooth chip, with lessened shock to the tool.

The application of correct amount of heat, in the required place, is of maximum importance. Hence, the type of heat and its application needs to be studied with care. Heating of the workpiece also influences tool wear. Therefore, heating in the cutting process improves machinability, when the increase in tool life, due to the reduction of the work done in cutting, is greater than the detrimental effect of the high temperature on the tool, leading to increased wear. It has been established that the temperature- interval in machining with heating of the workpiece should be taken 35 to 40°C lower than the temperature- interval for annealing and aging.

The heating temperature depends upon the cutting speed and the rate of feed, since the amount of heat generated in cutting increases with the speed and feed. Thus, in turning a particular grade of stainless steel, heating temperature is

> $> 500°C$ at cutting speed of 19 m/min
> $= 350°C$ at cutting speed of 300 m/min
> $= 230°C$ at cutting speed of 375 m/min

Advantages

1. The process is economical and in many case has reduced the operating costs.

2. Production gets increased.

3. Good surface finish can be obtained, superior to that obtained on these materials at room temperature.

4. Little evidence of any adverse microstructural change.

Heating Devices : The work piece can be heated by various methods of heating as : high-frequency induction heating or electric-arc heating devices mounted on the carriage, by resistance heating with the application of an electric current in the cutting zone, by flame heating, by Plasma arc heating. Sometimes, the blank is preheated in a furnace before being loaded into the machine tool.

12.2. UNIT HEADS

Basically a unit head is a power operated slide with provisions for advancing different types of cutting tools to the component. Unit heads are mounted on standardised bases. A unit head consists of a cast iron body which houses the gears driven from the motor to rotate the spindle. The body has longitudinal movement along the base which is effected from the main motor, (see Fig. 12.1), through a lead screw and nut.

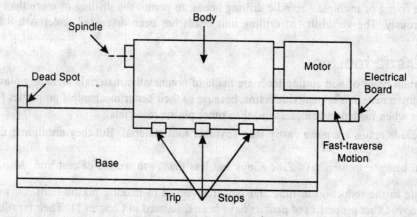

Fig. 12.1. A Unit Head.

The idle motions are carried out with the help of a fast traverse motor and its electrical brake. Depths of cut and various intermittent motions are controlled by a series of trip stops secured to the head, while a dead stop can be used to ensure the accuracy of cutter depth. The longitudinal movement of the head can be actuated also through the rotation of a plate or cylindrical cam, or when required for arduous duties, by hydraulic power.

The "unit head" has opened up avenues of multiple-operation machines for the completion of components which would need a line of machine tools, each of which would need to be fully tooled and manned. Also interstage handling and storage have been eliminated.

It is possible to load one or more components and not to remove them from the fixture on the machine until the completion of a wide range of operations. On the completion of the machining of these parts, the heads can be dismantled from the bases, and these with the bases, passed into stores until required for the machining of other components. The "unit heads" have made considerable headway in the production of medium to large-scale components.

Advantages.

1. Unit heads allow for maximum versatility.

2. They can be mounted and remounted in a variety of positions on standard interchangeable bases.

3. High production rates, along with consistent high accuracy.

4. Number of handling times reduced.

5. Less floor space needed for machines and for spring.

6. Operators more fully employed.

7. Physical efforts of operators reduced.

8. Good economical recovery rate.

The unit head is available in a wide range of sizes. Power rating of driving motors ranges from about 0.2 kW to 22 kW, with spindle speeds from 41 to 200 rev/min, and with feeds of 0.025 to 3.50 mm/rev.

Each unit head needs a control panel and such panels can be housed in separate cabinets or enclosed within a standard base. When a machine setup includes several heads, a combined control board can be enclosed within the framework of the base.

The majority of the unit heads are designed for boring, broaching, chamfering, counter boring, countersinking, drilling, end milling, face milling, gang milling, reaming, sawing, shot - facing, tapping, thread rolling and turning. The front faces of most of the heads are provided with means to allow the fixing of multiple - spindle drilling heads, to permit the drilling of more than one hole simultaneously. The versatility of drilling unit heads has been discussed under Art. 8.3.9. (Fig. 8.50).

12.3. PLASTIC TOOLING

Certain types of non cutting tools are made of nonmetallic materials including plastics. The most common materials are epoxide resins, because of their better mechanical properties (excellent properties when loaded in compression) than other plastic materials.

Epoxide resins are more costly than anyother tool material. But they are lighter than other materials, being $\frac{1}{4}$th weight of Zinc alloys and less than $\frac{1}{4}$th weight of cast iron. Also, the cost saving due to the reduction in time and labour involved in making plastic tools, outweighs the material cost. Other properties of plastics have been discussed in Chapter 11. Their tensile strength can be increased by reinforcing with fibre glass.

Epoxide resins can be poured, cast, laminated or moulded into intricate shapes with negligible shrinkage, and finish with a minimum amount of surface finishing. Consequently, the greatest saving in cost is obtained with tools of complex shape, for which the cost of machining and final finishing will be very high.

Compared with any of the tooling metals, plastics are soft and have a much shorter life than comparable tools in steel. It is not economical, therefore, to use plastic tools when : tool shapes are conventional, the component material is thick and quantities are large. Plastic tools, too, can be damaged more easily by faulty handling.

Applications. Plastic tools are being used in many industries :

(1) For drilling jigs, Routing jigs and fixtures for assembling, brazing and welding. In the majority of cases inserts are provided to prevent undue wear.

(2) **In plastic industry** for the production of moulds for both thermo-setting and thermoplastic materials, for vacuum forming and for the injection blow moulding of polythene products.

(3) **In foundries** for the production of patterns and core boxes. The entry orifice of the latter is normally fitted with a hardened steel insert to counteract the abrasive effect of the blown sand.

(4) Metal forming tools for drop hammers, hammer blocks, multipart press tools, piercing - punch plates, rubber press tools, spinning chucks and stretch press formers. Most of these tools can be given extra support by the inclusion in the mould of metal or fibre glass frames or supports.

(5) Plastic tools also offer many advantages where short runs and prototypes are required or where a set of tools is required very quickly.

General tapers and blending radii assist in producing a strong tool. The thickness of component metal should rarely exceed about 1.5 mm while radii less than 4.75 mm are to be avoided.

The metal formed by plastic tools include :

Aluminium alloys, brass and other copper alloys, mild steel, nimonic, stainless steel and titanium.

Production of Plastic tools. Plastic tools can be produced by two methods : by Casting and by building up reinforced layers of resin and glass fibre. The casting process is used for the production of tools of large mass, such as forming dies and punches. Selected fillers are added to the resin to reduce the cost of the mass and to provide the properties required in the tool. Inserts and supports can be embodied in the casting to provide strength where required. Casting is least time - consuming and the more reproducible of the two methods.

12.4. ELECTRO-FORMING

Electro-forming is a process of producing precision metal parts, that are usually thin in section, by electro-deposition on to a form (variously called as mandrel, mould, matrise or die) which is shaped exactly to the interior form of the product and which is subsequently removed.

In the process, a slab or plate of the material of the product is immersed into electrolyte (an aqeous solution of a salt of the same metal) and is connected to the positive terminal of a low voltage, high current d.c. power. So, it becomes an anode. A correctly prepared master mandrel or pattern of correct shape and size is immersed at some distance from the anode and is connected to the negative terminal (cathode). The mandrels are made from a variety of materials, both metallic or non - metallic. If the material is non - conducting, a conductive coating must first be applied in order to perform electroplating. The mandrel should possess mirror like finish. When the circuit is closed, metal ions are removed from the anode, transported through the electrolyte towards the cathode (master) and deposited there. After the deposition, the master is removed or destroyed. A metal shell is left, which conforms exactly to the contours of the master. It may take hours or days to get a deposit of sufficient thickness. The thickness of electro - forms ranges from 0.25 to 25 mm. The process is very much similar to electro - plating, with the difference that whereas in electro-plating, the deposit stays in place (on the cathode), in electro - forming, it is stripped from the form. The electro-formed products are typically made from Nickel, Iron, Copper or Silver, and more recently from copper - tin, nickle - cobalt and nickle - manganese alloys.

Advantages

1. Low plant cost, cheap tooling and absence of heavy equipment.

2. Low labour operating costs.

3. The process can be designed to operate continuously through out day and night.

4. Electro - deposition can produce good dense deposits, and compared with castings, electroforming offers high purity, freedom from porosity with a homogeneous structure. These important qualities are seldom obtained to such a degree in machined parts, stampings or forgings.

5. There is no restriction on the internal complexity of electro- forms, and this advantage eliminates in many instances, the costly joining processes.

6. The process has no equal for the reproduction of fine or complex details.

7. The use of inserts has widened the application of the process. Metal inserts are attached to or are embedded in a wax or fusible alloy master, and, when the master is melted, the inserts remain attached to the electroform.

8. A high quality surface finish is obtained on both internal and external surfaces of the electro-forms. Accuracies as close as 0.005 mm with surface finishes upto 0.125 μm can be produced.

9. Complex thin-walled parts can be produced with improved electrical properties.

10. Shell-like parts can be produced quickly and economically.

Note. Some care must be exercised to minimize residual stresses.

Mandrels. The mandrel, the mould or the master, is the most expensive item in the elector - forming process. The type of master and its precision are major factors in the economics of the process. As noted above, the mandrels can be made of a variety of metallic and non - metallic materials. The common metallic materials are : aluminium, brass, carbon steel, chromium - plated steel, stainless steel and titanium. A common feature of all these materials is their oxide passivation film, which facilitates their separation from the electro - form without any special surface treatment.

Depending upon the shape of the electro - forms, the mandrels are of three types : permanent, semi - permanent and expendable.

1. Permanent Mandrels. These mandrels are usually made of metals or of glass or rigid plastic. The surface of the non - metallic mandrels is made conductive by metallizing by electro - plating or a chemical deposition technique. For close tolerances work, such as gears and gauges, stainless steel is recommended. Such mandrels can be used indefinitely, with a minimum of treatment to preserve the smooth surface. Adhesion is minimized by the application of a thin coating of a parting compound. Mandrels are also slightly tapered to facilitate stripping. permanent mandrels are used for long runs and convex surfaces.

2. Semi-permanent Mandrels. For straight-sided components, or components which have undercuts upto about 0.013 mm, semi - permanent mandrels are used. These are made from steel with fusible coatings, compounded usually from wax and graphite. To remove the electro - form the fusible layer is melted, and after removal the mandrel is cleaned and rebuilt to form.

3. Expendable Mandrels. Expendable mandrels for complex electro - forms are made from :

    (*i*) plaster, which after electro-forming are removed by breaking.

    (*ii*) plastic resins and fusible alloys (Sn-Zn alloy) which are melted.

    (*iii*) aluminium and zinc which are dissolved chemically.

    (*iv*) brass

Plastic resins are commonly used for decorative work where tolerances are wide without undercuts. The surface finish of mandrels made from the fusible metal alloys can be improved by electroplating a layer of copper 0.025 to 0.050 mm thick. This copper layer is dissolved from the electro - form after the fusible alloy is melted.

Applications. There is a wide range of applications of electroforming process :

1. Moulds and dies feature high in the list. Moulds for the production of artificial teeth, rubber and glass products, and high - strength thermosetting plastics are now commonplace. The moulds can be made with undulating parting lines which have made a considerable impact upon the production of thermoplastic toys and novelties.

2. Radar and electronic industry : Radar wave - guides, probes, complicated grids, screens and meshes can be produced much more easily, to fine accuracies and at lesser cost.

3. Spline, thread and other types of form gauges.

4. Cathodes for ECM and electrodes for EDM.

5. Electro-formed core boxes with inbuilt heating elements. Electro-formed moulds for the wax patterns.

6. Electro-formed precision tubing, parallel and tapered, formed to different shapes to eliminate the need for bending which distorts the bore.

7. Electrotypes, floats, bellows, venturi tubes, fountain pen caps, reflectors, heat exchanger parts, honeycomb sandwich, parts for gas appliances and musical instruments, radio parts, spraying masks and stencils, seamless screen cylinders for textile printing, filters and dies for stamping of high-fidelity records.

Electro-forming is particularly useful for :

(a) High-cost metals.

(b) Low production quantities.

(c) Quantity of identical parts, for example a multi - impression mould.

(d) The possibility of using a single master for the production of a number of electro - forms.

(e) Whereas intricate female impression is required, so that is would be much easier to produce a male form, that is, the master.

12.5. SURFACE CLEANING AND SURFACE TREATMENTS

During the manufacture of virtually all metal parts, filings, fine metal chips, pieces of chips, remnants of waste or abrasive grit may get into holes or channels of parts. Also, oil, dirt, grease, scale and other foreign materials remain adhered to the part surface. The purpose of surface cleaning and getting rid of all the above materials is two fold : Firstly, they may get into holes or channels of parts. Subsequently, in operation of the finished machine, they may be carried by the lubricants into the bearings, where they may lead to overheating and premature wear of the bearings and even to a breakdown of the whole machine. This can be avoided by properly cleaning the parts and units. Thorough cleaning of parts is essential for high quality of their assembly.

The second purpose of surface cleaning is to prevent corrosion, and to combine a decorative appearance with the protective coating. All metals will oxidize and corrode, when exposed to certain environments, unless protected with an antirust coating. Before application of any protective or decorative coating, it is essential that the surfaces of the part be prepared by proper cleaning to assure good adhesion. Neglect of this preparation can be the cause of poor quality coatings. Removal of oxide scales, dirt, grease, oil, and temporary coatings is absolutely necessary.

The various surface cleaning methods are discussed below :

12.5.1. Mechanical Cleaning and Finishing Methods. These methods have already been discussed in Chapter 3, Art. 3.10 (Cleaning and finishing of Castings) and in Chapter 4, Art. 4.3.8. (Cleaning and finishing of forgings).

"Barrel tumbling" may be employed for any of the following purposes :

1. Removing fins, flashes and scales from parts.

2. Cleaning of forgings, stampings and castings.

3. Deburring.

4. Improving micrometer finish.

5. Finishing high precision work to a high lustre.

6. Forming uniform radii.

7. Finishing gears and threaded parts without damage.

8. Removing paint or plating.

After tumbling, the parts must be thoroughly washed and dried by sawdust or infrared lamps and then oiled to prevent the formation of rust.

Tumbling is an inexpensive cleaning method. It can be done dry or wet.

Other methods under mechanical cleaning and finishing methods include : Abrasive blast cleaning, such as sand blasting or shot blasting, airless shot blasting and hydro-blasting.

12.5.2. Chemical Cleaning Methods : 1. Alkaline Cleaning. In this method, the parts are cleaned by dipping them in aqueous solution of alkaline silicates, caustic soda, or similar cleaning agents. Some type of soap is added to aid in emulsification. Wetting agents may also be added to the solution to help in thorough cleaning of the parts. The method satisfactorily removes grease and oil. The cleaning action is by emulsification of oils and greases.

Special washing machines are employed in lot and mass production, Washing machines may be of the single-, two- and three chamber types.

(*a*) In a single chamber washing machine, the washing chamber is equipped with a bank of pipes with nozzles. A pump delivers the cleaning fluid, drawn up from the drain tank, to the pipes. The nozzles are arranged so that the part or unit is washed from all sides simultaneously with powerful streams of fluid. The parts may be traversed in the washing machine by a chain conveyer. The cleaning fluid is heated by a steam coil to $60 - 80°C$, and therefore the parts ejected from the machine dry fairly soon. After washing, the cleaning fluid drains into a collector, wherefrom, passing a filter, it comes back to the pump.

(*b*) A two-chamber washing machines have two washing chambers. The parts are cleaned in the first chamber as explained above and then rinsed of the washing solution in the second chamber.

(*c*) In three-chamber machines, the third chamber is used for drying.

This method should not be used on aluminium, zinc, tin or brass.

2. Solvent Cleaning. Small parts are cleaned of oils, dirt, greases and fats etc. by dipping in commercial organic solvents, such as, naphtha, acetone, trichloro - ethylene, or carbon tetrachloride. The parts are then rinsed once or twice in a clean solution of the same solvent. The vapours of these solvents are toxic and therefore require ventilation. The method is particularly suitable for parts of aluminium, lead and Zinc, which are chemically active and might get attacked by alkaline cleaners.

3. Emulsion Cleaning. In this method, the action of an organic solvent is combined with that of an emulsifying agent. The solvent is generally of petroleum origin and the emulsifying agents, which are soap or a mixture of soap and kerosene oil, include : nonionic polyethers, high molecular weight sodium or amino soaps of hydrocarbon sulphonates, amine salts of alkyl aryl sulphonetes, fatty acid esters of polyglycerides, glycerols and polyalcohols. Cleaning (removal of oils, greases etc.) is done either by spraying or dipping the part (metals and non-metals) in the solution (at room temperature) and then rinsing and drying. The method is particularly suitable for parts having deep pockets that will trap the solution. Again, the method is particularly suitable for parts of aluminium, lead or zinc while are attacked by alkaline solutions.

4. Vapour Degreasing. Vapour degreasing is a similar process, except that the solvent vapours are used as the cleaning agent. The solvent is heated to its boiling point and the parts to be cleaned, are hung in its vapours. The vapours condense on the surface of the parts and washe off the oil and grease.

5. Pickling. As discussed in chapter 4, the pickling process is used to remove dust or oxide scale from the surface of the components. For this, the parts are immersed in a tank filled with an acid solution, which is 12 to 15% concentrate of sulphuric acid in water, and is at temperatures from $65°C$ to $85°C$. The solution acts to loosen the hard scale from the component surface and remove it. The acid solution should not react with the clean metal while removing the scale. For this, an inhibitor agent is added to the acid solution. In should be noted that the pickling process only removes the oxide scale. It will not clean the dirt or oil from the part surface. Therefore, the parts should first be cleaned by alkaline cleaning method before doing pickling process.

6. Ultra-sonic Cleaning. Very dirty small parts, especially those of intricate shape with hard-to-access inside surfaces, are difficult to clean in ordinary washing facilities. Such parts are cleaned much more efficiently by the "ultra-sonic cleaning method". The method is effected in three stages : preliminary washing, ultrasonic cleaning, and rinsing of parts in a clean washing medium (kerosene, trichloroethylene, tetra- chlorated carbon, etc.).

Ultrasonic energy is produced by a high-frequency generator which feeds high-frequency electric energy to transducers that transform the electric energy into inaudible sound energy (at 20 to 25 kHz). The transducers are fixed to the bottom or sides of a stainless steel tank designed to afford the optimum acoustic conditions. High velocities are imparted to the particles of cleaning liquid in the tank. Cavitation bubbles of microscopic dimension are formed on the surface of the component. The cleaning action is caused by the formation and bursting of bubbles which practically blast all contaminants from all types of materials in seconds, penetrating every crack or crevice and removing all loose matter. The cleaning liquids include water, water based solutions, mild acids and caustic solutions which are thermostatically controlled to operate at temperatures of about 45°C. The effectiveness of ultrasonic cleaning is 99%. Components cleaned by this method can be immediately plated without further treatment.

Rinses are required in all cases to ensure thorough removal of the cleaning agent before coating.

After being washed, machine parts should be carefully dried. This is usually accomplished with compressed air. Such air blasting proves expedient in assembly before each operation. Special care should be taken to blow through holes, grooves, slots and other places, where dust and dirt may readily accumulate.

Advantages

1. The process can be manned easily by trained labour.

2. The process reduces the time element.

3. The process produces cleaner surfaces and eliminates many manual operations and the quality hazards associated with the human element.

4. The cleaning of intricate assemblies after final assembly can reduce testing time.

Applications. The process is used in all types of engineering factories, cafes, dairies, hospitals and hotels, and by manufacturing jewellers. Components which have been cleaned by the process include : ceramics, cutlery, electronic equipment, engine parts, jewellery, machine-tool assemblies, porcelain and watch parts.

Other components which need to be scrupulously cleaned include air craft parts, ball-race assemblies, engine components, fuel gauges, gas turbine parts, gears, glass components, hydraulic devices, jet-engine parts, opthalmic frames and lenses, parts to be plated, refrigerator parts, Satellite components and parts for semi-conductors, teleprinter parts and timing devices.

7. Surface Polishing. Mechanical polishing of pressed or extruded metal products and many such articles (done manually or automatically) is by using a wide range of wire brushes or mops, in conjunction with specially blended greases and waxes. The two non-mechanical techniques for this purpose have economic advantages over mechanical polishing are: "Chemical polishing" and "Electrolytic polishing". Chemical polishing has made greater progress due to the increased use of aluminium for a variety of applications. Electrolytic polishing has made slower progress, because it is more expensive to instal and operate, as compared to chemical polishing.

(*a*) **Chemical Polishing.** In this process, the metallic objects are immersed in baths of selected acids. During the process, certain amount of metal, mainly from the peaks is dissolved, producing a bright surface without the formation of an etched pattern. For chemical polishing of aluminium alloys the most successful of the solutions used contain phosphoric, nitric and sulphuric acids. The production cycle consists of the following steps :

(*i*) Immerse for 1 to 3 min. at 100°C

(*ii*) Remove and rinse in hot water (70°C) to remove the viscous film formation.

(*iii*) Rinse in a mixture containing equal amounts of water and 1.42 sp. gr. nitric acid at room temperature.

(*iv*) If anodising required, rinse in cold water.

(*v*) If lacquering is called for, rinse in hot water.

The resultant surface finish is of the order of 0.45 to 0.50 with a high reflection factor of about 88%.

The polishing solution for copper alloys contain phosphoric and nitric acids to which water may be added, according to the alloy being polished. The polishing times range from 30 sec. to 5 min., at temperatures from 60 to 80°C. An improved specular reflectivity with superior surface leveling is obtained when either of the above two acids are added to nitric- arsenic acid mixtures.

Advantages

1. The process is comparatively cheap, with low operating costs.
2. The equipment has a long life.
3. It is very suitable for delicate, thin - walled, embossed or fluted components.
4. Both the inside and outside surfaces are cleaned easily.
5. The process can be combined with barrel - polishing to reduce time and cost.
6. The process can be included in the aluminium anodising cycle.
7. Improved reflectivity usually is obtained.

(*b*) **Electrolytic Polishing.** The principle of electrolytic polishing is the same as that of ECM. A surface layer of the workpiece is removed by anodic dissolution of the metal, leaving the component usually with a highly polished surface. This "deplating" process is known as electro-polishing. ECM is a highly accelerated version of this depleting process.

When a metallic object is immersed in an electro-polishing electrolyte, the current line leads from the surface peaks, tangentially, causing a higher current density on the peaks than on the valleys. Thus greater metal dissolution takes place on the peaks to produce a smoother surface, and as the process proceeds, a viscous film is formed on the metallic surface. This viscous film protects the micro valleys from the action of the current, but permits the minute peaks to be dissolved. The rate of metal removal ranges from 3 to 10 microns per minute. The length of time required for polishing is 4 to 10 minutes for ferrous and non-ferrous metals, and from 3 to 5 minutes for light alloys.

If an increased current density is produced at the cutting edge of a tool, thereby intensifying the process of dissolution, it is possible to effect electrolytically assisted sharpening of cutting tools.

A wide range of metals and alloys can be electrolytically polished, but the main industrial uses of this process are for the polishing of alloy and stainless steel, Copper alloys, nickle and aluminium alloys.

12.5.3. Surface Coatings. The various surface coatings on machine parts are used for protective, decorative, wear resistant and processing purposes. The different types of surface coatings used for this purpose are : Metallic coatings, Plastic coatings, Conversion coatings, Organic coatings and Inorganic coatings.

(A) **Metallic Coatings** are applied by : Electro-deposition, hot immersion, chemical deposition or metal spraying (Metallizing).

(a) **Electro-deposited Coatings.** This process of coating also known as "Electro-plating", comprises preparation of the surface to be plated, plating itself, and polishing (where ever necessary). The preparatory operations include grinding, polishing and degreasing of the surface. The part to be electro - plated is made the cathode and the metal to be deposited is made the anode and both are placed in a tank containing an electrolyte. The process is carried out at a voltage of 10 V (D.C.) and current density of upto $10A/dm^2$. When the circuit is closed, metallic ions from the anode migrate to the cathode and get deposited there. Some characteristics of electrodeposited coatings are given below :

(i) **Copper plating.** Used for masking of steel parts from carburi- zation in case of hardening heat treatment, plating for improved running- in of plated surfaces and as an underlayer for multi - layer coatings. Coating thickness : 5 to 25 μm.

(ii) **Chrome plating.** Wear - resistant protective and decorative coating. It results in improved retention of lubricant and lower co-efficient of friction. Coating thickness : 30 - 40 μm.

(iii) **Cadmium plating.** Coating for protection against corrosion of steel in moist atmosphere (marine corrosion) and for improved running in of mating surfaces. Plating thickness: 15 μm.

(iv) **Nickle plating.** Undercoat of chrome, corrosion protection for steel, wear qualities and for decoration. Plating thickness : Upto 25 μm.

(v) **Lead plating.** Resistance to chemical corrosion.

(vi) **Zinc plating.** Low-cost protection of steel and iron against atmospheric corrosion and for decoration. Plating thickness : Upto 15 μm.

(vii) **Silver plating.** Electrical contacts. Good antigalling and siezing qualities at high temperature. Plating thickness : 2.5 to 12.5 μm.

(viii) **Tin plating.** Coating for protection against weak acidic media, non-toxic protection in food, for subsequent soldering and for masking in nitriding. Plating thickness : 3 to 12 μm.

(ix) **Gold plating.** Infrared reflectors, electrical contacts, jewellery.

(x) **Borating.** High hardness coating.

(xi) **Phosphating.** Anti-corrosive coating. Plating thickness : 0.5 - 1 μm.

(xii) **Lead - indium plating.** Electro-deposit of lead on a silver plated surface followed by indium plating forms a satisfactory bearing surface.

(xiii) **Brass plating.** Brass plating is frequently used as a base for bonding rubber and rubberlike materials to the metal. It improves appearance, provides soldering surface which is abrasive resistant. Since brass tarnishes (it is satin yellow to bronze initially and then turns to black to green on exposure), it must be covered with lacquer, when used for decorative purposes. Brass plating is used on steel, zinc, aluminium, and copper plate.

(ivx) The coatings of Nickle-Cobalt, Zinc-cadmium and Tin-lead are obtained by methods which are called "thermo electro-plating" or "thermo-diffusion". The latter consists in that individual metals are successively deposited on the part and in the course of subsequent heating these diffuse and form a plating of some alloy. Nickle-cobalt plating increases hardness, Zinc Cadmium plating upgrades corrosion resistance and tin-lead plating reduces porosity and improves appearance.

Electro-less Plating. This method of plating differs from the conventional method of plating, that is, electro-plating, in that no external source of electricity is used in the process. The plating is obtained with the help of a chemical reaction. For example, for nickel plating, a metallic salt of nickel, nickel chloride is reduced with a reducing agent, such as sodium hypophosphite. Nickel metal so obtained is deposited on the workpiece. Nickel and copper are the two most commonly used metals for this process.

Advantages :

1. The process can be used for plating nonconducting materials such as plastics and ceramics.

2. The process does not produce hydrogen embrittlement.

3. Cavities, recesses and inner surfaces of tubes can be plated successfully.

4. Coating thickness is uniform.

5. The coating has excellent wear and corrosion resistance.

Disadvantage : The process is costlier as compared to electro-plating.

Sometimes, some portions of the base of a workpiece are not to be electro-plated for decorative purpose or for the sake of economy. This is known as "Blacking out". For this the complete base is prepared for electroplating. The base is heated to 100°C. Paraffin wax is applied to the portions to be blocked out and then the workprice is completely cooled. After that the electroplating process is carried out.

Electro-plated parts are usually dull and possess little or no metallic lustre. To provide finish, shine and lustre to the electro-plated parts, they are finished by `mops' and `compos' The mop should be moved slowly over the surface to avoid removal of any portion of electro-plated leyer, the final finish/colour is obtained by mopping with chalk. Compos which contain abrasives should not be used with soft metals.

(*b*) **Hot - Dip Coatings.** Many metal parts are given anti - corrosion coatings by dipping them into certain molten metals. Most commonly used metal coatings are of tin, Zinc, lead and an alloy of lead and tin, before the parts are coated by hot - dip method, they are thoroughly cleaned.

(*i*) **Tin Coating.** Tin coated sheets are used for making food containers due to the nontoxity of tin. To remove the excess tin, the sheets are passed through rollers (immersed in palm oil) after these come out of the bath.

(*ii*) **Zinc Coating.** Giving a coating of Zinc is called "Galvanizing". One method of doing so is by "electro-plating". In the hot-dip method, the parts or steel sheets are fluxed by immersing them into a solution of Zinc chloride and hydrochloric acid. After that they are dipped into a molten Zinc bath. Again, to remove excess Zinc, the sheets are passed through rollers after they leave the bath. Galvanized steel sheets (and more recently, also one sided galvanized sheet) find increased use in automotive and appliance industry in addition to their use for roofing.

(*iii*) **Lead Coating.** Load-coated sheet provides anticorrosion properties in some media, where tin coated and Zinc coated sheets can not resist corrosion. However, lead coated sheets can not be used for food applications, because lead is toxic. An alloy of 15% to 20% tin and the remaining lead can also be used for this coating. Lead coating method is also called ©Terne[a] coating.

(*iv*) **Aluminium - Coating.** Aluminium - coated sheets can resist corrosion by hot gases. Due to this, these are suitable for heat exchanges, automotive exhaust systems and grill parts etc.

(*c*) **Metallization.** Metallization means spraying molten metal with the aid of compressed air. The metal particles moving at a speed of 100 to 150 m/s strike the surface of a part being coated and adhere to it, thus forming a layer of strong, finely porous metal coating. The layer has a fairly high compressive strength, even though it is brittle. The coating thickness varies from a few hundredths of a mm to 3 - 4 mm. Parts after being coated can be turned and ground. The method is used to obtain decorative, protective, antifriction and heat-resistant coatings, to restore worn out parts and correct defects of castings. The metal being sprayed is melted by OA flame (gas metallization) or by electric arc (electrometallization). The initial material is metal wire. Sometimes use is made of equipment operating on meltable powders. The surface to be coated is cleaned of oil and oxides. Sand blasting and rough turning is employed for better adhesion of the metal being sprayed to the surface.

(*d*) **Cementation.** This is another method of obtaining metallic coatings. The method is similar to heat treatment method of hardening (pack carburizing), in that the parts are heated in a closed container having suitable metal powder. However, it differs from the hardening method in that where as in the hardening method, the chemical composition of the outer layers of the parts in changed, in cementation process, metal alloy is formed on the surface layers of the part. Depending upon the powders used in the container (commonly used powders are of : Zn, Al and Cr), there are variations of this process :-

(*i*) **Sheardizing :** Powder used is of Zn. Temperature in the box is 365 to 375°C. The method is used for coating threaded work, chains and small parts.

(*ii*) **Calorizing :** Powder is a mixture of Al powder, $Al_2 O_3$ and Aluminium chloride powders. The temperature in the box : 850 – 920° C in an non-oxidizing atmosphere. Used for coating parts of iron and steel to protect from high temperature oxidation.

(*iii*) **Chromizing :** Powder is of Cr. used for iron and steel parts. Temperature in the box : 800 – 1050°C. Powder is of ferro Cr in granular form or ferro – Cr with ammonium iodide and non-vitrified kaoline. Parts : taps, dies, files, hacksaws, bandsaws etc. For corrosion and high temperature resistance.

B. Plastic coating. Plastics are used as decorative, anti - corrosive, and anti - friction coatings. These are applied in liquid and powder form. The primary materials used are thermo - plastics such as : polyethylene, polypropylene, polyamide, polyvinyl butyral, poly - urethane, fluoroplastic and Caprolactum etc. These are used in the form of fine powders which, on heating, change to plastic state. The coat thickness ranges from 0.15 to 0.35 mm. Before coating, the parts are heated to 180–300°C depending on the plastic to be used. The treatment itself lasts from 2 to 5 s. Plastic coatings make it possible to use carbon steel instead of alloy steels or nonferrous metals.

C. Conversion Coatings. These are the coatings produced when a film is deposited on the base material as a result of chemical or electro-chemical reaction. Many metals particularly steel, aluminium and zinc can be conversion coated. The coatings can be phosphate coatings, chromate coatings and oxalate coatings. After degreasing and cleaning in alkali, the part is soaked in suitable acid bath, for example, for chromate coatings, in chromic acid bath.

Conversion coatings are obtained for corrosion protection, prepainting and decorative finish. Another important application of this coating is as a lubricant carrier in cold forming operations, such as wire drawing.

The various conversion coatings are :—

Phosphate coatings

Chromate coatings

Oxide coatings

Anodic coatings

(*i*) **Phosphate Coatings :** A coating, mainly for steel, as a preparation for painting, adhesive bondings or rust proofing. It also reduces wear on the sliding surfaces and facilitates cold working of iron and steel. However, it can also be used for non-ferrous and light metals. The process involves the chemical development of a protective film containing ferrous insoluble crystalline phosphates of manganese and ferrum, or ferrum and zinc, by treatment with a dilute solution of phosphoric acid and other elements. Phosphate coatings are also applied for increasing inter laminar electrical resistance of laminations made of Si sheets for electric motors and transformers.

Depending upon the coating structure and the method of surface preparation, the film may be 2 to 15 μm thick. The process resulting in thin coatings is called " Bonderizing". The process is rapid and the coating may be applied as a solution at 57 to 85° C by dipping for about 2 minutes or by spraying at 65 to 85°. The method is widely used in automotive and electrical appliances industries for preparing motor car bodies, bicycles, washing machines, refrigerators and similar products, to receive an organic finish. The paint will stick tightly to the surface produed by bonderizing.

The process of obtaining thick coatings is called " Parkerizing". It consists of the following steps :

1. Cleaning and Rinsing with water 2. Dipping in a bath containing solution (either powder or liquid chemical and water at 65 to 90°C) for 5 to 60 minutes. 3. Rinse again with water 4. Drying or water staining to get black finish by dipping in staining solution and then drying. 5. Finally oil is applied on the surface. Used for : nuts, bolts, washers, small coatings,

(*ii*) **Oxide Coating.** Oxide coating of steel parts is done for decoration, rust proofing and to obtain low friction surfaces. The coating is obtained by thermal, chemical and electro-chemical methods.

The thermal methods involve heating the part in air, steam or molten nitre. An oxide film of 1 μm thick is formed on the part surface ; the film colour varies with the process temperature. Heating in the air serves to form thin oxide films on electrical components.

The chemical methods include alkaline and acidic oxidation. In the first method, steel parts are treated with a hot concentrated solution of caustic alkali containing oxidants. In the second method, solution contains ortho-phosphoric acid and oxidants. The acidic oxidation is much quicker as compared to alkaline oxidation and provides a stronger oxide film with improved corrosion resistance. The oxide films on steel parts are thin (0.8 to 3 μm) and porous, and therefore do not reliably protect the parts from corrosion. Their corrosion - resistance can be increased by subsequent varnishing.

The chemical methods are used to oxidate parts made of aluminium, magnesium, copper, Zinc and their alloys. The field of the process application is the manufacture of instruments, tools and consumer goods.

Electro - chemical oxidation of parts made of ferrous and non- ferrous metals and alloys is carried out in solutions of caustic alkali. The parts being processed form an anode. The process runs at lower temperatures and requires less chemical agents than the chemical alkaline oxidation. Prior to treatment of parts, these are cleaned of corrosion spots and degreased, and after oxidation they are rinsed in water. Decorative oxidation takes from 30 to 40 min ; corrosion - resistant films require upto 1.5 – 2 hours for their formation.

(*iii*) **Anodizing.** Anodizing or Anodic coating is a process of providing corrosion resistant and decorative films on metals, particularly aluminium. The process is the reverse of electro - plating, in that the part to be coated is made anode, instead of cathode, as in electro - plating.

When the circuit is closed, a layer of aluminium oxide is formed on the anode (aluminium) by the reaction of aluminium with the electrolyte. The layer of aluminium oxide on the surface is highly protective.

There are two processes used for anodizing :

(*a*) **Chromic acid process.** In this process, 3% solution of chromic acid is made as the electrolyte at a temperature of about 38°C. This process is applicable only to those aluminium alloys containing not more than 5% copper or a total alloy content of not more than $7\frac{1}{2}\%$. The process produces a light grey colour.

(*b*) **Sulphuric acid process.** The electrolyte is 15 to 25% solution of sulphuric acid. The process is applicable to aluminium alloys containing more than 5% copper or a total alloy content of more than $7\frac{1}{2}\%$. The process produces a light yellow colour.

These processes shall not be applied to parts having joints or recesses in which solution may be retained. Normal anodized coatings are 0.0050 to 0.0075 mm thick.

Anodic coatings are also applied by : Oxalic acid and Boric acid bath processes.

The steps for obtaining anodic coatings are :

1. Degrease 2. Rinse 3. Clean in alkali 4. Rinse 5. Apply anodic coating (3 to 10% solution of chromic acid). 6. Rinse 7. Dry.

(*iv*) **Chromate Coatings :** These coatings are mainly used for corrosion protection of galvanized sheet. The result is added corrosion resistance and base for paint. The product is called "Passivated" or " Stablized". These coatings which are very thin (0.0005 mm) are used on non-ferrous materials like Al. Mg and Zn - coated materials and cadmium coated parts.

The steps involved are :

1. Degrease 2. Rinse 3. Clean in Alkali 4. Rinse 5. Soak in solution of chromic acid, Cr salts together with hydro-fluoric acid or hydro-fluoric acid salts, phosphoric acid, or other mineral acid 6. Rinse 7. Place in di-chromate bath (45 min. soak) 8. Rinse 9. Dry.

Note : The process should not be used on galvanized steel parts which are to be resistance welded or phosphated and painted.

A chromate coating is less expensive than an anodic coating, because it is faster and the overheads are less. It has greater resistance to corrosion. However, anodic coatings have superior wear-resistance.

Bicycle Wheel Rim plating Plant Process Chart

The rims are loaded on the fixture. The fixture can carry up to twenty rims at a time and after the loading is done, the robot is switched on which takes control of the whole process. The rims undergo various processes before being unloaded for use in Body Assembly shop. The various process of Electroplating of the Rims is as in the table below :

Serial Number	Process Sequence	Chemical Concentration	Temperature (° C)	Density (deg. Be)	Checking
1.	Kerosene Oilcleaning	M.T. kerosene oil 100%	Room	–	Once daily
2.	Abrasive Cleaning	Surclean-504 70-80 cc/litr. NAON-80-100-80-ltr	60-80	8-10	Once daily
3.	Water Rinse	Running Water	Room	–	–
4.	Soak Cleaning	Steelex80-100 gm/ltr.	60-80	8-10	Once daily
5.	Water Rinse	Running Water	Room	–	–
6.	ElectroCleaning	Ginbond-80880-100 gm/ltr.	60-80	8-10	Once daily
7.	Water Rinse	Running Water	Room	–	–
8.	Acid Dipping	HCl 30-40%	Room	8-10	Once daily
9.	Water rinse (I)	Running Water	Room	–	–
10.	electro Cleaning	Ginbond-808 80-100 gm/ltr.	60-80	8-10	Once daily
11.	Water Rinse (II)	Running Water	Room	–	–
12.	Acid Dip	Sulphuric Acid10-15%	Room	8-10	Once daily
13.	Water Rinse (II)	Running Water	Room	–	–
14.	Semi-Bright Ni Plating (II)	Nickel Sulphate 250-300 gm/ltr.	45-55	18-25	Once daily
15.	Tri-Nickel Plating	Nickel Sulphate 250-300 gm/ltr.	45-55	18-25	Once daily
16.	Bright Nickel Plating	Nickel Sulphate 250-300 gm/ltr.	45-55	18-25	Once daily
17.	Drag out	D.M. Water Tank	Room	–	Once daily
18.	Water Rinse (III)	Running Water	Room	–	–
19.	Chrome Plating	Chromic Acid 275-325 gm./ltr.	40-50	24-30	Once daily
20.	Drag out	D.M. Water Tank	Room	–	Once daily
21.	Drag out	D.M. Water Tank	Room	–	Once daily
22.	Water Rinse (IV)	Running Water	Room	–	–
23.	Unloading of the rims				

Nickle Plating : is done as a protective coating as it has excellent adhesive properties which form good base for chrome plating.

Chrome plating is corrosion resistant and also enhances the looks of the component.

(*D*) **Paint Coating and Slushing.** Metal parts are painted to protect their surfaces against corrosive action of the surrounding medium and also to improve their appearance. The process of coating with paints and varnishes is carried out in three stages : preparation of the surface to be coated, painting, and drying with finishing.

These coatings are known as "Organic Coatings".

Preparation for painting consists in cleaning and degreasing surfaces. The surface so prepared is then primed for better adhesion of the subsequently deposited coatings. Use is made of oil-varnish, Oleo- bituminous, water - soluble and nitro - soluble primers. The primed surface is then treated with a filler, whose layer should be as thin as possible. Oil- varnish fillers and quick - drying pyroxylin fillers are commonly used. In the case of machines, the clearance surfaces (those that do not mate with surfaces of other parts during operation) are painted and the preparation for painting consists in cleaning and degreasing the surfaces, priming, luting (puttying) and smoothing down the luted surfaces with emery cloth.

Painting is done by applying one or several layers of paint. Oil and enamel paints and varnishes are used for this purpose. Enamel paints include oil enamels, nitro-enamels and spirit enamels. Nitro-enamels dry in 30 to 40 min ; after drying these form a hard glossy layer. Oil and spirit enamels dry for 24 to 48 hours.

Methods of Painting : The various methods of industrial painting are: Brush painting, Spray painting, Dip coating, Flow coating and painting in drums.

(1) **Brush painting.** Brush painting is used in piece and small lot production. It is done by hand and is a slow and cumbersome method, where quick-drying paints are used.

The method requires minimum of equipment but maximum of labour. The point losses are upto 5%.

(2) **Spray painting.** The method consists in applying fluid paint in the atomized form. This method is the most common and productive, but requires premises equipped with exhaust devices and spraying equipment. There are various ways of spray painting : mechanical spraying, air spraying, airless spraying, and electrostatic spraying. The method allows coating with quick- drying paints (nitrolacquers and enamels) and formation of smooth coated surface. The method can be easily automated by the aid of special installations and industrial robots.

(*i*) **Mechanical spraying.** In this method, the paint is delivered to a spray gun by a pump.

(*ii*) **Air spraying.** In this method, the paint is sprayed by a jet of compressed air which carries the paint mist to the surface being painted. The method is capable of coating 30 to 80 m^2 of surface per hour, but the losses are high (40 to 50%).

(*iii*) **Air-less spraying.** In this method, point heated to $70 - 90°C$ is forced through a nozzle at a pressure of 2 to 4 N/mm^2 and so sprayed. The method allows the use of highly viscous paints, which cuts the solvent requirements and drying time. The production rate can be $50 - 200$ m^2 of surface per hour and paint losses amount to $25 - 50\%$.

(*iv*) **Electro-static spraying.** In this method, a negatively charged sprayer delivers paint which gets onto the surface of a positively charged metal part being painted. The charging is provided by a high-voltage constant-current source. The method can also be used for non-metallic parts by setting up metal screens behind the parts. The paint losses are less than 5%. The method makes it possible to improve working conditions, to provide for fairly high productivity (50 m^2 of surface per hour) and for the possibility of developing a fully automated painting process.

(3) **Dip coating.** Dipping or dip - coating is used in automatic production. The method consists in dipping the parts suspended from a chain conveyor, in a paint bath. The method is used in large - lot and mass production for painting parts of simple shape. Operating conditions present no

hazard to health and are fire - safe. The method offers high productive output and low cost. Paint losses are less than 5%.

(4) **Flow coating.** In this method, the part being painted is put for some time under the jets of paint, whereby the paint flows over the part surface, forming a smooth, dense and uniform coat.

(5) **Drum painting.** Painting in drums is employed for small parts in mass production. The parts may be either stationary or may travel on a conveyor. The method is used to form a single - layer coat of quick drying paints on small single - type parts. Roller coating is used to paint sheet material.

Drying. After being painted, the parts, units or machines undergo drying. The quality of paint coatings depend on the method of drying. Drying is a complex chemical process involving evaporation of the solvent and oxidation or polymerization of the coating film. Drying can be natural or artificial.

The natural or air drying is carried out at a temperature of 18 to 25°C over a long time. The artificial drying makes it possible to speed up solidification of the coat and also to greatly improve its quality.

The most common method of artificial drying is by convective heating. The drying is carried out in a closed chamber which is air - heated by gas, electricity or steam to a temperature of 55° to 220°C or by means of a reflector equipped with banks of special electric lamps. The latter method takes only from one fourth to one half as much time as hot - air drying. other drying methods utilize high - frequency currents (induction heating) and infrared rays. The latter are used in drying parts coated with lacquers and enamels.

Finishing. The finishing of a painted surface includes : varnishing, polishing and decorative design. Varnishing increases stability of the paint and makes it glossy; the varnish is applied on the painted surface in one or several layers. Polishing is used to obtain a shiny surface by means of felt wheels or bands with special polishing pastes. Decorative design involves the application of narrow decorative lines, ornaments and trade marks to the painted surface.

Note. Sometimes parts are painted without preliminary preparation of the surfaces and without finishing. This simplified procedure is used for parts such as automobile rear axles, gearbox cases, etc. Machine components are usually painted before assembly, but in some cases painting is done after the product has been fully assembled and tested, for example, machine tools and other manufacturing equipment. After coating the parts with the slushing compound they are wrapped in waste paper.

Varnishes. Varnishes are homogeneous mixtures of synthetic or natural resins in a solvent. The commonly used resins are : amber, copal, shellac or lac. The common solvents are : turpentine oil, methylated spirit, alcohol and linseed oil. A dryer is also added to hasten the drying of varnish.

The varnish is applied as a protective and decorative coating. When it dries, it leaves a hard, transparent, glossy and hard lustrous film on the surface of the part.

When the solvent is methylated spirit, we get "Spirit varnish". This varnish is very quick drying. However, the film produced on the surface has a tendency to crack and peel off. Such varnishes are usually used for polishing wooden surfaces.

When the solvent is linseed oil or turpentine oil, we get "oil varnishes". These varnishes take longer to dry, but the coating is hard, lusturous and durable.

Lacquers. Lacquer is a "film forming material which dries very quickly by the evaporation of solvent. Most lacquers are made of nitrocellulose dissolved in volatile organic solvents, with pigments added for colour.

Because of their quick drying property, they find a great application in auto industry. A coat of primer is a must because of the poor adhesive property of lacquers on metal surfaces. Clear lacquers are used for protection against indoor atmospheres (painting of indoor woodwork, metal surfaces, furniture etc.), while pigmented lacquers are useful for outdoor applications as well.

Vinyl lacquers are impermeable to water, are chemically resistant and are free from odour, taste and toxicity. So, they find applications in linining food and beverage containers.

Shellac. It is a solution of natural resin (lac) in an alcohol. It hardens by the evaporation of the thinner used. It does not penetrate wood surfaces deeply. So, it is often used as a sealing coat on wood and will give a durable film. Since it is soluble only in an alcohol, varnishes and lacquers can be used over it without the two running together.

(*E*) **Inorganic Coatings.** These coatings are made up of refractory compounds. They are harder, more rigid, and have greater resistance to elevated temperature than organic coatings (paints, varnishes, Lacquers, Shellac etc.) Inorganic ocatings include :

Porcelain enamels

Ceramic coatings

For porcelain enamels see Art. 13.6.

Ceramic coatings are viterous and metallic oxide coatings. They contain a higher percentage of alumina than porcelain enamels and are more refractory than these. These coatings protect the metal from oxidation and corrosion and increase its strength and rigidity and hence its wear resistance. The chief ingredient of these coatings is silicate powder. However, coatings are based on oxide materials, carbides, silicides and phosphates. They are applied by : dipping, spraying, flow coating etc.

12.5.4. Temporary Coatings or Corrosive Proofing:-

The protective coatings discussed under Art. 12.5.3 are known as "permanent coatings" and these are used for parts in service, so that they do not get corroded while in service. These coatings remain on the surface permanently.

However, parts intended for long-term storage or transportation are subjected to "Temporary Coatings" or "Corrosive Proofing". These coatings can be removed from the surface without damaging it. Such coatings are produced by applying a slushing compound (Vaseline, Rifle grease): With brushes, by dipping in a hot slushing solution or by spraying. Use is also made of anti corrosive varnishes, which can be removed by de-slushing with petrol or other solvents. Effective corrosive proofing is also done by dipping parts for 2-3 min in a tank with 30% solution of sodium nitride heated to 40-50°C, and by wrapping in paper impregnated with a 10% solution of sodium nitride and other corrosion inhibitors.

12.6. ADHESIVE BONDS

Permanent joints can be made by means of adhesives applied in a thin layer between the connected parts. They are employed to fasten together metal elements, metal and non-metallic elements (textolite, foam plastic etc.) and two non-metallic elements.

Advantages

1. Reliable connection of parts made of very thin sheet materials.
2. Dissimilar materials can be joined.
3. The process is used to reduce production costs.
4. It is used to lessen the mass of parts.
5. Highly skilled labour is not required for bonding.
6. The process provides for tight and corrosion - free joints.
7. Smooth bonded surfaces.
8. Exterior surfaces remain smooth.
9. Only low temperatures are involved, therefore, absence of stresses or their lower concentration.
10. Heat sensitive materials can be joined without any damage.
11. Complex assemblies can be made at low cost.
12. Adhesives contribute towards absorption of shocks and vibrations.

13. Adhesive bonds can tolerate the thermal stresses of differential expansion and contraction.
14. Because the adhesives bond the entire joint area, good load distribution and fatigue resistance are obtained.
15. The joints are sufficiently strong in shear and withstand dynamic and variable loads.
16. Compared to welded, soldered and riveted joints, adhesive bonded parts have uniformly spread stresses and do not tend to warp.
17. The process is very fast.
18. Stress concentrations are reduced or entirely absent.
19. Adhesives are indispensable where welding, brazing or soldering fails or where bolts and rivets can not be used for fear of stress concentration, e.g., honeycombings structures.

Disadvantages

1. Comparatively low operational temperatures (maximum upto about 100°C for most adhesives).
2. Low resistance to tear - off.
3. Reduced strength of some adhesives in the course of timing (ageing).
4. Tendency to creep, if subjected to long standing and heavy loads.
5. The need for extended polymerization time.

Applications

Adhesive bonds have been particularly developed in the air-craft industry : The appearance of honeycomb elements is entirely due to this method. The method is used in critical structures such as control surfaces in air craft and entire aircraft body. In machine tools, adhesives are employed to bond carriage - guide - ways to beds, and in automobile industry to fasten friction linings to clutch - disks and brake - bands. Adhesive bonds are also used in appliance and consumer goods fields and also for sealing, vibration damping and insulating etc.

12.6.1. Adhesive-bonded Joints. Adhesive-bonding of parts is effected on the following types of surfaces :

1. On cylindrical surfaces, for example, placing bushings into holes in housing - type parts and discs onto shafts, coupling pipes together, fitting plugs, and fastening linings to brake blocks etc.
2. On flat surfaces, for example, lap-type joining of sheet parts with one or two straps and so on.

Typical adhesive-bonded joints are shown in Fig. 12.2.

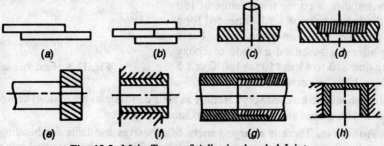

Fig. 12.2. Main Types of Adhesive-bonded Joints.

The strength of an adhesive joint is dependent on the amount of clearance in it, which is normally kept at 0.05 to 1.5 mm. With increased clearance, the strength of the joint decreases. As the length of over lapping of the joint increases, the force needed to break down the joint increases asymptotically approaching a certain limit. Surface roughness of the parts bonded should be held to within 6.3 to 1 µmRa. Increase in curing time has a favourable effect on the strength of the adhesive - bonded joint. With cold - curing, the strength grows continuously over a long period of time. The strength of joints bonded with cold curing adhesives increases if the polymerization process is accompanied by heating. Heating also greatly reduces the curing time.

Making an adhesive-bonded Joint

An adhesive-bonding process comprises the following steps :

(*i*) Preparation of part surfaces.

(*ii*) Preparation and application of the adhesive.

(*iii*) Assembly of parts under a pressure determined by the grade of the adhesive.

(*iv*) Heating of the assembled product.

The surfaces to be bonded must be cleaned and degreased. Cleaning is done with wiping wastes, brushes or in a sand blaster. The substances used for degreasing are : acetone, trichloroethylene, Carbon tetra chloride and other organic solvents. Aluminium- alloy parts are prepared by pickling. Where necessary, the surfaces to be joined are machined to obtain a surface finish that provides for better holding of the adhesive.

Adhesives are prepared in special polychloroethylene or metallic containers ; the latter need to be chrome-plated or coated with silicone varnish. Hot curing adhesives can be stored in closed containers for a long time. Cold - curing adhesives are prepared just before use as their pot life is only 30 to 40 min.

The method of application of an adhesive depends on its viscosity. Liquid adhesives, that can be applied with brushes or sprayers, are used most commonly. Some grades of adhesives are convenient to apply with spatulas, rollers or injectors.

The adhesive is spread in an even thin layer (0.1 – 0.2 mm) with a bristle brush or a spatula. To prevent frothing, the adhesive must be applied moving the brush in one direction.

In hand pneumatic injectors, (Fig. 12.3), compressed air is supplied through an inlet connection. The air extrudes the adhesive by means of a piston through a nozzle having a diameter of 1 mm.

After the application of adhesive, the parts are assem-bled in special fixtures and clamped by means of lever mechanisms, springs, or pneu-matic clamping devices. Clamping force must ensure a unit pressure of 0.05 to 1.0 MN/m^2.

Lastly, heating is effected in cabinets equipped with electric or gas heaters. The heating temperature and curing time depends on the composition of the adhesive. For instance, a curing temperature of 150 to 160°C and a curing time of 1.5 h is needed for a cold-curing adhesive based on epoxy resin. For a hot - curing adhesive based on a grade of epoxy resin, a curing time of 3 to 4 h at 150° to 160°C or 1.5 to 2 h at 180° to 190°C is recommended.

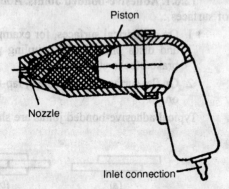

Fig. 12.3. Hand Pneumatic Injector.

Adhesives should be handled very carefully as their constituents are toxic. The work, therefore, should be done with gloves on, under proper exhaust ventilation.

12.6.2. Adhesives. There is a large variety of adhesives available for bonding metals with metals and metals with structural non - metallic materials. They can be classified into the following main groups :

1. Adhesives based on epoxy resins. The available epoxyresin- based adhesives are both cold and hot curing. These are used for cold and hot joining of metals, ceramics, plastics, wood and other materials.

In cold curing adhesives, a curing agent, such as polyethylene polymide (8 to 10 parts by mass) or hexamethylenediamine (20 parts by mass) is added to 100 parts by mass of the resin.

Maleic anhydride (40 parts by mass) is added as a curing agent to the resin in making hot curing adhesives. The various epoxy resins used as adhesives are given below with the curing temperatures given within brackets :

Epoxy (room temperature cure, 16 to 32°C)

Epoxy (elevated temperature cure, 93 to 177°C)

Epoxy nylon (121 to 177°C)

Epoxy phenolic (121 to 177°C).

2. Phenol-resin based resins. These are modified by various compounds. Curing takes place at a temperature of about 150°C with the jointed components being held against each other. Phenol polyvinyl acetate adhesives are available ready-made without subsequent introduction of curing agent. These adhesives can sustain temperatures upto 70°C. Phenolic rubber and phenolic resin-based adhesives modified by organic polymers and silicone compounds feature high temperature resistance. Phenol formaldehyde is used to bond foam plastics, textile laminate etc. The other common adhesives in this group are :

Neoprene - phenolic (135 – 177°C)

Nitrile - phenolic (135 – 177°C)

Butyral - phenolic (135 – 177°C)

3. Polyurethane adhesives. These adhesives have resistance to temperature of 100 to 120°C and the same strength as Phenol polyvinyl acetate adhesives.

4. Special grade adhesives. These are used for higher temperature resistance and possess high shearing strength.

Bonding Plastic parts. The above mentioned adhesives and special- purpose adhesives are used to bond plastic parts. For many thermoplasts, their solvents serve as adhesives, for example, dichloroethane for organic glass, benzol for polystrene, acetone for viniplast etc. The scope of automation of adhesive-bonding processes is the application of the adhesive to mating surfaces, assembly and accurate location of the parts bonded, and subsequent curing. Adhesives can be applied with rollers, or fed with an injector into the clearance between the mating parts ; dipping the mating parts into it is also practicable.

12.7. SURFACE COATINGS FOR TOOLING

In almost every type of production tooling, the most desirable feature to have is a very hard surface layer on a low strength but tough body. Toughness is needed to survive mechanical shocks, that is, impact loading in interrupted cuts. Shocks occur in even continuous chip formation processes, when the tool encounters a localized hard spot. The examples of such tooling include : metal cutting tools, rock drills, cutting blades, forging dies, screws for extrusion of plastic and food products and saw mills and so on. Other applications include : parts for earth moving machinery, valves and valve seats for diesel engines, and many such parts involving high heat applications and in general, applications requiring wear resistance. The various techniques employed for this purpose are discussed below :

1. Hard Facing. This is a welding technique and has already been discussed in Chapter 5 on "Welding Process", under Art. 5.11.

2. Nitriding Case Hardening. Discussed in Chapter 2.

3. Hard Chrome Plating. Hard chrome plating is done by the Electrolytic electro - plating technique (See Art. 12.5.3). It is the most common process for wear resistance.

4. Flame Plating. Flame plating is a process developed to prolong the life of certain types of cutting tools and for severe wear applications. By this process, a carefully controlled coating of tungsten carbide, chromium carbide ($Cr_3 C_2$) or aluminium oxide is applied to a wide range of base metals. The more common materials which have been successfully flame - plated include : aluminium, brass, bronze, Cast iron, ceramics, copper, glass, H.S.S., magnesium, molybdenum, nickle, steel and titanium and their alloys.

The process uses a specially designed gun into which is admitted metered amounts of oxygen and acetylene. A change of fine particles of the selected plating mixtures is injected into the mixture of oxygen and acetylene. Immediately after this, a valve opens to admit a stream of nitrogen to protect the valves during the subsequent detonation. The mixture is now ignited and an explosion takes place, which plasticises the particles and hurls them from the gun barrel at 750 m/s. The particles get embedded in the surface of the component and a microscopic welding action takes place, which produces a highly tenacious bond.

Each particle in the coating is elongated and flattened into a thin disc. The coating has a dense, fine - grain laminar structure with negligible porosity and an absence of voids or visible oxide layers.

The layer of the plated material is about 0.006 mm, and this layer can be built up, by repeating the explosions, to thicknesses ranging from 0.05 to 0.75 mm, according to the requirements of any subsequent operations. The resultant coating is dense, hard and well bonded.

Because of the hard dense structure of the coatings, flame - plating has provided industry with a valuable tool for the solving of many abrasion, erosion and wear problems. For example, bushes for many applications, core pins for powder metallurgy, dies, gauges, journals, mandrels and seals for high - duty pumps, have all been given much longer lives.

The process has influenced considerably certain types of cutting processes, especially in the glass, leather, paper, rubber, soap and textile industries and has proved to be of great advantage for components involving high heat applications such as "hot-end" of gas turbines.

The coatings show an excellent resistance to galling and corrosion. Flame-plated coatings can be ground and lapped, if necessary. Resultant surface finish can be within the region of 0.025 Another advantage is that the components can be masked to enable the coatings to be placed precisely where required.

The mixture of tungsten carbide coating material consists of cobalt ranging from 7 to 17% and the balance of tungsten carbide.

Aluminium oxide plating mixture is almost of Al_2O_3 (Above 99%). Chromium carbide plating mixture consists of about 75 to 85% of Cr_3C_2 and balance of (Ni - Cr).

5. Chemical Vapour Deposition. Chemical vapour deposition (CVD) uses volatile metal compounds which are carried as vapours in a gas stream and deposited as metal upon any surface that is hot enough to produce the desired reaction.

Vapour phase deposition may be done by two methods :

(*i*) In decomposition method, a metal halide is vapourised, metered and transported by means of an inert carrier gas to the heated component, where it decomposes on the surface to yield pure metal.

(*ii*) In the second method, a reduction process, hydrogen is used as the carrier gas through a purifier and dry hydrogen chemically reduces the halide to pure metal on the part surface, as shown in Fig. 12.4.

For Carbide tools, single coat- ings can be given of Al_2O_3 TiC, TiN, HfC or HfN. Multiple coatings of Al_2O_3 or TiN can also be given on top of Al_2O_3 or TiC. Coating thickness is in icrometres.

For depositing a layer of TiC on Carbide tool inserts, a mixture of hydrogen, methane and Titanium tetrachloride gases is formed in the mixing chamber. The mixture of these gases then flows to another chamber in which carbide inserts (WC) are heated upto about 1000°C by induction heating or by

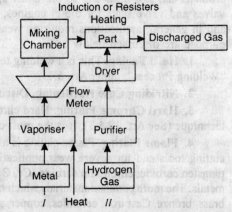

Fig. 12.4. Reduction Method of C.V.D.

resistance heating. The following chemical reaction takes place near the surface of the parts :

$$TiCl_4 + CH_4 \rightarrow TiC + 4HCl \uparrow$$

TiC so produced gets adhered to the surface of the substrate, that is, WC.

The main advantages of CVD process is its ability to produce :

(a) High - density coatings because the coating is built up atom by atom.

(b) High - purity materials

(c) High - strength materials

(d) and complex shapes

An emerging coating technology, used particularly for multiple-phase coatings, is Medium-temperature CVD (MTCVD). It is being developed to machine ductile iron and stinless steels and to provide higher resistance to crack propagation than conventional CVD.

6. Physical Vapour Deposition (PVD). In the basic form of PVD method, metal or an oxide is evaporated by applying sufficient heat with the help of one of the many techniques. The atoms or molecules so produced move in all directions. When they come into the atomic or molecular attraction of the component, that is, the substrate, they condense on it to form a uniform coating.

In a variation of the method, a cathode target (substance to be deposited) is bombarded by accelerated ions (usually of an inert gas such as Argon). This impact dislodges or drives off (Sputtering) single atoms or small clusters into the surrounding gas for deposition on a nearby substrate surface. To increase coating adhesion and improve film structure, the substrate surface is heated to temperature from about 200°C to 500°C.

PVD process is particularly suited to TiN coating of H.S.S. tools, because it being a relatively low temperature process, the tempering temperature point of HSS is not reached. So, after the PVD process, the heat treatment is not needed.

7. Diffusion Coatings. The surface hardness of low carbon steels (with C < 0.2%) can be increased by making them hardenable by diffusing carbon or nitrogen into the surface. On heating and quenching, the carbon- nitrogen enriched surface becomes very hard, but the core remains tough. The surface can also be hardened by 'ion nitriding' method, where the steel surface is bombard by low energy nitrogen ions produced in a plasma.

8. Ion-plantation. In this method, high energy ions are penetrated into the surface. For cutting tools, nitrogen ions are most commonly used.

There is virtually no change in dimensions in the last two processes.

12.8. FINE BLANKING

In sheet metal working, there is a great demand for blanks with very clean-cut edges, perpendicular to the sheet surface and of a surface finish sufficiently smooth to allow immediate use of the parts, for example, as gears in lightly loaded machinery and close-tolerance contacting members in instruments. Clearly sheared edges square to the stock surface can also be advantageous in wleding operations and for accurate location of parts in an assembly fixture. Fine-blanking (Fine-edge blanking, Smooth-edge blanking, Fine-flow blanking) process produces precision blanks in a single operation, without the fracture edges characteristically produced in conventional blanking or piercing. The process eliminates the need for in-process secondary operation, such as `shaving for conventionally blanked or pierced parts. A quick touch up on an abrasive belt or a short treatment in a vibratory finisher may be used to remove the small burr on the blank.

We know that fracture can be delayed by the imposition of a high hydrostatic pressure. This principle is exploited in the process of fine blanking. A specially shaped blank holder (A V-shaped impingement ring) is forced into the stock, to lock it tightly against the die, just prior to the beginning of the cut. The deformation zone is kept in compression and the whole thickness is plastically deformed. The material being sheared is not structurally separated, until the punch has fully penetrated the stock thickness. This results in the production of precise blanks. Die clearance is extremely small and punch speed is much slower than in conventional blanking. A counter punch operates with the main punch, eliminating any curvature of the part.

A specially designed triple-action hydraulic press or a combination hydraulic and mechanical press is used. The outer slide holds the stock firmly against the die ring and forces a V-shaped impingement ring into the metal surrounding the outline of the part. An ineer slide carries the main blanking punch. A lower slide furnishes the counteraction to hold the blank flat and secure it against the blanking punch, (Fig. 12.5) The counter punch also ejects the blank. The stripping and ejection actions are delayed, until after the die has opened at least to twice the stock thickness, to provent the blank from being forced into the stock strip or slugs from being forced into the blank.

The process is completed in the following steps :

(*i*) The stock to be blanked is held against the die-ring, with the help of the ring indentor. This superimposes compressive stresses on the stock. According to Siebel, for a suffi- ciently high, superimposed compressive stress, the shear fracture stress will become larger than the shear flow stress, thereby, reducing the chances of crack formation. In conventional blanking, the shear fracture stress is lower than the shear flow stress. Bridgeman has also shown that by super- imposing a pure hydrostatic compressive stress fully smooth sheared surface can be obtained.

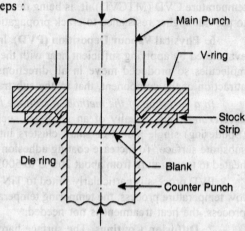

Fig. 12.5. Fine Blanking.

(*ii*) The stock is then pressed by a counter punch against the main blanking punch, and the two punches move down- wards.

(*iii*) After shearing, the main blank- ing punch and the impingement ring move upward. Simultaneously, the counterpuch moves upwards and ejects the blank out of the die-ring.

Fine blanking is not restricted to compund dies only, but also utilizes progressive and transfer tooling technology. Forming, bending and coining are some of the features that can be combined into fine blanking tools and applications.

Advantages of fine-blanking process are :

1. Clearly sheared edges over the whole material thickness.

2. Improved flatness.

3. Maintenance of close tolerance dimensions.

4. Part repeatability for the life of the tool.

12.9. COUNTER-BLANKING

In this recently developed method, two punches are employed for completing the blanking: main blanking punch and a counter punch. Blanking

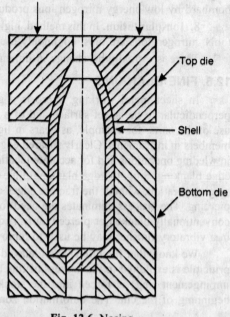

Fig. 12.6. Nosing.

is completed in three stages :

1. The main punch (top punch) penetrates into the stock only slightly.

2. Counter-blanking takes place, that is, the bottom punch (Counter punch) comes into action (starts moving upwards).

3. In the last stage, the top punch completely penetrates the stock and completes the blanking process.

The process is carried out in a transfer tooling and three sets of punches are employed. For every stage, clearances are matched.

This process does not produce blanks of the same quality as produced by fine blanking process, but, sheared surfaces, completely free from burr, with an increased smooth portion can be obtained.

12.10. NOSING

Nosing is a hot or cold forming process in which the open end of a shell or tubular component is closed by axial pressure with a shaped die, Fig. 12.6.

PROBLEMS

1. Why is 'hot machining' needed for some materials ?
2. Write a short note on "Hot machining".
3. Write a short note on 'Unit heads'. What are the advantages of unit heads ?
4. Give the various applications of Plastic tooling.
5. Name the materials for plastic tooling. How are plastic toolings produced ?
6. What is "Electro-forming" process Give its advantages.
7. Give the various types of mandrels used in electro-forming process.
8. Give the applications of electro-forming process.
9. What are the needs of surface cleaning and surface treatments ?
10. Discuss the following methods of Surface cleaning :
    - (a) Alkaline cleaning
    - (b) Solvent cleaning
    - (c) Vapour cleaning
    - (d) Pickling
    - (e) Ultra-sonic cleaning
11. What are the advantages of ultra-sonic cleaning ? Write the applications of this process.
12. What is Surface polishing ?
13. Discuss the following methods of surface polishing :
    - (a) Chemical polishing.
    - (b) Electrolytic polishing.
14. What is the use of surface coatings ?
15. What is "electro - deposited coating" ?
16. What is the function of the following types of electro - deposited coatings: Copper coating, chrome plating, cadmium plating, Nickle plating, Lead plating, Zinc plating, Silver plating, Tin plating, Gold plating, borating, phosphating and lead-indium plating ?
17. Discuss the following types of Coatings :
    - (a) Phosphate coating
    - (b) Oxide coating
    - (c) Plastic coating
    - (d) Metallization
    - (e) Anodizing.
18. Discuss the various hot-dip coatings.
19. Write a short note on "Paint coating and Slushing".
20. Write the advantages, disadvantages and applications of Adhesive bonded joints.
21. Write about the various adhesive bonded joints.
22. Discuss the steps of making an adhesive joint.

23. How the adhesives are applied at the joint ?
24. Discuss the various adhesives used for adhesive joints.
25. What is the significance of 'surface coating' for tools ?
26. Discuss the process of "flame plating" of tool surfaces.
27. What are CVD and PVD processes of surface coatings ? Write their applications.
28. What are : Diffusion Coating and Ion - plantation ?
29. Write short notes on:-
    (a) Fine blanking   (b) Counter blanking
    (c) Nosing
30. Discuss the machanical methods of cleaning and finishing of surfaces.
31. What is emulsion cleaning of surfaces ?
32. Write the advantages of chemical polishing.
33. What is brass plating ?
34. What is "thermo-electro-plating" or "thermo-diffusion" ?
35. What are conversion coatings ?
36. Discuss the various methods of paint coating.
37. Write on the "Drying" and "Finishing" processes after the operation of painting.
38. Write briefly on: Varnishes, Laquers and Shellac.
39. Write briefly on "Inorganic Coatings".
40. Name the common conversion coatings.
41. What are primers ?
42. What is preparation of the base ?
43. What is the principle of electro-plating ?
44. Compare the dipping process with electro-plating.
45. Describe the main characteristics of an anodized surface.
46. List the advantages of fine blanking.
47. Compare fine blanking and Counter blanking.
48. List the main advantages of CVD process.
49. Compare diffusion and ion plantation.
50. Why parts have to be coated with ceramics ?
51. How is hot dipping performed ?
52. Where is metallizing used ?
53. List the main drawback of lacquers.
54. What products have made use of vinyl lacquers ?
55. What are the main ingredients of an oil paint ? Explain their functions.
56. What is electro-less plating ? Write its advantages and disadvantages.
57. Explain the difference between electro-plating and electro-less plating.
58. List the similarities between electro-plating and anodizing.
59. How is hot dipping performed ?
60. Why is galvanizing important for automotive body sheet ?
61. List some applications of mechanical surface treatment.
62. Give the main specifications of different Unit Heads.

      Unit Head   Main Specifications

    (i) Unit Heads, Boring : Bore ϕ, Power (kW)

    (ii) Unit Heads, Drilling : Drill ϕ, Power (kW)

    (iii) Unit Heads, Milling: Cutter ϕ, Power (kW)

    (iv) Unit Heads : Combination/SPM: No. of heads, Product.

13

Ceramic Materials and Their Processing

13.1. GENERAL

The word "Ceramic" is derived from the Greek "Keramos", which means potter's earth or clay. Therefore, ceramics may be considered as materials made from naturally occuring clay or earth. Thus, to the common man, ceramics mean pottery, Chinavares and like materials. In a narrower definition, ceramics are compounds of metallic and non-metallic elements. However, the above definition of ceramics is not complete, because it leaves out such manufactured ceramic materials as diamond, SiC and Si_3N_4 and so on. Thus, in modern applications, a broader definition regards ceramics as everything that is not a metal or organic material. That is, ceramics are inorganic and non-metallic materials and which are processed or used at high temperatures. The American Ceramic Society has defined ceramic products as those manufactured" by the action of heat on raw materials, most of which are of an earthy nature (as distinct from metallic, organic etc.) while of the constituents of these raw materials, the chemical element silicon, together with its oxide and the compounds thereof (the silicates), occupies a predominant position."

Ceramic materials are used in industry for many purposes. They account for nearly 7% of the tonnage of major engineering materials, compared to about 11% of that of the steel. Ceramic articles of industry are : Dinner ware, electrical and chemical porcelain, refractory bricks and tiles, glass, porcelain enamels, abrasives, cutting tools, bricks and tiles, cements and concretes, whitewares, mineral Ores, slags and fluxes and insulators etc.

13.2. CLASSIFICATION OF CERAMICS

A general classification of ceramics is difficult to make, because of the great versatility of these materials. However, ceramics may be classified as given under : -

(1) Ceramics can be natural or manufactured.

(a) **Natural Ceramics :** The most frequently used, naturally occuring Ceramics are : Silica (SiO_2), Silicates and Clay minerals.

(b) **Manufactured Ceramics :** Such ceramics include : SiC, Al_2O_3, Silicon Nitride (Si_3N_4) and many varieties of Oxides, Carbides, Nitrides, Borides and more complex ceramics. Some of the naturally occuring ceramics are also, manufactured which results in their enhanced properties, as compared to natural ceramics. For example, Magnesia (Magnesium Oxide, MgO) also occurs in nature, but for industrial use, it is made from the Carbonate or Hydroxide. However, all the ceramics not available naturally, are manufactured.

The natural ceramics are also called as "traditional ceramics", while manufactured ceramics are usually called as "High-tech ceramics" or "fine ceramics".

(2) Functional Classification : This classification indicates particular industries and industrial applications of the ceramics, as given below :

    (*a*) Abrasives : Alumina, Carborundum

    (*b*) Pure Oxide Ceramics : MgO, Al_2O_3, SiO_2, Zirconia (ZrO_2) and Berylia (BeO) etc.

    (*c*) Fired-clay products : Bricks, Tiles, Porcelain etc.

    (*d*) Inorganic glasses : Window glass, lead glass etc.

    (*e*) Cementing materials : Portland cement, Lime etc.

    (*f*) Rocks : Granites, Sandstones etc.

    (*g*) Minerals : Quartz, Calcite etc.

    (*h*) Refractories : Silica bricks, Magnesite etc.

(3) Structural Classification : This classification indicates the structural criteria as given below:

(*i*) Crystalline Ceramics	:	Single phase like MgO or multiphase from the MgO to Al_2O_3 binary system.
(*ii*) Non-Crystalline Ceramics	:	Natural and synthetic inorganic glasses *e.g.*, window glass.
(*iii*) "Glass-bonded" Ceramics	:	Fired clay products - Crystalline phases are held in glassy matrix.
(*iv*) Cement	:	Crystalline or Crystalline and non-Crystalline phases.

The American Ceramic Society has classified "Ceramics" into the following groups :

1. Whitewares
2. Glass
3. Refractories
4. Structural clay products
5. Enamels.

13.3. PROPERTIES OF CERAMICS

The co-valent bonding of ceramic materials, alongwith their high melting point and relative resistance to oxidation, make ceramics good candidates for high temperature applications. In addition, they are relatively cheap and abundant and are not dependent on import for supply.

In general, ceramics are hard, brittle and high melting point materials with :-

— desirable electrical, magnetic and optical properties, i.e., low electrical and thermal conductivity.

— good chemical and thermal stability, that is, high hot-strength and high corrosion resistance, and freedom from oxidation.

— good creep resistance, and

— High compressive strength and excellent resistance to wear

— Their low density is also an attractive feature to minimise centrifugal stresses in parts rotating at high speed. Many ceramics retain strength to much higher temperatures than metals. Despite the generally excellent high temperature strength, many of the ceramics are susceptible to thermal shock (Due to brittleness). Porous ceramics (for thermal insulation) are resistant to thermal shock, whereas the same ceramic, in dense form, for structural use may be susceptible.

Since ceramics are brittle materials, their use in the past has severely been limited in structural applications. They have no yield strength and fail when the local stress exceeds the material fracture strength. For that reason, they are very sensitive to the distribution of flaws. However, with the development of higher-purity ceramic materials, with improved high temperature strength, such as Si_3N_4 and SiC and with the development of processing methods to produce the new materials with low porosity and more consistent properties, the building of high temperature air-craft structural components from ceramic materials is being seriously considered. Ceramics are much stronger under compressive loading.

They have low tensile strength. The tensile strength of Alumina is of the order of 190 MPa as compared to its compressive strength which is of the order of 1950 to 3500 MPa.

There being virtual absence of ductility in ceramics, so, in general, they can not be machined or built up from stock. However shaping and turning of unfired or slightly fired material is sometimes possible with small articles.

13.4. PROCESSING OF CERAMICS

The processing of ceramics, except glass, follows the Powder Metallurgy route, that is, consists of the following steps :-

1. Preparation of powders.
2. Mixing and Blending of powders.
3. Compacting of powders.
4. Firing or Sintering.

1. Preparation of Powders : As discussed above, ceramics are natural or manufactured. Natural ceramics are mined in open-pit mines whenever possible, and reduced to powder in crushers and hammer and ball mills. Undesirable components are removed by screening, magnetic separation, filtering or floating.

Among the manufactured ceramics, the two most important ceramics are : Alumina [Aluminium oxide, Al_2O_3] and Silicon Carbide, SiC. The methods of their preparation have already been discussed in Chapter 8 under Art. 8.6.1. Another ceramic of increasing importance is silicon nitride, Si_3N_4. It is made by high temperature reaction of silicon metal with N_2 gas. Many other varieties of manufactured ceramics (oxides, carbides, nitrides and borides etc.) are also made by this process. The manufactured mass is reduced to powder to controlled sizes and size distributions.

2. Mixing and Blending : The aims of mixing and blending of ceramics are the same, as discussed under the chapter on Powder Metallurgy. A ceramic is mixed and blended with other ceramic/ceramics or with lubricants and binders. Binders may be organic, such as, polymers, waxes, gums, starches etc., or inorganic, such as, clays, silicates, phosphates etc.

Lubricant reduces the wall friction of the mould, reduces internal friction between particles during moulding, increases the flowability of the powders and aids in the ejection of compacted parts. A wetting agent (like water) is added to improve mixing. A plasticizer is added to make the mix more plastic and formable. Deflocculents such as Na_2CO_3 and Na_2SiO_3 (in amounts of less than 1%) are added to make the ceramic-water suspension. Some other additives are also added to control foaming and sintering.

For example, clay-based ceramic products are made by combining several different clay minerals (SiO_2, Al_2O_3 etc.) with certain amount of non-plastic materials, such as crushed and ground quartz, feldspar, talc or "gorg", a finely ground fire clay material. Non-plastic materials, in general, alter the plasticity of the clay-body, making it more suitable for various processes, act as fluxes causing greater degree of vitrification during firing, and reduce the drying and firing shrinkages of the clay-body.

3. Compacting of Ceramics : All the techniques employed for compacting powders (under Powder Metallurgy porcess) can be used for compacting ceramic powders to the desired shape.

The techniques can be : pressing into steel dies on mechanical or hydraulic presses, cold isostatic pressing, extrusion, slip casting and injection moulding.

(*i*) **Pressing in dies :** Most ceramic compacts are made by pressing in dies.

(*a*) **Dry pressing :** Dry pressing of ceramics requires high tonnage presses and expensive dies. However, the parts can be mass produced to close tolerances. Lubricants and binders are used as required.

(*b*) **Wet pressing :** Here, the percentage of binders or other additives or liquids (mainly water) is such that the mixture can be processed by plastic forming techniques. This method is frequently used for clay-type ceramics, but can also be used for other ceramics.

The main limitation of pressing in dies is that since the granular ceramic material is limited in its plasticity, complex shapes in the lateral plane cannot be formed successfully.

(*ii*) **Iso-static pressing :** For more uniform density of the compact, "iso-static pressing" can be employed, as discussed in chapter on Powder Metallurgy.

Typical product is : Automotive spark plug insulators. HIP is used for forming high-technology ceramics such as SiC, Si_3N_4 (vanes for high temperature use).

(*iii*) **Extrusion :** In extruding, the raw material is mixed to a plastic state. It can be a ceramic-binder blend or a ceramic-water blend. It is then extruded in the extrusion press (usually screw type). Variable shapes can be obtained by this method (such as long lengths). Mandrels can be placed in position in the nozzle or die of the extrusion press, so that the extruded rod can have a variety of internal openings. The method is a low cost process, but the binder must be removed afterwards. Also, the orientation of the ceramic particles is fixed by the flow of the blend.

(*iv*) **Injection moulding :** The method is similar to that used for plastics (see chapter 11). The raw material is ceramic-plastic blend. The method is : fast, can be automated, complex cross-sections can be obtained in high volumes. However, the tooling cost is high and the binder must be removed at the end of the process.

The process is used for precision forming of ceramics for high technology applications, such as rocket engine parts.

(*v*) **Slip casting :** The method of "Slip Casting" or "Drain Casting" has already been discussed in the Chapter on Powder Metallurgy. The raw material is slurry. It is poured in a gypsum mould. The moisture is absorbed by the porous mould and the body is cast against the walls of the mould. To get hollow components, the excess slurry is poured off once the correct wall thickness of the part has been obtained. The advantages of the process are that complex shapes of large sizes can be obtained and the tooling cost is low. However, the process is labour intensive and the cycle time is long.

Typical product applications include : Large and complex parts, such as plumbing ware, art objects and dinner ware etc.

There are Variations of Slip Casting Method :

(*a*) **Doctor-blade method.** Here, the slip is cast over a moving plastic belt and its thickness is controlled by a blade. Typical application is : Thin sheets of ceramics less than 1.5 mm thick.

(*b*) **Rolling.** The slip is rolled between a pair of rolls and the slip is cast over a paper tape. The paper tape is subsequently burned off during firing operation.

(*vi*) **Jiggering :** Jiggering is usually an automatic forming process. It operates on the pattern of potter's wheel and is mainly used for clay products. The raw material is placed in a heavy mould, made of plaster of paris. The inside shape of the mould is the desired outside shape of the product. The inner shape of the product is obtained by forcing a shaped tool into the material, while the mould is rotated.

The process is limited to axisymmetric parts and has limited dimensional accuracy.

4. Firing or Sintering : The ceramic product, after compacting, is in the green state. To get the desired strength of the product, it is fired or sintered. However, before it is fired or sintered, it should undergo a drying process, by holding at room temperature and by low temperature heating. This is done to drive away any moisture of organic carriers, thereby minimizing the stresses, distorsion and cracking during the firing process. Then the compact is fired or sintered to obtain the desired level of strength. The complete firing process (Slow heating and cooling) may take days or even weeks. Getting the desired strength of the compact by firing is called "maturing".

If the ceramic product is to be glazed, it can be achieved in two ways. Either the glaze is applied to the product (green compact) and then the product and the glaze are matured in a single firing. Or, first the green compact is matured with a bisque fire and then the glaze is applied, which is matured with a lower temperature firing, known as a "ghost fire".

The matured compact is called "bisque".

Glazing makes the porous ware water tight. Glazes are glassy coatings made of inorganic compounds such as quartz, feldspar, boric oxide and lead oxide. These are finely powdered and mixed with water to form slurry (slip). Feldspar is a group of crystalline minerals consisting of aluminium silicate, potassium, calcium or Sodium, for example, Potash feldspar is $K_2O.Al_2O_3.6SiO_2$; Sodium feldspar is $Na_2O, Al_2O_3, 6SiO_2$ and Limefeldspar is $CaO.Al_2O_3.2SiO_2$.

Machining of Ceramics : Most ceramics are sintered to their finish dimensions. However, sometimes, they are machined to get better dimensional accuracy and surface finish. Machining of ceramics can be done with Diamond abrasives, LBM, EBM and CHM.

13.5. PRODUCT APPLICATIONS

1. Clay products : Clay body ceramics include whitewares and stoneware. Whitewares include such families of products as earthenwares, China and porcelain. Whitewares are largely used as tile, sanitary ware, low and high voltage insulators, and high frequency applications. It is still used extensively in Chemical industry as crucibles, jars and components of chemical reactors. Heat resistant applications include : pyrometer tube, burner tips, and radiant heater supports.

(a) **Earthenware :** Apparent porosity is usually 6 to 8% and may exceed 15%. Firing range is 800 to 950°C and may exceed 1000°C. Typical applications are : Porous drainage pipes, ceramic filter, wall tiles and bricks.

(b) **Fine China :** Apparent porosity is usually less than 1%. Firing range is 1100 to 1200°C. Typical product application : Tableware.

(c) **Stoneware :** Apparent porosity is less than 3%. It is usually 1 to 2%. Firing temperature is above 1250°C. Typical applications are : Glazed pipes, roofing tiles and tableware.

(d) **Porcelain :** Apparent porosity is less than 1% and is usually zero. Firing range is 1300 to 1450°C. Typical applications : Fine tableware, Scientific equipment and spark plug insulators for automobiles.

A typical composition of a vitrified porcelain for spark-plug insulators is : Kaolin 30%, Ball Clay 20%, **Feldspar** 30%, and Silica 20%. "Sintex" ceramic material, developed for spark plugs, is sintered Alumina, with small amounts of silica and some organic material added that provides for better crystal formation to give improved mechanical and electrical properties. "Sintex" is a good conductor of heat, its thermal conductivity is 20 times that of porcelain and slightly more than steel. Its abrasion resistance is remarkable.

2. Refractories : Refractory ceramics are the materials which are capable of withstanding high temperature in various situations. The refractory materials are of three types :-

(a) Acidic refractories.

(b) Basic refractories.

(c) Neutral refractories.

Acidic refractories are based on alumina-silica composition, varying from pure silica to nearly pure alumina, through a wide range of alumina silicates.

The basic constituent of basic refractories is magnesia, MgO. Basic refractories include chrome-magnesite, dolomite, limestone and magnesite.

Neutral refractories include substances which do not combine with either acidic or basic oxides. With increasing alumina content, silica-alumina refractories may gradually change from an acidic to neutral type. A typical neutral character is exhibited by such refractories as Carbon, graphite, carbide, chromite, bauxite and forsterite.

Refractory powders or porous blocks serve as thermal insulation in high temperature applications. Basic refractories are often used in metal processing applications, to provide compatibility with the metal. Neutral refractories are used to separate the acidic and basic materials, because they tend to attack one another.

Acidic refractories are not attacked by acidic medium but are sensitive to basic surroundings. Similarly Basic refractories are attacked by acidic medium.

Refractories are used in the construction or lining of furnaces, boilers, flues, regenerators, convertors, crucibles, dryers, pyrometer tubes and in many others, primarily to withstand the high temperature to which it is likely to be subjected without cracking, disintegrating or softening.

In recent years, new refractories have been developed for service at very high temperatures produced in gas-turbines, ram jet engines, missiles, nuclear reactors, and similar processes and operations. These refractories are relatively simple crystalline bodies, composed of pure metallic oxides, carbides, boxides, nitrides and sulphides.

The most widely used oxide refractory ceramic is alumina, Al_2O_3. It is sintered into cutting tool bits, spark plug insulators, high temperature tubes, melting crucibles, wear components and substrates for electronic circuits and resistors.

Carbides have the highest melting point of all the substances. Silicon carbide, SiC, is difficult to sinter, but pressure sintered or reactive sintered solid bodies of SiC are used as high-temperature resistance-heating elements, rocket nozzels and sand blast nozzles. Ceramics such as UO_2, UC and UC_2 are used in nuclear applications as fuel elements, fuel containers, moderators, control rods and structural parts. Boron carbide, B_4C, is extremely hard and is used as a grinding grit. In the sintered form, it is used for wear-resistant parts and body armour. Other carbides (Tungsten Carbide, Tantalum Carbide and Titanium carbide) are used in the sintered form as cutting tool materials.

Nitrides have only slightly lower melting points than carbides. Cubic boron nitride, CBN, is the hardest material after diamond and is used as cutting tool material. Silicon nitride, Si_3N_4, is used for ceramic engine components, turbine disks and rocket nozzles. Sialon (Si - Al - O - N), that is oxynitrides, have better oxidation resistance and is used for cutting tools and welding pins.

Borides (of Chromium, Zirconium and Titanium) are used as turbine- blades, Rocket nozzles and Combustion chamber liners.

Lastly, Cermet, a composition of ceramic and metal, has been developed. This material shows better thermal shock resistance than ceramics, but at the same time retains their high refractoriness.

It is used as cutting tool material, as crucibles and as jet engine nozzles.

3. Cutting Tool Materials : As discussed above, the various ceramics, which can be used as cutting tool materials are : Carbides, nitrides and oxides and cermets. Cemented carbides are expensive materials, since they contain comparitively rare elements, such as W, Ti, Ta and Co. Cemented oxides (Al_2O_3) are efficient substitutes for Cemented Carbides in many cases. Their manufacturing process is also relatively inexpensive, so that ceramic oxide tips are considerably cheaper than those of Cemented Carbides.

4. Abrasives : An abrasive is a hard material used to wear away a softer material. Ceramics are the hardest materials. Hence their selection as abrasive purposes. Abrasives are used for operations, such as scratching, grinding, cutting, rubbing and polishing.

Abrasives have been discussed in detail in chapter, 8 under the article 8.6.1 on Grinding process.

5. Electrical and Magnetic Applications : Ceramics find wide applications in electrical and electronic industries. As insulators, semi-conductors, dielectrics, ferroelectrics, piezoelectric crystals. Ceramics such as glass, porcelain, alumina, quartz and mica, are getting heavy demands. Ceramics, such as SiC, are used as resistors and heating elements for furnaces. Ceramics, having semiconducting properties, are used for thermistors and rectifiers. Barium titantate, for example, is used in capacitors and transducers. High density clay bed ceramics and Al_2O_3 make excellent high-voltage insulators.

6. Optical Applications : Optical applications of ceramics are not unknown. Ceramics are notably useful as a pigment, because it is exceptionally durable. It is completely oxidised and not subject to chemical attack and variation. Yttralox (a new ceramic material) is useful in optical applications, becuase it is as transparent as window glass and can resist very high temperature. Generally, Ceramics are opaque, because of the presence of tiny pores within them that scatter light. Yttralox is completely free from pores.

7. Phosphorescence. Ceramic phosphors emit light of a characteristic wave-length when excited or pumped by some appropriate energy source (an electric discharge or electron beam). Light tubes, VDT's and colour T.V. rely on this phenomenon. Of increasing interest are Laser materials. The most widely used Laser is ruby (an Al_2O_3 crystal doped with Cr ion). They are being used for machining, welding and cutting etc.

13.6. ENAMELS

Enamels are one of the many types of finishes/coatings applied to metal products. Enamels can be : Organic coatings or Inorganic coatings. In organic finishes, pigment is dispersed in either a varnish or a resin or a combination of both. Enamels may dry by either or both oxidation and polymerization. Both air-drying and baking-type enamels are available.

Enamels, belonging to the category of ceramics, are inorganic coatings. They are made up of refractory compounds and have a glasslike finish (glaze) when applied to both ferrous and non-ferrous surfaces. They are better than organic coatings and provide excellent resistance to both corrosion and elevated temperature and good resistance to abrasion. Inorganic coatings include : Porecelain enamels and ceramic coatings which are fused to base metals.

Porcelain enamels can be defined as highly durable alkaliborosilicate glass coatings that are bonded by fusion to various metal substrates at temperatures above 425°C. These coatings are widely used for industrial products, household appliances, plumbing fixtures, signs and architectural applications and for jet engine components.

The basic material of the porcelain enamel is called "frit", a special glass of friable particles produced by quenching a molten glass mixture. The frit is ground to a fine powder and is suspended in water with the addition of antiflocculants etc. Clay or organic binders are added to it to impart pseudo-plastic behaviour, so that it can retain the slip on vertical surfaces. Thus, enamels are glassy or partially crystalline coatings, applied in the form of a slurry. Glazes are also glassy coatings made of inorganic compounds.

13.7. Glass : Glasses are, by definition, "Ceramics" because the starting materials needed to produce glass are typical of ceramic materials. However, they are produced by the melt processing route, instead of the powder metallurgy route used for other ceramics. The techniques to process glass are closer to those used for thermo-plastic polymers.

In ceramic science, the word "glass" signifies any amorphous component of ceramic mixture. However, in general terms, glass is a transparent silica product which may be amorphous or crystalline, depending on heat treatment. Glasses may be either inorganic or organic. Vitreous materials or inorganic glasses are the fusion products which during solidification from a liquid state failed to crystallise. During the cooling process, the glasses exhibit no discontinuous change at any temperature and only a progressive increase in viscosity is noticed. In fact, glass is a hard liquid.

Glass is one of the most verstatile of all materials. It is :

— woven into cloth.

— made into doors, cookware and self de-frosting wind shields.

— used as a glazing material for buildings.

— made into filters, prisms and other light separating devices, and

— made into bottles, jars and many other products. Glass has good corrosion resistance, poor resistance to thermal shock and good electrical resistivity.

13.7.1. Glass Forming Constituents : Silica, which is obtained from high-purity silica sand is the most widely used glass-forming constituent. Other glass forming constituents are the oxides of boron, vanadium, germanium and phosphorous. Some other elements and compounds such as tellurium, selenium and BeF_2 can also form glasses.

The oxide components added into a glass batch can be grouped on the basis of function they perform within the glass. These are :- Network formers, intermediates, and modifiers.

Network Formers : These are indespensible in the formation of glass, since they form the basis of the random three dimensional network of glasses. Silica, SiO_2, is the main network forming constituent. Other network formers include oxides such as : B_2O_3, GeO_2, P_2O_5, V_2O_5 and As_2O_3.

Intermediates : These are added in high proportions for linking up with the basic glass network to retain structural continuity. These oxides include : Al_2O_3, Sb_3O_2, ZrO_2, TiO_3, PbO, BeO and ZnO. In general, Al_2O_3 increases hardness and reduces thermal expansion. PbO reduces hardness and increases the refractive index.

Modifiers : These oxides are added to modify the properties of glasses. These include: MgO, Li_2O, BaO, CaO, SrO, Na_2O and K_2O. These reduce the melting and working temperatures.

Alongwith the above oxides, fluxes are also added to the charge for a glass. Fluxes lower the fusion temperature of the glass and render the molten glass workable at reasonable temperature. However, fluxes may reduce the resistance of glass to chemical attack, render it water soluble or make it subject to partial or complete devitrification (that is, crystallisation) upon cooling. Such a glass is undesirable since the crystalline are extremely weak and brittle. Stabilizers are therefore, added to the glass batch to overcome these problems. The various fluxes used are : arsenic oxide, As_2O_3, Antimony oxide Sb_2O_3, boron oxide B_2O_3, borax $Na_2B_4O_7$, Calcium fluoride CaF_2, $NaNO_3$, KNO_3, and ammonium sulphate $(NH_4)_2SO_4$,

13.7.2. Types of Glasses : There are four principal types of glasses, on the basis of their chemical composition : Silica glass, Borosilicate glass, Lead glass and Sodalime glass. Their chemical compositions are given in Table 13.1.

Table 13.1. Composition of Glasses

Composition, %	Silica glass	Borosilicate glass	Lead glass	Sodalime glass
SiO_2	96	73 – 82	53 – 68	70 – 50
Na_2O	–	3 – 10	5 – 10	12 – 18
K_2O	–	0.4 – 1	1 – 10	0 – 1
CaO	–	0 – 1	0 – 6	0 – 4
PbO	–	0 – 1	1540	–
B_2O	3	5 – 20	–	–
Al_2O_3	–	2 – 3	0 – 2	0.5 – 2.5
MgO	–	–	–	0 – 4

Table 13.2. shows a comparison of these types of glasses.

Table 13.2. Comparison of Types of Glasses

Property	Silica glass	Boro Silicate	Lead glass	Sodalime glass
Cost	Highest	Moderate	Low	Lowest
Weight	Lightest	Medium	Heaviest	Heavy
Electrical Resistance	High	High	Highest	Moderate
Strength	Highest	Good	Low	Low
Thermal Shock Resistance	Highest	Good	Low	Low
Hot workability	Poor	Fair	Best	Good
Chemical Resistance	Highest	Good	Fair	Poor
Impact Abrasion Resistance	Best	Good	Poor	Fair
Heat Strengthening Possibilities	None	Poor	Good	Good
Ultraviolet light Transmission	Good	Fair	Poor	Poor

Silica glasses are mainly used where high temperature resistance is required. They can be regularly used at temperatures upto about 900°C. They have a very low co-efficient of thermal expansion and so have a high resistance to thermal shock. Silica glass is also called as "Quartz glass"

In borosilicate glass, a part of silica is replaced by boron oxide to impart desirable properties to glass. Borsoilicate glasses have fair hot workability and still have high strength, high chemical stability, high electrical resistance and low thermal expansion. Because of all this and a lower cost than silica glass, borosilicate glasses have wide industrial applications. Typical applications include : Kitchenware, High tension insulators, telescope mirror and laboratory glassware, sight glasses, gauge glasses. A special glass of this type is manufactured under the trade name "pyrex".

Lead glasses, also called "flint glasses" have low melting point, but exhibit, good hot workability, high electrical resistance and high refractive indices (1.50 to 2.20). Therefore, these glasses are used for products such as : optical purposes, cut glassware (art objects) and jewellery, High quality tableware, thermometer tubing, fluorescent lamps, lamp tubing and television tubes, for windows and shields to protect personnel from X-ray radiation.

Soda lime glasses are the cheapest and have good hot workability (low temperature is needed to melt these glasses). They comprise the largest tonnage of glass manufacture. These glasses are used as : window glass, bottles, lamp globes, ordinary chemical apparatus like test tubes, beakers and so on.

Some Other Types of Glasses

1. Coloured Glasses : Sometimes, various substances are added to the glass fusion to get coloured glasses. For example, the following colours will be obtained by the addition of the substances mentioned against each :

Yellow	:	Ferric salt
Green	:	Ferrous and Chromium salts (Cr_2O_3)
Blue	:	Cobalt salts (Cobaltous oxide)
Purple	:	MnO_2
Red	:	Nickle salts or Cu_2O
Lemon Yellow	:	CdS

Fluorscent greenish yellow : Uranuim oxide

Opaque milky-white : Cryolite, $Na_3 AlF_6$ or Calcium phosphate.

Photo-sensitive eye glasses are made from glass that contains AgCl. When this glass is energized, by ultraviolet rays, Ag ions form and impart a deeper colour to the glass.

2. Recrystallised Glass : By adding nucleating agents, such as sodium fluoride, phosphorous pentaoxide, titanium oxide or vanadium oxide to the glass melt, we get recrystallised glass, which is also known as "Polycrystalline glass". After the glass is formed, it is heat treated to promote crystallisation. Compared to ordinary glasses, such glasses possess : a high hardness and impact strength and better thermal conductivity. Their main application is in the manufacture of the so-called refrigerator-to-oven cooking wares.

3. Fibre Glasses : Fibre glass or glass fibre is glass in fibre form. It is obtained by drawing molten glass through dies into fibres 3 to 20 μm in diameter. Unlike normal glass, this glass possesses high tensile strength and is almost free from surface defects. Glass fibres are ; non-flammable, bad conductors of both heat and electricity, poor conductor of sound and are chemically inactive. They are used for insulating fabric and reinforcing fibre for plastics.

"Glass Plastics" are the materials having a synthetic resin as a binder and fibre glass (glass laminate and glass fibre) as a filler. These materials are three or four times lighter than steel but are just as strong. Such materials are widely used to build the hulls of small vessels (boats, yachts), bodies of cars and aircraft parts.

4. Glass Wools : Glass wools are relatively short fibres of about 20 to 30 μm in diameter. These are made by forming molten glass through some vents by centrifugal force, in the process known as "Crown process". Glass wools are suitable for insulation.

5. Foam Glasses : Foam glasses are produced by introducing innumerable air cells or pores into molten glass. On cooling, this glass becomes very light and can even float on water. It is cut into suitable sizes and then used as heat insulating material.

13.7.3 Forms of Glass and Their Manufacture

Glass is available in many forms, such as : Sheet, plate, rod, tube, and various finished forms. First of all, molten glass is obtained by fusing together the various glass forming ingredients. These are first finely broken into small particles, blended and then melted in a melting furnace (the temperature may be 1800°C). For example, a typical charge for soft glass (soda-lime glass) is made up of sand, limestone ($CaCO_3$), soda ash (Na_2CO_3) and cullet (broken glass scrap). A typical charge for borosilicate glass will consist of sand, borax, alumina, soda, pottasium carbonate and cullet. During melting, the carbonates decompose and react with SiO_2,

$$CaCO_3 + SiO_2 \rightarrow CaSiO_3 + CO_2 \uparrow$$

$$Na_2CO_3 + SiO_2 \rightarrow Na_2SiO_3 + CO_2 \uparrow$$

Gas evolution helps to homogenize the melt, but bubbles would remain. In order to promote refining, that is, the removel of small gas bubbles, materials such as sodium sulphate, sodium nitrate, sodium chloride, Arsenic oxide, calcium fluoride and carbon etc. are added to the glass charge. Decolouring agents such as Selenium, ceruim oxide, neodynmium oxide and nitre etc are also added to the melt. Cullet facilitates melting and produces a more uniform product. From the furnace, the melt flows to a "Forehearth" which is an extension of the melting furnace. Here, the melt is kept agitated, by electric current or mechanical stirrers, to main uniformity. The temperature of the melt is also controlled to impart the optimum viscosity for the subsequent forming processes.

1. Sheet Glass : Sheet glass is usually a soda-lime glass. Its thickness ranges from 0.8 to 10 mm. It is produced by drawing or rolling from the forehearth. It can also be produced by extruding vertically from the forehearth. It cools as it descends. Sheet glass is not free of imperfections. So, it is not recommended for automotive or aircraft glazing. However, it is widely used as window glass for domestic and commercial buildings. It is also used as mirrors, table tops and photographic plates.

Sheet glass can be heat-treated, which increases its tensile strength by 2 to 5 times. It, then, can be used as fire screens, safety mirrors, gauge shields and office building glazing.

A stronger sheet glass can be made by imbedding wiremesh in the glass in its molten state. This glass can withstand penetration of missiles and is less vulnerable to fragmentation.

2. Plate Glass : Plate glass is obtained by rolling the plastic glass upto a thickness of about 31.75 mm. It is then ground and polished to get optically flat surfaces. This glass is used for automotive glazing, storefront windows, tracing tables and surface plates. Plate glass can be heat-treated to get extra strength. Now a days, heavy plate glass is obtained by casting on to the surface of a molten tin bath in a controlled atmosphere.

3. Laminated Glass : Laminated glass is obtained by placing transparent vinyl plastic between two layers, of plate glass. The plastic layer prevents the splintering of the outside glass layers if broken. That is why it is known as "Safety glass'". Product applications include : automotive and air-craft glazing, protection shields and storefront windows.

4. Glass Tube : Glass tubing and rod come under the group "drawn glassware". They are used in gauge glasses, chemical pipe and insulation.

Molten glass from the furnace is wrapped around a hollow rotating cylindrical mandrel and is mechanically drawn out by a set of rolls. Air is blown through the hollow mandrel to prevent the glass tube from collapsing which gradually stiffens. To produce rods, air is not blown through the hollow mandrel.

5. Pressed Glassware : Pressed glassware is produced by pressing a measured guantity of molten glass (gob) in steel or iron moulds. The process is similar to closed-die forging. Product applications include : eyeglases, household appliances, glass gauges, and decorative and ornamental pieces.

6. Blown Glassware : This method is used for producing hollow pieces of thinner walls and with reentrant sections. The gob is dropped into a mould and a preform (parison) is obtained by pressing with a punch. The parison is reheated and transferred to a split mould. The product is formed by blowing a jet of air, so that it takes the form of the closed mould, upon solidification, Fig. 13.1. Products include : Bottles, jars, vases and bulbs.

7. Sagging. In this process, a sheet of glass is placed over a mould and is heated. The glass becomes plastic and sags under its own weight and conforms to the shape of the mould. No pressure or vacuum is applied. Typical product applications include : Shallow dischies, sunglass lenses, mirrors for telescopes, and lighting panels.

8. Spinning. This process which is also known as "Centrifugal Casting" is similar to the process used for metals. The molten glass is forced against the walls of the rotating mould, by the centrifugal force, where it cools and solidifies. Typical product applications include : TV picture tubes, Missile nose cones etc.

13.7.4. Strengthening of Glass. Glass can be strengthened by the following methods :

1. **Thermal Tempering.** This method is also known as "Physical tempering" or "Chill tempering". In this method the hot glass is cooled rapidly. As the glass begins to cool, it contracts and shrinks. As a result tensile stresses are set up on the surface.

2. **Chemical Tempering.** In this method, the glass is heated in a bath of molten KNO_3, K_2SO_4, or $NaNO_3$ (depending upon the type of glass). Ion exchange takes place. Larger atoms replace the smaller atoms on the surface. Due to this, residual compressive stresses are set up on the surface of the glass.

13.7.5. Finishing Operations

To relieve the glass surface of residual stresses, glass is annealed (similar to the method used for metals). Glass may also be subjected to some finishing operations such as : cutting, drilling, grinding and polishing etc. Sharp edges and corners are smoothened by grinding or by "fire polishing" where a torch is held against the edges which rounds them by localized softening and surface tension.

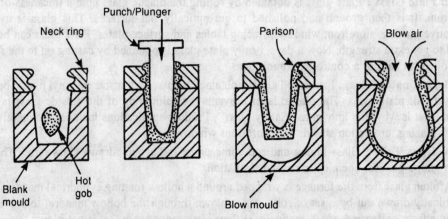

Fig. 13.1 Glass Blowing.

13.8 Design Considerations of Ceramic Products : The ceramics are brittle and have low meehanical and thermal shock resistance. Therefore, designing ceramic products needs special considerations, so as to make use of their advantages and avoid their limitations. Since the ceramics are about 10 times stronger in compression than in tension, therefore, every effort should be made to load ceramics in compression and to avoid tensile loading. Ceramics are sensitive to stress concentration, being brittle. Therefore, features like sharp corners, notches and unstrengthened holes should be avoided. Ceramics can be successfully attached to steel by press fits and shrink fits. This allows prestressing the ceramic part in compression, which increases its load carrying capacity.

Other design considerations are :

1. Avoid large flat surfaces, to eleminate warping of the product.

2. Avoid large changes in thickness, to eliminate non-uniform drying and cracking.

3. Provide generous dimensional tolerances, to avoid the need for machining, which is usually difficult and expensive.

PROBLEMS

1. What are ceramic materials ?
2. Classify ceramic materials.
3. Write the names of the various types of ceramics.
4. Write the properties of ceramics.
5. Write the steps for processing ceramics.
6. What is jiggering process ?
7. Write the product applications of ceramics.
8. What is glass ?
9. What are the various glass forming constituents ?
10. Write about the various types of glasses.
11. Write about the various forms of glasses and their manufacture.
12. What are the attractive features of ceramics in comparison with metals ?
13. Why should sharp corners and large changes in thickness be avoided, when designing ceramics ?
14. How glass is strengthened ?
15. Write about the finishing operations done on glass.
16. Write a short note on " Manufactured ceramics".

As noted on P. 675, 'manufactured ceramics' also known as : 'High tech. ceramics, 'Fine ceramics', Advanced ceramics', 'Engg. ceramics' or 'technical ceramics' exhibit superior mechanical properties, Corrorion/ oxidation resistance, and thermal, electrical, optical or magnetic properties as compared to 'natural ceramics, Advanced ceramics are classified as :

1. **Structural ceramics** : Such as industrial wear parts, bioceramics, cutting tools, and engine components.

2. **Electrical and Electronic ceramics** : Include : capacitors, insulators, substrates, IC packages, magnets, semi conductors and super conductors. The electronic, industry would not exist without ceramics. It is hard to imagine not having cell phones, computers, T.V. and other electronic consumer products. These ceramics have the largest market.

3. **Ceramic Coatings** : Find application in engine components, cutting tools, and industrial wear parts.

4. **Chemical processing and environmental ceramics** : include filters, membranes, catalysts and catalyst supports.

Ceramics can be defined as inorganic, non-metallic materials that are produced using clays and other minerals from the earth or chemically processed powders. They form one of three large classes of solid materials. The other two being : metals and polymers. The combination of two or more of these materials together to produce a new material whose properties would not be attainable by conventional means in called 'Composite', see chapter 14.

Chapter
14

Composite Materials and Their Processing

14.1. GENERAL

Composite materials can be defined as, the structures made up of two or more distinct starting materials. The starting materials can be organic, metals or ceramics. The components of a composite material do not occur naturally as an alloy, but are separately manufactured, before these are combined together mechanically or metallurgically. Due to this, they maintain their identities, even after a composite material is fully formed. However, the starting materials combine to rectify a weakness in one material by a strength in another. Hence, a composite material exhibits properties distinctly different from those of the individual materials used, to make the composite. Thus, a composite material or structure possesses a unique combination of properties, such as stiffness, strength, hardness, weight, conductivity, corrosion resistance and high temperature performance etc. that is not possible by the individual materials.

Thus, the search for materials with special properties to suit some specific stringent conditions of use has given rise to the development of materials called "Composite Materials".

Advantages of Composite Materials :

1. High stiffness-to-weight and strength-to-weight ratios.
2. Elimination of corrosion and stress corrosion problem
3. Significant reduction in fatigue problems.
4. Reduction in structural mass.
5. Improved control of surface contour and smoothness.
6. Improved appearance.

14.2. TYPES OF COMPOSITE MATERIALS

Composite materials may roughly be classified as :

1. Agglomerated materials or Particulate Composites
2. Reinforced materials
3. Laminates
4. Surface-Coated materials.

The particulate composites and reinforced composites are constituted by just two phases, the matrix phase and the dispersed phase. The matrix phase is continuous and surrounds the dispersed phase. The aim is to improve the strength properties of the matrix material. The matrix material should be : ductile with its modulus of elasticity much lower than that of the dispersed phase. Also, the bonding forces between the two phases must be very strong.

In fact, the particulate composites also fall in the category of reinforced composites. Depending upon the nature of the reinforcing materials (shape and size), the reinforced composites can be classified as:

1. Particle reinforced composites or particulate reinforced composites.

2. Fibre reinforced composites.

In particle reinforced composites, the dispersed phase is in the form of exi-axed particles, whereas in fibre-reinforced composites, it is in the form of fibres.

The particulate composites can be further classified as : Large particle composites and Dispersion-strengthened composites, depending upon the size of the reinforcing particles.

The characteristic property of many materials (particularly brittle one) that small sized particles (fibres etc.) are much stronger than the bulk materials, is used in reinforced composites.

14.2.1. Agglomerated Materials : Agglomerated materials or particulate composites consist of discrete particles of one material, surrounded by a matrix of another material. The materials are bonded together into an integrated mass. Two classic examples of such a composite material are : Concrete formed by mixing gravel, sand, cement and water and agglomeration of asphalt and stone particles, that is used for paving the highway surfaces. Other examples of particulate composite materials include :-

1. Grinding and cutting wheels, in which abrasive particles (Al_2O_3, SiC, CBN or diamond) are held together by a vitreous or a resin bond.

2. Cemented carbides, in which particles of ceramic materials, such as WC, TaC, TiC and of Cobalt and nickle, are bonded together via Powder Metallurgy process, to produce cutting tool materials. Cobalt acts as the binder for ceramic particles. During sintering, the binder melts and forms a continuous matrix between the ceramic particles. This method is called as "Vitreous sintering", that is, sintering with the formation of liquid phase.

Many powdered metal parts and various magnetic and dielectric ceramic materials are produced by solid sintering, which requires diffusion and no liquid phase in the process of sintering.

3. Cermets (Ceramics + metals), see chapter 7. Metals (W, Mo, Ni, Co) act as binders and the product is made by Powder Metallurgy method. The sintering temperature is the melting point of the metal. In the resulting composite material, the metal contributes high toughness and thermal shock resistance, while the ceramic contributes higher refractoriness and creep resistance, superior chemical stability and abrasion resistance.

4. Electrical contact points from powders of tungsten and silver or copper and processed via powder metallurgy method (See chapter 10)

5. Electrical brushes for motors and heavy duty frictional materials for brakes and clutches by combining metallic and non-metallic materials (See chapter 10)

6. Copper infiltrated iron and silver infiltrated tungsten (for nozzles for rockets and missiles)

7. Heavy metal (W + 6% Ni + 4% Cu), See chapter 10

8. Electric resistance welding electrodes from mixtures of copper and tungsten.

9. Dispersion strengthened materials, See Chapter 10 : In these materials, hard, brittle, and fine particles (usually oxides) are dispersed in a softer and more ductile matrix. Examples are : Copper welding electrodes with dispersed alumina, thoriated dispersed nickle with 2% Tho_2 (for jet engine components), UO_2 dispersed in alumina or stainless steel (for nuclear fuel elements) and sintered aluminium powder consisting of an aluminium matrix strengthened by Al_2O_3, and so on.

The particle size ranges from 10 to 100 nm. The mechanism of strengthening here is similar to that of precipitation hardening (See Art. 2.4).

10. Shell moulding sand, using a resin binder, which is polymerized by a hot pattern.

11. Metal-polymer structures (metal bearings infiltrated with nylon or PTFE).

12. Particle board, in which wood chips are held togather by a suitable glue.

13. Elastomers and plastics are also reinforced with suitable particulate materials. The best example is : addition of 15 to 30% of carbon black in the vulcanised rubber for automobile types. It increases : tensile strength, roughness and tear and abrasion resistance of the product.

Because of their unique geometry, the properties of particulate composites can be isotropic. This property is very important in many engineering applications.

14.2.2. Reinforced Materials : Reinforced materials form the biggest and most important group of composite materials. The purpose of reinforcing is always to improve the strength properties. Reinforcement may involve the use of a dispersed phase (discussed in the last article) or strong fibre, thread or rod.

Fibre-reinforced Materials : In a large number of applications, the material should have high strength, alongwith toughness and resistance to fatigue failure. Fibre-reinforced materials offer the solution. Stronger or higher modulus filler, in the form of thin fibres of one material, is strongly bonded to the matrix of another. The matrix material provides ductility and toughness and supports and binds the fibres together and transmits the loads to the fibres. The fibres carry most of the load. The toughness of the composite material increases, because extra energy will be needed to break or pull out a fibre. Also, when any crack appears on the surface of a fibre, only that fibre will fail and the crack will not propagate catastrophically as in bulk material. Failure is often gradual, and repairs may be possible.

Due to the above mentioned desirable properties of the matrix materials, the commonly used matrix materials are : Metals and polymers, such as, Al, Cu, Ni etc. and commercial polymers.

Fibre-reinforced materials can be made quite anisotropic through directional control of the strong fibres in the relatively weak matrix. Like this, it is possible to produce parts where strength control is developed in different directions. If the part is loaded parallel to the fibres, the matrix material yields plastically and under equal strain, the stress within the fibres will be much greater than in the matrix. Even if the fibre breaks, the softness of the matrix hinders the propagation of crack. The fibre directions are tailored to the direction of loading.

Reinforcing Fibres : A good reinforcing fibre should have : high elastic modulus, high strength, low density, reasonable ductility and should be easily wetted by the matrix. Metallic fibres such as patented steel, stainless steel, tungsten and molybdenum wires are used in a metal matrix such as aluminium and titanium. Carbon fibres and whiskers are also used to produce ultra-high strength composites. Fibres need not be limited to metals. Glass, ceramic and polymer fibres are used to produce variety of composites having wide range of properties. The high modulus of ceramic fibres make them attractive for the reinforcement of metals. The ductile matrix material can be aluminium, magnesium, nickle or titanuim and the reinforcing fibres may be of boron, graphite, alumina or SiC.

Forms of Reinforcing Fibres : The fibres used for reinforcing materials are available in different forms :

(a) **Filaments :** These are very long and continuous single fibres.

(b) **Yarn :** This is twisted bundle of filaments.

(c) **Roving :** These are untwisted bundles of gathered filaments.

(d) **Tows :** These are bundles of thousands of filaments.

(e) **Woven fabrics :** These are made from filaments, yarn or roving which have been woven at 90° to each other.

(*f*) **Mats :** Fibre form is said to be mat form when the continuous fibre is deposited in a swirl pattern or chopped fibre is deposited in a random pattern.

(*g*) **Combination mats :** Here, one ply of woven roving is bonded to a ply of chopped-strand mat.

(*h*) **Surface mats :** These are very thin, monofilament fibre mats for better surface appearance.

(*i*) **Chopped fibres or roving :** These are of 3 to 50 mm in length.

(*j*) **Milled fibres :** These are of brittle materials, usually 0.5 to 3 mm in length.

(*k*) **Whiskers :** Whiskers are single crystals in the form of fine filaments, a few microns in diameter (20-50 nm diam) and short in length (a few mm). These single crystal whiskers are the strongest known fibres. Their high strength is due to the high degree of perfection and the absence of dislocation in their structure. Their strength is many times greater than that of the normal metals. For example, the strength of an iron whisker is found to be 13450 MN/m^2, compared to about 294 MPa for a piece of pure iron. Besides metal whiskers, long nonmetallic whiskers (Al$_2$O$_3$, SiC, Si$_3$N$_4$) and of graphite are being produced. They are introduced into resin or metallic matrix for the purpose of high strength and high stiffness at high temperatures.

The properties of reinforced materials will depend on :

(*i*) The properties of the matrix material.

(*ii*) The properties of the fibre material.

(*iii*) The proportion of the reinforcement in the composite material. It is never less than 20% and may go upto 80% in oriented structures.

(*iv*) The orientation of the fibres, relative to the load application and relative to one another.

(*v*) The degree of bonding between the fibres and the matrix material.

(*vi*) The length-to-diameter ratio (aspect ratio) of the fibres.

There has to be some minimum fibre length, known as, critical length, l_c, to get the desired strength and stiffness of the composite material. It is given as :

$$l_c = \frac{\sigma_f \cdot d}{\tau}$$

where, σ_f = Tensile strength of fibre material

           d = diameter of fibre

and τ = shear yield strength of the fibre-martix bond

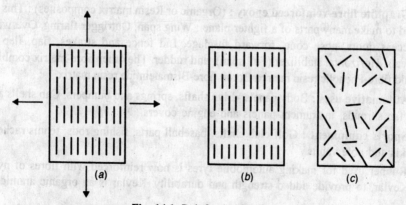

Fig. 14.1. Reinforcing Fibres.

For example, for carbon and glass fibres, the critical length is of the order of 1 mm, which may be 20 to 150 times the diameter of the fibre.

The fibre reinforcement can be done in three ways :

1. Continuous and aligned, Fig. 14.1a.
2. Discontinuous and aligned, Fig. 14.1b.
3. Continuous and randomly oriented, Fig. 14.1c.

If the fibre length is considerably greater than l_c, e.g., 15 times or more, it is called a "continuous fibre", otherwise it is called "Short" or "Discontinuous fibre".

As noted above, the properties of a composite having aligned fibre reinforcements, are highly anisotropic, that is, they depend upon the direction in which these are measured. Their maximum strength is along the direction of alignment. They are very weak in the transverse direction. The strength of the randomly oriented reinforcements, lies between the above two extremes. This arrangement is best suited for applications involving multi-directional applied stresses, for example, bi-axial stresses in pressure vessels or a tube. The same results can be achieved by using bi-axially oriented or cross-ply fibres. It is apparent that the strength of the discontinuous and aligned arrangement will be less than that of the continuous and aligned arrangement.

Applications : As discussed in the beginning, composite structures combine the desirable properties of two or more materials. This has greatly expanded the scope of application of all engineering materials. We can produce components with exceptional strength-to-weight and stiffness-to-weight ratios (many composites are stronger than steel, lighter than aluminuim and stiffer than titanium). Also, they have low conductivity, good heat resistance, good fatigue life, adequate wear resistance and are free from corrosion.

Reinforced concrete is a classic example of reinforced materials. Steel rods used in the concrete to reinforce the material take all the tensile load since concrete is weak in tension but strong in compression.

1. **Glass-fibre reinforced plastics :** Here, we have glass fibres in a matrix of unsaturated polyester. To get better qualities to use at high temperatures, high temperature polyamide resin is used with pure SiO_2 fibres. A special type of glass fibre can be used with cement bond to form flexible type of concrete. Glass fibre-reinforced plastics are used to make : boat hulls, Car bodies, truck, cabins and aircraft fittings. The other matrix materials can be : Vinylester and Phenolic.

2. **C-C Composites :** These composites have graphite fibres in a carbon matrix. This material is being used to make : Nose cone and leading edge of the missiles and space shuttles, racing car disk brakes, aerospace turbine and jet engine components, rocket nozzles and surgical implants.

3. **Graphite fibre-reinforced epoxy :** (Organic or Resin matrix composites) : This material is being used to make many parts of a fighter plane : Wing span, Outrigger flaring, Overwing flaring, engine access doors, nose cone, forward fuselage, Lid fence and strakes, flap, flap slot door, Aileron seals, Horizontal stabilizer (Full span), and rudder. The other fibre-matrix combination can be : Aramid fibre-Phenolic resin matrix, Boron fibre-Bismaleimide resin matrix.

4. **Automative uses :** Body panels, drive shafts, springs and bumpers, Cab shells and bodies, oil pans, fan shrouds, instrument panels and engine covers.

5. **Sports equipment :** Golf club shafts, baseball parts, fishing rods, tennis rackets, bicycle frames, skis and pole vaults.

6. Rubber used for making automobile tyres is now reinforced with fibres of nylon, rayon steel or Kevlar, to provide added strength and durability. Kevlar is an organic aramid fibre with

very high tensile strength and modulus of elasticity. Its density is about half of that of aluminuim and it has negative thermal expansion. It is flame retardant and transparent to radio signals. This makes it very attractive for military and aerospace applications. It is also being used for making bullet proof jackets. The trade name "Kevlar" is given by Du Pont.

7. Metal-matrix composites (MMC) : As already noted, these composites are obtained by impregnating high-strength fibres (of stainless steel, boron, tungsten, molybdenum, graphite, Al_2O_3, SiC and Si_3N_4 etc.) with molten metal (aluminuim, titanuim, Ni, and cobalt etc). These composites offer higher strength and stiffness especially at elevated temperatures and lower co-efficient of thermal expansion as compared to metals. And as compared to Organic-matrix composites, these composites offer greater heat resistance and improved thermal and electrical conductivity. Hence metal-matrix composites are used where operation temperature is high or extreme strength is desired. These will find applications in a variety segments like automobiles and machinery.

Aluminium oxide reinforced aluminium is used for making automotive connecting rods. Aluminium reinforced with Si C whiskers is used to make air craft wing panels. Fibre reinforced superalloys are used for making turbine blades. Graphite fibres in aluminium matrix is used for Satellite, missile, and helicopter structures. Graphite fibres in magnesium matrix is used for space and satellite structures. Graphite fibres in lead matrix is used for Storage-battery plates. Graphite fibres in Copper matrix is used for bearings and electrical contacts. Other examples of MMC are:

(*a*) Boron fibre in Aluminium : Compressor blades and structural supports.

(*b*) " " " Magnesium : Antenna structures.

(*c*) " " " Titanium : Jet-engine fan blades.

(*d*) Alumina " " Lead : Storage-battery plates.

(*e*) " " " Magnesium : helicopter transmission structures.

(*f*) SiC " " Super alloy (Cobalt based) : High-temperature engine components.

(*g*) Tungsten and Molybdenum fibres in Superalloy matrix : High-temperature engine components.

8. Ceramic-matrix composites (CMC). As already noted, ceramics are strong, stiff, can resist high temperatures, but generally lack toughness. Ceramic matrix materials are : Al_2O_3, SiC, Si_3N_4, and mullite (a compound of Al, Si, and O_2). They can retain their strength upto 1700°C, and also resist corrosive environments.

Typical product applications of Ceramic-matrix composites are : in jet and automotive engines, deep-sea mining equipment, pressure vessels, structural components, cutting tools, and dies for extrusion and drawing operations.

In Japan, Toyota have made automotive engine pistons and connecting rods from a hybrid MMC. This material has fine particulates, ceramic whiskers or both on continuous SiC or Carbon fibres that then are cast in an aluminium matrix. The resulting MMC is twice as strong as conventional SiC or Carbon-reinforced aluminium composite materials. Los Alamos National Lab. (U.S.A.) has developed a SiC-reinforced molybdenum disilicide intermetallic that at temperatures greater than 1200°C is 15 times stronger than current intermetallic alloys.

Composites in the Development Stage : The following fibre reinforced composites are in the developmental stage :-

(*i*) Advanced bismaleimide resin matrix series for high temperature service.

(*ii*) Polyether etherketone thermoplastic matrix series for higher temperature service.

(*iii*) Hybrid reinforcements and Knitted/stacked ply fabrics and three-dimensional (special shape) woven fabric reinforcements.

(*iv*) Selective stiching of Collated plykits.

In hybrid reinforced composites, two or more different types of fibres are used in a common matrix. Such composites exhibit better properties as compared to a single fibre reinforced composite. A very common example is of glass- and carbon-fibre reinforced resins. They combine the strength, stiffness and low density of carbon fibres with low cost of glass fibres. Such hybrid composites possess low weight, toughness, higher impact resistance and are of reduced cost.

Hybrid composites are finding use in light weight transport (land, water or air), light weight orthopeadic components, sports equipment and structural components.

In the hybrid composites, the reinforcing fibres can be arranged in the following ways :

1. Reinforcing fibres positioned in alternate layers, known as, interply.

2. Mixed reinforcing fibres in the same layer (intraply).

3. Combination of 1 and 2, that is, inter-ply-intra-ply.

4. Selected layup. Here, costlier fibre is used where it is necessary.

5. Stiching the plies of different reinforcing materials together, known as interply knitting.

14.2.3. Laminates : Laminates or laminar composites are those structures which have alternate layers of materials bonded together in some manner. Some common examples of laminar composites are given below:

1. **Plywood** is the most common material under this category. Here, thin layers of wood veneer are bonded with adhesives. The successive layers have different orientations of the grain or fibre, Structural parts capable of carrying a load are made of multi-plywood board from 25 to 30 mm thick.

2. **Bimetallic** strips used in thermostat and other heat sensing applications.

3. **Safety glass :** Discussed under Art. 13.7.3.

4. **Sandwich material :** Here, low density core is placed between thin, high strength, high density surfaces, for example, corrugated cardboard. Cores of polymer foam or honeycomb structures can also be used. Wood substitutes based on red mud polymer have been developed to be used for door shutters, windows, partitions and false ceilings.

The sandwich or honeycomb structures possess high specific strength and specific stiffness, that is, strength to weight ratio and stiffness-to-weight ratio, and high resistance to bending forces. The corrugated cardboard is extensively used in packaging for consumer and industrial goods. Due to the above mentioned properties, the honeycomb structures are used for aircraft and aerospace components such as wings, fuselage and tailplane skins. For these honeycomb structures, aluminium alloys are the most commonly used materials.

5. **Roll cladding (bonding) and explosive cladding (welding)** of one metal upon another : See chapter 5, Art. 5.5. The main aim of clad materials is to improve corrosion resistance while retaining low cost, high strength and/or light weight. Mild steel-Stainless steel combination, copper-stainless steel combination are examples of metal-to-metal laminates. Another example is "Alclad", which is formed by cladding duralumin with thin sheets of pure aluminium. The material is a high strength composite in which aluminium cladding provides galvanic protection for the more Corrosive duralumin. The above claddings are done by "hot roll bonding" method.

6. **Laminated plastic sheet :** This structure is usually made from sheets of paper or cloth and a suitable resin. The resins used include : phenolics, polyesters, silicones and epoxides. The paper or cloth provides the bulk of the strength, while the resin acts as a semirigid binder. Laminated plastic sheet can be machined, drilled, punched and pressed to shape. It is used in the production of gears, bearings, electrical components, and small cabinets. Laminate fabric base gears have the advantages over metal gears of being silent in operation and stable against the attack of various aggressive media. In many cases, laminate fabric base gears have completely replaced nonferrous

gears. They are employed to transmit rotation from electric motors in high speed machine tools, they are mounted on the camshafts of internal-combustion engines etc. In chemical industry, laminate fabric base gears are used in various apparatus and instruments where they resist corrosive attack much more efficiently than gears of bronze, brass or leather. In addition to gears, certain other transmitting devices : rollers, rings, etc are also made of laminate fabric base. Laminated sheets/ plates are available in sizes of : 900 × 900 mm, 900 × 1800 mm, 1200 × 2400 mm. The minimum thickness of sheet is 0.8 mm and it vaires as follows :-

Thickness range, mm	0.8 – 1.6	1.6 – 4.8	6.4 – 9.6	12.8 – 19.2	25.6 – 38.4
Step, mm		0.4	0.8	1.6	3.2	6.4

7. **Tufnol :** This is a laminated material consisting of layers of woven textiles impregnated with a thermosetting resin. The polymer imparts rigidity, while the woven textile provides great tensile strength. Paper or asbestos may also be used as alternative reinforcements. The material (with woven textile) can be used for making seat covers and carpets.

8. **Laminated carbides :** In laminated carbides, laminates consisting of a hard thin surface layer of TiC and in the form of throw-away tips, are bonded by epoxy resin to the rake face of a tip body of WC. This increases the crater wear of WC cutting tool (See chapter 7).

9. **Laminated wood :** Thin sheets of wood (veneer), impregnated with special resins and compressed hot, form what is called 'laminated wood', which finds extensive application in textile machinery and electrical engineering, as well as a substitue for nonferrous metals in bearings of hydraulic machinery and mechanisms operating in abrasive media. Parts of wood are machined in ordinary machine tools and wood working machinery.

14.2.4. Surface Coated Materials : The surface coatings are applied to the materials for various purposes :- protection of the material against corrosion; for decorative, wear resistant and processing purposes. They may also be used to : (*i*) improve visibility through luminescence and better reflectivity (*ii*) provide electrical insulation, and (*iii*) improve the appearance. Surface coatings are usually classified as : Metallic coatings, Inorganic chemical coatings and Organic chemical coatings.

1. **Metallic coatings :** Metallic coatings of copper, chromium, Nickle, Zinc, Lead and tin etc. are applied by hot dipping, electro-plating or spraying techniques to protect the base metal from corrosion and for other purposes (for details, refer to Art. 12.5.1).

2. **Inorganic chemical coatings :** These surface coatings may be divided into : Phosphate coating, Oxide coating and Vitreous coatings. Oxide and phosphate coatings are done to make iron or steel surfaces free from rust and this is done by chemical action. These coatings also provide protection against corrosion (For details, refer to Art. 12.5.1). Vitreous coatings are commonly applied to steel in the form of a powder or frit and are then fused to the steel surface by heat. These coatings are relatively brittle, but offer absolute protection against corrosion. Enamel is an example of a ceramic coating on metal and glaze on tiles is an example of a glassy ceramic on crystalline ceramic base. The glazing as a protective coating on porcelain and stoneware ceramic is performed for the purpose of protection from moisture absorption in ceramic materials.

Coatings of TiC, TiN, Al_2O_3 or HFN on WC base are examples of ceramics on ceramic and coatings of TiC and TiN on HSS base are examples of ceramics on steel. These coatings increase the life of cutting tools (For details, refer chapter 7 and Art. 12.7).

3. **Organic coatings :** Organic coatings include paints, varnishes, enamels and lacquers. They serve to protect the base metal and to improve its appearance (for details refer to Art. 12.5.2).

Polymer coatings on paper are used for making milk cartons. Polymer coated textiles are used for making seat covers and carpets, Polymer coatings on metals act as wire insulation. Polymer coated metals are used for making beverage cans.

14.3. PRODUCTION OF COMPOSITE STRUCTURES

14.3.1. Fabrication of Particulate Composites : As discussed under Art. 14.2. a majority of the particulate composits are made via the Powder Metallurgy route. So, for details, readers should refer to Chapter 10. However, a few particulate composites are made by dispersing the particles in the matrix meterials through introduction into a slurry (Concrete) or into a liquid melt (agglomeration of asphalt and stone particles).

14.3.2. Fabrication of Fibre Reinforced Composites : Many processes have been developed to fabricate fibre-reinforced composite structures. Their aim is to combine the fibre and the matrix into a unified form. The various fabrication techniques depend on : the size and form of the fibres and their orientation in the matrix material; the shape, size and the quantity of the product. The common fabrication processes are : Open-Mould proceses, Filament winding, Pultrusion and Matched-die-Moulding, and Laminating.

Before these processes are discussed, the following terms should be understood :

(*i*) **Prepregs :** Prepregs means "Preimpregnated with resin". It is a ready-to-mould material in sheet form. These are made by impregnating rovings and mats with resin matrix under the condition in which the resin undergoes only a partial cure. These are stored for subsequent use. These are supplied to the fabricator, who lays up the finished shape in stacks which is subjected to heat and pressure. This completes the curing of the resin into a continuous solid matrix. "Lay-up" is positioning of the reinforcement material, sometimes resin-impregnated, in the mould.

(*ii*) **BMCs -** are "Bulk Moulding Compounds". These are thermosetting resins mixed with chopped reinforcements or fillers and made into a viscous compound for compression moulding.

(*iii*) **SMCs -** are "Sheet Moulding Compounds". These comprise chopped fibres and resin in sheet form approximately 2.5 mm thick. These are processed further to fabricate large sheet like parts. They can replace sheet metal, where light weight, corrosion resistance and integral colour are attractive features.

(*iv*) **Thick Moulding Compounds.** Thick moulding compounds (TMC) combine the lower cost of BMC and higher strength of SMC. These are usually injection moulded using chopped fibres of various lengths. Used for electrical components due to their high dielectric strength.

1. **Open - Mould Process :** In this process, only one mould (Die) is employed to fabricate the reinforced part. The mould may be made of : wood, plaster or reinforced plastic material. The various techniques in this category are :-

(*a*) **Hand Lay-up technique :** In this method, the successive layers of reinforcement mat or web (which may or may not be impregnated with resin) are positioned on a mould by hand. Resin is used to impregnate or coat the reinforcement. It is then followed by curing the resin to permanently fix the shape. Curing may be at room temperature or it may be speeded up by heating. The technique in which resin-saturated reinforcements is placed in the mould is called "Wet lay-up".

(*b*) **Bag Moulding :** This is a technique of moulding reinforced plastics composites by using a flexible cover (bag) over a rigid mould. The composite material is positioned in the mould and covered with the plastic film (bag). Pressure is then applied byá: Vacuum, auto-clave, press or by inflating the bag. An auto-clave is a closed pressure vessel for inducing a resin cure or other operation under heat and pressure.

(*i*) **Vacuum-bag moulding :** In this technique for moulding reinforced plastics, a sheet of flexible, transparent material is placed over the lay-up on the mould. After sealing the edges, the entrapped air between the sheet and the lay-up is mechanically worked out and removed by the vacuum. Finally, the part is cured, (Fig. 14.2.)

(*ii*) **Pressure-bag moulding :** It is a process for moulding reinforced plastics in which a tailored, flexible bag is placed over the contact lay-up on the mould, sealed and clamped in place. Compressed air forces the bag against the part to apply pressure while the part cures.

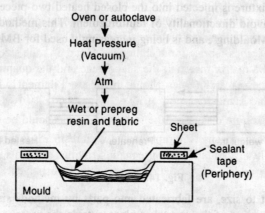

Fig. 14.2. Vacuum Bag Moulding.

(*c*) **Spray-up :** In this technique, a spray gun supplies resin in two converging streams into which chopped roving fibre is forced with the help of a chopper. The composite material stream is then deposited against the walls of the mould cavity. It is a low-cost method of fabricating meduim strength composite structures.

All the above open-mould techniques are extensively used for fabricating parts such as: boats, tanks, swimming pools, ducts and truck bodies.

2. **Matched-die moulding :-** Matched metal dies are used for moulding composite structure when : production quantities are large, tolerances are close and surface quality has to be the best. The dies are heated to complete the curing of the product during the moulding process. [See Fig. 14.3. for "Compression moulding" of composite parts.]

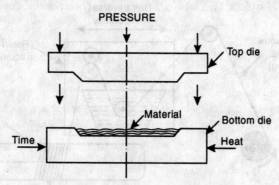

Fig. 14.3. Compression Moulding.

(*i*) Compression moulding is essentially employed for moulding BMCs.

(*ii*) **Resin-Transfer Moulding or Resin Injection Moulding :** In this technique (RTM or RIM), two piece matched cavity dies are used with one or multiple injection points and breather holes. The reinforcing material, which is either chopped or continuous strand material is cut to shape and draped in the die-cavity. The die-halves are clamped together and a polyester resin is pumped through an injection port in the die. The pressure used in the die is low, which allows use of low cost tooling. The method is used for moulding small non-load bearing parts.

In a variant of the above technique, instead of the injection of only resin into the die-cavity, the reinforcement (flake glass) is mixed with the resin in a mixing head and the mixture is injected into the closed heated two-piece die. Flake glass is preferred to avoid directionality of reinforcement. This method is known as "Reaction Injection Moulding", and is being increasingly used for BMCs.

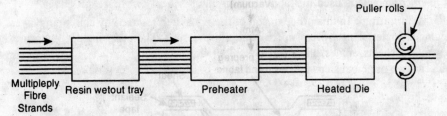

Fig. 14.4. Pultrusion.

(*iii*) SMCs, cut to size, are fabricated into parts by methods similar to metal pressing. However, curing of the part takes place outside the press.

3. **Pultrusion :** This is the process of extrusion of resin-impregnated roving (a bundle of fibres) to manufacture rods, tubes and structural shapes (Channels, I-beams and Z-Sections etc.) of a constant cross-section. After passing through the resin-dip tank, the roving is drawn through a heated die (where curing takes place) and cured to form the desired cross-section, as it continuously runs through the machine, (Fig.14.4.) After the Puller rolls, a saw cutter cuts the extruded section to the required lengths.

In "Pulmoulding", the process begins with pultruding; then the part is placed in a compression mould.

Product applications are :- Golf club shafts, vehicle drive shafts, because of their high damping capacity, and structural members for vehicle and aerospace applications.

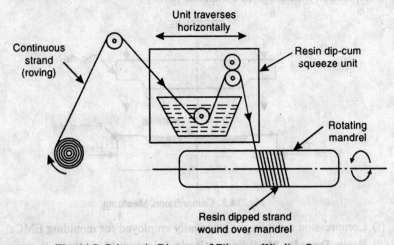

Fig. 14.5. Schematic Diagram of Filament Winding Process.

4. **Filament winding :** In this process, resin-impregnated strands are applied over a rotating mandrel, to produce high strength, reinforced cylindrical shapes. Fibres or tapes are drawn through

a resin bath and wound onto a rotating mandrel Fig. 14.5. The process is relatively slow, but the fibre direction can be controlled and the diameter can be varied along the length of the piece. In a variation, the Fibre bundle (made up of several thousand carbon fibres) is first coated with the matrix material, to make a prepreg tape (endless strip with width equal to several cms, to a metre). With both the fibre and tape winding processes, the finished part is cured in an autoclave and later removed from the mandrel. In axial winding, the filaments are parallel to the axis and in circumferential winding, these are essentially perpendicular to the axis of rotation.

Cylindrical, spherical and other shapes are made by filament winding, for example, pressure bottles, missile canisters, industrial storage tanks and automobile drive shafts. C-fibres with epoxy-basin resin composite is used for fabricating strength-critical aerospace structures.

5. **Laminating :** In this process, composite parts are produced by combining layers of resin-impregnated material in a press under heat and pressure. The parts include; standard structural shapes, plates, sheets, angles, channels, rods, tubes etc. However, mainly it is used for comparatively flat pieces. Two principal steps in the manufacture of laminated fibre-reinforced composite materials are :-

(*a*) Lay-up which consists of arranging fibres in layers,

(*b*) Curing

We start with a prepreg material (partially cured composite with the fibres aligned parallel to each other). A pattern of product's shape is cut out, and the prepreg material is then stacked in layers into the desired laminate geometry. A final product is made by curing the stacked pile under heat and pressure in an autoclave, or by tool press moulding. Tubes are produced by winding the impregnated fibre on a mandrel of suitable diameter. The assembly is then cured in a moulding press and then the mandrel is removed, See Fig. 14.5.

14.3.3. Fabrication of MMC. Basically, three approaches are followed for fabricating MMC:

1. **Liquid Phase Approach.** In this technique, the matrix material is in the molten phase and the reinforcement is in the solid state. Either one of the conventional casting processes can be used to fabricate MMC or "Pressure infiltration casting method" can be used. In this method, a preform is made (usually a sheet or wire) of reinforcing fibres and the liquid metal matrix is forced into it with the help of a pressurized gas.

2. **Solid Phase Technique.** Here the Powder Metallurgy route is used to fabricate MMC. The best example is of manufacturing WC tool material where Cobalt is used as the matrix material.

3. **Two Phase Processing.** Here the metal matrix contains both the solid and liquid phases. The reinforcing fibres are mixed with the matrix. The mixture is then atomized when it leaves the nozzles and is sprayed and deposited over the surface of a mould cavity to fabricate MMC.

14.3.4. Processing of CMC. The most common method of fabricating CMC is of "Slurry infiltration". A preform of reinforcing fibres is prepared which is then hot pressed. A slurry containing matrix powder, a carrier liquid and an organic binder is prepared. The preform is then impregnated with the slurry to fabricate CMC.

14.3.5. Fabrication of Laminates : As already discussed, the two common methods of fabricating laminar composites, are : Roll welding or Roll bonding or Roll cladding and Explosive welding or cladding (Chapter 5, Art. 5.5). In Roll welding (a cold process), two or more sheets of similar or dissimilar metals are joined together by simultaneously passing them through a rolling mill. The method is also used for cladding one material onto another and for producing bimetallic structures (Fig. 5.42 a). Wide plates and dissimilar materials with large difference in mechanical properties are fabricated by Explosive welding or bonding (Fig. 5.41). Composite coins are also made by these two methods. The aim is to save more costly high nickle material and at the same time retain the desired lustre and corrosion resistance. Another method of fabricating laminates has been discussed in the last article.

There are two ways of stacking the plastic sheets in layers (The thickness of sheet may be as small as 0.05 to 0.12 mm). In one, the direction of continuous and aligned fibre reinforcements is the same in all the sheets, whereas in the second, the two consecutive sheets are stacked with the fibre direction at right angles to each other. In the first arrangement, the structure will be very strong if loaded in the direction of fibre alignment and it will be very weak in the transverse direction. However, in the second case, the structure will be equally strong in the two dimensional normal planes. For example, adjacent wood sheets in plywood are aligned with the goain directions at right angles to eachother.

Honeycomb Structures and Sandwich Panels

To fabricate honeycomb structures, the first step is to fabricate the core (honeycomb panel or the sandwich panel). Two methods are used for this :

1. **Corrugated Process.** The flat sheet is passed through a pair of specially designed rolls (just similar to straight tooth spur gears). The flat sheet is converted into corrugated sheet. The continuous corrugated wheet coming out of the rolls is cut into desired lengths. The individual cut corrugated sheets are stacked together with adhesive applied at nodal points. The complete assembly is then cured to produce a honeycomb block.

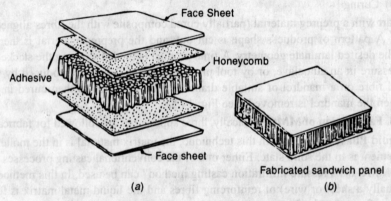

Fig. 14.6. Honeycomb Structure.

2. **Expansion Process.** Flat sheets are cut from a roll. Adhesive is applied at intervals along nodal lines. The individual sheets are stacked together and are then cured in a furance. Strong joints will be created along nodal lines. The c ured sheet is then cut into slices of desired dimensions. These are then stretched or expanded to get the honeycomb block.

To fabricate the honeycomb structure, the face sheets are attached with adhesives or by brazing, to the top and bottom surfaces of the honeycomb block, Fig. 14.6. The face materials can be : plywood, aluminium alloys, stainless steels, nickle alloys, titanium and fibre reinforced plastics (such as aramid-epoxy). The honecomb block (core) materials include : synthetic rubbers, foamed polymers and inorganic cements etc.

14.3.6. Fabricating Surface-Coated Composite Structures : For this, the readers shoulc refer to Art. 12.5.3, 12.5.4 and Art. 12.7.

14.4. MACHINING, CUTTING AND JOINING OF COMPOSITES

Conventional processes and tools are generally not suited for machining, cutting and joining of composites. Therefore, special methods are employed to the final processing operations for the composites.

· 1. **Machining :** Machining of composite materials should ensure that there is no splintering, cracking, fraying, or delamination of cured composite edges. Standard machine tools can be used with appropriate modifications. Cutting tools for composites include : drills, reamers, countersinks, cut-off wheels and router bits. Common cutting tool materials are :- HSS and WC. However, poly-crystalline diamond insert tool performs satisfactorily and is cost effective. Tools must be kept sharp, to provide quality cuts and avoid de-lamination. Tool and its geometry should be carefully selected. Cutting speeds and feeds will depend on the type of composite material, its thickness and the cutting method.

2. **Cutting :** The conventional methods for cutting uncured composites, such as prepreg ply include : manual cutting with Carbide disk cutter, scissors and power shears. For cutting cured composites, the main techniques are : reciprocating knife cutting, High pressure water jet cutting, ultrasonic knife cutting and laser cutting.

3. **Joining :** The common joints provided for composite structures are : Bolted joints and Adhesive bonded joints.

PROBLEMS

1. What are composite materials?
2. What are the various types of composite materials ?
3. What are Fibre-reinforced materials ?
4. What are the common reinforcing materials ?
5. Give the application of :-
    (a) Glass-fibre reinforced plastics.   (b) C-C composites.
    (c) Resin-matrix composites.
6. What are Laminates ? Write about the common laminates.
7. What are surface coated materials ?
8. Write about the various techniques of fabricating fibre reinforced composites.
9. What are : (a) Prepregs (b) BMCs (c) SMCs (d) TMCs"
10. Write about the following processes :-
    (a) Resin Injection Moulding.   (b) Pultrusion.
    (c) Filament Winding.   (d) Laminating
11. What are MMC and CMC ?
12. How are MMC and CMC fabricated ?
13. How a honeycomb structure is fabricated ?.
14. List the advantages of composite materials.
15. Distinguish between alloys and composite materials.
16. What is a hybrid composite?
17. What is the range of length and diameter of reinforcing fibres'
18. What are the basic functions of a honeycomb structure? What are its basic components?
19. Explain the functions of the matrix and the reinforcing fibres. What is the fundamental difference in the characteristics of the two?
20. Compare the advantages and disadvantages of MMC, CMC and reinforced plastic composites.
21. List the product applications of "Pultrusion" method.
22. List all possible applications for filament wound plastics.
23. List the product applications of open-mould process.
24. What are the various forms of reinforcing fibres?

25. What are: Continuous and aligned, discontinuous and aligned and continuous and randomly oriented fibres?

26. Write a short note on the material "Kevlar".

    Kevlar :– Kevlar is the trade name of "Aramids", Aromatic polyamides (thermosetting plastics). It is 5 times stronger than the same weight of steel, does not rust, does not corrode and is extremely light weight. Applications : As fibres for reinforced plastics, in bullet proof vests, in underwater cables, brake linings, radial tyres, space vehicles, boats, parachutes, and skis.

    Kevlar Protera is a new material from Du Pont (1996). It is a high performance fabric that allows lighter weight, more flexibility and greater ballistic protection in a vest design due to the molecular structure of the fibre. Its tensile strength and energy absorbing capabilities have been increased by the development of a new spinning process. (Also see Art. P 692).

27. Classify 'Composites'.

    See P 688. With respect to the matrix constituent, the composites are : Organic Matrix Composites (OMCs) or polymer Matrix Composites (PMCs). These also include Carbon Matrix Composites, known as Carbon -Carbon Composites), Metal Matrix Composites (MMCs) and Ceramic Matrix Composites (CMCs).

    On the basis of reinforcements used, composites are : Fibre Reinforced, Laminar and Particulate Composite (See P 689).

28. Write the Constituents of Composites : These are : Matrix, Rein forcements and Fillers. For matrix material, see Q 27. Its roles are : (See P 688 and 690 also). The properties of matrix material are, in addition to given on PP 688 and 690: Reduced Moisture absorption, Low shrinkage, low co-efficient of thermal expansion, excellent chemical resistance, dimensional stability, both elevated temperature and Low temperature capacity, etc. For Reinforcements, See P 689 and P 690 (Art. 14.2.2).

    The common reinforcing materials are : Thermosetting Polymer, Thermoplastic polymer, Metals, Carbon and glass (GFRC).

    Fillers are generally present to improve properties of composites other than strength, e.g., decorative finish, handling, fire retardancy, light stabilization, air inhibition reduction, air release promotion, improved modulus, very low densities, radar transparency and electrical and magnetic properties etc. Fillers can be : minerals, metal powder ceramics, polymers or metal oxides etc. Some common filters are : particles of alumina, silica, hollow or solid glass particles, wood chips, fly ash and carbon black.

29. Write the advantages and limitations of composites.

    Advantages : In addition to given on P 688 : Improved dent resistance, improved torsional stiffness, are dimensionally stable, improved marine ability, simplified manufacture and assembly, close tolerances, greater reliability, Directional tailoring properties and fibre to fibre redundant load path etc.

    Limitations : High cost of raw materials and fabrication, are more brittle than wrought metals, Reuse and disposal difficult, environmental degradation, New problems for repair etc.

30. **Define Composites** : Also see P 688. They are a combination of two or more materials, see P 687, and exhibit the best properties of the individual materials and include other properties that none of the individual materials possess. They are widely used in electronic industry for producing PCBs' A recent addition to composites is: Syntactic foam, which is gas filled material consisting of hollow spherical inclusions in a polymer/metallic matrix. It has good thermal and water insulation, vibration damping, low dielectric constant etc.

Chapter

15

Tracer Controlled
Machine Tools

15.1 GENERAL

In tracer controlled machine tools (also known as duplicators, contour producing or copying tools), an attachment is provided that enables the machine tool to machine all types of shaped components from a master form or model of the desired shape. The master form may consist of a previously machined part or a specially made template. The cutting tool is made to follow a path that duplicates the path of a stylus or tracer finger that scans the model either automatically or by hand. The machine tool cutter is made to mechanical, hydraulic, electrical, electro-hydraulic or optical contact. A taper turning attachment is an example of a simple straight line copying device. 'Duplicators' are capable of reproducing external and internal profiles from templates in three dimensions, whereas 'Profilers' do so in two dimensions.

A tracer controlled lathe will machine irregular contours, including steps, tapers, right-angle or tapered shoulders, recesses, grinding necks, radii formed surfaces, bore contours and so on. A tracer lathe is generally faster than a manually operated lathe for two or more diameters, shoulders or faces on a workpiece because the man or handling time to adjust the tool from one surface to another is eliminated. The advantages of a tracer lathe over the manually operated lathe increase as the part becomes more complex. To meet the initial cost of making and setting the template, a tracer lathe will be economical as compared to ordinary centre lathe) only if a number of pieces of one type are to be made on it.

The components made on a tracer lathe, can also be produced on turret and automatic lathes and at faster rate because in these machinnes, several tools can be made to machine a component at the same time. However, more expensive tooling and set up and more powerful machines are required. These machines will prove economical only for relatively large quantities of components. The use of a copy lathe substantially reduces the setting costs and can enable small batches to be economically produced. Tracer machines are designed to operate on an automatic cycle and will produce components to within the limits associated with automatic lathes. Also, turret lathes and some designs of automatic lathes cannot be used for parts that must be turned whilst held between centres.

Tracer control is equally fast and easy to control as numerical control. But it is more expensive and more lead time is needed to make a template for many parts (particularly the more complex one) than preparing a programme for a *NC* machine. However, tracer control is much cheaper than a numerical control. Its initial cost may be of the order of 1/10 or less of the cost of numerical control.

Tracer cotrol can be used with all the machine tools, but major development has been done for milling machines. Parts of complex shapes, such as blanking and bending dies, metal foundry patterns, permanent moulds, plastic moulds, propellar blades and turbine blades, are milled on tracer controlled milling machines.

15.2. MECHANICAL COPYING MACHINES

In these machines, the movement of the cutter is controlled through mechanical means, from a tracer or follower, following a master or a model. Mechanical tracing system is used in small machines which do engraving work and also for light milling operations such as the cutting of lettering or other fine details in dies and similar work. They are also used for milling complex surfaces of small parts of templates, in cases where the required machining accuracy is within 0.1or 0.2 mm. Many designs and forms of mechanical copying machines are available, but, here, we shall discuss only three of the common machines.

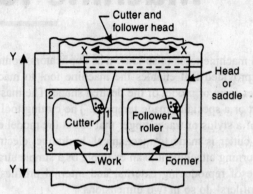

Fig. 15.1. Mechanical Copying Machine.

1. The first design is shown in Fig. 15.1. Both the work and the former or master are secured to the work-table. A provision may be made to adjust the relative positions of the two. The work table can be traversed in the direction *YY* on the bed ways of the machine. A cutter and a follower are carried by a head or saddle that can slide on ways on the column of the machine in the direction *XX*. Usually, either the work-table or the cutter head is left free to slide and is acted on by a spring or other force which keeps the follower and master in contact while a steady feed motion is given to the other member. Thus, when machining the portions 1-4 and 2-3, the feed motion will be given to the work-table and the cutter head would be left free so as to move towards the left or right. Similarly, when machining the portions 1-2 and 3-4, the feed motion would be given to the follower and cutter head, keeping the work-table free to move forwards or backwards. The force to keep the follower and the master in contact with each other can be supplied by a spring, a compressed air or hydraulic cylinder or by a dead-weight acting through a cable. if the cutter and follower head is carried on a slide that can move up and down vertically, the machine could be made to copy a three dimensional contour. For exact copying of the master, the shape and size of the follower and cutter should be exactly similar.

2. Another design of a machanical copying machine is shown in Fig. 15.2. It consist of two rotary tables which are carried by a saddle which can move along the bed ways. The two rotary tables are rotated in synchronism by a mechanical feed motion. One of the tables known as work-table carries the work and the cutter. The other table carries the master and the follower which are kept in contact by a force acting on the saddle. The master thus imparts the longitudinal motion of the saddle that enables the cutter to copy the shape of the master. The axes of the cutter and the follower are fixed during cutting, but their relative position can be adjusted relative to each other.

In an alternative arrangement, the rotary tables are carried direct on the bed of the machine and the longitudinal motion is given to the saddle which carries the follower and cutter and which can slide on the column of the machine. By making the cutter and follower capable of moving vertically, the machine can be adapted for three dimensional copying.

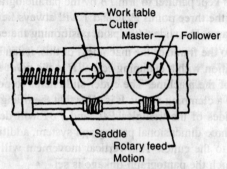

Fig. 15.2. Mechanical Copying Machine.

Disadvantages of the Above Machines

(a) Frequently, large forces may have to act between the follower and the master. This will necessitate the use of a large diameter follower and hence a large diameter cutter, which imposes restriction on the forms that can be reproduced. This difficulty can, however, be overcome by modifying the shape of the master making it possible to use a cutter of smaller diameter than the follower.

(b) The master should be strong enough to withstand the forces imposed on it by the follower. This will make the master somewhat expensive.

(c) Such machines tend to become single-purpose machines with a limited range of work.

3. **Pantograph Machine.** The Pantograph machine is extensively used for engraving and for diesinking operations. The machine utilizes the pantograph mechanism. The cutter is carried by one point of the pantograph and a tracer by the corresponding point. The ratio of the cutter movement to tracer movement is obtained by adjusting the links of the pantograph. The reproduced part can

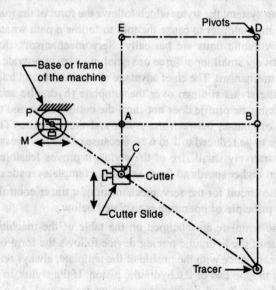

Fig. 15.3. Pantograph Linkage.

either be an enlargement or reduction of the size of the master. For very small work, the model or master used is larger than the work. The tracer or stylus is moved around the master by hand and thus imparts the necessary motion to the cutter.

A typical two dimensional pantograph linkage for an engraving machine is shown in Fig. 15.3. The arm *CA* is always kept parallel to arm *TB* by the parallelogram *ABDE*. Also points *P* and *C* must be adjusted so that the three points *P*, *C* and *T* will always lie on a straight line regardless of the positions of the linkage. The slide *M* helps in positioning the entire linkage

system with respect to the frame of the machine. For this, it can be moved along line *PA*. It is fastened at the desired position with a clamping screw. *P* is the pivot for the entire linkage system with respect to the frame of the machine. The cutter slide helps to position the cutter on the link *CA*. It is then fastened with a clamping screw. It is clear that the triangles *PAC* and *PBT* are always similar. The ratio of the sides of the triangles *PAC* and *PBT* will depend upon the reduction or enlargement desired. In a three dimensional pantograph system, additional arrangement is done to impart vertical movement to the cutter. This vertical movement will be at the same enlarged or reduced scale as that at which the pantograph linkage is set.

On a lathe, the simplest type of mechanical tracer-controlled contouring device is similar to taper-turning attachment in which the straight guide bar has been replaced by a template of the required shape and the guiding block by a roller or stylus.

In mechanically controlled tracer machines, it is necessary to ensure reliable contact between the stylus and the template.

A typical pantograph die-sinking and engraving machine (also known as pantograph mill) consists of two tables, copy table and the work table. The template or the model is held on the copy table. The copy table is held on horizontal slideway, with vertical and rotary movement. The worktable has movements in three directions controlled by screws and indicating sleeves. The patograph mechanism is carried above the two tables ad incorporates the tracer pointer and the cutter head, the spindle being driven by round or V-belt from a vertically mounted motor. The correct depth of cut is obtained by the cutter spindle feed mechaism and the form of the cutter imparts the profile to the mould or cavity.

15.3. HYDRAULIC TRACING DEVICES

In hydraulic tracing system, the stylus which follows the form of the master, gives a continuous signal to the hydraulic unit, in order to cause the tool to follow a path which is a copy of the form on the master. These hydraulic units are basically 'Servomechanism", that is, a control system which magnifies a relatively small input force or signal in order to provide a large output force or signal for operating the mechanism. The chief advatage of nonmechanical tracing systems (hydraulic and electrical) is that the stylus slidingn over the template (hydraulic and electrical) is that the stylus sliding over the template profile does not carry the cutting force and the cutting force has no influence on the force of contact between the stylus and the template. This enables the contact pressure on the template to be reduced to 1 to 6 N. Because of the low pressure of the stylus on the template and the comparatively small size of the stylus, it proves feasible to tur steep transition surfaces of the contour at higher speeds ad feeds and to use templates made of iexpensive materials.

A simple hydraulic circuit for the servomechanism of a tracer controlled milling machine is shown in Fig. 15.4. Its principle of operation is explaied below :

The blank and the template are clamped on the table of the machine. As the table moves longitudinally, the stylus of the hydraulic tracing device follows the form of the template and will move up and down in accordance with the profile of the template, always remaining in contact with it by spring pressure on the top end of the hydraulic piston. If the stylus, in following the template form, moves downward, ports *b* and *d* of the tracer valve are opened. As a result, oil delivered by the oil pump is admitted through port *b* of the valve, to the headend of the hydraulic actuating cylinder. The pressure of oil in this end of the cylinder forces the piston together with its rod and spindle head to move downward, reproducing the template shape on the blank. The oil from the rod end of the cylinder drains through port *d* back to the tank. The spindle head will cotinue to move downward until the ports *b* and *d* are covered by the body of the tracer valve.

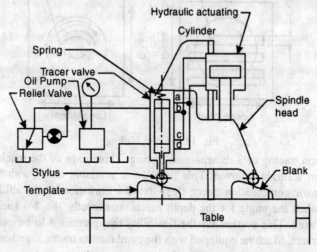

Fig. 15.4. Hydraulic Tracer-controlled Milling Machine.

When the stylus moves upward, ports a and c of the tracer valve are uncovered. Oil from the pump is admitted through the port a to the rod end of the actuating cylinder, while the oil from the head end drains through port c back to the tank. The piston, together with piston rod and the spindle head travels upward until the ports *a* and *c* are again closed by the valve body. In this manner, the power cylinder which is rigidly linked to the spidle head, reproduces the motions of the tracer system. The tracing efficiency may be very high, of the order of 0.01 or 0.02 mm.

The various tracing functions employed in tracer controlled milling machines are discussed below. One or more of these functions may be used simultaneously to generate the desired complex surfaces.

1. Depth tracing. Here the depth of the entire shape to be duplicated in the workpiece may be varied relative to the master or model. Depth tracing positions only one machie slide or axis which is controlled from the tracing follower, while one or more of the machine slides or axes are fed by hand or automatically, as discussed above (Fig. 15.4).

The principle of a copy millig machine, three dimensional system (under depth tracing) is illustrated in Fig. 15.5 (*a*). The vertical movement of the knee is controlled by a hydraulic tracer valve. The stylus scans the master in the vertical plane, while the machine table moves in the logitudinal direction. The milling cutter moves vertically in unison with the vertical movement of the tracer.

Straight line feeding path across the three dimensional master are employed as shown, by the movement of the machine table in the longitudinal direction. At the ned of each longitudinal traverse, the cross feed is advanced through a pick feed mechanism.

2. **360°** or 2-axis tracing. This system is illustrated in Fig. 15.5 (*b*). The tracer and the milling cutter remain at a constant depth during a complete tracing. In order to machine a three dimensional shape, several tracings are made as shown. These machines use flat templates and irregular contours, radial cam profile and constant depth grooves of any contour on a flat face can be milled on such machines. Other applications include the cases where form cutters are used to great advantage.

Substituting one of the two machine slide axes with a rotating axis makes it possible to machine aerofoil blades for gas turbines or grooves in drum cams.

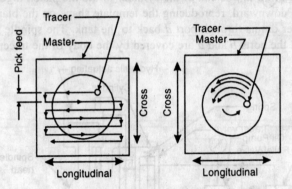

Fig. 15.5. Copy Milling.

3. **Combination tracing or 3-dimensional tracing.** Three axes of the machine are controlled simultaneously from a single follower. This function is available either with automatic or hand feed. For the automatic combination tracer, there exists a limitation on the ability of the tracer to follow the model when the angle for the depth functions exceeds 35°. No such limitations exist when hand feed is used. This system has the flexibility that permits it to be used as only a depth tracer or as a 360° tracer. Machine equipped with the combination tracer, together with servocontrol to the three axes are very versatile.

4. **Depth Control and 360° tracing.** In this system two separate models are used. The making of the models is greatly simplified compared with the complexity of the three dimensional models required in combination tracing.

Die-Sinkers. Milling machines with depth tracing and contouring functions are known as die-sinkers. In "hand die-sinkers" power and hand feed is employed for machine slides, without feed rate modifications to the feeding slides. The feed rate is varied manually according to the contour of the master or model. "Automatic die-sinkers" are equipped with power and hand feed to the machine slides with feed rate modifications, automatic feed reversal and pick feed or progression. Automatic feed rate modifications will produce a constant feed rate between the cutter and the surface being generated. In such machines, provision for 360° profiling is also made.

Copying Lathes. As discussed under Article 15.1, copying lathes are used for profile turning. These machines are used for turning of parts such as shafts, axles, piston rods, internal and external stepped and form surfaces etc., in batch production. The latest version of copying lathes have a slant bed to facilitate heavy duty copy turning.

One and two dimensional systems are employed on turning equipment for engine lathes.

1. **One Dimensional System.** In this system, the longitudinal movement of the tool is provided by the carriage driven by the standard feed mechanisms and does not depend on the tracer system. The working of the hydraulic tracer system is identical to that for milling machine explained above (Fig. 15.4). Upon longitudinal feed of the carriage, the stylus follows the profile of the template and operates a hydraulic valve that admits or exhausts oil under pressure on the opposite ends of a piston which transmits its motion to the tool slide. The neutral position of the control valve corresponds to tracing on a section of the template parallel to the spindle axis, *i.e.*, when the cross feed should be disengaged.

In one dimensional system, three classifications are found :

(*i*) Tool slide at 45° to the centre line of the machine. The compound rest of the engine lathe is removed and the tracer controlled tool slide is mounted in its place at an angle. When this angle is to the line of centres, it is not necessary to stop the longitudinal feed of the carriage to produce shoulders at right angles to the centre line of the job. The carriage feeds continuously and the cut is uninterrupted, Fig.15.6(a).

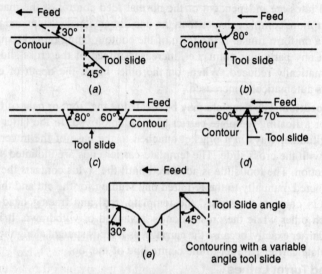

Fig. 15.6. Tool Slide Angle Settings.

(ii) Tool Slide angle 90°, Fig. 15.6 (b, c). The standard carriage provides longitudinal feed. The stylus controls the in-and-out motion of the cross-slide and also actuates a hydraulic clutch and brake that stops the carriage feed for right angle facing cuts. When the stylus contacts a shoulder, it disengages the clutch and applies the brake while lesser deflection produce in-and-out motion of the tool.

(iii) Tool-slide angle variable, Fig. 15.6 (d, e): This feature permits setting the tool slide at the optimum angle for the most difficult cutting conditions in the contour. The greatest angle of the contour is bisected by the angle of the tool slide. For step shafts, the tool slide normally is set at when set at the stepest practical contour that can be traced continuously is one with a included angle in the downward direction and a included angle outward.

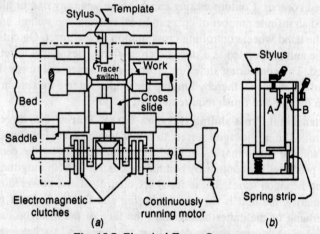

Fig. 15.7. Electrical Tracer System.

2. Two Dimensional Control. Two co-ordinate hydraulic-tracer-controlled systems, in which longitudinal feed is dependent on cross feed, are usually used in automatic lathes at the present time. This system is similar to one dimensional system with the addition of carriage-feed control. Feed rates for both motions are arranged in the hydraulic control valve to give a resultant feed rate tangential to the point of contact between the stylus and the template, *i.e.*, uniform across the entire template. The feed rates are independent of the normal feed control of the machine. This type of control can contour more complex shapes than the one dimensional system and provides a uniform feed rate and thus a uniform finish. If the form of the contour being turned requires an increase in the depth of cut at any particular point, i.e., increased infeed of the cross slide, the longitudinal feed will be automatically reduced. When, on the other hand, the depth of cut is reduced, the longitudinal feed is automatically increased.

Template Location. The template may be located at the front or near of the lathe. It may be fixed in position or a floating template carrier may be employed. In the latter case, the template carrier fits in longitudinal ways in a bracket attached to the base of the tracer unit. The Bracket moves in and out with the cross slide. The template-carrier ends are mounted so they can slide in the transverse direction. The tool slide is advanced until the stylus contacts the template, then the cross slide is advanced manually to the required dial reading for the cut and the longitudinal feed is engaged. Once in contact, the stylus, the template, tool and tracing head remain in correct relationship to each other while the cross slide is advanced or withdrawn. It is not necessary to align the template carrier exactly, because the carriage, as it feeds straight along the bed, automatically positions the template carrier parallel to the centre line of the job.

Tracer Controlled Turret Lathes

1. **Slide-tool Type Tracer.** A hydraulic slide tool type contouring attachment that can be mounted to a face of the hexagon turret is used for contour boring and turning. These tools are single directional. The tool is mounted vertically into the tracer slide tilted back to a 60° angle to the machine centre line to allow climbing a 90° shoulder. The longitudinal turret apron feed is used to traverse the template and the tracer slide advances or retreats on the 60° angle to follow the contour. Short to medium length contour bores are ideal jobs for this tracer. The bores are roughed out using other hexagon turret tools and the tracer used for finish operations.

2. **Single Directional cross-sliding Hexagon Turret Tracer.** This type of control is adapted to the cross motion of the cross-sliding hexagon turret to provide a means of contour machining of deep grooves (bores). The standard longitudinal saddle feeds are used to move the unit along the ways as the cross-sliding turret moves laterally under control of the template and tracing unit to produce the desired contour. Contour cutting can be done with any one or all six stations on the hexagon turret, and an infinite number of cuts can be taken from one station, an adjustment for size is made through the hand wheel controlling cross motion of the turret. On cuts that do not require contour control, the unit is operated as a standard cross-sliding hexagonal turret and the mechanical feeds are employed. The contouring slide (the cross-sliding hexagonal turret slide) operates at 90° to the centre line of the machine, thereby limiting the angles cut to a maximum of between 45° and 60°, depending on the cut and finish requirements of the job.

3. **Two Dimensional Cross-sliding Hexagon Turret Traces.** Two directional contouring is also adapted to cross-sliding hexagon turrets to allow tracing complex shapes. This unit has no angle limitations and the shape that it can produce is limited only by the geometry of the cutter. This arrangement produces the contour by combining control of both longitudinal and cross feeds of the cross-sliding hexagon turret. These feeds are controlled and powered either electrically or hydraulically. Primarily, the unit is for contour boring and facing. Contour turning is limited in length by the overhang of the cutter holder from the face of the hexagon turret. As with single directional unit above, contouring can be done from any one or all six hexagon turret stations and the tracing unit can be disengaged to allow use of carriage feed for standard operation.

15.4. ELECTRIC TRACING SYSTEMS

An electric tracing device has an electrically coupled tracer which follows a master profile of the shape to be produced. Through an electric control, it imparts an identical motion to the spindle of the machine tool.

In a three dimensional, copy milling machine, the tracer and the cutter are identical in size and shape. Under the automatic electric control the tracer slowly scans the area covered by the master profile. The depth of cut is automatically controlled by the tracer. At the end of the each stroke of the tracer, the operator reverses the direction of motion and puts on an increment of feed to cause the action to advance a small distance from the previous passage. Thus, the entire surface of the master is covered by the tracer in a series of narrow parallel lines with the cutter faithfully following the path of the tracer and reproducing the shape of the master. The action of the tracer is very light and the master can be made of any material. Also, the sensitivity is very fine and it is possible to reproduce the most delicate gradations of surface.

For a two dimensional work, the profile tracer guides the vertical and horizontal movements of the machine after the cutter has been set into the depth required. This operates against four contacts at corresponding to the four directions of travel and changes in direction of travel are obtained by energising or deenergising magnetic clutches which operate the movements of the machine. The sensitivity is so high that a movement less than 0.025 mm on its point is enough to cause a change in direction of machine travel. Parts such as moulds for plastic lavatory seats and drop forging dies for a crankshaft can be made on such machines.

Fig. 15.7 shows an 'on off' electrical system as applied to a lathe. In the figure, the tool is shown to be operating on a parallel portion of the work. The tracer switch, Fig. 15.7 (*b*), will be in its neutral position with both the contacts *A* and *B* open. Because of this, neither of the electro-magnetic clutches will be engaged and the cross-feed screw will be stationary. When the tracer or

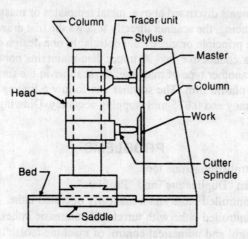

Fig. 15.8. Keller Die-Sinking Machine.

stylus reaches the inclined portion of the template (due to the longitudinal movement of the saddle), it will get deflected inwards. When this deflection is sufficient to close the contacts *A*, the electromagnetic clutch giving outward motion of the cross-slide will be engaged. The cross-slide feed screw will make the cross-slide to move outwards a constant rate. This will continue until the deflection of the tracer is reduced. The contacts *A* open again and the cross-feed will stop. With the continued longitudinal feed of the saddle, the tracer will again get deflected and the complete above cycle will be repeated. Thus, the cross-feed is not continuous so as to obtain a smooth curve. Instead a series of steps will be obtained. The size of these steps will depend on the magnitude of the tracer movement required to make and break the contacts A. With proper design of the system, the size of the steps can be made very small—usually smaller than the totool marks left by a sharp-nosed tool in ordinary turning. The inclination of the steps will depend upon the saddle feed rate/crossfeed rate. it can be made larger by using a low saddle feed rate and a high cross-feed rate, it cannot equal Thus, in this system, square shoulder cannot be copied. In spite of this defect, the system is popular because it is simple and reliable.

Keller Die-Sinking Machine. A keller die-sinking machine based on "on-off" electrical tracing system is shown in Fig. 15.8. The cutter spindle and the tracer unit are carried on the head which moves up and down the column. This column in turn can move perpendicular to the plane of paper on ways provided in the saddle. The saddle can itself slide in or out along the bedways of the machine. Both the master and the work are clamped to the face of the right hand column, which is an integral part of the machine. The machine can work in two manners :

1. By giving a constant downward feed motion to the head and a step by step motion to its column (left) on its ways in the saddle, or

2. By giving a constant cross feed to the column (left) and a step-by-step motion on the head.

In either case, the appropriate member is returned to its starting position between the steps and the contour of the work would be obtained by the in-and-out motion of the saddle, which is controlled by the tracer unit. The in-and-out motions of the saddle are obtained from constantly running electric motors which by means of electro-magnetic clutches can be connected to the lead-screws which move the saddle. These clutches are controlled by contacts which are made or broken by the movement of the tracer. Since only a limited number of downwards (or sideways) traverses can be made in covering the whole area of the master, it is clear that the surface produced will consist of a series of ridges and hollows which must be removed by subsequent processes, usually by hand grinding and filing.

15.5. AUTOMATIC TRACING

In all the tracing systems discussed above, metal templates or masters are employed to guide the cutters. In automatic tracing, the scanner directly follows the line drawings. Such machines may operate on the pantograph principle or electrical controls. In one design of such machines, the line drawings are made with a conductive ink. A tracer disc maintains contact with the line through control of a spark gap. In another type of machine, the scanner in the form of electric eyes follows regular ink lines on clear plastic film. The scanner can follow a line as fast as 125 mm/min with 0.025 mm travelling accuracy and 0.075 mm stopping accuracy. Drawing are made to a scale of as much as 10 : 1.

PROBLEMS

1. Define a tracer controlled machine tool.
2. Differentiate between "Duplicators" and "Profilers".
3. Compare a tracer controlled lathe and a manually operated lathe.
4. Compare a tracer controlled lathe with turret and automatic lathes.
5. Compare tracer control and numerical control of machine tools.
6. Explain with the help of neat diagrams, the mechanical copying machines. Discuss their drawbacks.
7. Explain the principle of a pantograph machine.
8. With the help of a neat diagram, explain the working of a hydraulic tracer controlled milling machine.
9. With the help of neat diagrams, explain the following principles of copying :
   (a) Three dimensional system.   (b) Two dimensional system.
10. With the help of a neat diagram, explain the tracing system.
11. With the help of a neat diagram, explain the working of Keller Die-Sinking machine.
12. Explain automatic tracing.

Numerically Controlled Machine Tools

16.1. GENERAL

In the modern age of business competition, the aim of manufacturing activity is to manufacture the parts of desired quality at the minimum possible cost resulting in profit to the organisation. To compete in the market, the quality of the product will have to be reliable and consistent with delivery of the product offered on schedule.

For consistency in quality especially in the manufacture of complex components, human intervention has to be eliminated. This necessitates the use of special purpose or automatic machine tools. These machine tools are highly specialised and have high rates of production. However, their initial costs are high. Due to these factors, these machine tools are suitable and economical for mass production only. Moreover, these machine tools are inflexible (that is, the complete set up will have to be changed for a new product). Due to this inflexibility also, these machine tools are not suitable for job or small batch production. Thus, when the main requirement is : quantity, consistency in quality and delivery schedule, mass production or automation is the answer. Mass production machine tools include : automatic unit machine tools and automatic transfer machines etc.

However, the mass production system of manufacturing accounts for only about 20% of the total of manufactured parts.

The remaining demand is met by jobbing and the batch production systems. More than half of the total machine tools are engaged in small lot and piece production. These include general purpose machine tools, hydraulic tracer controlled machine tools and programmed operation cycle machine tools. The general purpose machine tools, eventhough highly flexible (can easily change from one product to another), are not suitable for mass production, because of longer set up times, machine and tool adjustments, and very low machine utilization time (maximum upto about 30% of the total time). All this results in low rates of production and delays in the delivery schedule. Also, they require too highly skilled operators. Because of the intervention of operators, (eventhough skilled) the consistency in quality can not be assured. Therefore, when consistency in quality and delivery schedule are of prime importance, these machine tools are not suitable. Similarly, hydraulic tracer controlled machine tools etc. (which are mainly used for small batch productions) require longer set up times while changing over to new jobs as these machines require cams, templates, stops, electrical trip dogs etc.

Because of the above factors, a great need was felt for machine tools that could bridge the gap between highly flexible general purpose machine tools (which are not economical for mass production) and highly specialized, but inflexible mass production machines. Numerically controlled machine tools have taken up this role very well. These machines are highly flexible and are economical for producing a single or a large number of parts.

Numerical control, NC, can be defined simply as control by numbers. Electronics Industries Association defines NUMERICAL CONTROL as "a system in which actions are controlled by the direct insertion of numerical data at some point. The system must automatically interpret at least some protion of these data." In numerically controlled machine tools, the input information for controlling the machine tool motion is provided by means of punched paper tapes, plastic tapes(Mylar), floppy disk, hard disk or magnetic tapes in a coded language. Thus, with numerical control, the operation and motions of a machine tool are controlled electronically. NC machine tools are thus automated production machines.

The key difference in this system is that of "reprogrammability". In NC, a changeover to a new product, does not require extensive physical changes in the machine set up. Only a change in the control program itself is required. Thus, the flexibility of general purpose machine tools can be combined with the precision and accuracy of special-purpose machine tools. The human intervention, as an interface translating the design information into machine activities, is replaced by some form of information processing device, such as a computer.

The principles of NC were established in 1950s. However, with the availability of low-cost programmable control, based around the microprocessor in 1970s, this technology diffused widely. This opened up the development of the concept of Computer Numerical Control (CNC), and other functions such as automatic tool change or part manipulation. All this led to highly sophisticated, multipurpose machining centres, complete with a range of support functions such as tool change, head change, transport and manipulation and so on-all under computer control. The next development was the idea of Direct (or distributed) Numerical Control (DNC), in which more than one machine tool (alongwith associated functions) could be grouped into a manufacturing cell under the overall control of a larger, supervisory computer. The early numerically controlled machine tools were milling and profiling machines that provided faster and less expensive means for producing aircraft parts. Now, NC, has been applied to other machine tools, such as lathes, drilling and boring machines, welding and flame cutting machines, punching machines and inspection devices

16.2. WORKING OF NC MACHINE TOOL

To understand the working of a NC machine tool, let us refer to Fig.16.1. The first two steps, component drawing and process planning are similar in both operator and NC machine tools. In the operator controlled machine tools, the operator controls the cutter position during machining. He also makes the necessary adjustments and corrections to produce the desired component. However, in numerically controlled system, the place of the operator is taken by the data processing part of the system and the control unit. In the data processing unit, the co-ordinate information regarding the component is recorded on a tape by means of a teleprinter. Tape is fed to the control unit which sends the position command signals to slide-way transmission elements of the machine tool. At the same time, the command signal is constantly compared with the actual position achieved, with the help of position feedback signal derived from automatic monitoring of the machine tool slide position. The difference in the two signals, if any, is corrected until the desired component is produced.

The conventional NC system consists of basically two parts : Machine Tool and Machine Control Unit (MCU).

The main elements of a NC machine tool are shown in Fig. 16.2. These are :

1. The machine control unit (MCU), also known as N.C. console or Director.

2. The drive units, or actuators.

3. The position feed back package.

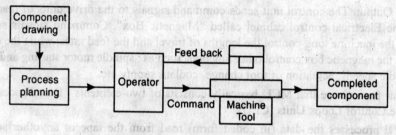

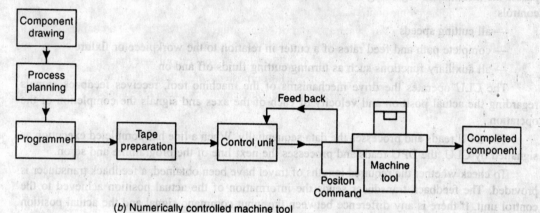

(a) Operator controlled machine tool

(b) Numerically controlled machine tool

Fig. 16.1.

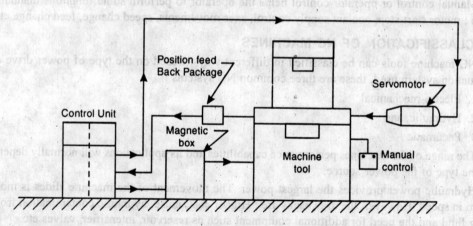

Fig. 16.2. Main Elements of a NC Machine.

4. Magnetic Box.

5. Manual control.

The hardware also includes the associated circuits.

The functional elements involved in MCU are :

1. **Data Input.** The instructions for manufacturing the component are written in a Coded language (Paper tape is the most commonly used device) are read by a tape reader.

2. **Data Processing.** The instruction undergo electronic processing resulting in information in the form of electrical signals (pulsed commands).

3. **Data Output.** The control unit sends command signals to the drive units of machine tool and also to the Electrical control cabinet called "Magnetic Box". Command signals sent to the drive units of the machine tool, control the lengths of travel and the feed rates, while the command signals sent to the magnetic box control other functions such as : spindle motor starting and stopping, selecting spindle speeds, actuation of tool change, coolant supply etc.

It is clear from above that MCU basically consists of two elements : Data Processing Unit (DPU) and the Control Loops Units (CLU).

The DPU processes the data (in coded form) read from the tape or anyother source and passes the information regarding the various controls to CLU. NC is used to provide the following controls:

— all cutting speeds

— complete path and feed rates of a cutter in relation to the workpiece or fixture

— all auxiliary functions such as turning cutting fluids off and on.

The CLU operates the drive mechanisms of the machine tool, receives feedback signals regarding the actual position and velocity of each of the axes and signals the completion of the operation.

The DPU reads and processes the data sequentially. When a line has completed execution as signalled by CLU, the DPU reads and processes the next line of the programme and so on.

To check whether the required lengths of travel have been obtained, a feedback transducer is provided. The feedback transducer sends the information of the actual position achieved to the control unit. If there is any difference between the input command signal and the actual position achieved, the drive unit is actuated by suitable amplifier from the error signal.

Manual control or operator control helps the operator to perform some functions manually such as : motor start-stop, coolant supply control, axes movements, speed change, feed change etc.

16.3. CLASSIFICATION OF NC MACHINES

NC machine tools can be classified in different ways. Based on the type of power drive or the actuation system used, these are three common NC systems :

1. Electro-mechanical
2. Hydraulic, and
3. Pneumatic

The range of the machines performance capabilities and its applications will normally depend upon the type of the power source.

Hydraulic power provides the largest power. The movement of the machine slides is more uniform in speed. However, the drawbacks are : Higher cost, noise, hydraulic contamination from leaking fluid and the need for additional equipment such as reservoir, intensifier, valves etc.

Pneumatic power is least expensive, because the shop air can be tapped for this purpose. However, the motion of the worktable is not uniform.

Electro-mechanical drives are the most precise and the most commonly used power sources.

The group of electro-mechanical, hydraulic or pneumatic equipment used to control the motion of an NC machine is called the "Servo".

Based on control system features, NC machines are classified as :

1. Point-to-Point system
2. Straight line system
3. Contour system

These three systems are illustrated in Fig. 16.3.

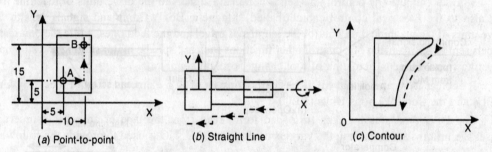

(a) Point-to-point   (b) Straight Line   (c) Contour

Fig. 16.3. NC Control System.

In point-to-point system, the machining is done at specific positions. The working-piece remains unaffected as the tool moves from one position to the next. This system is the simplest. In Fig. 16.3 (a), after drilling the hole at position A, the tool moves to position B, along the dotted line. A drilling machine is the best example of point-to-point system.

Straight line system, Fig. 16.3 (b) is an extension of point-to-point system. Here the tool moves at a controlled feed rate in one axis direction at a time. The examples of straight line system are; stepped turning on lathe, pocket milling etc.

In contour or continuous path system, Fig. 16.3 (c), there are continuous, simultaneous and co-ordinated motions of the tool and the workpiece along different co-ordinate axes. The various profiles, contours and curved surfaces are machined by this system.

Depending on the feedback, NC machine systems are of two types :

1. Open loop system
2. Closed loop system

As discussed above, a command signal is sent to the machine tool to carry out a certain operation. In the open loop system, there is no 'feedback' and no return signal to indicate whether the tool has reached the correct position at the end of the operation, or not. Hence, there are no means of knowing whether there is an error or not between the input command signal and the result achieved. An example of open loop system is a co-ordinate drilling machine.

Fig. 16.4 (a) illustrates an **"open loop system"**. The command signal from the MCU is given to the servo-motor (here a stepper motor). The motor is driven a precise angular rotation for every pulse issued by CLU. So, the response of the motor is in incremental steps. An incremental step of is common. This will result in a corresponding linear movement of the lead screw (depending upon its lead) and hence of the machine slide.

In closed loop system, a 'feedback' is built into the system, which automatically monitors the position of the tool. From the feedback signal to the control unit, it is known whether the tool has moved correctly to its new position or not. If not, its position is automatically controlled until it is in the right position. Such a device is known as a position feed back transducer. Common position feed back devices used on modern NC machines are : shaft encoders, linear scales or Inductosyns. In the contour or continuous path system, velocity control is also essential to ensure that the cutter path is as required by the profile. In this system, a velocity feed back is provided by a transducer known as tacho-generator attached to the feed drive system.

A closed loop system is more expensive than an open loop system.

A block diagram of a closed-loop system is shown in Fig. 16.4 (b). Since, there is a continuous monitoring of the positions, the drive is a continuous-position device. These servomotors provide a smoother and continuously controllable movement of the work-table.

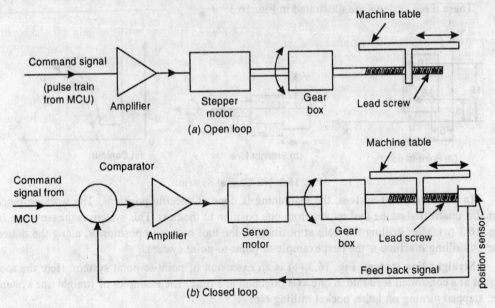

Fig. 16.4. Control Systems.

A.C. servo-motors have better reliability, better performance-to-weight ratio and lower power consumption. So, these are rapidly replacing the DC servomotor on new NC machine tools.

16.4. PROGRAMMING FOR NC MACHINES

As discussed above, the complete information for producing a component on an NC machine, is punched on a paper tape. The information punched on the paper tape includes :

1. the co-ordinate values of the entire tool path.

2. the co-ordinate values are prefixed with certain codes indicating the type of movement of the tool (point-to-point, straight line, contour) from one co-ordinate to the next.

3. the co-ordinate values are also suffixed with certain codes indicating the various machine functions, such as, start/stop, spindle coolant etc. The co-ordinate values are also supplemented with other functions such as feed rates, spindle speeds, etc.

Programming to obtain the punched paper tape can either be done manually or with the help of a computer. Simple point-to-point programs can be easily developed manually, but more complex ones, as well as almost all contouring programs are developed with the help of computers.

Before making the part programme, the programmer first studies the part drawing and decides upon : the proper sequence of operations, the cutting tools, the path of the cutter/tool, speeds and feeds at various points and the other related information, such as starting and stopping of the machine etc.

16.4.1. Manual Programming. The first step is to establish the zero reference axes on the part drawing and determine the co-ordinate dimensions for each operation. Also, the set up instruments to establish the workpiece properly on the machine table with respect to the tool, are established. Then, all the data and the instructions are entered in a 'program sheet' in a particular format acceptable to the machine tool-control unit combination. This sheet includes the following information : the co-ordinate dimensions for each operation, the spindle traverse that determines the depth of cut, the spindle speed and feed, tool change. After preparing the 'programme sheet', the programmer uses it to prepare the punched paper tape on a typewriter-like tape punching machine.

16.4.2. Computer Programming. To develop the program with the help of a computer, specialized programming languages, such as APT (Automatically Programmed Tool) have been developed to facilitate the production of punched paper tapes with relatively little knowledge of computers. The various steps in computer programming are :

1. Writing the 'part programme manuscript' using the simplified programming language.

2. Copying the part programme manuscript onto a deck of punched cards with the help of a keypunch operator. This is known as the 'part programme'. On each card, a specific machine-tool instruction is punched.

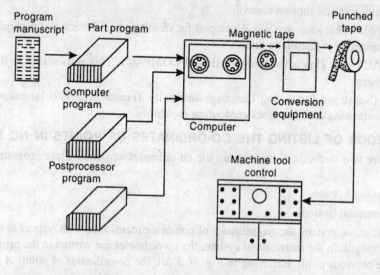

Fig. 16.5. Computer Programming.

3. The 'part programme' alongwith 'computer programme' and 'post-processor programme' are then fed to a general-purpose computer. The 'computer programme' is a previously prepared deck of punched cards, or tape, that contain instructions for the computer for executing the part-programme instructions, and also those from 'post-processor programme'. The computer translates the 'part programme' into numbers and computing instructions and performs the calculations. The output of the computer, which is translated with the aid of 'post processor programme' into a form acceptable to the particular machine tool, may be in the form of a magnetic tape or a punched paper tape. If the output is in the form of a magnetic tape, it is converted into punched tape with the help of conversion equipment. The punched tape is now ready to be fed into machine tool control. The complete scheme of computer programming is shown in Fig. 16.5.

APT the first programming language used for NC machine tools was developed in 1950. It used English type statements. After that, many subsets of APT and new languages have been developed. In APT-II, the complete job of part program preparation from the part drawing was undertaken by the computer.

Then came the APT Long Range Program (ALRP). In 1965, ALRP was changed to Computer-Aided Manufacturing-I (CAM-I).

The subsets of APT and its expanded forms and other new languages are given below :

ADAPT (Adaptation of APT) :for smaller components.

UNIAPT :handles full power of APT on a smaller computer. It differs from APT only in its internal design of processor.

NELAPT :developed by National Engineering Laboratory in U.K.

This language contains advanced features not available in APT. EXAPT (Extended APT) : was developed in Germany. It is both geometrically and technologically oriented. Its various versions are available :

(*i*) EXAPT 1 : for positioning machine tools, e.g., drilling machines,

(*ii*) EXAPT 2 : for turning centres.

(*iii*) EXAPT 3 : for milling operations.

AUTOSPOT (Automatic System for Positioning Tools) : was developed by IBM in 1962 for three axes, point-to-point motion control.

COMPACT :This language was developed for simultaneous servising of multiple users from a remote computer over telephone lines.

COMPACT - II :This is the latest version of COMPACT. This is available to the users on a time sharing basis.

SPLIT (Sunstrand Processing Language Internally Translated) : This language can handle upto 5-axis positioning and possesses contouring capability.

16.5. METHODS OF LISTING THE CO-ORDINATES OF POINTS IN NC SYSTEM

There are two methods of mentioning the co-ordinates of points while programming for an NC system :

1. Absolute System.

2. Incremental System.

In the absolute system, the co-ordinates of points are mentioned with respect to one reference point, that is, datum. In the incremental system, the co-ordinates are written in the programme with respect to the previous point. Referring to Fig. 16.3 (*a*), the co-ordinates of points *A* and *B*, in the two system, are given as below :

Absolute system	X-Co-ordinate	Y-Co-ordinate
Point A	5	5
Point B	10	15
Incremental System		
Point A	5	5
Point B	5	10

16.6. APPLICATIONS OF NC MACHINES

The major applications of NC machines are :

1. For parts, which are complex and it will not be possible to manufacture them very accurately on conventional machines, due to human error involved.

2. For parts which are frequently subjected to design changes.

3. Repetitive and precision quality parts which are to be produced in low to medium batch quantity.

4. In situations where the investment on tooling and fixture inventory will be high if the parts are made on conventional machine tools.

5. To cut down 'lead time' in manufacture.

16.7. ADVANTAGES AND DISADVANTAGES OF NC MACHINES
Advantages

1. Greater accuracy.

2. Lesser production cost per piece due to reduction in lead time and also set up time.

3. Improved product quality and provision of high order of repeatability.

4. High production rates as the machining conditions (feeds and speeds) are optimised and the non-machining times are reduced to a minimum.

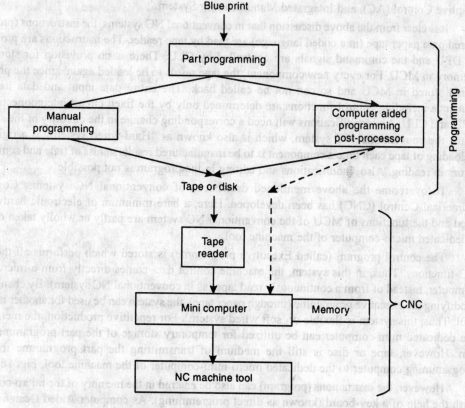

Fig. 16.6.

5. Less scrap due to consistent accuracy and absence of operator errors

6. Reduced inventory of 'parts in process' because parts can be made economically in smaller quantities.

7. Less operator skill is required to run NC machine.

8. Due to reduced idle time, the machine utilization is better.

9. Changes in part design can be incorporated very easily and at a low cost by simply changing parts of tape program.

10. Excellent reliability as the control equipment now is virtually all made of solid state modulus.

11. Lower tooling costs as expensive jigs and fixtures are not required.

12. Reduced cycle time and increased tool life.

The major disadvantage of NC machines are their costs. Therefore, the machines must have sufficient use to justify the investment. Programming of NC machines has been greatly simplified and machine availability above 95% is common.

16.8. COMPUTER NUMERICAL CONTROL (CNC) AND DIRECT NUMERICAL CONTROL (DNC)

Computer has been associated with NC right from the begining, and over the years this association has resulted in many new conceptions like : Computer Numerical Control (CNC). Direct Numerical Control (DNC), Computer Aided Design (CAD), Computer Aided Manufacture (CAM), adaptive Control (AC), and Integrated Manufacturing System.

It is clear from the above discussion that in conventional NC systems, the instructions (program) stored on a paper tape (in a coded language) are read by tape reader. The instructions are processed by DPU and the command signals are controlled by CLU. There is no provision for storage or memory in MCU. For every new component, the tape needs to be loaded again, since the program is not stored in MCU and so can not be called back. The entire data input and data handling sequence including control functions are determined only by the fixed circuit interconnections of DPU and CLU. Any modifications will need a corresponding change in the circuitry of the system. Thus, the conventional NC system, which is also known as "Hard-wired system" is a rigid one. Reloading of tape each time a component is to be manufactured results in loss of time and sometimes errors in reading. Also, modifications and editing in the program is not possible.

To overcome the above mentioned drawbacks of conventional NC systems, Computer Numerical Control (CNC) has been developed. Here, a bare minimum of electronic hardware is used and the functions of MCU of the conventional NC system are partly or wholly taken over by a dedicated micro-computer of the machine tool.

The control program (called Executive programme) is stored which performs all the basic NC functions. Thus, in this system, the machine control data comes directly from a micro-mini-computer, instead of from a continuously read tape (as in conventional NC system). By changing or modifying the executive programme (through paper tape), the system can be used for another machine tool. Thus, this system is flexible or 'soft wired system'. For repetitive production, the memory of the dedicated mini-computer can be utilized for temporary storage of the part programme being run. However, tape or disc is still the medium of transmitting the part programme from the programming computer to the dedicated micro-mini-computer of the machine tool, Fig. 16.6.

However, the instructions (program) can also be entered in the memory of the micro-computer with the help of a key-board (known as direct programming). As computer-Aided Design (CAD) systems become more common generating data bases, the use of tape for storing program will decrease with the corresponding increase in the use of floppy disk, hard disk and other computer storage devices for this purpose. Again, computer-aided programming is being replaced by computer-aided manufacturing (CAM), where the programs for the NC machine tools can be generated on the graphic terminal directly from the data base created by CAD (CAD file), with the help of CAD/CAM software.

Advantages of CNC Systems over Conventional NC Systems

1. Because the computer can be readily and easily reprogrammed, therefore, the system is very flexible. The machine can manufacture a part followed by other parts of different designs.

2. More versatility. Editing and debugging programs, reprogramming; and plotting and printing part shapes are simpler.

3. Program to manufacture a component can be easily called. This saves time and eliminates errors due to tape reading.

4. Greater accuracy.

5. Ease of operation.

6. The micro-processors used in place of hard-wired NC circuits are very reliable and have self diagonistic features. This makes trouble shooting extremely easy.

7. The dedicated computers need less memory storage and even small computers possess large memory.

In DNC system, several NC machines can be controlled by a large central computer. Here, direct link may be established between the programming computer and the large central control computer. But, this system is very expensive and a highly skilled software knowledge is needed and can usually be justified only in large corporations or if the system is expanded to include process management and control (CAM and CAD) Fig. 16.7.

The NC units used in the conventional DNC system may be :

1. of the conventional hard-wired type, with the tape reader being replaced by a direct communicating link to the Central Computer, or

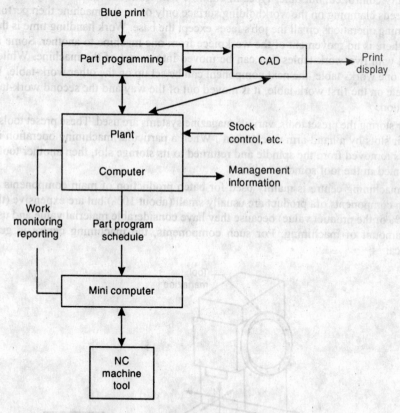

Fig. 16.7.

2. Speicialized units which like CNC system, use a micro/mini computer as the MCU.

DNC system has the main drawback that if the Central mainframe computer goes down, all the machine tools become inoperative. This drawback has been overcome by a more recent definition of DNC as "Distributed Numerical Control" in place of "Direct Numerical Control", still abbreviated as DNC. In this system, a Central large computer is still used as in conventional DNC. But, the individual NC machines are not directly controlled by this central computer. Each NC machine has its own dedicated on-board micro-computer just like a CNC system. All these invidual micro-computers are linked to the central large computer, which serves as the Central control system.

This arrangement overcomes the main drawback of the conventional DNC system, in that if the central computer goes down, the NC machines will not become inoperative. Moreover, this system provides a larger memory and computational capabilities and increased flexibility.

DNC, system appeared in the market earlier than CNC system. but with the development of dedicated mini-computers, the benefits of DNC system can be realised in CNC system.

Moreover, with the availability of small computers with large memory, micro-processors, and program editing capabilities, CNC machines are widely used at present. Also, the availability of low cost-programmable logic controllers (PLCs) has helped in the successful implementation of CNC systems.

16.9. MACHINING CENTRE

A machining centre or work centre consists of a single, but sometimes, two machine tools with the specific feature of an automatic tool changer and capable of performing a number of operations (drilling, tapping, milling, boring and turning etc.) on a workpiece. Most machines are numerically controlled, but other types of controls will work as well. The major advantage is that the job needs clamping on the workholding surface only once; the machine then performs a variety of machining operations on all the job's faces except the base. Work handling time is thus decreased because there is no movement of the workpiece from one machine to another. Some machines are equipped with two work-tables that can be moved into or out of the machine. While the work is going on one works table, the next component can be set up on the other work-table. When the job is complete on the first work-table, it is moved out of the way and the second work-table is moved into position.

For storing the preset tools, various magazine systems are used. These preset tools are removed from their slots by a hand-arm mechanism'. When a particular machining operation is completed, the tool is removed from the spindle and returned to its storage slot, then another tool is picked up and mounted in the tool spindle.

A machining centre is mainly used for batch production of main components of a product. The main components ofa product are usually small (about 10%) but are expensive (they represent about 50% of the product value) because they have considerable material value and usually require a large amount of machining. For such components, the machining centre is generally most economical.

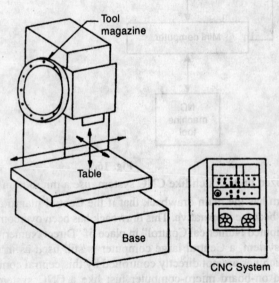

Fig. 16.8

Machining centres have high metal removal rate capabilities. The high degree of accuracy and multi-operation in the same set up, make the machining centres highly versatile and increase productivity. Some models are made with manual tool change facility. Fig. 16.8 shows a typical machining centre.

16.10. ADAPTIVE CONTROL

Adaptive control (AC) is another step towards true automation, wherein the vital element of decision making is added. As the component is being manufactured, the important variables are measured and then if need be, certain variables are altered within programmed limits, to get as accurate the finished part as possible. For example, in drilling, the torque on the drill is measured and speed and feed or both are adjusted within programmed limits. Similarly, in milling process, feed and/or speed and depth of cut are controlled in response to signals from torque, force, vibration and dimensional transducers. The limits set by the process, e.g., surface finish, maximum feeds, speeds and depth of cut, cutting force and torque; and those set by the machine tool, e.g., vibration and elastic deformation, are programmed.

Adaptive control is still in its infancy, since, the effect of the various process variables on the finished part, is still relatively unknown. For the adaptive control to grow, process reliability has to be improved and also a more quantitative understanding of the process has to be gained. Another major problem is the on line measurement of the dimensional, without which the tool wear can not be compensated for with any great accuracy.

PROBLEMS

1. Justify the need for NC machines.
2. Define NC
3. With the help of a diagram, explain the working of a NC machine tool.
4. List the main component of a NC machine tool and explain their functions.
5. Compare a closed loop system with an open loop system.
6. Classify the NC machines.
7. Discuss the programming of NC machines.
8. Give the applications of NC machines.
9. List the advantages and disadvantages of NC machines.
10. Define CNC and DNC.
11. List the advantages of CNC systems over the conventional NC systems.
12. List the main advantages of DNC.
13. What is "Distributed Numerical Control" ?
14. What is a machining centre ?
15. List the main advantages of a machining centre.
16. What is "Adaptive Control" ?
17. Write briefly, how numerical control works ?
18. Explain the main difference between point to point and continuous path type of numerically controlled machine tools.
19. Under what conditions of production the numerically controlled machine tools are employed ?

20. What is point-to-point type of path motion of NC ? For which machines this system is employed ?

21. What is straight line NC ?

22. What is continuous path NC ?

23. How manual programming of a NC machine is done ?

24. How computer programming of a NC machine is done ?

25. Discuss the control system of a NC machine.

26. Write the functions of MCU, DPU and CLU, in a NC machine.

27. Write on some of the programming languages used for NC machine tools.

28. Write on the methods of listing the co-ordinates of points in NC system.

29. What are "information sources" is an NC machine tool?

30. Write the information carriers in an NC systems ?

31. Write the aim of the manufacturing activity in the modern age of business competition?

32. How are the NC Machines classified?

33. On the basis of power drive, what are the various types of NC systems?

34. What is pneumatic control?

35. What is its drawback?

36. Write the advantages and drawbacks of hydraulic control.

37. What is electro-mechanical drive?

38. What is "Servo"?

39. Write on different types of feedback systems in NC machines.

40. What is the difference between NC and CNC machines?

41. When should an NC machines be used from the point of view of economy?

42. Write on : CNC scene in India.

43. What are PLCs?

44. What is Retro-fitting ?

The medium and small scale industries (which play a significant role in the economy of developing countries) can ill afford NC machine tools, because of their very high initial nvestment. Their problem can be overcome by providing assessories to their conventional general purpose equipment so as to get the advantages of advanced CNC technology. Their performance is not equal to that of CNC machines, but is much higher than the conventional machine tools. This is know as "Retro-Fitting.

$$R_a = (\text{CLA}) \times R = \frac{1}{L} \int_0^L |h| dx$$

$$= \frac{\sum h}{n}$$

Chapter

17

Surface Finishing Processes

17.1 INTRODUCTION

Whatever may be the manufacturing process, an absolutely smooth and flat surface can not be obtained. The machine elements or parts retain the surface irregularities left after manufacturing. The surface of a part is its exterior boundary and the surface irregularities consist of numerous small wedges and valleys that deviate from a hypothetical nominal surface (Fig. 17.1, which shows a surface on a highly magnified scale). These irregularities are responsible to a great extent for the appearance of a surface and its suitability for an intended application of the component. These surface irregularities are usually understood in terms of surface finish, surface roughness, surface texture or surface quality. Heat exchanger tubes transfer heat better when their surfaces are slightly rough rather than highly finished. Brake drums and clutch plates etc. work best with some degree of surface roughness. However, if a film of lubrication must be maintained between two moving parts, the surface irregularities must be small enough (smooth surface) so that they do not penetrate the oil film under the most severe operating conditions. The examples are : Bearings, journals, cylinder bores, piston pins, bushing, helical and worm gears, seal surfaces and machine ways etc. In gears, smooth surfaces are also necessary to ensure quiet operations. For components which are subjected to load reversals, sharp irregularities act as stress raisers constituting the greatest potential source of fatigue cracks. Therefore, the surfaces of components which are subjected to high stresses and load reversals are finished highly smooth.

Fig. 17.1. A Profile of Surface Irregularities.

Evaluation of Surface Roughness : As per B.I.S (Bureau of Indian Standards), it is assessed in terms of Centre Line Average (CLA) or Arithmatic Average (AA) and is denoted as R_a. Referring to Fig. 17.2, Arithmatic average or Centre line average is difined as : the average value of the ordinates from the center line (the centre line AB is located such that the sum of areas above the line is equal to sum of areas below the line), the algebra sign of the ordinates is not considered that is,

$$AA = CLA = R_a = \frac{1}{L}\int_0^L |y(x)|\, dx$$

Where L = Roughness width cut-off or the sampling length. This is the maximum width of surface irregularities that is included in the measurement of rougness height.

$$\text{Approximately, } R_a = \frac{\sum_1^n |Y_i|}{n}$$

Where n = number of vertical ordinates

i.e.
$$R_a = \frac{y_1 + y_2 + y_3 + \ldots + y_n}{n}$$

$$= \frac{A_1 + A_2 + A_3 + \ldots + A_n}{L}$$

$$= \frac{\Sigma A}{L}$$

Units of Surface Roughness: Surface rougness or surface finish is measured in microns or micrometres,

$$1 \text{ micron} = 10^{-3} \text{ mm}$$
$$= 10^{-6} \text{ m} = 1\ \mu\text{m}.$$

The secondary manufacturing processes (the conventional metal machining methods, Chapter 8) are all finishing processes. The range of surface finish obtained with these methods for average applications is given in Table 17.1. To achieve better surface finish, other surface finishing processes such as lapping,

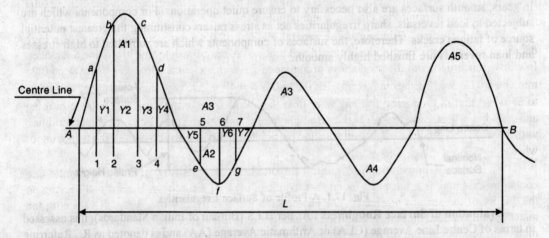

Fig. 17.2. Surface Roughness.

Honing, Buffing and super finishing etc. are used. These processes will be discussed in this chapter. The typical ranges of surface finish obtained by these methods is given in Table 17.1.

Table 17.1. Typical Ranges of Surface Finish, Ra, μ m

Process	Average applications
Turning, Boring	0.4 to 6.3
Reaming	0.8 to 3.2
Shaping, Planing	1.6 to 12.5
Drilling	1.6 to 6.3
Milling	0.8 to 6.3
Broaching	0.8 to 3.2
Grinding	0.1 to 1.6
Roller burnishing	0.2 to 0.8
Lapping	0.05 to 0.4
Honing	0.1 to 0.8
Buffing	0.05 to 0.5
Super finishing	0.05 to 0.2

17.2. SURFACE FINISHING PROCESSES

The various methods used for finishing the surfaces of the parts are discussed below:

17.2.1 Diamond Turning and Boring. It is customary to find, where the application demands it, light alloys, bronzes and tin alloys, bearing metal, being turned or bored using diamond tools with a geometric control of about 0.0125 mm or below and with surface rougness measurement of between 0.075 and 0.125 μ m (AA). Fine finishing by the diamond tools is more or less confined to those materials which do not include hard or abrasive particles in their make up which would chip or damage the stone, and which cut cleanly with a definite chip. Materials which come away in an abrasive powder rapidly erode the cutting edge and thus make the use of diamond tools expensive and uncertain. The machines employed for fine turning and boring must obviously be in perfect condition, with all ways and guides straight and true and all bearings and spindles running in perfect truth with minimum clearance and no vibration.

17.2.2. Grinding. Grinding is the general method of finishing steel but it requires a high degree of skill to repeat continuously a restricted grade of surface finish to fine geometric tolerances. In works concerned with the production of hardened components with tolerances of between 0.05 mm and 0.025 mm, finishes in the range of 0.2 to 0.3 μ m (AA) are commonly produced and it has to be noted that in producing finishes finer than the above figures, the danger of surface burning and cracking is greatly increased. Machine employed for fine griding must be in first class condition with all ways and guides straight and true and particular attention must be paid to the balancing of wheels.

Wheel surface preparation is of utmost importance. Adequate flow of chip and granule free coolant is essential as it has been found that the cleanliness of the coolant has a direct bearing on the quality of the surface produced. The choice of wheel grit, speeds coolants will vary with the material being cut and the finish demanded. Whilst grinding is convenient and a reasonable economic method of producing fine surface, it brings in its train a number of pitfalls. An inevitable result of grinding is the formation by the high temperature generated at the work and wheel contact line, of an extremely thin layer of decarburised material which has a considerable effect on the initial efficiency of a surface as a bearing and has to be removed in many cases before really satisfactory bearing conditions are attained. A further effect of high temperature is burning of the surface and the formation of grinding cracks which are large enough to affect the fatigue strength of the component. Chatter is also evident on ground cylindrical components, particularly on those which have been centreless ground.

17.2.3. Lapping: Lapping is a surface finishing process used on flat or cylindrical surfaces (mainly external). Lapping is the abrading of a surface by means of a lap (which is made of a material softer than the material to be lapped), which has been charged with the fine abrasive particles. When the lap and the work surface are rubbed together with the fine abrasive particles between them, these particles become embedded in the softer lap. It then becomes a holder for the hard abrasive. As a charged lap is rubbed against a hard surface, the hard particles in the surface of the lap remove small amounts of materials from the harder surface. Thus it is the abrasive which does the cutting and the soft lap is not worn away, because the abrasive particles become embedded in its surface, instead of moving across it.

In lapping, the abrasive is usually carried between the lap and the work in some sort of a vehicle. The vehicle or lubricant controls to some extent the cutting action and prevents scoring the work and caking of the abrasive. Some of the vehicles used include: kerosene plus a small amount of machine oil, greases, fine sperm oil for fine job, olive oil, lard oil, spindle oil, and soapy water. Naphtha is used to clean the laps.

Laps may be made of almost any material soft enough to receive and retain the abrasive grains. They may be made of soft cast iron, wood, leather, brass, copper, lead or soft steel. The most common lap is fine grain cast iron. Copper is used rather often and is the common materials for lapping diamonds. For lapping hardened metals for metrolographic examination, cloth laps are used.

For steel surfaces, artificial corrundum is used as an abrasive for preparatory lapping and again used in a final state for finishing. Silicon carbide gives good results on cast iron and alumina for finest lapping. For lapping small components, diamond dust or boron carbide in the finest grain size give good results. The other abrasives used are: rough (Ferric oxide Fe_2O_3), green rough (chromium oxide Cr_2O_3) and crocus powder. The abrasive particles are from 120 grit up to the finest powdered sizes. In nearly all cases, a paraffin lubricant is used. The exception being for soft materials when a soluble oil or water lubricant is used.

In lapping, the material removal is usually less than 0.025 mm, although rough lapping may remove as much as 0.075 mm and finish lapping as little as 0.0025 mm. Commercial lapping operations can produce parts to limits of 0.000625 mm. Since it is such a slow metal removal process, it is used only to remove scratch marks left by grinding orhoning or to obtain very flat or smooth surfaces such as required on gauge blocks or liquid tight seals where high pressures are involved. Materials of almost any hardness may be lapped. However, it is difficult to lap soft materials since the abrasives tend to become embedded.

Thus, lapping is done:

(*i*) to produce geometrically true surface.

(*ii*) to correct minor imperfections is shape.

(*iii*) to obtain fine dimensional accuracy to provide a very close fit between the contact surfaces.

(*iv*) to secure a fine surface finish.

Lapping Methods:– Lapping may be done by hand or mechanically with the help of special lapping machines.

(*a*) *Hand lapping for flat work* : Here, the lap is a flat similar to a surface plate. Grooves are usually cut across the surface of a lap to collect the excessive abrasive and chips. For finishing of the work surface, either the lap or the workpiece is held by one hand and the irregular rotary motion of the other by the second hand, enables the abrading of the two surfaces in contact. The work is turned frequently to obtain uniform cutting action. The method is used for lapping: press work dies, dies and metallic moulds for castings etc., surface plate, engine valve and valve seat, gauge blocks and piston rings etc. Piston rings are customarily made parallel and to high precision by hand lapping. Manual lapping is used to bring gauge blocks to their final stage of dimensional accuracy and parallelism, a finish of 0.025 to 0.050 μ m and a tolerance as small as ± 0.000025 mm.

(*b*) *Hand lapping for external Cylindrical work (Ring Lapping)* : An external lap for external workpieces (round) is shown in Fig. 17.3. It is split by a saw cut and can be closed in by tightening one or more screws. The diameter of the hole is made the same as that of the piece to be lapped, and the hole is, of course bored before the saw cut is made. Internal laps are made to expand.

The ring lap is reciprocated over the work piece surface. The method is usually used for stepped plug gauges or gauges made in small quantities.

(*c*) *Machine Lapping* : Mechanical lapping is a high production process, for example gudgeon pins 25 mm diameter and 75 mm long are lapped at the rate of 500 pieces per hour, removing 0.05 to 0.075 mm

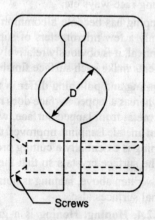

Fig. 17.3 External Lap.

of material with a limit of accuracy of roundness, straightness and size within 0.025 mm. Mechanical lapping machines are of vertical construction with the work holder mounted on the lower table which is given an oscillating motion. The upper lap is stationary and floating, while the lower one revolves at about 60 rev/min. Several types of lapping machines are available for lapping round surfaces. A special type of centreless lapping machine is made for lapping small parts such as piston pins, ball bearing races etc.

A general purpose machine for lapping both cylindrical and flat surfaces is shown in Fig. 17.4 A number of workpieces are placed between the upper and the lower lap, whose surfaces have previously been lapped flat. The workpieces are placed in slots in a work holder so that their axes X-X are not quite radial. The shape of the slots will depend upon that of the workpieces. The two laps are rotated and the work holder is given as oscillation of about 25 mm amplitude. A stream of vehicle in which fine abrasive flour is suspended is fed to the centre of the laps and flows outwards and the workpieces are thus gradually lapped to size.

During machine lapping a pressure of 0.007 to 0.02 N/mm^2 for soft materials and upto

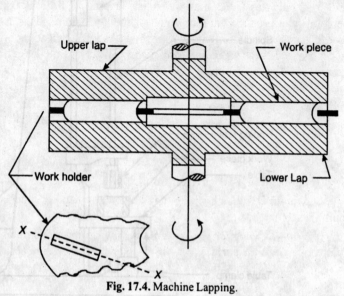

Fig. 17.4. Machine Lapping.

0.07 N/mm^2 for hard materials is satisfactory. Mechanical lapping machines can be used for lapping: (*i*) External cylindrical surfaces, and (*ii*) flat surfaces.

The following are examples of work done by lapping: aircraft piston pins, automotive wrist pins, diesel engine injector-pump parts and spray nozzles, plug gauges, certain dies and moulds, gauge blocks, refrigerator-compressor parts, oil-burner parts, micro-meter spindles, roller bearings, taper rollers, worm and worm gears, crankshafts, camshafts, ball bearing race-ways etc.

Lapping has become a common production process with the demand for hardened surfaces having only a few micrometers of surface finish. However, because, it is such a slow method of metal removal, it is obviously relatively expensive and is not economically justified unless operating requirements make such surface finishes absolutely necessary.

Lapping and polishing differ in the following manner-Polishing is meant to produce a shiny surface whereas a lapped surface does not usually have a bright shiny appearance. Lapping definitely removes metal from lapped surface, whereas, polishing as a rule does not remove any appreciable amount of metal. Lapping improves the geometrical shape of the body, whereas, polishing does not. Lapping is essentially a cutting process, while polishing consists of producing a kind of plastic flow of the surface crystals so that the high spots are made to fill the low spots.

As written above, lapping is normally adopted for external surfaces. However, it can be used for internal surfaces also.

17.2.4. Honing. Honing is a grinding or abrading process. In it, a very little material is removed. This process is used primarily to remove the grinding or tool marks left on the surface by previous operations. The cutting action is obtained from abrasive sticks (aluminium oxide or silicon carbide) mounted in a mandrel or fixture. A floating action between the work and the tool prevails so that any pressure exerted on the tool is exerted and transmitted equally on all sides. The honing

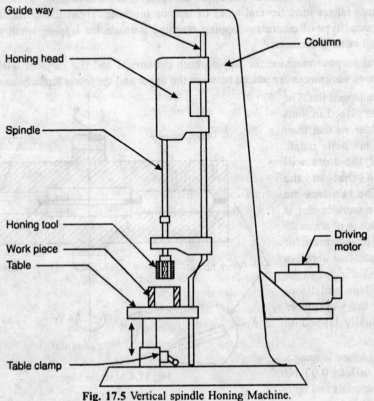

Fig. 17.5 Vertical spindle Honing Machine.

tool is given a slow reciprocating motion as it rotates, having resultant honing speeds from 15 to 60 mpm. This action results in rapid removal of stock and at the same time, the generation of a straight and round surface. Defects such as slight eccentricity, a wavy surface, or a slight taper caused by previous operations can be corrected by this process. Parts honed for finish remove only 0.025 mm or less. However, when certain inaccuracies must be corrected, amounts upto 0.50 mm represent usually practice. Collants are essential to the operation of this process to flush way small chips and keep temperatures uniform. Sulphurised mineral base or lard oil mixed with kerosene is generally used. Paraffin is also used.

Most honing is done on internal surfaces, or holes, such as automobile cylinders. There are a few applications of honing to external surfaces. Parts can be of any shape, but the surface must be cylindrical. Practically any material can be honed. Soft materials which cannot be lapped, can be honed because of the use of bonded abrasive. Hard and soft cast iron, steel, carbides, bronze, aluminium, brass and silver, as well as glass, ceramics and some plastic can be honed.

Honing machines are similar in general construction to vertical drilling machines Fig. 17.5 but the spindle reciprocation is usually by hydraulic means. The rotary motion may be from a hydraulic motor or by gearing. The speed ratio of two motions affects the work finish and may be varied throughout the operation or for different materials. For cast iron, the speed ranges from 60 to 150 mpm for rotation; with 15 to 21 mpm for reciprocation. The corresponding speeds for steel are : 45 to 60 mpm for rotation and 12 mpm for reciprocation. The reciprocation motion distributes the wear over the whole length of the sticks and keeps the bore cylindrical. Semi-automatic honing machines used in the finishing of automobile cylinder bores are of vertical type. Both single and multi spindle machines are used for this operation. The abrasive stones are mounted on a honing tool. In order to expand the abrasive stones outward to fit the hole to be honed, the conical wedge is moved relative to the honing tool.

A general arrangement of a vertical honing machine is shown in fig. 17.6. The abrasive sticks (upto 8 in number) are expanded while honing takes place, if required, by micrometer controlled, mechanical or hydraulic, means. The honing tool will follow the axis of the original

hole, therefore, the honing tool or fixture must be free to float. This is done by using universal joints as shown in the figure. Due to this, the honing tool becomes self centring and it is not necessary to line up the hole and hone axes precisely. Vertical machines have been designed for work upto 500 mm diameter.

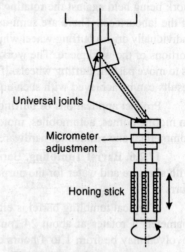

Fig. 17.6 Vertical Honing Machine.

Horizontal honing machines are used only for honing large, long gun barrels and similar work. The workpiece is held on the left and the tool is rotated and reciprocated by the head on the right end of the bed of the machine. Machines of this type are made with strokes of upto 22.5 m and hone holes as large as about 1 m in diameter.

All honing gives a smooth finish with a characteristic cross hatch appearance. The depth of these hone marks can be controlled by variations in pressures, speed and type of abrasive used. Accurate dimensions can be maintained by the use of automatic size controlled devices in

connection with honing. Typical applications of honing are finishing of automobile engine cylinders, bearings, gun barrels, ring gauges, piston pins. Shafts and flange faces.

The grit size of abrasive material used in abrasive sticks is 80 to 180 for primary honing and 300 to 500 for secondary honing. Surface finish of the order of 0.05 μ m R can be obtained by honing.

17.2.5. Buffing. Buffing is a polishing operation in which the workpiece is brought in contact with a revolving cloth buffing wheel, that usually has been charged with a very fine abrasive Fig. 17.7. The polishing action in buffing is very closely related to lapping in that when a polishing medium such as 'rouge' is used, the cloth buffing wheel becomes a carrying vehicle for the fine abrasives. In (this action the abrasive removes amounts of metal from the workpiece, thus

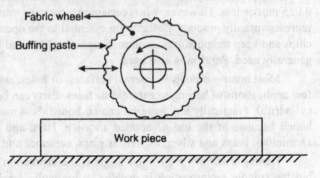

Fig. 17.7 Buffing.

eliminating the scratch marks and producing a very smooth surface. When softer metals are buffed, particularly without the use of an abrasive, there is some indication that a small amount of metal flow may occur which helps to reduce the high spots and produce a high polish.

Buffing wheels are made of discs of linen, cotton, broad cloth and canvass. They are made more or less firm by the amount of stitching used to fasten the layers of the cloth together. Buffing wheels for very soft polishing or which can be used to polish into interior corners may have no stitching, the cloth layers being kept in position by the centrifugal force resulting from the rotation of the wheel. Buffing wheel speeds are in the range of 32.5 to 40 m/s.

Various types of buffing rouges are available. Most of them being primarily ferric oxide in some soft type of binder. Buffing should be used only to remove very fine scratches or to remove oxide or similar coatings which may be on the work surface. It ordinarily, is done manually, the work being held against the rotating wheel. This procedure is apt to be relative expensive because of the labour cost. There are semi-automatic buffing machines available consisting of a series of individually driven buffing wheel which can be adjusted to the desired position so as to buff different portions of the workpiece. The workpieces are held in fixtures on a rotating circular worktable so as to move past the buffing wheels. If the workpieces are not too complex in shape, very satisfactory results can be achieved with such equipment and the buffing cost will be low.

Product applications of buffing process which produces mirror-like finish are : objects used on mobile homes, automobiles, motor-cycles, boats, bicycles, sporting items, tools, store fixtures, commercial and residential hardware and household utensils and appliances.

17.2.6. Barrel Tumbling. Barrel tumbling is the process of revolving workpiece in a barrel with abrasive and water for the purpose of producing a high lustre or for the purpose of removing burrs.

A typical tumbling barrel is eight sided, lined with wood and about 1.8 m long and 1.2 m in diameter. It rotates at about 24 rpm. The barrel may have one to six compartments. The time involved may be from 1 to 4 hours depending upon the job.

Parts are packed into the barrel or drum until it is nearly full, together with slugs; stars or jacks or some abrasive such as sand, granite chips or aluminium oxide pallets. The barrel is then rotated. The movement of the parts as they tumble and roll over one another and the accompanying impingement of the slug or abrassive against the parts produce a fine cutting action, Fig. 17.8. Delicate parts should not shift loosely during tumbling and in some cases the parts must be attached to racks within the barrel so that they will not strike against one another. Tumbling is an inexpensive cleaning method. Various shapes of slug materials may be used. Several shapes may be mixed in a given load since shapes must be provided which will reach into all sections and corners that must be cleaned. Tumbling usually is done dry, but sometimes it may also be wet.

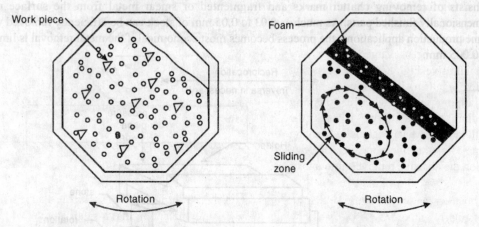

Fig. 17.8. Barrel Tumbling.   Fig. 17.9 Barrel Rolling.

Tumbling may be employed for any of the following purposes:

(a) Removing fins, flashes and scales from parts.

(b) Cleaning of forgings, stampings and castings.

(c) Deburring.

(d) Improving micrometer finish.

(e) Finishing high precision work to a high lustre.

(f) Forming uniform radii.

(g) Finishing gears and threaded parts without damage.

(h) Removing paint or plating.

After tumbling, the parts must be thoroughly washed and dried by sawdust or infrared lamps and then oiled to prevent the formation of rust.

17.2.7. Barrel Rolling. Barrel Rolling is similar to tumbling except that the barrel is loaded only about 40 to 60% full and its purpose is not to clean but to cut down the surfaces through the use of suitable cutting abrasive,Fig. 17.9. Rolling is done either in open tilted barrels or in close horizontal barrels. The workpieces, abrasive and water or dilute acid solutions are loaded into the barrel to such a height that as barrel turns, the mass will be carried about 3/4 of the distance up the side and then roll over and fall to the bottom. The abrasives most commonly used are: slag, cinders, sharp sand, granite chips, broken chips of glass or carborundum. The abrasives vary in shape from round to triangular and in size from about 5 mm to 25 mm. The rolling action must be such that there is a relative motion between the work and the abrasive particles, since no cutting action will occur unless the sharp edges of the abrasive pass across the surfaces to be finished. Rolling usually is done wet since this gives a faster cutting action. However dry rolling is also done usually with an abrasive mixed with saw dust to brighten small parts.

By using the proper abrasive, a wide range of finishes can be obtained. Rolling time varies from 10 minutes for non-ferrous parts to 2 or 3 hours for steel. Since it usually is done as a batch process, it is simple and very economical. The resulting surface is remarkably uniform, but deep scratches must be removed prior to rolling.

17.2.8. SUPER-FINISHING

Super-finishing is a micro finishing process that produces a controlled surface condition on parts which is not obtainable by any other method. The operation which is also called 'microstoning' consists of scrubbing a stone against a surface to produce a fine quality metal finish. The process consists of removing chatter marks and fragmented or smear metal from the surface of a dimensionally finished parts. As much as 0.03 to 0.05 mm of stock can be efficiently removed with some production applications, the process becomes most economical if the metal removal is limited to 0.005 mm.

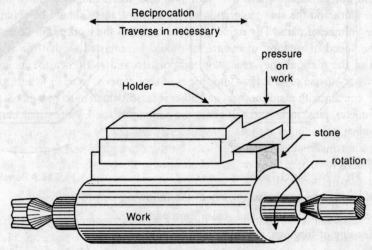

Fig. 17.10. Supper Finishing.

The method is performed by rapidly reciprocating a fine grit stone with a soft bond and pressing it against a revolving round work-piece, Fig. 17.10. The stone quickly wears to conform to the contour of the work-piece. The work-piece and tool are flooded with a cutting fluid to carry away heat and particles of metal and abrasive. The time needed for super finishing is quite small. Parts may be super-finished to a smoothness of 0.075 μm as rapidly as 15 to 50 seconds. However, to obtain a better finish 2 or 3 minutes may be required. Product applications of super-finishing are: computer memory drums, sewing machine parts, automotive cylinders, brake drums, bearings, pistons, piston rods and pins, axles, shafts, clutch plates, tappet bodies, guide pins etc.

17.2.9. Burnishing: Burnishing operation is the process of getting a smoth and shiny subface by contact and rubbing of the surface against the walls of a hard tool [punch and/or die, rollers and balls etc.). It is a finishing and strengthening process. Burnishing is basically a cold surface plastic deformation process. Cold working of surfaces improves the surface finish and induces surface compressive residual stresses, thus improving the fatigue life of the component. Fig. 10.6 shows the sizing operation with the help of a punch or mandrel and a die to get burnished inside and outside surfaces, inside surface of the bush is burnished when the mandrel gets forced through it and the external surface is burnished when the bush is forced through the die. The surface finish of the gear both is also improved by burnishing. A special hardened gear shaped burnishing die subjects the tooth surfaces to a surface rolling action. In this method, the gear is rolled under pressure with hardened accurately formed burnishing gear. In this cold working process, any high points on the tooth surface are plastically deformed to get accurate and finished tooth profile.

Some other burnishing methods are discussed below:—

(a) Barrel Burnishing. Results very nearly comparable with those obtained by buffing may often be obtained by barrel burnishing. It is similar to barrel rolling except that instead of using an abrasive medium, medium balls, shots or round pins are added to the work in the barrel. There is no cutting action in burnishing. Instead, the slug material producing peening and rubbing action on the work rough surface, spreading the minute surface irregularities to an even surface. Burnishing will not ordinarily remove visible scratches or pits, but will produce a smooth, uniform surface and reduce the porosity in surfaces which are to be or have been plated. Parts which are to be barrel burnished, usually first should be rolled with a fine abrasive. Barrel burnishing normally is done wet, using water to which has been added some lubricating or cleaning agents such as soap. The barrel should not be loaded more than half full with work and shot. Since the rubbing action between the work and the shot material is very important, there should be about two volumes of shots to one volume of parts. The ratio should be such that the workpieces do not rub against one another. The speed of rotation of the barrel should be adjusted so that the workpieces are not thrown out of the mass as they reach the top position and roll down the inclined surface. It is usually necessary to use several sizes and shapes of shot material in order to ensure that the material can come in contact with inside corners and other recesses which must be rubbed. Balls from 3 mm to 6 mm diameter, pins, jacks and ball cones are commonly used. Parts which cannot be permitted to bump against one another may be burnished successfully by fastening them in racks inside the barrel. The shot material is then added and burnishing carried out in the usual manner. When proper conditions have been achieved, barrel burnishing is economical and produces surfaces suitable for subsequent painting or plating.

(b) Roller/Ball Burnishing:–

Flat, cylindrical or conical surfaces (both internal and external) are burnished with hardened steel or cemented carbide rollers or with steel balls mounted in a holder, fig. 17.11.

Fillets and grooves are burnished by rollers rounded to a radius, fig. 17.11 (c). Where strengthening is the aim of the treatment, the burnishing pressure is to be increased. However, this condition results in somewhat lower machining accuracy. Hole burnishing is performed with multi-roller tools on drill presses, turret lathes, horizontal borers, unit built machines and automatic lathes. Burnishing raises the hardness of the surface by 20 to 50% and its wear resistance by 1.5 to 2 times. Internal surfaces are also burnished with the help of balls, the process being called as "ball burnishing" or "Ballizing". Smooth balls or mandrels slightly larger than the bore diameter are pushed through the length of the hole, see fig. 10.6

Typical product applications of roller burnishing include: Hydraulic system components, Seals, valves, spindles and fillets on shafts.

17.2.10. Powder Coating:– In powder coating, a suitable plastic formation in the form of pulverised powder is spread over the surface to be coated. After that, the surface is subjected to heat. The powder changes to plastic state allowing it to flow and fuse into a uniform continuous coating. The method was discussed briefly in chapter 12 under Art. 12.5.3, under the heading "Plastic Coatings".

Both thermo-plastic resins and thermo-setting resins are used. In addition to thermo-plastic resins mentioned in Art. 12.5.3, the other plastics used include: nylon, PVC, and thermo-plastic polyester. Thermo-setting resins include: epoxy, polyester and acrylic. We get thicker coatings with thermo-plastic resins. Thermo-setting resins are mainly used where thin paint like surface coatings are desired. For epoxy resin the baking temperature ranges from about 120°C to 135°C and a baking time of 20 to 30 minutes. It is used both as thick coating (functional end uses) and for this film decorative coating.

For thermo-plastic resins, the *"fluidised bed"* technique is used. Here, a preheated part is immersed into a fhuidised powder bed. The thickness of coating will depend upon the temperature of the heated part and the time it remains immersed in the powder bed.

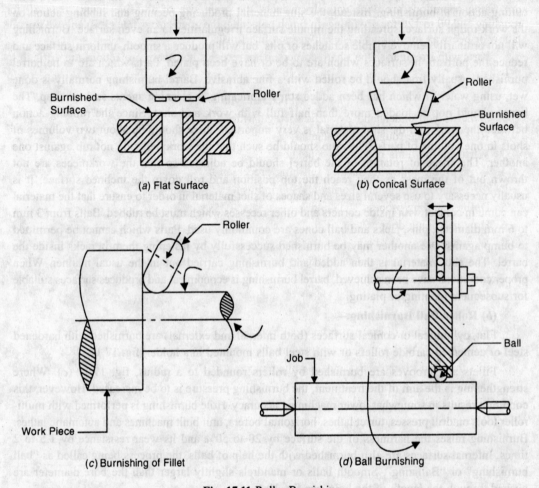

Fig. 17.11 Roller Burnishing.

Another common method of coating is "Electrostatic fluidised bed" process. Here, a cloud of charged powder particles is created above the powder bed. The components (hot or cold) are covered into the cloud. An electrical field of attraction is established between the powder particles and the components, due to which powder is deposited over the surface of the components. The resins used in this process include: epoxy, polyester, acrylic, polyethylene and polypropylene.

The most widely used method of powder coating is "electrostatic spraying". The equipment includes: a powder feed unit, powder spray guns, spray booth, electrostatic voltage source and powder recovery unit.

Note: The other methods of coating such as metal coating, electro-plating, chrome plating and anodizing etc. have been discussed in detail in chapter 12.

17.2.11. Polishing:- Polishing is a process used to get a smooth and lustrous surface finish on a part. It is done with soft/resilient polishing wheels (made of felt, cloth, wood or coarse calico etc.) coated with abrasive (Al_2O_3 or diamond) paste or used with fluid carrying abrasives. The process is based on the simultaneous action of the tool (polishing wheel) and the surface active agents of the pastes. It reduces surface roughness to 0.032-0.012 μm Ra. Unlike lapping, polishing does not improve machining accuracy.

Polishing operations may be classified as : roughing, dry fining and finishing. Roughing and dry fining operations are done with dry wheels, the grain size of abrasive being 20 to 80 for roughing and 90 to 120 for dry fining. In finish polishing, the grain size is fine (150) and we use oil, tallow or beeswax for making pastes. It gives a fine finish.

Parts with irregular shape, sharp corners, deep recesses and sharp projections are difficult to polish.

PROBLEMS

1. What do you understand by surface irregularities?
2. How is surface roughness evaluated?
3. What are the units of surface roughness?
4. Write on the following surface finishing processes:–
   (a) Diamond turning and boring.   (b) Grinding
5. Define Lapping process.
6. How is lapping done?
7. Write the materials of laps.
8. Name the abrasives used in lapping process.
9. List the functions of lapping process.
10. Write briefly on:
    (a) Hand lapping of flat surfaces.
    (b) Hand lapping of external cylindrical work.
11. With the help of a neat diagram, explain the process of Mechanical lapping.
12. List the product applications of lapping process.
13. Define honing process.
14. With the help of a neat diagram, explain the honing process.
15. Write the product applications of honing process.
16. Define Buffing operation.
17. With the help of neat diagrams, discuss:–
    (a) Barrel tumbling process.
    (b) Barrel rolling process.
18. What is the difference between barrel tumbling process and barrel rolling process.
19. With the help of a neat diagram, explain the super-finishing process.
20. List the product applications of super-finishing process.
21. Define Burnishing process.
22. Write briefly on Barrel burnishing process.
23. With the help of neat diagrams, explain the Roller/Ball burnishing processes.
24. List the product applications of roller burnishing process.
25. Write a short note on: Powder Coating.
26. What is "Electrostatic Fluidised Bed" process of powder coating?
27. What is "Electrostatic Spraying"?
28. What is "Polishing" operation?
29. Name the materials used for polishing wheels.
30. How is the polishing operation classified?
31. Give the limitations of polishing operations.
32. What is the level of surface roughness achieved after polishing operation?
33. Does polishing improve machining accuracy?

APPENDIX—I

A Representation of Welds of Drawing IS : 813-1961

Table I-1

Form of weld	Sectional representation	Appropriate symbol
Fillet		
Square butt		
Single V butt		
Double V butt		
Single U butt		
Double U butt		
Single bevel butt		
Double bevel butt		
Single J butt		
Double J butt		
Stud		
Bead edge or seal		
Sealing run		
Spot		
Seam (Continuous)		
Stitch, Seam		

B. Classification of carbide tips according to their range of application   (IS : 2428 – 1964)

Designation Indentification colour	Increasing direction of the characteristic of		Range of application	
	Carbide tip	Cutting	Material to be machined	Machining conditions
P_{01}	Resistance to wear	Toughness — Cutting speed — feed	Steel, steel casting	Precision turning and find boring Cutting speed : high. Feed : Low
P_{10}			Steel, steel casting	Turning, threading and milling Cutting speed : high. Feed : low or medium
P_{20}			Steel, steel casting, malleale cast iron forming long chips	Turning, milling. Cutting speed and feed : medium planing : with low feed rate
P_{30}			Steel, steel casting, malleable cast iron forming long chips	Turning, planning, milling. Cutting speed : medium to low. Feed : medium to high even if operating conditions are unfavourable
P_{40}			Steel, steel casting with stand inclusions or shrinkage cavities	Turning, planing, shaping. Cutting speed : low, Feed : high. Rake angle : high for machining under favourable conditions and work on automatic machines
P_{50}			Steel, steel castings of medium or low tensile strength with sand inclusions or shrinkage cavities	Turning, planning, shaping. Cutting speed : low. Feed : high Rake angle large for machining under unfavourable conditions and work on automatic machines
M_{10}	Resistance to wear	Toughness — Cutting speed — feed	Steel, steel casting, manganese steel, grey cast iron, alloyed cast iron	Turning. Cutting speed : mediuum to high. Feed : low to medium
M_{20}			Steel, steel casting, austenitic steel, manganese steel, grey cast iron, sphrodised cast iron and malleable cast iron	Turning, milling, Cutting speed : medium Feed : medium
M_{30}			Steel, steel casting, austenitic steel, grey cast iron, heat resisting alloys	Turning, milling, planing. Cutting speed : medium Feed : medium or high
M_{40}			Free cutting steel, low tensile strength steel, brass and light alloy	Turning, profile turning, parting off especially in automatic machines
K_{01}	Resistance to wear	Toughness — Cutting speed — feed	Very hard grey cast iron, chilled casting of hardness up to 60 HRC. Alluminium alloys with high silicon content, hardened steel, plastics of abrasive type, hard board and cermics	Turning, precision turning and boring, milling, scraping
K_{10}			Grey cast iron of hardness more than 220 HB, malleable cast iron forming short chips, tempered steel, aluminium alloys containing silicon, copper alloys, plastics, glass, hard rubber, hard cardboard, porcelain, stone	Turning, milling, boring, reaming, broaching, scraping
K_{20}			Grey cast iron of hardness up to 220 HB, non-ferrous metals, such as copper, brass, aluminium, laminated wood of abrasive type	Turning, milling, planing, reaming, broaching
K_{30}			Soft grey cast iron, low tensile strength steel laminated wood	Turning, planing, shaping, milling. rakeangle large. even under unfavourable conditions
K_{40}			Soft or hard natural wood, nonferrous metals	Turning, milling, planing, shaping. Rakeangle : large, even under unfavourable maching conditions

C. Super-Alloys : Super-alloys are those materials which, under stressed conditions, can with stand high temperatures (600 to 1100°C). Thus, these materials do not loose their strength at high temperature. There are three types of Super-alloys :

1. Iron-Based
2. Ni-Based
3. Co-Based

All the three have Cr as one of major constituents, Its main function are : it aids in Carbide formation and also imparts Corrosion-Resistance properties to the alloys. Super-alloys have major fields of application in Aero-gas turbines and Nuclear Reactors, Ni-based super alloys are widely used in the manufacture of turbine disks for turbo-jet engine applications. The nominal compositions of these super-alloys are given in a table I.3.

D. Specifications of Manufacturing Equipment :

1. **Foundry :**
(a) Moulding Machines : Pressure, Mould box size, Pressing cylinder φ
(b) Die-Casting Machines : Job weight, Tonnage (Locking Force).
(c) Centrifugal Casting Machines :–
    (i) Bush Casting Machines   : Bush φ × Bush length..
    (ii) Water-pipe   "   "   : Pipe φ.
    (iii) Canal-pipe   "   "   : Pipe φ

2. **Metal Forming Equipment :**

(a) **Forging and Stamping Machines**   :
    Forging Machines (Heading and Upsetting)   :   Job φ
    Swaging M achines   :   Tube φ
    Roll Forming Machines   :   Tonnage
    Stamping Machines :   :   Plate Thickness

(b) **Bending and Forming Machines :**
    (i) Bending Rolls (Pipes/Bars/Shapes/Angles)   :   Plate thickness
    (ii) Rotary head and Ram type Bending Machines
        (Pipes/Bars/Shapes/Angles)   :   Section size
    (iii) Folding and Bending/Angles)   :   Bend length
    (iv) Flattening and Straightening Machines   :   Plate thickness
    (v) Press Brakes   :   Tonnage

(c) **Punching and Shearing Machines**   :
    (i) Punching Machines   :   Plate thickness
    (ii) Guillotine Shearing Machines   :   Plate thickness
    (iii) Shearing and Cropping Machines   :   Section size
    (iv) Rotary Shears   :   Plate thickness
    (v) Combination Punching, Shearing,
        Notching and Cropping Machines   :   Plate thickness
    (vi) Gang slitting Machines
    (vii) Nibbling Machines   :   Plate Thickns.
    (vii) Slab, Ingot and Billet Shearing Machines   :   Job size

(d) **Drawing Machines :**
    (i) Wire and Metal Ribbon drawing Machines   :   Wire φ
    (ii) Tube and Bar drawing Machines   :   Tube φ / Bar φ

(e) **Other Metal Forming Machines :**
    (i) Spring manufacturing machines   :   Wire φ
    (ii) Chain making machines   :   Chain size
    (iii) Container making machines   :   Job size
    (iv) Wire/Rope/Cable making machines   :   Job size

Table I.3: Super-Alloys

Alloy	C	Mn	Cr	Ni	Mo	Ti	Al	W	Fe	Co
Iron-Based										
A—286	0.08	1.35	15	26	1.25	2	—	—	54	—
V–57	"	0.25	15	25.5	"	3	—	—	64	—
19-9DL	0.30	1.10	19	9	"	0.3	—	—	68	—
16-25-6	0.06	1.35	16	25	6	—	—	—	51	—
Ni-Based										
Hastelloy										
R-235	0.10	0.25	16	61.25	5.5	2.5	2	—	10	1.9
Inconel										
X-750	0.04	0.5	15	73	—	2.4	0.6	—	0.6	0.4
Udimet–500	0.09	—	19	52	4	3	2.8	—	2	17
Waspaloy	0.06	0.5	19.5	57.25	4.2	3	1.2	—	1	13.5
Co-Based										
J-1570	0.2	—	20	28	—	4	—	7	2	39
S-816	0.38	—	20	20	4	—	—	4	4	44

Nominal Composition, %

(v)	Nails/Rivets making machines	:	Job size
(vi)	Needles and Pins making machines	:	Wire ϕ
(vii)	Special nut and bolt forming machines	:	Thread ϕ

3. Joining and Assembly Equipment :

(i)	Gas welding machines	:	Tip size
(ii)	Electric arc welding machines	:	kVA
(iii)	Plasma arc welding machines	:	kVA
(iv)	Resistance welding machines	:	kVA
(v)	Friction welding machines	:	kVA
(vi)	Ultrasonic Welding machines	:	W
(vii)	Electron-Beam welding machines	:	kW
(viii)	Laser-Beam welding machines	:	W
(ix)	Brazing and Soldering machines	:	kVA

4. Machine Tools :

(a) Lathes

(i)	Copying lathes; Multi-tool and production lathes; crankshaf lathes; Relieving lathes; wheel and Axle lathes; Flow turning lathes and spinning lathes.	:	Swing ϕ
(ii)	Roll turning lathes	:	Swing ϕ, Job weight
(iii)	Diamond turning lathes	:	Swing ϕ
(iv)	Facing and Boring lathes	:	Face plate (work table) ϕ or Swing ϕ
(v)	Capstan lathes, Turret lathes	:	Swing ϕ
(vi)	Vertical turning and Boring mills	:	Swing ϕ
(vii)	Automats, Single spindle, Bar type, Horizontal, Sliding head (Swiss type) and others	:	Bar ϕ
(viii)	Automats, Multi-spindle, Bar type (Hor., Vert.)	:	Bar ϕ
(ix)	Automats, Chucking type (Single-spindle/ Multi-spindle; Hor./Vert.)	:	Chucking ϕ

(b) Planner :

	Plate edge Planner	:	Tool travel

(c) Rifling Machines :   :   Stroke

(d) Drilling Machines :

(i)	Deep hole (including gun drilling) :	Drill ϕ, Drill length
(ii)	Facing and Centering	:	Job ϕ

(e) Milling Machines :

(i)	Pantograph milling machines	:	Table size
(ii)	Plano-milling	:	Table width

(f) Grinding Machines :

(i)	Slideway grinders	:	Table size
(ii)	Tool and cutter grinders	:	Wheel ϕ
(iii)	Grinders, Drill point sharpening	:	Drill ϕ
(iv)	Grinders, Tap sharpening	:	Tap ϕ
(v)	Grinders, Broach sharpening	:	Broach ϕ, Broach length

(vi)	Grinders, Circular saw sharpening	:	Saw ϕ
(vii)	Grinders, Band saw blade sharpening	:	Module, Hob ϕ
(viii)	Grinders, Hob sharpening	:	Module, Hob ϕ
(ix)	Spline grinders	:	Job length
(x)	Jig grinders	:	Bore ϕ
(xi)	Abrasiver band grinders	:	Band width
(xii)	Centre grinders	:	Job ϕ, Job length
(xiii)	Bearing raceway grinders (exit., int.)	:	Job ϕ
(xiv)	Grinders (Brake drum, Piston)	:	Job ϕ
(xv)	Polygon grinders	:	Job ϕ
(xvi)	Duplex grinders	:	Wheel ϕ
(xvii)	Grinders (Form, Profile, Valve seat,		
	Bench, Wing frame	:	Wheel ϕ

Note :- The main specifications of the conventional and more commonly used **Manufactur**ing machines/equipment and Machine tools, have been given at appropriate places in the **text.**

APPENDIX—II

Machining Variables and Related Relations :

As already discussed under Art 6.6, the three machining elements of any machining process are : feed, f (mm/rev.), depth of cut, d (mm), and cutting speed, V (m/min.).

1. **Lathes.** Refer to Art. 6.6 and Fig. 6.13.

$$V = \frac{\pi\, DN}{1000}, \text{m/min} \qquad \qquad \dots (1)$$

Area of Uncut Chip : The cross-sectional area, Ac, of the layer of the work material being removed is

$$A_C = \text{width of chip} \times \text{thickness of uncut chip.}$$
$$= b \times t$$

Now if C_s = side cutting edge angle, then

$$b = \frac{d}{\text{Cos}\, C_s} \text{ and } t = f\, \text{Cos}\, C_s$$

$$\therefore \qquad b \times t = f.d\ \text{mm}^2$$

∴ Metal removal rate, (MRR) is given as

$$\text{MRR} = \pi.D.A_c.N\ \text{mm}^3/\text{min}$$

$$\therefore \qquad \text{MRR} = 1000\, A_c.\text{V mm}^3/\text{min} \dots \text{(From Equation .1}^{\cdot}$$

$$= 1000\ \text{fdV, mm}^3/\text{min}$$

Machining Time : The machining time is given as,

$$T_m = \frac{L}{fN}\ \text{min, per pass (cut)}$$

where $\quad L$ = Total length of travel of the tool or of the workpiece

$\qquad$ = (Length of surface to be machined) + (Tool approach) + (Tool overtravel)

Tool approach = Distance a tool is fed from the time it touches the workpiece, until it is cutting to the full depth.

Tool overtravel = Distance a tool is fed, while it is not cutting.

It is the distance over which the tool idles, before it enters and after it leaves the cut.

Approach of most of the single point cutting tools is negligible. Refer to Fig. II.1.

$$L = l + x + y$$

where $\qquad\qquad x$ = Tool approach = $d \tan C_s$ or $d\, Cot\, \lambda$ mm

$\qquad\qquad\qquad y$ = Tool overtravel = 1 to 2 mm

$\qquad\qquad\qquad \lambda$ = Tool approach angle = $90 - C_s$

For facing operation,

$$L = D/2 + x + y, \text{mm}$$

Now, Total machining time = $T_m \times i$

where i = number of passes or cuts = $\dfrac{\text{Total machining allowance}}{\text{Material removed per cut}}$

Now, total machining allowance = $\dfrac{D_i - D_f}{2}$, for turning and = $\dfrac{D_f - D_i}{2}$, for boring

where $\qquad\qquad\qquad D_i$ = initial diameter of the workpiece

$\qquad\qquad\qquad\qquad D_f$ = finished diameter of the workpiece

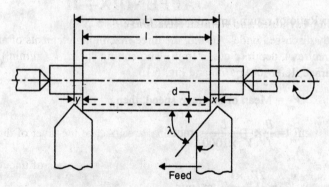

Fig. II.1. Turning Operation.

Material removed per cut = Depth of cut,

Depth of cut is half the difference between the work diameter at the start of the cut and the diameter of machined surface obtained after the cut.

$$\therefore \qquad d = \frac{\text{Total machining allowance}}{i}$$

In practice, the depth of cut per pass is not constant. For roughing operations, it is much greater than for the finishing operations.

2. Shapers, Planers, Slotters : Refer to art. 8.2.4.,

$$\text{MRR} = f.d.L.N, \text{ mm}^3/\text{min}$$

Here,
$\qquad L$ = Length of the workpiece, mm

$\qquad N$ = Number of the complete strokes /min.

$\qquad f$ = feed, mm/stroke

Machining Time,
$$T_m = \frac{B+x+y}{f\,N}, \text{min}.$$

$\qquad B$ = Width of the machined surface

$\qquad x$ = Side approach of the tool = d cot λ

$\qquad y$ = Side over travel of the tool = 2 to 3 mm.

Another Method of Calculating the Machining Time

$$T_m = \frac{B}{f}\left(\frac{L}{V_w \times 1000} + \frac{L}{V_r \times 1000}\right), \text{min}$$

where L = Length of stroke (for Shaper) or length of Table travel (for Planer), mm

$\qquad$ = Length of workpiece + Approach + Overtravel

$\qquad V_w$ = working stroke speed or cutting speed, m/min

$\qquad V_r$ = Return stroke speed, m/min; See Fig. 8.38

$\qquad B$ = Width of job, mm

$\qquad f$ = Cross-feed per full stroke of table (For Shaper) and of tool head (for Planer), mm.

V_w can be determined as,

$$V_w = \text{Cutting speed} = \frac{L \times N \times (1+K)}{1000}, \text{m/min}.$$

V_w is 'V' as under Art. 8.2.4.

where N = Number of full (double) strokes/min, that is, working plus return strokes

$$K = \text{Ratio of return time to cutting time, or } = \frac{V_w}{V_r}$$

On an average, $K = \frac{2}{3}$ to $\frac{3}{4}$

Now, if $\quad V_m = $ Mean or Average speed, then

$$T_m = \frac{B}{f} \times \frac{2L}{V_m \times 1000}, \text{min}.$$

V_m is given as, $V_m = \dfrac{2V_w \times V_r}{V_w + V_r}, \text{m/min}.$

3. Drilling :

Cutting speed, $V = \dfrac{\pi DN}{1000}, \text{m/min}$

Here $D = $ Drill diameter, mm
            $N = $ rotational speed of the drill, / min

$$\text{MRR} = \frac{\pi D^2}{4} \cdot f.N, \text{mm}^3 / \text{min}$$

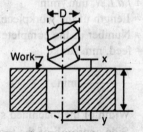

Fig. II.2. Drilling Operation.

Machining time, $\quad T_m = \dfrac{L}{fN} = \dfrac{l+x+y}{fN}, \text{min}.$

where $l = $ hole length or depth, mm (Fig. II.2)
                 $x = $ Tool approach, 0.29D (with point angle of 118°)
                 $y = $ Tool over travel, 1 to 2 mm

4. Milling : See Art. 8.5.6.,

(a) Peripheral Milling : See Fig. 8.62(a),
                 $\text{MRR} = b.d.F \text{ mm}^3/\text{min}$

where $b = $ cutting edge engagement = width of job
                 $d = $ depth of cut
                 $F = $ table feed, mm/min.
Now $F = f \text{ (mm/rev of cutter)} \times N = f_t \times n \times N, \text{mm/min}.$
                 $f_t = $ feed per tooth, per rev., mm.
                 $n = $ number of teeth in the cutter

Machining time, $\quad T_m = \dfrac{l+x+y}{F}, \text{min}$

                 $l = $ length of job

where, x = cutter approach
                                y = over travel = 1 to 5 mm

x is given as :

$$x = \sqrt{d\,(D-d)}\;\;\text{[See Fig. I.3 (a)]}.$$

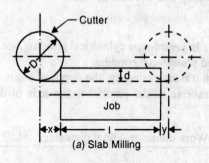

(a) Slab Milling

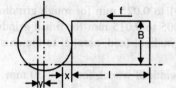

(b) Face Milling
Fig. II.3. Milling Operaton.

(b) **Face Milling :**
For face milling, the tool approach is given as, [Fig. II.3 (b)]

$$x = 0.5\left(D - \sqrt{D^2 - B^2}\right)$$

B is the width of the job.

5. **Broaching:** The cross - sectional area, Ac, of uncut chip per tooth is

$$A_c = f_z\,b\;\text{mm}^2\;\text{for a keyway broach}$$

$$= f_z.b.n.\;\text{mm}^2,\;\text{for a multiple-Spline"} = f_z.\pi.D,\;\text{mm}^2\;\text{for a round broach}$$

where f_z = cut per tooth mm
      = Difference in height between two successive cutting teeth
  b = width of broach
  n = number of splines
  D = diameter of round broach, mm
MRR/pass = MRR/tooth × z
∴ MRR/tooth = $1000.A_c.V.$ mm³/min
  Where z = number of teeth simultaneously in operation.

Machining time, $T_m = \dfrac{l_w + l_b}{V}$

where l_w = Length of workpiece
           l_b = Length of broach
However, machining time per piece

$$T = \frac{L}{1000\,V} + \frac{L}{1000\,V_r}$$

where L = Length of stroke, mm

                               V_r = Return velocity of broach.

or $$T = \frac{L}{1000\,V}k.$$

where k = Co-efficient, taking into account the ratio of working and return stroke speeds = 1.4 to 1.5

6. Grinding :

(*a*) **Cylindrical grinding :** In centre-type cylindrical grinding, we have two types of grinding operations; traverse grinding and plunge-cut grinding.

(*i*) **Traverse grinding :** In traverse grinding, the depth of cut is the layer of metal removed by the grinding wheel in one traverse stroke parallel to the axis of the job. It is also called "in feed". So, depth of cut is,

$$d = \frac{\text{Work diameter} - \text{final diameter}}{2} = \frac{D_w - D_f}{2}$$

where d = 0.01 to 0.025 mm for rough grinding

                               = 0.005 to 0.015 mm for finish grinding

The traverse feed is the longitudinal feed, parallel to the axis of the job, mm/rev for rough grinding,

$$f = '(0.3 \text{ to } 0.5) \text{ width of wheel, for } D_w < 20 \text{ mm}$$

$$= (0.7 \text{ to } 0.85 \text{ width of wheel, for } D_w \geq 20 \text{ mm}$$

For finish grinding, f = (0.2 to 0.4) + width of wheel. Table traverse will be,

$$f_t = f.Nw, \text{ mm/min}$$

where N_w = work speed, rev/min.

Peripheral speed of work,

$$V_w = \frac{\pi D_w N_w}{1000}, \text{ m/min}$$

Peripheral Speed of the Wheel (Cutting speed),

$$V_g = \frac{\pi D_g N_g}{1000}$$

where D_g = grinding wheel diameter, mm

                               N_g = grinding wheel speed, rev/min.

When the work and the wheel rotate in opposite direction to each other, the cutting speed can be taken as,

$$V = V_g + V_w$$

Metal Removal Rate : It can be taken approximately as

$$\text{MRR} = \pi\, d\, D_w\, f.N_w, \text{ mm}^3/\text{min}$$

Machining Time :

$$T_m = \frac{L}{f\,N_w} \times i \times k, \text{ min}$$

i = number of passes

$$= \frac{\text{machining allowance on each side}}{\text{depth of cut (infeed)}}$$

k = sparking out factor

This factor takes into account the removal of metal even in passes in which there is no infeed. This occurs due to: the springing of the work, non-uniform wear of the wheel, breaking out of grains and the absence of continuous cutting edge. All this leads to an increase in machining time.

k is about 1.2 for rough grinding, and = 1.4 for finish grinding

(*ii*) **Plunge- cut Grinding :**

$$MRR = \pi D_w.B_g.f_p \ mm^3/min$$

where
B_g = wheel width
f_p = rate of radial feed, mm/min.

Machining time, $T_m = \dfrac{\text{Machining allowance}}{f_p}$

$$f_p = f \times N_w, f \text{ is in mm/rev.}$$

(*b*) **Surface grinding :**

Cutting speed,
$$V = \frac{\pi D_g N_g}{1000}, \ m/min$$

$$MRR = fp.d f_t$$

where
f_p = cross-feed per stroke, mm/stroke
f_t = table traverse rate, mm/min
d = depth of cut per pass.

Machining time
$$T_m = \frac{L.B}{V.1000.f_p} i.k.$$

Where
L = Length of workpiece to be ground
B = Width of workpiece to be ground
V = Traverse Velocity of table, m/min.
f_p = Crossfeed of grinding wheel, mm/stroke

SOLVED EXAMPLES

Example II.1: *A workpiece of 76 mm diameter is to be machined on a lathe to 68 mm diameter. The total length of the workpiece is 250 mm. The recommended values of the machining elements are : feed = 0.25 mm/rev, a cutting speed of 60 mpm, and a maximum depth of cut of 2.5 mm. How long will it take to finish, the part? Also, determine the metal removal rate.*

Solution : The machining time is given as,

$$T_m = \frac{L}{f \times N} \times i, min.$$

where,
$L = l + x + y$
x = Tool approach $= d \cot \lambda$

Now
$d = 2.5$ mm, Let $\lambda = 75°$ ($C_s = 15$ to $30°$)

$\therefore$
$x = 2.5 \cot 75° = 0.67$ mm
y = over travel = 2mm (say)
$f = 0.25$ mm/rev.

$$N = \frac{1000\,V}{\pi D} = \frac{1000 \times 60}{\pi \times 76} = 251 \ rev./min.$$

$$i = \frac{76-68}{2\times 2.5} = 2$$

$$\therefore \qquad T_m = \frac{250+0.67+2}{0.25\times 251}\times 2 = \textbf{8.05 min.}$$

$$\text{MRR} = 1000\, f\, d\, V$$
$$= 1000 \times 0.25 \times 2.5 \times 60 = \textbf{37.5} \times \textbf{10}^3\ \textbf{mm}^3\textbf{/min.}$$

Example II.2 : *A part of 25cm in diameter and 50 cm length is to be turned down to 23.5 cm for the entire length. The suggested feed is 1 mm per rev. and the cutting speed is 135 mpm. The maximum allowable depth of cut is 5.0 mm. What are the feed speed, spindle rpm, MRR, and cutting time. Assume the over travel is 12.5mm.*

Solution : Spindle rpm, $= \dfrac{1000\, V}{\pi\, D}$

$$= \frac{1000\times 135}{\pi\, D} = 172\ \text{rev./min.}$$

$$\text{feed speed} = f \times N = 1 \times 172 = 172\ \text{mm/min.}$$
$$\text{MRR} = 1000\, .\, f\, .\, d\, .\, V = 1000 \times 1 \times 5 \times 135 = \textbf{67.5} \times \textbf{10}^4\ \textbf{mm}^3\textbf{/min.}$$

Cutting time, $T_m = \dfrac{L}{f\, N}\times i$

Here, $i = \dfrac{250-235}{2\times 5} = 2$

and $L = 500 + 12.5 = 512.5\ \text{mm}$

$$\therefore \qquad T_m = \frac{512.5}{172}\times 2 = \textbf{5.96 min}$$

Example II.3 : *A hole of 25 mm diameter and 62.5 mm depth is to be drilled. The suggested feed is 1.25 mm per rev. and the cutting speed is 60 mpm. What are the feed speed, spindle rpm, and cutting time. Assume the clearance height is 5 mm. Also find the MRR.*

Solution : Spindle rpm, $N = \dfrac{1000\, V}{\pi\, D}$

$$= \frac{1000\times 60}{\pi\times 25} = 764\ \textbf{rev./min}$$

$$\text{feed speed} = f\, N = 1.25 \times 764 = \textbf{955 mm/min.}$$

Cutting time $= \dfrac{L}{f\, N}$

Now $L = 62.5 + 5 = 67.5\ \text{mm.}$

$$\therefore \qquad T_m = \frac{67.5}{955} = \textbf{0.0707 min}.$$

$$\text{MRR} = \frac{\pi\, D^2}{4}\, f \times N = \frac{\pi\times 625}{4}\times 955 = \textbf{46.8974}\times \textbf{10}^4\ \textbf{mm}^3\textbf{/min.}$$

Example II.4 : A 50 cm 15 cm surface of cast iron block 50 cm long 15 cm wide 10 cm thick, is to be machined on a shaper. Ram speed is 20 mpm, length of stroke is 510 mm, depth of cut is 4 mm, feed is 1.5 mm/stroke, stock to be removed is 6 mm, side cutting edge angle of the tool is 45°, ratio of time taken in return stroke to the time taken in cutting stroke is 0.5. Determine the metal removal rate and the total cutting time.

Solution: Now refer to Art. 8.2.4,

$$V = \frac{LN\,(1+K)}{1000}$$

$\therefore$
$$N = \frac{1000 \times 20}{510 \times 1.5} \cong 26. \text{ full strokes/min.}$$

$$\text{MRR} = f.\,d.\,L.\,N = 1.5 \times 4 \times 510 \times 26$$
$$= \mathbf{79.56 \times 10^3 \ mm^3/min.}$$

Cutting Time, $$T_m = \frac{B+x+y}{f\,N}$$

$$B = 150 \text{ mm}$$

$$x = d \cot \lambda = 4 \text{ mm}$$

$$y = 3 \text{mm (say)}$$

Now number of passes $= \dfrac{\text{Stock to be removed}}{\text{depth of cut}} = \dfrac{6}{4} = 2 \text{ (say)}$

$\therefore$ Total cutting time, $$T_m = \frac{150+4+3}{1.5 \times 26} \times 2 = \mathbf{8.05 \ min.}$$

Example II.5 : *Evaluate the cutting parameters for the slab milling operation for the following data: Diameter of milling cutter = 100 mm, cutter speed = 500 rpm, width of cutter = 100 mm, depth of cut = 5 mm, table feed = 100 mm/min , length of workpiece = 50 cm, width of workpiece = 80 mm, number of teeth in the cutter = 8,*

Solution : Cutter diameter = 100 mm. Cutter speed   = 500 rpm.

Cutting speed, $$V = \frac{\pi\,DN}{1000} = \frac{\pi \times 100 \times 500}{1000} = 157 \text{ m / min}$$

$$\text{MRR} = b.\,d.\,F$$

where
$$b = \text{width of job} = 80 \text{ mm}$$
$$d = \text{depth of cut} = 5 \text{ mm}$$
$$F = \text{Table feed} = 100 \text{ mm/min.}$$

Machining time, $$T_m = \frac{l+x+y}{F}$$

Here
$$l = 500 \text{ mm.}$$
$$y = 4 \text{ mm (say)}$$
$$x = \sqrt{d\,(D-d)} = \sqrt{5 \times 95} = 21.8 \text{ mm.}$$

$$T_m = \frac{500 + 21.8 + 4}{100} = 5.258 \text{ min.}$$

Example II.6 : *Determine the machining parameters for the broaching operation from the following date; cutting speed = 12 m/min., return speed of broach = 25 m/min., length of workpiece*

= 200 mm, length of broach = 300 mm, length of stroke = 600 mm, width of workpiece = 10 mm, rise per tooth = 0.10 mm.

Solution: $MRR = 1000 \, fz \cdot b \cdot V$

$$f_z = \text{cut per tooth} = 0.10 \text{ mm}$$
$$b = \text{width of contact} = 10 \text{ mm}$$
$$V = 12 \text{ m/min}$$

$\therefore$ $MRR/\text{tooth} = 0.10 \times 10 \times 1000 \times 12 = 12000 \text{ mm}^3/\text{min}.$

Machining time, $T_m = \dfrac{l_w + l_b}{V}$

$$l_w = 200 \text{ mm}, l_b = 300 \text{ mm}$$

$\therefore$ $T_m = \dfrac{200 + 300}{12 \times 1000} = 0.042 \text{ min}.$

Machining time per piece $= \dfrac{L}{1000 \, V} + \dfrac{L}{1000 \, V_r}$

Now $L = 600$ mm, $V_r = 25$ m/min.

$\therefore$ $\text{Time} = \dfrac{600}{1000 \times 12} + \dfrac{600}{1000 \times 25} = \mathbf{0.074 \, min}.$

Example II.7 : *Determine the machining parameters for the rough grinding of medium steel shaft from the following date : Work diameter = 38 mm, length of part = 200 mm, Total stock = 0.25 mm, grinding wheel = 50 mm face, depth of cut = 0.025 mm, cutting speed = 15 m/min.*

Solution : Now $Dw = 38$ mm

$\therefore$ $f = \text{feed /rev.} = (0.7 \text{ to } 0.85) \times \text{width of wheel}$

Width of wheel = 50 mm

$\therefore$ $f = 0.8 \times 50 = 40$ mm.

Number of cuts $i = \dfrac{\text{Total stock}}{\text{Depth of cut per pass}} = \dfrac{0.25}{0.025} = 10$

Wheel speed $= \dfrac{1000 \, V}{\pi \, D_w} = \dfrac{1000 \times 15}{\pi \times 38} = 125 \text{ rev./min}.$

$\therefore$ $T_m = \dfrac{L}{f \, N_w} \times i \times k = \dfrac{200}{40 \times 125} \times 10 \times 1.1 = \mathbf{0.44 \, min}.$

Example II.8. A workpiece 200 mm × 300 mm is to be machined on a shaper. Calculate the machining time. Take,

$V_w = 10$ m/min, $Vr = 20$ m/min, $f = 5$ mm/full stroke, min clearance of each end = 50 mm.

Solution: $B = 200$ mm

$L = 300 + 2 \times 50 = 400$ mm

$\therefore$ $T_m = \dfrac{B}{f}\left(\dfrac{L}{V_w \times 1000} + \dfrac{L}{V_r \times 1000} \right)$

$= \dfrac{200}{5} \times \left(\dfrac{400}{10 \times 1000} + \dfrac{400}{20 \times 1000} \right)$

$= \mathbf{2.4 \, min}.$

Now Average speed,

$$V_m = \frac{2 \times V_w \times V_r}{V_w + V_r} = \frac{2 \times 10 \times 20}{10 + 20} = \frac{40}{3} \text{ m/min}$$

$$\therefore \quad T_m = \frac{B}{f} \times \frac{2L}{V_m \times 1000}$$

$$= \frac{200}{5} \times \frac{2 \times 400 \times 3}{40 \times 1000}$$

$$= \textbf{2.4 min.}$$

Example II.9. A plain surface, width = 100 mm and length = 320 mm is to be face-milled on a vertical milling machine. The milling allowance is 4 mm. The cutter has 16 teeth and the feed per tooth is 0.25 mm. The spindle speed is 125 rev./min. Calculate the machining time. Diameter of cutter = 160 mm.

Solution. $\qquad T_m = \frac{l + x + y}{F}$, min.

Where $\qquad l$ = length of job = 320 mm

x = cutter approach or Added table travel

$$= 0.5 \, (D - \sqrt{D^2 - B^2})$$

$$= 0.5(160 - \sqrt{160^2 - 100^2}) = 17.5 \text{ mm}$$

Let $\qquad y$ = over travel be = 3 mm.

F = Table feed per min, mm/min.

= Feed per tooth per rev. (mm)

$\qquad\qquad$ × number of teeth in cutter × spindle revolution min.

$$= 0.25 \times 16 \times 125 = 500 \text{ mm/min.}$$

$$\therefore \quad T_m = \frac{320 + 17.5 + 3}{500} = \textbf{0.68 min.}$$

Example II.10. The top surface of a slab, 520 mm wide and 4000 mm long is to be planed on a planer. Take cutting speed as 18.8 m/min. and return speed as 75 m/min. Take machining allowance as 10 mm. the tool approach angle is 45°. Calculate the machining time. Cross feed of tool = 3 mm/full stroke.

Solution. Refer Art. 8.2.4., the cutting speed or working speed is given as,

$$V = \frac{LN(1 + K)}{1000}, \text{ m/min}$$

Where $\qquad L$ = Length of table stroke (for planer)

= length of job + table overtravel on both sides

= 4000 + 325 (say) = 4325 mm.

N = Number of full strokes/min

$$K = \frac{\text{Return time}}{\text{Cutting time}} = \frac{\text{Cutting speed}}{\text{Return speed}}$$

$$= \frac{18.8}{75} \cong 0.25$$

$$\therefore \quad N = \frac{1000 \times 18.8}{4325(1.25)} = 3.5$$

Now, Cutting time, $T_m = \dfrac{B + x + y}{fN}$

B = Width of job = 520 mm

x = Side approach of tool = $d \cot \lambda$

    = 10. $\cot 45°$ = 10 mm

y = Side overtravel of tool = 2 to 3 mm, Take 3 mm

∴ $T_m = \dfrac{520 + 10 + 3}{3 \times 3.5} = \textbf{51.7 min.}$

Example II.11. A premachined cylindrical bore 55 mm in diameter and length 62 mm is to be broached on a horizontal broaching machine. Overall length of broach is 570 mm and shank length of broach is 265 mm. Cutting speed is 8 m/min. and return speed is 20 m/min. Take tool overtravel as 50 mm. Determine the broaching time.

Solution. $T_m = \dfrac{L}{1000V} \cdot k$

$k = 1 + \dfrac{V}{V_r} = 1 + \dfrac{8}{20} = 1.4$

L = Length of stroke

  = Length of working part of broach + length of job

                                                          + tool overtravel

  = (570 − 265) + 62 + 50 = 417 mm

∴ $T_m = \dfrac{417}{1000 \times 8} \times 1.4 = \textbf{0.073 min}$

Example II.12. A shaft of length, 210 mm and 40 mm in diameter is to be longitudinally ground in one pass on a cylindrical grinding machine. The allowance per side is 0.2 mm. Wheel diameter is 600 mm and its width is 63 mm. Cutting speed is 35 m/min. Determine the grinding time.

Solution. $T_m = \dfrac{L}{f \cdot N_w} \cdot i \cdot k$

L = Length of table stroke

  = Length of workpiece + wheel overtravel on each side

  = $210 + 2 \times 0.5\, B_g$

Now, B_g = 63 mm (width of grinding wheel)

∴ L = 273 mm

N_w = Work speed = $\dfrac{1000 V_w}{\pi D_w} = \dfrac{1000 \times 35}{\pi \times 40} = 280$ rpm

f = traverse feed, mm/rev.

  = (0.2 to 0.4) × B_g for finish grinding

  = $0.3 \times 63 = 18.9$ mm/rev.

i = number of passes

  = $\dfrac{\text{machining allowance on each side}}{\text{depth of cut (infeed)}}$

For finish grinding, depth of cut = 0.005 to 0.015 mm

  = 0.005 mm (say)

$$\therefore \qquad i = \frac{0.2}{0.005} = 40$$

Let $\qquad k = 1.4$

$$\therefore \qquad T_m = \frac{273}{18.9 \times 280} \times 40 \times 1.4$$
$$= 2.89 \text{ min.}$$

Example II.13. A flat surface of a workpiece is to be ground, workpiece width is 110 mm and length is 280 mm. Machining allowance per side = 0.35 mm. Traverse velocity of table is 16 m/min. Downward feed of the grinding wheel (depth of cut) per pass is 0.015 mm per reverse of the grinding wheel. Cross feed of grinding wheel = 32 mm/table stroke. Determine the total machining time.

Solution. $\qquad T_m = \frac{L.B}{1000.V.f_p}.i.k$

$$L = 280 \text{ mm}$$
$$B = 110 \text{ mm}$$
$$V = 16 \text{ m/min}$$
$$f_p = 32 \text{ mm/table stroke}$$
$$i = \text{number of pass}$$
$$= \frac{0.35}{0.015}$$
$$k = 1.4 \text{ (say)}$$

$$\therefore \qquad T_m = \frac{280 \times 110}{1000 \times 16 \times 32} \times \frac{0.35}{0.015} \times 1.4$$
$$= 1.965 \text{ min.}$$

PROBLEMS

1. A 100 mm diameter brass bar of 250 mm length is to be turned to a new diameter of 99.75 mm.
   (a) Determine the rpm setting for the lathe
   (b) Determine the cutting time assuming an allowance of 6.25 mm
   (c) Determine the metal removal rate
   Take cutting speed = 150 mpm and feed = 0.25 mm/rev.
2. A 19 mm diameter hole is to be drilled in a piece of C-20 steel of thickness 25 mm. Taking cutting speed as 400 rev/min. and feed as 0.50 mm/rev.
   (a) Calculate the cutting speed in mpm.
   (b) Determine the machining time assuming an allowance of 12.5 mm.
   (c) Determine the metal removal rate
3. A 100 mm diameter aluminium bar of 300 mm length is to be turned to a new diameter with a speed of 157.5 mpm, feed of 0.50 mm/rev. and 0.75 mm depth of cut.
   (a) Determine the rpm to be set on the machine tool.
   (b) Determine the machining time assuming an allowance of 6.25 mm.
   (c) Determine the metal removal rate.
4. A slot 6.25 mm wide and 6.25 mm deep is to be milled in one pass in a component. The component is 450 mm long and milled with a 150 mm diameter, 10-tooth cutter. Take cutting speed = 45 mpm and feed = 0.125 mm/tooth
   (a) Determine the rpm setting.
   (b) Determine the feed rate in mm/min.
   (c) Calculate the machining time by taking allowance equal to one cutter diameter.
   (d) Calculate the metal removal rate.

5. A 63.5 mm diameter plain milling cutter having 6 teeth is used to facemill a block of aluminium 18 cm long and 3 cm wide. The spindle speed is 1500 rpm and the feed is 0.125 mm/tooth/rev.

(a) Determine the table feed in mm/min.

(b) Total table travel.

(c) Cutting time.

6. Calculate the time required on the shaper to complete one cut on a plate 600 mm × 900 mm, if the cutting speed is 6 m/min. The return time to cutting time ratio is 1 : 4, and the feed is 2 mm/stroke. The clearance at each end is 75 mm.

7. Determine the machining time for one pass longitudinal turning of a shaft from 70 mm to 64 mm over a length of 200 mm. The speed of lathe spindle is 600 rev./min. Tool feed is 0.4 mm/rev. and plan approach angle of tool is 45°.   **[Ans. 0.85 min.]**

8. Determine the machining time in facing a workpiece of 165 mm diameter on a lathe in one pass. The speed of the spindle is 480 rev/min. and tool feed is 0.3 mm/rev. Machining allowance is 3.5 mm and plan approach angle of tool is 45°.   **[Ans. 0.61 min]**

9. A surface 90 mm wide and 200 mm long is machined on a Shaper. The machining allowance is 2 mm. Take: Cutting speed = 23.8 m/min. Ratio of cutting speed to return speed = 0.8, cross-feed of table = 0.6 mm/full stroke, tool overtravel on each side as 25 mm, plan approach angle of the tool = 45°.

         [Ans. 2.95 min.]

10. A through hole of diameter 20 mm is to be drilled to a depth of 80 mm on a vertical drilling machine. Take cutting speed as 22.3 m/min. and drill feed as 0.4 mm/rev.   **[Ans. 0.62 min.]**

11. A plain surface 70 mm wide and 600 mm long is to be face milled on a vertical-spindle milling machine. The machining allowance is 3.7 mm, to be removed in one pass. cutter diameter is 110 mm and the cutting speed is 172.7 m/min. Number of teeth on the cutter is 4 and the feed is 0.2 mm/tooth/rev. Find the machining time.   **[Ans. 1.54 min.]**

12. A plain surface 100 mm wide and 320 mm long is to be face milled on a vertical milling machine. Cutter diameter is 160 mm and number of cutter teeth is 16. Cutting speed is 63 m/min. Feed per tooth is 0.25 mm/tooth. Determine the machining time.   **[Ans. 0.68 min.]**

13. The peripheral milling of a plain surface, 75 mm wide and 300 mm long is carried out on the horizontal milling machine. Cutter diameter is 90 mm, cutting speed is 28.3 m/min, Number of cutter teeth is 8 and feed per tooth is 0.2 mm. The machining allowance is 3 mm to be removed in a single pass. Determine the machining time.   **[Ans. 1.98 min]**

14. A plain surface 65 mm wide and 225 mm long is to be machined on a horizontal milling machine. The machining allowance is 1.5 mm. Cutter diameter is 63 mm, cutting speed is 49.5 m/min, number of cutter teeth is 14 and feed per tooth is 0.11 mm. Determine the machining time.   **[Ans. 0.59 min.]**

15. A slot 32 mm wide, 15 mm deep and 250 mm is to be rough machined in a single pass by a disk-type milling cutter on a horizontal milling machine. Cutter diameter is 150 mm, cutting speed is 37.6 m/min, Number of teeth on cutter is 16 and the feed per tooth is 0.078 mm. Determine the machining time.

         [Ans. 3 min.]

16. A through slot 32 mm wide, 15 mm deep and 300 mm long is to be milled by an end mill cutter on a vertical milling machine. The cutter diameter is 32 mm and it has 6 teeth. Cutting speed is 20 m/min. and the feed per tooth is 0.083 mm/tooth. Determine the machining time.

         [Ans. 3.19 min. Hint: Take tool approach = $\dfrac{D}{2}$]

17. Determine the metal removal rate (a) Based on mean diamater (b) Based on the difference in initial and final diamter, for the turning operation for the following data: feed = 0.5 mm / rev; Spindle speed = 200 rer./min. Initial diameter = 50 mm Final Diameter = 42 mm.

Solution : Depth of cut, $d = \dfrac{D_i - D_f}{2} = \dfrac{50 - 42}{2} = 4$mm

(a)   MRR = d.f. π Dave × N

                 $= 4 \times 0.5 \times \pi \times 46 \times 200 \cong 5.78 \times 10^4$ mm^3 / min.

(b)   MRR $= \dfrac{\pi}{4}\left(50^2 - 42^2\right) \times f \times N$

                 $= \dfrac{\pi}{4}\left(50^2 - 42^2\right) \times 0.5 \times 200 = 5.78 \times 10^4$ mm^3/min

Thus, there is no difference in the two results, It is the personal choice about the method to be used.

APPENDIX III
Problems From Competitive Examinations
(GATE, IES, IAS)
CHAPTER 2

1. Match the terms used in connection with heat-treatment of steel with the microstructural/physical characteristics:

Terms	Characteristics
(A) Pearlite	(P) Extremely hard and brittle phase
(B) Martensite	(Q) Cementite is finely dispersed in ferrite
(C) Austenite	(R) Alternate layers of Cementite and Ferrite
(D) Eutectoid	(S) Can exist only above 723°C
	(T) Pertaining to state of equilibrium between three solid phases
	(U) Pertaining to state of equilibrium between one liquid and two solid phase

    (*GATE 1992*) (**Ans.** A – R, B – P, C – S, D– T)

2. The Iron–Carbon diagram and the TTT curves are determined under:
    (A) equilibrium and non-equilibrium conditions respectively
    (B) non-equilibrium and equilibrium conditions respectively
    (C) equi-librium conditions for both
    (D) non-equilibrium conditions for both   [*GATE 1996*] (**Ans.** A)

3. On completion of heat treatment, the following structure will have retained Austenite if
    (A) rate of cooling is greater than the critical cooling rate
    (B) rate of cooling is less than the critical cooling rate
    (C) martensite formation starting temperature is above the room temperature
    (D) martensite formation finish temperature is below the room temperature
    [*GATE 1997*] (**Ans.** C)

4. Cast steel crankshaft surface is hardened by
    (A) nitriding   (B) normalising   (C) carburising   (D) induction heating
    [*GATE 2000*] (**Ans.** D)

5. The alloying element mainly used to improve the endurance strength of steel materials is:
    (A) Nickle   (B) Vanadium   (C) Molybdenum   (d) Tungsten
    [*GATE 1997*] (**Ans.** B)

6. Decreasing grain size in a polycrystalline material
    (A) increases yield strength and corrosion resistance
    (B) decreases yield strength and corrosion resistance
    (C) decreases yield strength but increases corrosion resistance
    (D) increases yield strength but decreases corrosion resistance.   [*GATE 1998*] (**Ans.** A)

7. Carburised machine components have higher endurance limit, because carburization
    (A) raises the yield point of the material
    (B) produces a better surface finish
    (C) introduces a compressive layer on the surface
    (D) suppresses any stress concentration produced in the component.
    [*GATE 1992*] (**Ans.** C)

8. Match List I with List II and select the correct answer using the codes given below the lists:

List I	List II
(Mech. properties)	(Related to)
(A) Malleability	1. Wire drawing
(B) Hardness	2. Impact loads
(C) Resilience	3. Cold rolling
(D) Isotropy	4. Indentation

5. Direction

Codes.	A	B	C	D		A	B	C	D
(a)	4	2	1	3	(b)	3	4	2	5
(c)	5	4	2	3	(d)	3	2	1	5

(Ans. b) (IES 1993)

9. Match List I with List II and select the correct answer using codes given below the lists:

List I	List II
(Steel type)	(Product)
A. Mild steel	1. Screw driver
B. Tool steel	2. Commercial beams
C. Medium Carbon steel	3. Crane hooks
D. High carbon steel	4. Blanking dies

Codes.	A	B	C	D		A	B	C	D
(a)	1	4	3	2	(b)	2	4	1	3
(c)	1	3	4	2	(d)	2	4	3	1

[IES 1993] (Ans. d)

10. Which of the following statements are true of annealing of steels?
    1. Steels are heated to 500 to 700°C
    2. Cooling is done slowly and steadily
    3. Internal stresses are relieved
    4. Ductility of steel is increased

    Select the correct answer using the codes given below:

    Codes:

    (A) 2, 3 and 4   (B) 1, 3 and 4   (C) 1, 2 and 4   (D) 1, 2 and 3

    [IES 1993] (Ans. A)

11. Duralumin alloy contains aluminium and copper in the ratio of

	% Al	% Cu
(A)	94	4
(B)	90	8
(C)	98	10
(D)	86	12

    [IES 1993] (Ans. A)

12. Eutectic reaction for iron-carbon system occurs at

    (A) 600°C   (B) 723°C   (C) 1147°C   (D) 1493°C

    [IES 1993] (Ans. C)

13. The blade of a power saw is made of

    (A) boron steel   (B) high speed steel   (c) stainless steel   (D) malleable cast iron

    [IES 1993] (Ans. B)

14. Quartz is a
    (A) ferroelectric material   (B) ferromagnetic material
    (C) piezo electric material   (D) diamagnetic material **[IES 1993] (Ans. C)**

15. Match List I with List II and select the correct answer using the codes given below the lists:

List I (Material/Part)	List II (Techniques)
A. Ductile iron	1. Inoculation
B. Malleable iron	2. Chilled
C. Rail steel joints	3. Annealing
D. White cast iron	4. Thermit Welding
	5. Isothermal annealing

Codes:

	A	B	C	D		A	B	C	D
(a)	1	3	4	2	(b)	5	3	2	1
(c)	2	1	4	5	(d)	1	4	2	3

[IAS 1995] (Ans. a)

16. Consider the following treatments:
    1. Normalising
    2. Hardening
    3. Martempering
    4. Cold working
    Hardness and tensile strength in austenitic steel can be increased by
    (A) 1, 2 and 3   (B) 1 and 3   (C) 2 and 4   (D) 4 alone
                                                              [*IES 1994*] (**Ans. D**)

17. Killed steels
    (A) have minimum impurity level
    (B) have almost zero percentage of phosphorus and sulphur
    (C) are produced by LD process
    (D) are free from O_2 [*IES 1994*] (**Ans. D**)

18. Which of the following pairs are correctly matched:
    1. Silicon steels .... Transformer stampings
    2. Duralumin .... Cooking utensils
    3. Gun metal .... Bearings
    Select the correct answer using the codes given below:
    Codes:
    (A) 1, 2 and 3   (B) 1 and 2   (C) 1 and 3   (D) 2 and 3
                                                              [*IES 1994*] (**Ans. A**)

19. Match List I with List II and select the correct answer using the codes given below the lists:
    List I (Materials)   *List II (Applications)*
    A. Engineering Ceramics   1. Bearings
    B. Fibre reinforced plastics   2. Control rods in nuclear reactors
    C. Synthetic carbon   3. Aerospace industry
    D. Boron   4. Electrical insulator

Codes	A	B	C	D		A	B	C	D
(a)	1	2	3	4	(b)	1	4	3	2
(c)	2	3	1	4	(d)	4	3	1	2

                                                              [*IES 1994*] (**Ans. d**)

20. Which of the following pairs are correctly matched?
    1. Lead screw nut ...... Phosphor bronze
    2. Piston ...... Cast iron
    3. Cam .... EN 31 steel
    4. Lead screw ...... Wrought Iron
    Select the correct answer using the codes given below:–
    Codes.
    (A) 2, 3 and 4   (B) 1, 3 and 4   (C) 1, 2 and 4   (D) 1, 2 and 3
                                                              [*IES 1994*] (**Ans. D**)

21. Babbit lining is used on brass/bronze bearings to
    (A) increase bearing resistance   (B) increase compressive strength
    (C) provide any friction properties   (D) increase wear resistance
                                                              [*IES 1995*] (**Ans. D**)

22. In low carbon steels, presence of small quantities of sulphur improves:
    (A) Weldability   (B) formability   (C) machinability   (D) hardenability
                                                              [*IES 1995*] (**Ans. C**)

23. Match List I with List II and select the correct answer using codes given below the lists:

List I (heat treatment)   List II (effect on properties)
A Annealing   1. Refines grain structure
B Nitriding   2. Improves hardness of the whole mass
C Martempering   3. Increases surface hardness
D Normalising   4. Improves ductility

Codes.	A	B	C	D		A	B	C	D
(a)	4	3	2	1	(b)	1	3	4	2
(c)	4	2	1	3	(d)	2	1	3	4

[IES 1995] (Ans. a).

24. Consider the following statements:
Addition of Silicon to cast iron
1. promotes graphite nodule formation
2. promotes graphite flake formation
3. increases fluidity of the molten metal
4. improves the ductility of cast iron
Of these statements
(A) 1 and 4 are correct   (B) 2 and 3 are correct
(C) 1 and 3 are correct   (D) 3 and 4 are correct   [IES 1995] (Ans. B)

25. Eutectoid reaction occurs at
(A) 600°C   (B) 723°C   (C) 1147°C   (D) 1493°C
[IES 1995] (Ans. B)

26. Match List I with List II and select the correct answer using the codes given below the lists:

List I (Name of Material)   List II (% Carbon Range)
A. Hypo-eutectoid steel   1. 4.3 – 6.67
B. Hyper-eutectoid steel   2. 2.0 – 4.3
C. Hypo-eutectic cast iron   3. 0.8 – 2.0
D. Hyper-eutectic cast iron   4. 0.008 – 0.8

Codes	A	B	C	D		A	B	C	D
(a)	4	3	2	1	(b)	1	3	2	4
(c)	4	1	2	3	(d)	1	2	3	4

[IES 1995] (Ans. a)

27. Which one of the following constituents is expected in equilibrium cooling of a hypereu-tectoid steel from austenitic state?
(A) Ferrite and Pearlite   (B) Cementite and Pearlite
(C) Ferrite and bainite   (D) Cementite and Martensite
[IES 1995] (Ans. B)

28. Addition of Magnesium to cast iron increases its
(A) hardness   (B) ductility and strength in tension
(C) Corrosion resistance   (D) Creep strength
[IES 1995] (Ans. B)

29. Small amount of which one of the following elements/pairs of elements is added to steel to increase machinability
(A) Nickle   (B) Sulphur and Phosphorous
(C) Silicon   (D) Manganese and copper
[IES 1996] (Ans. B)

30. Which of the following pairs regarding the effect of alloying elements in steel are correctly matched?
1. Molybdenum : Forms abrasion resisting particles
2. Phosphorus: Improves machinability in free cutting steels
3. Cobalt: Contributes to red hardness by hardening ferrite
4. Silicon: Reduces oxidation resistance
Select the correct answer using the codes given below:
(A) 2, 3, 4   (B) 1, 3 and 4   (C) 1, 2 and 4   (D) 1, 2 and 3
[IES 1996] (Ans. D)

31. Machine tool guideways are usually hardened by
    (A) Vacuum hardening   (B) Martempering
    (C) Induction hardening   (D) Flame hardening   [IES 1996] (Ans. D)
32. 18/8 stainless steel contains:
    (A) 18% Ni, 8% Cr   (B) 18% Cr, 8% Ni
    (C) 18% Cr, 8% W   (D) 18% W, 8% Cr.   [IES 1996] (Ans. B)
33. Tin base white metals are used where the bearings are subjected to:
    (A) large surface wear   (B) elevated temperatures
    (C) high load and pressure   (D) high pressure and load
                                                             [IES 1996] (Ans. D)
34. Alloy steel which is work hardenable and which is used to make the blades of bull dozers
    bucket wheels excavators and other earth moving equipment contains iron, carbon and
    (A) Mn   (B) Si   (C) Cr   (D) Mg
                                                             [IES 1996] (Ans. A)
35. Guide ways of lathe beds are hardened by
    (A) Carburising   (B) Cyaniding   (C) nitriding   (D) Flame hardening
                                                             [IES 1997] (Ans. D)
36. A given steel test specimen is studied under metallurgical microscope. Magnification used
    is 100 X. In that different phases are observed. One of them is Fe_3C.
    The observed phase Fe_3C is also known as
    (A) ferrite   (B) cementite   (C) austenite   (D) martensite
                                                             [IES 1997] (Ans. B)
37. Match List I (Alloying elements in steel) with List II (Property conferred on steel by the
    element) and select the correct answer using the codes given below the lists:
    List I   List II
    A Nickle   1. Corrosion resistance
    B Chromium   2. Magnetic permeability
    C Tungsten   3. Heat resistance
    D Silicon   4. Hardenability
    Codes:

	A	B	C	D		A	B	C	D
(a)	4	1	3	2	(b)	4	1	2	3
(c)	1	4	3	2	(d)	1	4	2	3

                                                             [IES 1998] (Ans. a)
38. Match List I (Alloys) with List II (Applications) and select the correct answer using the
    codes given below the lists:
    List I   List II
    A Chromel   1. Journal bearing
    B Babbit alloy   2. Milling Cutter
    C Nimonic alloy   3. Thermocouple wire
    D High speed steel   4. Gas turbine blades
    Codes

	A	B	C	D		A	B	C	D
(a)	3	1	4	2	(b)	3	4	1	2
(c)	2	4	1	3	(d)	2	1	4	3

                                                             [IES 1998] (Ans. a)

39. Match List I with List II and select the correct answer using the codes given below the lists:
List I (Materials)

A. Tungsten Carbide
B. Silicon nitride
C. Aluminium Oxide
D. Silicon Carbide

List II (Applications)

1. Abrasive wheels
2. Heating elements
3. Pipes for conveying liquid metals
4. Drawing dies

Codes.

	A	B	C	D		A	B	C	D
(*a*)	3	4	1	2	(*b*)	4	3	2	1
(*c*)	3	4	2	1	(*d*)	4	3	1	2

[*IES 1999*](**Ans.** *d*)

40. Heating the Hypoeutectoid steels 30° above the upper critical temperature line, soaking at that temperature and then cooling slowly to room temperature to form a pearlite and ferrite structure is known as

(A) hardening   (B) normalising   (C) tempering   (D) annealing

[*IES 1999*] (**Ans.** D)

41. In a eutectic system, two elements are completely

(A) insoluble in solid and liquid states   (B) soluble in liquid state
(C) soluble in solid state   (D) insoluble in liquid state

[*IES 1999*] (**Ans.** B)

42. A steel with 0.8% C is called

(A) Hypo-eutectoid steel   (B) Hyper-eutectoid steel
(C) Eutectoid steel   (D) None of these

(**Ans.** C)

43. A steel with 0.8% C contains:

(A) 100% pearlite   (B) 100% austenite
(C) ferrite and pearlite   (D) pearlite and cementite   (**Ans.** A)

44. The lower critical temperature for all steels is:

(A) 700°C   (B) 723°C   (C) 650°C   (D) 910°C

(**Ans.** B)

45. A steel with 0.8% C has

(A) One critical point   (B) Two critical points
(C) No critical point

(**Ans.** A)

46. Cementite consists of:

(A) 13% ferrite and 87% pearlite   (B) 6.67% C and 93.33% Iron
(C) 13% C and 87% ferrite

(**Ans.** B)

47. Pearlite consists of:

(A) 87% ferrite and 13% Cementite   (B) 87% cementite and 13% ferrite
(C) 6.67% C and 93.33% Iron

(**Ans.** A)

48. In the austempering heat treatment process, austenite decomposes into:

(A) Sorbite   (B) Troostite   (C) Bainite   (D) Martensite

(**Ans.** C)

49. Do we need tempering operation on a component hardened by austempering process?

(**Ans.** *No*)

50. The upper critical temperature for steel

(A) is constant
(B) depends upon the rate of heating
(C) varies according to the carbon content in steel
(D) none of the above

(**Ans.** C)

51. The lower critical temperature for steel
    (A) is constant
    (B) depends upon the rate of heating
    (C) varies according to the carbon content in steel
    (D) None of the above   (Ans. A)

52. The beginning of separation of ferrite from solid solution of Austenite is represented by
    (A) A_1 line   (B) A_3 line   (C) Acm line   (D) None of the above
                                                                            (*Ans.* B)

53. The completion of transformation of austenite into ferrite and pearlite is represented by
    (A) A_1 line   (B) A_3 line   (C) Acm line   (D) None of the above
                                                                            (Ans. A)

54. The limit of Carbon solubility in austenite is represented by
    (A) A_1 line   (B) A_3 line   (C) Acm line   (D) None of the above
                                                                            (Ans. C)

55. Fine grains of austenite
    (A) decrease hardenability
    (B) increase hardenability
    (C) first decrease, then increase hardenability
    (D) first increase, then decrease hardneability
                                                                            (Ans. A)

56. Dissolved alloying elements in steel
    (A) decrease hardenability   (B) increase hardenability
    (C) has no effect on hardenability   (D) first decrease, then increase hardenability
                                                                            (Ans. B)

57. The temperature at which the first new grain appears is known as
    (A) Melting temperature   (B) Critical temperature
    (C) Boiling temperature   (D) Recrystallisation temperature   (Ans. D)

58. The recrystallisation temperature depends upon:
    (A) grain size   (B) type of metal
    (C) extent of cold deformation   (D) annealing time
    (E) purity of metal   (F) all of the above
    (G) None of the above
                                                                            (Ans. F)

59. The recrystallisation temperature for pure metals is
    (A) $0.2\,T_m$ (B) $0.3\,T_m$ (C) $0.5\,T_m$ (D) $0.8\,T_m$
    Where T_m = melting temperature   (Ans. B)

60. The recrystallisation temperature for alloys is approximately:
    (A) $0.2\,T_m$ (B) $0.3\,T_m$ (C) $0.5\,T_m$ (D) $0.8\,T_m$ (Ans. C)

61. Carbon occurs in steel in the combined state with iron to form the component:
    (A) Ferrite   (B) Cementite   (C) Pearlite   (D) Bainite
                                                        (*I.MECH, E, L.U., D.U.*) (Ans. B)

62. When a steel is heated to above its upper critical temperature, the structure produced is one of:
    (A) Martensite   (B) Austenite   (C) Pearlite   (D) Sorbite
                                                                            (Ans. B)

63. The predominant structure of a hypereutectoid steel that has been quenched at above its upper critical temperature will be:–
    (A) Austenite   (B) Martensite   (C) Troostite   (D) Sorbite
                                                        (*B.U., D.U., AIME*) (Ans. B)

64. Which one of the following structures is predominant in a normalized steel:–
    (A) Troostite   (B) Bain ite   (C) Sorbite   (D) Martensite
                                                                    (AMIE, UPSC) (Ans. C)

65. When a steel is heated in a furnace and then cooled in air at ordinary temperature, the process is one of
    (A) Annealing   (B) Hardening   (C) Normalizing   (D) Tempering
                                                                    (AMIE, L.U., P.U.) (Ans. C)

CHAPTER 3

1. In a green-sand moulding process, uniform ramming leads to
   (A) less change of gas porosity
   (B) uniform flow of molten metal into the mould cavity
   (C) greater dimensional stability of the casting
   (D) less sand expansion type of casting defect   [GATE 1992] (Ans. C)

2. Match the following moulding casting processes with the product:

   Moulding/Casting processes   *Product*
   (A) Slush casting   (P) Turbine blades
   (B) Shell moulding   (Q) Machine tool bed
   (C) Dry sand moulding   (R) Cylinder block
   (D) Centrifugal casting   (S) Hollow castings like lamp shades
                                             (T) Rain water pipe
                                             (U) Cast iron shoe brake
                        [GATE 1992]   (Ans. A – S, B – P, C – R, D – T)

3. Centrifugally cast products have
   (A) large grain structure with high poror"ity
   (B) fine grain structure with high density
   (C) fine grain structure with low density
   (D) segregation of slag towards the outer skin of the casting   [GATE 1993] (Ans. B)

4. List I gives a number of processes and List II gives a number of products. Match correct pairs:

   List I   *List II*
   (A) Investment casting   1. Turbine rotors
   (B) Centrifugal casting   2. Turbine blades
   (C) Die-casting   3. Connecting rods
   (D) Drop forging   4. Galvanized iron pipe
   (E) Extrusion   5. Cast iron pipes
   (F) Shell moulding   6. Carburettor body
                                                                    [GATE 1994]
                        (Ans. A – 2, B – 5, C – 6, D – 3, E – 4, F – 1).

5. Light impurities in the molten metal are prevented from reaching the mould cavity by providing a
   (A) Strainer   (B) Bottom well   (C) Skim bob   (D) all of the above
                                                                    [GATE 1996] (Ans. C)

6. Chills are used in moulds to
   (A) achieve directional solidification
   (B) reduce the possibility of blow holes
   (C) reduce freezing time
   (D) Smoothen metal flow for reducing splatter   [GATE 1998] [IAS 1994] (Ans. A)

7. Which of the following materials requires the largest shrinkage allowance, while making a pattern for casting?

(A) Aluminium   (B) Brass   (C) Cast iron   (D) Plain carbon steel
[GATE 1999] (Ans. D)

8. Disposable patterns are made of
(A) wood   (B) rubber   (C) metal   (D) polystyrene
(Ans. D)

9. Match List I with List II and select the correct answer using the codes given below the lists:

List I (Equipments)
A. Hot chamber machine
B. Muller
C. Dielectric baker
D. Sand blasting

List II (Functions)
1. Cleaning
2. Core making
3. Die casting
4. Annealing
5. Mixing

Codes:

	A	B	C	D		A	B	C	D
(a)	3	5	2	1	(b)	4	2	5	3
(c)	4	2	3	1	(d)	3	5	1	2

[IES 1993] (Ans. a)

10. Which of the following materials can be used for making patterns?
1. Aluminium 2. Wax 3. Mercury 4. Lead
Select the correct answer using the codes given below:
Codes:
(A) 1, 3 and 4   (B) 2, 3 and 4   (C) 1, 2 and 4   (D) 1, 2 and 3
[IES 1994] (Ans. D)

11. Which of the following materials will require the largest size of riser for the same size of casting?
(A) Aluminium   (B) cast iron   (C) steel   (D) copper
[IES 1995] (Ans. A)

12. Directional solidification in castings can be improved by
(A) Chills and chaplets   (B) Chills and padding
(C) Chaplets and padding   (D) Chills, chaplets and padding
[IES 1995] (Ans. B)

13. Match List I with List II and select the correct answer taking the help of codes given below the lists:

List I (Products)
A. Automobile piston in aluminium alloy
B. Engine crankshaft in spherioidal graphite iron
C. Carburettor Housing in aluminium alloy
D. Cast titanium blades

List II (Process of Manufacture)
1. Pressure die-casting
2. Gravity die-casting
3. Sand casting
4. Precision investment casting
5. Shell moulding

Codes:

	A	B	C	D		A	B	C	D
(a)	2	3	1	5	(b)	3	2	1	5
(c)	2	1	3	4	(d)	4	1	2	3

[IES 1995] (Ans. a)

14. Consider the following ingredients used in moulding:
1. Dry silica sand 2. Clay 3. Phenol formaldehyde 4. Sodium silicate
Those used for shell mould casting include:
(A) 1, 2 and 4   (B) 2, 3 and 4   (C) 1 and 3   (D) 1, 2, 3, 4
[IES 1996] (Ans. C)

15. Which of the following methods are used for obtaining directional solidification for riser design:

1. Suitable placement of chills 2. Suitable placement of chaplets 3. Employing padding
Select the correct answer:
(a) 1 and 2   (b) 1 and 3   (c) 2 and 3   (d) 1, 2 and 3
                                                                     [IES 1996] (Ans. b)

16. Misrun is a casting defect which occurs due to
(A) very high pouring temperature of the metal
(B) insufficient fluidity of the molten metal
(C) absorption of gases by the liquid metal
(D) improper alignment of the mould flasks   [IES 1996] (Ans. B)

17. Which of the following pairs are correctly matched?
1. Pit moulding .... for large jobs   2. Investment moulding .... Lost wax process   3. Plaster moulding ...... Mould prepared in gypsum
(A) 1, 2 and 3   (B) 1 and 2   (C) 1 and 3   (D) 2 and 3
                                                                     [IES 1996] (Ans. A)

18. Which one of the following pairs is not correctly matched?
(A) Aluminium alloy Piston ...... Pressure die casting
(B) Jewellery .... Lost wax process
(C) Large pipes .... Centrifugal casting
(D) Large bells ...... Loam moulding   [IES 1997] (Ans. A)

19. If the melting ratio of a cupola is 10 : 1, then the coke requirement for one ton melt will be
(A) 0.1 ton   (B) 10 tons   (C) 1 ton   (D) 11 tons
                                                                     [IES 1997] (Ans. B)

20. Which one of the following are the requirements of an ideal gating system?
1. The molten metal should enter the mould cavity with as high a velocity as possible
2. It should facilitate complete filling of the mould cavity
3. It should be able to prevent the absorption of air or gases from the surroundings of the
molten metal while flowing through it
Select the correct answer using the codes given below:
(A) 1, 2 and 3   (B) 1 and 2   (C) 2 and 3   (D) 1 and 3
                                                                     [IES 1998] (Ans. C)

21. A spherical drop of molten metal of radius 2 mm was found to solidify in 10 seconds. A
similar drop of radius 4 mm will solidify in
(A) 14.14 s   (B) 20 s   (C) 28.30 s   (D) 40 s
                                                                     [IES 1998] (Ans. D)

(Hint: Solidification for sphere is $\alpha \left(\dfrac{V}{A} \right)^2$)

22. In solidification of metal during casting, compensation for solid contraction is
(A) provided by the oversize pattern
(B) achieved by properly placed risers
(C) obtained by promoting directional solidification
(D) made by providing chills.   [IES 1999] (Ans. A)

23. Disk-shaped components are cast by
(A) True Centifigural casting   (B) Semi-Centrifugal casting
(C) Centifuge casting
                                                                     (Ans. B)

24. Consider the following ingredients used in moulding:
1. Dry silica sand 2. Clay 3. Ethyl silicate 4. Phenol formaldehyde
Those used for Lost Wax casting method include:
(A) 1, 2 and 4   (B) 2, 3 and 4   (C) 1 and 3   (D) 1, 2, 3 and 4
                                                                     (Ans. C)

25. Metal patterns require ...... (more/less) draft allowance than wooden patterns. (**Ans.** more)
26. The molten metal is poured from the pouring basin to the gate with the help of a
    (A) Riser   (B) Sprue   (C) Runner   (D) Core   (**Ans.** B)
27. In cold chamber die-casting process, only non-ferrous alloys with ...... (high melting point/
    low melting point) are cast. (Ans. High melting point)
28. In the casting of large pipes by true centrifugal casting
    (A) Core is of sand   (B) Core is of metal   (C) no core is used   (**Ans.** C)
29. Core prints are provided on patterns
    (A) to support the core
    (B) to locate the core in the mould
    (C) to support as well as locate the core in the mould   (**Ans.** C)
30. Contraction allowance is provided on a pattern:
    (A) for machining of castings   (B) for contraction in metal on cooling
    (C) for making a good casting   (**Ans.** B)
31. To provide the machining allowance, a pattern should be made ...... (larger/smaller) than the
    size of the finished casting required. (Ans. Larger)
32. An ingate
    (A) acts as a reservoir for the molten metal
    (B) delivers molten metal into the mould cavity
    (C) delivers molten metal from the pouring basin to runner
    (D) all of the above   (**Ans.** B)
33. A riser
    (A) acts as a reservoir for the molten metal
    (B) delivers molten metal into the mould cavity
    (C) delivers molten metal from the pouring basin to runner
    (D) feeds the molten metal to the casting in order to compensate for solid shrinkage
                                                                                    (**Ans.** D)

34. The function of a core is:
    (A) to improve mould surface
    (B) to form internal cavities in the casting
    (C) to form a part of a green sand mould
    (D) None of the above
    (E) All of the above   (**Ans.** E)
35. When the molten metal flows into the cavity of a metallic mould by gravity, the method of
    casting is known as:
    (A) Die-casting   (B) Centrifugal casting
    (C) Permanent mould casting   (D) Plaster mould casting   (**Ans.** C)
36. The toys and ornaments of non-ferrous alloys are made by:
    (A) Die-casting   (B) Lost-wax method
    (C) Permanent mould casting   (D) Slush casting   (**Ans.** D)
37. Two castings of the same metal have the same surface area. One casting is in the form of a
    sphere and the other is a cube. What is the ratio of the solidification time for the sphere to
    that of a cube. [*GATE 1998*]

Solution. According to Chvorinov's rule, solidification time is $\alpha \left(\dfrac{V}{A} \right)^2$, where

$$V = \text{Volume of casting}$$
$$A = \text{Surface area of casting}$$

Now $As = Ac$

∴ Ratio of solidification time $= \left(\dfrac{V_s}{V_c}\right)^2$

$$= \left(\dfrac{\frac{4}{3}\pi R^3}{a^3}\right)^2$$

$$= \dfrac{16\pi^2 R^6}{9a^6}$$

Where R = Radius of sphere, and
a = side of the cube.

38. Risering is not needed when casting Gray cast iron, True/False.   (Ans. True)

39. Calculate the ratio of the solidification times of two steel cylindrical risers of sizes 30 cm in diameter by 60 cm height and 60 cm in diameter by 30 cm in height subjected to identical conditions of cooling.   [GATE 1992]

Solution. According to Chvorinov's rule solidification time is $\alpha\left(\dfrac{V}{A}\right)^2$ (See problem 37)

Riser 1.

$$\dfrac{V}{A} = \dfrac{\frac{\pi}{4}d^2 \times h}{\pi d h + 2 \times \frac{\pi}{4}d^2}$$

$$= \dfrac{\frac{1}{4}\times 900 \times 60}{30\times 60 + \frac{1}{2}\times 900} = \dfrac{13500}{2250} = 6$$

Riser 2:

$$\dfrac{V}{A} = \dfrac{\frac{1}{4}\times 3600 \times 30}{60\times 30 + \frac{1}{2}\times 3600} = \dfrac{27000}{3600} = 7.5$$

∴ Ratio of solidification times, $= \left(\dfrac{7.5}{6}\right)^2 = 1.5625$

40. An aluminium cube of 10 cm side has to be cast along a cylindrical riser of height equal to its diameter. The riser is not insulated on any surface. If the volume shrinkage of aluminium during solidification is 6%, calculate

(i) Shrinkage volume of cube on solidification, and
(ii) minimum size of the riser so that it can provide the shrinkage volume.

[GATE 1993]

Solution:

(i) Volume of casting $= 10 \times 10 \times 10 = 1000 \text{ cm}^3$,

Shrinkage volume = 6% = 60 cm³ (Depending upon metal, this shrinkage varies from 2.5 to 7.5%)

Now from practice,

Minimum volume of riser is approximately three times the shrinkage volume,

∴ Minimum volume of riser = 3 × 60 = 180 cm³

$$\therefore \qquad \frac{\pi}{4}d_r^2 \times h_r = 180$$

now $$\qquad h_r = d_r$$

$\therefore$ From here, $$\qquad d_r = 5.2 \text{ cm}$$

Now for sound casting, the metal in the riser should be the last to cool, that is, the riser should have a longer solidification time than the casting, so

$$\left(\frac{A}{V}\right)_r \leq \left(\frac{A}{V}\right)_c \quad \text{or} \quad \left(\frac{V}{A}\right)_r \geq \left(\frac{V}{A}\right)_c$$

Now $$\left(\frac{A}{V}\right)_r = \frac{6}{d_r} = \frac{6}{5.2} \quad \text{(it is simple to prove this, with } d_r = h_r\text{)}$$

$$\left(\frac{A}{V}\right)_c = \frac{6 \times 10 \times 10}{10 \times 10 \times 10} = \frac{3}{5}$$

As is clear, $\left(\frac{A}{V}\right)_r$ is $> \left(\frac{A}{V}\right)_c$, which is not desirable.

$$\therefore \qquad \left(\frac{A}{V}\right)_r \leq \left(\frac{A}{V}\right)_c$$

$$\leq 0.6$$

or $$\frac{6}{d_r} \leq 0.6, \qquad \therefore \frac{10}{dr} \leq 1, \qquad \therefore d_r \geq 10.$$

$\therefore$ Minimum size of riser = <u>10 cm diameter × 10 cm height</u>

$$\therefore \qquad V_r = \frac{\pi}{4} \times 100 \times 10 = 785.4 \text{ cm}^3.$$

41. With cylindrical riser, prove that for a longer solidification time, diameter of riser = height of riser.

Solution: We know that for longer solidification time, the ratio $\left(\frac{V}{A}\right)$ should be maximum

or the ratio, $\left(\frac{A}{V}\right)$ should be minimum.

Now, $$V = \frac{\pi}{4}d^2 \times h$$

$$\therefore \qquad h = \frac{4V}{\pi d^2}$$

$$A = \pi d.h + 2.\frac{\pi}{4}d^2$$

$$\therefore \qquad A = \pi d.\frac{4V}{\pi d^2} + \frac{\pi}{2}d^2$$

$$\therefore \qquad A = \frac{4V}{d} + \frac{\pi}{2}d^2$$

For A to be minimum for a given V, $\partial A / \partial d = 0$, and it will be seen that for this, $d = h$.

i.e. $-\dfrac{4V}{d^2} + \pi d = 0$

or $d^3 = \dfrac{4V}{\pi}$

Also, $\dfrac{4V}{\pi} = hd^2$

$\therefore$ $d^3 = hd^2$

or $d = h$

This optimum ratio is true only for a side riser, Fig. 3.22 (a). For a top riser,

$$A = \pi dh + \dfrac{\pi}{4} d^2$$

Doing the analysis as above, it will be seen that

$$d = 2h$$

or $\dfrac{h}{d} = \dfrac{1}{2}$

42. Shrinkage allowance on pattern is provided to compensate for shrinkage when
    (a) the temperature of liquid metal drops from pouring to freezing temperature
    (b) the metal changes from liquid to solid state at freezing temperature
    (c) the temperature of solid phase drops from freezing to room temperature
    (d) the temperature of metal drops from pouring to room temperature

                                                        [GATE 2001] (Ans. c)

43. Two solid workpieces (i) Sphere with radius R, (ii) a cylinder with diameter equal to its height, have to be sand cast. Both workpieces have the same volume. Show that the c ylindrical workpiece will solidify faster than the spherical work piece.   [GATE 2001]

Solution.   Volume of sphere $= \dfrac{4}{3} \pi R^3$

                        Volume of cylinder $= \dfrac{\pi}{4} d^2 . h$

                                             $= \dfrac{\pi}{4} d^3$

                        $\dfrac{\pi}{4} d^3 = \dfrac{4}{3} \pi R^3$

$\therefore$ $d^3 = \dfrac{16}{3} R^3$

Now solidification time is $\alpha \left(\dfrac{V}{A} \right)^2$

Now, $\left(\dfrac{V}{A} \right)_{cyl} = \dfrac{\dfrac{\pi}{4} d^2 . h}{\pi dh + 2 . \dfrac{\pi}{4} d^2} = \dfrac{d}{6}$ (with $d = h$)

$$\therefore \qquad \left(\frac{V}{A}\right)_{cyl} = \frac{1}{6} \cdot \left(\frac{16}{3}\right)^{\frac{1}{3}} \cdot R = 0.29\,R$$

Again,
$$\left(\frac{V}{A}\right)_{sphere} = \frac{\frac{4}{3}\pi R^3}{4\pi R^2} = \frac{R}{3} = 0.33\,R$$

Now, it is known that risers with a higher value of $\left(\frac{V}{A}\right)$ loose heat at a slower rate. Thus, it is clear from above, that a solid casting of cylindrical section will solidify faster than the spherical work piece.

44. The primary purpose of sprue in a casting mould is to
   (a) Feed the casting at a rate consistent with the rate of solidification
   (b) Act as a reservoir for molten metal
   (c) Feed molten metal from the pouring basin to the gate
   (d) Help feed the casting until all solification takes place   (*GATE 2002*) (**Ans.** c)

45. In centrifugal casting, the impurities are
   (*a*) Uniformly distributed
   (*b*) Forced towards the outer surface
   (*c*) trapped near the mean radius of the casting
   (*d*) collected at the centre of casting   [*GATE 2002*] (**Ans.** *a*)

46. Match 4 correct pairs between List I and List II

List I	*List II*
(A) Sand casting	(1) Symmetrical and circular shapes only
(B) Plaster mould casting	(2) Parts have hardened skin and soft interior
(C) Shell mould casting	(3) Minimum post casting processing
(D) Investment casting	(4) Parts have a tendency to warp
	(5) Parts have soft skin and hard interior
	(6) Suitable only for non-ferrous metals

   [*GATE 1998*] (**Ans.** A – 2, B – 6, C – 1, D – 3)

CHAPTER 4

1. The thickness of the blank needed to produce, by power spinning a missile cone of thickness 1.5 mm and half cone angle 30°, is
   (*a*) 3.00 mm   (*b*) 2.5 mm   (*c*) 2.0 mm   (*d*) 1.55 mm
                                                                      [*GATE 1992*] (**Ans.** *a*)

2. The true strain for low carbon steel bar which is doubled in length by forging is
   (*a*) 0.307   (*b*) 0.5   (*c*) 0.693   (*d*) 1.0
                                                                      [*GATE 1992*] (**Ans.** *c*)

3. The process of hot extrusion is used to produce
   (*a*) curtain rods made of aluminium   (*b*) steel pipes for domestic water supply
   (*c*) stainless steel tubes used in furniture   (*d*) Large size pipes used in city water mains
                                                                      [*GATE 1994*] (**Ans.** *a, c*)

4. Match 4 correct pairs between List I and List II

    List I
    (a) Rivets for air craft body
    (b) Carburettor body
    (c) Crank shafts
    (d) Nails

    List II
    1. Forging
    2. Cold heading
    3. Aluminium-based alloy
    4. Pressure die casting
    5. Investment casting

    [*GATE 1996*] (**Ans.** a– 3, b – 4, c – 1, d – 2)

5. In a progressive Die (Sheet metal work), the tonnage of the press can be reduced by
    (a) Grinding the cutting edges sharp.
    (b) Increasing the hardness of punches.
    (c) Increasing the hardness of die.
    (d) Staggering the punches.   (**Ans. D**)

6. *List I*
    (A) Aluminium brake shoe
    (B) Plastic water bottle
    (C) Stainless steel cups
    (D) Soft drink can (aluminium)

    List II
    (1) Deep drawing
    (2) Blow moulding
    (3) sand casting
    (4) Centrifugal casting
    (5) Impact extrusion
    (6) Upset forging

    [*GATE 1998*] (**Ans.** A – 3, B– 2, C – 1, D – 5).

7. In sheet metal work, the cutting force on the tool can be reduced by
    (A) grinding the cutting edges sharp   (B) increasing the hardness of tool
    (C) providing shear angle on tool   (D) increasing the hardness of die
                                                            [*IES 1993*]   (**Ans. C**)

8. Tandem drawing of wires and tubes is necessary because
    (A) it is not possible to reduce in one stage
    (B) annealing is needed between stages
    (C) accuracy in dimensions is not possible otherwise
    (D) surface finish improves after every drawing stage   [*IES 1993*] (**Ans. A**)

9. In order to get uniform thickness of plate by rolling process, one provides
    (A) Camber on the rolls   (B) offset on the rolls
    (C) hardening of the rolls   (D) antifriction bearings [*IES 1993*] (**Ans.** *A*)

10. A moving mandrel is used in
    (A) wire drawing   (B) tube drawing   (C) metal cutting (D) forging
                                                            [*IES 1993*] (**Ans. B**)

11. Which of the following methods can be used for manufacturing 2 metre long seamless metallic tubes?
    1. Drawing   2. Extrusion   3. Rolling   4. Spinning [*IAS 1994*]
    Select the correct answer using the codes given below:
    Codes.
    (A) 1 and 3   (B) 2 and 3   (C) 1, 3 and 4   (D) 2, 3 and 4   (**Ans. B**)

12. In blanking operation, the clearance provided is
    (A) 50% on punch and 50% on die
    (B) on die
    (C) on punch
    (D) on die or punch depending upon designers choice   [*IAS 1995*] (**Ans. C**)

13. Consider the following states of stress:
    1. compressive stress in flange   2. tensile stress in the wall
    3. tensile stress on the bottom part

During drawing operation, the states of stress in cup would include

(a) 1 and 2   (b) 1 and 3   (c) 2 and 3   (d) 1, 2 and 3

[IAS 1995] (Ans. a)

14. The following operations are performed while preparing the billets for extrusion process:
1. Alkaline cleaning 2. Phosphate coating
3. Pickling   4. Lubrication with reactive soap
The correct sequence of these operations is

(A) 3, 1, 4, 2   (B) 1, 3, 2, 4   (C) 1, 3, 4, 2   (D) 3, 1, 2, 4

[IAS 1995] (Ans. D)

15. Match List I with List II and select the correct answer using the codes given below the lists:

List I (Metal forming process)   List II (A similar process)
A. Blanking   1. Wire drawing
B. Coining   2. Piercing
C. Extrusion   3. Embossing
D. Cup drawing   4. Rolling
                                       5. Bending

Codes:	A	B	C	D		A	B	C	D
(a)	2	3	4	1	(b)	2	3	1	4
(c)	3	2	1	5	(d)	2	3	1	5

[IES 1994] (Ans. b)

16. In sheet metal blanking, shear is provided on punches and dies so that

(A) press load is reduced   (B) good cut edge is obtained
(C) warping of sheet is minimised   (D) cut blanks are straight

[IES 1994] (Ans. A)

17. Which of the following pairs of process and draft are correctly matched?
1. Rolling 2   2.Extrusion.........50   3.Forging......4
Select the correct answer using the codes given below:
Codes:

(A) 1, 2 and 3   (B) 1 and 2   (C) 1 and 3   (D) 2 and 3

[IES 1994] (Ans. A)

18. The mode of deformation of the metal during spinning is

(A) bending   (B) stretching
(C) rolling and stretching   (D) bending and stretching

[IES 1994] (Ans. D)

19. In drop forging, forging is done by dropping
(A) the work piece at high velocity
(B) the hammer at high velocity
(C) the die with hammer at high velocity
(D) a weight on hammer to produce the requisite impact   [IES 1994] (Ans. C)

20. Metal extrusion process is generally used for producing
(A) uniform solid sections   (B) uniform hollow sections
(C) uniform solid and hollow sections (D) varying solid and hollow sections

[IES 1994] (Ans. C)

21. Which one of the following is an advantage of forging?
(A) Good surface finish   (B) Low tooling cost
(C) close tolerance   (D) Improved physical property

[IES 1996] (Ans. D)

22. In wire drawing process, the bright shining surface on the wire is obtained if one

(A) does not use a lubricant   (B) uses solid powdery lubricant
(C) uses thick paste lubricant   (D) uses thin fluid lubricant
[IES 1996] **(Ans. D)**

23. Match List I with List II and select the correct answer
List I (Metal forming process)   *List II (Associated force)*
A. Wire drawing   1. Shear force
B. Extrusion   2. Tensile stress (force)
C. Blanking   3. Compressive force
D. Bending   4. Spring back force

Codes:	A	B	C	D		A	B	C	D
(a)	4	2	1	3	(b)	2	1	3	4
(c)	2	3	1	4	(d)	4	3	2	1

[IES 1996] **(Ans. c)**

24. In metals subjected to cold working, strain hardening effect is due to
(A) slip mechanism   (B) twining mechanism
(C) dislocation mechanism   (D) fracture mechanism   *[IES 1997]* **(Ans. A)**

25. Which one of the following processes is most commonly used for the forging of bolt heads of hexagonal shape?
(A) closed die drop forging   (B) open die upset forging
(C) closed die press forging   (D) open die progressive forging
[IES 1998] **(Ans. D)**

26. The bending force required for V-bending, U-bending and Edge bending will be in the ratio of
(A) 1 : 2 : 0.5   (B) 2 : 1 : 0.5   (C) 1 : 2 : 1   (D) 1 : 1 : 1
[IES 1998] **(Ans. A)**

27. Match List I with List II and select the correct answer using the codes given below the lists:
List I   *List II*
A. Drawing   1. Soap solution
B. Rolling   2. Camber
C. Wire drawing   3. Pilots
D. Sheet metal operations using progressive dies   4. Crater
     5. Ironing

Codes:

	A	B	C	D		A	B	C	D
(a)	2	5	1	4	(b)	4	1	5	3
(c)	5	2	3	4	(d)	5	2	1	3

[IES 1999] **(Ans. d)**

28. Which one of the following is the correct temperature range for hot extrusion of aluminium?
(A) 300 – 340° C   (B) 350 – 400°C   (C) 430 – 480°C   (D) 550 – 650°C
[IES 1999] **(Ans. B)**

29. Major operations in the manufacture of steel balls used for Ball bearings are given below:
1. oil lapping 2. cold heading 3. Annealing 4. Hardening 5. Rough grinding
The correct sequence of these operations is
(A) 3, 2, 4, 1, 5   (B) 3, 2, 1, 4, 5   (C) 2, 3, 4, 5, 1   (D) 2, 3, 5, 4, 1
[IAS 1994] **(Ans. C)**

30. In metal working processes, the stresses induced in the metal are
(A) less than the yield strength of the metal

(B) greater than the yield strength of the metal

(C) less than the breaking strength of the metal

(D) greater than the breaking strength of the metal   (Ans. B, C)

31. In cold working of metals, the working temperature is

(A) room temperature   (B) below the recrystallisation temperature

(C) above the recrystallisation temperature (D) less than the room temperature   (Ans. B)

32. In hot working of metals, the working temperature is

(A) below the recrystallisation temperature

(B) above the recrystallisation temperature

(C) equal to the melting point of the metal

(D) 150°   (Ans. B)

33. Which mechanical property a metal should possess to enable it to be mechanically formed?

(A) ductility   (B) malleability   (C) elasticity   (D) machinability

(Ans. A)

34. Mass production of cooking utensils is usually done by

(A) metal spinning   (B) deep drawing   (C) coining   (D) embossing   (Ans. B)

35. The equipment generally used for metal spinning is

(A) mechanical press (B) hydraulic press   (C) drop hammer   (D) speed lathe (Ans. D)

36. Collapsible tubes are made by

(A) direct extrusion   (B) Indirect extrusion

(C) cold impact extrusion   (D) piercing   (Ans. C)

37. Large size Rivet heads are made by

(A) swaging   (B) hammerzing   (C) upset forging   (D) drop forging (Ans. C)

38. In blanking operation, the clearance is provided on ....   (Ans. Punch)

39. In punching operation, the clearance is provided on ....   (Ans. Die)

40. In punching operation, shear is provided on ....   (Ans. Punch)

41. In blanking operation, shear is provided on ....   (Ans. Die)

42. In punching operation, the size of hole is dependent on the size of punch or die?

(Ans. Punch)

43. In Blanking operation, the size of blank is dependent on the size of punch or die?

(Ans. Die)

44. For the same thickness of sheet, the clearance is more for hard or ductile materials?

(Ans. Hard)

45. Blanking and Punching operations can be performed simultaneously on

(A) combination die (B) compound die   (C) progressive die   (D) simple die   (Ans. B)

46. Cutting and forming operations can be performed simultaneously on

(A) combination die (B) compound die   (C) progressive die   (D) simple die   (Ans. A)

47. Cold working of metal increases

(A) tensile strength   (B) hardness   (C) yield strength   (D) all of these (Ans. D)

48. The cutting force in punching and blanking operations mainly depends on

(A) the modulus of elasticity of metal   (B) the shear strength of metal

(C) the bulk modulus of the metal   (D) the yield strength of metal

[GATE 2001] (Ans. B)

49. Hot rolling of mild steel is carried out

(A) at recrystallisation temperature.   (B) Below 100°C and 150°C

(C) Above recrystallisation temperature   (D) Below recrystallisation temperature

(GATE 2001) (Ans. C)

50. When a steel undergoes a cold working process, it becomes progressively
    (A) Softer   (B) Harder
    (C) Ductile   (D) Malleable   (*UPSC, AMIE*) (**Ans.** B)
51. When a cold worked metal is heated upto its recrystallization temperature, it becomes :-
    (A) Harder   (B) Softer
    (C) Stays unchanged is hardness   (D) Staysunchanged in softness
                                                        (*L.U., A.M.I.E.*) (**Ans.** B)

CHAPTER 5

1. For resistance spot welding of 1.5 mm thick steel sheets, the current required is of the order
   of
   (A) 10 A   (B) 100 A   (C) 1000 A   (D) 10,000A
                                                        [*GATE 1992*] (**Ans.** D)
2. In an explosive welding process, the ..... (maximum/minimum) velocity of impact is fixed
   by the velocity of sound in the .... (flyer/target) plate material.
                                          [*GATE 1992*] (**Ans.** *maximum, flyer*)
3. In *d.c.* welding, the straight polarity (electrode negative) results in
   (A) lower penetration   (B) lower depositing rate
   (C) less heating of work piece   (D) smaller weld pod [*GATE 1993*] (**Ans.** B)
4. The electrodes used in arc welding are coated electrodes. The coating is not expected to
   (A) provide protective atmosphere to weld (B) Stabilize the arc
   (C) Add alloying elements   (D) Prevent electrode from contamination
                                                        [*GATE1994*] (**Ans.** D)
5. The ratio of acetylene to oxygen is approximately ...... for a neutral flame used in gas
   welding.   [*GATE 1994*] (**Ans.** 1 : 1)
6. Preheating before welding is done to
   (A) make the steel softer
   (B) burn away oil, grease etc. from the plate surface
   (C) prevent cold cracks
   (D) prevent plate distortion   [*GATE 1996]* (**Ans.**
7. Match 4 correct pairs between List I and List II
   List I   *List II*
   (A) Welding of aluminium alloy   1. Submerged arc welding
   (B) Ship building   2. Electron beam welding
   (C) Joining of HSS drill bit to carbon steel shank 3. TIG welding
   (D) Deep penetration precision welds 4. Gas welding
                          [*GATE 1996*] (**Ans.** A – 3, B – 1, C – 4, D – 2)
8. For butt-welding 40 mm thick steel plates when the expected quantity of such jobs is 5000
   per month over a period of 10 years, choose the best suitable welding process out of the
   following available alternatives
   (A) Submerged arc welding   (B) Oxy–acetylene gas welding
   (C) Electron beam welding   (D) MIG welding   [*GATE 1999*] (**Ans.** B)
9. Electron–beam welding can be carried out in
   (A) open air   (B) a shielding gas environment
   (C) a pressurised inert gas chamber (D) vacuum
                                                        [*IES 1993*] (**Ans.** D)
10. In gas welding of mild steel using an oxy-acetylene flame, the total amount of acetylene
    used was 10 litre. The oxygen consumption from the cylinder is
    (A) 5 litre   (B) 10 litre   (C) 15 litre   (D) 20 litre
                                                        [*IAS 1994*] (**Ans.** B)

[**Hint:** For gas welding of M.S. neutral flame is used].

11. Which one of the following welding processes uses non-consumable electrodes:
    (A) TIG welding   (B) MIG welding
    (C) Manual arc welding   (D) Submerged arc welding
                                                          [*IES 1994*] (**Ans.** A)

12. Match List I with List II and select the correct answer using the codes given below the lists:
    List I (Filler)   *List II (Joining process)*
    A. Cu, Zn, Ag alloy   1. Braze welding
    B. Cu, Sn, alloy   2. Brazing
    C. Pb, Sb alloy   3. Soldering
    D. Iron oxide and aluminium powder   4. TIG welding of Al
    Codes:

	A	B	C	D		A	B	C	D
(a)	2	1	3	–	(b)	1	2	4	–
(c)	2	1	3	4	(d)	2	–	3	4

                                                          [*IES 1994*] (**Ans.** *a*)

13. Consider the following statements:
    MIG welding process uses
    1. consumable electrode   2. non-consumable electrode
    3. D.C. power supply   4. A.C. power supply
    Of these statements
    (A) 2 and 4 are correct   (B) 2 and 3 are correct
    (C) 1 and 4 are correct   (D) 1 and 3 are correct   [*IES 1997*] (**Ans.** D)

14. In oxy-acetylene gas welding, for complete combustion, the volume of oxygen required per unit ton of acetylene is
    (A) 1   (B) 1.5   (C) 2   (D) 2.5
                                                          [*IES 1998*] (**Ans.** D)

15. The voltage-current characteristics of a dc generator for arc welding is a straight line between an open circuit voltage of 80 V and short circuit current of 300 A. The generator setting for maximum arc power will be
    (A) 80 V and 150 A   (B) 40 V and 300 A   (C) 40 V and 150 A   (D) 80 V and 300 A
                                                          [*IES 1998*] (**Ans.** C)

16. Which of the following joining processes are best suited for manufacturing pipes to carry gas products?
    1. riveting   2. welding   3. nuts and bolts
    Select the correct answer using the codes given below:
    Codes :
    (A) 1 and 2   (B) 1 and 3   (C) 2 alone   (D) 1, 2 and 3
                                                          [*IES 1998*] (**Ans.** C)

17. The correct sequence of the given materials in descending order of their weldability is
    (A) MS, Cu, C.I, Al   (B) C.I., M.S., Al, Cu   (C) Cu, C.I., MS, Al   (D) Al, Cu, C.I., M.S.
                                                          [*IES 1999*] (**Ans.** A)

18. Failure of a bead weld between a heavy steel section and a thin section is mainly due to the formation of
    (A) spheriodite
    (B) bainite
    (C) carbon free zone due to burning of carbon at high temperature
    (D) martensite   [*GATE 1998*] (**Ans.** C)

19. The open circuit voltage (OCV) in arc welding ranges from:
    (A) 40 to 80 V   (B) 100 to 100 V   (C) 200 to 220 V   (D) 400 to 440 V
                                                                       (**Ans.** A)

20. In thermit welding, heat is generated
    (A) From combustion of gas
    (B) By an arc
    (C) By chemical reaction between aluminium and iron oxide
    (D) None of the above   **(Ans. C)**

21. For resistance welding
    (A) voltage is high, current is low   (B) voltage is low, current is high
    (C) both voltage and current are low   (D) both voltage and current are high
                                                                                             (Ans. B)

22. In resistance welding, the greatest resistance, when the power is switched on, is:
    (A) At the point of contact between the electrode and the job.
    (B) At the point of contact of work pieces to be joined
    (C) At the surface
    (D) None of the above   **(Ans. B)**

23. The maximum temperature produced by oxy-hydrogen flame is about:
    (A) 3300°C   (B) 2500°C   (C) 2000°C   (D) 1800°C   **(Ans. B)**

24. Majority of the oxy-acetylene welding is done with:
    (A) Neutral flame   (B) Reducing flame   (C) Oxidising flame   **(Ans. A)**

25. Brasses and Bronzes are welded by:
    (A) Neutral flame   (B) Reducing flame   (C) Oxidising flame   **(Ans. C)**

26. Fluxes are used while welding :
    (A) to increase the rate of welding
    (B) to clean the joint
    (C) to prevent oxidation of metal during welding
    (D) all the above   **(Ans. D)**

27. The selection of welding electrodes depends upon:
    (A) the thickness of the metal to be joined (B) the type of metal to be joined
    (C) position of welding   (D) strength of joint
    (E) all the above   **(Ans. E)**

28. Low pressure OAW is the name given to the welding process in which
    (A) Oxygen is supplied at low pressure
    (B) Acetylene is supplied at low pressure
    (C) Both oxygen and Acetylene are supplied at low pressure   **(Ans. B)**

29. In arc welding, the electric arc is produced between the job and the electrode due to
    (A) Voltage   (B) flow of current   (C) contact resistance (D) All of the above
                                                                                             (Ans. D)

30. In submerged arc welding, the arc is struck between
    (A) Consumable coated electrode and job (B) Non-consumable electrode and job
    (C) Consumable bare electrode and job   (D) Two tungsten electrodes and the job
                                                                                             (Ans. C)

Note: For MIG, the answer will be C
TIG, the answer will be B
SMAW, the answer will be A.

31. Resistance spot welding is performed on two plates of 1.5 mm thickness with 6 mm diameter electrode, using 15000 A current for a time duration of 0.25 s. Assuming the interface resistance to be 0.0001 ohm, the heat generated to form the weld is
    (A) 5625 W-sec   (B) 8437 W-sec   (C) 22500 W-sec   (D) 33750 W-sec
                                                                        [GATE 2001] **(Ans. A)**

32. Two plates of the same metal having equal thickness are to be butt welded with electric arc. When the plate thickness changes, welding is achieved by
    (A) adjusting the current   (B) adjusting the duration of current
    (C) changing the electrode size   (D) changing the electrode coating
                                                          (GATE 2001) **(Ans. A, C)**.

33. Which of the following arc welding processes does not use consumable electrodes :
    (A) SAW   (B) GMAW
    (C) GTAW   (D) None of these   *(GATE 2002)* **(Ans. C)**

34. The temperature of a carburising flame in gas welding is .... that of a neutral or oxidising flame.
    (A) Lower than   (B) Higher than
    (C) Equal to   (D) Unrelated to   *(GATE 2002)* **(Ans. A)**

35. The arc length-voltage characteristic of a D.C. arc is given by the equation $V = 24 + 4L$, where V is voltage in volts and L is arc length in mm. The static volt-ampere characteristic of the power source is approximated by a straight line with a no load voltage of 80 V and a short circuit current of 600 A. Determine the optimum arc length for maximum power.
                                                                              (GATE 2002)

Solution :

$V = 24 + 4L$

The static volt-ampere characteristic of power source is given as,

$$\frac{V}{80} + \frac{I}{600} = 1$$

Now Power, $P = V \times I$

$$= (24 + 4L) \times \left(1 - \frac{V}{80}\right) \times 600$$

$$= (24 + 4L) \times \left(\frac{80 - 24 - 4L}{80}\right) \times 600$$

$$= \frac{6 + L}{20} \times (56 - 4L) \times 600$$

$$= 120 (6 + L) (14 - L)$$
$$= 120 (84 + 8L - L^2)$$

For Max. P, $\dfrac{\partial P}{\partial L} = 0$

$\therefore$ $0 + 120 \times 8 - 2L \times 120 = 0$

$\therefore$ $L = 4$ mm

36. The purose of a gas-welding flux is to:
    (A) Lower the melting point of the metal
    (B) Lower the melting point of the oxide
    (C) Remove oxides from the surface of the metal
    (D) Remove elements from paront metal   *(L.U., BTE, M.U.)* **(Ans. C)**

37. The flux coating of an electric arc electrode has a melting point:
    (A) Higher than the metallic core
    (B) Lower than the metallic core
    (C) The same as the metallic core
    (D) The same as the metal being welded.   **(Ans. A)**

38. Which gas from the following will form a hard constituent when it combines with molten steel and remains after solidification has taken place:
    (A) O_2 (B) N_2
    (C) H_2 (D) He   (*BHU, BTE, AMIE, I.Mech.E*) (**Ans.** B)
39. The purpose of preheating low-alloy steel pipes, before they are electric arc welded is to:
    (A) Refine grain structure
    (B) Relieve internal streesses
    (C) Retard rapid cooling
    (D) Regulate excessive expansion   (*L.U., AMIE, UPSC*) (**Ans.** C)
40. Hard-Zone cracking in low-alloy steel due to welding is the result of an absorption of:–
    (A) N_2 (B) O_2
    (C) H_2 (D) C^2 (*BTE, UPSC, DU*) (**Ans.** C) .
41. A low carbon steel plate is to be welded by the manual metal are welding process using a linear V – I characteristic D – C. Power source. The following data are available :
    OCV of Power source = 62 V
    Short circuit current = 130 A
    Arc length, L = 4 mm
    Traverse speed of welding = 15 cm/mm
    Efficiency of heat input = 85%
    Voltage is given as V = 20 + 1.5 L
    Calculate the heat input into the workprice   (*GATE 1992*)
    Solution. Volt ampere characteristic of source is given as

    $$\frac{V}{62} + \frac{I}{130} = 1$$

    Now V = 20 + 1.5 × 4 = 26 Volts

    $$\therefore \; I = 130\left(1 - \frac{26}{62}\right) = 75.5 \text{ A}$$

    $\therefore$ Power consumed, P = V × I = 75.5 × 26 = 1963 W
    Efficiency of heat input = 85%
    $\therefore$ Heat input into workpiece = 0.85 × 1963 = 1668.5 watts

CHAPTER – 6, 7, 8

1. The effect of rake angle on the mean friction angle in machining can be explained by
   (A) sliding (Coulomb) model of friction   (B) sticking and then sliding model of friction
   (C) sticking friction
   (D) Sliding and then sticking model of friction   [*GATE 1992*] (**Ans.** D)
2. In horizontal milling process ..... (up/down) milling provides better surface finish and ...... (up/down) milling provides longer tool life.   [*GATE 1992*] (**Ans.** *down, down*)
3. Match the following components with the appropriate machining process:

Component	Process
(A) Square hole in a high strength alloy	(P) Milling
(B) Square hole in a ceramic component	(Q) Drilling
(C) Blind hole in a die	(R) ECM
(D) Turbine blade profile on high strength alloy	(S) Jig boring
	(T) EDM
	(U) USM

   [*GATE 1992*] (**Ans.** A – T, B – U, C – P, D – R)
4. The cross-feed on a shaper consists of a lead screw having 0.2 threads per mm. A ratchet and pawl on the end of the lead screw is driven from the shaper crank such that the pawl indexes the ratchet by one tooth during each return stroke of the ram. Ratchet has 20 teeth.

(A) Find the feed in mm

(B) If a plate 100 mm wide has to be machined in 10 minutes, find the cutting speed in metres/sec. The ratio of return speed to cutting speed is 2 : 1, and the length of the stroke is 150 mm.   [GATE 1992]

Solution.   Pitch of lead screw = $\dfrac{1}{0.2}$ = 5 mm

Now,   the pawl indexes $\dfrac{1}{20}$ revolutions per stroke

∴   (A) Cross feed = $\dfrac{5}{20}$ = 0.25 mm,

(B) Number of cutting strokes = $\dfrac{\text{width of job}}{\text{cross feed per stroke}}$

$$= \dfrac{100}{0.25} = 400$$

Refer to Art 8.2.4.

$$V = \dfrac{LN(1+K)}{1000} \text{ min}$$

L = Length of ram stroke = 150 mm
N = Number of full strokes/min

$$= \dfrac{400}{\text{Time}} = \dfrac{400}{10} = 40$$

$$K = \dfrac{\text{Return time}}{\text{Cutting time}} = \dfrac{\text{Cutting speed}}{\text{Return speed}} = \dfrac{1}{2}$$

∴ $$V = \dfrac{150 \times 40 \times 1.5}{1000} = 9 \text{ m/min.}$$

$$= 0.15 \text{ m/s}$$

5   A milling cutter having 8 teeth is rotating at 150 rpm. If the feed per tooth is 0.1 mm, the value of the table speed in mm/min is
(A) 120   (B) 187   (C) 125   (D) 70
[GATE 1993] (Ans. A)

6. To get good surface finish on a turned job, one should use a sharp tool with a .... feed and ...... speed of rotation of the job.   [GATE1994] (Ans. *Minimum, maximum*)

7. Among the conventional, machining process, maximum specific energy is consumed in
(A) Turning   (B) Drilling   (C) Planing   (D) Grinding
[GATE 1995] (Ans. D)

8. Cutting power consumption in turning can be significantly reduced by
(A) increasing rake angle of the tool   (B) increasing the cutting angle of the tool
(C) widening the nose radius of the tool   (D) increasing the clearance angle
[GATE 1995] (Ans. A)

9. Plain milling of mild steel plate produces
(A) irregular shaped discontinuous chips   (B) regular shaped discontinuous chips
(C) continuous chips without built up edge(D) jointed chips   [GATE 1995] (Ans. C)

10. Diamond wheels should not be used for grinding steel components.
[GATE 1995] (Ans. *True*)

11. Match 4 correct pairs

List I	List II
(Manufacturing Processes)	(Conditions)
(A) Finish turning	1. Backlash eliminator
(B) Forming	2. Zero rake
(C) Thread cutting	3. Nose radius
(D) Down milling	4. Low speed

    [*GATE 1995*] (**Ans.** A – 2, B– 3, C– 4, D– 1).

12. The rake angle in a drill
    (A) increases from centre to periphery   (B) decreases from centre to periphery
    (C) remains constant   (D) is irrelevant to the drilling operation

    [*GATE 1996*] (**Ans.** D)

13. Helix angle of a fast helix drill is normally
    (A) 35°   (B) 60°   (C) 90°   (D) 5°

    [*GATE 1997*] (**Ans.** A)

14. In machining using abrasive material, increasing abrasive grain size
    (A) increases the material removal rate
    (B) decreases the material removal rate
    (C) first decreases and then increases the material removal rate
    (D) first increases and then decreases the material removal rate   [*GATE 1998*]   (**Ans.** D)

15. Abrasive material used in grinding wheel selected for grinding ferrous alloys is
    (A) Silicon carbide   (B) diamond   (C) aluminium oxide (D) boron carbide

    [*GATE 2000*] (**Ans.** C)

16. Match List I with List II and select the correct answer using the codes given below the lists:

List I	List II
(Cutting tool Material)	(Major characteristic constituent)
A. High Speed Steel	1. Carbon
B. Stellite	2. Molybdenum
C. Diamond	3. Nitride
D. Coated Carbide tool	4. Columbium
	5. Cobalt

Codes:	A	B	C	D		A	B	C	D
(a)	2	1	3	5	(b)	2	5	1	3
(c)	5	2	4	3	(d)	5	4	2	3

    [*IES 1993*] (**Ans.** b)

17. Consider the following parameters:
    1. Grinding wheel diameter
    2. Regulating wheel diameter
    3. Speed of grinding wheel
    4. Speed of the regulating wheel
    5. Angle between the axes of grinding and regulating wheels
    Among these parameters, those which influence the axial feed rate in centreless grinding would include:
    (A) 2, 4 and 5   (B) 1, 2 and 3   (C) 1, 4 and 5   (D) 3, 4 and 5

    [*IES 1993*] (**Ans.** A)

18. It is required to cut screw threads of 2 mm pitch on a lathe. The lead screw has a pitch of 6 mm. If the spindle speed is 60 rpm, then the speed of the lead screw will be
    (A) 10 rpm   (B) 20 rpm   (C) 120 rpm   (D) 180 rpm

    [*IES 1993*] (**Ans.** B)

19. A dynamometer is a device used for the measurement of
    (A) chip thickness ratio   (B) forces during metal cutting
    (C) wear of the cutting tool   (D) deflection of the cutting tool
                                                          [IES 1993] (Ans. B)
20. The main purpose of boring operation, as compared to drilling is to:
    (A) drill a hole   (B) finish the drilled hole
    (C) correct the hole   (D) enlarge the existing hole
                                                      [IES 1993] (Ans. B, C, D)
21. Climb milling is chosen while machining because
    (A) the chip thickness increases gradually
    (B) it enables the cutter to dig in and start the cut
    (C) the specific power consumption is reduced
    (D) better surface finish can be obtained   [IES 1993] (Ans. D)
22. In centreless grinding, the workpiece centre will be
    (A) above the line joining the two wheel centres
    (B) below the line joining the two wheel centres
    (C) on the line joining the two wheel centres
    (D) at the intersection of the line joining the wheel centres with the work plate plane
                                                          [IES 1993] (Ans. A)
23. A hole of 30 mm diameter is to be produced by reaming. The minimum diameter permissible is 30.00 mm while the maximum diameter permissible is 30.05 mm. In this regard, consider the following statements about the reamer size:
    1. The minimum diameter of the reamer can be less than 30 mm
    2. The minimum diameter of the reamer can not be less than 30 mm
    3. The maximum diameter of the reamer can be more than 30.05 mm
    4. The maximum diameter of the reamer must be less than 30.05 mm
    Of these statements
    (A) 1 and 4 are correct   (B) 1 and 3 are correct
    (C) 2 and 3 are correct   (D) 2 and 4 are correct   [IES 1993] (Ans. A)
24. A standard dividing head is equipped with the following index plates
    1. Plate with 15, 16, 17, 18, 19,20 holes circles
    2. Plate with 21, 23, 27, 29, 31, 33 holes circles
    3. Plate with 37, 39, 41, 43,47,49 holes circles
    For obtaining 24 divisions on a workpiece by simple indexing
    (A) hole plate 2 alone can be used   (B) hole plates 1 and 2 can be used
    (C) hole plates 1 and 3 can be used   (D) any of the three hole plates can be used
                                                          [IAS 1994] (Ans. D)
25. Size of a shaper is given by
    (A) stroke length   (B) motor power
    (C) weight of the machine   (D) table size   [IAS 1995] (Ans. A)
26. Consider the following tool materials:
    1. Carbide 2. Cermet 3. Ceramic 4. Borazon
    Correct sequence of these tool materials in increasing order of their ability to retain their hot hardness is
    (A) 1, 2, 3, 4   (B) 1, 2, 4, 3   (C) 2, 1, 3, 4   (D) 2, 1, 4, 3
                                                          [IES 1994] (Ans. C)
27. Enlarging an existing circular hole with a rotating single point tool is called
    (A) boring   (B) drilling   (C) reaming   (D) internal turning
                                                          [IES 1994] (Ans. A)

28. Consider the following statements regarding grinding of high carbon steel
    1. Grinding at high speeds results in the reduction of chip thickness and cutting forces per grit.
    2. Aluminium oxide wheels are employed
    3. The grinding wheel has to be of open structure. Of these statements
    (A) 1, 2 and 3 are correct   (B) 1 and 2 are correct
    (C) 1 and 3 are correct   (D) 2 and 3 are correct   [IES 1994] (Ans. B)

29. Consider the following operations:
    1. Cutting keyways on shafts   2. Cutting external screw threads
    3. Cutting teeth of spur gears 4. Cutting external splines
    Those which can be performed with milling cutters would include:
    (A) 1 and 2   (B) 2, 3 and 4   (C) 1 and 3   (D) 1, 2, 3 and 4
                                                                  [IES 1994] (Ans. D)

30. In reaming process
    (A) metal removal rate is high   (B) high surface finish is obtained
    (C) high form accuracy is obtained   (D) high dimensional accuracy is obtained
                                                                  [IES 1994] (Ans. B)

31. Cubic boron nitride is used
    (A) as lining material in induction furnaces (B) for making optical quality glass
    (C) for heat treatment   (D) for none of the above [IES 1993] (Ans. D)

32. The compositions of some of the alloy steels are as under :
    1. 18 W 4 Cr 1 V   2. 12 Mo 1 W 4 Cr 1 V
    3. 6 Mo 6W 4 Cr 1 V   4. 18 W 8 Cr 1 V
    The compositions of commonly used high speed steels would include :
    (A) 1 and 2   (B) 2 and 3
    (C) 1 and 4   (D) 1 and 3   (IES 1995)(Ans. C)

33. The straight grades of cemented carbide cuttingtool materials contain
    (A) Tungsten carbide only   (B) tungsten carbide and titanium carbide
    (C) tungsten carbide and cobalt.   (D) tungsten carbide and cobalt carbide
                                                                  (IES 1995) (Ans. C)

34. In the grinding wheel of A60G7B23, B stands for
    (A) resinoid bond   (B) rubber bond
    (C) shellac bond   (D) silicate bond   (IES 1995) (Ans. A)

35. Soft materials can not be economically ground due to
    (A) the high temperature involved   (B) frequent wheel clogging
    (C) rapid wheel wear   (D) low work piece stiffness.
                                                                  (IES 1995) (Ans. B)

36. In a milling operation, two side milling cutters are mounted with a desired distance between them so that both sides of a workpiece can be milled simultaneously. This set up is called
    (A) gang milling   (B) straddle milling
    (C) Side milling   (IES 1995) (Ans. B)

37. In a mechanical shaper, the length of stroke is increased by
    (A) increasing the centre distance of bull gear and crank pin
    (B) decreasing the centre distance of bull gear and crank pin
    (C) increasing the length of ram.
    (D) decreasing the length of slot in the slotted lever   (IES 19995) (Ans. A)

38. Cubic Boron Nitride
    (A) has a very high hardness which is comparable to that of diamond

(B) has a hardness which is slightly more than that of HSS.

(C) is used for making cylindrical blocks of aircraft engines

(D) is used for making optical glasses   [*IES 1996*] (**Ans. A**)

39. The limit to the maximum hardness of a work material which can be machined with HSS tools even at low speeds is set by which of the following tool failure mechanisms?

(A) Attrition   (B) Abrasion

(C) Diffusion   (D) Plastic deformation under compression

[*IES 1996*] (**Ans. A**)

40. A machanist desires to turn a round steel block of outside diameter 100 mm at 1000 rpm. The material has tensile strength of 75 kg/mm^2. The depth of cut chosen is 3 mm at a feed rate of 0.3 mm/rev. Which one of the following tool materials will be suitable for machining the component under the specified cutting conditions?

(A) Sintered Carbides (B) Ceramic   (C) HSS   (D) Diamond

[*IES 1996*] (**Ans. B**)

[**Hint:** Find cutting speed]

41. In turning of slender rods, it is necessary to keep the transverse force minimum mainly to

(A) improve the surface finish   (B) increase productivity

(C) improve cutting efficiency   (D) reduce vibrations and chatter.

[*IES 1996*] (**Ans. D**)

42. A grinding wheel of 150 mm diameter is rotating at 3000 rpm. The grinding speed is

(A) 7.5 π m/s   (B) 15 π m/s   (C) 45 π m/s   (D) 450 π m/s

[*IES 1996*] (**Ans. A**)

43. Which of the following statements are correct?

1. A boring machine is suitable for job shop.

2. A jig boring machine is designed specially for doing more accurate work when compared to a vertical milling machine.

3. A vertical precision boring machine is suitable for boring holes in cylindrical blocks and lines

(A) 1, 2 and 3   (B) 1 and 2   (C) 2 and 3   (D) 1 and 3

[*IES 1996*] (**Ans. C**)

44. Match List I (Type of drill) with List II (Application) and select the correct answer using the codes given below the lists:

List I	*List II*
A. Straight shank	1. Soft materials
B. Taper Shank	2. Deep holes
C. Single flute	3. General purpose
D. High helix	4. Small hole diameter

Codes:

	A	B	C	D		A	B	C	D
(a)	3	4	1	2	(b)	3	4	2	1
(c)	4	3	2	1	(d)	4	3	1	2

[*IES 1997*] (**Ans. c**)

45. Which of the following are the advantages of a hydraulic shaper over a mechanically driven shaper?

1. More strokes can be obtained per minute at a given cutting speed.

2. The cutting stroke has a definite stopping point

3. It is simpler in construction

4. Cutting speed is constant throughout most of the cutting stroke

Select the correct answer using the codes given below:

(A) 1 and 2   (B) 1 and 4   (C) 2 and 4   (D) 1, 3 and 4

[*IES 1997*] (**Ans. B**)

46. Consider the following operations:
    1. Under cutting 2. Plain turning 3. Taper turning 4. Thread cutting
    The correct sequence of these operations in machining a product is
    (A) 2, 3, 4, 1   (B) 3, 2, 4, 1   (C) 2, 3, 1, 4   (D) 3, 2, 1, 4
                                                                        [*IES 1997*] **(Ans. C)**

47. Which one of the following materials is used as the bonding material for grinding wheels?
    (A) Silicon carbide   (B) Sodium silicate   (C) Boron carbide   (D) Aluminium oxide
                                                                        [*IES 1997*] **(Ans. B)**

48. Consider the following statements:
    In up-milling process
    1. The cutter starts the cut from the machine surface and proceeds upwards
    2. The cutter starts the cut from the top surface and proceeds downwards
    3. The job is fed in a direction opposite to that of cutter rotation
    4. The job is fed in the same direction as that of cutter rotation. Of these statements:
    (A) 1 and 3 are correct   (B) 1 and 4 are correct
    (C) 2 and 3 are correct   (D) 2 and 4 are correct   [*IES 1997*] **(Ans. A)**

49 The type of quick return mechanism employed mostly in shaping machines is:
    (A) D.C. reversible motor   (B) Fast and loose pulleys
    (C) Whit worth motion   (D) Slotted link mechanism
                                                                        [*IES 1997*] **(Ans. D)**

50 A 400 mm long shaft has a 100 mm tapered step at the middle with 4° included angle. The
    tail stock offset required to produce this taper on a lathe would be
    (A) 400 sin 4°   (B) 400 sin 2°   (C) 100 sin 4°   (D) 100 sin 2°
                                                                        [*IES 1998*] **(Ans. B)**

51 A single start thread of pitch 2 mm is to be produced on a lathe having a lead screw with
    a double start thread of pitch 4 mm. The ratio of speeds between the spindle and lead screw
    for this operation is
    (A) 1 : 2   (B) 2 : 1   (C) 1 : 4   (D) 4 : 1
                                                                        [*IES 1998*] **(Ans. D)**

52. Match List I with List II and select the correct answer using the codes given below the lists
    List I   *List II*
    A. Reaming   1. Smoothing and squaring surface around the hole for proper seat
                                   ing
    B. Counter-boring   2. Sizing and finishing the hole
    C. Counter-sinking   3. Enlarging the end of the hole
    D. Spot facing   4. Making a conical enlargement at the end of the hole
    Codes:

	A	B	C	D		A	B	C	D
(a)	3	2	4	1	(b)	2	3	1	4
(c)	3	2	1	4	(d)	2	3	4	1

                                                                        [*IES 1998*] **(Ans. d)**

53. Which one of the following pairs of parameters and effects is not correctly matched?
    (A) Large wheel diameter ...... Reduced wheel wear
    (B) Large depth of cut .... Increased wheel wear
    (C) Large work diameter .... Increased wheel wear
    (D) Large wheel speed ...... Reduced wheel wear   [*IES 1998*] **(Ans. D)**

54. A component requires a hole which must be within two limits of 25.03 and 25.04 mm
    diameter. Which of the following statements about the reamer size are correct?
    1. Reamer size can not be below 25.03 mm

2. Reamer size can not be above 25.04 mm

3. Reamer size can be 25.04 mm

4. Reamer size can be 25.03 mm

Select the correct answer using the codes given below:

(A) 1 and 3   (B) 1 and 2   (C) 3 and 4   (D) 2 and 4

[IES 1998] **(Ans. D)**

55. In metal cutting operation, the approximate ratio of heat distributed among chip, tool and work, in that order is

(A) 80 : 10 : 10   (B) 33 : 33 : 33   (C) 20 : 60 : 10   (D) 10 : 10 : 80

[IES 1998] **(Ans. A)**

56. Which one of the following sets of forces are encountered by a lathe parting tool while groove cutting:

(A) Tangential, radial and axial   (B) Tangential and radial

(C) Tangential and axial   (D) Radial and axial   *[IES 1999]* **(Ans. A)**

57. In a single-point turning operation of steel with Cemented carbide tool, Taylor's tool life exponent is 0.25. If the cutting speed is halved, the tool life will increase by

(A) two times   (B) four times   (C) eight times   (D) sixteen times

[IES 1999] **(Ans. D)**

58. Match List I (ISO classification of carbide tools) with List II (applications) and select the correct answer using the codes given below the lists :

List I	List II
A. P – 10	1. Non-ferrous roughing cut
B. P – 50	2. Non-ferrous, finishing cut
C. K – 10	3. Ferrous materials, roughing cut
D. K – 50	4. Ferrous materials, finishing cut

Codes:

	A	B	C	D		A	B	C	D
(a)	4	3	1	2	(b)	3	4	2	1
(c)	4	3	2	1	(d)	3	4	1	2

[IES 1999] **(Ans. d)**

59. Consider the following statements:

For precision machining of non-ferrous alloys, diamond is preferred because it has

1. low co-efficient of thermal expansion 2. high wear resistance

3. high compression strength 4. low fracture toughness

Which of the following statements are correct?

(A) 1 and 2   (B) 1 and 4   (C) 2 and 3   (D) 3 and 4

[IES 1999] **(Ans. A)**

60. Which one of the following processes results in the best accuracy of the hole made?

(A) Drilling   (B) Reaming   (C) Broaching   (D) Boring

[IES 1999] **(Ans. D)**

61. Consider the following reasons:

1. Grinding wheel is soft   2. RPM of grinding wheel is too low

3. Cut is very fine   4. An important cutting fluid is used

A grinding wheel may become loaded due to reasons stated at

(A) 1 and 4   (B) 1 and 3   (C) 2 and 4   (D) 2 and 3

[IES 1999] **(Ans. B)**

62. Consider the following statements regarding reaming process:

1. Reaming generally produces a hole larger than its own diameter

2. Generally rake angles are not provided on reamers

3. Even numbers of teeth are preferred in reamer design

Which of these statements are correct?

(A) 1 and 2   (B) 2 and 3   (C) 1 and 3   (D) 1, 2 and 3

[IES 1999] (Ans. D)

63. Match List-I (Drill bits) with List-II (Applications) and select the correct answer using the codes given below the lists:

   List I   *List II*
   A. Core drill   1. To enlarge a hole to a certain depth so as to accommodate the bolt head of a screw
   B. Reamer   2. To drill and enlarge an already existing hole in a casting
   C. Counter bore drill   3. To drill a hole before making internal threads
   D. Tap drill   4. To improve the surface finish and dimensional accuracy of the already drilled hole

   Codes:

	A	B	C	D		A	B	C	D
(a)	1	3	2	4	(b)	2	3	1	4
(c)	2	4	1	3	(d)	3	2	4	1

[IES 1999] (Ans. c)

64. When milling a slot 20 mm wide × 10 cm long in a rectangular plate 10 cm × 20 cm, the cutting speed = 60 m/min; Diameter of end drill = 20 mm
   Number of flutes = 8, Feed = 0.01 mm/flute
   Depth of cut = 3 mm
   Find the cutting time for the operation to be completed in a single pass.   [GATE 1994]

   Solution. Cutting time is given as,

   $$T_m = \frac{l+x+y}{F}, \text{ min}$$

   Where l = length of job = 100 mm

   $$x = \text{Cutter approach} = \frac{D}{2} = 10 \text{ mm}$$

   y = Cutter overtravel = 5 mm (say)
   F = Table feed, mm/min
   $= f_t \times n \times N$
   f_t = feed per tooth, per rev. = 0.01 mm
   n = number of flutes = 8
   N = Spindle rev./min.

   $$= \frac{V \times 1000}{\pi D} = \frac{60 \times 1000}{\pi \times 20}$$

   $$= 955 \text{ rev./min}$$

   $$\therefore \quad T_m = \frac{100+10+5}{0.01 \times 8 \times 955}$$

   $$= \frac{115}{76.4} = 1.505 \text{ min.}$$

65. A grinding wheel A24K7V is specified for finish grinding of a HSS cutting tool. What do you understand about the wheel from the above code? Is this an appropriate choice?
   [GATE 1994]

   Solution.   Code is A 24 K 7 V

   $A \longrightarrow$ Abrasive type, it is Al_2O_3.

Appendix III

24 ⟶ Grain size, it is coarse

K ⟶ grade, it is medium grade

7 ⟶ Structure, it is medium structure

V ⟶ Bond type, it is Vitrified bond

For finish grinding of HSS tool, fine grit is needed. The grit size in the grinding wheel is coarse, so it is not an appropriate choice.

66. Why can we use higher cutting speeds with H.S.S. tools than with carbon steel tools? [GATE 1994]

[Hint: Because of the presence of alloying elements]

67. State the Taylor's equation for tool life. [GATE 1994]

68. Tool life testing on a lathe under dry cutting conditions gave n and C of Taylor's tool life equation as 0.12 and 130 m/min respectively. When a coolant was used, C increased by 10%. Find the percentage increase in tool life with the use of coolant at a cutting speed of 90 m/min. [GATE 2001]

Solution. $V.T_1^n = C_1$

∴ $90.T_1^{0.12} = 130$

From here, $T_1 = 21.42$ min.

Now $C_2 = 130 + 13 = 143$

$90.T_2^{0.12} = 143$

∴ $T_2 = 47.40$ min

∴ Percentage increase in tool life = 121.29%

69. A lead-screw with half nuts in a lathe, free to rotate in both directions has
(A) V-threads
(B) Whitworth threads
(C) Buttress threads
(D) ACME threads. (GATE 2002) (Ans. D)

70. The time taken to drill hole through a 25 mm thick plate with the drill rotating at 300 rpm and moving at a feed rate of 0.25 mm/rev is
(A) 10 s
(B) 20 s
(C) 100 s
(D) 200 s (GATE 2002) (Ans. B)

71. The hardness of a grinding wheel is determined by the
(A) hardness of abrasive grains
(B) ability of the bond to retain abrasives
(C) hardness of the bond
(D) ability of grinding wheel to penetrate the work piece (GATE 2002) (Ans. B)

72. A built-up-edge is formed while machining
(A) ductile material at high speed
(B) ductile material at low speed
(C) brittle material at high speed
(D) brittle material at low speed (GATE 2002) (Ans. B)

73. Trepanning is performed for
(A) Finishing a drilled hole
(B) Producing a large hole without drilling
(C) Truing a hole for alignment
(D) Enlarging a drilled hole (GATE 2002) (Ans. B)

CHAPTER 9

1. In Ultrasonic Machining (USM) the material removal rate would
(A) increase
(B) decrease
(C) increase and then decrease
(D) decrease and then increase with increasing mean grain diameter of the abrasive material. [GATE 1992] (Ans. A)

2. The two main criteria for selecting the electrolyte in Electrochemical Machining (ECM) is that the electrolyte should
   (A) be chemically stable   (B) not allow dissolution of Cathode material
   (C) not allow dissolution of anode material (D) have high electrical conductivity
                                                    [GATE 1992] (Ans. A, D)
3. In ultrasonic machining process, the material removal rate will be higher for materials with
   (A) higher toughness (B) higher ductility   (C) lower toughness (D) higher fracture strain
                                                    [GATE 1993] (Ans. C)
4. Electrical discharge machining imposes larger forces on tool than Electrochemical machining
                                                    [GATE 1994] (Ans. True)
5. Electric Discharge machining is more efficient than Electrochemical machining for producing large non-circular holes.
                                                    [GATE 1994] (Ans. True)
6. Ultrasonic machining is about the best process for making holes in glass which are comparable in size with the thickness of the sheet.   [GATE 1994] (Ans. True)
7. Selection of electrolyte for ECM is as follows:
   (A) non-passivating electrolyte for stock removal and passivating electrolyte for finish control
   (B) passivating electrolyte for stock removal and non-passivating electrolyte for finish control
   (C) selection of electrolyte is dependent on current density
   (D) electrolyte is based on tool-work electrodes   [GATE 1997] (Ans. D)
8. Inter electrode gap in ECG is controlled by
   (A) controlling the pressure of electrolyte flow
   (B) Controlling the applied static load
   (C) Controlling the size of diamond particle in the wheel
   (D) Controlling the texture of the workpiece   [GATE 1997] (Ans. C)
9. Match 4 correct pairs

   List I   List II
   (A) ECM   (1) Plastic Shear
   (B) EDM   (2) Erosion/Brittle fracture
   (C) USM   (3) Corrosive reaction
   (D) LBM   (4) Melting and vapourization
                                  (5) Ion displacement
                                  (6) Plastic shear and ion displacement
                      [GATE 1998] (Ans. A – 5, B – 1, C – 2, D – 4).
10. In Electro-Discharge Machining (EDM), the tool is made of
    (A) Copper   (B) High speed steel (C) Cast iron   (D) Plain carbon steel
                                                    [GATE 1999] (Ans. A)
11. Deep hole drilling of small diameter, say 0.2 mm is done with EDM by selecting the tool material as
    (A) copper wire   (B) tungsten wire   (C) brass wire   (D) tungsten Carbide
                                                    [GATE 2000] (Ans. D)
12. Match List I (Machining Process) with List II (Associated Medium) and select the correct answer using the codes given below the lists :
    List I   List II
    A. USM   1. Kerosene
    B. EDM   2. Abrasive slurry
    C. ECM   3. Vacuum
    D. EBM   4. Salt solution

Codes:

	A	B	C	D			A	B	C	D
(a)	2	3	4	1		(b)	2	1	4	3
(c)	4	1	2	3		(d)	4	3	2	1

[IES 1998] **(Ans.** *b***)**

13. Match List I with List II and select the correct answer using the codes given below the lists:

    List I
    A. Die-sinking
    B. Deburring
    C. Fine hole drilling (thin material)
    D. Cutting/hardening sharp materials

    List II
    1. Abrasive Jet machining
    2. Laser Beam Machining
    3. EDM
    4. Ultrasonic machining
    5. Electrochemical grinding

    Codes:

	A	B	C	D			A	B	C	D
(a)	3	5	4	1		(b)	2	4	1	3
(c)	3	1	2	5		(d)	4	5	1	3

[IES 1999] **(Ans.** *a***)**

14. For machining a complex contour on Tungsten Carbide work-piece, which process will be used?
    1. ECM   2. EDM   3. USM   4. EBM   **(Ans.** 2**)**

15. The current density used in ECM process is of the order of:
    (A) 100,00 A/cm^2 (B) 1000 A/cm^2 (C) 200 A/cm^2 (D) 10 A/cm^2 **(Ans.** C**)**

16. In ECM process, the electrolyte used is
    (A) kerosene   (B) water   (C) air   (D) Brine solution
                                                           (Ans. D**)**

17. In EDM process, the workpiece is connected to:
    (A) Cathode   (B) Anode   (C) Earth   (D) Any of these
                                                           (Ans. *B***)**

18. USM is best suited for which materials?
    (A) soft and ductile materials   (B) hard and brittle materials
    (C) Both of these materials
                                                           (Ans. B**)**

19. With increase in the frequency of tool oscillation, the MRR in USM will
    (A) first increase and then remain constant (B) first decrease and then remain constant
    (C) increase   (D) decrease   **(Ans.** A**)**

20. With increase in the abrasive slurry concentration, the MRR in USM will
    (A) increase   (B) decrease
    (C) first increase and then remain constant (D) first decrease and then remain constant
                                                             (Ans. C**)**

21. Holes in Nylon buttons are made by:
    (A) EDM   (B) CHM   (C) USM   (D) LBM   **(Ans.** D**)**

22. Integrated circuits and printed circuits are produced by
    (A) EDM   (B) CHM   (C) USM   (D) LBM   **(Ans.** B**)**

23. Which one of the following processes does not cause tool wear?
    (A) USM   (B) ECM
    (C) EDM   (D) Anode mechanical machining
                                                           [IES 1997] **(Ans.** B**)**

24. In ECM, the material removal is due to
    (A) Corrosion   (B) Erosion   (C) Fusion   (D) Ion displacement
                                                           [GATE 2001] **(Ans.** D**)**

CHAPTER 10

1. Generally cylindrical parts produced by powder metallurgy should not have non-uniform cross-section and a length to diameter ratio exceeding .... *[GATE 1994]* **(Ans. 2.5)**
2. Which of the following components can be manufactured by powder metallurgy methods?
   1. Carbide tool tips   2. Bearings   3. Filters   4. Brake linings
   Select the correct answer using the codes given below:
   (A) 1, 3 and 4   (B) 2 and 3   (C) 1, 2 and 4   (D) 1, 2, 3 and 4
                                                             [IES 1997] **(Ans. D)**
3. In Powder metallurgy, the operation carried out to improve the bearing property of a bush is called
   (A) Infiltration   (B) Impregnation   (C) Plating   (D) Heat treatment
                                                             [IES 1998] **(Ans. B)**
4. The correct sequence of the given processes in manufacturing by powder metallurgy is
   (A) blending, compacting, Sintering, sizing (B) blending, compacting, sizing, sintering
   (C) compacting, sizing, blending, sintering (D) compacting, blending, sizing and sintering
                                                             [IES 1999] **(Ans. A)**
5. The operation of filling the pores of a sintered component with molten metal is known as:
   (A) Sizing   (B) Coining   (C) Impregnation   (D) Infiltration **(Ans. D)**
6. For producing self lubricated bearings by powder metallurgy process, the secondary operation carried out is called:
   (A) Infiltration   (B) Impregnation   (C) Sintering   (D) Coining   **(Ans. B)**
7. The method of Powder Metallurgy is used for:
   (A) Mass production   (B) Small lot production
   (C) Intricate shaped components   (D) None of the above   **(Ans. A)**
8. In Powder Metallurgy, the strength of the green compact is achieved by
   (A) Tempering   (B) Compressed tempering
   (C) Sintering   (D) None of the above   **(Ans. C)**
9. The operation of "Pre-Sintering" is done with
   (A) Soft and ductile material   (B) Hard and strong materials
   (C) Blended powders   (D) None of the above   **(Ans. B)**
10. The simultaneous compacting and sintering is achieved by which method:
    (A) Cold Isostatic pressing   (B) Hot isostatic pressing
    (C) P/M forging   (D) None of the above   **(Ans. B)**

CHAPTER 11

I. Which of the following pairs are correctly matched?
1. Cellulose nitrate .... Table tennis ball
2. Phenol furfurol ...... Brake linings
3. Epoxies .... Jigs and Fixtures
Select the correct answer using the codes given below:
Codes:
(A) 1 and 2   (B) 2 and 3   (C) 1 and 3   (D) 1, 2 and 3
                                                         [IES 1993] **(Ans. A)**
2. To reduce consumption of synthetic resins, the ingredient added is
   (A) accelerator   (B) elastomer   (C) modifier   (D) filler
                                                            [IAS 1994] **(Ans. D)**
3. Which of the following pairs of plastics and their modes of formation are correctly matched?
   1. Polythene .... Condensation polymerisation
   2. Polycarbonate .... Addition polymerisation
   3. Polystyrene .... Addition polymerisation

4. Polyamide .... Either by addition or by condensation polymerisation
Select the correct answer using the codes given below:
(A) 1 and 2   (B) 2 and 4   (C) 1 and 4   (D) 3 and 4
[IES 1994] (Ans. D)

4. Match List I (materials) with List II (applications) and select the correct answer using the codes given below the lists:

List I	List II
A. Engineering Ceramics	1. Bearings
B. Fibre reinforced plastics	2. Control rods in nuclear reactors
C. Synthetic carbon	3. Aerospace industry
D. Boron	4. Electrical insulator

Codes:

	A	B	C	D		A	B	C	D
(a)	1	2	3	4	(b)	1	4	3	2
(c)	2	3	1	4	(d)	4	3	1	2

[IES 1994] (Ans. d)

5. Consider the following statements:
Thermosetting plastics are
1. Formed by addition polymerisation
2. Formed by condensation polymerisation
3. Softened on heating and hardened on cooling for any number of times
4. Moulded by heating and cooling. Of the statements
(a) 1 and 3 are correct   (b) 2 and 4 are correct
(c) 1 and 4 are correct   (d) 2 and 3 are correct

[IES 1996] (Ans. b)

6. Match List I with List II and select the correct answer

List I (Material)	List II (Nature of product)
A. Polyethylene	1. Adhesive
B. Polyurathane	2. Film
C. Cyano–acrylate	3. Wire
D. Nylon	4. Foam

Codes	A	B	C	D		A	B	C	D
(a)	2	4	3	1	(b)	4	2	3	1
(c)	2	4	1	3	(d)	4	2	1	3

[IES 1996] (Ans. c)

7. Consider the following statements:
Fibre Reinforced Plastics are:
1. made of thermosetting resins and glass fibre
2. made of thermoplastic resins and glass fibre
3. anisotropic
4. isotropic. Of these statements
(A) 1 and 4 are correct   (B) 1 and 3 are correct
(C) 2 and 3 are correct   (D) 2 and 4 are correct   [IES 1996] (Ans. B)

8. Match List I with List II and select the correct answer using the codes given below the lists:

List I	List II
A. Neoprene	1. Electric switches
B. Bakelite	2. Adhesive
C. Foamed polyurethane	3. Thermal insulator
D. Araldite	4. Oil seal

Codes:

	A	B	C	D		A	B	C	D
(a)	4	1	2	3	(b)	1	4	2	3
(c)	4	1	3	2	(d)	1	4	3	2

[*IES 1997*] (**Ans.** *c*)

9. Which one of the following materials is used for car tyres as a standard material?
   (A) Styrene-Butadiene Rubber (SBR)   (B) Butyl rubber
   (C) Nitrile rubber   (D) Any of the above depending upon the need

   [*IES 1997*] (**Ans.** A)

10. Which one of the following refractory materials is recommended for steel furnaces containing CaO slags?
    (A) Alumina   (B) Silica   (C) Magnesia   (D) Fireclay

    [*IES 1997*] (**Ans.** B)

11. Consider the following statements:
    The strength of the fibre reinforced plastic product
    1. depends upon the strength of the fibre alone
    2. depends upon the fibre and the plastic
    3. is isotropic
    4. is anisotropic
    Which of these statements are correct?
    (A) 1 and 3   (B) 1 and 4   (C) 2 and 3   (D) 2 and 4

    [*IES 1999*] (**Ans.** B)

12. Consider the following pairs of plastics and their distinct characteristics:
    1. Acrylics .... Very good transparency to light
    2. Polycarbonate .... Poor impact resistance
    3. PTFE .... Low co-efficient of friction
    4. Polypropylene .... Excellent fatigue strength
    Which of these pairs are correctly matched?
    (A) 2 and 3   (B) 1 and 3   (C) 1 and 4   (D) 2 and 4

    [*IES 1999*] (**Ans.** C)

13. The bottles from thermo-plastic materials are made by
    (A) Compression moulding   (B) Extrusion
    (C) Injection moulding   (D) Blow moulding   (**Ans.** D)

14. The long plastic rods and tubes are produced by
    (A) Compression moulding   (B) Extrusion
    (C) Injection moulding   (D) Blow moulding   (**Ans.** B)

15. The process of producing thin sheets by squeezing a thermo-plastic material between revolving cylinders, is known as:
    (A) Transfer moulding   (B) Injection moulding
    (C) Blow moulding   (D) Calendering   (**Ans.** D)

16. The process of producing plastic components in moulds without the application of pressure, is known as
    (A) Moulding   (B) Laminating   (C) Calendering   (D) Casting   (**Ans.** D)

CHAPTER 16

1. In a point to point type of NC system
   (A) Control of position and velocity of tool is essential
   (B) Control of only position of the tool is sufficient
   (C) Control of only velocity of the tool is sufficient
   (D) Neither position nor velocity need be controlled   [*GATE 1992*] (**Ans.** B)

2. With reference to NC machines which of the following statements is wrong:

(A) both closed-loop and open-loop control systems are used
(B) paper tapes, floppy tapes and cassettes are used for data storage
(C) digitizers may be used as interactive input devices
(D) post processor is an item of hardware   *[GATE 1993]* (**Ans.** D)

3. CNC machines are more accurate than conventional machines because they have a high resolution encoder and digital readouts for positioning.   *[GATE 1994]* (**Ans.** *True*)

4. CNC machines are more economical to use even for simple turning jobs.
     [GATE 1994] (**Ans.** *False*)

5. A block of information in N.C. machine program means:
(A) one row on tape   (B) a word comprising several rows on tape
(C) one complete instruction   (D) one complete program for a job
     [IES 1993] (**Ans.** C)

6. Feed drives in CNC milling machines are provided by
(A) Synchronous motors   (B) induction motors
(C) stepper motors   (D) servo-motors   *[IES 1994]* (**Ans.** D)

7. Consider the following characteristics of production jobs:
1. Processing of parts frequently in small lots
2. Need to accommodate design changes of products
3. Low rate of metal removal
4. Need for holding close tolerances
The characteristics which favour the choice of NC machines would include
(A) 1, 2 and 3   (B) 2 and 3, 4   (C) 1, 3 and 4   (D) 1, 2 and 4
     [IES 1995] (**Ans.** D)

8. Which of the following pairs are correctly matched?
1. CNC machine .... Post processor   2. Machining Centre ..... Tool Magazine
3. DNC ...... FMS
(A) 1, 2 and 3   (B) 1 and 2   (C) 1 and 3   (D) 2 and 3
     [IES 1996] (**Ans.** A)

9. Which of the following is/are the advantage (s) of numerical control of machine tools?
1. Reduced lead time   2. consistently good quality
3. Elaborate fixtures are not required
(A) 2 and 3   (B) 1 and 2   (C) 1 alone   (D) 1 and 3
     [IES 1996] (**Ans.** A)

10. Which of the following are the rules of programming NC machine tools in APT language?
1. Only capital letters are used
2. A period is placed at the end of each statement
3. Insertion of space does not affect the APT word
Select the correct answer using the codes given below:
(A) 1 and 2   (B) 2 and 3   (C) 1 and 3   (D) 1 alone
     [IES 1998] (**Ans.** C)

11. Consider the following components
1. A dedicated computer   2. Bulk memory
3. Telecommunication lines
Which of these components are required for a DNC system?
(A) 2 and 3   (B) 1 and 2   (C) 1, 2 and 3   (D) 1 and 3
     [IES 1999] (**Ans.** C)

12. Consider the following statements regarding NC machine tools:
1. They reduce non-productive time   2. They reduce fixturing
3. They reduce maintenance cost
Which of these statements are correct?

(A) 1, 2 and 3   (B) 1 and 2   (C) 2 and 3   (D) 1 and 3
                                                                    [IES 1999] (**Ans.** A)

IES 2002

1. Which of the following fibre materials are used for reinforcement in composite materials :-
   1. Glass   2. Boron Carbide
   3. Graphite
   Select the correct answer using the codes given below :
   Codes
   (*a*) 1 and 2   (*b*) 1 and 3
   (*c*) 2 and 3   (*d*) 1, 2 and 3   (Ans *d*)

2. Consider the following statements :
   The strength of a single point cutting tool depends upon
   1. Rake angle   2 Clear ance angle
   3. Lip angle
   Which of these statements are correct ?
   (*a*) 1 and 3   (*b*) 2 and 3
   (*c*) 1 and 2   (*d*) 1, 2 and 3   (**Ans.** d)

3. Which of the following materials are used in grinding wheels ?
   1. Aluminium oxide   2. Cubic boron nitride
   3. Silicon carbide
   Select the correct answer using the codes given below :-
   Codes :
   (*a*) 1, 2 and 3   (*b*) 1 and 2
   (*c*) 2 and 3   (*d*) 1 and 3   (**Ans.** *a*)

4. Consider the following statements related to piercing and blanking :
   1. Shear on the punch reduces the maximum cutting force.
   2. Shear increases the capacity of the press needed.
   3. Shear increases the life of the punch.
   4. The total energy needed to make the cut remains unaltered due to provision of shear.
   Which of the above statements are correct ?
   (*a*) 1 and 2   (*b*) 1 and 4
   (*c*) 2 and 3   (*d*) 3 and 4   (**Ans. :** *b*)

5. Consider the following steps involved in hammer forging a connecting rod from bar stock:
   1. Blocking   2. Trimiming
   3. Finishing   4. Fullering
   5. Edging
   Which of the following is the correct sequency of operations ?
   (*a*) 1, 4, 3, 2 and 5   (*b*) 4, 5, 1, 3 and 2
   (*c*) 5, 4, 3, 2 and 2   (*d*) 5, 1, 4, 2 and 3   (**Ans.** *b*)

6. Match List I (Parts) with List II (Manufactiring processes) and select the correct answer
   using the codes given below the lists :

List I (Parts)	List II (Manufacturing Process)
A. Seamless tubes	1. Roll forming
B. Accurate and Smooth tubes	2. Shot peening
C. Surface having higher hardness and fatigue strength.	3. Forging
	4. Cold forming

   Codes :-

	A	B	C
(a)	1	4	2
(b)	2	3	1
(c)	1	3	2
(d)	2	4	1

(Ans. *a*)

7. Match List I (Machine tools) with List II (Machine tool parts) and select the correct answer using codes given below the lists :

List I	List II
A. Lathe	1. Lead screw
B. Milling machine	2. Rocker arm
C. Shaper	3. Universal indexing
D. Drilling machine	4. Flute

Codes :-

	A	B	C	D
(a)	4	2	3	1
(b)	1	3	2	4
(c)	4	3	2	1
(d)	1	2	3	4

(Ans. b)

8. T.T.T. diagram indicates time, and temperature transformation of
   (A) Cementite   (B) Pearlite
   (C) Ferrite   (D) Austenite   (Ans. *D*)

9. The correct conposition of austenitic stainless steel used for domestic utensils is :
   (A) 0.08% C, 18% Cr, 8% Ni, 2% Mn, 1% Si
   (B) 0.08% C, 24% Cr, 12% Ni, 2% Mn, 1% Si
   (C) 0.15% C, 12% Cr, 0.5% Ni, 1% Mn, 1% Si
   (D) 0.30% C, 12% Cr, 0.4% Ni, 1% Mn, 1% Si   (Ans. *A*)

10. The rate of production of a powder metallurgy part depends on
    (*a*) flow rate of powder   (*b*) green strength of powder
    (*c*) apparent density of compact   (*d*) Compressibility of powder   (Ans. *a*)

11. In a machining process, the percentage of heat carried away by the chips is typically
    (*a*) 5%   (*b*) 25%
    (*c*) 50%   (*d*) 75%   (Ans. *d*)

12. Match List I (Machine tools) with List II (Features) and select the correct answer using the codes given below the list :

List I	List II
(*Machine Tool*)	(*Features*)
A. Lathe	1. Push or Pull tool
B. Drilling machine	2. Ratchet and pawl mechanism
C. Shaper	3. Dividing head
D. Broaching machine	4. Hollow tapered spindle
	5. Face plate

Codes :-

	A	B	C	D
(a)	2	4	5	1
(b)	5	3	2	4
(c)	2	3	5	4
(d)	5	4	2	1

(Ans. *d*)

13. Which of the following are fabricated using engineering plastics ?
   1. Surface plate   2. Gears
   3. Guideways for machine tools   4. Foundry patterns
   Select the correct answer using the codes given below
   Codes :
   (a) 1, 2 and 3   (b) 1
   (c) 2, 3 and 4   (d) 1, 2, 3 and 4   (Ans. c)
14. Which one of the following is the hardest cutting tool material next only to diamond ?
   (a) Cemented Carbides   (b) Ceramics
   (c) Silicon   (d) Cubic boron nitride   (Ans. d)
15. Crater wear on tools always starts at some distance from the tool tip because at that point
   (a) Cutting fluid does not penerate. (b) normal stress on rake face is maximum
   (c) temperature is maximum   (d) tool strength is minimum   (Ans. c)
16. A 31.8 mm H.S.S. drill is used to drill a hole in a cast iron block 100 mmthick at a cutting
   speed of 20 m/min and feed 0.3 mm/rev. If the overtravel of the drill is 4 mm and approach
   9 mm, the time required to drill the hole is
   (a) 1 min 40 s   (b) 1 min 44 s
   (c) 1 min 49 s   (d) 1 min 53 s   (Ans. d)
17. A side and face cutter 125 mm diameter has 10 teeth. It operates at a cutting speed of 14 m/
   min. with a table traverse 100 mm/min. The feed per tooth of the cutter is
   (a) 10 mm   (b) 2.86 mm
   (c) 0.286 mm   (d) 0.8 mm   (Ans. c)
18. Which one is not a method of reducing cutting forces to prevent the overloading of press ?
   (a) providing shear on die   (b) providing shear on panch
   (c) increasing die clearance   (d) stepping punches.   (Ans. c)
19. In which one of the following welding techniques is vacuum envrionment required ?
   (a) Ultrasonic welding   (b) Laser beam welding
   (c) Plasma arc welding   (d) Electron beam welding   (Ans. d)
20. Match list I (Material) with List II (Application) and select the correct answer using the
   codes given below the lists :

	List I (Material)		List II (Application)
A.	Ceramics	1.	Construction of Chemical plants
B.	Refractories	2.	Columns and pillars
C.	Stones	3.	Lining of furnaces
D.	High silica glass	4.	Tiles

   Codes :

	A	B	C	D
(a)	4	3	2	1
(b)	2	1	4	3
(c)	4	1	2	3
(d)	2	3	4	1

                                                                            (Ans. a)
21. Match list I (Ingredients) with List II (Welding functions) and select the correct answer
   using the codes given below the lists :

	List I (Ingredients)		List II (Welding functions)
A.	Silica	1.	Arc stabilizer
B.	Potassium silicate	2.	De-oxidizer
C.	Ferro-silicon	3.	Fluxing agent
D.	Cellulose	4.	Gas forming material

Codes :

	A	B	C	D	
(a)	3	4	2	1	
(b)	2	1	3	4	
(c)	3	1	2	4	
(d)	2	4	3	1	(Ans. c)

22. In a CNC machine tool, encoder is used to sense and control
    (a) table position   (b) table velocity
    (c) spindle speed   (d) coxland flow   (Ans. a)
23. In rolling a strip between two rolls, the position of the neutral point in the arc of contact does not depend on
    (a) amount of reduction   (b) diameter of the rolls
    (c) co-efficient of friction   (d) material of the rolls   (Ans. d)
24. Match list I (NC machine tool systems) with List II (Features) and select the correct answer using the codes given below the lists :

List I
(*NC machine tool systems*)

List II
(*Features*)

A. NC system
1. It has integrated automatic tool changing unit and a component indexing device.

B. CNC system
2. A number of machine tools are controlled by a computer. No tape reader, the part programme is trasmitted directly to the machine tool from the computer memory.

C. DNC systen
3. The controller consists of soft-wired computer and hard-wired logic system. Graphic display of tool path is also possible.

D Machining centre
4. The instructions on tape are prepared in binary decimal form and operated by a series of coded instructions.

Code :

	A	B	C	D	
(a)	4	2	3	1	
(b)	1	3	2	4	
(c)	4	3	2	1	
(d)	1	2	3	4	(Ans. c)

25. Compare die-casting with investment casting w.r.t. production rate, melting point of work materials and ability of producing complex shaped products.
26. Name three processes of manufacturing long low carbon steel tubes.
27. What are the advantages of submerged arc welding over conventional open air manual arc welding and why ?
28. Why are the lathe-spindles made hollow ?
29. How does application of cutting fluid help in reducing cutting forces and inproving tool life and surface quality ?
30. In which machine tools, teeth of internal spur gears can be cut and which one of those machine tools work fastest ?
31. What are meant by 'A – 60 – K – 8 – V' when used for a grinding wheel specification ?
32. What are the major constituents of high speed steel (HSS) and uncoated single carbides which are used as cutting tool materials ? How are these carbide tool inserts manufactured ?

IES 2003

1. During heat treatment of steel, the hardness of various structures in the increasing order is
   (A) martensite, fine pearlite, coarse pearlite, spheroidite
   (B) fine pearlite, coarse pearlite, spheroidite, martensite
   (C) martensite, coarse pearlite, fine pearlite, spheroidite
   (D) spheroidite, coarse pearlite, fine pearlite, martensite.   (*GATE 2003*) (**Ans. D**)

2. Hardness of green sand mould increases with
   (A) increase in moisture content beyond 6 per cent
   (B) increase in permeability   (C) decrease in permeability
   (D) increase in both moisture content and permeability   (**Ans. C**)

3. In oxyacetylene gas welding, the temperature at the inner cone of the flame is around
   (A) 3500°C   (B) 3200°C
   (C) 2900°C   (D) 2550°C   (**Ans. A**)

4. Cold working of steel is defined as working
   (A) at its recrystallisation temperature   (B) above its recrystallisation temperature
   (C) below its recrystallisation temperature
   (D) at two thirds of the melting temperature of the metal   (**Ans. C**)

5. As tool and work are not in contract in EDM process
   (A) no relative motion occurs between them.
   (B) no wear of tool occurs
   (C) no power is consumed during metal cutting
   (D) no force between tool and work occurs   (**Ans. D**)

6. Hardness of steel greatly improves with
   (A) Annealing   (B) Cyaniding
   (C) normalising   (D) tempering   (**Ans. B**)

7. With a solidification factor of 0.97×6^6 s/m^2, the solidification time (in seconds) for a spherical casting of 200 mm diameter is
   (A) 539   (B) 1078
   (C) 4311   (D) 3233   (**Ans. B**)

   Hint : In chvorinov's equation

   $$t = K \cdot \left(\frac{V}{SA}\right)^2, \quad K = 0.97 \times 10^6 \ s/m^2$$

8. Match the following

Work material	Type of joining
P Aluminium	1. Submerged Arc Welding
Q Die Steel	2. Soldering
R Copper wire	3. Thermit welding
S Titanium sheet	4. Atomic Hydrogen Welding
	5. Gas Tungsten Arc Welding
	6. Laser Beam Weldign

(A)	(B)	(C)	(D)
P – 2	P – 6	P – 4	P – 5
Q – 5	Q – 3	Q – 1	Q – 4
R – 1	R – 4	R – 6	R – 2
S – 3	S – 4	S – 2	S – 6 (**Ans. D**)

IES – 2004

1. Write the Chemical equation for the reaction going on in the oxy-acetylene flame. Where do you get the most part of the oxygen; is it from the cylinder or the atmosphere ?

2. Clearances have to be provided on the press tools. What is the order of clearances for shearing operation and deep drawing operation ? On what tool will you provide the clearance in :

   (i) Punching operation

   (ii) Blanking operation

3. What is the three high rolling mill ? Indicate the movement of rolls and the workpiece.

4. What are the steps involved in making of carbide tool bits ? What do you understand by the green density of a metal powder compacted part ? What are the chief merits of a bush made by metal powder compaction.

5. An iron-carbon binary allow has 0.5% C by weight. What is this alloy called ?

   (a) Eutectoid alloy   (b) Eutective alloy

   (c) Hypo-eutectioid alloy   (d) Hyper-eutectoid alloy

   (Ans. c)

6. Match List–I (Name of alloy) with List - II (Major alloying elements) and select the correct answer using the codes given below the list :

List – I	List – II
(Name of alloy)	(Major alloying elements)
A. Invar	1. Manganese
B. Hadfield steel	2. Chromium
C. Stellite	3. Nickel
D. Stainless steel	4. Tungsten
	5. Molybdenum

Codes :	A	B	C	D
(a)	5	1	4	2
(b)	3	2	5	1
(c)	5	2	4	1
(d)	3	1	5	2

   (Ans. d)

7. Match-list – I (Name of Treatment) with List – II (media used) and select the correct answer using the codes given below the lists :-

List – I	List – II
(Name of treatment)	(Media used)
A. Pack Carburising	1. Ammonia gas
B. Gas Carburising	2. Sodium Cyanide
C. Cyaniding	3. Carburising Compound
D. Nitriding	4. Ethane

Codes :

	A	B	C	D
(a)	3	4	2	1
(b)	2	1	3	4
(c)	3	1	2	4
(d)	2	4	3	1	(Ans. a)

8. Consider the following pairs :

Heat Treatment		**Effects on medium Carbon steel**
1. Normalising	:	Grain refinement
2. Full annealing	:	Uniform grain structure
3. Martempering	:	Decreased ductility
4. Spheoroidizing	:	Maximum softness

Which of the pairs given above are correctly matched ?

(a) 1 and 2   (b) 2 and 3

(c) 3 and 4   (d) 1, 2, 3 and 4   (Ans. : c)

9. Match List – I (Type of Moulding) with list – II (Mechanism involved) and select the correct answer using codes given below the lists :

List – I (Type of moulding)	List – II (Mechanism involved)
A. Compression moulding	1. Mould cavity must be heated to cure the plastic forced into it
B. Injected moulding	2. Similar to hydraulic extrusion
C. Jet moulding	3. Analogous to hot pressing of powdered metals
D. Extrusion moulding	4. Analogous to die casting of metals.

Codes :

	A	B	C	D
(a)	2	4	1	3
(b)	3	1	4	2
(c)	2	1	4	3
(d)	3	4	1	2	(Ans. : d)

10. Match List – I (Steel type) with List – II (Product) and select the correct answer by using the codes given below the list :

List – I (Steel type)	List – II (Product)
A. Mild steel	1. Screws
B. Tool steel	2. Commercial beams
C. Medium Carbon steel	3. Crane hooks
D. High Carbon steel	4. Blanking dies

Codes :

	A	B	C	D
(a)	2	4	1	3
(b)	3	1	4	2
(c)	2	1	4	3
(d)	3	4	1	2	(Ans. a)

11. Match List – I (Alloy) with List – II (Application) and select the correct answer using the codes given below the lists :–

List – I (Alloy)	List – II (Application)
A. Silicon steel	1. Marine Bearings
B. High Carbon steel	2. Cutting tools
C. High speed steel	3. Springs
D. Monel metal	4. Transformer laminations

Codes :

	A	B	C	D
(a)	1	2	3	4
(b)	4	3	2	1
(c)	4	2	3	1
(d)	1	3	2	4

(Ans. : b)

12. Consider th following statements :

In comparison to hot working, in cold working,

1. higher forces are required

2. no heating is required

3. less ductility is required

4. better surface finish is obtained

Which of the statements given above are correct ?

(a) 1, 2 and 3   (b) 2 and 4

(c) 1 and 3   (d) 2, 3 and 4   (Ans. : b)

13. Consider the following factors :

1. Size and shape that can be produced economically

2. Porosity of the parts produced.

3. Press Capacity

4. High density

Which of the above are the limitations of powder metallurgy ?

(a) 1, 3 and 4   (b) 2 and 3

(b) 1, 2 and 3   (d) 1 and 2   (Ans. : c)

14. Match List – I (Welding problems) with List – II (Causes) and select the correct answer using codes given below the Lists :

List – I (Welding problems)	List – II (Causes)
A. Cracking of weld metal	1. Excessive stresses
B. Cracking of base metal	2. High joint rigidity
C. Porosity	3. Failure to remove slag from previous deposit
D. Inclusions	4. Oxidation
	5. Excessive H_2, O_2, N_2, in the welding atmosphere

Codes :

	A	B	C	D
(a)	2	1	5	3
(b)	3	4	2	1
(c)	2	4	5	3
(d)	3	1	4	2

(Ans. : a)

806

A Textbook of Production Technology

15. Consider the following statements :
The size of heat affected zone HAZ) will increase with
1. increased starting temperature
2. increased welding speed
3. increased thermal conductivity of the base metal
4. increase in base metal thickness
Which of the statements given above are correct ?
(a) 1, 2 and 3　　　　　　　　　(b) 1 and 3
(c) 1 and 4　　　　　　　　　　(d) 2 and 3　　　　　　　　　(Ans. b)

16. Consider the following statements :-
The magnitude of residual stresses in welding depends upon
1. Design of weldment
2. Support and clamping of components
3. Welding process used.
4. amount of metal melted/deposited.
Which of the statements given above are correct ?
(a) 1, 2 and 4　　　　　　　　(b) 1, 2 and 3
(c) 1 and 3　　　　　　　　　(d) 2 and 3　　　　　　　　　(Ans. : a)

17. The cutting speed of a milling cutter while cutting brass is :
(a) 45 to 60 m/min　　　　　　(b) 30 to 40 m/min.
(c) 25 to 35 m/min　　　　　　(d) 15 to 20 m/min　　　　　(Ans. : a)

18. Consider the following statements :
The helical flute in a twist drill provides the necessary
1. Clearance anagle for the cutting edge.
2. Rake angle for the cutting edge
3. Space for the chip to come out during drilling.
4. Guidance for the drill to enter into the workpiece.
Which of the statements given above are correct ?
(a) 1 and 2　　　　　　　　　(b) 2 and 3
(c) 3 and 4　　　　　　　　　(d) 1 and 4　　　　　　　　　(Ans. c)

19. For improving the strength of steel at elevated temperature, which one of the following alloying elements is used :
(a) Copper　　　　　　　　　(b) Tungsten
(c) Aluminium　　　　　　　　(d) Zinc　　　　　　　　　　(Ans. b)

20. Match List – I (cutting tools) with List – II (Features) and select the correct answer using the codes given below the lists :

List – I (Cutting tools)　　　　　　**List – II (Features)**
A. Turning tool　　　　　　　　1. Chiesel edge
B. Reamer　　　　　　　　　　2. Flutes
C. Milling cutter　　　　　　　3. Axial relief
　　　　　　　　　　　　　　4. Side relief

Codes :

	A	B	C		A	B	C
(a)	1	2	3	(c)	4	2	3
(b)	4	3	2	(d)	1	3	2	**(Ans.** b**)**

21. Match List – I (Milling Problem) with List – II (Probable Causes) and select the correct answer using the codes given below the lists :

List – I (Milling problem)	List – II (Probable Causes)
A. Chatter	1. Too high feed
B. Poor surface finish	2. Lack of rigidity in machine, fixtures, bar or workpiece
C. Loss of accuracy	3. High cutting load
D. Cutter burrs	4. Radial relief too great
	5. Not enough lubricant

Codes :

	A	B	C	D		A	B	C	D
(a)	2	1	5	3	(c)	4	5	2	3
(b)	2	1	3	5	(d)	4	2	3	5

(Ans. b**)**

22. Consider the following statements with respect to the relief angle of cutting tool :

1. This affects the direction of chip flow.

2. This reduces excessive friction between the tool and workpiece

3. This affects tool life.

4. This allows better access of coolant to the tool-workpiece interface. Which of the statements given above are correct ?

(a) 1 and 2   (b) 2 and 3

(c) 2 and 4   (d) 3 and 4   **(Ans.** b**)**

23. One brand of milling machine has the following two index plates supplied alongwith the indexing head :

Plate 1 : 15, 16, 17, 18, 19, 20 hole circles

Plate 2 : 21, 23, 27, 29, 31, 33 hole circles

It is proposed to mill a spur gear of 28 teeth using simple indexing method. Which one of the following combinations of index plate and number of revolutions is correct ?

(a) Plate 1 : 1 revolution and 9 holes in 18 hole circles.

(b) Plate 2 : 1 revolution and 9 holes in 21 pole circles.

(c) Plate 2 : 1 revolution and 9 holes in 33 hole circles.

(d) Plate 1 : 1 revolution and 9 holes in 15 hole circles.   **(Ans.** b**)**

24. Match List – I with List – II and select the correct answer using the codes given below the lists

List – I	List – II
A. Plan approach angle	1. Tool face
B. Rake angle	2. Tool flank

C. Clearance angle   3. Tool face and flank
D. Wedge angle   4. Cutting edge
                                                  5. Tool nose

Codes :

	A	B	C	D			A	B	C	D
(a)	1	4	2	5	(c)		4	1	2	3
(b)	4	1	3	2	(d)		1	4	3	5

(Ans : c)

25. Match List – I (Cutting tool materials) with List – II (Manufacturing methods) and select the correct answer using the codes given below the list :

List – I (Cutting tool materials)	List – II (Manufacturing methods)
A. HSS	1. Casting
B. Stellite	2. Forging
C. Cemented Carbide	3. Rolling
D. UCON	4. Extrusion
	5. Powder metallurgy

Codes :

	A	B	C	D			A	B	C	D
(a)	3	1	5	2	(c)		3	5	4	2
(b)	2	5	4	3	(d)		2	1	5	3

(Ans. : d)

26. A medium carbon steel workpiece is turned on a lathe at 50 m/min. speed (cutting), 0.8 mm/rev. feed and 1.5 mm depth of cut. What is the rate of metal removal ?

(a) 1000 mm³/min.   (b) 60,000 mm³/min.
(c) 20,000 mm³/min   (d) can not be calculated with the given data.

(Ans. : b)

27. Match list – I (Machining processes) with List – II (Operating media) and select the correct answer using the codes given below the lists :

List – I (Machining processes)	List – II (Operating media)
A. Abrasive Jet machining	1. Dielectric
B. Electron – beam machining	2. Electrolyte
C. Electro-chemical machining	3. Abrasive slurry
D. Electro-discharge machining	4. Vacuum
	5. Air

Codes :

	A	B	C	D			A	B	C	D
(a)	5	4	2	1	(c)		4	2	3	5
(b)	4	5	2	1	(d)		2	5	3	4	**(Ans. a)**

GATE – 2005

1. Match the items of List I (Equipment) with the items of List II (Process) and select the correct answer using the given codes.

   List – I (Equipment)   **List – II (Process)**
   P – Hot Chamber Machine   1 – Cleaning
   Q – Muller   2 – Core making
   R – Dielectric Baker   3. Die Casting
   S – Sand Blaster   4 – Annealing
                                    5 – Sand mixing

   (A) P–2, Q–1, R–4, S–5   (B) P–4, Q–2, R–3, S–5
   (C) P–4, Q–5, R–1, S–2   (D) P–3, Q–5, R–2, S–1   **(Ans. D)**

2. When the temperature of a solid metal increases,

   (A) strength of the metal decreases but ductility increases.

   (B) both strength and ductility of the metal decrease

   (C) both strength and ductility of the metal increase

   (D) strength of the metal increases but ductility decreases   **(Ans. A)**

3. The strength of a brazed joint

   (A) decreases with increase in gap between the two joining surfaces.

   (B) Increases with increase in gap between the two joining surfaces.

   (C) decreases upto certain gap between the two joining surfaces beyond which it increases.

   (D) increases upto certain gap between the two joining surfaces beyond which it decreases

   (Ans. : D)

4. A zig zag cavity in block of high strength alloy is to be finish machined. This can be carried out by using

   (A) electric discharge machinery

   (B) electrochemical machining

   (C) laser beam machining

   (D) abrasive flow machining   **(Ans. :A)**

5. Which among the NC operations given below are continuous path operations ?

   Arc Welding (AW)   Milling (M)

   Drilling (D)   Punching in sheet Metal (P)

   Laser cutting of sheet Metal (LC) Spot welding (SW)

   (A) AW, LC and M   (B) AW, D, LC and M

   (C) D, LC, P and SW   (D) D, LC, and SW   **(Ans. : A)**

6. A 600 mm × 30 mm flat surface of a plate is to be finish machined on a shaper. The plate has been fixed with the 600 mm side along the tool travel direction. If the tool over-reach at each end of the plate is 20 mm, average cutting speed is 8m/min, feed rate is 0.3 mm/stroke and

809

A Test Book of Production Technology

the ratio of return time to cutting time of tool is 1 : 2, the time required for machining will be

(A) 8 minutes   (B) 12 minutes   (C) 16 minutes   (D) 20 minutes   (Ans. : B)

7. Spot welding of two 1 mm thick sheets of steel (density = 800 kg/m^3) is carried out success-fully by passing a certain amount of current for 0.1 second through the electrodes. The resultant weld nugget formed is 5 mm in diameter and 1.5 mm thick. If the latent heat of fusion of steel is 1400 kJ/kg and the effective resistance in the welding operation is 200 μΩ, the current passing through the electrodes is approximately,

(A) 1480 A   (B) 3300 A (C) 4060 A   (D) 9400 A

Solution. :– Welding nugget volume $=\dfrac{\pi}{4}\times 5^2 \times 1.5 \cong 30\, mm^3$

Welding nugget mass = 0.008 × 30 = 0.24 gm

∴ Heat needed   = 0.24 × 1400 = 336 J

Now $Q = I^2Rt$

∴   336 = I^2× 200 × 10^{-6} × 0.1

∴ I^2 = 16.8 × 10^6

∴ I = 4100 A   (Ans. : C)

8. A mould has a downsprue whose length is 20 cm and the cross-sectional area at the base of the downsprue is 1cm^2. The downsprue feeds a horzontal runner leading into the mould cavity of volume 1000 cm^3. The time taken to fill the mould cavity will be

(A) 4.05 s   (B) 5.05 s   (C) 6.05 s   (D) 7.25 s   (Ans. B)

Solution. :– Velocity at the bottom of the sprue,

$$V = \sqrt{2gh} = \sqrt{2\times 981 \times 20} = 198.1 \text{ cm/s}$$

Now area of cross-section at the base = 1 cm^2

∴ $A \times V \times t = Q$

Now Q = 1000 cm^3

∴   1 × 198.1 × t = 1000

∴ t = 5.05 s

APPENDIX IV
Additional Material

IV.I. Sheet-Metal Formability:

In sheet metal forming process, a blank (cut from a larger sheet) is formed into various shapes. All sheet metal forming operations involve a pair of tools (punch and die) to form the blank into the desired shape. During sheet metal forming operation, the material undergoes two basic modes of deformations: Mainly stretching and also drawing or bending. Before selecting a forming process, it is important to determine whether the blank can be formed into the desired shape without failure or not. This is decided on the basis of what is known as "Sheet-metal formability". It may be defined as the ability of the sheet metal to undergo the desired shape change without failure, such as by necking or tearing.

The sheet metal formability depends upon certain sheet metal characteristics as discussed below:-

1. Elongation:- Since the material undergoes stretching and drawing/bending, during forming, large uniform elogation is desirable for good formability.

At the onset of necking,

True strain, $\varepsilon =$ strain – hardening exponent, $n(\sigma = k, \varepsilon^n; k$ is strength coefficient).

Thus, higher the value of n, larger will be the uniform elongation before it begins to neck.

Again,
$$\sigma = C \dot{\varepsilon}^m$$

where ε is strain rate, m is strain-rate sensitivity exponent and C is the strength coefficient.

The magnitude of the strain rate sensitivity exponent, m, significantly influences necking. With an increasing m, the material stretches farther before it fails. Thus, an increasing m delays necking. Elongation is nothing but a measure of the ductility of the material. Thus higher the ductility, higher will be the formability.

In addition to uniform elongation and necking, the total elongation of the specimen is also a significant factor in the formability of sheet metals. The total elongation of the material increases with increasing values of n and m.

Sheet metal grain size is also important. Grain size affects mechanical properties and it influences the surface appearance of the formed part. The coarser the grains, the rougher is the surface appearance.

Formability is also dependent upon; thickness of sheet, friction and lubrication at the punch-die-sheet metal interface, anistropy and yield point elongation.

It has been proved that the thicker the sheet, the larger is its formability. However, in actual practice, a thick blank may not bend as easily around small radii without cracking.

With well lubricated interface between sheet and punch/die, the strains are more uniformly distributed over the punch. Surface scratches, deep cuts and blemishes can reduce formability and cause premature tearing and failure.

Again, the formability of a metal is a function of its tensile strength. The tensile strength and yield point must not be high or too much work will be required for forming the metal.

Sheet Formability Tests:- During the various sheet metal forming processes, the stresses and strains developed in the material are quite complex. So, any measure of the formability of the sheet metal on the basis of material properties derived from a simple tension test(for example, % elongation as an index of ductility of the material) is not very accurate. Over the years, a number of tests have been developed to evaluate the formability of a sheet metal. These tests are discussed below:-

Cupping Tests:- These are the earliest developed tests. The various tests in this category are:-

1. Erichsen Test:- Here, the standard sheet metal specimen (90 mm wide) is clamped between two ring dies having 27 mm diameter openings. A steel ball or a round punch (of 20 mm diameter) is then hydraulically forced against the sheet until a crack begins to appear on the bottom face of the specimen as it is stretched into the die opening (Fig. IV. 1). The depth, d, is a measure of the formability of the sheet.

2. Olsen Test :- This test is just similar to the Erichsen test with one difference that the die opening size is 50 mm.

3. Swift Test :- Swift flat bottom cup test is a standard test for deep drawing process. The sheet formability is measured in terms of Limiting Draw Ratio, LDR (See Art. 4.8.11).

4. Fukui Test :- Erichsen and Olsen tests mainly evaluate the stretchability and the Swift test the deep drawability of the sheet metal. However, the actual conditions during any forming process are quite complex (mainly a combination of stretching and drawing/bending). The Fukui test uses a hemispherical punch and produces a conical cup. Thus; this test provides a combination of both stretching and deep drawing.

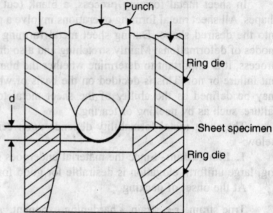

Fig. IV.1. Erichsen Test.

The latest test methods which nearly relate to the actual conditions are discussed below:-

5. Forming Limit Diagrams, FLD:- This is a very useful technique for controlling failure in sheet metal forming and thus giving an accurate forming limit criteria. The surface of the sheet metal specimen is covered with a grid-pattern of circles (typically 2.5 mm to 5 mm is diameter), using electrochemical or photoprinting techniques. During testing, when the sheet gets deformed, the circles distort into ellipses. The major and minor axes of an ellipse give the two principal strain directions during forming. These strains are determined as the % change in the lengths of major and minor axes. These strains at any point on the surface of the sheet are then compared with the Keeler Good win diagram for the material (See Fig. IV. 2). Strain positions above the curve indicate failure. For enhanced accuracy, the diameter of circles in the grid can be reduced. (The failure curve for the tension-tension region was determined by Keeler and that for the tension-compression region was determined by Goodwin). The strain distribution can be altered (for example, by changing the dieradius) so that the strain position moves to the safe region.

6. Stretch-Draw Shape analysis:- Here, the forming limit of the sheet metal is determined by the Olsen and Swift cupping tests. Then the specimen is broken into simple shapes and the % of stretch and draw are determined from the geometry. Then, with the help of FLD for the material, the degree of severity of the part can be determined.

7. Formability Charts:- Very useful formability charts have been developed for many processes, such as, brake forming, linear stretch forming, rubber forming, dimpling, beading and metal spinning etc.

8. Computer-analysis Program:- Just like the bulk deformation processes, computer-aided design and analysis have been applied in determining the sheet metal forming limits. The total program includes: Constitutive relations for the material, a program for analysis of FLD and an analysis program for determining the critical strains.

IV. 2 Super-Plastic Forming (SPF): 'Superplasticity' refers to large neck-free extensions before fracture, (between 100 and 1000 %) when deforming certain metals and alloys. Extreme examples of superplastic materials are : Bubble gum and molten glass which can be drawn from melt into glass fibres without the fibres necking down. The preconditions for super plastic behaviour of a material are listed under Art. 4.3.12 on "Super-plastic forging". Materials with a high strain-rate sensitivity $(0.3 < m > 1.0)$ exhibit pronounced resistance to necking (Here m is strain-rate sensitivity index in the equation $\sigma = C\dot{\varepsilon}^m$; $\dot{\varepsilon}$ is the strain-rate, for grass, $m = 1$). Generally, this condition is satisfied in materials with a very fine grain size (of the order of 1 μm) and at deformation temperatures of > 0.4 Tm. Also, for superplastic materials, there is a limiting strain rate (generally below $0.0.1s^{-1}$), at which they should be formed.

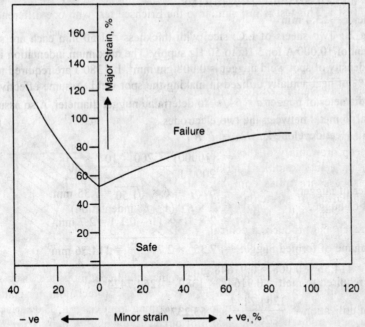

– ve $\longleftarrow$ Minor strain $\longrightarrow$ + ve, %

Fig. IV.2. : Forming Limit Diagram.

Advantages of SPF :- 1. High ductility and Low flow stress (of the order of 5 to 30 MPa) exist at superplastic condition. These lead to lower tooling costs and forging of difficult-to-work super-alloys (see Art. 4.2.12) or in embossing of fine details in other applications.

2. Forming of complex shapes with fine details and close tolerances.

3. Savings in materials as secondary operations are eliminated.

4. Little or no residual stresses in components.

Draw backs:- (*i*) Very low strain-rates, resulting in large forming times. So, best suited for batch production.

(*ii*) The component material must not be super-plastic at service temperature.

Common super-plastic materials used are : - Zn–22Al and Ti – 6Al – 4V. Their bulk deformation can be done by – forging, coining, compression moulding (see chapter 11), extrusion and hubbing. Sheet forming of these materials can be done by : thermo-forming, vacuum forming and Blow moulding (see Chapter 11).

IV. 3. Peen Forming :- Peen forming is a sheet metal working process utilizing the method of shot preening, which has been discussed in detail under Art. 4.10, along with its advantages and applications in industry. Another very useful application is to produce curvatures on thin metal sheets by striking shots on one side of the sheet. The main product application is the forming of smooth and complex curvatures on aircraft wing skins. When the sheet metal is subjected to shot peening, the surface layer expands, while the bottom layer remains rigid. The shots may be of cast steel about 2.5 mm is diameter striking the sheet surface at about 60 m/s. For thicker sections, the shots diameter can be as larger as 6 mm.

IV. 4. Some Numerical Problems :-

Problem 1 : Determine the choke area to fill C.I. castings neglecting directional flow and flow losses. Casting mass = 30 kg; t = 20s : ρ = 0.007 gm / mm³, h = 160 mm ; Gate = Top gate.

Solution : $CA = \dfrac{m}{c\rho t\sqrt{2gH}}, mm^2$

Now c for taper sprue = 0.85

and $H = h = 160$ mm for top gate

$$\therefore CA = \frac{30 \times 1000}{0.85 \times 0.007 \times 20 \sqrt{2 \times 9810 \times 160}} \cong 141 \text{ mm}^2$$

$\therefore$ Diameter = **13.4 mm**

Problem 2 : Two sheets of L.C. steel with thickness = 1.50 mm each are spot welded by passing a current of 10,000 A for 5 Hz to 50 Hz supply. The maximum indentation is 10% of sheet thickness and density of spot weld nugget is 0.008 gm/mm^3. If 1380 J are required to melt 1 gm of steel, find the % of heat actually utilized in making the spot weld. Assume effective resistance as 200 μ Ω and diameter of nugget $d = 6\sqrt{t}$ to determine nugget diameter. Also assume the nugget size to be equal to metal between the two electrodes.   (*GATE, 1992*)

Solution : Heat developed, $H = I^2 R t$

$$= (10000)^2 \times 200 \times 10^{-6} \times \frac{5}{50}$$
$$= 2000 \text{ J}$$

Diameter of nugget, $d_n = 6\sqrt{t} = 6 \times \sqrt{1.50} = 7.35$ mm
Height of nugget $= 2 \times t \times (1 - \%$ indentation$)$
$= 2 \times 1.5 \times (1 - 0.1) = 2.7$ mm

$\therefore$ Volume of formed nugget $= 7.35^2 \times 2.7 \times \dfrac{\pi}{4} = 114.56$ mm^3

$\therefore$ Mass $= 114.56 \times 0.008 = 0.91648$ gm

$\therefore$ Heat required to melt $= 0.91648 \times 1380 = 1264.7424$ J

$\therefore$ % heat utilization $= \dfrac{1264.7424}{2000} = $ **63.237%**

Problem 3 : Calculate the suitable gear train for cutting 8 TPI in a lathe with a lead screw having 4 TPI.

Solution : Ratio $i_{cg} = \dfrac{\text{Driver teeth}}{\text{Driven teeth}} = \dfrac{P}{L}$

P = Pitch of screw thread to be cut $= \dfrac{1}{8}$

L = Pitch of lead screw $= \dfrac{1}{4}$

$\therefore$ $i_{cg} = \dfrac{4}{8} = \dfrac{4 \times 5}{8 \times 5} = \dfrac{20}{40}$

$\therefore$ Driver gear on spindle = 20 teeth
Driven gear on lead screw = 40 teeth.

Problem 4 : Determine the dimensions of the pattern for the casting: 300 × 200 × 150 mm cuboid with a central hole of 100 mm diameter. Material is C.I. Consider only the shrinkage allowance of 20 mm / m.

Solution : Shrinkage allowance = 20 mm / m =0.02 mm / mm.
$\therefore$ Outer dimensions of the pattern = 306 × 204 × 153 mm
Diameter of hole in the pattern = 100 – 2 = 98 mm.

Problem 5 : Find the dimensions of the pattern by considering draft allowance also, which is 1° for external surfaces and 3° for internal surfaces.

Solution : We know that the draft allowance is provided only on the vertical surfaces.
$\therefore$ Draft allowance for exterior surface = 153 tan 1° = 4 mm / side
$\therefore$ Draft allowance for interior surface = 153 tan 3° = 8 mm / side
It is also clear from Fig. 3.8 that after the provision of draft allowance, the dimension of the pattern is minimum at the parting line for exterior surfaces and maximum at the parting line for interior surfaces.

$\therefore$ Top outer dimension of the pattern   = 306 + 2 × 4 = 314 mm
and   = 204 + 2 × 4 = 212 mm
and top inner dimension of the pattern hole = 98 – 2 × 8 = 82 mm

IV.5 Hydraulic Drive for Shapers: There are two systems of hydraulic drive for shapers. Constant pressure system (Fig. 8.3 Art. 8.2.1) and the constant volume system. The pump used in the constant pressure system is of the plunger type and by varying its stroke, the rate of oil flow and its pressure can be varied as per the need of the machine.

In the constant volume system, Fig. IV.3, a fixed quantity of oil is delivered by a gear or vane pump to both the sides of the piston. The effective area of the piston on the head side is smaller than on the cover side (due to the presence of piston rod), the return stroke will be faster, since volume of oil /unit time = velocity × area of cross-section

$$\left(m^3/s\right) \qquad\qquad (m/s)\ \times\ m^2$$

Or, as the pump is a constant discharge one, the same amount of oil is pumped into smaller volume. The pressure of oil is risen automatically which increases the speed during return stroke.

Again, the speed of the cutting stroke can be varied by a throttle valve in the discharge pipe from the head end of the cylinder. By restricting the flow of oil, the cutting speed can be reduced without affecting the ram return speed. A relief valve is provided in the system to permit excess oil delivered by the pump to return to the reservoir.

The constant pressure system is preferred for heavy and variable duty, where as, the constant volume system is favoured for machines not needing excessive power or wide variations in speed.

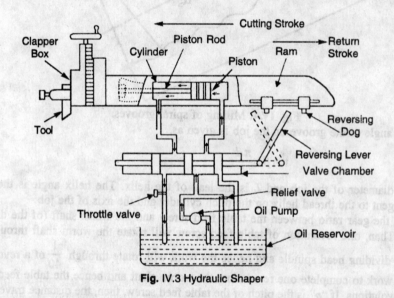

Fig. IV.3 Hydraulic Shaper

IV.6 Creep Feed Grinding: Conventional grinding is considered to be a finishing process (MRR being very low). To get higher MRR in grinding, a few techniques have been developed. One such method is Creep feed grinding where depth of cut is quite big at a very slow feed rate (opposite to that for conventional grinding). The method has been developed for machining Ni-alloys in Aircraft industry. Grinding wheels are of extremely hard material such as CBN or diamond held in metal matrix. These materials are prone to damage by vibrations and Chatter, but the large contact area of the process reduces this tendency, while the harder material retains it shape better than with the conventional approach to grinding.

IV.7 Some Special Milling Operations:-

(*a*) **Milling of Helical Grooves** (Cutting of helical teeth) : To facilitate the cutter to cut helical grooves, the workpiece must be given two simultaneous motions normal to each other : the linear motion along its axis and a rotary motion. The workpiece is held in the dividing head (mounted on the machine table) whihc is connected by means of gears to the table feed screw of the machine.

When the table feed screw rotates, the spindle of the dividing head and hence the work will rotate through change gears, worm and worm wheel of the dividing head. Also, when the table feed screw rotates in the nut, the machine table and hence the dividing head has linear motion.The milling cutter is mounted on the arbor of the machine. To cut the helix, it is necessary to swing the machine table through an angle equal to the helix angle, on the vetical axis. Due to this, the spiral grooves are cut on a universal milling machine. Fig. (IV).4.

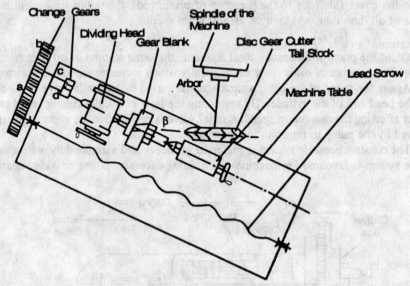

Fig. IV.4. Milling of spiral grooves.

The helix angle of the groove on the job is given as,

$$\tan \beta = \frac{\pi d}{L}$$

where d is the diameter of the job and L is the lead of the helix. The helix angle is the angle between the tangent to the thread helix on the pitch cylinder and the axis of the job.

Supposing the gear ratio between the table feed screw and the worm shaft (of the dividing head) is 1 : 1. Then, one revolution of table feed screw will rotate the worm shaft through one revolution. The dividing head spindle and hence the work will rotate through $\frac{1}{40}$ of a revolution. That is, for the work to complete one revolution, the worm shaft and hence the table feed screw will make 40 revolutions. If "p" is the pitch of the table feed screw, then, the distance travelled by the the table feed screw for one revolution of the work will be 40p. This is called the "Lead of the machine". Hence, the lead of the machine is defined as the distance travelled by the machine table corresponding to one complete revolution of the dividing head spindle (and hence of the work) when the gear ratio between the table feed screw and worm shaft is 1 : 1. Thus,

Lead of helix will be = Lead of machine = 40p.

The diameter of the job and the lead of the helix to be cut will determine the setting of the machine and the gear ratio. The hand of the helix will determine whether an idler is needed or not in the gear train. The work must rotate left handed for left hand helix and right handed for right hand helix. Thus, for right handed helix, the table feed screw and the worm shaft should rotated in the same direction and for left handed helix, they should rotate in the opposite directions.

$$\text{Gear ratio} = \frac{a}{b} \times \frac{c}{d} = \frac{\text{Drivers}}{\text{Driven}}$$

$$= \frac{\text{Lead of the machine}}{\text{Lead of the helix be cut}}$$

$$= \frac{40p}{L} \times n$$

$$= \frac{40pn}{\pi d} \times \tan \beta = \frac{40 \, pn \tan \beta}{\pi . z . m}$$

Where n = No. of starts of the milling table lead screw

z = Number of teeth on helical gear

m = module of the tech

Example. *A right hand helix is to be cut on a job with diameter 40 mm. Lead of helix to be cut is 450 mm, and the pitch of the table screw is 6 mm. Determine the setting of the machine and the change gears.*

Solution. Helix angle of the groove to be cut.

$$\beta = \tan^{-1} \frac{\pi d}{L} = \tan^{-1} \frac{\pi \times 40}{450}$$

$$= \tan^{-1} 0.2792$$

$$= 15.6°$$

Gear ratio, $i = \dfrac{\text{Drivers}}{\text{Driven}} = \dfrac{\text{Lead of the machine}}{\text{Lead of the helix}}$

$$= \frac{40p}{450} = \frac{40 \times 6}{450}$$

$$= \frac{8}{15} = \frac{2 \times 4}{5 \times 3}$$

$$= \frac{40 \times 32}{100 \times 24}$$

It is a compound gear drive.

Use a gear of 40 teeth on table feed screw, gear of 24 teeth on worm, 100 teeth gear on first gear on stud and second gear of 32 teeth on stud, and no idle gear.

After mounting the gears, the job and the cutter, the machine feed table should be swung at an angle of 15.6°.

(*b*) **Cam-Milling.** Cams can be machined on milling machines by :

(*i*) Special purpose milling machines, known as "Cam millers", discussed under Art. 8.5.1. This method is best suited for Disk-Cams. A master cam is held in contact with a fixed roller on the machine table and controls the table movements. The work is mounted on a face plate and slowly fed against the rotating cutter, its outline being controlled by the master cam. Shank-type end mills are used for cutter. This method is economical when cams are to be produced in sufficiently large numbers.

(*ii*) When only one or a few cams are needed and the cams rise and fall at a uniform rate, these can be machined on a universal milling machine, equipped with a universal dividing head and a swivelling type vertical milling attachment (or on a vertical milling machine).

The cam blank is mounted on the dividing head psindle by means of a mandrel or a chuck. An end milling cutter is held in the vertical milling attachment and is aligned with the dividing head so that the periphery of the cam blank is square with its face.

The blank moves linearly towards the cutter when the feed is given to the machine table. It simultaneously rotates because the dividing head is geard to the machine table feed screw (similar to spiral groove milling). The combined action of these two motions will result in the machining of the cam.

The spindle of the dividing head can be set at any angle from the horizontal to the vertical position. However, if the angle of the tilt of the spindle lies between 0° and 90°, then the cam can be given any lead (the cam lead is its rise or fall in its one revolution) between zero and the lead for which the gearing has been set. It should be noted that the axis of the dividing head spindle and that of the cutter spindle must always be parallel to each other.

From Fig. IV.5, it is clear that,

$$\sin \alpha = \frac{\text{Lead of Cam}}{\text{Table Travel}}, \qquad \alpha \text{ is the angle of tilt}$$

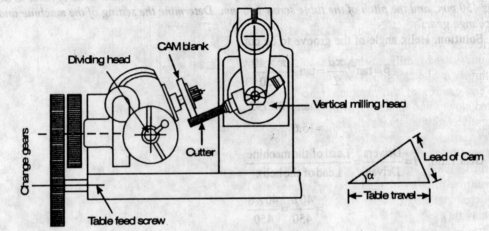

Fig. IV.5. Cam Milling

The gearing ratio, $i = \dfrac{\text{Drivers}}{\text{Driven}}$

It is clear that for one revolution of table feed screw, the dividing head spindle and hence the cam will rotate through $i/40$ revolutions.

Now, $\dfrac{\text{Work - rotation}}{\text{Table travel}} = \dfrac{i}{40 \times p} = \dfrac{i}{40 p}$

Now, for one revolution of spindle,

Table travel $= 40p/i$

Also, table travel $= \dfrac{\text{Lead of Cam}}{\sin \alpha}$

$\therefore$ $40p/i = \dfrac{\text{Lead of Cam}}{\sin \alpha}$

Now, $40p = \text{Lead of machine}$

$\therefore$ $i = \dfrac{\text{Lead of machine}}{\text{Lead of Cam}}$

IV.8. Thread Milling

In thread milling, the threads are cut by a revolving form milling cutter conforming to the shape of the thread to be produced. Both external and internal threads can be cut by this method. Thread milling has got the following characteristics :

1. This is a fast thread cutting method for producing threads usually of too large a diameter for die heads.

2. The threads produced are more accurate than those cut by dies, butless accurate than produced by grinding.

3. Threads running upto a shoulder on the workpiece can be cut without any difficulty.

4. Worms and lead screws which are too large to be cut with a single point tool can be milled.

5. This method is more efficient than cutting thread on a lathe, especially when the job is long or when large amounts of metal are to be removed.

6. The method is more efficient than cutting thread on a lathe, especially when the job is long or when large amounts of metal are to be removed.

For thread milling either single or multiple cutters may be used. A single-form cutter has a single, annular row of teeth, lying in one plane. While thread cutting with a single cutter, it is tilted through an angle equal to the helix angle of the thread to avoid interference while cutting. To start milling the threads, the cutter is fed radilly inward equal to the depth of the thread, while the job is stationary, being held between centres of the machine. The job is then rotated slowly and the cutter, while rotating, is also traversed longitudinally parallel to the axis of the job, or vice versa, by means of a lead screw. This operation is stopped when the thread is completed. This method of thread milling is used for cutting coarse (large pitch or multiple-pitch) threads. The threading can be completed in a single cut or roughing and finishing cuts may be used.

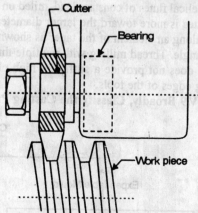

Fig. IV.6. Thread Milling with Single-Thread Cutter.

The method of cutting threads with single-thread or single-rib milling cutters is chiefly employed to cut long threads (chiefly of square and trapezoidal profiles) on various lead screws and worms. Usually, the threads are cut rough by milling and then these are finished by chasing with a single-point tool a formed grinding wheel. The method is shown in Fig. IV.6.

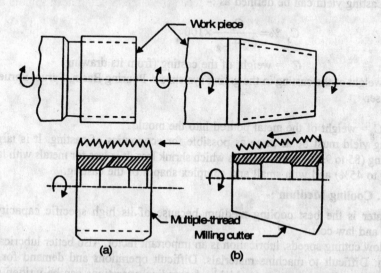

Fig. IV.7. Thread Milling with Multiplethread Cutters. (a) External Threads; (b) Taper.

Multiple cutter is used when the thread to be cut is not too long and it is desired to cut the threads in one revolution of the work. The width of the cutter has to be slightly more than the length of the thread. The cutter is set parallel to the axix of the job and is fed readily inward equal to the depth of the thread while the job is stationary. The job is equal to the depth of the thread while the job is stationary. The job is then rotated slowly, with the cutter moving axially a distance equal to the lead of the thread plus a small overtravel to complete the thread in one pass.

Thread milling with multiple-thread or multiple-rib cutters is illustrated in Fig. IV.7. Fig. IV.7 (*a*) is for cutting external threads.

The profile of the cutter teeth should be the same as that of the thread to be cut (Usually vee threads are cut by this method). Taper threads can also be cut by this method, Fig. IV.7. Cutters have helical flutes of constant lead, miled on the conical surface of the cutters. The spacing between the flutes is more toward the larger diameter of the cutter. The cutter rotates and is displaced one pitch along an element of the taper as shown. The taper threads cut on the job will have a variable helix angle. Thread milling with multiple-thread cutters is widely employed for cutting dies or die heads, does not provide a sufficient high class of surface finish, or leads to rapid dulling of the cutting edges of the tools.

IV.9 Broadly, Classify the Casting Process :-

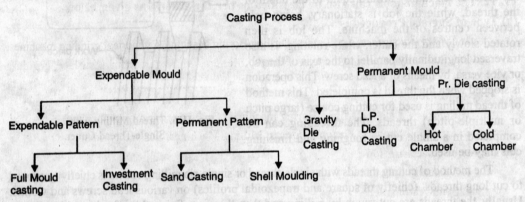

IV.10. Define Casting yield. How does it depend upon some casting factors .

Ans. Casting yield can be defined as :-

$$C_y, \% = \frac{C_w}{C_w + C_g} \times 100$$

Where C_w = weight of the casting (from its drawing)

C_g = weight of the casting in the gating system *i.e.* Pouring Basin, Sprue, Sprue well, Runner, gate and Riser.

etc.

$C_w + C_g$ = weight of the metal poured into the mould.

Casting yield must be as large as possible for economics of casting. It is large for big and simple casting (85 to 95%) and for metals which shrink less. It is less for metals with large shrinkage, e.g., Al (25 to 45%) and with small and complex shapes of the casting.

IV. 11. Cooling Medium :-

1. Water is the best cooling medium because of its high specific capacity and thermal onductivity and law cost.

2. Al low cutting speeds, lubrication is an important factor. Also better lubcrication should be sought with: Difficult to machine materials. Difficult operations and demand for better surface finish. Low demanding operations to highly demanding operations can be written as :- Grinding, Turning, Milling, Drilling, Reaming, Boring, Deep hole drilling, Gear Cutting, Threading, Broaching, Drawing and Extrusion.

3. Compressed Air or CO_2 can be used as cutting fluid, but have limited cooling power. They are usually limited in use, for example, in band sawing where the work-material does not need cooling, but the cutting tool material may benefit slightly.

4. Soft and ductile materials generate lot of heat and tend to form B.U.E. They need a cutting fluid with good cooling properties and anti-welding properties.

Table : Write about selection of cutting Fluid.

Process / Work Material	Mg alloys	Al alloys	Cu Alloys	Alloy Steels	C Steel	C-I
Turning	–	SO	SO	SO	SO	SO
Milling	–	–	SO	SO	SO	SO
Grinding / Drilling	MO/SO	SO	MO/FO	SO/MO	SO/EP	SO/EP
Heavy turning	MO/SO	MO	MO/FO	MO	EP	EP
Heavy Milling			MO/FO	MO	EP	EP
Tapping, Broaching				MO	EP	EP

SO = Soluble oil; MO: Mineral Oil, FO: Fatty Oil EP: Extreme Pressure oil.

IV. 12. The machine tools can also be classified as per the criteria as given below :–

(a) Type of Surface Produced :-

1. *Cylindrical surface*, e.g., Lathes, Dirlling/Boring Machine, Cylindrical grinding machines.

2. **Flat Surface**, e.g., Shapers, Planers, Slotters, Milling machines surface grinding machines.

(b) Type of Motion :-

1. *Rotary* : - Lathes, Drilling/Boring machines, Cylindrical grinding machines.

2. *Linear* : - Shapers, Planers, Slotters, Milling Machines, Surface grinders.

(c) Degree of Specialisation :

1. Manually operated
2. Semi-Automatic
3. Automatic Machine Tools

(d) Duty Cycle : e.g. Light Duty, Medium duty and Heavy duty machine tools.

(e) Type of Energy used. (1) Conventional Machine tools, (2) Non-conventional Machine tools, e.g., EDM, ECOM, WJM etc.

IV. 13 All tool-work movements display at least one of the 3 basic axial/linear motions, but with the exception of one or two processes (Broaching etc.), all those using multi-point tools involve rotational motion of the cutting trol. This is essential inorder to present each toolh to the w/p in the correct attitude for cutting.

IV. 14 Angle of Repose :- It is another measure of flow rate. It is the base angle of a cone of powder resting on a circular plate. Lower the angle of repose, greater is the flowability or flow rate. It has been noted above that flow rate can be increased by the addition of stearate to the mix. This is due to the fact that the addition of stearate to the mix reduces the inter granular frictions. Again, it has been noted that smaller and spherically shaped particles have the maximum flow rate. It is due to the fact that the spherical and finer particles have higher apparent density or lower porosity. Both the above factors result in lower angle of repose for increased flow rate.

IV. 15 Selection of Plastics Processing Method.

The correct choice of a production process for a particular component made of plastic material, often requires a deep understanding and knowledge of polymer processing methods and a wide range of practical experience. The following are the factors to be considered while selecting a production process for plastics :-

1. The type of plastic material (polymer): Whether thermo-setting or thermo-plastic.
2. The form of the starting material : Liquid, granule powder or sheet.
3. The type of additions : Solid, Liquid, metallic or gaseous.

4. The size of the component and the complexity of its shape.
5. The volume (quantity) of production.
6. Whether inserts are required or not.

The following is a guide for the three basic plastic moulding processes :-

Factor / Process	Type of Polymer	Production rate	Complexity of shape	Suitability for Inserts	Component size	Waste Material	Machine Capital Cost	Mould Capital Cost
1. Compression Moulding	Mainly thermo-setting	Low or Med.	No	No	Med to Large	Little or None	Med.	Low
2. Transfer Moulding	-do-	Low	Yes	Yes	-do-	Considerable	-do-	Med.
3. Injection Moulding	Thermo-plastic	High	Yes	Yes	small to Med.	None	High	High

IV.16. Moulding of Plastics can be done in :- Automatic Presses, Semi-automatic presses or in simple hand moulds.

The desired method of moulding is governed by :-
1. Plastic material being processed.
2. The rate of production of components.
3. Size, geometry and tolerances on the work piece
4. Number of inserts to be moulded into the work piece.

General Guide Lines for Mould Design :- Some guide lines, in additions

1. Specifiy the number of cavities to be present in the mould. Identify each cavity and its location in the mould.
2. Provide eye bolts on two sides 90° apart, for handling purposes. A typical eye bolt diameter is 16 mm.
3. Consider Parting line location and the location and size of ejector pins in both the mould cavities and in the runner.
4. Provide for venting to avoid any gas trapping problem.
5. Provide adequate channels in the mould for the circulation of cooling water.
6. Specify runner size. In case of a doubt, start with a smaller one which can always be increased.
7. Specify gate position and gate size.
8. Specify mould finish
9. Adopt a working tolerance.
10. Specify the material from which the mould cavity is to be fabricated. For vinyl plastic, stainless steel and hard chrome plasting is recommended to avoid corrosion.

IV. 17 Some Problems from Gate 2009 examination :-

1. A typical Fe–C alloy containing greater than 0.8% C is known as :-
   (a) Eutectoid steel
   (b) Hypo-eutectoid steel
   (c) Mild steel
   (d) Hyper-eutectoid steel   [Ans. (d)]

2. Hot chamber die casting is not suitable for
   (a) Lead and its alloys
   (b) Zinc and its alloys
   (c) Tin and its alloys
   (d) Aluminium and its alloys   [Ans. (d)]

3. The total angular movement (in degrees) of a lead screw with a pitch of 5 mm to draw a worktable 200 mm in a NC machine is :-
   (a) 14400
   (b) 28800
   (c) 57600
   (d) 72000   [Ans. (a)]

4. Anistropy in rolled components is caused by
   (a) Change in dimension
   (b) Scale formation
   (c) Closure of defects
   d) grain orientation   [Ans. (d)]

5. Which of the following process is used to manufacture products with controlled porosity?
   (a) Casting   (b) Welding
   (c) Metal Forming   (d) Powder Metallurgy   [Ans. (d)]
6. Which of the following powders should be fed for effective dry-fuel cutting of stainless steel ?
   (a) Steel   (b) Aluminium
   (c) Copper   (d) Ceramic   [Ans. (a)]
7. Diamond cutting tools are not recommended for making of ferrous metals due to
   (a) High tool hardness   (b) High thermal conductivity of work-material
   (c) Pro tool roughness   (d) Chemical affinity of tool material with iron
                                                            [Ans. (d)]
8. Auto-geneous gas tungsten arc welding of a steel plate is carried out with welding current of 500 A, voltage of 20 V and weld speed of 20 mm/sec. Consider the heat transfer efficiency from the arc to the weld pool as 90%. The heat input per unit length (in kJ/mm) is
   (a) 0.25   (b) 0.05
   (c) 0.45   (d) 0.53   [Ans. (c)]
9. A solid cylinder of diameter D and height equal to D and a solid cube of side L are being sand cast by using the same material. Assuming there is no imperfect in both the cases, the ratio of solidification time of cylinder to the solidification time of cube is
   (a) $(L/D)^2$ (b) $(2L/D)^2$
   (c) $(2D/L)^2$ (d) $(D/L)^2$ [Ans. (a)]
10. Following are some possibility characteristics of a pile of powder mixture
    P. Low inter particle frictions
    Q. High inter particle frictions
    R. Low porosity
    S. High porosity
    If the angle of repose for a pile of powder mixture is low it will exibit
    (a) P and R   (b) P and S
    (c) Q and S   (d) Q and R   [Ans. (a)]
11. Resistance spot welding of two steel sheets is carried out in lap joint configurations by using a welding current of 3kA and a weld time of 0.2s. A molten weld nugget of 20 mm³ is obtained. The effective contact resistance is 200 kΩ. The material properties of steel are given as (i) Latent heat of melting 1400 kJ/kg (ii) density 8000 kg/m³ (iii) melting temperature 1520°C (iv) Specific heat: 0.5 kJ/kg °C. The ambient temperature is 20°C. Determine the heat in Joules used for producing weld nugget assuming 100% heat transfer efficiency.
    Sol. $Q = I^2 Rt$
               $= 3 \times 3 \times 10^6 \times 200 \times 10^{-6} \times 0.2 = 360$ J.
12. In the above question : Heat (in Joules) dissipated to the base metal will be (neglecting all other heat losses)
    (a) 10   (b) 16
    (c) 22   (d) 32   [Ans. (b)]
    Sol. Heat in nugget melt = $m \times L$, J
         m = mass of metal melted = $8 \times 20 \times 10^{-3} = 0.16$ gm
         L = latent heat = 1400 J/gm
         ∴   Heat in melt = $1400 \times 0.16 = 224$ J
         ∴   Total heat dissipated = $360 - 224 = 136$ J
         Heat dissipated in nugget = $mC \Delta T = 0.16 \times 0.5 \times 1500 = 120$ J
         ∴   Heat dissipated to the base metal = $136 - 120 = 16$ J

INDEX